R. M. Kocan
M.S.U. Fall 1964

PRINCIPLES OF BIOCHEMISTRY

Principles of
BIOCHEMISTRY

ABRAHAM WHITE, Ph.D., *Dan Danciger Professor of Biochemistry,*
Albert Einstein College of Medicine,
Yeshiva University

PHILIP HANDLER, Ph.D., *James B. Duke Professor of Biochemistry,*
School of Medicine,
Duke University

EMIL L. SMITH, Ph.D., *Professor of Biological Chemistry,*
Center for the Health Sciences,
University of California, Los Angeles

THIRD EDITION

The Blakiston Division

McGRAW-HILL BOOK COMPANY
NEW YORK   TORONTO   LONDON

TO OUR WIVES

PREFACE

Two major problems presented themselves in the preparation of the third edition of *Principles of Biochemistry*. The first was Dr. DeWitt Stetten's withdrawal as one of the authors because of the pressures of his new duties. We would like to express our indebtedness to Dr. Stetten for his critical role in the preparation of the previous two editions. We greatly regret that his new responsibilities made it impossible for him to participate in the preparation of this third edition.

The second major problem arose from the very success of current biochemical research. The rapid development and expansion of every phase of biochemical knowledge not only has markedly enhanced our understanding of the nature of life, but also has made biochemistry the very language of biology, encompassing phenomena as diverse as the function of subcellular units such as the chromosomes and metabolic processes in the intact mammalian organism and providing explanation of metabolic aberrations in human disease. The burgeoning biochemical literature gives serious pause to authors contemplating a new edition of a textbook of biochemistry; it necessitated the almost complete rewriting of this one.

Despite the growing scope and importance of biochemistry, textbooks on this subject are, by tradition, smaller than those readily accepted in fields such as physiology or pharmacology. Rather than break with tradition, we resisted the obvious pressures to increase the size of this edition, leaving to others the preparation of more detailed compendia and encyclopedias. It is our continuing intent to present the fundamental principles and concepts of biochemistry, based upon our own teaching experiences. Although more detail and information has been presented than can usually be encompassed by a student in a single course in biochemistry, it seemed desirable to provide a book not only useful to a student in formal course work, but also of value to him as a reference work in later years. Because of this approach, it is hoped that this book will be used by medical and graduate students, as well as by college students with a major interest in biochemistry.

We realize that, although our colleagues and fellow biochemists as well as graduate students in the field may find insufficient detail in the material presented, many medical students may feel overwhelmed by the amount of detail. We direct the attention of the former group to the many valuable reviews, monographs, and specialized treatises cited herein. For the latter group, we hope that their teachers will assure them that not all the information in this book need be learned initially and that they will direct the students' attention to selected reading by indicating page rather than chapter assignments.

In this edition an effort has been made to retain the goals of the previous editions: to provide the basic principles of mammalian biochemistry and to illustrate these principles as often as possible by referring to the human species. In this sense, the volume is designed primarily for students of medicine and of mammalian biochemistry. Nevertheless, considerable emphasis is given to comparative biochemistry, since processes in lower forms, *e.g.*, microorganisms and plants, frequently provide insight into biochemical mechanisms in higher forms. Moreover, it seemed imperative, for the full appreciation of chemical biology, to present diverse processes which occur in some species but which cannot be duplicated by mammals, *e.g.*, biosynthesis of the essential amino acids and of vitamins, or photosynthesis, as well as a glimpse of the structure of bacterial cell walls. Indeed, the total material dealing with nonmammalian biochemistry has been significantly expanded.

In this edition, certain changes in the arrangement of material were made which, we hope, will ease the tasks of both student and teacher and which reflect the changes in our own viewpoints, produced by new discoveries. In certain of the more fully discussed areas of biochemistry, such as biological oxidations and amino acid metabolism, the subject matter has been divided into groups of chapters. In general, the fundamental principles and more general features of a particular subject are presented in the first chapter of such a group. Subsequent chapters then deal with more detailed aspects of the subject, and, in most instances, these chapters can be utilized by a student who desires a deeper consideration of the particular subject. This arrangement also should make easier the selection of material by the teacher for reading assignment.

A few other changes in presentation of subject matter may be noteworthy. Much of the pertinent information formerly in the chapter, Milk, now appears in the chapter, Specialized Fluids. The material previously presented under Protein Metabolism is now discussed under Amino Acid Metabolism, since, except for the role of proteins in nutrition and their fate in the gastrointestinal tract, other aspects of what has generally been termed protein metabolism are all phases of amino acid metabolism. This discussion has been divided into four chapters; the first and last deal with fundamental principles and basic information whereas the other two, concerned with the biosynthesis of the essential amino acids and the role of amino acids as precursors of other nitrogen-containing substances, contain information that should be of particular interest to the student who desires more knowledge in this area of biochemistry.

The great advances in biochemical genetics necessitated a group of three chapters called Genetic Aspects of Metabolism. These chapters include the discussion of protein biosynthesis, formerly in the chapter, Protein Metabolism, but now more appropriately in one of these three chapters. The material on cell structure, formerly appearing in the introductory chapter of the part devoted to Biochemistry of Specialized Tissues, is now presented in the chapter entitled Introduction to Metabolism. The authors well recognize the inadequacy of this treatment which can serve only to acquaint the student with the techniques for cell fractionation that are in general use and to which frequent reference is made throughout this text.

The discussion of the chemistry of amino acids and proteins has been revised and considerably expanded so as to present current concepts of protein structure. Similarly, in this edition, the chapter, Nucleic Acids and Nucleoproteins, has been expanded in the light of newer information now available. The chapter, Specificity of Enzymes, has been revised so as to emphasize modern concepts of the mechanism of action of these biocatalysts. Biological Oxidations is presented in three chapters, the third of which is concerned with a somewhat more detailed description of the enzymes and coenzymes that function in such systems. Carbohydrate Metabolism is discussed in two chapters; the first deals with digestion of carbohydrates and fundamental aspects of glucose metabolism, including glycolysis, the phosphogluconate oxidative pathway, and photosynthesis; the second is concerned with interconversions among the carbohydrates and with the metabolism of polysaccharides. The digestion of lipids and the metabolism of triglycerides and fatty acids are to be found in the first of two chapters entitled Lipid Metabolism, the second of which deals with phosphatides and sterols.

The former chapter, Blood, has been significantly modified and combined with the chapter, Plasma Proteins, to provide a new chapter, Blood Plasma. The less biochemical aspects of the former chapter on blood have been largely deleted.

The general organization of this edition has not been greatly altered. The subject matter is again divided into parts which appear to be logical in sequence and content. Part One presents the chemical nature of the diverse substances found in living systems; Part Two discusses the concepts of catalysis, the chemical nature of enzymes, and the manner in which they are thought to function; and Part Three, Metabolism, then deals with the reactions in which the chemical components of cells participate and with the enzymes that catalyze these reactions. Part Four is concerned with the composition and behavior of body fluids. Part Five treats of the chemistry and physiology of certain tissues and organs which, by virtue of either their composition or their synthesis of a highly specialized product, effect structural localization of a unique body function. Part Six presents, from a biochemical point of view, the nature and function of hormones as physiological regulators of prime importance in mammalian homeostasis. Part Seven contains a description of nutrition that not only includes the chemistry of, and requirements for, particular dietary components, but also interprets these requirements and the apparent consequences of deficiency in the light of the known functions of these substances in cellular phenomena.

Perhaps with questionable validity, the authors have assumed that the beginning student of biochemistry has had little or no formal training in physical chemistry. Therefore, necessary concepts from this discipline are presented as they are required in the course of this text rather than in a separate introductory section. It has been our experience that the interest of the student is much greater when particular chemical concepts are illustrated with a biological or biochemical principle close at hand. Extending this point of view, we have again omitted the classical chapter on digestion; rather, this aspect of biochemistry remains an integral part of the chapters dealing with the metabolism of the major foodstuffs.

In the preparation of this book, it has been difficult in many instances to distinguish between the substantive matter of biochemistry and what might be considered more appropriate to a textbook of physiology, microbiology, or, perhaps, cytology. For example, the present text includes discussions of energy metabolism, water and electrolyte metabolism, and endocrinology. Although much of the information in these chapters may also be considered to be within the province of physiology, an effort has been made to emphasize chemistry and to present this material from a biochemical standpoint. Indeed, this very dilemma indicates the success of biochemical research in the past two decades.

The method used in the preparation of this edition was the same as that for its predecessors. Preparation of the first draft of each of the chapters was assigned to one of the authors. Each complete first draft was then subjected to the suggestions and criticisms, frequently painful, of each of the other authors who also rewrote paragraphs, sections, or, on occasion, even the whole chapter. In addition, the authors convened at intervals, for meetings of several days' duration. These afforded opportunities for criticism, suggestions, deletions (always welcome), additions (always resisted), as well as appraisal of the extent to which this edition was in keeping with our original goals. In effect, therefore, each chapter was written by all three authors, who, accordingly, share responsibility for the entire work.

We are deeply indebted to the many colleagues, friends, and students who have provided critical evaluation and helpful suggestions during the course of this revision. Gratefully, we acknowledge the kindness of the many publishers who have permitted us to reproduce tables and illustrations which have been published elsewhere. We wish particularly to thank the staff of the Blakiston Division of the McGraw-Hill Book Company for their patient and helpful assistance in the production of this volume. Mrs. Ida Wolfson, of the editorial staff, and Mr. W. T. Shoener, Production Manager, have facilitated the day-to-day tasks involved in the preparation of the third edition. Mr. William Keller, Editor-in-Chief and General Manager, has continued to provide an understanding catalytic influence.

Abraham White
Philip Handler
Emil L. Smith

CONTENTS

1. General Considerations

The fundamental importance of biochemistry in biology stems from the recognition that every activity of all living cells results from underlying chemical processes. It is this concept which has channeled teaching and research in biochemistry along two major lines of endeavor: (1) the qualitative and quantitative characterization of the chemical components of cells, and (2) the elucidation of the nature and mechanism of the reactions in which these components participate.

Investigations in each of these two major areas have revealed that, regardless of the species studied, there exists both an extraordinary similarity in the chemical composition of all cells and an underlying unity in the nature of the processes in which these cellular constituents participate. It is now evident that the major mechanisms and pathways of energy production, biosynthesis, and degradation do not differ remarkably in microorganisms, plants, and animals, including man. As a consequence, information derived from experiments with nonmammalian forms has had great significance for the understanding of the normal and certain of the deranged states in man. Indeed, elucidation of numerous fundamental biochemical processes in man has derived from investigations with other forms, *i.e.*, plants and microorganisms, which are more readily susceptible to study and controlled manipulation in the laboratory. For example, the major advances made toward revealing the basic biochemical mechanisms underlying genetics have stemmed in large part from use of mutant strains of microorganisms. Also, the ready availability of bacterial extracts and fractions of bacterial cells has facilitated description of the mechanism of protein biosynthesis. Again, the transformations of carbohydrate in the photosynthetic process in plants are, except for the first reaction initiated by light, strikingly similar to those occurring in pathways of carbohydrate metabolism in mammals.

The boundary between living and nonliving forms is not always well delineated. For example, certain diseases are caused by infective agents termed *filtrable viruses*. These substances, invisible even with the aid of the ordinary microscope, pass through very fine filters, and reproduce when introduced into the environment of living cells. Certain viruses have been isolated in highly purified crystalline form and studied extensively in the laboratory. The chemical properties of the crystalline viruses, *e.g.*, the tobacco mosaic virus, indicate that they are nucleoproteins, with properties characteristic of this group of substances (Chap. 10). Yet these substances, isolated in the laboratory and having no apparent or obvious features characteristic of living matter, when inoculated into a healthy leaf of a tobacco plant multiply rapidly and cause the appearance in the leaf of the pathological lesions of tobacco mosaic disease. An inanimate crystalline compound, when intro-

1

duced into the proper environment, appears to behave as though it were a living viral agent. In discussing the question of whether or not crystalline viruses are "alive," Wendell M. Stanley, the first investigator to isolate a virus in crystalline form, concluded as follows:

> With the realization that there is no definite boundary between the living and the nonliving, it becomes possible to blend the atomic theory, the germ theory, and the cell theory into a unified philosophy, the essence of which is structure or architecture. The chemical, biological, and physical properties of matter, whether atoms, molecules, germs, or cells, are directly dependent upon the chemical structure of matter, and the results of the work with viruses have permitted the conclusion that this structure is fundamentally the same regardless of its occurrence.

The concept that the chemical structure of all matter is essentially the same is of importance in considering the chemical composition of cells, the fundamental units of all living forms. Multicellular organisms have differentiated and evolved into structures of varying sizes and shapes, containing aggregations of cells in the form of tissues and organs which, with the increasing complexity of the organism, were joined through the circulation. The various cells, comprising the tissues and organs of the body, have differentiated structures adapted to specific functions, with their own life cycles, but integrated physically and physiologically with other cells of the body to constitute an organism.

It has long been apparent that an understanding of the characteristic processes in living cells is based on the application of our knowledge of the nonliving components of these cells. There is available to the biochemist, therefore, a large body of information derived from the physical and chemical sciences and applicable to the study of the diverse chemical reactions which occur in living cells. Our understanding of the laws of chemistry and physics, coupled with an insight into the nature of the chemical components of living systems, will permit us to begin to construct a picture of the reactions in which these components may participate in the cell.

Three historic discoveries led to the concept that the fundamental laws of physics and chemistry, which apply to nonliving systems, also apply to living structures. These discoveries are (1) the establishment by Lavoisier and Laplace in 1785 of the law of conservation of energy in its applicability to animals, (2) the synthesis of urea from ammonium cyanate by Wöhler in 1828, and (3) the preparation of a cell-free extract, capable of fermenting sugar, by the Büchner brothers in 1897. These observations were of paramount importance. The work of Lavoisier and Laplace showed that fundamental chemical and physical principles, derived from investigations with inanimate objects, also applied to living organisms. Prior to the studies of Wöhler, it was held generally that a substance synthesized by living cells, e.g., urea, could not be synthesized in the laboratory and, until the experiments of the Büchners, that the fermentation of sugar could be conducted only by intact living cells. Thus, these studies succeeded in demolishing forever the concept of vitalism, i.e., that there existed in living cells a "vital force," or "spirit," which accounted for the differences between living and lifeless forms and operated in disregard of fundamental laws of chemistry and physics. Once this progress-restraining influence had been dissipated, rapid progress could be made in the application of basic physical and chemical principles to living systems. Certain of these principles will be described in subsequent pages of this book, and numerous examples of their application to living systems will be presented. It will suffice at this point to mention two of the most important of these principles, the *first* and *second laws of thermodynamics.* The first law is the principle of the conservation of energy, applied with the recognition that heat is a form of energy. It is comprised in the statements that the energy of an isolated system is constant and that any exchange of energy between a system and its surroundings must occur without the creation or destruction of energy. The second law of thermodynamics has been described in several ways, one of which is in terms of work, as stated by G. N. Lewis: "Every process that occurs spontaneously is capable of doing work; to reverse any such process requires the expenditure of work from the outside" (Chap. 12).

In living, as in nonliving, systems, therefore, these laws of physical chemistry require that energy must be supplied in order to accomplish the reversal of a spontaneous process or for the synthesis of a new compound from precursors of lower energy content. The coupling of energy-yielding with energy-consuming reactions is a prominent feature of cellular life.

CHEMICAL COMPOSITION OF CELLS

Cells of various tissues and organs differ from one another chiefly in (1) the nature and quantity of chemical substances present, (2) the nature of the reactions in which the constituents participate, and (3) the rates of these reactions.

Analytical data reveal the presence of some twenty elements in the human body, with oxygen present in the greatest quantity, approximately 65 per cent of the total elemental composition, whereas other elements, *e.g.,* cobalt, zinc, and molybdenum, are present in barely detectable quantities. As will be evident in subsequent pages, the total quantity of an element in an organism may not be a true index of its functional significance. Thus, many reactions of cells will not take place unless a minute quantity of a particular ion is present.

Analysis of tissues for the substances of which the elements are components reveals the values of Table 1.1. It is immediately evident that water is the most prominent compound in the body. Indeed, most body processes operate in dilute aqueous solutions, and these reactions are controlled by the physical and chemical laws of dilute solutions. Although the average water content of the body is 65 per cent of the fresh weight of tissue, this value may vary considerably in diverse tissues. Thus, the brain and the lungs contain 84 per cent and 78 per cent, respectively, of their fresh weight as water; bone contains approximately 22 per cent of water, and the dentine of the teeth only 10 per cent.

Just as the *quantity* of a particular constituent may be different in one type of cell as compared with another, so also may the *quality* of cellular components show some degree of variation. For example, while all cells contain proteins, the kind of protein appears to be specific for certain organs and for species. Thus, within a given

Table 1.1: APPROXIMATE PERCENTAGE COMPOSITION OF SOME MAMMALIAN TISSUES

Component	Tissue					
	Striated muscle	Whole blood	Liver	Whole brain	Skin	Bone (free of marrow)
Water................	72–78	79	60–80	78	66	20–25
Solids................	22–28	21	20–40	22	34	75–80
Proteins..............	18–20	19	15	8	25	30
Lipids................	3.0	1	3–20	12–15	7	Low
Carbohydrates........	0.6	0.1	1–15	0.1	Present	Present
Organic extractives....	1.0	0.14	High	1.0–2.0	Present	Low
Inorganic extractives....	1.0	0.9	.....	1.0	0.60	45

SOURCE: After E. S. West and W. R. Todd, "Textbook of Biochemistry," The Macmillan Company, New York, 1951.

species the chief *kind* of protein found in epithelial tissue is quite different in composition from that which predominates in glandular tissue.

As might be anticipated, the variations among cell types in the nature and quantity of their chemical constituents may be reflected in one or more reactions or functions characteristic of a given tissue or structure. Thus, the presence of a particular protein, hemoglobin, in the erythrocyte endows this cell with a special function in the respiratory cycle. The highly insoluble protein in epithelial tissue contributes uniquely to the protective or resistant nature of this tissue. Again, the presence of the protein myosin in high concentration in muscle tissue contributes specifically to the mechanics and chemistry of muscle contraction.

Finally, it is recognized that cells may differ from one another in the rate at which they perform chemical reactions. Thus, the rate of protein synthesis by a muscle cell is considerably less than half that of a liver cell, although presumably the fundamental mechanism underlying this synthesis is the same in both cells. The synthesis of certain compounds, *e.g.*, specific lipids, may be relatively slow in brain tissue as compared with the rate in liver or kidney cells.

Thus, the composition of cells is, broadly speaking, similar from tissue to tissue. Differences in histology or in structure are paralleled generally by differences in relative chemical composition, functions, and relative rates at which similar functions, processes, or reactions may proceed.

Subsequent chapters in this part are concerned with the chemistry of the chief organic constituents of cells, *viz.*, the carbohydrates, the lipids, the proteins and their fundamental constituents, the amino acids, and the nucleic acids and nucleoproteins. A chapter on important cellular pigments, the porphyrins, is also included in this part. Somewhat later in the book other cellular components, *i.e.*, water, inorganic salts, and additional organic compounds, will be discussed in relation to the organs and tissues that are chiefly concerned with the functions and metabolism of these substances.

2. Chemistry of Carbohydrates

*Classification, Formulation, and
Stereochemistry*

CLASSIFICATION

The carbohydrates include a large group of compounds which are polyhydroxyaldehydes or polyhydroxyketones, and their derivatives. For classification, these compounds may be divided into:

Monosaccharides
Derived monosaccharides
Oligosaccharides (di- and trisaccharides, etc.)
High molecular weight polysaccharides

In general, carbohydrates are white solids, sparingly soluble in organic liquids but, except for certain polysaccharides, soluble in water. Many carbohydrates of low molecular weight have a sweet taste.

Monosaccharides. Although formaldehyde and hydroxyacetaldehyde (glycolaldehyde) conform to the empirical formula of the carbohydrates, the smallest molecules generally termed carbohydrates are glyceraldehyde and dihydroxyacetone. These two compounds are the only possible trioses, the 3-carbon sugars.

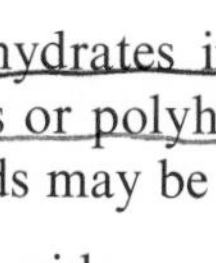

$$HC\!\!=\!\!O$$
$$|$$
$$CHOH$$
$$|$$
$$CH_2OH$$

Glyceraldehyde

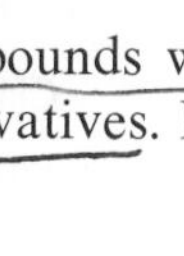

$$CH_2OH$$
$$|$$
$$C\!\!=\!\!O$$
$$|$$
$$CH_2OH$$

Dihydroxyacetone

Consideration of these formulas reveals several characteristics common to the entire group:

(1) The carbon skeleton is usually unbranched. (2) Each carbon atom except one bears a hydroxyl group. (3) One carbon atom bears a carbonyl oxygen. (4) This carbonyl oxygen may reside on a terminal carbon atom, giving an aldehyde, or on a centrally placed carbon atom, giving a ketone.

One of the methods of naming sugars relates to the last point. Thus glyceraldehyde may be termed an *aldo*triose, and dihydroxyacetone is then called a *keto*-triose. Among the common ketoses, or ketonic monosaccharides, the carbonyl oxygen is found on the C-2 carbon atom (adjacent to the uppermost one).

Monosaccharides containing four carbon atoms are called tetroses, those con-

5

taining five carbon atoms are termed pentoses, whereas the hexoses contain six and the heptoses seven carbon atoms. Generic names for the ketoses are formed by insertion of "ul," thus; pentulose, hexulose, heptulose.

Derived Monosaccharides. In this group is included a variety of compounds structurally very similar to the monosaccharides but deviating in one or another regard from the aldoses and ketoses just described. Three main varieties of carboxylic acids are found among oxidation products of the simple sugars. There are those in which the aldehydic group is oxidized to the carboxyl level, *e.g.*, gluconic acid. There are acids in which the primary hydroxyl group remote from the aldehyde is oxidized to the carboxyl level, *e.g.*, glucuronic acid. Finally there are dicarboxylic acids, oxidized at both ends, such as saccharic acid.

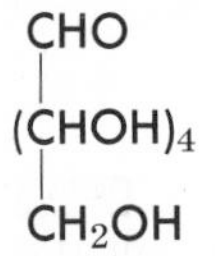

$$
\begin{array}{cccc}
\text{CHO} & \text{COOH} & \text{CHO} & \text{COOH} \\
| & | & | & | \\
\text{(CHOH)}_4 & \text{(CHOH)}_4 & \text{(CHOH)}_4 & \text{(CHOH)}_4 \\
| & | & | & | \\
\text{CH}_2\text{OH} & \text{CH}_2\text{OH} & \text{COOH} & \text{COOH}
\end{array}
$$

Aldohexose	Hexonic acid	Uronic acid	Dicarboxylic acid
(glucose)	(gluconic acid)	(glucuronic acid)	(saccharic acid)

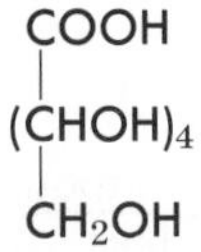

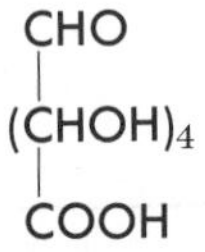

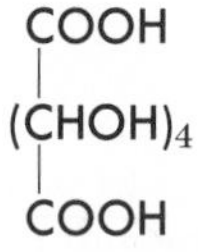

Upon reduction of aldoses or ketoses, polyhydric alcohols are obtained, *e.g.*, sorbitol. Related to such sugar alcohols are carbocyclic alcohols, such as inositol.

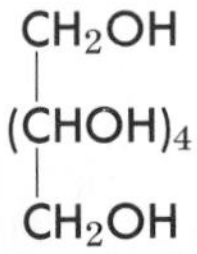

$$
\begin{array}{cc}
\text{CH}_2\text{OH} & \\
| & \\
\text{(CHOH)}_4 & \\
| & \\
\text{CH}_2\text{OH} &
\end{array}
$$

Hexitol (sorbitol) 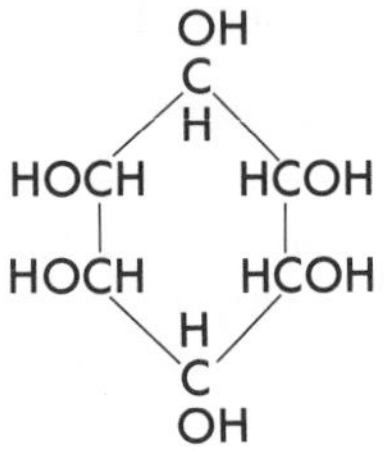   **Hexahydroxycyclohexane** (inositol)

The carbocyclic alcohols are isomeric with the true monosaccharides, sharing with them the empirical formula $(\text{CH}_2\text{O})_n$.

Replacement of a hydroxyl group by an amino group yields an amino sugar, whereas replacement of a hydroxyl group by hydrogen yields a deoxysugar.

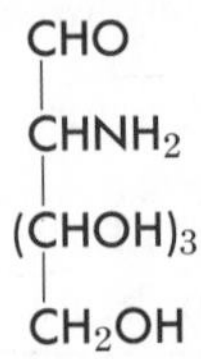

$$
\begin{array}{cc}
\text{CHO} & \text{CHO} \\
| & | \\
\text{CHNH}_2 & \text{CH}_2 \\
| & | \\
\text{(CHOH)}_3 & \text{(CHOH)}_2 \\
| & | \\
\text{CH}_2\text{OH} & \text{CH}_2\text{OH}
\end{array}
$$

Hexosamine (glucosamine) 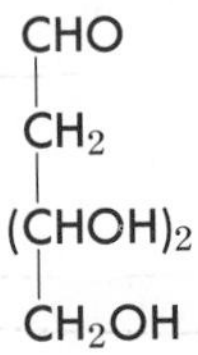   **Deoxypentose** (deoxyribose)

Monosaccharides are also known with an empirical formula $C_n(\text{H}_2\text{O})_{n-1}$, and these are called anhydrosugars.

Numerous other modifications of the basic monosaccharide formula exist, but the above examples are among the most important and most frequently encountered.

Oligosaccharides. Monosaccharides may be attached one to another in so-called glycosidic linkage, to be discussed later (page 21). Molecules which on hydrolysis yield two monosaccharide moieties are called disaccharides. The two halves may be either the same sugar as in maltose (a glucosylglucose) or different, as in lactose (a galactosylglucose). Trisaccharides yield on hydrolysis three fragments rather than two, and compounds containing up to ten monosaccharide fragments are usually included in the class of oligosaccharides.

Polysaccharides of High Molecular Weight. The process of coupling monosaccharides in glycosidic linkage may be extended to yield products of very high molecular weight. Such polysaccharides are classified according to the nature of their hydrolysis products, their specific physical and immunological properties, and their products after enzymic degradation. On the basis of chemical structure one may distinguish polysaccharides yielding only one product on hydrolytic cleavage, homopolysaccharides, and those yielding a mixture of products, heteropolysaccharides. In the former group are polysaccharides of pentoses, termed pentosans, as well as of hexoses, or hexosans. The hexosans include such important members as glycogen, the starches, and cellulose. Chitin is a polysaccharide in which the N-acetyl derivative of glucosamine is the repeating unit.

Many polysaccharides yield on hydrolysis mixtures of hexoses and derivatives of hexoses. An example is hyaluronic acid, which contains N-acetylglucosamine and glucuronic acid as repeating units in equimolar amounts.

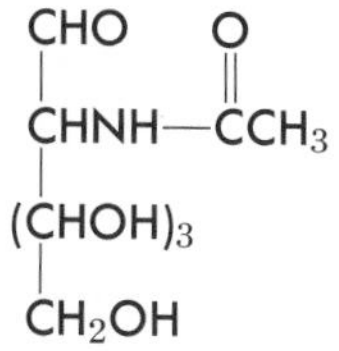

$$
\begin{array}{ll}
\begin{array}{l}
\text{CHO} \\
| \\
\text{CHNH}\!\!-\!\!\overset{\text{O}}{\overset{\|}{\text{C}}}\text{CH}_3 \\
| \\
(\text{CHOH})_3 \\
| \\
\text{CH}_2\text{OH}
\end{array}
&
\begin{array}{l}
\text{CHO} \\
| \\
(\text{CHOH})_4 \\
| \\
\text{COOH}
\end{array}
\\[1em]
\text{N-Acetylglucosamine} & \text{Glucuronic acid}
\end{array}
$$

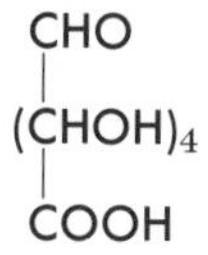

The polysaccharide components of the cell walls of bacteria are also heteropolysaccharides (page 57).

An example has been given of a polysaccharide containing an acetyl residue. This is but one of many polysaccharides known to contain a noncarbohydrate component. Other acidic groups, sulfuryl and phosphoryl, exist as integral parts of certain naturally occurring polysaccharides.

OPTICAL ROTATORY POWER

The development of carbohydrate chemistry is so closely associated with polarimetry that a brief discussion of the principles involved is appropriate at this point. Biot, commencing about 1815, in addition to observing the optical rotatory power of pure solids, liquids, and gases, studied the rotatory power of optically active materials in solution, noted the dependence of observed rotation upon concentration of solute and length of the path of light through the solution, and formulated the definition of specific rotation, $[\alpha]$,

$$[\alpha] = \frac{100 \times A}{c \times l}$$

where A is the observed rotation (plus or minus) in degrees, c is the concentration in grams per 100 ml. of solution, and l is the length, in decimeters, of the optical path through the solution. The specific rotation is thus the actual rotation imparted to a beam of plane-polarized light passing through 1 decimeter of a hypothetical solution of 100 g. of optically active solute in 100 ml. of solution. The specific rotation is a complex function of the wavelength of light and the nature of the solvent used. Monochromatic light, most frequently the D line of the sodium spectrum, is employed and specified. The temperature, often 20°C., must also be recorded, as rotatory power is temperature-dependent. These quantities are indicated as follows:

$$[\alpha]_D^{20} = \text{rotation value (solvent used)}; \ e.g., \ + 23° \ (CHCl_3)$$

Since the dependence of observed rotation upon concentration is not always strictly linear, it is customary to specify the concentration of solute at which the rotation is determined.

The dependence of optical rotary power upon the wavelength or frequency of light employed is expressed as the *optical rotatory dispersion*. The measurement of optical rotatory dispersion has contributed data for understanding of structural features of many biologically important substances, *e.g.*, the secondary structures of certain proteins (page 156).

Molecular Asymmetry. Pasteur recognized that for a compound to possess optical activity it must be asymmetric. This asymmetry may be restricted to the crystal structure as is the situation with crystalline quartz, but more frequently it resides in the molecule proper. Pasteur's study of the tartaric acids culminated in the definitions of "meso" acid and "racemic" acid,

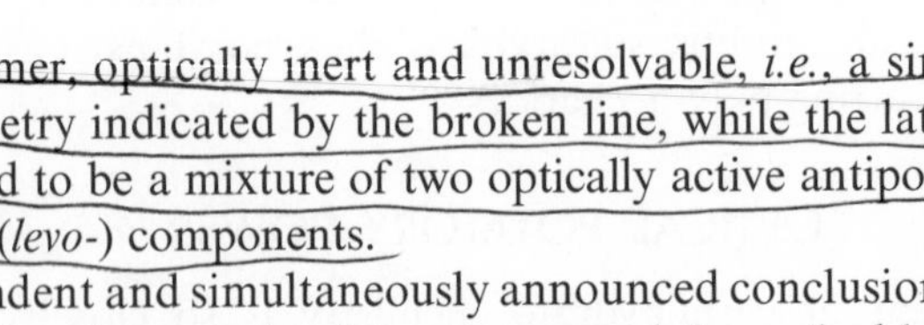

"Meso" acid   "Racemic" acid

of which the former, optically inert and unresolvable, *i.e.*, a single substance, has a plane of symmetry indicated by the broken line, while the latter, devoid of such symmetry, proved to be a mixture of two optically active antipodes, resolvable into *d* (*dextro-*) and *l* (*levo-*) components.

The independent and simultaneously announced conclusions of van't Hoff and LeBel, in 1874, placed stereochemistry on a sound theoretical basis. It was pointed out that the geometrically most probable orientation of the bonds of tetravalent carbon was to the apexes of an equilateral tetrahedron and that this assumption would account for all the then known phenomena of molecular asymmetry. This hypothesis has proved to be one of the most generally applicable in all of chemistry and, in conjunction with subsidiary hypotheses relating to freedom of rotation about the axes of valence bonds, has accounted for virtually all types of stereochemical relationships. Placing the two central carbon atoms of tartaric acid at the centers of tetrahedrons, the formulas become as shown.

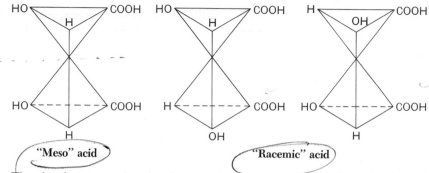

"Meso" acid   "Racemic" acid

The simplest type of molecular asymmetry that can arise from this hypothesis results from the occurrence of an atom asymmetrically located in the molecule, and, in the case of carbon, any carbon atom which bears four different substituents on its four valences becomes an asymmetric center. Carbon atoms bearing double or triple bonds are at once excluded from this category. Every compound the formula of which has one asymmetrically situated carbon atom is either optically active, *i.e.*, rotates the plane of polarized light, or is resolvable into optical antipodes, a pair of substances each of which is optically active. Whereas the general chemical properties of such antipodes are very similar (cf. Resolution of *dl* Mixtures and Racemates, below), they will differ from each other in that one will be *dextro-rotatory*, the other *levorotatory*, while the numerical value of [α], disregarding sign, will be the same for both compounds. The steric formulas of these two compounds will meet the criterion of being mirror images of each other but not superimposable,

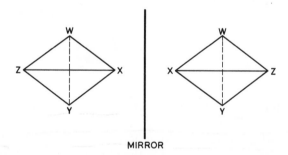

MIRROR

in the same relationship as that existing between the right and left hands. Because of the difficulties involved in drawing numerous tetrahedrons, the convention adopted in stereochemistry is to represent these antipodes in plane projection as

$$z-\underset{y}{\overset{w}{C}}-x \qquad\qquad x-\underset{y}{\overset{w}{C}}-z$$

Here an added restriction arises from the two-dimensional representation, *viz.*, the test for superimposability must be conducted without removing the formula from the plane of the paper.

Returning to the tartaric acids, it will be seen that the *d* and *l* components of *racemic* acid fulfill the requirements of being nonsuperimposable mirror images. The *meso* acid, however, is readily superimposed on its mirror image by rotation in the plane of the paper.

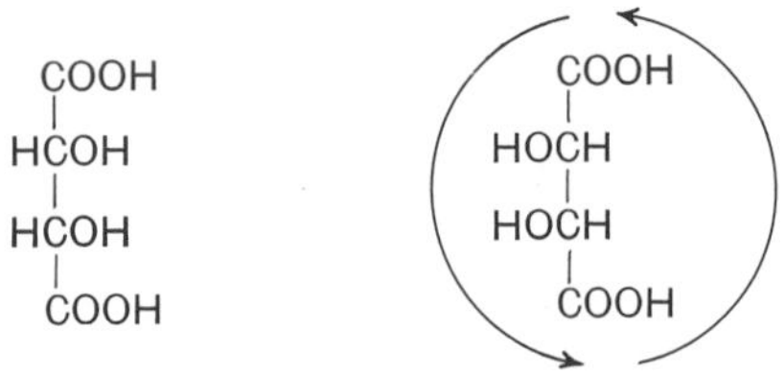

```
        COOH                    COOH
         |                       |
       HCOH                    HOCH
         |                       |
       HCOH                    HOCH
         |                       |
        COOH                    COOH
```

"Meso" acid

Consequently, the *meso* acid is not resolvable and is optically inert, despite the fact that it contains two atomic centers of asymmetry. This situation is termed "internal compensation" and may be pictured as resulting from opposing rotatory powers of opposite sign at the two ends of the molecule. The general conclusion is that, regardless of asymmetrically substituted atoms, optical activity will be absent if the molecule exhibits any plane of symmetry.

Asymmetric Behavior of Certain Symmetrical Compounds. There are certain molecules which, although possessed of a plane of symmetry, behave under certain circumstances as though they were asymmetric. These molecules all contain one carbon atom which bears *a pair of like and a pair of unlike substituents*.

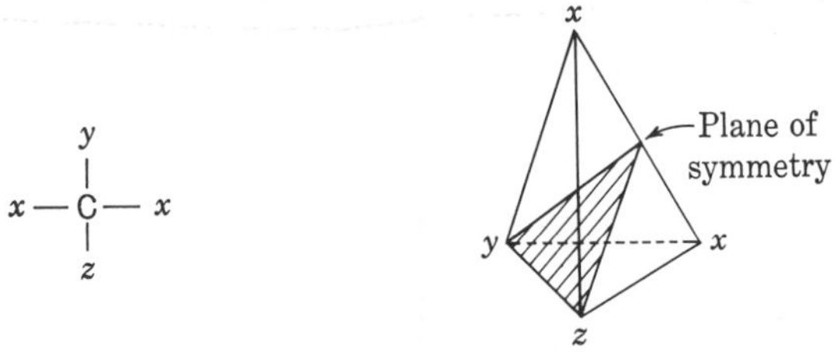

```
          y
          |
     x — C — x
          |
          z
```

x

Plane of symmetry

y -------- x

z

The tetrahedral representation of such a molecule clearly has a plane of symmetry, yet experimentally it can readily be shown that the two x substituents do not react equally when presented with an asymmetric reagent. The reason for this resides in an extension of the principles already outlined. Whereas the two x substituents are symmetrically disposed, and the two half-molecules generated by cleavage of the molecule along the plane of symmetry are mirror images, these two half-molecules are not superimposable one upon the other. Thus these two *half-molecules* may be said to be antipodal, just as the whole molecules of d- and l-tartaric acid are antipodal. Precisely as the two tartaric acids, d and l, will not be distinguished by symmetrical reagents but will react differentially with an asymmetric reagent, so will the two x groups in the molecule $C(xxyz)$ react at different rates if the reagent is itself unsymmetrical. *Meso*-tartaric acid is characterized by a molecular plane that divides the molecule into two halves which are nonsuperimposable mirror images. Since this condition is also met by the carbon atom in $C(xxyz)$, such an atom is referred to as a *meso* atom. This type of *meso* symmetry is of especial importance in biochemistry because virtually all reactions involve enzymes, and these are highly asymmetrical; examples will be encountered later (cf. Chaps. 14 and 18).

Number of Optical Isomers. The principles outlined permit computation of the expected number of optical isomers of any given structure. A molecule having one center of asymmetry will exist in two configurations corresponding to the *d* and *l* antipodes. Barring *meso* forms and steric incompatibilities, with two centers of asymmetry one finds four possible forms, or two antipodal pairs, *a* and *b*, and *c* and *d*.

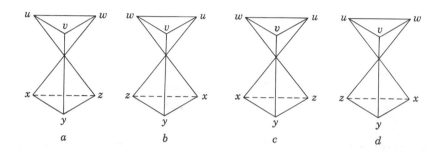

All other steric modifications that can be drawn will be found to be superimposable on, hence identical with, one of these. The expected relationship, again barring situations of internal compensation and restricted rotation of the molecule about some bond or bonds, is that for *n* centers of asymmetry, 2^n optically active isomers may be anticipated.

It should also be pointed out that, whereas optical antipodes *a* and *b* will be identical in most chemical and physical properties, *a* will not resemble *c* as closely as two isomers usually resemble each other. The *dl* mixture of *a* + *b* will in general be readily separable from the *dl* mixture of *c* + *d*.

Resolution of dl Mixtures and Racemates. When a living cell, incident to biosynthetic processes, establishes a new center of asymmetry in a molecule, it will usually produce an optically active product, often with complete exclusion of its antipode. For the most part, products isolated from living sources will, if they contain an asymmetric carbon atom, be optically active and usually pure from the stereochemical point of view. Not only do living cells, or enzyme systems derived therefrom, apparently synthesize only one of two antipodes, but they also utilize the two antipodes of a given compound at differing rates or in different ways, often completely consuming the one and leaving the other unattacked.

When the chemist, starting with optically inactive materials, synthesizes a compound containing an asymmetrically substituted carbon atom, he almost invariably obtains a product in which the *d* and *l* antipodes are equally represented. Thus reduction of 2-butanone yields an optically inactive mixture of products, since the probability of formation is the same for each antipode. Such *dl* mixtures are called racemic compounds. A frequently encountered problem involves the separation, or "resolution," of such materials into pure *d* and *l* components.

The crystals of *d*- and *l*-tartrates (sodium ammonium salts) separate from solution, under certain conditions, in crystalline forms which are themselves of two

$$
\begin{array}{ccc}
\text{CH}_3 & \text{CH}_3 & \text{CH}_3 \\
| & | & | \\
\text{C}=\text{O} \xrightarrow{\text{H}_2} & \text{HCOH} + & \text{HOCH} \\
| & | & | \\
\text{C}_2\text{H}_5 & \text{C}_2\text{H}_5 & \text{C}_2\text{H}_5 \\
\text{2-Butanone} & \multicolumn{2}{c}{\textit{dl}\text{-2-Butanol}}
\end{array}
$$

varieties, one being the nonsuperimposable mirror image of the other. Thus difference in crystalline forms permitted Pasteur to accomplish the tedious manual resolution of the mixture of crystals. A more generally useful method of resolution involves preparation of diastereoisomers, *i.e.*, derivatives with an optically active reagent. Alkaloids such as *l*-brucine or terpene acids such as *d*-camphoric acid are often employed in this manner. If an equal mixture of *d*- and *l*-tartaric acids is treated with *l*-brucine, two salts will be produced, *l*-brucine *d*-tartrate and *l*-brucine *l*-tartrate. These two compounds are now no longer antipodes, since the antipode of *l*-brucine *d*-tartrate will necessarily be *d*-brucine *l*-tartrate. They will consequently have different physical properties and can be separated by fractional crystallization or some other physical means.

A third general method of resolution depends upon the basic asymmetry of living systems and their enzymes. Thus in many cases a *dl* mixture can be offered as substrate to a microorganism, a tissue, or an enzyme, and the one antipode will be quantitatively destroyed while the other remains. A modification of this method involves preparation of a derivative of the *dl* mixture, which is then treated with an enzyme that splits one antipodal derivative but not the other. These biochemical resolution methods serve to emphasize the fundamental asymmetry of enzyme-catalyzed reactions, attributable to the asymmetry of the enzymes themselves.

Designation of Configuration. The employment of *d* and *l* or (+) and (−) to designate the sign of rotation of plane-polarized light by a given substance is useful to indicate which of a pair of antipodes is being discussed. It gives, however, no information as to the *configuration* of the several substituents about the center or centers of asymmetry in the molecule. Thus the glucose of nature is dextrorotatory, $[\alpha]_D^{20} = +52.7°$, while fructose is levorotatory, $[\alpha]_D^{20} = -92.4°$; yet these two hexoses prove to be configurationally intimately related.

$$
\begin{array}{ccc}
\text{CHO} & 1 & \text{CH}_2\text{OH} \\
| & & | \\
\text{HCOH} & 2 & \text{C}=\text{O} \\
| & & | \\
\text{HOCH} & 3 & \text{HOCH} \\
| & & | \\
\text{HCOH} & 4 & \text{HCOH} \\
| & & | \\
\text{HCOH} & 5 & \text{HCOH} \\
| & & | \\
\text{CH}_2\text{OH} & 6 & \text{CH}_2\text{OH} \\
d\,(+)\text{-Glucose} & & l\,(-)\text{-Fructose}
\end{array}
$$

It will be observed that the configurations about carbon atoms 3, 4, and 5 are identical for the two substances. A convention of nomenclature has been devised based upon configurational rather than optical properties. The actual sign of rotation may still be indicated by the italic letters *d* and *l*, but the configuration is

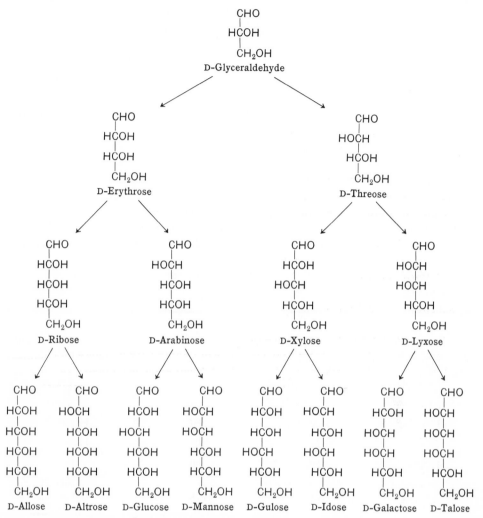

FIG. 2.1. Relationships of the D-aldoses. The formulas of the L-aldoses are in each case the mirror images of those structures given in the figure.

shown by the prefixed symbols in roman small capitals D and L. For the common sugars, the rule relates to that center of asymmetry most remote from the aldehydic end of the molecule; in hexoses this is carbon atom 5. Arbitrary configurations, now known to be correct in the absolute sense, have been assigned to the two glyceraldehydes,

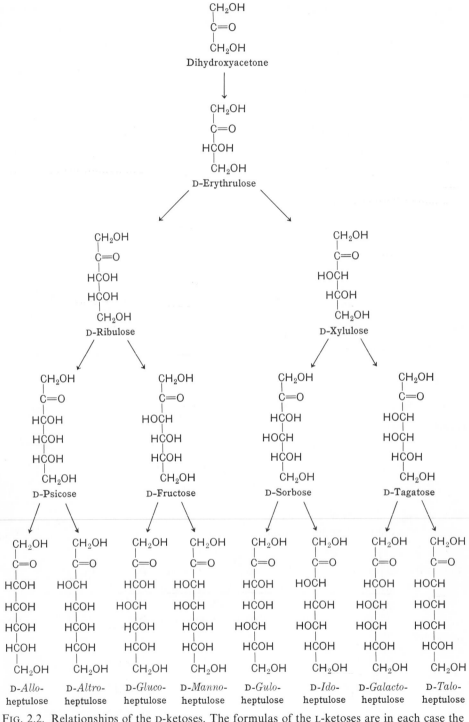

Fig. 2.2. Relationships of the D-ketoses. The formulas of the L-ketoses are in each case the mirror images of those structures given in the figure.

and all sugars terminating in these configurations are said to belong accordingly to the D or L configurational series. Thus both glucose and fructose are of the D series, and if the sign of rotation is to be included in the name, it is usually indicated as follows: D (+)-glucose, D (−)-fructose. The consistent utilization of these conventions permits the reasonable arrangement of sugars, as will be seen from the accompanying charts (Figs. 2.1 and 2.2) of the D-aldoses and D-ketoses.

It should be pointed out that these conventions can be employed only after configurational relationships have been established by unequivocal chemical means. Optically active materials of undetermined configuration must still be designated with respect to the sign of rotation. It should also be mentioned that some confusion may occasionally arise in nomenclature. Thus the products of oxidation of D-glucose and L-gulose to the dicarboxylic acid level are identical and may be given either of two names with equal justification.

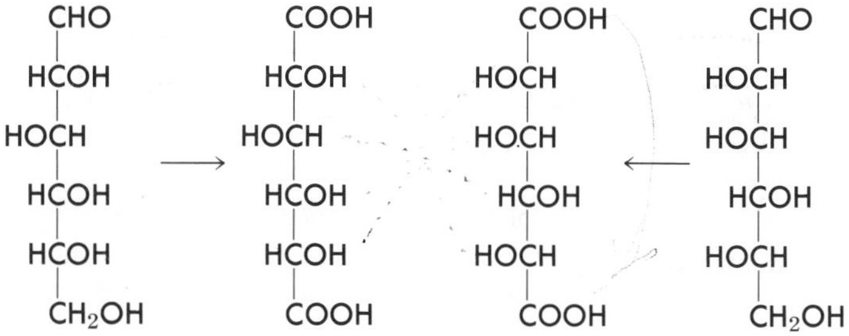

CHO	COOH	COOH	CHO
HCOH	HCOH	HOCH	HOCH
HOCH	HOCH	HOCH	HOCH
HCOH	HCOH	HCOH	HCOH
HCOH	HCOH	HOCH	HOCH
CH₂OH	COOH	COOH	CH₂OH
D-Glucose	D-Glucosaccharic acid	L-Gulosaccharic acid	L-Gulose

$$\text{CHO} \quad \xrightarrow{\hspace{1cm}} \quad \text{COOH} \qquad \text{COOH} \quad \xleftarrow{\hspace{1cm}} \quad \text{CHO}$$

Identical Products

FORMULATION OF MONOSACCHARIDES

Formula of D-Glucose, Linear Form. In writing structural and configurational formulas it is the intent of the organic chemist to indicate in shorthand as many of the characteristics of a compound as possible. When the earlier Fittig-Baeyer structural formula for glucose was replaced by the Fischer configurational formula,

CHO
HCOH
HOCH
HCOH
HCOH
CH₂OH

CHO
(CHOH)₄
CH₂OH

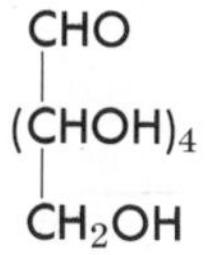

Glucose
(Fittig-Baeyer)

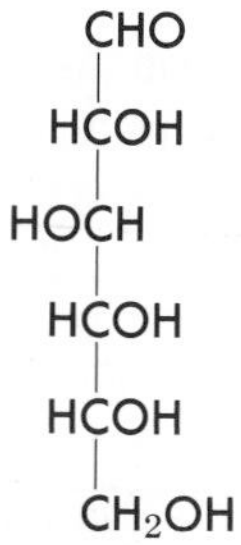

D-Glucose
(Fischer)

certain additional properties were taken into account. According to this formula, there were four asymmetric centers in the molecule, from which it could be calculated that D-glucose was one of 2^4 or 16 stereoisomers, and further stereoisomers were excluded. However, it soon became apparent that even this formulation failed to describe certain chemical properties of glucose.

Cyclic Structure of Glucose. The earliest indication that D-glucose existed in more than one configurational modification came from the finding that the specific rotation of a freshly prepared glucose solution changed under observation in the polarimeter. Ultimately two differing species of D-glucose could be prepared which in aqueous solution were found to exhibit widely differing optical activities. For the one, α-D-glucose, $[\alpha]_D^{20} = +112.2°$; for the other, β-D-glucose, $[\alpha]_D^{20} = +18.7°$. If these solutions were subjected to continued polarimetric observation, the specific rotations of each would approach the value of $+52.7°$, after which no further change would occur. This finding clearly meant there were two distinct stereoisomeric modifications of glucose, which were interconverted in aqueous solution to yield an equilibrium mixture represented by the final rotation. This phenomenon, termed *mutarotation*, is not peculiar to glucose but is a general phenomenon of sugars and has been observed for a variety of pentoses and hexoses, as well as certain disaccharides.

The demonstrated existence of two isomers of D-glucose requires that there be an additional asymmetric center in the formula. It was established that carbon atom 1 was the locus of this asymmetry, and formulas for α- and β-D-glucose have been assigned.

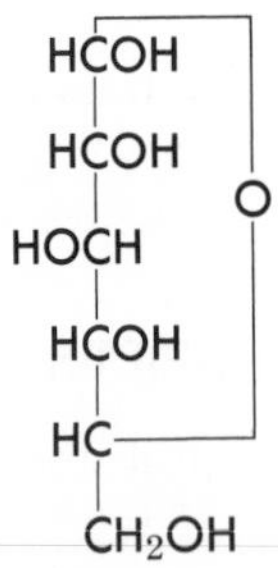

HCOH

HCOH

HOCH   O

HCOH

HC——

CH₂OH

α-D-Glucose
$[\alpha]_D^{20} = +112.2°$

HOCH

HCOH

HOCH   O

HCOH

HC——

CH₂OH

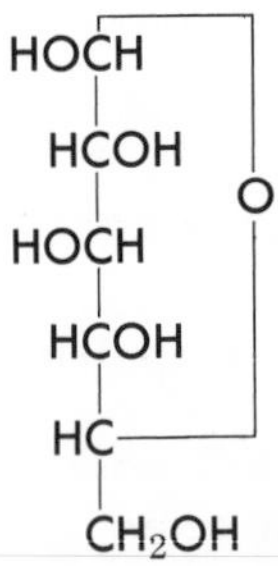

β-D-Glucose
$[\alpha]_D^{20} = +18.7°$

In this formulation there are five centers of asymmetry, hence $2^5 = 32$ possible isomers, permitting an α and β modification of each aldohexose. The α designation is used to indicate that the hydroxyl group on carbon atom 1 is on the same side of the structure as the ring oxygen; the β modification refers to the form in which the C-1 hydroxyl group is on the side of the structure opposite to the ring oxygen. It may be noted that among sugars of the D configuration, the α isomer always has an optical rotation higher than that of the β isomer.

This formulation also accounts for the fact that when glucose is treated with methanol and mineral acid, two distinct methyl glucosides are produced. The formulas of these may be written:

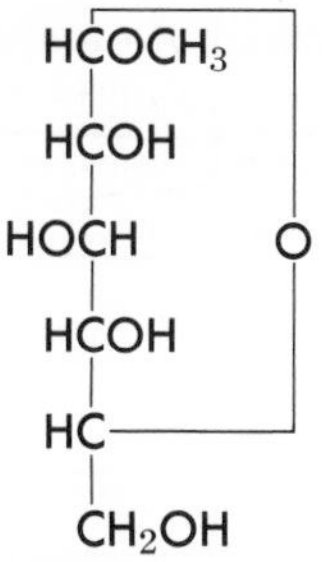

HCOCH₃
HCOH
HOCH   O
HCOH
HC
CH₂OH

Methyl α-D-glucoside
$[\alpha]_D^{20} = +158.9°$

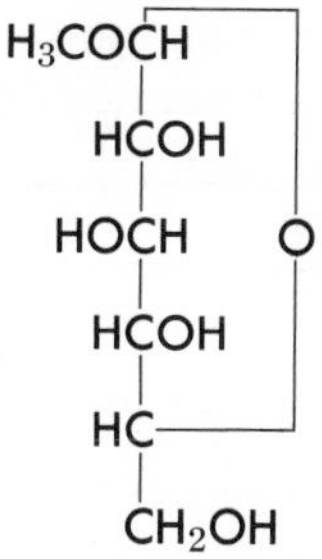

H₃COCH
HCOH
HOCH   O
HCOH
HC
CH₂OH

Methyl β-D-glucoside
$[\alpha]_D^{20} = -34.2°$

The oxygen bridge between the first and fifth carbon atoms results in a six-membered ring which resembles that of pyran,

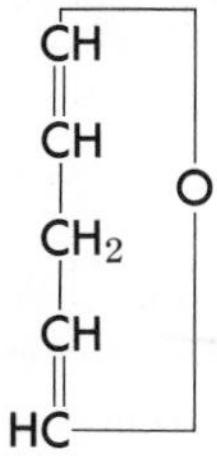

CH
CH
CH₂   O
CH
HC

Pyran

and sugars containing such a ring are termed *pyranoses.* Thus the above methyl α-D-glucoside may correctly be named methyl α-D-glucopyranoside. Among certain other sugars, the aldopentoses and ketohexoses, as they commonly occur in oligosaccharides, the ring is predominantly five-membered, and five-membered rings have also been prepared among certain aldohexoses (galactose, mannose).

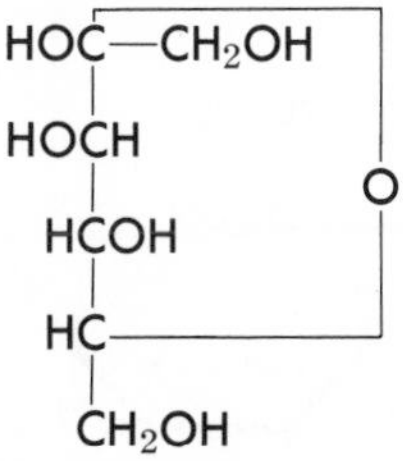

HOC—CH₂OH
HOCH
HCOH   O
HC
CH₂OH

β-D-Fructofuranose

HOCH
HOCH   O
HCOH
HC
CH₂OH

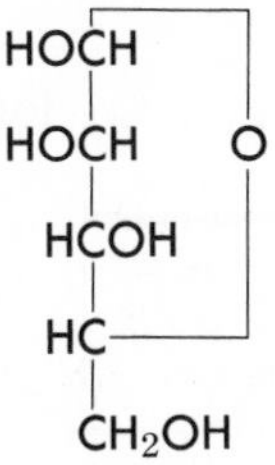

β-D-Arabinofuranose

The nomenclature here is based on the similarity of this ring to that of furan,

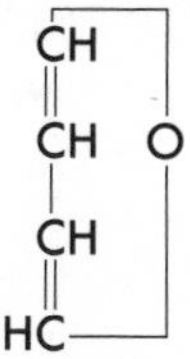

CH
CH   O
CH
HC

Furan

and sugars containing this type of ring are termed *furanoses*. It is generally supposed, albeit without evidence, that mutarotation, which involves mutual interconversion of α- and β-pyranoses and α- and β-furanoses, occurs through the intermediate formation of the open-chain aldehyde or its hydrate.

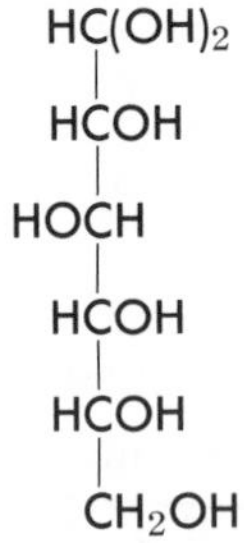

$$HC(OH)_2$$
$$|$$
$$HCOH$$
$$|$$
$$HOCH$$
$$|$$
$$HCOH$$
$$|$$
$$HCOH$$
$$|$$
$$CH_2OH$$

D-Glucose monohydrate

In aqueous solution the open-chain aldehyde is a very minor constituent of the equilibrium mixture. For glucose it has been estimated to represent 0.024 per cent of the total.

Hexagonal or Pentagonal Formulation. With the intent of writing structural formulas which more accurately summarize the properties of pyranoses and furanoses, Haworth has advocated that these formulas be written as more or less regular hexagons and pentagons. These rings are now no longer in the plane of the paper, and this is shown by shading those cyclic bonds which are indicated to be nearer to the reader.

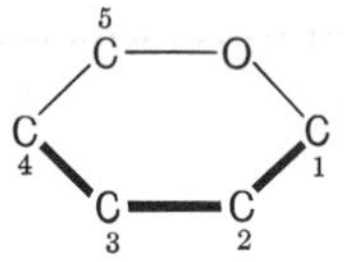

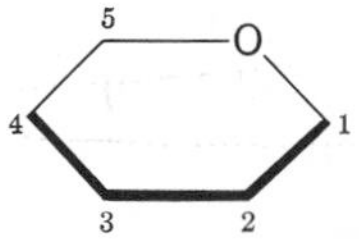

In this convention the two forms of D-glucopyranose become

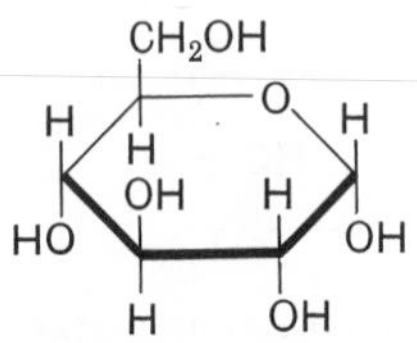

α-D-Glucopyranose 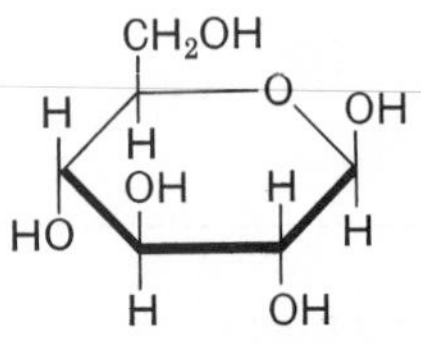   β-D-Glucopyranose

Similarly, in pentagonal form, the furanoses may be represented as follows:

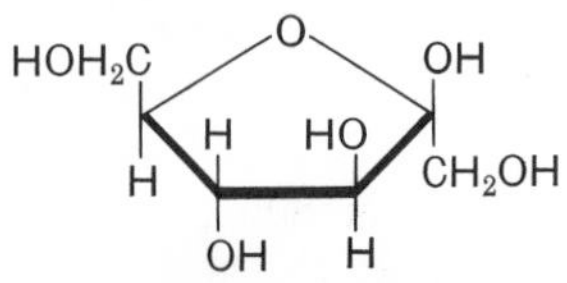

β-D-Fructofuranose 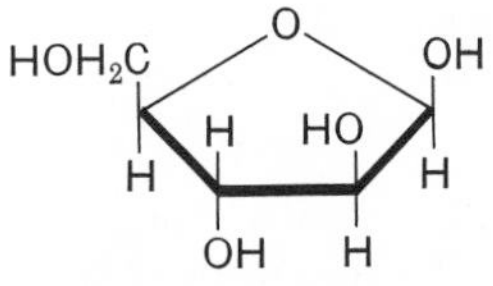   β-D-Arabinofuranose

The transition from one convention to the other relates the left and right sides of the carbon chain of Fischer to the upper and lower aspects, respectively, of the plane of the ring of Haworth. Exceptions do occur, as will be seen by comparing the arrangement about carbon-5 of glucose in the two conventions. In the linear formulation the hydrogen at this position is to the left of the carbon, while in the hexagonal formulation it is below the plane of the ring. The reader is referred to texts on carbohydrate chemistry for a detailed discussion of this transition.

Conformational Representation. Whereas the six atoms in the benzene ring lie in one plane, the normal valence angle of the carbon atom precludes a stable planar arrangement for the six carbon atoms of cyclohexane. From atomic model studies, two types of arrangement in space, *conformations,* are readily shown to exist, the "chair" and "boat" forms.

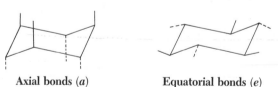

Chair   Boat

Cyclohexane

It is now established, on energetic grounds, that the chair form is quite rigid and by far the more stable. Considerable force is needed to distort the chair form or to convert it to another form. The boat form is, however, completely flexible and has an infinite number of possible actual conformations in solution. The 12 hydrogen atoms of cyclohexane now fall into two classes, those on C—H bonds parallel to the axis of symmetry of the ring, *axial,* and those which radiate more or less in the plane of the ring, or *equatorial.* These relationships are shown in the following conformational formulas.

Axial bonds (*a*)   **Equatorial bonds (*e*)**

It will be noted from the above, as well as from the previously indicated chair form of cyclohexane, that at each carbon atom one hydrogen is up or directed upwards, and the other is down or directed downwards. The six hydrogens that are up are termed β-hydrogens and are represented by solid lines; those that are down are α-hydrogens and are represented as dotted lines.

The conformational method of representation is far more than an exercise in projectional geometry. It reveals properties of the molecule that are not at once apparent from other representations of structure. A generalization of importance is that a substituent, particularly a large substituent, is at a lower energy state in the equatorial than in the axial location. An equatorially disposed substituent is more remote from its neighbors than is an axial substituent. Therefore, for example, in the equilibrium between the conformational isomers of methylcyclohexane,

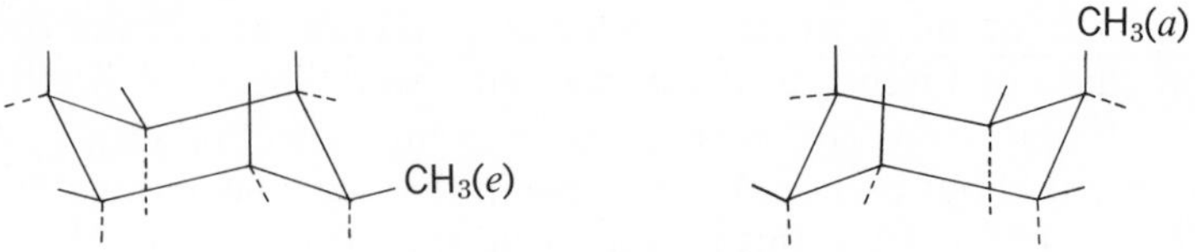

CH₃(a)

CH₃(e)

Methylcyclohexane

the equatorial form preponderates. As might be expected, equatorial hydroxyl groups are more readily esterified than axial hydroxyls, and there are many known instances of differences in chemical reactivity of groups, depending upon whether they are axially or equatorially disposed.

Conformational formulas are also useful in the field of sugar chemistry and will again be encountered in the consideration of steroid chemistry. Conformational formulation of aldohexoses is particularly meaningful in interpreting reactivity of hydroxyl groups.

The conformational representation of glucose, in this convention, is:

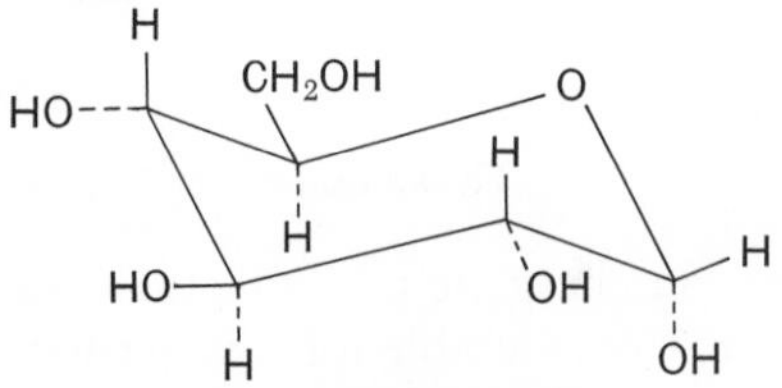

α-D-**Glucose**

Hemiacetal and Acetal Bonds. A pair of stereoisomers related to each other as are α- and β-D-glucose are said to be *anomers*, and since their sole configurational difference resides in steric arrangement about carbon atom 1, the "carbonyl" carbon of the linear formula, this atom has been termed the *anomeric carbon atom*. Considerable interest attaches to the arrangement of substituents about this reactive center.

When an aldehyde is allowed to react with two equivalents of alcohol, the product is called an acetal.

$$\underset{}{RCHO + 2HOR'} \longrightarrow R\overset{\overset{\displaystyle H}{|}}{\underset{\underset{\displaystyle OR'}{|}}{C}}-OR' + H_2O$$

Acetal

If the quantity of alcohol is restricted, the expected product is a hemiacetal,

$$RCHO + HOR' \longrightarrow R\overset{\overset{\displaystyle H}{|}}{\underset{\underset{\displaystyle OH}{|}}{C}}-OR'$$

Hemiacetal

and it will be noted that the formerly aldehydic carbon atom now bears four different substituents, —H, —OH, —OR', and —R. Every carbon atom similarly located is a hemiacetal carbon atom, and this is precisely the arrangement of substituents about the anomeric carbon atom in position 1 of glucopyranose. A distinctive feature of the hemiacetal carbon in monosaccharides is that the —OR′ and R substituents stem from the same molecule, making intramolecular hemiacetals. In this these compounds bear an analogy to the lactones, which are intramolecular esters. Fructofuranose, in which the anomeric carbon atom 2 bears R, R′, OR″, and OH as substituents, has a structure analogous to that of the reaction product of a ketone and alcohol,

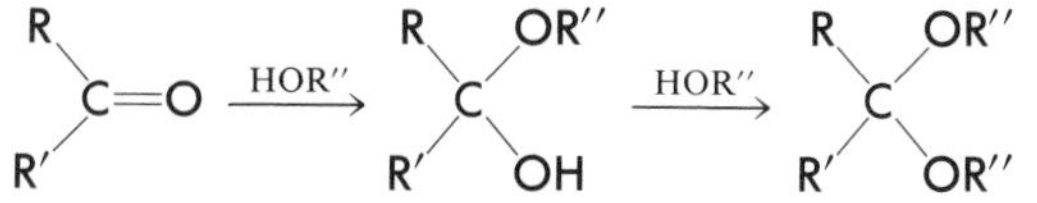

$$
\underset{\text{Hemiketal}}{\overset{R}{\underset{R'}{\diagup}}C=O \xrightarrow{\text{HOR''}} \overset{R \quad OR''}{\underset{R' \quad OH}{C}}} \xrightarrow{\text{HOR''}} \underset{\text{Ketal}}{\overset{R \quad OR''}{\underset{R' \quad OR''}{C}}}
$$

and may therefore be designated as a hemiketal.

Glycosidic Bond. The residual hydroxyl group of a hemiacetal can react with an alcohol to yield an acetal. This is what occurs when methanol reacts with glucose,

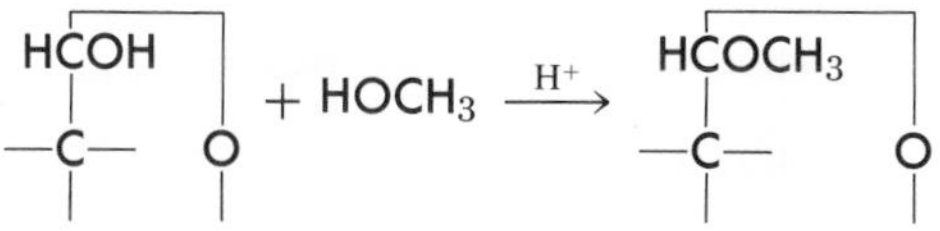

$$
\begin{array}{c} \text{HCOH} \\ | \\ -\text{C}- \quad \text{O} \\ | \quad | \end{array} + \text{HOCH}_3 \xrightarrow{\text{H}^+} \begin{array}{c} \text{HCOCH}_3 \\ | \\ -\text{C}- \quad \text{O} \\ | \quad | \end{array}
$$

and the product, a mixed acetal, wherein one alcoholic contribution comes from outside while the other is intramolecular, is called a *glucoside.* This is one of a group of compounds known as *glycosides,* formed when the hydroxyl group on the anomeric carbon atom of a monosaccharide has reacted with an alcohol to form an acetal. Since this reaction may occur with either the α- or β-stereoisomer, there exist the corresponding groups of α- and β-glycosides. The members of these groups are named in accordance with the monosaccharides from which they are derived, e.g., α- and β-glucosides, α- and β-galactosides, etc. It should be noted particularly that in reactivity the hemiacetal hydroxyl is quite different from an alcoholic hydroxyl group, and likewise the glycoside oxygen bridge, though bearing some superficial resemblance to an ether bridge, has none of the chemical stability generally found in aliphatic ethers.

Relatively few monosaccharides occur free in nature. Much more frequently they are found either conjugated one to another or bound to noncarbohydrate materials. In most cases, this coupling is effected through the anomeric carbon atom, and the bond proves to be a glycosidic bond. In the polysaccharides the pattern is one of glycosidic bonds between the anomeric carbon of one monosaccharide and an alcoholic hydroxyl group of an adjacent monosaccharide. Occasionally (cf. sucrose), the glycosidic bond is between two anomeric carbon atoms.

REFERENCES

See list following Chap. 4.

3. Chemistry of Carbohydrates

Monosaccharides

Whereas only glucose and fructose occur abundantly in nature as free mono-saccharides, several other simple sugars are repeatedly encountered, either as units of disaccharides and polysaccharides or in other types of linkage. The hexoses which commonly are present in these combined forms are the aldohexoses, *viz.*, glucose, galactose, and mannose, and the 2-ketohexose, fructose.

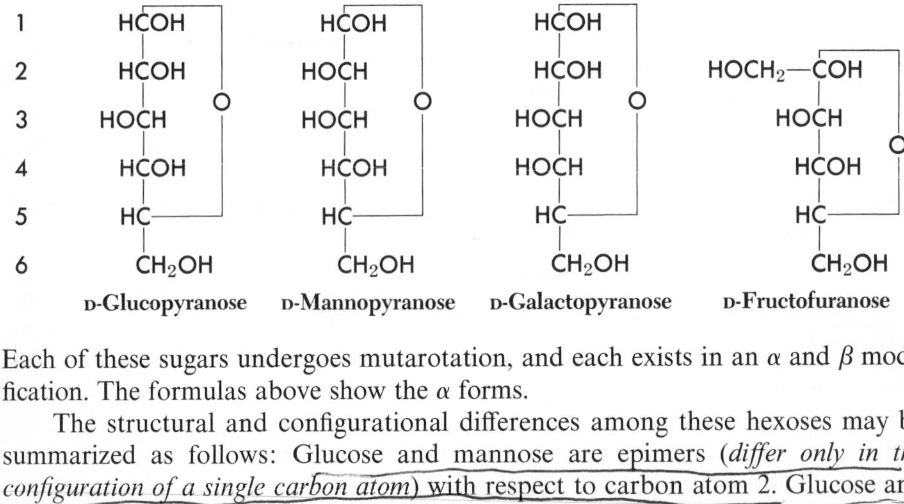

1	HCOH	HCOH	HCOH	
2	HCOH	HOCH	HCOH	HOCH$_2$—COH
3	HOCH	HOCH	HOCH	HOCH
4	HCOH	HCOH	HOCH	HCOH
5	HC—	HC—	HC—	HC—
6	CH$_2$OH	CH$_2$OH	CH$_2$OH	CH$_2$OH

D-Glucopyranose   D-Mannopyranose   D-Galactopyranose   D-Fructofuranose

Each of these sugars undergoes mutarotation, and each exists in an α and β modification. The formulas above show the α forms.

The structural and configurational differences among these hexoses may be summarized as follows: Glucose and mannose are epimers (*differ only in the configuration of a single carbon atom*) with respect to carbon atom 2. Glucose and galactose represent an epimeric pair with respect to carbon-4. Fructose differs from the others in that its anomeric carbon atom is 2 rather than 1. With respect to configuration about atoms 3, 4, and 5, fructose is identical with glucose and mannose.

The cyclic formulations for mannose, galactose, and fructose are shown:

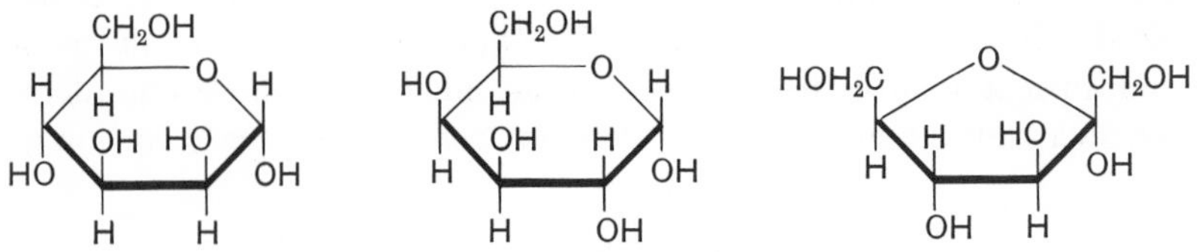

α-D-Mannopyranose α-D-Galactopyranose α-D-Fructofuranose

Only one other hexose occurs in natural products; this is the ketohexose, sorbose.

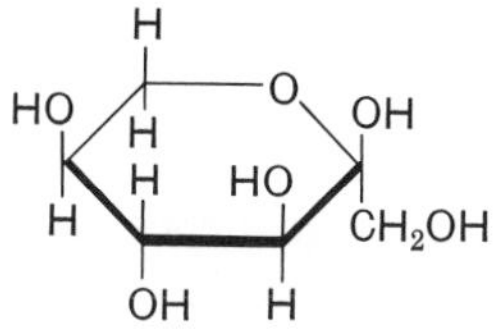

α-L-**Sorbopyranose**

Among the naturally occurring pentoses are the aldoses, L-arabinose, D-ribose, and D-xylose, and the ketopentose, L-xylulose.

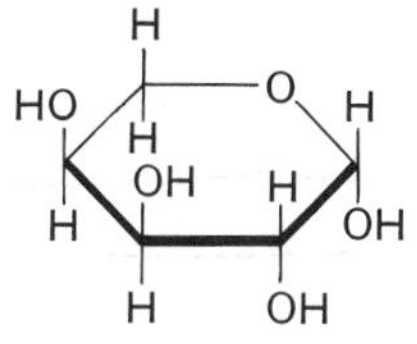

β-L-**Arabinopyranose**

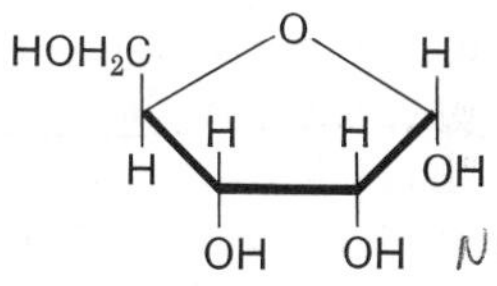

α-D-**Ribofuranose**

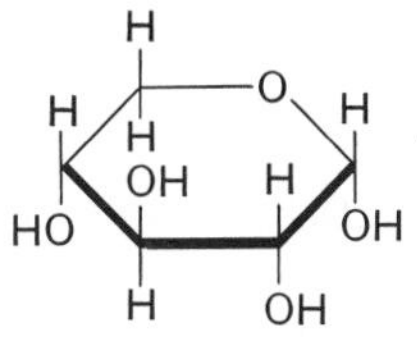

α-D-**Xylopyranose**

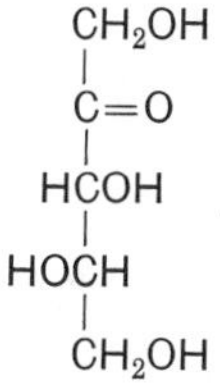

L-**Xylulose**

Whereas arabinose and xylose are found chiefly in plant products, ribose occurs as the characteristic sugar in certain nucleic acids (Chap. 10) of both plants and animals, and xylulose is an abnormal constituent of urine (Chap. 37).

GENERAL REACTIONS OF MONOSACCHARIDES

Additions to the Anomeric Carbon. The method of elongation of the carbon skeleton of an aldose, which has been widely employed both as a synthetic device and as an aid to proof of configuration, is the cyanohydrin synthesis.

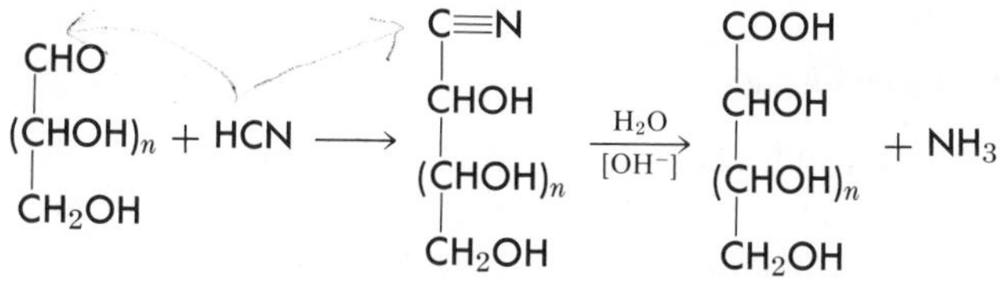

The lactone of such a sugar acid may in turn be reduced to the corresponding hemiacetal by sodium amalgam.

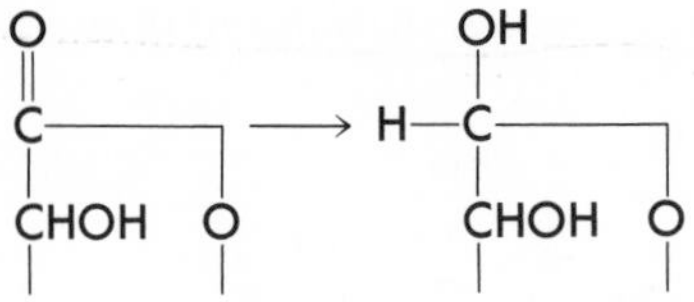

The final products of such a reaction sequence are two aldoses, epimeric at carbon atom 2. Thus, from β-D-arabinose there is obtained a mixture of D-glucose and D-mannose, with the latter predominating. The two products are not obtained in equal amounts, since the asymmetry of the pentose favors one of the two configurations. This phenomenon is known as *asymmetric induction*. It is worth noting that all the D-aldoses can be formed by repetitive syntheses from D-glyceraldehyde, while L-aldoses can be made from L-glyceraldehyde. Ketoses, similarly treated, give rise to branched-chain structures.

Mention has been made (page 21) of glycosides in which the alcoholic hydroxyl of one monosaccharide portion has lost the elements of water in reaction with the hemiacetal hydroxyl of an adjacent monosaccharide. This type of linkage, the fundamental linkage of most di- and trisaccharides and all polysaccharides, is shown in maltose (4-O-α-D-glucopyranosyl-D-glucose).

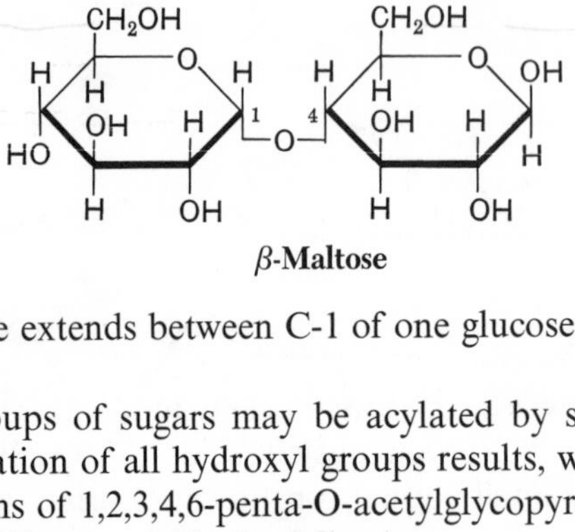

β-**Maltose**

Here the acetal linkage extends between C-1 of one glucose moiety and C-4 of the other.

The hydroxyl groups of sugars may be acylated by suitable reagents. With acetic anhydride, acylation of all hydroxyl groups results, with formation of either the α or β modifications of 1,2,3,4,6-penta-O-acetylglycopyranose, depending upon conditions employed. Glucose yields the following:

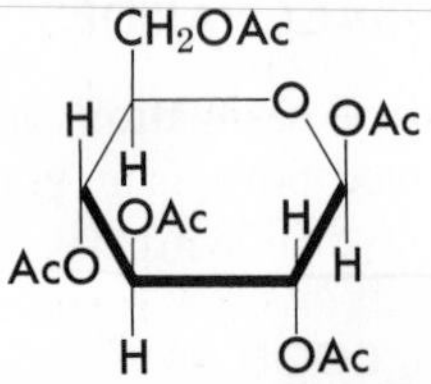

Penta-O-acetyl-β-D-glucose

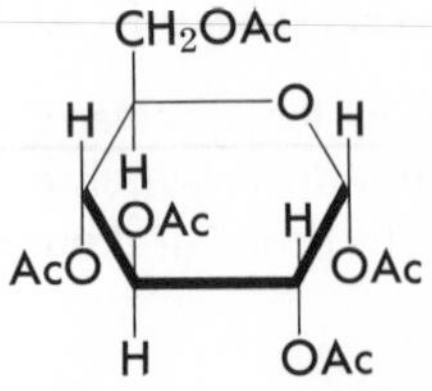

Penta-O-acetyl-α-D-glucose

In strong acid, these products yield an equilibrium mixture which, for glucose, is approximately 90 per cent α form and 10 per cent β form. From such esters the initial sugars may be regenerated by cautious hydrolysis or transesterification:

Glucose pentaacetate + 5 methanol $\longrightarrow$ 5 methyl acetate + glucose

This reaction proceeds effectively with sodium methylate at low temperature.

Phosphoric Acid Esters. Among the many known sugar esters, those of phosphoric acid occupy a unique position in biochemistry. Phosphoric acid esters are encountered with trioses, tetroses, pentoses, hexoses, and heptoses, as well as with derived sugars such as sugar acids and sugar alcohols. Indeed, phosphorylation of all sugars is the initial step in their metabolism. Thus, glucose is converted to glucose 6-phosphate. In many living systems, this compound may be further transformed into α-glucose 1-phosphate. Glucose 6-phosphate may also be converted to fructose 6-phosphate, which upon further phosphorylation yields fructose 1,6-diphosphate. The formulas of these esters are given below.

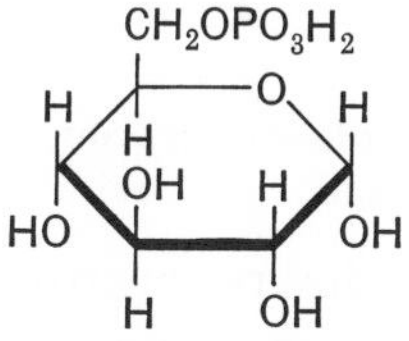

Glucose 6-phosphate

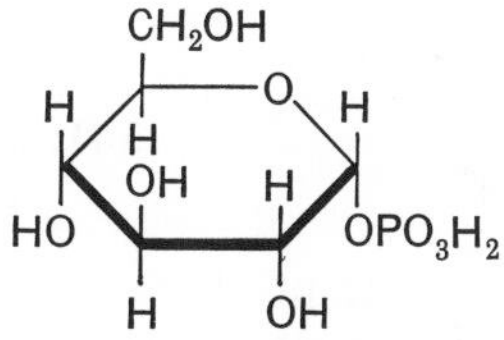

Glucose 1-phosphate

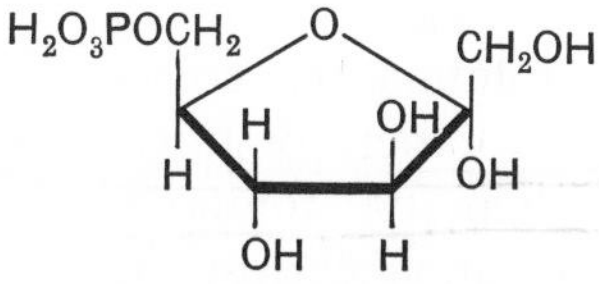

Fructose 6-phosphate

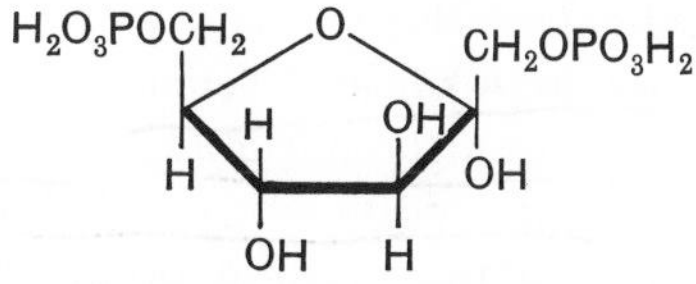

Fructose 1,6-diphosphate

Methylation of Hydroxyl Groups. In addition to esterification, the hydroxyl groups may undergo etherification. Methylation of the *hemiacetal* hydroxyl on the anomeric carbon atom proceeds readily with methanol and acid catalyst and yields a glycoside, which is an acetal, not an ether. Methylation of the *alcoholic* hydroxyl groups requires much more vigorous conditions, *e.g.*, dimethyl sulfate plus alkali or methyl iodide plus silver oxide. Repeated treatment is often required to obtain etherification of all the hydroxyl groups. The reaction has been extensively employed to ascertain which hydroxyl groups in a sugar are free and available for reaction. Thus methyl glucopyranoside is methylated in positions 2, 3, 4, and 6, but not in position 5, which is involved in the hemiacetal link. Similarly with disaccharides and with polysaccharides, exhaustive methylation followed by hydrolysis—the ether link is very resistant to hydrolysis—yields methylated monosaccharides, the study of which may provide much information.

Reactions in Acid Solution. In strong mineral acid the characteristic reaction of sugars is dehydration. From pentoses, the product obtained is furfural.

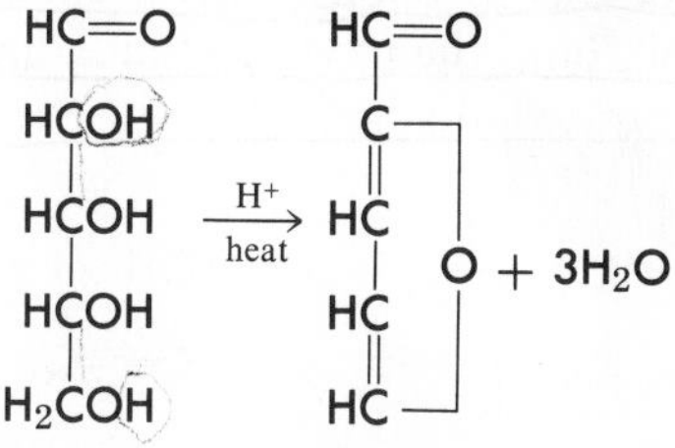

Furfural

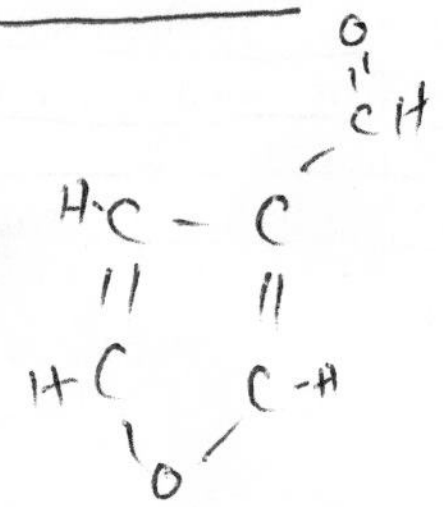

With hexoses, the analogous reaction leads to formation of 5-hydroxymethyl-furfural, which on further heating is transformed to levulinic acid.

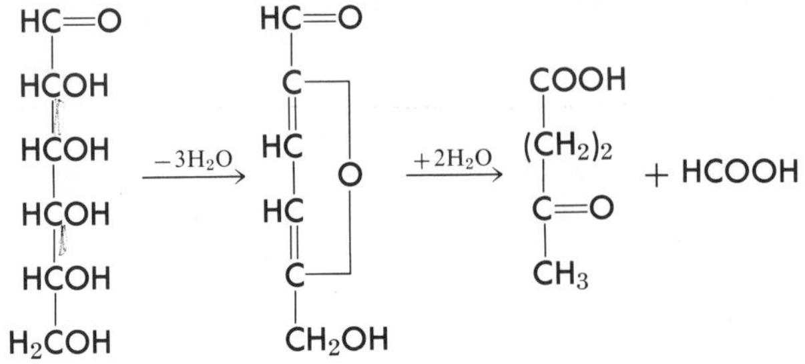

$$
\begin{array}{c}
HC{=}O \\
| \\
HCOH \\
| \\
HCOH \\
| \\
HCOH \\
| \\
HCOH \\
| \\
H_2COH
\end{array}
\xrightarrow{-3H_2O}
\begin{array}{c}
HC{=}O \\
| \\
C{-} \\
\| \\
HC \quad O \\
\| \\
HC \\
| \\
C{-} \\
| \\
CH_2OH
\end{array}
\xrightarrow{+2H_2O}
\begin{array}{c}
COOH \\
| \\
(CH_2)_2 \\
| \\
C{=}O \\
| \\
CH_3
\end{array}
+ \; HCOOH
$$

| 5-Hydroxymethyl-
furfural | Levulinic
acid | Formic
acid |

The aldehydic products of these reactions readily polymerize to give brown tars. They also condense with various phenols to give characteristically colored products, and many of the color tests for sugars depend upon such condensations (see Table 3.1, page 30).

Reactions in Alkaline Solution. In alkaline solution the common monosaccharides are extremely unstable. They undergo a variety of fragmentations, rearrangements, and polymerizations, and more than 100 compounds have been identified among the reaction products of alkali upon glucose. These reactions may lead to the appearance of branched chains, as in saccharinic acid.

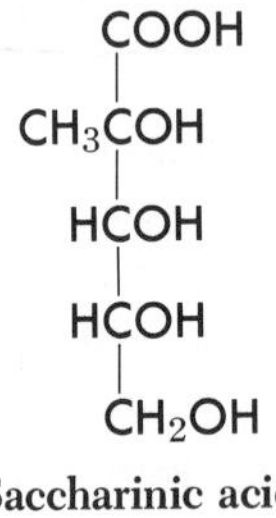

$$
\begin{array}{c}
COOH \\
| \\
CH_3COH \\
| \\
HCOH \\
| \\
HCOH \\
| \\
CH_2OH
\end{array}
$$

Saccharinic acid

Formaldehyde and glycolaldehyde as well as triose and tetrose fragments have been isolated from the alkaline degradation of hexoses.

One reaction observed at low temperatures with dilute alkali merits special consideration because of the analogy that it bears to certain biochemical transformations. This is the Lobry de Bruyn–van Ekenstein transformation. If glucose is treated under these conditions, as the glucose disappears, fructose and mannose appear. The mechanism of this reaction involves enolization, the migration of a proton from a carbon atom onto the oxygen of an adjacent carbonyl group, with the formation of an unsaturated alcohol, an enol (*-ene* indicates unsaturation, *-ol* indicates a hydroxyl group).

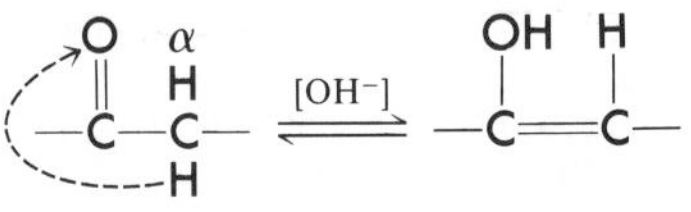

$$
\begin{array}{c}
\overset{O}{\underset{\|}{}} \; \overset{\alpha}{} \\
-\overset{}{C}-\overset{H}{\underset{}{C}}- \\
\quad\;\; {-}{-}{-}H
\end{array}
\xrightleftharpoons{[OH^-]}
\begin{array}{c}
OH \quad H \\
| \qquad | \\
-C{=}C- \\
\end{array}
$$

| Ketone or
aldehyde | Enol |

Enolization is a general phenomenon of aldehydes or ketones, the α-carbon of which bears a hydrogen atom. When a hydroxyaldehyde or hydroxyketone undergoes enolization, the product is termed an ene*diol*.

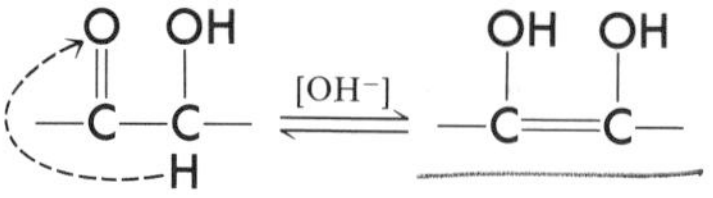

$$-\overset{\displaystyle O}{\underset{\displaystyle |}{C}}-\overset{\displaystyle OH}{\underset{\displaystyle |}{C}}- \quad \underset{[OH^-]}{\rightleftharpoons} \quad -\overset{\displaystyle OH}{C}=\overset{\displaystyle OH}{C}-$$
$$\overset{}{\underset{H}{|}}$$

Enediol

Present evidence indicates that the transformation of glucose into fructose and mannose is a stepwise reaction proceeding via enediol formation as follows:

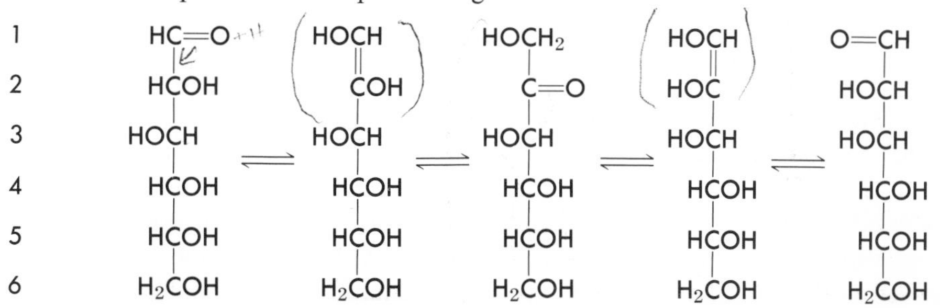

	Glucose	*trans*-Enediol	Fructose	*cis*-Enediol	Mannose
1	HC=O	HOCH	HOCH₂	HOCH	O=CH
2	HCOH	COH	C=O	HOC	HOCH
3	HOCH	HOCH	HOCH	HOCH	HOCH
4	HCOH	HCOH	HCOH	HCOH	HCOH
5	HCOH	HCOH	HCOH	HCOH	HCOH
6	H₂COH	H₂COH	H₂COH	H₂COH	H₂COH

This relationship among glucose, fructose, and mannose is one of the consequences of the identical steric configurations in these compounds about carbon atoms 3, 4, and 5.

Probably related to the phenomenon of enolization is the fact that the common sugars exhibit properties of weak acids. Under suitable circumstances salts of sugars with cations may be isolated from alkaline solution, a characteristic reminiscent of the much-studied enol, acetoacetic ester. The acidic dissociation constants of several monosaccharides that have been measured are approximately 10^{-12}, which means that they are considerably less acidic than phenol, yet more acidic than water.

Reduction of Monosaccharides. When a simple sugar is treated with H_2 gas under pressure in the presence of a metal catalyst, or with an active metal, such as Ca, in water, the carbonyl group is reduced to an alcoholic hydroxyl group, yielding a polyhydric alcohol. D-Glucose, under these circumstances, yields sorbitol, which, it will be noted, is also a product of the reduction of L-sorbose.

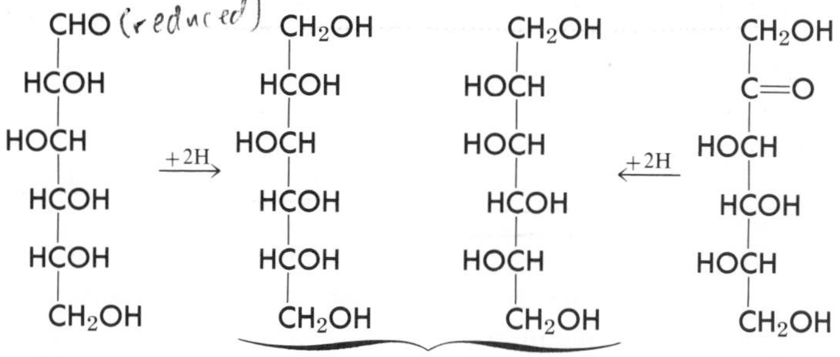

D-Glucose		Sorbitol		L-Sorbose
CHO	$\xrightarrow{+2H}$	CH₂OH	$\xleftarrow{+2H}$	CH₂OH
HCOH		HCOH		C=O
HOCH		HOCH		HOCH
HCOH		HCOH		HCOH
HCOH		HCOH		HOCH
CH₂OH		CH₂OH		CH₂OH

Reduction of mannose yields mannitol, and galactose, similarly treated, yields dulcitol.

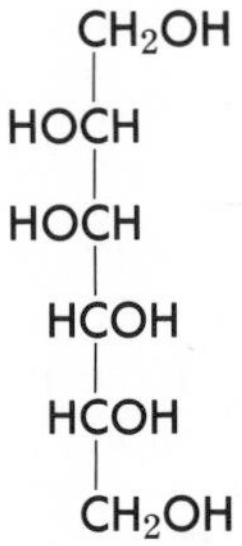

$$
\begin{array}{cc}
\text{CH}_2\text{OH} & \text{CH}_2\text{OH} \\
\text{HOCH} & \text{HCOH} \\
\text{HOCH} & \text{HOCH} \\
\text{HCOH} & \text{HOCH} \\
\text{HCOH} & \text{HCOH} \\
\text{CH}_2\text{OH} & \text{CH}_2\text{OH} \\
\text{D-Mannitol} & \text{Dulcitol}
\end{array}
$$

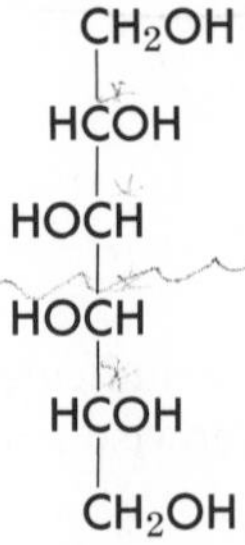

It may be noted that dulcitol is a *meso* compound, possessing four asymmetric carbon atoms, but with a plane of molecular symmetry between carbon atoms 3 and 4.

Sorbitol is widely distributed in plants, and the other two alcohols mentioned have also been isolated from vegetable sources. Although not abundant in animal tissues, both sorbitol and xylitol occur in mammals as products of enzymic reduction of appropriate monosaccharides.

Oxidation of Monosaccharides. Many oxidizing agents attack aldoses. Among these perhaps the simplest to picture is alkaline hypohalite. When iodine is dissolved in alkali it undergoes a dismutation.

$$
2\text{NaOH} + \text{I}_2 \longrightarrow \text{NaI} + \text{NaOI} + \text{H}_2\text{O}
$$

Sodium   Sodium
iodide   hypoiodite

Sodium hypoiodite in turn reacts with aldoses to give the sodium salts of the aldonic acids.

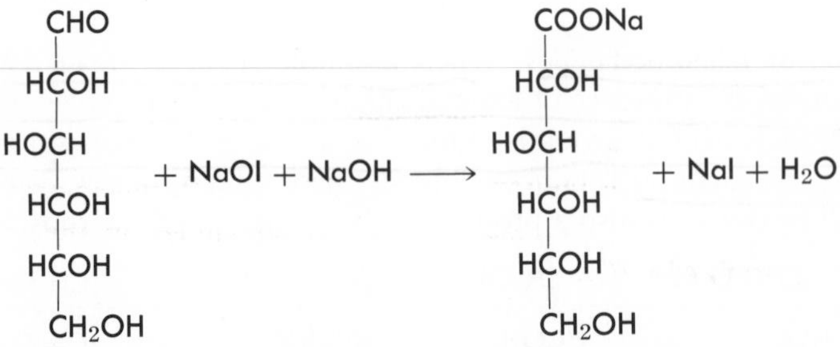

$$
\begin{array}{ccc}
\text{CHO} & & \text{COONa} \\
\text{HCOH} & & \text{HCOH} \\
\text{HOCH} & +\ \text{NaOI} + \text{NaOH} \longrightarrow & \text{HOCH} \quad +\ \text{NaI} + \text{H}_2\text{O} \\
\text{HCOH} & & \text{HCOH} \\
\text{HCOH} & & \text{HCOH} \\
\text{CH}_2\text{OH} & & \text{CH}_2\text{OH} \\
\text{D-Glucose} & & \text{Sodium D-gluconate}
\end{array}
$$

This oxidation is specific for the aldoses and is the basis for an analytical method that distinguishes them from ketoses. In this method the unspent NaOI is reconverted into I_2 by acidification, and the I_2 may then be titrated with sodium thiosulfate. The specific nature of this reaction and the excellent yields obtained make it a valuable preparative method as well.

In alkaline solution monosaccharides are susceptible to oxidation by a variety of agents, including cupric ion, silver ion, and ferricyanide ion. Although these reagents are widely employed in analytical methods for sugars, mixtures of products are generally obtained, rendering them of little value in preparative chemistry.

An oxidant that has proved useful in the elucidation of structural relationships is nitric acid. This reagent, in addition to oxidizing the aldehydic group, also attacks the primary alcoholic group and yields dicarboxylic acids, generically called saccharic acids.

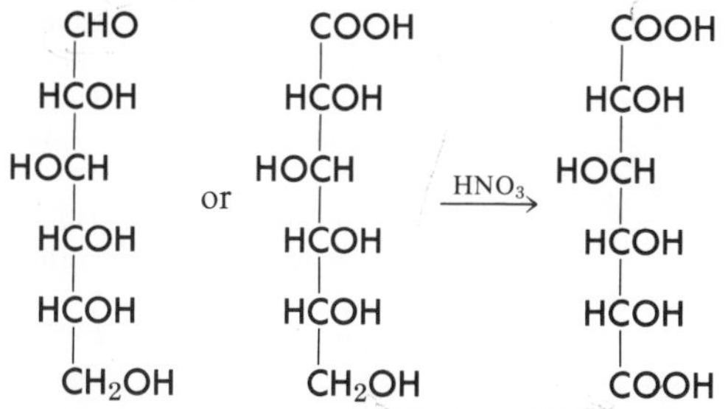

$$
\begin{array}{ccc}
\text{CHO} & \text{COOH} & \text{COOH} \\
\text{HCOH} & \text{HCOH} & \text{HCOH} \\
\text{HOCH} & \text{HOCH} & \text{HOCH} \\
\text{HCOH} & \text{HCOH} & \text{HCOH} \\
\text{HCOH} & \text{HCOH} & \text{HCOH} \\
\text{CH}_2\text{OH} & \text{CH}_2\text{OH} & \text{COOH} \\
\text{D-Glucose} & \text{D-Gluconic acid} & \text{D-Glucaric acid}
\end{array}
$$

D-Glucose   or   D-Gluconic acid $\xrightarrow{\text{HNO}_3}$ D-Glucaric acid (saccharic acid)

The corresponding product of oxidation of galactose, mucic acid, has two noteworthy properties. Because of internal compensation mucic acid is devoid of optical activity.

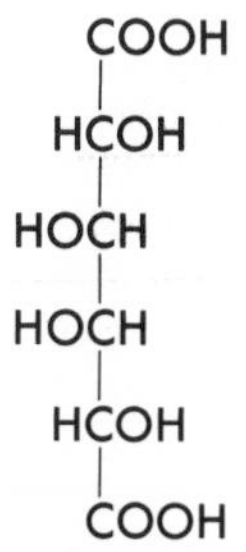

$$
\begin{array}{c}
\text{COOH} \\
\text{HCOH} \\
\text{HOCH} \\
\text{HOCH} \\
\text{HCOH} \\
\text{COOH}
\end{array}
$$

Mucic acid

Of the common members of the family of saccharic acids, mucic acid is the least soluble in acid solution, a fact that is used to advantage in the identification of galactose in sugar mixtures.

Sugar Derivatives and Identification of Individual Sugars. For the qualitative analysis of sugar or sugars present in a mixture the biochemist employs several approaches. Various more or less specific color tests for certain classes of sugars have been devised (Table 3.1), and the dietary habits of various microorganisms have been used to advantage. In addition to the native fermentative abilities of microorganisms, numerous types of organisms artificially adapted to the consumption of one or another carbohydrate have been used for analytical purposes.

The identification of a sugar, as of any organic compound, includes the

Table 3.1: COLOR REACTIONS OF SUGARS*

Reagent	Sugar type	Comment
α-Naphthol (Molisch reaction) Tryptophan Aminoguanidine	All aldoses and ketoses	More sensitive for ketoses
Resorcinol (Seliwanoff reaction)..	Ketohexoses	
Cysteine-carbazole............	Ketohexoses, ketopentoses, methylpentoses, dihydroxyacetone	
Carbazole...................	All carbohydrates, including uronic acids, deoxypentoses	Characteristically different colors with different sugars
Cysteine-H_2SO_4...............	Many sugars, including polysaccharides; generally used for hexoses	Different colors obtained with different sugars
Anthrone....................	Many sugars, including polysaccharides; generally used for hexoses	Different colors obtained with different sugars
Orcinol.....................	Pentoses, heptuloses, uronic acids	Colors due to other sugars may be corrected for by independent methods. Uronic acids decarboxylate to pentose and then give reaction
Naphthoresorcinol............	Uronic acids	
Acetylacetone-*p*-dimethylamino-benzaldehyde..............	Hexosamines	
Nitrite-indole.................	Hexosamines	Amino sugars give no color without prior deamination by nitrite
Diphenylamine...............	Mono- and dideoxypentoses	
Tryptophan-perchloric acid......	Deoxypentoses	
Indole-HCl...................	Deoxypentoses	
Leucofuchsin (Feulgen reaction)..	Deoxypentoses	

* The reagents commonly employed and the carbohydrates for which each is most useful are given. All reactions shown occur in strongly acidic solution. None is entirely specific; except for the tests for hexosamines, all the other reactions are given by polysaccharides as well as monosaccharides.

formation and characterization of one or more suitable derivatives. For this purpose, a frequently employed reagent is phenylhydrazine,

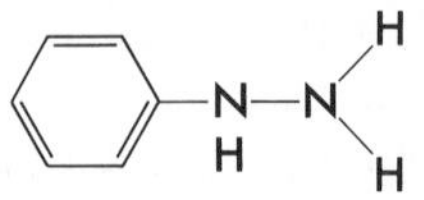

which reacts with carbonyl compounds in neutral or slightly acid aqueous solution to yield phenylhydrazones.

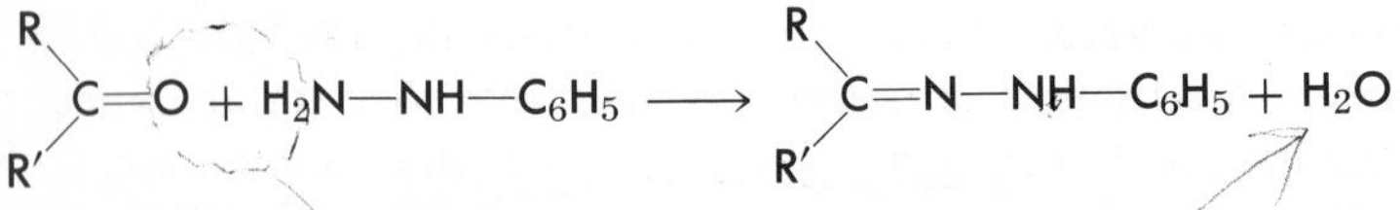

In certain instances the phenylhydrazone is sufficiently insoluble to separate from solution, and the reaction stops at that point. Thus mannose at low temperature yields a phenylhydrazone which is readily isolated.

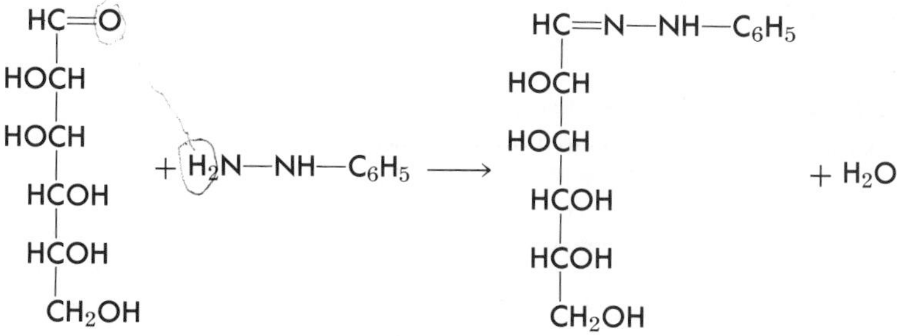

$$\begin{array}{ccc}
\text{HC=O} & & \text{HC=N—NH—C}_6\text{H}_5 \\
\text{HOCH} & & \text{HOCH} \\
\text{HOCH} & +\ \text{H}_2\text{N—NH—C}_6\text{H}_5 \longrightarrow & \text{HOCH} & +\ \text{H}_2\text{O} \\
\text{HCOH} & & \text{HCOH} \\
\text{HCOH} & & \text{HCOH} \\
\text{CH}_2\text{OH} & & \text{CH}_2\text{OH}
\end{array}$$

D-**Mannose**   **Phenylhydrazine**   D-**Mannose phenylhydrazone**

With many sugars, however, including galactose, fructose, glucose, and indeed mannose at higher temperatures, and in the presence of excess phenylhydrazine, the reaction proceeds further to yield a product called a phenylosazone,

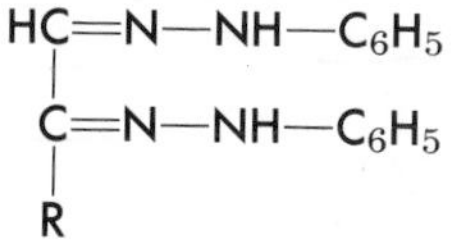

$$\begin{array}{c}
\text{HC=N—NH—C}_6\text{H}_5 \\
\text{C=N—NH—C}_6\text{H}_5 \\
\text{R}
\end{array}$$

Phenylosazone

and since such osazones are usually insoluble, they may readily be recovered.

In the course of osazone formation from the several hexoses, any differences in configuration about carbon atoms 1 and 2 will be abolished, and hexoses which differ from each other only in these positions, e.g., glucose, fructose, and mannose, yield the same phenylosazone.

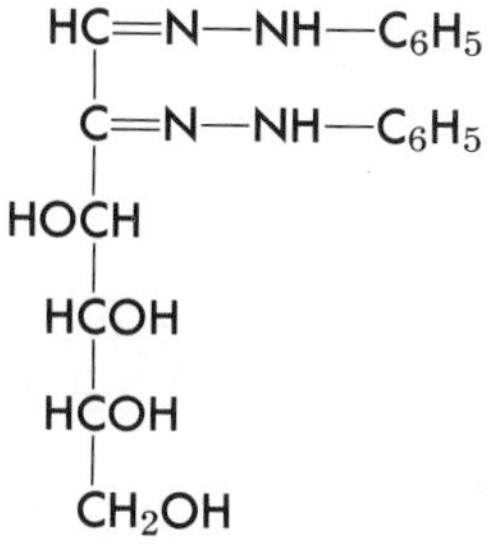

$$\begin{array}{c}
\text{HC=N—NH—C}_6\text{H}_5 \\
\text{C=N—NH—C}_6\text{H}_5 \\
\text{HOCH} \\
\text{HCOH} \\
\text{HCOH} \\
\text{CH}_2\text{OH}
\end{array}$$

D-**Glucose phenylosazone**

Osazone formation is not restricted to monosaccharides but is exhibited by most disaccharides. An important exception is sucrose, which, having no potential carbonyl group, is not susceptible to attack by phenylhydrazine.

A second useful series of derivatives of aldoses are the benzimidazole derivatives. These are readily prepared after initial oxidation of the aldose to the corresponding aldonic acid (page 28). The potassium salts of these aldonic acids separate from the alcoholic medium in which the oxidation is conducted and are then condensed in hot acid with orthophenylenediamine (*o*-diaminobenzene).

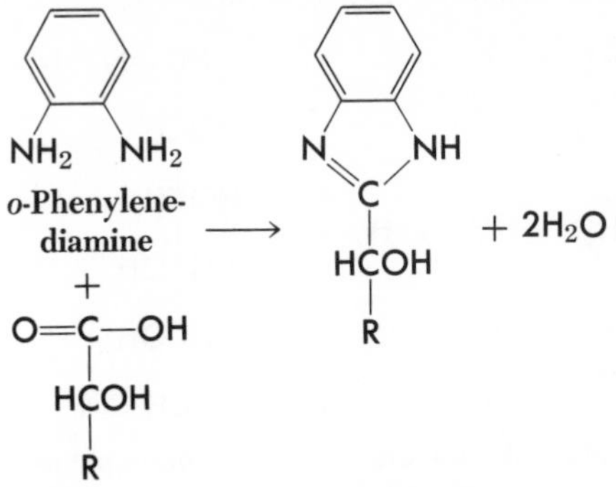

$$
\begin{array}{ccc}
\underset{\substack{\text{NH}_2 \quad \text{NH}_2 \\ \textit{o}\text{-Phenylene-}\\ \text{diamine}}}{} \\
+ \\
\underset{\substack{\text{HCOH} \\ |\\ \text{R}}}{\text{O}=\text{C}-\text{OH}}
\end{array}
\longrightarrow
\quad
\underset{\substack{\text{HCOH}\\|\\ \text{R}}}{\overset{\substack{\text{N} \quad \text{NH}}}{\underset{}{\text{C}}}}
\quad + 2\text{H}_2\text{O}
$$

Aldonic acid		**Benzimidazole** **derivative**

It should be noted that ketoses will not form this series of derivatives inasmuch as they are not oxidized by hypoiodite solution. However, with aldoses these derivatives have many advantages over the osazones. Asymmetry about carbon atom 2 is not disturbed; hence mannose and glucose give different products, whereas they yield the same osazone. The benzimidazole derivatives have sharp melting points which distinguish them one from another. In addition, though relatively insoluble in water, they have sufficient solubility in aqueous acid to permit measurement of specific rotation.

SUGAR ACIDS

Mention has already been made of the several types of sugar acids, of which the most important are the following:

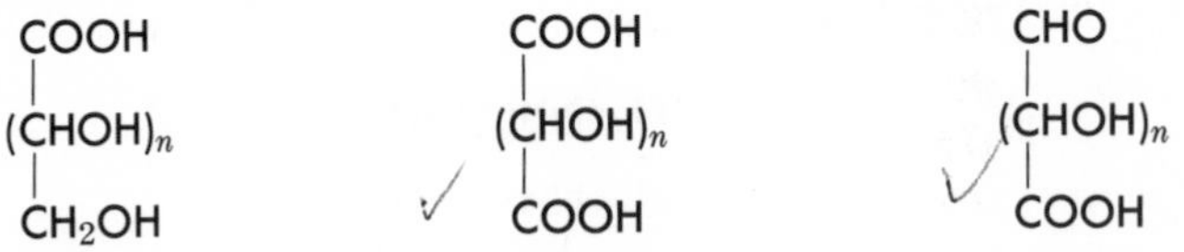

$$
\begin{array}{ccc}
\text{COOH} & \text{COOH} & \text{CHO} \\
| & | & | \\
(\text{CHOH})_n & (\text{CHOH})_n & (\text{CHOH})_n \\
| & | & | \\
\text{CH}_2\text{OH} & \text{COOH} & \text{COOH} \\
\textbf{Aldonic} & \textbf{Aldaric} & \textbf{Uronic}
\end{array}
$$

All these compounds, like other γ- and δ-hydroxy acids, tend to form inner esters or lactones, usually with the establishment of a five- or six-membered ring.

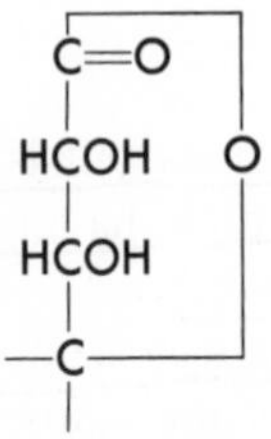

$$
\begin{array}{cc}
\begin{array}{c}
\text{C}=\text{O} \\
| \\
\text{HCOH} \quad \text{O} \\
| \\
\text{HCOH} \\
| \\
-\text{C}-
\end{array}
&
\begin{array}{c}
\text{C}=\text{O} \\
| \\
\text{HCOH} \\
| \qquad \text{O}\\
\text{HCOH} \\
| \\
\text{HCOH} \\
| \\
-\text{C}-
\end{array}
\\
\boldsymbol{\gamma}\text{-Lactone} & \boldsymbol{\delta}\text{-Lactone}
\end{array}
$$

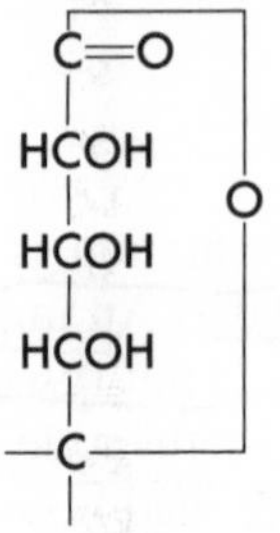

These compounds are strong acids, and their salts are soluble in water and yield neutral solutions. Gluconic acid, nontoxic and well metabolized, is often employed for the introduction into the body of a cation such as Ca^{++}.

δ-Gluconolactone may be formed in an aerobic oxidation catalyzed by an enzyme termed *glucose oxidase*. This enzyme, available from the mold *Penicillium notatum*, catalyzes the following reaction.

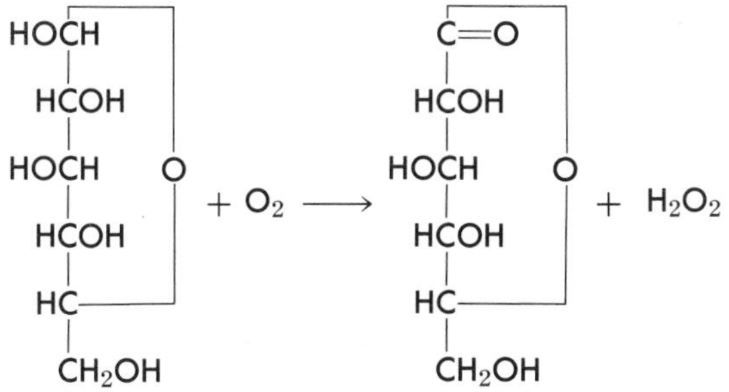

$$
\begin{array}{c}
\text{HOCH} \\
| \\
\text{HCOH} \\
| \\
\text{HOCH} \quad \text{O} \\
| \\
\text{HCOH} \\
| \\
\text{HC} \\
| \\
\text{CH}_2\text{OH}
\end{array}
\quad + \text{O}_2 \longrightarrow \quad
\begin{array}{c}
\text{C}=\text{O} \\
| \\
\text{HCOH} \\
| \\
\text{HOCH} \quad \text{O} \\
| \\
\text{HCOH} \\
| \\
\text{HC} \\
| \\
\text{CH}_2\text{OH}
\end{array}
\quad + \text{H}_2\text{O}_2
$$

β-D-Glucose   δ-Gluconolactone

Glucose oxidase exhibits marked specificity for β-D-glucose and has been applied to the quantitative determination of glucose, since the hydrogen peroxide which is stoichiometrically generated may be measured quantitatively.

The lower members of the series of aldonic and aldaric acids,

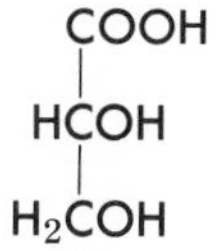

$$
\begin{array}{c}
\text{COOH} \\
| \\
\text{HCOH} \\
| \\
\text{H}_2\text{COH}
\end{array}
\qquad\qquad
\begin{array}{c}
\text{COOH} \\
| \\
\text{HCOH} \\
| \\
\text{HOCH} \\
| \\
\text{COOH}
\end{array}
$$

D-Glyceric acid 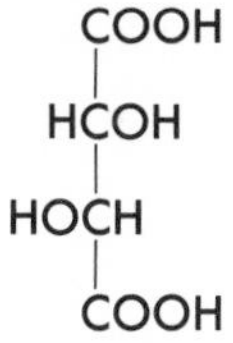   *dextro*-Tartaric acid

are found in nature as intermediates in glycolytic and fermentative processes. The hexuronic acids abound in nature, usually in glycosidic linkage.

Glucuronic acid,

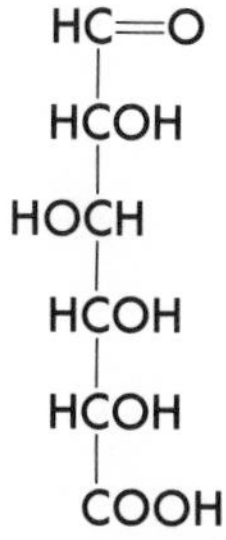

$$
\begin{array}{c}
\text{HC}=\text{O} \\
| \\
\text{HCOH} \\
| \\
\text{HOCH} \\
| \\
\text{HCOH} \\
| \\
\text{HCOH} \\
| \\
\text{COOH}
\end{array}
$$

D-Glucuronic acid

occurs in human urine where it is bound in glycosidic linkage to various hydroxylated compounds, *e.g.*, menthol, borneol, estrogens, etc. The enhanced solubility in water incident to glucosiduronic acid formation from these alcohols may well render them more readily disposable by the body. Glucuronic acid may also form esters, as with bilirubin, a bile pigment (Chap. 36). Glucuronic acid as a component of many polysaccharides is considered in the following chapter as well as in Chap. 40.

A special case of a sugar acid of great biological importance, widely distributed in animal and vegetable nature, is vitamin C, ascorbic acid (L-xyloascorbic acid). From its formula,

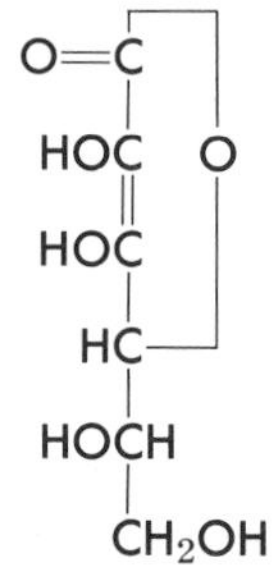

$$
\begin{array}{l}
O{=}C \\
HOC \quad O \\
HOC \\
HC \\
HOCH \\
CH_2OH
\end{array}
$$

Ascorbic acid   *Vit. C*

it will be recognized as a γ-lactone of a hexonic acid which differs from other examples previously discussed in that it contains a double bond between carbons-2 and -3, an enediol linkage. By virtue of this arrangement it is a very unstable compound, one of the most readily oxidizable substances isolated from natural sources. In air, it undergoes oxidation to dehydroascorbic acid.

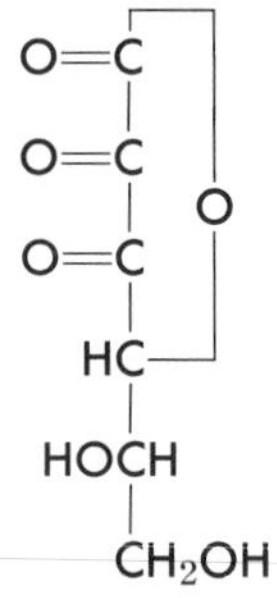

$$
\begin{array}{l}
O{=}C \\
O{=}C \\
O{=}C \quad O \\
HC \\
HOCH \\
CH_2OH
\end{array}
$$

Oxidised form of Vit. C

Dehydroascorbic acid

This is a reversible reaction. Further oxidation of dehydroascorbic acid is accompanied by cleavage of the carbon skeleton between carbons-2 and -3.

SUGAR ALCOHOLS OR POLYOLS

Whereas the linear alcohols of the types of sorbitol, dulcitol, and mannitol are of little biochemical interest, the 3-carbon member of the series, glycerol, is of enormous importance. Its chemistry will be considered with the chemistry of lipids in view of the fact that its fatty acid esters belong to this class of substances. Its intensely sweet taste serves as a reminder that structurally it belongs to the same class of compounds as sorbitol.

The carbocyclic polyols of interest in biochemistry are hexitols (page 27).

Nine stereoisomeric modifications are possible, and these are indicated as having the ring at right angles to the plane of the paper. Seven of these are internally compensated or *meso* forms, while two are a pair of optically active antipodes. The best-known compound of the group, called *myo*-inositol,

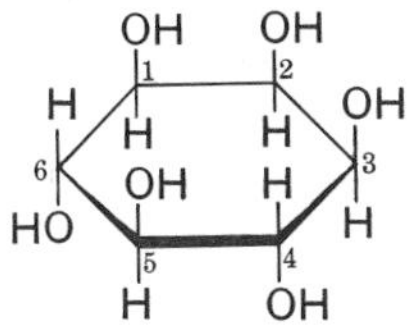

myo-**Inositol**

is widely distributed among microorganisms, higher plants, and animals. In plants it is found phosphorylated as phytic acid, the hexaphosphate, or as the mixed magnesium calcium salt of phytic acid, phytin. It also occurs in lower states of phosphorylation in plants as well as in animal tissues and as free inositol in muscle, heart, lung, liver, etc. It is a constituent of certain phosphatides called inositides (page 77). Biochemical interest in *myo*-inositol also relates to its nutritional essentiality, under certain circumstances, and to its role in lipid as well as in carbohydrate metabolism. *d*-Inositol, *l*-inositol, and scyllitol are stereoisomers of *myo*-inositol of more limited biological distribution.

AMINO SUGARS

In these compounds, the hydroxyl group is replaced by an amino group, $-NH_2$ on carbon atom 2 of aldohexoses. Two representatives of this class are D-glucosamine and D-galactosamine.

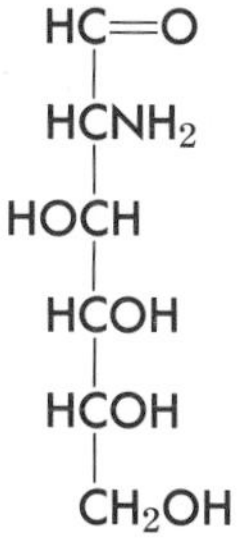

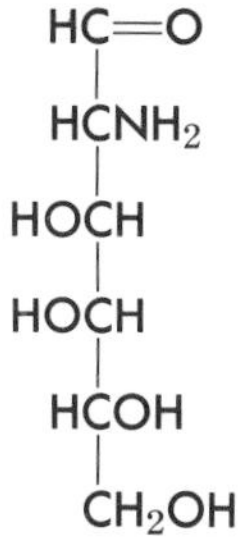

Glucosamine is the product of hydrolysis of chitin, the major polysaccharide of the shells of insects and crustaceans, and occurs in various mammalian polysaccharides (Chaps. 4 and 40) and in certain proteins (Chap. 8). Galactosamine is found in the characteristic polysaccharide of cartilage, chondroitin sulfate.

DEOXYSUGARS

Several examples of aldohexoses are known in which the terminal $-CH_2OH$ group is replaced by $-CH_3$; L-rhamnose (6-deoxy-L-mannose) and L-fucose (6-deoxy-L-galactose) are examples.

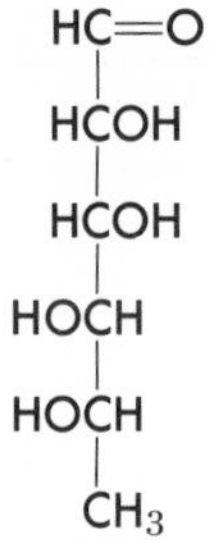

```
      HC=O                    HC=O
       |                       |
      HCOH                    HOCH
       |                       |
      HCOH                    HCOH
       |                       |
      HOCH                    HCOH
       |                       |
      HOCH                    HOCH
       |                       |
      CH₃                     CH₃
   L-Rhamnose              L-Fucose
```

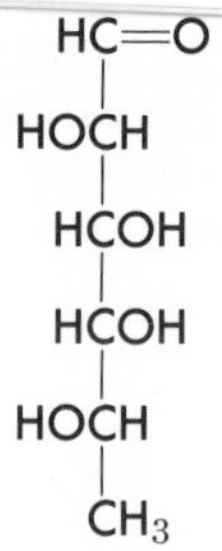

Of great interest in biochemistry is 2-deoxyribose,

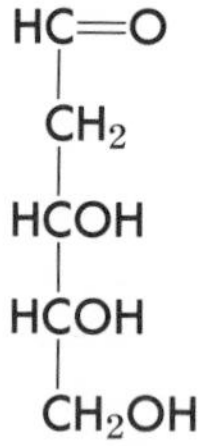

```
        HC=O
         |
        CH₂
         |
        HCOH
         |
        HCOH
         |
        CH₂OH
   2-Deoxy-D-ribose
```

which shares with ribose the sugar function in the group of compounds that includes nucleosides, nucleotides, and nucleic acids. The nucleic acids are generally classified according to whether they contain ribose or deoxyribose as their constituent sugar (Chap. 10).

Sialic Acids. Sialic acids are a group of naturally occurring N- and O-acyl derivatives of a 9-carbon, 3-deoxy-5-amino sugar acid called neuraminic acid. The sialic acids are ubiquitously distributed in tissues, having been identified as constituents of lipids, of polysaccharides, and of mucoproteins. Sialic acid from human plasma has the following structure.

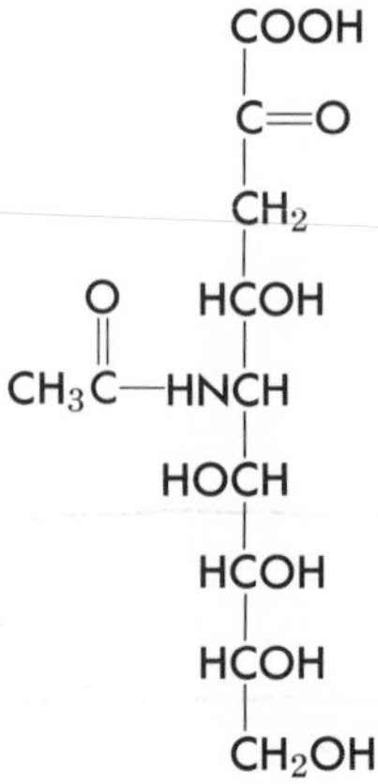

```
                COOH
                 |
                C=O
                 |
                CH₂
                 |
         O      HCOH
         ‖       |
   CH₃C—HNCH
                 |
               HOCH
                 |
               HCOH
                 |
               HCOH
                 |
               CH₂OH
      N-Acetylneuraminic acid
```

This substance may be envisaged as an aldol condensation product of N-acetylmannosamine and pyruvic acid, and certain bacterial enzymes can effect hydrolysis to these products.

Sialic acids present in bovine and sheep submaxillary gland mucin are diacetyl derivatives, with the additional acetyl group present as O-acetyl. In sialic acids found in pig submaxillary mucin, and pig, horse, and ox erythrocytes, the N-acetyl group is replaced by a glycolyl, $-\overset{O}{\underset{\parallel}{C}}-CH_2OH$, grouping. In mucoproteins containing sialic acid, the latter is linked in the molecule via a glycosidic bond at carbon-2.

Muramic Acid. The mucopeptides of bacterial cell walls are characterized by yet another complex sugar derivative which is also an N-acetylamino sugar acid. Like sialic acid, muramic acid may be regarded as derived from a 3-carbon acid, in this case D(-)-lactic acid and N-acetylglucosamine. The link between the two portions is an ethereal one, as the accompanying structural formula reveals.

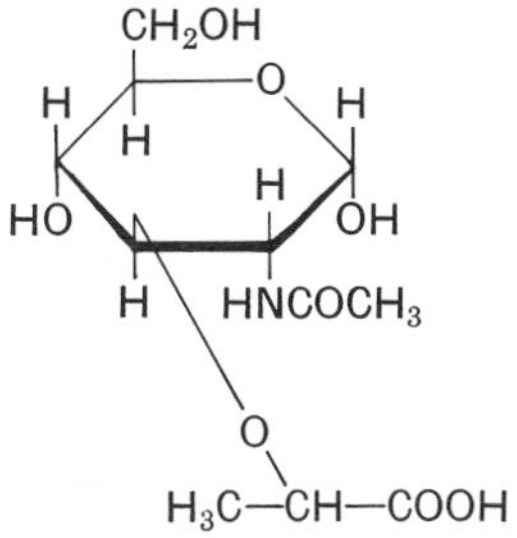

Muramic acid

SPECIAL METHODS OF SEPARATION, PURIFICATION, AND CHARACTERIZATION OF COMPOUNDS OF BIOCHEMICAL INTEREST

The methods to be described are not peculiar to biochemistry. They have, however, been extraordinarily useful to biochemists because of the small quantities of material that can be handled and the mildness of the conditions that may be used. Often simple in application yet very powerful in separations achieved, these methods have largely replaced the earlier techniques of fractional crystallization and fractional distillation.

Fundamentally, all the methods to be discussed entail the same general principle. The material to be purified or the mixture to be resolved is repeatedly distributed between two phases. One phase may be stationary, while the other flows past it, which is the situation in chromatography. Alternatively, both phases may move past each other in opposite directions, as occurs in countercurrent distribution. Both phases may be liquid, which is the case in countercurrent distribution and in partition chromatography. One phase may be solid, as in sorption chromatography or in ion exchange chromatography. In gas phase chromatography, as the name implies, the mobile phase is indeed gaseous. One of these methods (or more than one) has been successfully applied to each class of organic compound of concern to the biochemist. Thus, mixtures of sugars are often separated by partition chromatography on paper, as are amino acids, peptides, etc. Steroid mixtures are separable in most cases by sorption chromatography; gas-phase separations have superseded all other methods for the resolution of fatty acid mixtures. A general survey of some of these methods is introduced at this point even though their application is in no sense peculiar to carbohydrate chemistry. Because they are related to one another, both in theory and in operation, they are here treated together.

Chromatographic procedures are used to detect mixtures of substances and to separate the components of mixtures. The technique of chromatography depends on the use of solid adsorbents which have specific affinities for the adsorbed substances. It is customary to use the adsorbent in a column and allow the solution to percolate slowly down the column (Fig. 3.1, on left). The solutes may be completely adsorbed at the top of the column (Fig. 3.1, middle), in which case an eluting solvent is added to the column; this liberates each substance according to its adsorbing affinity. When the substances are colored, zones or bands may be observed on the column (Fig. 3.1, on right). Tswett, the Russian botanist who is generally credited with the discovery of this technique, showed that extracts of a green leaf contain two green pigments (chlorophylls a and b) and a number of yellow pigments (carotenoids).

Although the procedure is called chromatography since the behavior of colored substances is readily observed, the method can be applied to colorless substances also. However, some procedure is necessary for detecting colorless substances, and this may be done by illuminating with ultraviolet light and observing fluorescent

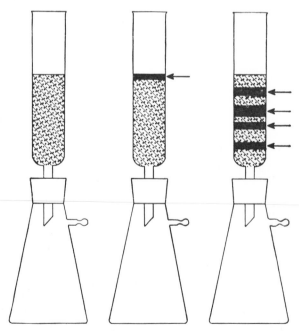

FIG. 3.1. A diagrammatic representation of the simplest type of chromatogram. A column of a suitable adsorbent is prepared (*left*). A solution of a mixture of four substances is poured on the column and is allowed to move slowly either by gravity or with a slight vacuum applied. The mixture is adsorbed as a narrow band at the top of the column (*middle*). When an eluting solvent is poured on the column, the substances are separated and, because they are colored, show four discrete zones (*right*).

substances or by using indicators or chemical procedures which give a color reaction. In many cases, it is more convenient to collect fractions of the eluting solvent as they emerge at the exit of the column. These fractions may then be tested by physical or chemical procedures or by biological assays if specifically active substances are present.

Homogeneous substances will give a single zone on the column or a single continuous fraction in the eluate. When suitable solvents are used, mixtures will give multiple zones or multiple eluted fractions, each of which is separated by a portion of the solvent. When uncharged substances, such as the chlorophylls, are separated by simple adsorption, the process is called *adsorption chromatography*. Ionic substances, *e.g.,* amino acids, can be readily separated by using polar particles as the adsorbing medium. This process is *ion exchange chromatography* (see Chap. 7).

The method of countercurrent distribution depends on the repetitive distribution of a solute between two immiscible solvents in a series of vessels in which the two solvent phases are in contact. The procedure may be carried out in a consecutive number of separatory funnels in which the solute in solvent *A* is shaken with solvent *B* until equilibrium is reached, the two phases are separated, and each is then equilibrated with fresh solvent. The process may be repeated as many times as desired. Automatic systems for the multiple extractions have been devised by Craig and his collaborators. These investigators have shown that at the end of the experiment, a homogeneous substance will be distributed in the various units (each separatory funnel represents a unit) in accordance with a constant termed the *dis-*

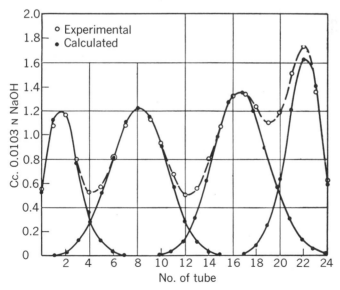

FIG. 3.2. Separation by countercurrent distribution of a mixture of four fatty acids. The maxima, from left to right, are acetic, propionic, butyric, and valeric acids, respectively. The acid content of each tube was determined by titration with sodium hydroxide. (*From L. C. Craig and D. Craig, in "Technique of Organic Chemistry," vol. 3, p. 171, Interscience Publishers, Inc., New York, 1950.*)

tribution coefficient or sometimes the *partition coefficient.* This constant represents essentially the ratio of the molecular concentration of the substance in the two solvents, which in turn is dependent upon the solubility coefficients. The separation of a mixture of fatty acids is shown in Fig. 3.2. A mixture will give a skewed curve or several distinct curves, depending on the solvents and the number of units used. The method of countercurrent distribution has been successfully used in the analysis and separation of many types of substances.

Partition chromatography applies the principle of countercurrent distribution to column chromatography. The procedure depends on using two immiscible solvent systems with a solid, supporting medium, such as silica gel or starch, in a column. One solvent phase, usually the aqueous one, is more strongly adsorbed to the solid phase. The other solvent, containing a mixture of substances, is allowed to percolate down the column. At each particle, a redistribution of solute occurs between the mobile and stationary phases, just as it does in a separatory funnel. The process is very efficient since relatively short columns act in the same manner as many separatory funnels. The process, as developed by Martin and Synge, can be employed for the separation of many types of substances.

One of the most ingenious methods of utilizing partition chromatography is the employment of filter paper as the supporting medium; hence the term, *filter paper chromatography.* In this method, a drop of solution containing a mixture of compounds is placed on one end or one corner of a sheet of filter paper. The filter paper is put into a sealed glass jar or cylinder which contains a small amount of an organic solvent saturated with water. The end of the paper nearest the mixture is inserted into the solvent-water mixture in the bottom of the container, with the paper being placed to hang freely without touching the sides of the vessel. Thus, the solvent will ascend into the paper, and this procedure is termed "ascending paper chromatography." Alternatively, the same end of the filter paper may be put into the solvent mixture contained in a narrow trough mounted near the top of the vessel. In this case, the solvent will descend into the paper; this procedure is termed "descending paper chromatography." After some time, the sheet of paper is removed and sprayed with a chemical developing agent, such as an alkaline silver reagent, which, by formation of a colored spot, serves to localize compounds on the paper. The paper may then be dried, and measurement may be made of the distance of migration of each compound from the point at which the mixture was placed on the filter paper. Since the rate of migration of each substance is a characteristic constant for each solvent system used, the identity of compounds on the filter paper may be established by measurement of the distance of migration with time. This migration rate is expressed as the R_F value, which is defined as the ratio of the distance moved of a particular solute to that moved by the solvent front. Thus, when a substance moves with the solvent front, the R_F is 1; when a substance moves half the distance of the front, the R_F is 0.5. Figure 3.3 illustrates schematically the separation of a mixture of six carbohydrates by filter paper chromatography.

A variation of the above-described filter paper chromatography has been termed "two-dimensional chromatography." After migration of the substances in one direction is completed, the sheet of filter paper may be turned 90° and placed

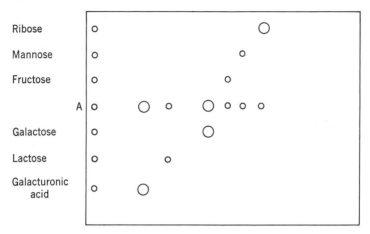

FIG. 3.3. Filter paper chromatogram of a mixture containing six sugars. The mixture was introduced in the circle at the left marked *A*, and the individual sugars were placed in the other circles at the left as indicated. The chromatogram was run in *s*-collidine. (*From S. M. Partridge, Biochem. J.,* **42**, 238, 1948.)

in a different solvent mixture to obtain further resolution. This type of procedure gives excellent separations; it is illustrated later in Chap. 7 (Fig. 7.4, page 118).

An important technical advance is *thin layer chromatography*. This combines many of the advantages of paper chromatography with those of chromatography on columns. Thin films of uniform thickness are prepared of adsorbents such as silica or alumina powder by bonding them to glass plates with plaster of paris. From this point on, these plates are treated much as described above for paper sheets, with an almost limitless range of available solvents. Because of the inorganic nature of the supporting medium, concentrated sulfuric acid spray followed by heating may be used to "develop" (locate substances on the chromatogram), in an entirely nonspecific way, by charring and rendering visible any spots of organic material.

Another important modification involves use of a granular dextran (page 53) preparation. Each granule behaves as though it were a small sac of dialyzing membrane. The two phases in a column packed with the dextran in water are (1) the water outside the granules, and (2) the water inside the granules. Small solute molecules distribute throughout both phases; large molecules are excluded from the inside phase. If a solution containing a mixture of large and small molecules is placed at the top of such a column, followed by a slow stream of solvent, the large molecules will appear at the effluent end of the column ahead of the small molecules. Columns of this sort conveniently separate large from small molecules regardless of their chemical natures. The cutoff between what is large and what is small is determined by the arbitrary choice of the packing material, granules of differing apparent porosities being available. The process has been likened to a *molecular sieve* and has been termed *gel filtration chromatography*.

Gas-liquid chromatography is a modification applicable to compounds and mixtures of compounds that exert significant vapor pressures at temperatures below those of excessive pyrolysis. Since this method has been particularly applicable to separation of lipids, it will be considered later (Chap. 5). It has also found some application in the separation and identification of carbohydrates. *Ion exchange chromatography,* particularly useful in the separation of amino acids, will be considered in Chap. 7.

REFERENCES

See list following Chap. 4.

4. Chemistry of Carbohydrates

Oligosaccharides and Polysaccharides

Many compounds on hydrolysis yield monosaccharides either exclusively or together with other products. Some of the properties of the more important compounds of this type will now be reviewed.

OLIGOSACCHARIDES

Oligosaccharides yield monosaccharides on hydrolysis and contain, per molecule, two to ten monosaccharide residues (*oligo-*, few). The distinction between oligo- and high molecular weight polysaccharides is arbitrary since properties of higher members of the class of oligosaccharides merge with those of the lower polysaccharides.

A large number of oligosaccharides have been described; many of these do not occur as such in nature but have been prepared by partial hydrolysis of higher oligosaccharides and polysaccharides. Most of the naturally occurring representatives occur in plant rather than in animal sources. The characteristics of oligosaccharides will be discussed with reference to the three most important disaccharides, sucrose, maltose, and lactose, and other representatives will be referred to only incidentally.

The methods employed in elucidating the structure of sucrose and other oligosaccharides may be mentioned briefly. The foremost of these involves exhaustive methylation, usually with dimethyl sulfate and alkali, followed by hydrolysis and identification of the methylated monosaccharides produced. Under these circumstances methoxyl groups (CH_3—O—) will be found to have replaced all hydroxyl groups except those participating in glycosidic or hemiacetal links, and from the distribution of these methoxyl groups the position of the glycosidic bond can be inferred. Additional information may also be secured from studies of periodate oxidation.

The determination of configuration of the glycosidic bond, whether α or β, often rests on the use of enzymes with known specificities. Thus there are *glucosidases,* enzymes which promote the hydrolysis specifically of glucosides, whose activity is restricted toward either α- or β-glucosides. Yeast maltase, for instance, attacks only α-glucosides, while almond emulsin is specific for β-glucosides.

SUCROSE ~Plants~

Sucrose, α-D-glucopyranosyl-β-D-fructofuranoside,

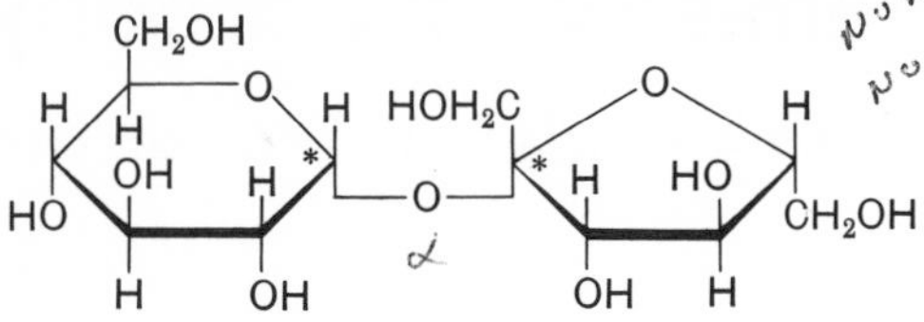

No mutarotation
Non-reducing
No carbonyl rxn

Sucrose

is the common sugar of commerce and the kitchen. It is derived commercially from either cane or beet but occurs in varying amounts in a variety of fruits, seeds, leaves, flowers, and roots. Together with its products of hydrolysis, glucose and fructose, it is the major carbohydrate of maple sugar.

In contrast to most other simple carbohydrates, the structure of sucrose contains neither a hemiacetal nor a hemiketal grouping. This results from the fact that the oxygen bridge between the two monosaccharide moieties extends between the anomeric carbon atoms (marked in the above formula with an asterisk) of the glucose and fructose portions.

As a consequence, sucrose contains no potentially active carbonyl group and lacks those properties of sugars which depend upon the presence of this group. Thus sucrose does not exhibit mutarotation and is incapable of reaction with specific reagents for carbonyl groups, such as phenylhydrazine. Sucrose is not a reducing sugar in that, unless hydrolyzed, it is not oxidized by alkaline solutions of Cu^{++} ions.

On hydrolysis, sucrose gives rise to an equimolar mixture of glucose and fructose. This mixture will readily reduce Cu^{++} ions to Cu^+ and will also react with phenylhydrazine to yield a single product, glucose phenylosazone.

All glycosides, including oligo- and polysaccharides, can be hydrolyzed with varying degrees of difficulty. The hydrolysis of sucrose, which proceeds more easily than that of most other disaccharides, has been called the *inversion of sucrose* because during the reaction, which may be followed polarimetrically, the sign of rotation changes from positive (*dextro-*) to negative (*levo-*). This reaction is catalyzed by a variety of enzymes called *invertases* and also by H^+ ions. In fact, in aqueous solution the rate of sucrose inversion is proportional to the activity of H^+, other things being equal, and this relationship provided an early method for the estimation of hydrogen ion concentration. The equimolar mixture of glucose and fructose, called "invert sugar," is sweeter than sucrose to the taste. Such a mixture is present in honey.

MALTOSE *Hydrolysis of starch*

This disaccharide is the most common example of a sugar which on hydrolysis yields two identical fragments. Its structure is 4-O-α-D-glucopyranosyl-D-gluco-pyranose.

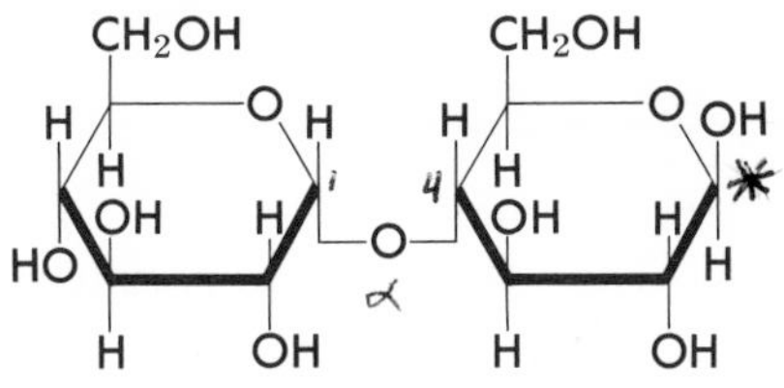

β-Maltose

In contrast to sucrose, maltose possesses an unattached anomeric carbon atom, a hemiacetal grouping, and is consequently a reducing sugar, capable of reaction with phenylhydrazine and exhibiting mutarotation. In the formula above this anomeric carbon atom is shown in the *β* configuration, hence the designation *β*-maltose. Although the anomeric carbon may exist in either the *α* or *β* configuration, the glycosidic linkage in maltose must be in the *α* configuration. This linkage joins carbon-1 of one glucose molecule and carbon-4 of the second unit and is abbreviated as an *α*,1,4 linkage. Occasionally in the literature the convention *α*,1,4′ is used to indicate that reference is made to C-1 and C-4 of different carbon chains. Also, the mode of linkage is often designated by use of an arrow, *e.g.*, *α*,1 → 4.

Although maltose does not occur abundantly, as such, in nature, its occurrence has occasionally been reported. This is not surprising as it is the major product of enzymic hydrolysis of starch (page 49). Low molecular weight oligosaccharides comprised of maltose residues have been isolated from mammalian liver and probably represent intermediates in the synthesis and degradation of glycogen (see below).

Maltose, with its *α*,1,4 glucosidic bond, is but one of several known glucosyl-glucose disaccharides. *Cellobiose,* in which the bond is *β*,1,4, is the repeating unit in the polysaccharide, cellulose; maltose is the analogous unit in the starch, amylose. In *gentiobiose* the link is *β*,1,6, whereas in *isomaltose* it is *α*,1,6. In *trehalose* the bridge between the two glucose moieties connects the two anomeric carbon atoms and this sugar, consequently, resembles sucrose in having no reducing activity. Trehalose is the principal sugar of insect hemolymph.

LACTOSE

This disaccharide, apparently solely of mammalian origin, is found in milk to the extent of about 5 per cent. Its structure is 4-O-*β*-D-galactopyranosyl-D-glucopyranose.

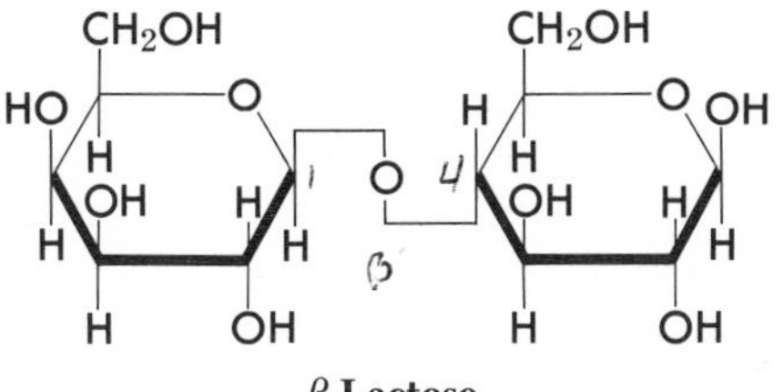

β-Lactose

Upon hydrolysis it yields an equimolar mixture of galactose and glucose. Lactose is a reducing sugar and forms a phenylosazone.

A minor quantity of lactose is also present in milk linked as an α-glycoside to the anomeric C-2 of N-acetylneuraminic acid (page 36) via the 3-hydroxyl of the galactose moiety of lactose. The compound has been termed neuramin lactose.

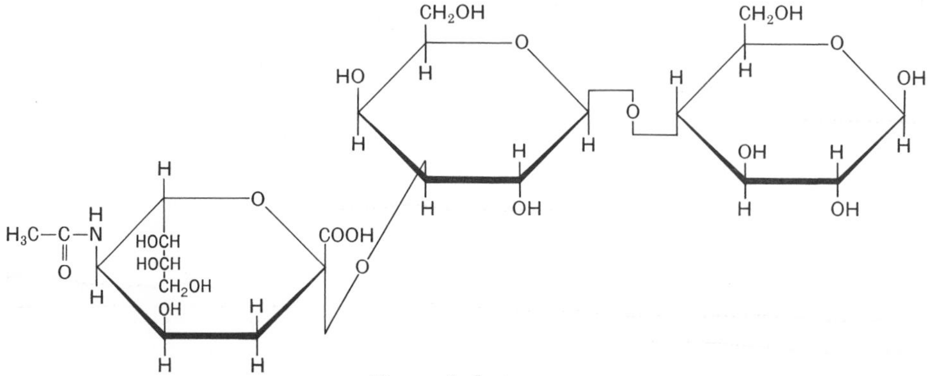

Neuramin lactose

GLYCOSIDES CONTAINING NONCARBOHYDRATE RESIDUES

In addition to glycosides of the oligosaccharide type, there are in nature many examples of compounds containing a sugar or a uronic acid linked in glycosidic bond to some noncarbohydrate residue. Among the most important of these is the group of compounds in which the noncarbohydrate portion of the molecule includes a nitrogenous base and one or more moles of phosphate (Chap. 10). No attempt will be made here to offer a comprehensive description of this class of compounds, but certain general characteristics should be mentioned. Examples of the participation of glucuronic acid in glycosidic linkage will be encountered later in this book.

Most of these glycosides occur in plants. Upon hydrolysis, one generally obtains a sugar or mixture of sugars and a nonsugar portion, termed the *aglycon*. Although the glycoside is a larger molecule than the aglycon derived from it, the glycoside is usually more soluble in water than the aglycon because of the hydrophilic hydroxyl groups on the sugar.

Among the interesting aglycons of nature are a wide variety of phenol derivatives. The glycosides of various flavones and anthocyanins occur as pigments in flowers, and rutin from buckwheat is such a compound. The poison phlorhizin, found in the roots of many fruit trees, is the glycoside of a closely related polyphenol, phloretin, and has had wide experimental use because of its depressant effect upon the renal threshold for glucose. Indoxyl, from which the dye indigo is prepared, also is found in nature as a glycoside.

In oil of bitter almond is found the glycoside amygdalin, which on hydrolysis yields two moles of glucose and one mole each of benzaldehyde and hydrogen cyanide. Noteworthy also is the fact that β-glucosidase, an enzyme that catalyzes the hydrolysis of amygdalin, is present in emulsin, a preparation derived from almonds, among other sources. The study of this enzyme-catalyzed reaction, dating back to 1830, is one of the earliest in the history of enzyme chemistry.

A number of phenanthrene derivatives are conjugated to sugars in nature. Of particular importance in medicine are the drugs of the digitalis group, the aglycons of which are closely related to the steroids (Chap. 6). The carbohydrate portions of these glycosides are often di- and trisaccharides containing 6-deoxy- and 2,6-dideoxyaldohexoses. Other dideoxysugars (2,6 and 3,6) occur in microbial polysaccharides.

POLYSACCHARIDES

The overwhelming bulk of all carbohydrates of nature exists in the form of molecules of high molecular weight, which on hydrolysis yield exclusively or chiefly monosaccharides or products related to monosaccharides, most frequently D-glucose. However, D-mannose, D- and L-galactose, D-xylose, L-arabinose as well as D-glucuronic, D-galacturonic, and D-mannuronic acids, D-glucosamine, D-galactosamine, and neuraminic acid also occur. The various polysaccharides differ from one another not only in constituent monosaccharide composition, but also in molecular weight and other structural features. Thus, some polysaccharides are linear polymers and others are highly branched. In all cases the linkage that unites the monosaccharide units is the glycosidic bond. This may be α or β and may join the respective units through linkages that are 1,2; 1,3; 1,4; or 1,6 in the linear sequence or between those units which are at "branch points" in the polymer. An enormous number of variants is therefore possible, and, indeed, a great many polysaccharides have been described. It is helpful to distinguish between homopolysaccharides which yield on hydrolysis a single monosaccharide and heteropolysaccharides which yield a mixture of constituent building units.

Methods of investigation of polysaccharides include a variety of techniques for estimation of molecular weight. Among these are osmotic pressure measurements, ultracentrifugation studies, observations of viscosity and of light scattering, and end group analysis (see below). Most if not all polysaccharides studied are *polydisperse*, *i.e.*, even though meeting other criteria of purity, each sample consists of molecules of various molecular weights. In this important regard, a sample of "pure" starch or glycogen differs from a pure, *monodisperse* protein.

Analysis of the products of complete and partial, often enzymic, hydrolysis may reveal the sequence of occurrence of various monosaccharide units in the chain. Study of the mixture obtained when an exhaustively methylated polysaccharide is hydrolyzed is also often revealing. If, for example, an unbranched polyglucoside (1,4) is studied in this way, the chain length may be estimated. One end of such a chain will still possess reducing activity; the opposite end will be occupied by a glucose residue unsubstituted at carbon-4. If the chain has 10 glucose residues, one should find 2,3,6-tri-O-methylglucose and 2,3,4,6-tetra-O-methylglucose in a ratio of 9:1. Wherever a branching of the polysaccharide chain occurs, there must be a glucose residue with an additional substituted hydroxyl and this should yield a di-O-methylglucose residue. This method of analysis thus gives information as to size, number of end groups, number of branchings, and positions of attachment of glucosidic bonds. This technique is supplemented by other methods. A study of the quantity of formic acid liberated on oxidation by periodate gives similar information as to average chain length. One of the most promising methods developed to date involves the successive use of selective enzymes that have been characterized with regard to the types of glucosidic bonds that they will or will not rupture (page 215).

Many of the larger molecular weight polysaccharides are strongly antigenic, *i.e.*, they lead to production of antibodies when injected into suitable animals (Chap. 32). Such an antibody, which reacts specifically with the antigen that elicited its production, also often cross-reacts with polysaccharides of similar structure. If the structure of the initial antigen is known, *i.e.*, the monosaccharide components and the linkages between them, the structures of cross-reacting polysaccharides may be inferred. By the use of a spectrum of antibodies of known specificity and measurement of the cross reaction to an unknown polysaccharide, important information regarding the structure of the latter has been gained in a number of cases by Heidelberger and his colleagues.

HOMOPOLYSACCHARIDES

CELLULOSE

Cellulose is unquestionably the most abundant organic compound in the world, comprising 50 per cent or more of all the carbon in vegetation. Though predominantly a plant polysaccharide, it has been found in certain tunicates. The purest source is cotton, which is at least 90 per cent pure cellulose.

On complete hydrolysis, cellulose yields glucose virtually quantitatively; partial hydrolysis yields the disaccharide cellobiose. Hydrolysis of fully methylated cellulose gives 2,3,6-tri-O-methylglucose almost quantitatively, indicating the absence of branching. From these and other considerations, the structure of the repeating unit of the cellulose chain joined by $\beta,1,4$ linkages is written as follows.

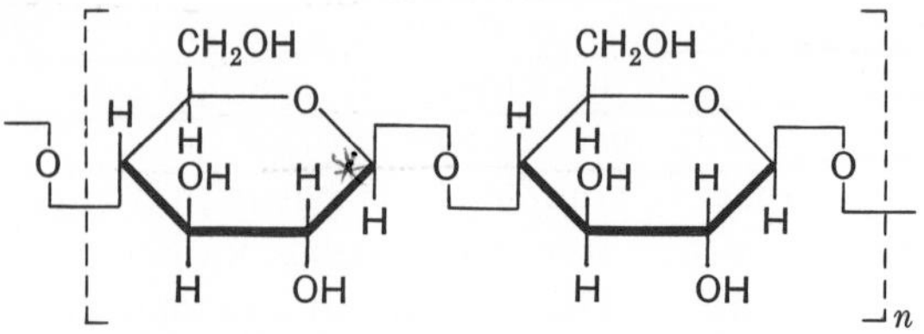

Repeating cellobiose unit of cellulose

Cellulose is insoluble in water but will dissolve in ammoniacal solutions of cupric salts. Its molecular weight has been estimated on different preparations to be between 50,000 and 400,000, corresponding roughly to 300 to 2,500 glucose residues per molecule, but these estimates may be far too low because of degradation in preparation of the sample.

STARCHES

Whereas cellulose, in which glucose units are joined in $\beta,1,4$ linkages, is the characteristic structural polysaccharide of plant cells, in starches, which serve as nutritional reservoirs in plants, the corresponding link is $\alpha,1,4$. The repeating disaccharide unit therefore is maltose rather than cellobiose.

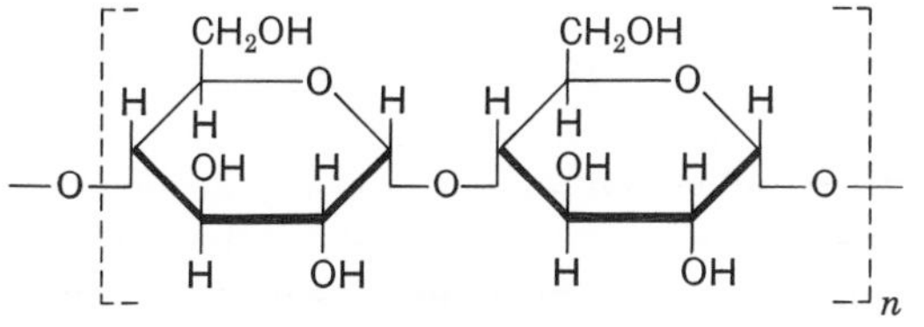

Repeating maltose unit of starch

Native starches are a mixture of two types of compounds which are separable from each other. *Amylose* is the component that is believed to be a long, un-branched chain, similar in this regard to cellulose. *Amylopectin* has been shown on the basis of methylation studies to be a branched-chain polysaccharide, one terminal glucose occurring for every 24 to 30 glucose residues. The glucose residue which is situated at each point of branching is substituted not only on carbon-4 but also on carbon-6. Isolation of the $\alpha,1,6$ disaccharide, isomaltose, from the products of incomplete hydrolysis of amylopectin proves the constitution of the branch points, which may be represented as shown:

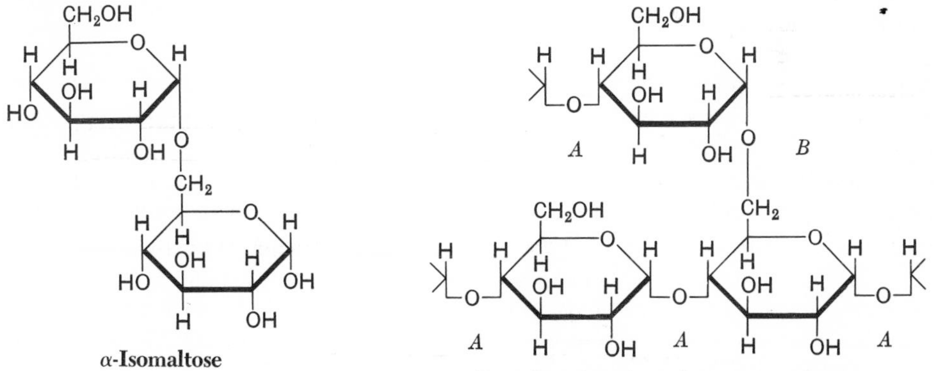

α-**Isomaltose**

Branch point of amylopectin or glycogen
$A = \alpha,1,4$-glucosidic bond
$B = \alpha,1,6$-glucosidic bond

Molecular weight determinations on various starch preparations have given results ranging from 50,000 up to several millions. In view of the likelihood of some degradation during isolation, the higher values probably represent more truly the sizes of native starch molecules.

The differences between the unbranched amylose and the branched amylopectin are most clearly understood from a consideration of the products of their enzymic hydrolyses. *Amylases*, the enzymes that catalyze the hydrolysis of starches, have been divided into two classes, formerly known as α- and β-amylases. This relatively general terminology has been replaced by more precise terms that indicate the nature of the action of these enzymes. The term α-amylase now connotes an α-1,4-glucan 4-glucanohydrolase and the term β-amylase an α-1,4-glucan maltohydrolase. The former enzyme, present for example in pancreatic juice and in saliva, splits α,1,4-glucosidic bonds, except for that of maltose, in an apparently random fashion, while the latter enzyme, such as that of barley malt, attacks polysaccharide chains, effecting successive removals of maltose units from the nonreducing ends. Neither type of enzyme exhibits activity against α,1,6 bonds or against β,1,4 bonds.

When amylose, which contains exclusively α,1,4-glucosidic bonds, is attacked by α-1,4-glucan 4-glucanohydrolase, random cleavage of these bonds gives rise to a mixture of glucose and maltose (Fig. 4.1), whereas attack by α-1,4-glucan malto-

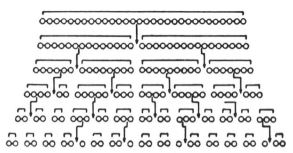

FIG. 4.1. Action of α-1,4-glucan 4-glucanohydrolase on amylose. (o) glucose unit; (-o-o-) α,1,4-glucosidic bond; (↓) action of enzyme. (*According to P. Bernfeld, Advances in Enzymol.,* **12**, 379, 1951.)

hydrolase gives pure maltose in almost quantitative yield (Fig. 4.2). Amylopectin, when treated with α-1,4-glucan 4-glucanohydrolase, undergoes random rupture of α,1,4 bonds and yields, as ultimate products, a mixture of branched and unbranched oligosaccharides in which α,1,6 bonds are abundantly present (Fig. 4.3). When amylopectin is hydrolyzed by the action of α-1,4-glucan maltohydrolase, successive maltose units are liberated, commencing at the nonreducing ends of the polysaccharide molecule. This process continues until a branch point is approached. Since the enzyme has no capacity to hydrolyze the α,1,6 bond that it here encounters, all reaction stops. The polysaccharide fragment that remains after such incomplete hydrolysis is called a *dextrin,* and specifically, since this dextrin is the limit of attack of α-1,4-glucan maltohydrolase upon amylopectin, it is called a *limit dextrin* (Fig. 4.4).

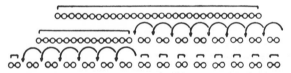

FIG. 4.2. Action of α-1,4-glucan maltohydrolase on amylose. (-o-o-) α,1,4-glucosidic linkage; (⌒) enzyme action. Maltose yield, 100 per cent. (*According to P. Bernfeld, Advances in Enzymol.,* **12**, 379, 1951.)

Starch in the native state is seen as microscopically visible granules, stained blue-black by iodine. On grinding with water, starch becomes dispersible, and "solutions" that are grossly clear can be prepared by this means. Some degree of degradation of the molecule may be presumed to accompany such treatment.

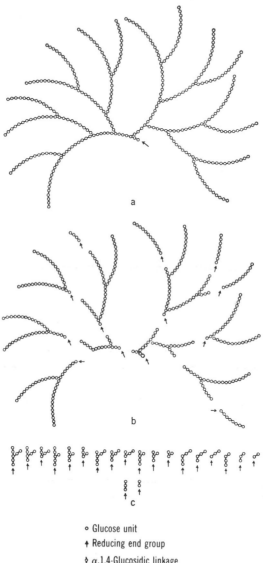

o Glucose unit

⬧ Reducing end group

⬦ α,1,4-Glucosidic linkage

FIG. 4.3. Action of α-1,4-glucan 4-glucanohydrolase on amylopectin. (a) Amylopectin model; (b) dextrins of medium molecular weight giving violet, purple, or red iodine color produced by splitting of 4 per cent of the glucosidic linkages of amylopectin; (c) possible structures of limit dextrins from amylopectin breakdown; the hepta-, hexa-, and pentasaccharides are probably split, more or less rapidly, into lower-molecular oligosaccharides. (*According to P. Bernfeld, Advances in Enzymol.*, **12**, 379, 1951.)

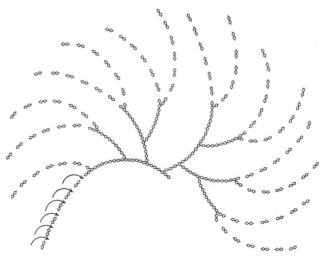

Fig. 4.4. Action of α-1,4-glucan maltohydrolase on amylopectin. Conversion limit, in this case, 61 per cent maltose. At the center, high-molecular limit dextrin. (⌒) enzyme action. (*According to P. Bernfeld, Advances in Enzymol., 12, 379, 1951.*)

Starch is readily hydrolyzed by dilute mineral acid, with ultimate production of glucose in quantitative yield. The course of hydrolysis may be followed by the gradual change in color produced by iodine (blue-black → purple → red → none) and by the increase in reducing-sugar concentration.

GLYCOGEN

The counterpart of starch in the animal is glycogen, which occurs in significant amount in liver and muscle and is particularly abundant in molluscs. A glycogen-like polysaccharide has also been described in corn.

Glycogen is a branched-chain polysaccharide, resembling amylopectin rather than amylose. Glycogen has variously been found to have 8 to 12 glucose residues per nonreducing end group, and molecular weights ranging from 270,000 to 100,000,000 have been reported. Even in single preparations, a wide distribution of molecular sizes is encountered.

Glycogen occurs in animal cells in particles much smaller than starch granules. It is readily dispersed in water to form opalescent "solutions" which give a violet-red color with iodine. Glycogen is fairly stable in hot alkali and is precipitated from aqueous solution by addition of ethyl alcohol. These properties were used advantageously in the original studies of glycogen by Claude Bernard and by Pflüger in the middle of the last century.

α-1,4-Glucan maltohydrolase attacks glycogen incompletely, yielding, as with amylopectin, maltose and limit dextrin. On complete acid hydrolysis, purified glycogen gives glucose in nearly theoretical yield. Analysis of tissues for glycogen usually depends upon solution of the entire tissue in hot alkali, precipitation of glycogen with alcohol, acid hydrolysis of this precipitate, and quantitative determination of the glucose formed.

Recent advances in understanding of details of the structures of the starches and glycogen depend largely upon experiments in which various enzymes of known specificity were employed to degrade these macromolecules. Further discussion of this evidence will be deferred (Chap. 21) until the characteristics of the enzymes employed have been presented (Chap. 12).

DEXTRANS

In addition to cellulose, starches, and glycogen, other polysaccharides of glucose have been found in nature. These include dextrans of yeast and bacteria, in which glucose residues are bound in α,1,6 linkages. Almost all preparations of dextrans exhibit some branching. The linkage at the branch point (1,2, 1,3, 1,4) and the distance between branch points is characteristic of the strain and species of the particular organism from which the dextran was obtained. The biochemistry of dextrans has been studied extensively because of their potential use as blood plasma substitutes or expanders in the treatment of shock.

FRUCTOSE HOMOPOLYSACCHARIDES

The best known member of this class of fructosans or *levans* is inulin, derived from the Jerusalem artichoke and certain other plants. It is apparently composed exclusively of fructose residues in furanose form linked to each other in linear fashion by a β,2,1 bond.

OTHER HOMOPOLYSACCHARIDES

A very highly branched galactose polysaccharide accompanies glycogen in certain species of snails. Mannose polysaccharides are found widely distributed in ivory nuts, orchid tubers, pine trees, yeasts, molds, bacteria, and elsewhere. Various pentosans, polymers of L-arabinose or of D-xylose, occur in woods, nuts, and other vegetable products.

Of the uronic acid polysaccharides, galacturonic acid polymers, partially esterified with methyl alcohol, comprise the pectins of fruits and berries; polymers of D-mannuronic acid have been described in seaweed.

Chitin in the shells of crustaceans and insects is a linear polymer of N-acetyl-D-glucosamine. Chitin is an analogue of cellulose (page 48) in which the hydroxyl group of glucose at C-2 is replaced by an N-acetylamino group. Except for cellulose, chitin is probably the most abundant polysaccharide of nature. Colominic acid, a homopolysaccharide that is a polymer of N-acetylneuraminic acid (page 36), has been prepared from *Escherichia coli* and is also found in other organisms.

HETEROPOLYSACCHARIDES

Polysaccharides which yield on hydrolysis mixtures of monosaccharides and derived products are numerous in both plants and animals. Great variety is made possible by virtue of the large number of available monosaccharides that might be included in such structures and by variation in the nature of the glycosidic linkages (α or β, 1,4, 1,6, 1,3, etc.). The simplest heteropolysaccharides are those constructed by repetitive use of a mixed disaccharide. The "specific soluble sugar," the immunochemically specific polysaccharide of type III pneumococcus, is an example of such a heteropolysaccharide since, on hydrolysis, it yields equimolar amounts of glucose and glucuronic acid. It has the following structure.

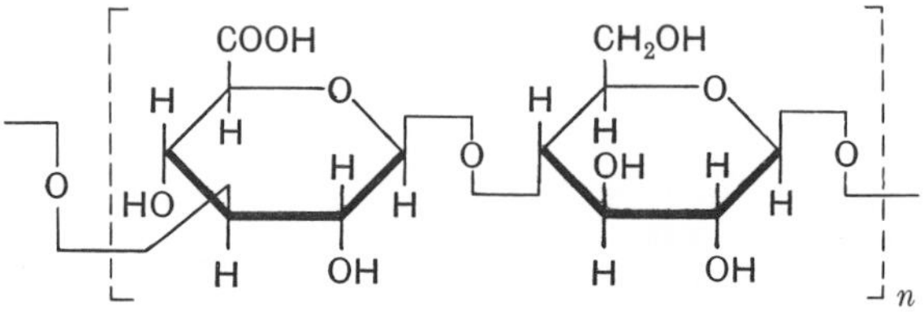

Repeating aldobiuronic acid unit of specific
soluble sugar of pneumococcus type III   *SSS*

Other heteropolysaccharides of a similar structure will be discussed later.

Acid Mucopolysaccharides. Widely distributed throughout the animal body in connective tissue are large quantities of a group of related heteropolysaccharides, each of which contains a hexosamine in its characteristic repeating disaccharide unit. Table 4.1 lists the more common mucopolysaccharides, their repeating disaccharide units, and the linkages between the individual hexoses. It will be seen that the repeating structure of each disaccharide involves alternate 1,4 and 1,3 linkages. These polysaccharides can be separated in the laboratory by fractional precipitation by addition of alcohol to a solution of the mucopolysaccharides containing calcium ions.

The most abundant member of this group is probably *hyaluronic acid.*

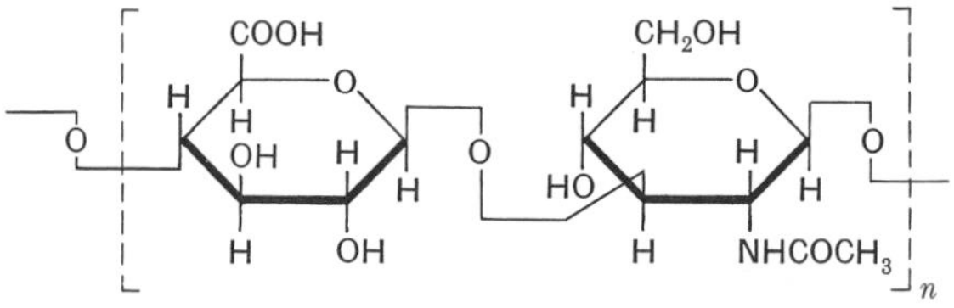

Repeating unit of hyaluronic acid

Solutions of this polysaccharide are characterized by their very high viscosity. Wharton's jelly from umbilical cord is usually employed as the starting material for preparation of hyaluronic acid. However, this polymer is ubiquitous in connective tissue throughout the body. Most of the procedures for its isolation result in partial degradation of the molecule. Thus, the viscosity of both vitreous and synovial fluids considerably exceeds that of a reconstructed solution of the isolated hyaluronic acid. Further, the isolated polymer yields a flocculent precipitate upon acidification, whereas acid produces a *mucin clot* when added to hyaluronate in the native state, because of the presence of small amounts of associated protein.

Chondroitin, which is of limited distribution, is a polymer of β-D-glucuronido, 1,3-N-acetyl-D-galactosamine joined in repeating β,1,4 linkages. The repeating unit of this polysaccharide differs from hyaluronic acid only in that it contains galactosamine rather than glucosamine. It may be regarded, however, as the parent material

Table 4.1: SOME MUCOPOLYSACCHARIDES AND THEIR REPEATING DISACCHARIDE UNITS

Mucopolysaccharide	Monosaccharides in the disaccharide units	Linkages*
Hyaluronic acid............	D-Glucuronic acid; N-acetyl-D-glucosamine	$\beta, 1 \to 3; \beta, 1 \to 4$
Chondroitin...............	D-Glucuronic acid; N-acetyl-D-galactosamine	$\beta, 1 \to 3; \beta, 1 \to 4$
Chondroitin sulfate A........	D-Glucuronic acid; N-acetyl-D-galactosamine 4-sulfate	$\beta, 1 \to 3; \beta, 1 \to 4$
Chondroitin sulfate C........	D-Glucuronic acid; N-acetyl-D-galactosamine 6-sulfate	$\beta, 1 \to 3; \beta, 1 \to 4$
Dermatan sulfate (formerly chondroitin sulfate B)......	L-Iduronic acid; N-acetyl-D-galactosamine 4-sulfate	$\alpha, 1 \to 3; \beta, 1 \to 4$
Keratosulfate..............	D-Galactose; N-acetyl-D-glucosamine 6-sulfate	$\beta, 1 \to 4; \beta, 1 \to 3$

*The linkages are given in the same order as the names of the monosaccharide units, *e.g.*, for chondroitin the linkages, as given, indicate that the linkage of glucuronic acid to acetylgalactosamine is $\beta, 1 \to 3$, and that of acetylgalactosamine to the next glucuronic acid is $\beta, 1 \to 4$, etc.

for two more widely distributed polysaccharides, *chondroitin sulfate A* and *chondroitin sulfate C,* which differ only in the position in which sulfate is esterified to the galactosamine moiety.

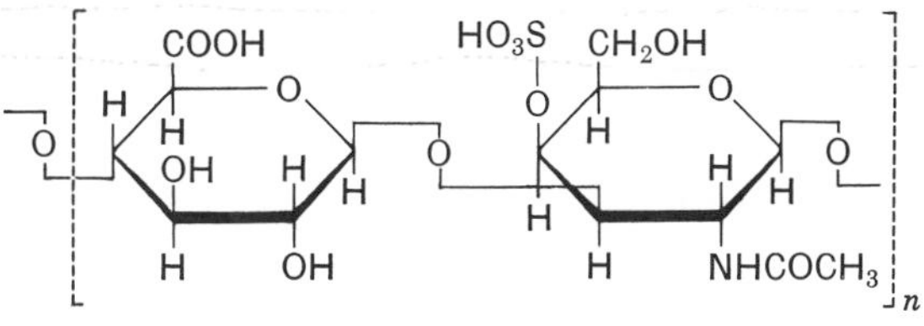

Repeating unit of chondroitin sulfate A

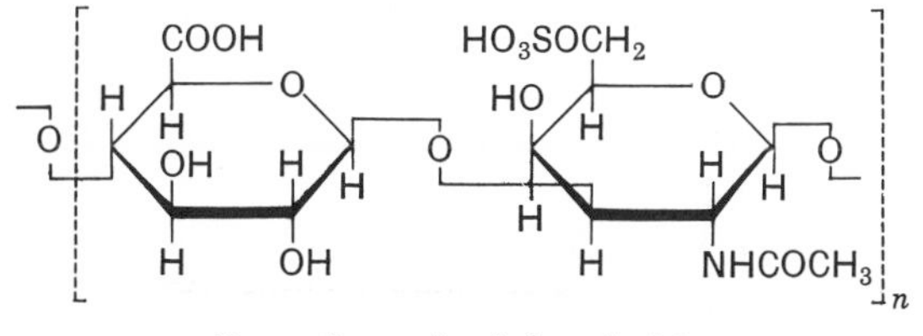

Repeating unit of chondroitin sulfate C

As shown in Table 4.1, the polymer that was long termed *chondroitin sulfate B* yields upon hydrolysis not D-glucuronic acid but L-iduronic, the two differing in configuration only at C-5. Hence, the conventional designation is a misnomer and current literature frequently refers to this compound as *dermatan sulfate* or *derman sulfate;* it was formerly also called *β-heparin. Keratosulfate* differs from the other members of this group in that the uronic acid component is replaced by D-galactose. Although this polymer is also constructed of alternating $\beta,1,4$ and $\beta,1,3$ linkages, in this instance the hexosaminidic linkage is $\beta,1,3$.

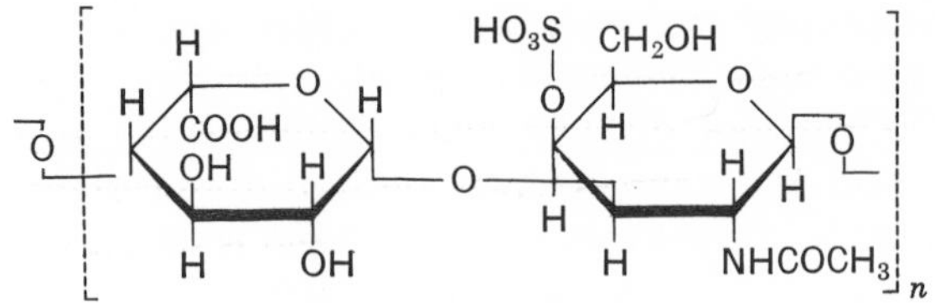

**Repeating unit of dermatan
sulfate**
(formerly chondroitin sulfate B)

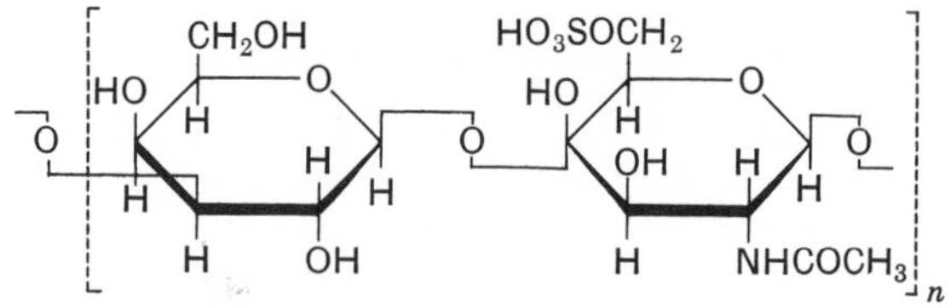

Repeating unit of keratosulfate

Related to the sulfated mucopolysaccharides is *heparin,* a polysaccharide early recognized because of its anticoagulant properties (Chap. 33) and present in liver, lung, the walls of large arteries, and, indeed, wherever mast cells are found. Heparin is a polymer in which the repeating unit consists of D-glucuronic acid with an O-sulfate group probably at C-2, and D-glucosamine N-sulfate with an additional O-sulfate group at C-6. Both the linkages of the polymer are alternating 1,4; it is not certain whether all or only a portion of the glucuronic acid residues in heparin carry an O-sulfate group. Both linkages are α-D.

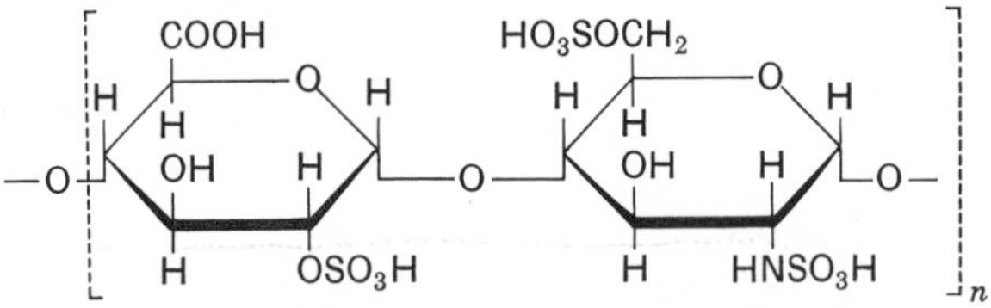

Postulated repeating unit of heparin

It appears that the acid mucopolysaccharides are present in their ubiquitous sites as mucoproteins, *i.e.,* combinations of the specific mucopolysaccharides with proteins. In no instance has the structure of the specific protein been established, nor are the stoichiometric relations between protein and carbohydrate known. It has been suggested that the carbohydrate moiety is linked to its protein component through a covalent bond, perhaps linked to the hydroxyl group of the serine residues of the protein. Partial enzymic hydrolysis of mucoproteins has yielded peptides, rich in glutamic and aspartic acids, threonine and serine, and linked to carbohydrate residues of the mucoproteins.

The heteropolysaccharides which have been discussed above are characterized by the presence of two different sugars in each monomer. More complex heteropolysaccharides occur in which the monomer unit may consist of more than two carbohydrates. In plants, the structures of such heteropolysaccharides remain to be established. The vegetable "gums" contain as many as four different types of monosaccharides in a single preparation. Most common in these structures are D-glucuronic acid, D-mannose, D-xylose, and L-rhamnose, but many others are also found in gums from various sources. Agar, derived from certain seaweeds, yields on hydrolysis D- and L-galactose in a ratio of 9:1 and is sulfated in varying degree.

In animal and microbial tissue, a wide variety of heteropolysaccharides have been described which on hydrolysis yield a variety of carbohydrates. As is the case for the acid mucopolysaccharides, which occur linked to proteins (see above), these more complex polysaccharides are also bound to proteins, as well as to lipids. Indeed, a large number of proteins and lipids can be classed as glycoproteins (page 122) and glycolipids (gangliosides, page 78) because of the presence of an oligosaccharide moiety. The cell membranes of animals are characterized by the presence of an oligosaccharide which on hydrolysis yields fucose, together with varying amounts of glucosamine, galactosamine, galactose, and occasionally sialic acid (Chap. 42). The same sugars are found in the mucoproteins derived from epithelial mucous secretions, viz., those of the respiratory and digestive tracts. These mucoproteins, in contrast to those of connective tissue in which polysaccharides are linked to proteins, have numerous small oligosaccharides linked covalently to a single protein molecule. An example is the "mucin" or mucoprotein of saliva, which contains, per protein molecule, numerous molecules of the disaccharide 6-(N-acetyl-α-neuraminyl)-N-acetyl-D-galactosamine.

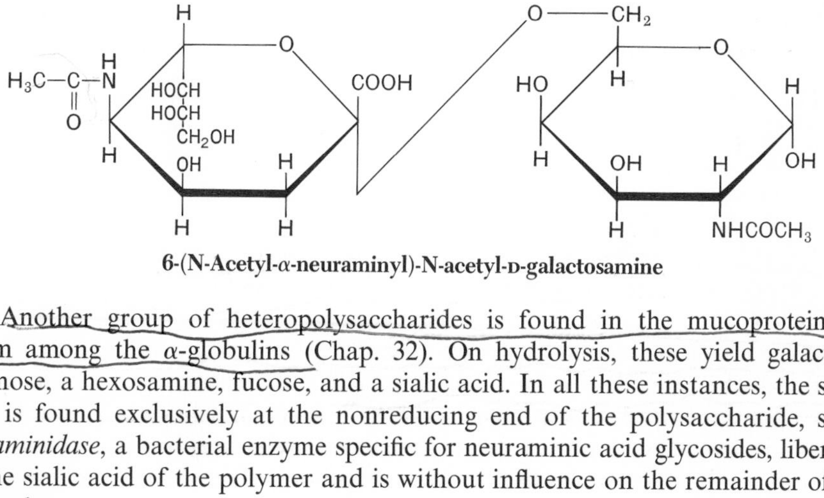

6-(N-Acetyl-α-neuraminyl)-N-acetyl-D-galactosamine

Another group of heteropolysaccharides is found in the mucoproteins of serum among the α-globulins (Chap. 32). On hydrolysis, these yield galactose, mannose, a hexosamine, fucose, and a sialic acid. In all these instances, the sialic acid is found exclusively at the nonreducing end of the polysaccharide, since neuraminidase, a bacterial enzyme specific for neuraminic acid glycosides, liberates all the sialic acid of the polymer and is without influence on the remainder of the molecule.

The specific "blood group substances" are also heteropolysaccharides; these will be considered in Chap. 42.

BACTERIAL CELL WALLS

It is the presence of a rigid and mechanically strong cell wall which permits bacterial cells to maintain normal volume and shape despite a markedly hypotonic medium. Although similar structures are not known in animals, the chemical structure of bacterial walls is of great interest. In recent years much has been learned concerning the structural components of the Gram-positive bacteria, which contain two major classes of polymers not previously discussed. The major component of the wall is a polymer of N-acetylglucosamine linked to a unique monosaccharide, muramic acid (page 37). The latter generally is present as its N-acetyl derivative. The repeating disaccharide units are presumably linked by $\beta,1,4$ and $\beta,1,6$ bonds. The postulated repeating disaccharide unit is shown below.

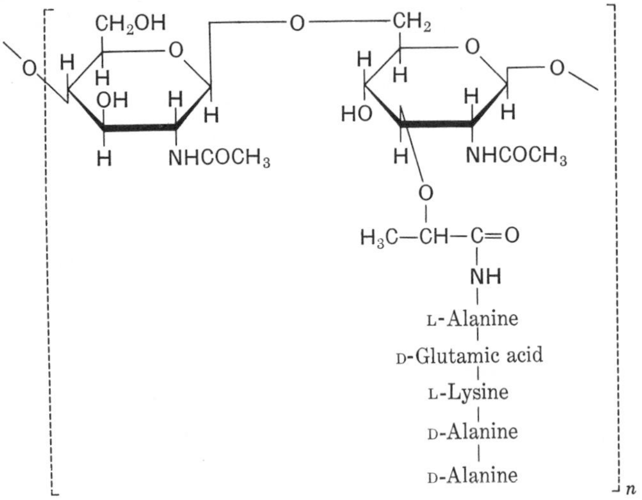

Postulated repeating unit of the muramic acid–containing mucopeptide

The carboxyl group of the lactic acid portion of muramic acid is bound in amide linkage to the α-amino group of L-alanine (page 92), which is the N-terminal member of a pentapeptide. Many bacterial cell wall peptides contain the dicarboxylic acid glutamic acid (page 96) and either the diamino acid lysine (page 97) or diaminopimelic acid (Chap. 25).

The $\beta,1,4$ bonds between muramic acid and N-acetylglucosamine are cleaved by *lysozyme*, an enzyme present in tears, gastric juice, and egg white and known to lyse some species of Gram-positive bacteria.

Polymers of the second group are termed *teichoic acids*, which are not limited to cell walls but are also found intracellularly. There appears to be a wide variety of such substances; each is a linear polymer of a polyol, ribitol or glycerol phosphate, in which adjacent polyol residues are linked by a phosphodiester bond. Both types bear D-alanine residues in ester linkage with hydroxyl groups in the polymer, and the latter also carry glycosidically bound sugar residues. The general features of these compounds, which are not polysaccharides, are shown in Fig. 4.5, which indicates that in *Bacillus subtilis* teichoic acid, ribitol is present, whereas glycerol is the polyol in *Lactobacillus arabinosus*. Many variants of these structures are known. The glucose units may be replaced by N-acetylglucosamine in both ribitol and glycerol polymers. A ribitol polymer is also present in the wall of *L. arabinosus* in which the alanine residues shown for the *B. subtilis* wall are replaced in part by second glucose units. In this case one glucose is in α linkage and the second in β linkage.

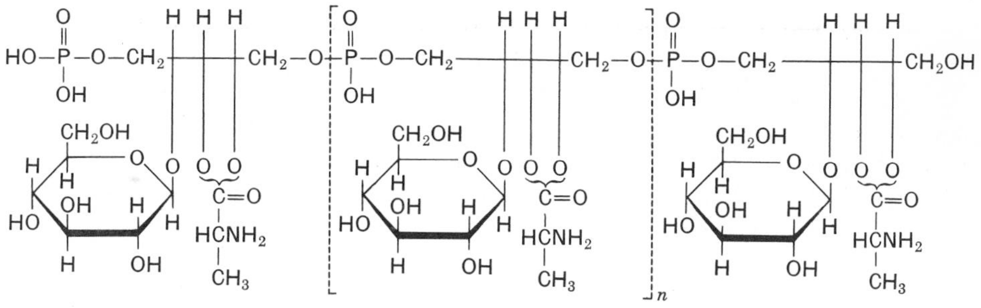

Bacillus subtilis teichoic acid (wall)

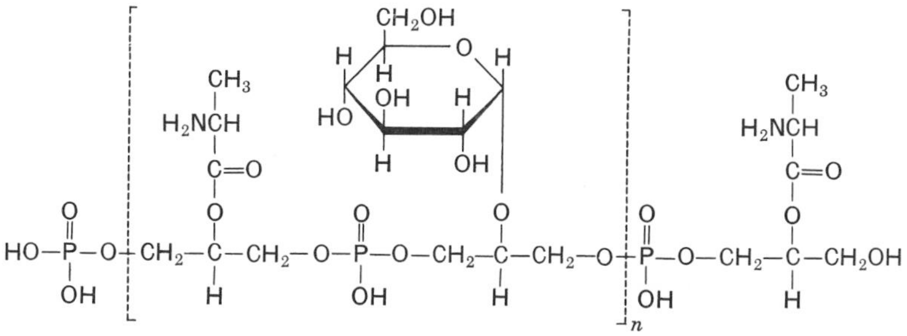

Lactobacillus arabinosus teichoic acid (intracellular)

Fig. 4.5. Proposed structures for two teichoic acids. The positions of the D-alanine residues in *Bacillus subtilis* teichoic acid are not established, but are at either C-2 or C-3 of the ribitol residues, as indicated.

REFERENCES

Books

Block, R. J., Durrum, E. L., and Zweig, G., "A Manual of Paper Chromatography and Paper Electrophoresis," 2d ed., Academic Press, Inc., New York, 1958.

Clark, F., and Grant, J. K., eds., "Biochemistry of Mucopolysaccharides of Connective Tissue," Cambridge University Press, New York, 1961.

Florkin, M., and Stotz, E., "Comprehensive Biochemistry," Carbohydrates, sec. II, vol. 5, Elsevier Publishing Company, New York, 1963.

Gottschalk, A., "The Chemistry and Biology of Sialic Acids," Cambridge University Press, New York, 1960.

Heidelberger, M., and Plescia, O. J., eds., "Symposium on Immunochemical Approaches to Problems in Microbiology," Rutgers University Press, New Brunswick, 1961.

Lederer, E., and Lederer, M., "Chromatography: A Review of Principles and Applications," 2d ed., Elsevier Publishing Company, New York, 1957.

Pigman, W. W., ed., "The Carbohydrates: Chemistry, Biochemistry and Physiology," Academic Press, Inc., New York, 1957.

Salton, M. R. J., "Microbial Cell Walls," John Wiley & Sons, Inc., New York, 1960.

Stacey, M., and Barker, S. A., "Polysaccharides of Microorganisms," Clarendon Press, Oxford, 1960.

Stacey, M., and Barker, S. A., "Carbohydrates of Living Tissues," D. Van Nostrand Company, Inc., Princeton, 1962.

Whistler, R. L., and Smart, C. L., "Polysaccharide Chemistry," Academic Press, Inc., New York, 1953.

Whistler, R. L., and Wolfrom, M. L., eds., "Methods in Carbohydrate Chemistry," Academic Press, Inc., New York, 1962.

Review Articles

Bell, D. J., Natural Monosaccharides and Oligosaccharides: Their Structure and Occurrence, in M. Florkin and H. S. Mason, eds., "Comparative Biochemistry," vol. III, part A, pp. 288–354, Academic Press, Inc., New York, 1962.

Hirst, E. L., The Structure of Polysaccharides, in D. J. Bell and J. K. Grant, eds., "The Structure and Biosynthesis of Macromolecules," pp. 45–62, Cambridge University Press, New York, 1962.

Jeanloz, R. W., Recent Developments in the Biochemistry of the Amino Sugars, *Advances in Enzymol,* **25,** 433–456, 1963.

Raymond, A. L., Carbohydrates II, in H. Gilman, ed., "Organic Chemistry," 2d ed., vol. II, pp. 1605–1663, John Wiley & Sons, Inc., New York, 1943.

Rogers, H. J., The Surface Structures of Bacteria, in D. J. Bell and J. K. Grant, eds., "The Structure and Function of the Membranes and Surfaces of Cells," pp. 55–104, Cambridge University Press, New York, 1963.

Roseman, S., Metabolism of Connective Tissue, *Ann. Rev. Biochem.,* **28,** 545–578, 1959.

Symposium, Synthesis of Complex Polysaccharides, *Federation Proc.,* **21,** 1064–1092, 1962.

Wolfrom, M. L., Carbohydrates I, in H. Gilman, ed., "Organic Chemistry," 2d ed., vol. II, pp. 1532–1604, John Wiley & Sons, Inc., New York, 1943.

Zilliken, F., and Whitehouse, M. W., The Nonulozaminic Acids, *Advances in Carbohydrate Chem,* **13,** 237–263, 1958.

Many special phases of carbohydrate chemistry have been reviewed in *Advances in Carbohydrate Chemistry,* Academic Press, Inc., New York, 1945–current.

5. Chemistry of Lipids

Fatty Acids, Fats, Phosphatides, and Related Substances

If animal or vegetable tissues are extracted with one or more of the so-called "fat solvents," *e.g.*, ether, chloroform, benzene, petroleum, carbon disulfide, etc., a portion of the material may dissolve; the name "lipid" is given to the components of this soluble fraction. The lipid (lipoid, lipide, lipin) fraction is an operational rather than a structural classification and is defined, simply, as that fraction of any biological material which is extractable by nonpolar solvents. It includes a heterogeneous group of structural types, of which the more prominent members are:

Fatty acids
Neutral fats (triglycerides)
Phosphatides
    Derivatives of glycerol phosphate
    Derivatives of sphingosine or of related compounds
Glycolipids
    Derivatives of sphingosine
    Derivatives of glycerol
Aliphatic alcohols and waxes
Terpenes
Steroids

THE FATTY ACIDS

In order to appreciate the physical and chemical properties of many of the classes of lipids, it is necessary to consider some of the properties and reactions of the fatty acids. Whereas *free* fatty acids occur only as minor ingredients in most naturally occurring lipids, they are found in abundance in *ester* linkage, and occasionally in amide linkage, in several of the classes of compounds listed above. The fatty acids encountered in nature have, with only occasional exceptions, certain properties from which generalizations may be drawn.

1. They are, for the most part, monocarboxylic acids with hydrocarbon residues which are both acyclic and generally unbranched.

2. The number of carbon atoms in the molecule is in most cases even; odd-numbered carbon atom fatty acids are also found in nature, although in much smaller quantities.

61

3. They may be saturated or may contain one or more double bonds. However, double bonds are not usually found in that portion of the molecule between the carboxyl group and the ninth carbon atom removed.

Saturated Fatty Acids. The common names and formulas of some of the saturated fatty acids are given in Table 5.1. Certain properties of these substances may be regarded as the sum of contributions by the polar hydrophilic carboxyl group and by the hydrophobic paraffin residue. Thus, acetic and propionic acids are

Table 5.1: SATURATED FATTY ACIDS

Molecular formula	Common name	Systematic name	Structural formula
$C_2H_4O_2$	Acetic	. . . .	CH_3COOH
$C_3H_6O_2$	Propionic	. . . .	CH_3CH_2COOH
$C_4H_8O_2$	n-Butyric	. . . .	$CH_3(CH_2)_2COOH$
$C_6H_{12}O_2$	Caproic	n-Hexanoic	$CH_3(CH_2)_4COOH$
$C_8H_{16}O_2$	Caprylic	n-Octanoic	$CH_3(CH_2)_6COOH$
$C_9H_{18}O_2$	Pelargonic	n-Nonanoic	$CH_3(CH_2)_7COOH$
$C_{10}H_{20}O_2$	Capric	n-Decanoic	$CH_3(CH_2)_8COOH$
$C_{12}H_{24}O_2$	Lauric	n-Dodecanoic	$CH_3(CH_2)_{10}COOH$
$C_{14}H_{28}O_2$	Myristic	n-Tetradecanoic	$CH_3(CH_2)_{12}COOH$
$C_{16}H_{32}O_2$	Palmitic*	n-Hexadecanoic	$CH_3(CH_2)_{14}COOH$
$C_{18}H_{36}O_2$	Stearic*	n-Octadecanoic	$CH_3(CH_2)_{16}COOH$
$C_{20}H_{40}O_2$	Arachidic	n-Eicosanoic	$CH_3(CH_2)_{18}COOH$
$C_{22}H_{44}O_2$	Behenic	n-Docosanoic	$CH_3(CH_2)_{20}COOH$
$C_{24}H_{48}O_2$	Lignoceric	n-Tetracosanoic	$CH_3(CH_2)_{22}COOH$
$C_{26}H_{52}O_2$	Cerotic	n-Hexacosanoic	$CH_3(CH_2)_{24}COOH$

* These are the most abundant saturated fatty acids encountered in animal fats.

miscible with water. Butyric acid has a limited solubility in water, 5.6 per cent; caproic acid has a solubility of 0.4 per cent; higher members of the series are virtually insoluble in water although readily soluble in nonpolar solvents. As the paraffin residue becomes longer, it appears to dominate in establishing physical properties. Boiling points and melting points of fatty acids rise with increasing chain length. Even-numbered–carbon atom saturated fatty acids of less than 10 carbon atoms are liquids at room temperature; longer-chained members are solids.

As implied by their name, the fatty acids are all acidic, undergoing dissociation in aqueous solution,

$$RCOOH \rightleftharpoons RCOO^- + H^+$$

where
$$K = \frac{[H^+][RCOO^-]}{[RCOOH]}$$

and $pK = -\log K$. Except for the first member of the series, formic acid ($pK = 3.75$), all the saturated fatty acids resemble acetic acid in their dissociation constants ($pK = 4.76$). However, many of the common properties of acids are evident only in so far as the acid in question is water-soluble. Thus although stearic acid possesses approximately the same acidic strength as does acetic acid, a saturated aqueous solution of stearic acid will not affect the color of indicators because of its extreme insolubility in water.

The mixture of fatty acids obtained upon hydrolysis of lipids derived from various sources will generally contain both saturated and unsaturated fatty acids. In typical animal lipids, the most abundant saturated fatty acid is usually palmitic (C_{16}), with stearic (C_{18}) second in amount. Shorter-chain fatty acids (C_{14} and C_{12}) do occur in small quantity, as do longer-chain members (up to C_{24}). Fatty acids of 10 carbon atoms or less are present in limited amounts in animal lipids. An exception is milk fat, which contains appreciable concentrations of lower molecular weight fatty acids.

Unsaturated Fatty Acids. The names and structures of certain of the more common unsaturated fatty acids are given in Table 5.2. Unsaturation, *i.e.*, the presence of one or more double bonds, markedly alters certain properties of a fatty acid. In general, the melting point is greatly lowered and solubility in nonpolar solvents is enhanced (Table 5.3). All the common unsaturated fatty acids of nature are liquids at room temperature.

The double bond in the singly unsaturated fatty acids of animal lipids is generally in the 9,10 position. Thus, the two most abundant singly unsaturated fatty acids of animal lipids are oleic acid and palmitoleic acid.

$$CH_3—(CH_2)_7—CH=CH—(CH_2)_7—COOH$$

Oleic acid

$$CH_3—(CH_2)_5—CH=CH—(CH_2)_7—COOH$$

Palmitoleic acid

Oleic acid is the most widely distributed and most abundant fatty acid in nature.

The introduction of a double bond gives rise to the possibility of a type of geometrical isomerism known as *cis-trans* isomerism. This results because the valence bonds lie in one plane and there is no freedom of rotation about the axis of the double bond. The isomeric forms of 9-octadecenoic acid may be written as follows:

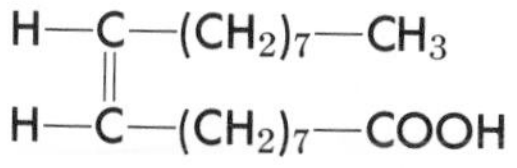

$$
\begin{array}{ll}
H—C—(CH_2)_7—CH_3 & CH_3—(CH_2)_7—C—H \\
\quad\| & \qquad\qquad\quad\| \\
H—C—(CH_2)_7—COOH & H—C—(CH_2)_7—COOH
\end{array}
$$

Oleic acid (*cis*) 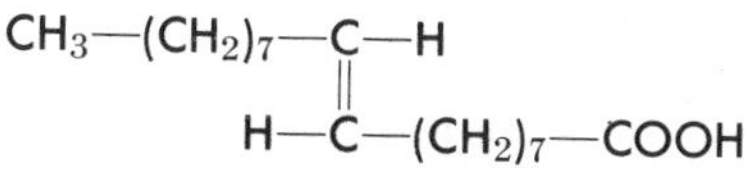   **Elaidic acid (*trans*)**

In this and in certain other known cases in which ethylenic double bonds occur in the fatty acid series, it is the *cis* configuration which is found in nature. However, among other classes of compounds this rule does not necessarily apply. In sphingosine (page 76) the configuration is *trans*, as it is in the abundant ethylene *di*carboxylic acid of nature, fumaric acid.

Fatty acids containing more than one double bond are also commonly found. When two double bonds occur in a carbon skeleton in the relationship

$$—CH=CH—CH=CH—$$

they are said to be in conjugation. Such conjugated double bonds are usually more readily oxidized than isolated double bonds or double bonds related to each other in any other fashion. Conjugated double bonds are found in the fatty acid series of

Table 5.2: Unsaturated Fatty Acids

Molecular formula	Common name	Systematic name	Structural formula
$C_{16}H_{30}O_2$	Palmitoleic*	9-Hexadecenoic	$CH_3(CH_2)_5CH=CH(CH_2)_7COOH$
$C_{18}H_{34}O_2$	Oleic*	cis-9-Octadecenoic	$CH_3(CH_2)_7CH=CH(CH_2)_7COOH$
$C_{18}H_{34}O_2$	Elaidic	trans-9-Octadecenoic	$CH_3(CH_2)_7CH=CH(CH_2)_7COOH$
$C_{18}H_{34}O_2$	Vaccenic	11-Octadecenoic	$CH_3(CH_2)_5CH=CH(CH_2)_9COOH$
$C_{18}H_{32}O_2$	Linoleic*	cis, cis-9, 12-Octadecadienoic	$CH_3(CH_2)_4CH=CHCH_2CH=CH(CH_2)_7COOH$
$C_{18}H_{30}O_2$	Linolenic	9, 12, 15-Octadecatrienoic	$CH_3CH_2CH=CHCH_2CH=CHCH_2CH=CH(CH_2)_7COOH$
$C_{18}H_{30}O_2$	γ-Linolenic	6, 9, 12-Octadecatrienoic	$CH_3(CH_2)_4CH=CHCH_2CH=CHCH_2CH=CH(CH_2)_4COOH$
$C_{18}H_{30}O_2$	Eleostearic	9, 11, 13-Octadecatrienoic	$CH_3(CH_2)_3CH=CH—CH=CH—CH=CH(CH_2)_7COOH$
$C_{20}H_{32}O_2$	Arachidonic	5, 8, 11, 14-Eicosatetraenoic	$CH_3(CH_2)_4CH=CHCH_2CH=CHCH_2CH=CHCH_2CH=CH(CH_2)_3COOH$
$C_{22}H_{34}O_2$	Clupanodonic	4, 8, 12, 15, 19-Docosapentaenoic	$CH_3CH_2CH=CH(CH_2)_2CH=CHCH_2CH=CH(CH_2)_2CH=CH(CH_2)_2CH=CH(CH_2)_2COOH$

* These are the most abundant unsaturated fatty acids in animal fats.

Table 5.3: MELTING POINTS OF THE COMMON 18-CARBON FATTY ACIDS

Fatty acid	Double bonds	M.p., °C.	Solubility in cold ethanol
Stearic acid..................................	0	70°	2.5%
Oleic acid....................................	1	14°	Infinitely soluble
Linoleic acid................................	2	−5°	Infinitely soluble
Linolenic acid...............................	3	−11°	Infinitely soluble

the vegetable world (eleostearic acid, Table 5.2), among the so-called "drying oils" of the paint industry. Linolenic acid (Table 5.2), in which the double bonds are not conjugated, is the principal constituent of linseed oil, the chief drying oil of industry. Multiple unsaturation as it occurs in the fatty acids of animal lipids is in general not conjugated but rather of the type:

$$\left(-CH=CH-CH_2-CH=CH-\right)$$

The fatty acids most frequently encountered in mammalian biochemistry exhibiting multiple unsaturation are linoleic acid, containing two double bonds,

$$CH_3(CH_2)_4-CH=CH-CH_2-CH=CH-(CH_2)_7-COOH$$
Linoleic acid

linolenic acid, with three double bonds,

$$CH_3-CH_2-CH=CH-CH_2-CH=CH-CH_2-CH=CH-(CH_2)_7-COOH$$
Linolenic acid

and arachidonic acid, with four double bonds,

$$CH_3(CH_2)_4CH=CHCH_2CH=CHCH_2CH=CHCH_2CH=CH(CH_2)_3COOH$$
Arachidonic acid

It will be observed that, in conformity with the general principles outlined above, no double bonds occur between the first (carboxyl) and ninth carbon atoms, except in γ-linolenic, arachidonic, and clupanodonic acids (Table 5.2), and that successive double bonds occur one carbon atom remote from conjugation.

Carbocyclic and Oxygenated Fatty Acids. Fatty acids carrying various substituents are occasionally encountered. Tuberculostearic acid, derived from the lipid of the tubercle bacillus, is one of the few branched-chain odd-numbered–carbon atom fatty acids of nature, being 10-methylstearic acid. Occasionally, alicyclic substituents are encountered, *e.g.*, in chaulmoogra oil, used in the treatment of leprosy. Chaulmoogric acid, derived from this source, has the formula

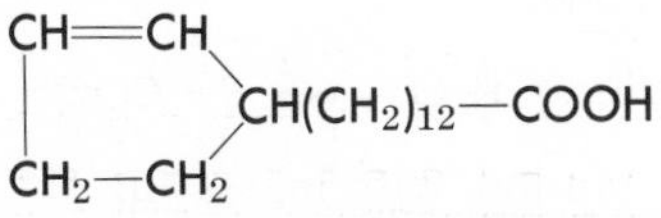

$$
\begin{array}{c}
CH=CH \\
| \qquad \diagdown \\
\qquad \quad CH(CH_2)_{12}-COOH \\
| \qquad \diagup \\
CH_2-CH_2
\end{array}
$$
Chaulmoogric acid

An interesting type of bacterial fatty acid containing a cyclopropane ring has been described.

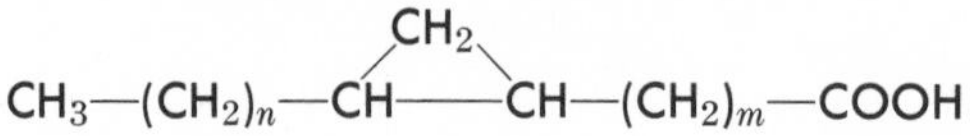

$$CH_3-(CH_2)_n-\overset{\displaystyle CH_2}{\overset{\diagup\quad\diagdown}{CH\text{------}CH}}-(CH_2)_m-COOH \qquad (n+m=14)$$

Oxygenated substituents, particularly among long-chain fatty acids, are also encountered. Examples are cerebronic acid,

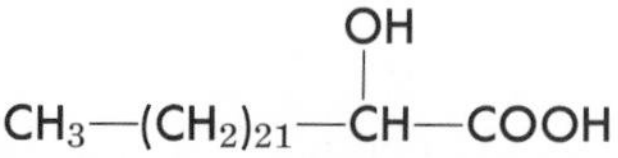

$$CH_3-(CH_2)_{21}-\overset{\overset{\displaystyle OH}{|}}{CH}-COOH$$

Cerebronic acid

present in animal lipids, and the characteristic fatty acid of castor oil, the unsaturated hydroxy acid, ricinoleic acid.

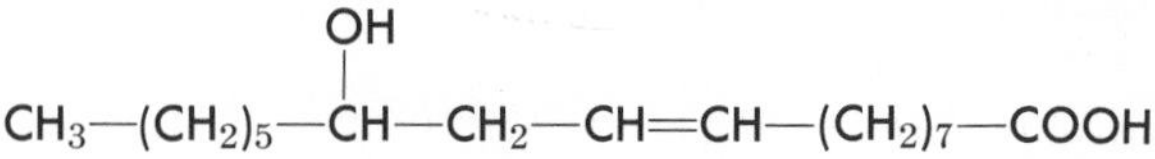

$$CH_3-(CH_2)_5-\overset{\overset{\displaystyle OH}{|}}{CH}-CH_2-CH=CH-(CH_2)_7-COOH$$

Ricinoleic acid

SOAPS AND DETERGENCY

The generic name "soap" has been given to any salt of fatty acids. The sodium and potassium soaps, the soaps of commerce, are more or less soluble in water, whereas the salts of fatty acids with other metal ions are quite insoluble. The potassium soaps are more soluble in water than are the sodium soaps, and, in accord with principles already mentioned, the soaps of unsaturated fatty acids are more soluble in water than are those of saturated fatty acids. Thus potassium linoleate gives a clear solution in water, whereas sodium stearate is sparingly soluble, and its solution is grossly opalescent, indicating the presence of micelles of polymolecular dimensions.

The common use of soap in cleansing is related to its capacity to render more intimate and more prolonged the mixing of oil and water. This is accomplished by means of the negative charge the soap anion confers on the small oil droplets; electrostatic repulsion then prevents their coalescence into an oil phase that would be large enough to separate. Retardation of separation of emulsions is the basis for the property called "detergency." Soaps are the most important but not the only "anionic detergents." In addition, there are "cationic detergents," in which a positively rather than a negatively charged particle is involved. All detergents share with soaps the structural characteristic of containing a highly hydrophilic grouping, together with a large hydrocarbon residue. Certain biologically important detergents will be discussed in later chapters.

Necessary Conditions for Detergency. Incident to hydrolysis, aqueous solutions of soaps are somewhat alkaline.

$$R-COO^- + Na^+ + H_2O \longrightarrow R-COOH + Na^+ + OH^-$$

If acid is added to such a solution, with increasing H^+ ion concentration the fatty acid is formed and precipitates.

$$R\text{---}COO^- + H^+ \longrightarrow R\text{---}COOH\downarrow$$

from solution, and "soapiness," as well as detergency, disappears. Thus the common soaps are not effective detergents in acid solutions, and if a detergent is required under these circumstances, use is made of synthetic alkyl sulfonates, $R\text{---}SO_3^- + Na^+$, which, as salts of far stronger acids, retain their ionic nature even at high H^+ concentrations.

The fatty acid salts of metals other than the alkali metals are practically insoluble in water. Thus calcium, magnesium, and iron soaps are completely devoid of detergent action. This is the chemical basis for "hardness" of water encountered where these ions are present in excessive amounts in water.

REACTIONS OF FATTY ACIDS

Esterification. The important chemical reactions of fatty acids relate to the carboxyl group and to the double bonds. The most prominent reaction of the carboxyl group is esterification, in which a molecule of acid and alcohol react reversibly to yield one molecule of ester and water.

$$\left(R\overset{\overset{O}{\|}}{\text{---}C}\text{---}OH + HOR' \rightleftharpoons R\overset{\overset{O}{\|}}{\text{---}C}\text{---}OR' + H_2O \right)$$

The reaction of esterification is extremely slow if uncatalyzed but may be accelerated either with heat or by addition of hydrogen ion, or both.

Reactions of the Double Bond. Reactions of double bonds of fatty acids include addition of hydrogen or halogen and oxidation by various reagents. Unsaturated fatty acids or their esters may readily be hydrogenated by gaseous hydrogen in the presence of catalysts, *e.g.*, finely divided platinum, palladium, or active nickel. If reduction is carried to completion, such unsaturated acids as linoleic and linolenic acids are quantitatively transformed into stearic acid.

$$CH_3(CH_2)_4CH\text{=}CHCH_2CH\text{=}CH(CH_2)_7COOH \xrightarrow[\text{Pt or Ni}]{H_2} CH_3(CH_2)_{16}COOH$$

| **Linoleic acid** | **Stearic acid** |

This reaction is of great technological importance in that it permits transformation of inexpensive, highly unsaturated liquid vegetable fats into solid shortenings.

Halogens, such as Br_2 and IBr, add readily to double bonds of fatty acids and their esters, the reaction proceeding spontaneously in suitable solvent and to completion in most cases. This reaction is the basis of the "iodine-number determination" (see below).

Whereas the saturated fatty acids are relatively insusceptible to oxidation, unsaturated fatty acids can be oxidized. This occurs slowly and spontaneously in the presence of air and contributes to the processes termed "rancidification." The reaction is believed to involve attack at the double bond by peroxide radicals, with formation of unstable hydroperoxides which decompose to keto and hydroxy keto acids. Oxidation of double bonds proceeds much more rapidly in the presence of ozone, O_3, where an unstable ozonide is pictured as forming initially, with subsequent cleavage by water to give rise to two aldehydic groups:

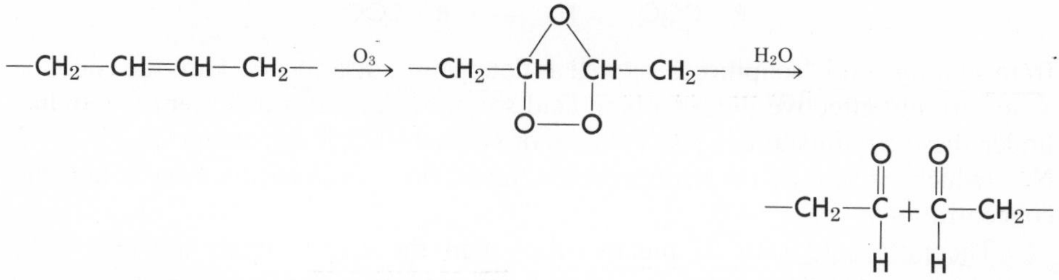

$$-CH_2-CH=CH-CH_2- \xrightarrow{O_3} -CH_2-\overset{\displaystyle O}{\underset{O-O}{CH\ \ CH}}-CH_2- \xrightarrow{H_2O}$$

$$-CH_2-\overset{O}{\underset{H}{\overset{\|}{C}}} + \overset{O}{\underset{H}{\overset{\|}{C}}}-CH_2-$$

This reaction has been extensively employed to establish the position of double bonds in fatty acid chains; the identification of the fragments derived from ozonolysis, followed by oxidative hydrolysis, often permits inference of structure. Potassium permanganate oxidation has also been employed for similar purposes. Under mild conditions, glycols are formed at the sites of double bonds.

$$CH_3(CH_2)_7CH=CH(CH_2)_7COOH \xrightarrow{KMnO_4} CH_3(CH_2)_7CHOH-CHOH(CH_2)_7COOH$$
                Oleic acid   9,10-Dihydroxystearic acid

Under vigorous conditions the same reagent cleaves the molecule at the double bond and oxidizes the termini to the carboxyl level.

$$CH_3(CH_2)_7CH=CH(CH_2)_7COOH$$
                                Oleic acid

$$\downarrow KMnO_4$$

$$CH_3(CH_2)_7COOH + HOOC(CH_2)_7COOH$$
            Pelargonic acid   Azelaic acid

CHARACTERIZATION OF FATTY ACID MIXTURES

Fatty acids of natural origin are usually obtained from their esters by alkaline hydrolysis. The fatty acids, which separate from the aqueous phase on addition of strong acids, may be collected by filtration or by extraction with ether or petroleum ether. In general, such procedures yield complex mixtures of fatty acids which were formerly resolvable with relative difficulty. Accordingly, a description of fatty acid mixtures has been frequently restricted to certain general characteristics indicating average chain length, average degree of unsaturation, etc., rather than to identification and relative quantities of individual fatty acids in the mixture. Among the commonly employed characterizations of such a mixture are the *iodine number,* the *titration equivalent weight,* the *acetyl number,* and the *Reichert-Meissl number.*

Iodine-number Determination. The determination of the iodine number depends on the already mentioned fact that most double bonds react quantitatively with Br_2 or IBr at room temperature in acetic acid or methanol solution. By conventional iodometric procedures the quantity of free halogen that remains after a weighed amount of fat or fatty acid has reacted with a measured excess of halogen can be determined. From this the iodine number, defined as the number of grams of iodine reacting with 100 g. of lipid, is calculated. The iodine number of saturated fatty acids is zero; of oleic acid, 90; of linoleic acid, 181; of linolenic acid, 274.

Titration Equivalent Weight. The average molecular weight of a fatty acid mixture is usually determined by titration of a weighed sample in aqueous alcohol with standard alkali. Titration is carried to a somewhat basic end point (phenolphthalein) with exclusion of CO_2, and the mean molecular weight is calculated.

$$\left(\text{Mean mol. wt.} = \frac{\text{mg. of fatty acid}}{(\text{ml. of alkali})(\text{normality of alkali})} \right)$$

Acetyl and Reichert-Meissl Numbers. The treatment of a fat or fatty acid mixture with acetic anhydride results in acetylation of all alcoholic hydroxyl groups. The *acetyl number,* which is a measure of the number of such hydroxyl groups, is defined as the number of milligrams of KOH required to neutralize the acetic acid contained in 1 g. of acetylated fat.

Fatty acids of 12 carbon atoms or less are volatile in steam, and those containing 6 carbon atoms or less are appreciably soluble in water. Their abundance may be estimated by the determination of the *Reichert-Meissl number,* which is defined as the number of milliliters of $0.1N$ alkali required to neutralize the volatile, soluble acids derived from 5 g. of fat.

Separation and Isolation of Fatty Acids. Complete and quantitative separation of a fatty acid mixture may be achieved by one of several procedures. Classical methods involve separation of unsaturated and saturated fatty acids by crystallization of the latter from cold acetone or precipitation of their lead salts from ethanol. Unsaturated fatty acids may be further separated by fractional crystallization of their bromo derivatives; saturated fatty acids, by meticulous fractional distillation of their methyl esters. More recently, unsaturated fatty acids have been separated as their mercuriacetate adducts.

These methods for separation of fatty acids have been largely replaced by chromatographic procedures, *viz.,* thin-layer (page 41), paper (page 39), and, particularly, gas-liquid chromatography. It may be noted that because of the relative insolubility of fatty acids in polar solvents, their separation on paper entails certain special features, *e.g.,* the use of silicic acid–impregnated and glass fiber paper.

In gas chromatography, a glass or metal tube (column), 1 to 2 m. long and 0.2 to 2 cm. in internal diameter, is filled with a finely divided inert solid, such as diatomaceous earth or ground firebrick impregnated with a nonvolatile liquid (lubricating greases, silicone oils, or polyesters of high molecular weight alcohols and dibasic acids). A mixture of methyl esters of fatty acids is flash-evaporated at one end of the column, the entire length of which is maintained at an elevated temperature (170 to 225°C.). The volatilized esters are swept through the column by a constantly flowing stream of an inert gas, *e.g.,* argon, helium, or nitrogen. Each component of the ester mixture moves on the column at a different rate determined by its ratio of partition between the gas phase and the nonvolatile liquid (stationary) phase. The presence of the individual esters in the gas emerging from the column is detected usually by physical or chemical means. The data are automatically recorded on a

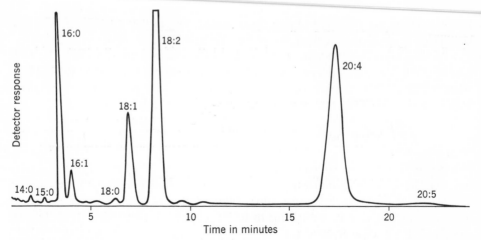

F<small>IG</small>. 5.1. Gas-liquid chromatographic analysis of the methyl esters of the fatty acids present in normal rat plasma as cholesterol esters. The numbers at the top or at one side of the peaks, to the left and right of the colon, indicate, respectively, the number of carbon atoms and double bonds present in each fatty acid. The areas under each peak reflect the relative quantities of each fatty acid present. (*Courtesy, Dr. L. I. Gidez.*)

chart as a series of peaks. The area under each peak is proportional to the concentration of the particular component in the mixture. Identification of components in a chromatogram is achieved by the use of standards. The resolution of a mixture of the methyl esters of fatty acids by this procedure is illustrated in Fig. 5.1. Members in a homologous group, *e.g.*, straight-chain saturated fatty acid methyl esters, may be identified from a plot of the logarithm of the volume of gas necessary to elute a component from the column (retention volume) versus the number of carbon atoms in the component. This plot will yield a straight line. This technique permits quantitative resolution of microgram quantities of mixtures of fatty acids.

It may be noted that gas-liquid chromatography has also been applied to separation of suitable volatile derivatives of carbohydrates and of amino acids, as well as of steroids (page 88).

NEUTRAL FATS

The neutral fats, or triglycerides, comprise by far the most abundant group of lipids in nature. These are esters of fatty acids with the trihydroxyl alcohol glycerol, $CH_2OHCHOHCH_2OH$, and have the generic formula

$$R\text{—}COO\text{—}CH_2$$
$$R'\text{—}COO\text{—}CH$$
$$R''\text{—}COO\text{—}CH_2$$

Neutral fat

in which RCOOH, R'COOH, and R''COOH represent three molecules of either the same or different fatty acids. The system for naming the neutral fats is based upon the names of the constituent fatty acids. Thus tristearin contains three stearic acid residues per molecule, and oleodistearin contains one of oleic and two of stearic acid.

Study of the distribution of a mixture of fatty acids among the triglycerides in a given sample of native fat has thus far failed to reveal any system in the formation of glyceryl esters. Indeed, it appears that the several fatty acids present in a sample of fat are randomly distributed in ester linkage to the glyceryl residues. From this random esterification and probability considerations it follows that molecules of triglyceride in which only one fatty acid is represented occur very infrequently except in samples of fat in which one species of fatty acid is represented to the extent of 50 per cent or more.

Physical and Chemical Properties. The general physical properties of fats are reminiscent of those of fatty acids. As a class, the fats are insoluble in water, soluble in nonpolar solvents. The solubility is greater, and the melting point lower, the richer the fat is in short-chain and unsaturated fatty acid residues. Saturation as well as increasing chain length tend to result in elevation of melting point such that, whereas tristearin is a solid at room temperature (melting point, 71°C.), triolein (melting point, −17°C.) and tributyrin (melting point < −75°C.) are liquids.

Table 5.4 contains examples of the fatty acid composition of neutral fats from various sources. Most samples of animal fat contain predominantly esters of palmitic, stearic, palmitoleic, oleic, and linoleic acids in various proportions. Fat from diverse portions of the same organism may differ widely in composition. Thus, subcutaneous fat of man has an average iodine number of 65, whereas fat from the liver, which is richer in unsaturated acids, has an average iodine number of 135. Butter or milk fat is a notable exception in having fatty acids of shorter chain length in higher abundance than elsewhere. Subcutaneous fat of different

Table 5.4: APPROXIMATE COMPOSITION, IN MOLAR PERCENTAGE, OF THE FATTY ACID MIXTURES OBTAINED FROM TRIGLYCERIDES FROM VARIOUS SOURCES

Acid	Depot fat				Liver fat, cow	Milk fat, cow
	Human	Cow	Pig	Sheep		
Butyric	..	..	..	..	...	9
Caproic	..	..	..	..	...	3
Caprylic	..	..	..	..	...	2
Capric	..	..	..	..	...	4
Lauric	..	..	..	..	...	3
Myristic	3	7	1	2	3	11
Palmitic	23	29	28	25	35	23
Stearic	6	21	10	26	5	9
Palmitoleic	5	..	..	..	10	4
Oleic	50	41	58	42	36	26
Linoleic	10	2	3	5	8	3
C_{20-22} unsaturated	..	..	..	..	3*	

* Average number of double bonds per molecule = 3.0.

SOURCE: Data adapted from T. P. Hilditch, "The Chemical Constitution of Natural Fats," John Wiley & Sons, Inc., New York, 1940, and from the literature.

mammalian species varies considerably in-degree of unsaturation, and this is reflected in the fact that, whereas the melting point of beef tallow is high, pork lard melts at a considerably lower temperature.

Vegetable fats, or oils, exhibit greater diversity in their fatty acid composition in regard to both chain length and degree of unsaturation of the constituent fatty acids. Many are liquids at room temperature, and it is among the vegetable oils that the unusual fatty acids, those with conjugated double bonds or carbocyclic structure, are encountered.

Hydrolysis and Saponification. The most important chemical reaction of the neutral fats is their hydrolysis to yield three molecules of fatty acid and one of glycerol.

$$
\begin{array}{ccc}
\text{R—COO—CH}_2 & & \text{R—COOH} \quad \text{HOCH}_2 \\
& & + \\
\text{R'—COO—CH} + 3\text{H}_2\text{O} \underset{}{\overset{(H^+)}{\rightleftharpoons}} & \text{R'—COOH} + \text{HOCH} \\
& & + \\
\text{R''—COO—CH}_2 & & \text{R''—COOH} \quad \text{HOCH}_2 \\
\textbf{Neutral fat} & & \textbf{Fatty acids} \quad \textbf{Glycerol}
\end{array}
$$

This reaction proceeds slowly in boiling water, partly because of immiscibility of the reagents, and is facilitated by addition of a detergent, which will increase the surface of contact between water and fat. It is a reversible reaction, its reversal being the reaction of esterification, and the attainment of equilibrium will be accelerated by the same catalysts employed in esterification. Frequently employed in the laboratory is H^+ in the form of a strong mineral acid. If an aryl or alkyl sulfonic acid is employed, it will serve both as a detergent and as a source of hydrogen ions. While the reaction of hydrolysis is a reversible one, it may be driven to virtual completion by addition of a large excess of water. The enzymes that catalyze this reaction in animals and plants are *esterases,* or more specifically, *lipases.*

In the laboratory it is generally found more convenient to decompose neutral fats by subjecting them to the action of alkali rather than to that of water. This reaction, termed *saponification,* is different in many respects from that of acid-catalyzed hydrolysis.

$$
\begin{array}{ccc}
\text{R—COOCH}_2 & & \text{R—COO}^-\text{Na}^+ \quad \text{HOCH}_2 \\
& & + \\
\text{R'—COOCH} + 3\text{NaOH} \longrightarrow & \text{R'—COO}^-\text{Na}^+ + \text{HOCH} \\
& & + \\
\text{R''—COOCH}_2 & & \text{R''—COO}^-\text{Na}^+ \quad \text{HOCH}_2 \\
\textbf{Neutral fat} & & \textbf{Soaps} \quad \textbf{Glycerol}
\end{array}
$$

It is completely irreversible, the carboxylate ions showing no tendency to recombine with the hydroxyl groups of glycerol. The progress of the reaction is further favored by the fact that the initial portion of soap that is formed itself acts as a detergent. It will be noted that when the reaction is completed, the products, soap and glycerol, are all soluble in water and insoluble in "fat solvents" such as ether. This fact gives rise to an operational separation frequently employed in lipid chemistry. The *saponifiable fraction* is defined as that portion of total lipid which, after treatment with hot alkali, is soluble in water and insoluble in ether. Neutral fats are thus said to be saponifiable. Examples of nonsaponifiable materials will be encountered in the following chapter. Although originally signifying "soapmaking," the term saponification has been extended to include alkaline hydrolyses of all esters.

Glycerol. Glycerol is a sweet, viscous liquid, infinitely miscible with water and with ethanol, but insoluble in ether. It forms esters with inorganic, as well as organic, acids. Thus, α-glycerophosphate is an important intermediate in carbohydrate (Chap. 20) and lipid (Chap. 23) metabolism.

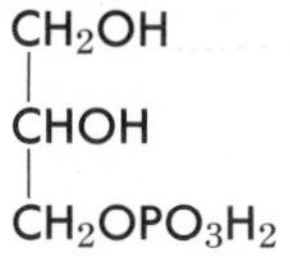

$$CH_2OH$$
$$CHOH$$
$$CH_2OPO_3H_2$$

α-**Glycerophosphate**

"Hardening" of Fats. Hydrogenation of vegetable and other liquid fats to yield solid fats and margarines is conducted under high pressure of hydrogen, most frequently in the presence of nickel catalyst. The reaction is essentially the same as that already discussed (page 67) and involves reduction of double bonds of constituent unsaturated fatty acids. Industrially the hydrogenation is generally not carried to completion but is interrupted when a fat of the required physical characteristics is procured.

PHOSPHATIDES

The next large class of lipids to be considered is the phosphatides, often called phospholipids. This class of substances comprises compounds that are derivatives of glycerol phosphate or of sphingosine, and may be further subdivided on the basis of the nature of the linkage of the hydrocarbon chains and of polar groups present in the molecule. In addition, further characterization may be based on the presence or absence of a nitrogen-containing base as a portion of the polar group.

The larger groups of naturally occurring phosphatides are derivatives of glycerol phosphate and most frequently contain a nitrogenous base. Therefore, in these phosphatides the atomic ratio N/P equals unity; in contrast are phosphatides which are derivatives of sphingosine and in which this ratio is 2 (page 76).

DERIVATIVES OF GLYCEROL PHOSPHATE

The compounds of this group may be regarded as derivatives of L-α-phosphatidic acid.

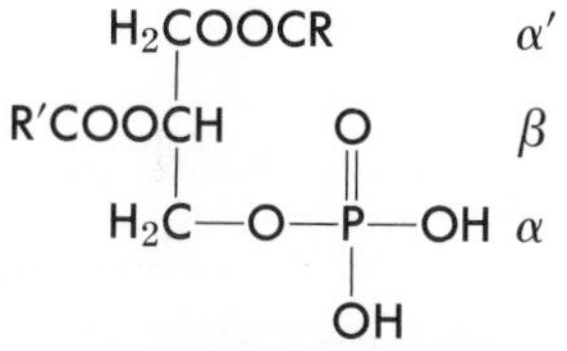

$$
\begin{array}{ll}
H_2COOCR & \alpha' \\
R'COOCH \quad O & \beta \\
H_2C\text{—}O\text{—}P\text{—}OH & \alpha \\
\qquad\qquad OH &
\end{array}
$$

L-α-**Phosphatidic acid**

It may be noted that this compound is designated as the L form because of its stereochemical relationship to L-glyceryl phosphate. Phosphatidic acid yields, on total hydrolysis, one equivalent each of glycerol and of phosphoric acid and two equivalents of fatty acid. The fact that the fatty acids obtained often contain about one-half a double bond per mole indicates that, in phosphatidic acids derived from some natural phosphatides, one molecule of each pair of fatty acids is saturated and the other unsaturated. It will be noted that the phosphoric acid is bound to glycerol in ester linkage at the terminal α-hydroxyl group.

In the phosphatides, the phosphoric acid is also bound in ester linkage to one of the following nitrogenous compounds:

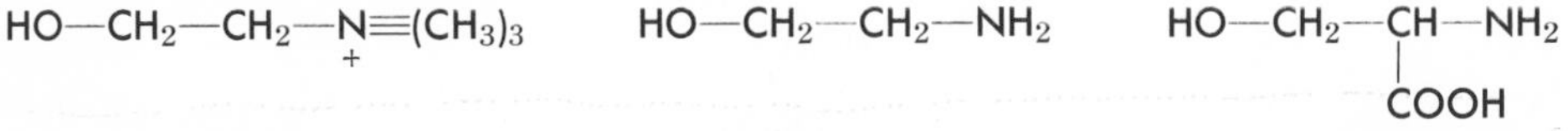

$$HO—CH_2—CH_2—\overset{+}{N}\equiv(CH_3)_3 \qquad HO—CH_2—CH_2—NH_2 \qquad HO—CH_2—\underset{\underset{COOH}{|}}{CH}—NH_2$$

$$\textbf{Choline} \qquad\qquad\qquad \textbf{Ethanolamine} \qquad\qquad\qquad \textsc{l}\text{-}\textbf{Serine}$$

The structural names of the three corresponding phosphatides are phosphatidyl choline, phosphatidyl ethanolamine, and phosphatidyl serine, respectively.

Lecithin. Phosphatidyl choline, or lecithin, has the following formula:

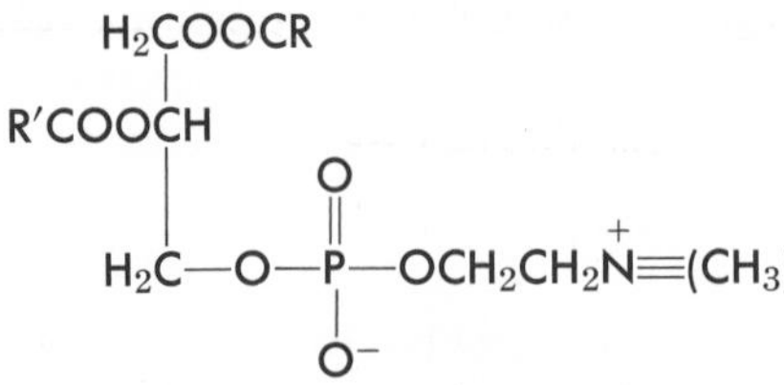

$$
\begin{array}{l}
H_2COOCR \\
\quad| \\
R'COOCH \\
\qquad| \qquad\qquad\quad O \\
\qquad| \qquad\qquad\quad || \\
\quad H_2C—O—P—OCH_2CH_2\overset{+}{N}\equiv(CH_3)_3 \\
\qquad\qquad\;\;| \\
\qquad\qquad\;\;O^-
\end{array}
$$

$$\textsc{l}\text{-}\alpha\text{-}\textbf{Lecithin}$$

On complete hydrolysis, choline, phosphoric acid, glycerol, and two molecules of fatty acid are obtained. The formula is written in dipolar form (Chap. 7), which is intended to convey the fact that choline is a strong base, that phosphoric acid is a moderately strong acid, and that over a wide pH range, including physiological pH, both groups exist predominantly in the ionic form. Partial hydrolysis of lecithin with removal only of one fatty acid yields a substance that has been termed *lysolecithin*. Hydrolysis of the β-ester is catalyzed by enzymes found in snake venoms, microorganisms, and in animal tissues (Chap. 23).

The basicity of choline is characteristic of all quaternary ammonium compounds, *i.e.*, compounds in which N bears four organic substituents. Free choline base,

$$(CH_3)_3\overset{+}{\equiv}N—CH_2—CH_2—OH + OH^-$$
$$\textbf{Choline}$$

exists in aqueous solution practically completely dissociated, much like KOH, and in striking contrast to NH_4OH. Salts of choline with strong acids, such as choline chloride,

$$(CH_3)_3\overset{+}{\equiv}N—CH_2—CH_2—OH + Cl^-$$
$$\textbf{Choline chloride}$$

react as neutral substances in aqueous solution.

The Cephalins. The cephalins include two well-characterized members, phosphatidyl ethanolamine and phosphatidyl serine.

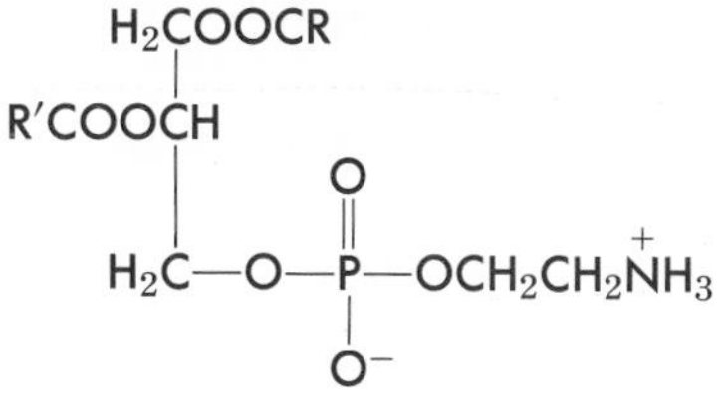

$$H_2COOCR$$
$$R'COOCH$$
$$H_2C-O-\overset{\overset{\displaystyle O}{\|}}{P}-OCH_2CH_2\overset{+}{N}H_3$$
$$O^-$$

Phosphatidyl ethanolamine

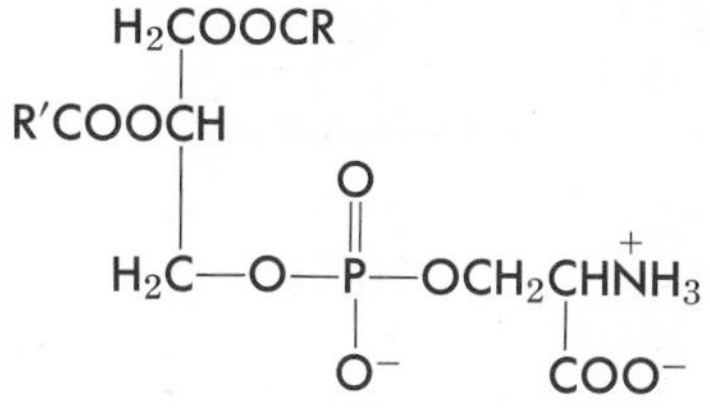

$$H_2COOCR$$
$$R'COOCH$$
$$H_2C-O-\overset{\overset{\displaystyle O}{\|}}{P}-OCH_2\overset{+}{CH}NH_3$$
$$O^-\qquad COO^-$$

Phosphatidyl serine

Like lecithin, these compounds are ionic at physiological pH, but since the primary amino group is much less basic than the quaternary ammonium group, the cephalins are more acidic than lecithin. Phosphatidyl serine, with its added carboxyl group, is the most strongly acidic member.

Plasmalogens. The plasmalogens are a class of phosphatides in which the fatty acid at the α' position is replaced by an α,β-unsaturated ether. Thus, the ethanolamine-containing plasmalogens have the following generic formula:

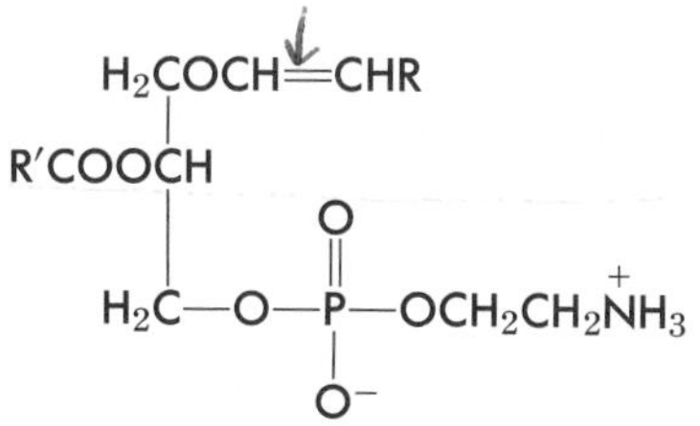

$$H_2COCH \overset{\downarrow}{=} CHR$$
$$R'COOCH$$
$$H_2C-O-\overset{\overset{\displaystyle O}{\|}}{P}-OCH_2CH_2\overset{+}{N}H_3$$
$$O^-$$

Phosphatidal ethanolamine

On mild acid hydrolysis of plasmalogens, the α,β-unsaturated ether gives rise to an aldehyde. The three principal classes of plasmalogens may be called phosphatidal ethanolamine, phosphatidal choline, and phosphatidal serine.

Plasmalogens occurring in nature appear to be of the L configuration. They are present in highest concentrations in brain and heart, and apparently are not found in significant quantity in nonanimal tissues. The aldehydogenic chains may be of lengths varying from C_{12} to C_{18}, including odd-numbered, branched, and unsaturated carbon chains. Nineteen different aldehydes have been obtained from the lipids of human red blood cells. Pure phosphatidal choline of beef heart showed 98 per cent of the fatty acyl chain to be unsaturated, whereas 94 per cent of the aldehydogenic chains were saturated. The α,β-unsaturated ether linkage has the *cis* configuration. Plasmalogens without a nitrogenous base, *i.e.*, α,β-unsaturated ethers of phosphatidic acid, have also been reported in animal tissues, *e.g.*, liver. Nonphosphatidic plasmalogens occur in low concentrations in structures analogous to triglycerides in which two chains are bound as acyl ester and one as unsaturated ether.

Diphosphatidyl Glycerol. A group of nitrogen-free derivatives of glycerol phosphate is present in animal and, particularly, plant tissues. The compounds of this group may be regarded as composed of one mole of glycerol and two moles of L-α-phosphatidic acid; hence the name diphosphatidyl glycerol. The generic formula is as follows:

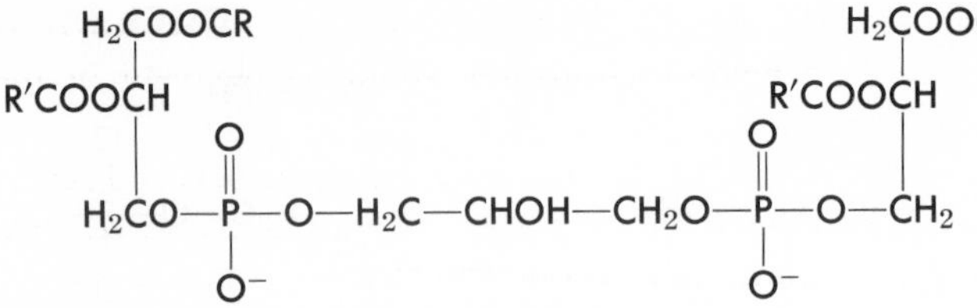

$$
\begin{array}{cc}
H_2COOCR & H_2COOCR \\
R'COOCH & R'COOCH \\
\end{array}
$$

$$
H_2CO-\overset{\overset{\displaystyle O}{\|}}{\underset{\underset{\displaystyle O^-}{|}}{P}}-O-H_2C-CHOH-CH_2O-\overset{\overset{\displaystyle O}{\|}}{\underset{\underset{\displaystyle O^-}{|}}{P}}-O-CH_2
$$

Diphosphatidyl glycerol

The single important example of a diphosphatidyl glycerol reported in animal tissue is cardiolipin, isolated from heart tissue. This is the only phosphatide with known immunological properties; it is utilized in the serological diagnosis of syphilis. Similar compounds are also present in plants; however, the major class of phosphatides in plants contains one mole of phosphatidic acid and, therefore, a monophosphatidyl glycerol. Members of the group differ from one another in the nature of the fatty acids yielded on hydrolysis.

DERIVATIVES OF SPHINGOSINE

Those phosphatides that have two nitrogen atoms contain, in addition to phosphoryl choline, the base sphingosine or a closely related structure dihydrosphingosine.

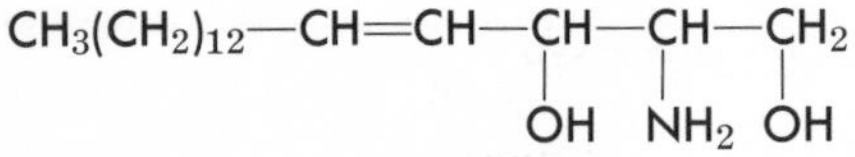

$$
\begin{array}{cc}
CH_3(CH_2)_{12}-CH{=}CH-\underset{\underset{\displaystyle OH}{|}}{CH}-\underset{\underset{\displaystyle NH_2}{|}}{CH}-\underset{\underset{\displaystyle OH}{|}}{CH_2} & CH_3(CH_2)_{14}-\underset{\underset{\displaystyle OH}{|}}{CH}-\underset{\underset{\displaystyle NH_2}{|}}{CH}-\underset{\underset{\displaystyle OH}{|}}{CH_2} \\
\text{Sphingosine} & \text{Dihydrosphingosine}
\end{array}
$$

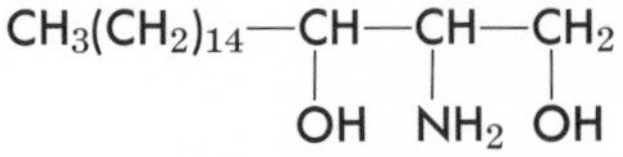

These bases, and related compounds, are also found in certain classes of glycolipids (page 78). In the latter instance, phosphoric acid is not present in the molecule.

Sphingomyelins. The sphingomyelins are the only group of sphingosine-containing phosphatides. They are found in significant concentration primarily in nervous tissue but are also present elsewhere, for example, in the phosphatides of blood. On hydrolysis, the sphingomyelins yield equimolar amounts of fatty acid, choline, phosphoric acid, and sphingosine or dihydrosphingosine but no glycerol. The structure assigned to this group of compounds is

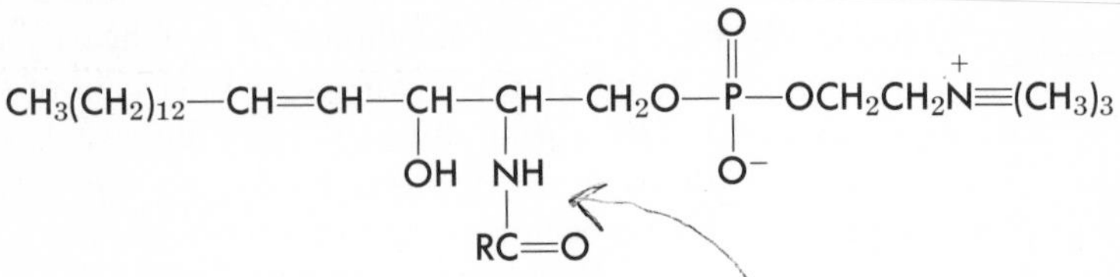

$$
CH_3(CH_2)_{12}-CH{=}CH-\underset{\underset{\displaystyle OH}{|}}{CH}-\underset{\underset{\underset{\displaystyle RC{=}O}{|}}{\underset{\displaystyle NH}{|}}}{CH}-CH_2O-\overset{\overset{\displaystyle O}{\|}}{\underset{\underset{\displaystyle O^-}{|}}{P}}-OCH_2CH_2\overset{+}{N}{\equiv}(CH_3)_3
$$

Sphingomyelin

in which the fatty acid residue (RC=O) is in amide linkage to the sphingosine amino group.

In brain slightly more than 90 per cent of the long-chain base is sphingosine, with an additional small amount of dihydrosphingosine. In plasma phosphatides the values are lower for sphingosine (approximately 75 per cent), with the amount of dihydrosphingosine the same as in brain; an as yet unidentified base, possibly dehydrosphingosine (see below), comprises about 15 per cent of the long-chain bases of plasma phosphatides.

Analyses of plant phosphatides have revealed the presence of several additional long-chain bases. These include phytosphingosine, a saturated C_{18} dihydroxy-sphingosine with the additional secondary alcohol group adjacent to that in sphingosine, and two homologues of phytosphingosine containing 20 carbon atoms. Unsaturated sphingosines (dehydrosphingosines) also appear to be present in plant and animal phosphatides.

GLYCOLIPIDS

Glycolipids, as the term indicates, contain one or more carbohydrate residues. One group of glycolipids is comprised of the phosphoinositides, which are also classified as phosphatides inasmuch as they are derivatives of phosphatidic acid.

Phosphoinositides. Inositol-containing phosphatides are of increasing interest because of evidence for their role in transport processes in cells and data indicating their rapid synthesis and degradation in brain (Chap. 39). On hydrolysis, phosphoinositides yield one mole of glycerol, one mole of the hexahydroxy alcohol, L-*myo*-inositol (page 35), two moles of fatty acid, and one, two, or three moles of phosphoric acid. A phosphoinositide containing three moles of phosphate is present in brain; the compound is 1-phosphatidyl-L-*myo*-inositol-4,5 diphosphate and probably represents more than half the total phosphoinositides in brain (Chap. 39).

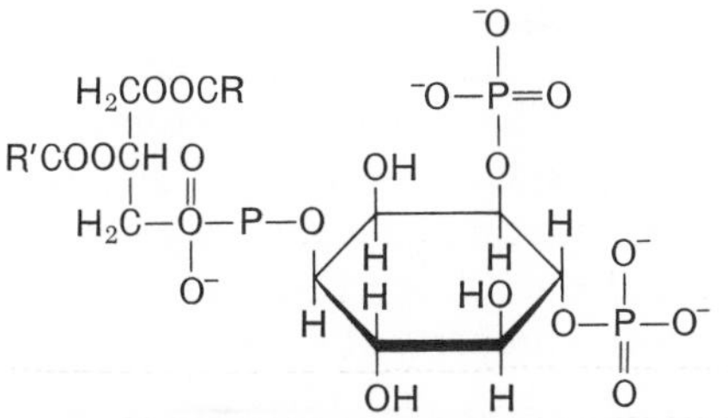

Triphosphoinositide

Cerebrosides. The members of this group differ from the foregoing in that they lack phosphorus. On hydrolysis they yield a hexose, most frequently D-galactose. For this reason members of the group are sometimes referred to as *galactolipids*. On complete hydrolysis each molecule of cerebroside yields one molecule each of sphingosine, galactose or occasionally glucose present in β-glycosidic linkage, and fatty acid. The generic formula is

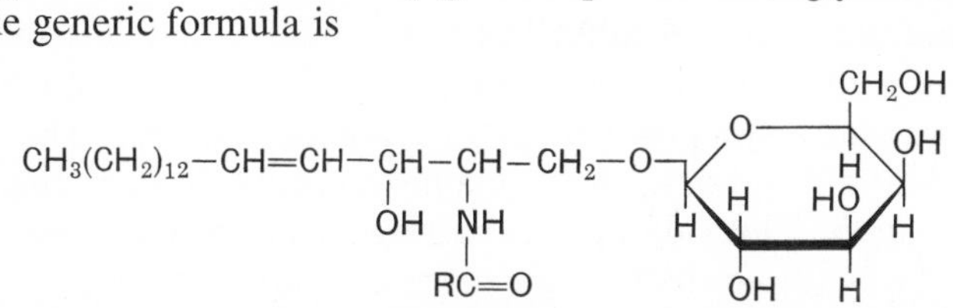

Cerebroside

with $R\overset{|}{C}{=}O$ representing the fatty acid residue in acid amide linkage to sphingo-sine. The name *ceramide* is used to designate the sphingosine–fatty acid (N-acylsphingosine) portion of cerebrosides.

The fatty acid component, RCOOH, appears to be chiefly of the 24-carbon variety, and members of the group differ from one another in the variety of their constituent fatty acids. The saturated C_{24} acid, lignoceric, occurs in the cerebroside kerasin, while its 2-hydroxy derivative, cerebronic acid, is found in phrenosin. Hydroxy fatty acids with 18 carbon atoms have also been described. As in the sphingomyelins, the bond between the sphingosine and fatty acid portions is an amide linkage, while the hexose is attached by an acetal or glycosidic bond.

Compounds of this group occur most abundantly in the myelin sheaths of nerves.

Galactose-containing lipids that are galactosyl glycerides have been found in plant tissues. An α-D-galactosyl (1,6) β-D-galactosyl diglyceride has been de-scribed in chloroplast lipids by Benson and his coworkers.

Gangliosides. This class of lipids is found in significant concentrations in nerve tissue and in other selected tissues, notably spleen. The structure of ganglio-sides is not yet definitely established but is related to that of cerebrosides, in that gangliosides contain a ceramide (see above) linked to carbohydrate. However, in addition to the mole of hexose (galactose or glucose) found in cerebrosides, gangli-osides generally contain several additional moles of carbohydrate, one mole of N-acetylgalactosamine, and at least one mole of N-acetylneuraminic acid (a sialic acid, page 36). In gangliosides from horse erythrocytes and bovine spleen, the sialic acid is N-glycolylneuraminic acid (page 37).

Ceramide Oligosaccharides. A number of other glycosphingolipids have been isolated recently from animal tissues. The most prominent of these is cytolipin H (ceramide lactoside), which displays immunological activity under certain condi-tions. Another, cytolipin K, is a ceramide glycoside containing one residue of glu-cose, two of galactose, and one of acetylgalactosamine. Immunological activity has been found to be a general property of glycosphingolipids such as cerebrosides, ceramide disaccharides (cytosides), and ceramide oligosaccharides. In contrast, only one phosphatide, cardiolipin (page 76), has this property.

Sulfur-containing Glycolipids. Several types of sulfur-containing glycolipids have been described. A sulfate ester analogue of phrenosin (see above) is abundant in the white matter of brain; the sulfate is present in ester linkage at C-3 of the galactose portion of the molecule. Similar sulfur-containing lipids have been reported in other tissues. Members of the group of cerebroside sulfuric esters have been designated as *sulfatides.*

A glycolipid that contains sulfur has been found widely distributed in plants and is apparently localized in the chloroplasts. This compound has also been identified in the chromatophores of photosynthetic bacteria. The sulfur in the molecule is present as a sulfonic group in a hexose; substances of this class may be designated *sulfolipids.* The sulfolipid occurring in all photosynthetic tissues has been shown to be 6-sulfo-6-deoxy-α-glucosyl monoglyceride. The sugar, 6-deoxy-glucose, is known as quinovose.

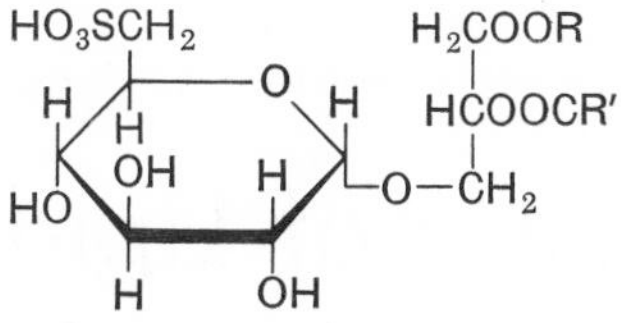

6-Sulfo-6-deoxy-α-glucosyl monoglyceride
(6-sulfoquinovosyl monoglyceride)

ALIPHATIC ALCOHOLS, WAXES, AND GLYCERYL ETHERS

Significant quantities of aliphatic alcohols have been recovered from certain lipid sources. Thus in the feces there are detectable amounts of cetyl alcohol, the primary alcohol corresponding to palmitic acid.

$$CH_3(CH_2)_{14}CH_2OH$$
Cetyl alcohol

In various highly specialized lipids, such alcohols occur as esters of fatty acids. The "head oil" of the sperm whale is largely cetyl palmitate, known as spermaceti, and beeswax is rich in myricyl palmitate.

$$CH_3(CH_2)_{14}-\overset{\displaystyle O}{\overset{\|}{C}}-OCH_2(CH_2)_{14}CH_3 \qquad CH_3(CH_2)_{14}-\overset{\displaystyle O}{\overset{\|}{C}}-OCH_2(CH_2)_{28}CH_3$$

Cetyl palmitate   **Myricyl palmitate**

The generic name "wax" is given to a naturally occurring fatty acid ester of any alcohol other than glycerol. It may be pointed out that the alcoholic components discussed here are part of the *nonsaponifiable fraction* (page 72) of a lipid hydrolysate.

The fatty alcohols are also found in ethereal linkage, as glyceryl ethers. Three such compounds have been isolated from shark oil.

$$\begin{array}{lll}
CH_2O(CH_2)_{15}CH_3 & CH_2O(CH_2)_{17}CH_3 & CH_2O(CH_2)_8CH=CH(CH_2)_7CH_3 \\
| & | & | \\
CHOH & CHOH & CHOH \\
| & | & | \\
CH_2OH & CH_2OH & CH_2OH \\
\textbf{Chimyl alcohol} & \textbf{Batyl alcohol} & \textbf{Selachyl alcohol}
\end{array}$$

Batyl alcohol is an ether of glycerol and octadecyl alcohol (C_{18} corresponding to stearic acid), while selachyl alcohol contains an unsaturated oleyl alcohol residue (corresponding to oleic acid). These alcohols occur naturally in a form in which the hydroxyl groups are acylated.

REFERENCES

See list following Chap. 6.

6. Chemistry of Lipids

Terpenes and Steroids

TERPENES

Throughout the biological world there are numerous compounds whose carbon skeletons suggest a structural relationship to isoprene, 2-methyl butadiene.

$$CH_2=\overset{\overset{\displaystyle CH_3}{|}}{C}-CH=CH_2$$

Isoprene

Many of these compounds contain multiples of five carbon atoms so related to each other as to make possible dissection of their structures into isoprene-like fragments. This class of compounds, called *terpenes* (from turpentine), includes essential oils such as citral, pinene, geraniol, camphor, and menthane; the resin acids and rubber; a variety of plant pigments, including carotenes, lycopene, and others; and vitamin A and squalene of animals. Examples of open-chain terpenes are phytol, the alcoholic fragment obtained on hydrolysis of chlorophyll,

$$CH_3-\overset{\overset{\displaystyle CH_3}{|}}{CH}-CH_2-CH_2-CH_2-\overset{\overset{\displaystyle CH_3}{|}}{CH}-CH_2-CH_2-CH_2-\overset{\overset{\displaystyle CH_3}{|}}{CH}-CH_2-CH_2-CH_2-\overset{\overset{\displaystyle CH_3}{|}}{C}=CH-CH_2OH$$

Phytol

and squalene, a hydrocarbon derived from shark-liver oil.

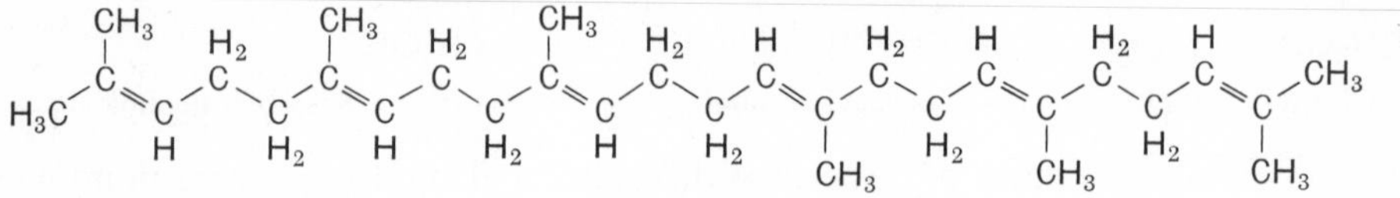

Squalene

Of particular interest are the carotenes, orange pigments occurring in plants. The formulas of α-, β-, and γ-carotene are shown.

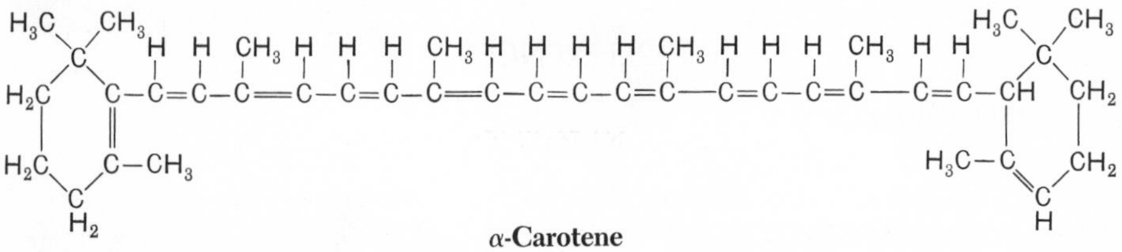

α-Carotene

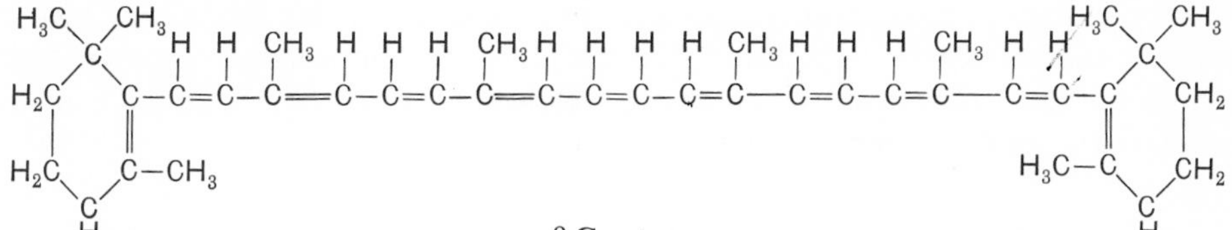

β-Carotene

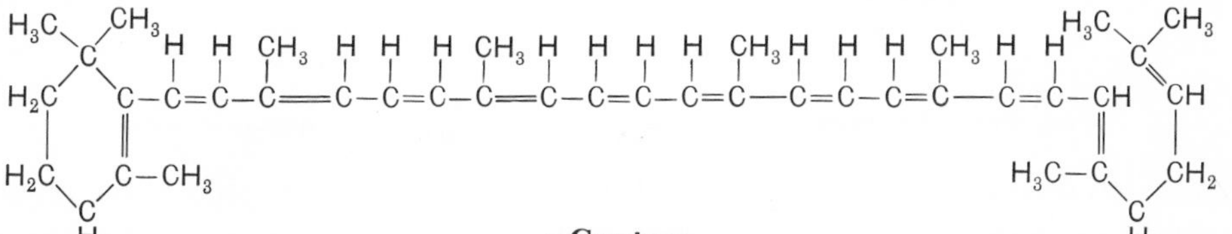

γ-Carotene

β-Carotene, as can be seen, is symmetrical with respect to the arrangement of the two termini of the chain. The ring structure is the same as in β-ionone.

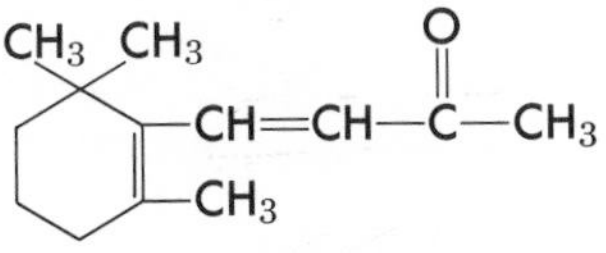

β-Ionone

Interest in these compounds relates to the fact that the carotenes are precursors of the group of vitamins A (Chap. 56); an example is vitamin A_1.

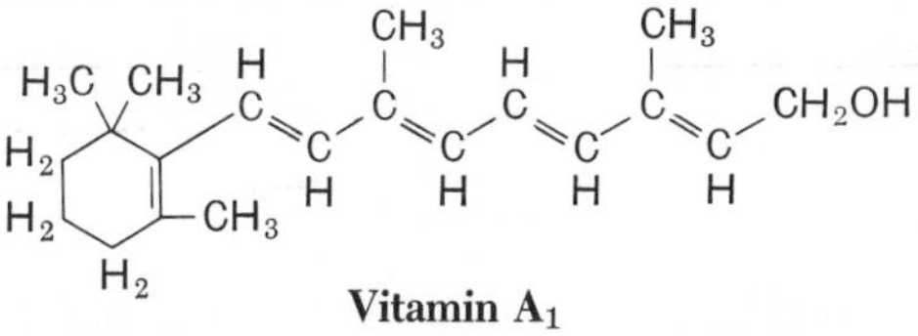

Vitamin A_1

Because of the many double bonds in the carotenoid side chain, *cis-trans* isomerism is possible. The major proportion of naturally occurring carotenoids have their double bonds in the all-*trans* configuration, as shown above for vitamin A_1. Small quantities of carotenoids containing one or more *cis* double bonds occur in nature, and isomerization can take place in animal tissues. A *cis* form of vitamin A is present in rat liver, and a carotenoid containing a *cis* double bond is present in the retina of the eye (Chap. 43).

Certain other accessory dietary factors are related chemically to the terpenes. The compounds that have been grouped as vitamins E (Chap. 56) are lipid-soluble aromatic compounds bearing side chains of the type seen among terpenes. The antihemorrhagic factor, vitamin K (Chap. 56), is a substituted 1,4-naphthoquinone bearing a phytyl side chain.

STEROIDS

This large group of compounds bears some structural resemblance to the terpenes. The diversity of their physiological activity makes it one of the most studied classes of biological compounds. The members of this group may be considered as derivatives of a fused, reduced ring system, perhydrocyclopentanophenanthrene, comprising three fused cyclohexane rings (A, B, and C) in the nonlinear or phenanthrene arrangement,

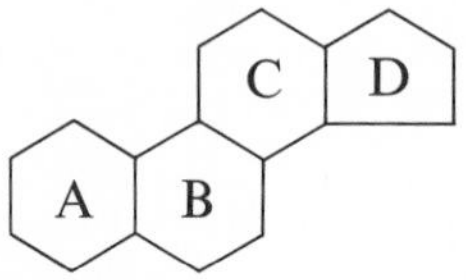

Perhydrocyclopentanophenanthrene 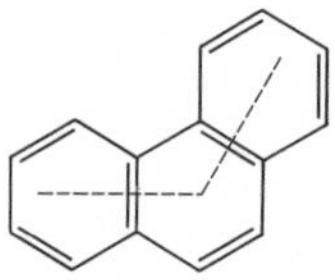   Phenanthrene

and a terminal cyclopentane ring (D). Certain general characteristics of the group may be considered with reference to a typical member, cholestanol; the conventional numbering of the carbon atoms is included in the formula.

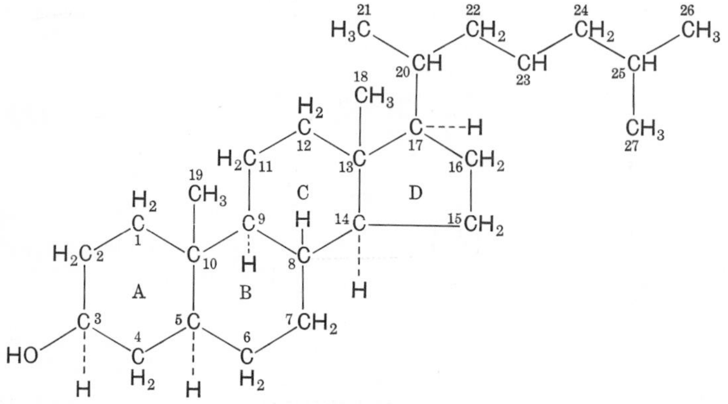

Cholestanol

The shorthand of steroid chemistry transforms this formula into the following:

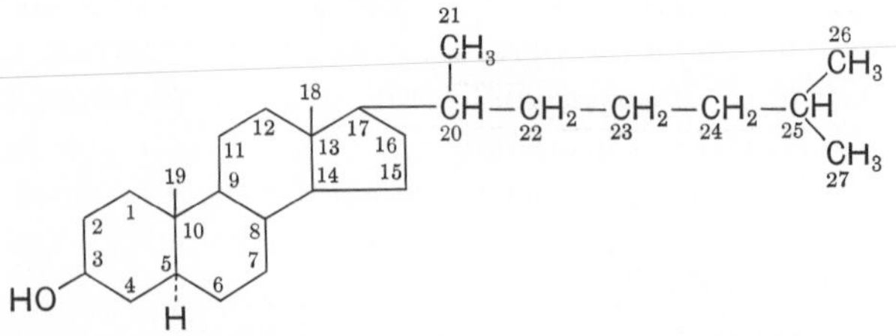

Note that each ring is completely saturated. In this shorthand, whenever double bonds occur they are specifically indicated.

General Considerations. Certain facts of general applicability may be pointed out in regard to this formula. There is an oxygenated substituent on carbon atom 3, a characteristic shared by almost all naturally occurring steroids. There are "angular" methyl groups, numbered 19 and 18, on carbon atoms 10 and 13. This also is a general characteristic. However, as will be seen later, in the estrogens, ring A is aromatic or benzenoid in character, and under these circumstances carbon atom 10 does not bear a methyl group. There may be an aliphatic substituent on carbon atom 17. This substituent serves as a convenient basis for classification of steroids, and in the present discussion steroids will be grouped according to the number of carbon atoms in this side chain. It contains 8, 9, or 10 carbon atoms in the sterols (total carbon atoms—27, 28, or 29, respectively), 5 carbon atoms in the bile acids (total of 24 carbon atoms), 2 in the adrenal cortical steroids and in progesterone (total of 21 carbon atoms), and none in the naturally occurring estrogens or androgens (total of either 18 or 19 carbon atoms).

Conformational and Steric Considerations. The conformational formula of cholestanol shows that the molecule is rigid. The small letters in the formula, *a* and *e*, refer to axial and equatorial substitutions, respectively. Not all hydrogen atoms have been represented; some are indicated by solid or dashed lines. The chair conformation of cyclohexane itself is more stable than the boat conformation. In cholestanol rings B and C are locked rigidly in the chair conformation by the *trans*

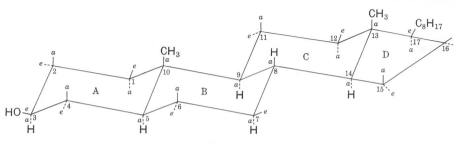

Cholestanol
(conformational structure)

fusions to rings A and D. Ring A is free to assume the boat form, but the instability associated with the boat form of cyclohexane itself would be enhanced by a strong interaction between methyl and hydroxyl groups at the bow (C-10) and stern (C-3) positions.

In cholestanol there are nine centers of asymmetry in the molecule; these are at carbon atoms 3, 5, 8, 9, 10, 13, 14, 17, and 20. In the structural representation of the steroid (see formulas above), substituents that are β-oriented (to the front) are indicated with a solid bond; those which are α-oriented (to the back) are represented with a dashed line. Thus the angular methyl groups at carbon atoms 10 and 13 are β-oriented, as is the 3-hydroxyl, the 8-hydrogen, and the side chain at carbon atom 17.

Two positions of asymmetry warrant further comment. The hydrogen atom on carbon-5 may be either on the same side of the plane of the molecule as the methyl group on carbon-10, or on the opposite side. In the former case, rings A and B will be *cis* to each other, and the molecule is said to belong to the *normal* configuration. If the hydrogen and methyl are on opposite sides, rings A and B are *trans* to each other, and the molecule is of the *allo* configuration.

CH$_3$	CH$_3$
A $\begin{smallmatrix}10\\5\end{smallmatrix}$ B	A $\begin{smallmatrix}10\\5\end{smallmatrix}$ B
H	H
A/B *cis* normal	**A/B *trans* allo**

The hydroxyl group on carbon-3 may similarly be α- or β-oriented.

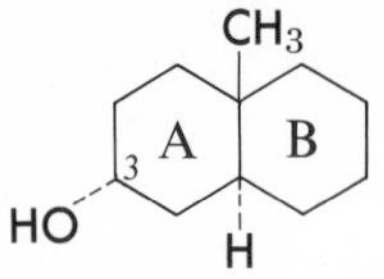

α, allo   β, allo

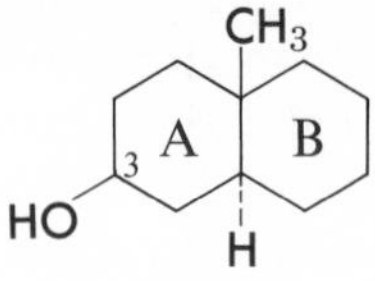

Steroids with the 3 β-hydroxy structures are precipitated by digitonin, itself the glycoside of a steroid. Many analytical methods for cholesterol depend upon an initial digitonin precipitation. This reagent is useful also in the determination of configuration of other steroids by virtue of this specific reactivity.

STEROLS

Steroids with 8 to 10 carbon atoms in the side chain at position 17 and an alcoholic hydroxyl group at position 3 are classed as sterols; the most abundant representative in animal tissues is cholesterol.

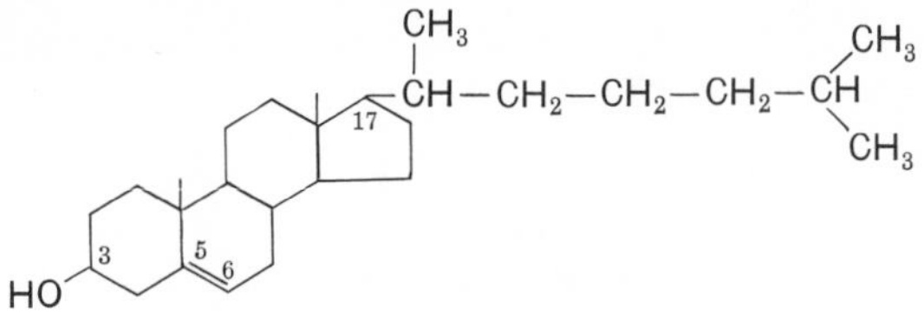

Cholesterol

In addition to a hydroxyl group at position 3, there is a double bond at the 5,6 position. Cholesterol occurs in almost all samples of animal lipid as well as in blood and bile. In the blood about two-thirds of the cholesterol is esterified, chiefly to unsaturated fatty acids, the remainder occurring as the free alcohol (Chap. 23). Reduction of the double bond gives rise to two products, both of which are naturally occurring, *viz.*, coprosterol (β, normal) and β-cholestanol (β, allo). The former is the major fecal sterol; the latter occurs as a minor constituent of the sterols of blood and other tissues. 7-Dehydrocholesterol arises from cholesterol on oxidation and possesses a conjugated pair of double bonds; this sterol is present in skin (Chaps. 23 and 56).

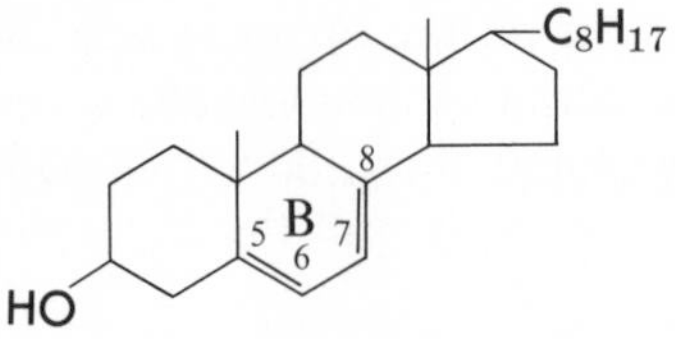

7-Dehydrocholesterol

A similar arrangement of double bonds is in the yeast sterol, ergosterol,

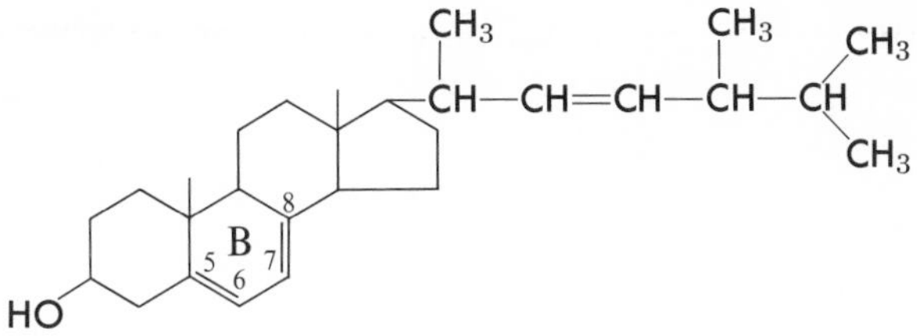

Ergosterol

which, in common with certain other plant sterols, has more than eight carbon atoms in the side chain and, in addition, a double bond.

As a result of the conjugated unsaturation of the B ring, ultraviolet irradiation of the latter two compounds yields products that result from rupture of the B ring; these possess vitamin D activity (Chap. 56). If one starts with 7-dehydrocholesterol, vitamin D_3 is obtained; from ergosterol, the product is vitamin D_2.

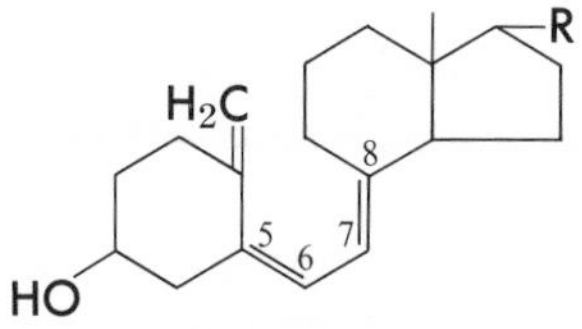

Vitamin D

R = C_8H_{17} in vitamin D_3.
R = C_9H_{17} in vitamin D_2.

Another type of important sterol is represented by lanosterol, first identified in wool lipid.

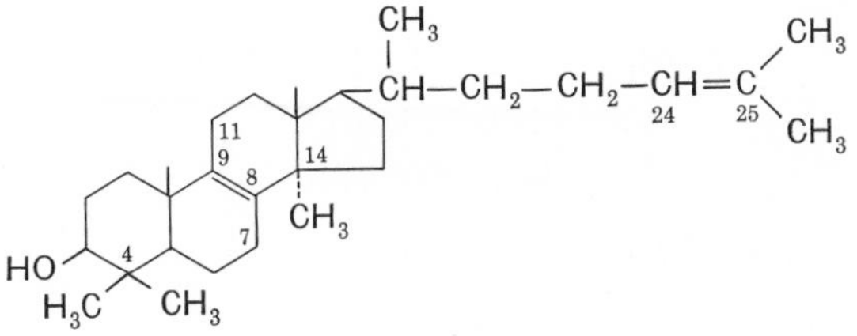

Lanosterol

The distinguishing structural features of this sterol are the *gem* (twin) dimethyl substitution on carbon-4 and the angular methyl group on carbon-14. There is a double bond in the side chain at position 24,25, and another in the nucleus at position 8,9. Lanosterol is an intermediate in cholesterol biosynthesis (Chap. 23).

BILE ACIDS—C_{24} STEROIDS

In bile acids, the side chain at carbon-17 is five carbon atoms in length, terminating in a carboxyl group. Four such acids have been isolated from human bile.

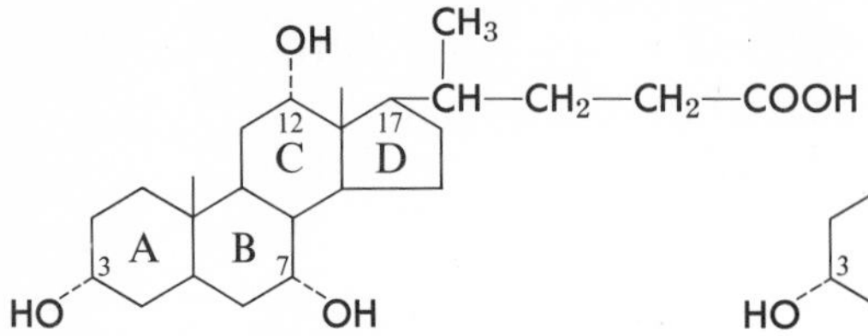

Cholic acid

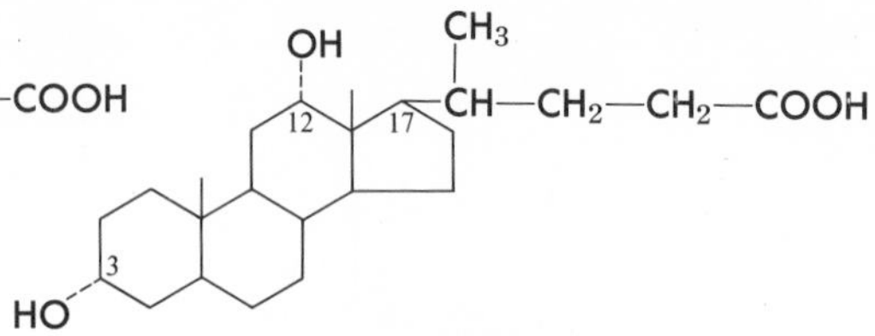

Deoxycholic acid

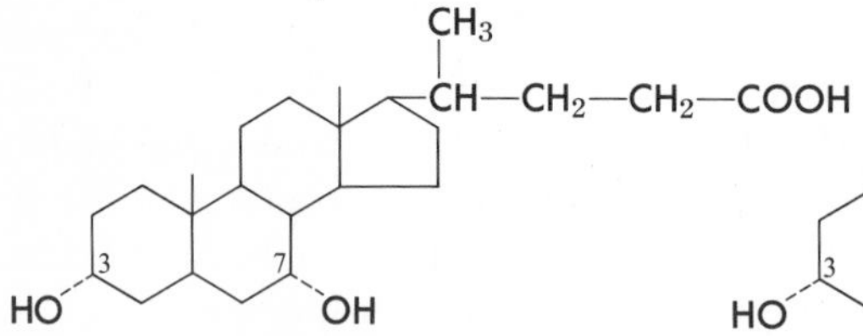

Chenodeoxycholic acid

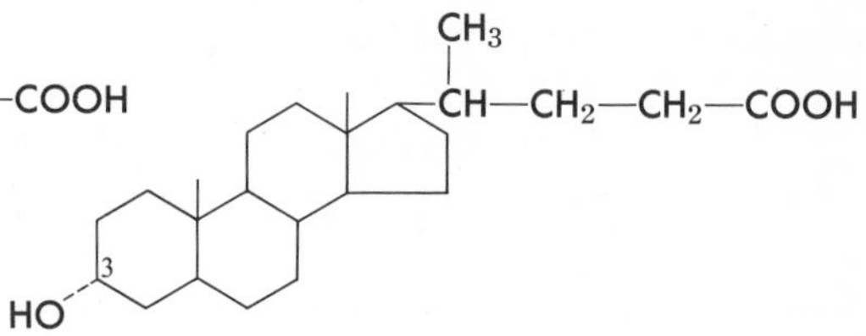

Lithocholic acid

All the hydroxyl groups are of the α configuration; these compounds are therefore not precipitable by digitonin. The A and B rings are of the *cis* or normal configuration. Cholic acid (3α, 7α, 12α-trihydroxycholanic acid) is by far the most abundant bile acid in human bile, but considerable species variation has been found.

In bile these acids are coupled in amide linkage to the amino acids glycine and taurine.

$$H_2N—CH_2—COOH \qquad H_2N—CH_2—CH_2—SO_3H$$

Glycine · Taurine

Thus glycocholic acid and taurocholic acid are the major representatives in human and ox bile.

$$\overset{O}{\overset{\|}{C_{23}H_{26}(OH)_3C}}—\overset{H}{N}—CH_2—COOH$$

Glycocholic acid
(cholylglycine)

$$\overset{O}{\overset{\|}{C_{23}H_{26}(OH)_3C}}—\overset{H}{N}—CH_2—CH_2—SO_3H$$

Taurocholic acid
(cholyltaurine)

The salts of these conjugated acids are water-soluble and are powerful detergents.

PROGESTERONE AND THE ADRENAL CORTICAL STEROIDS—C$_{21}$ STEROIDS

Since the steroids of endocrinological significance will be discussed in detail later in Part Six, only certain chemical features will be introduced at this point. Among the steroids with two carbon atoms in the side chain at position 17 is progesterone, produced in the corpus luteum.

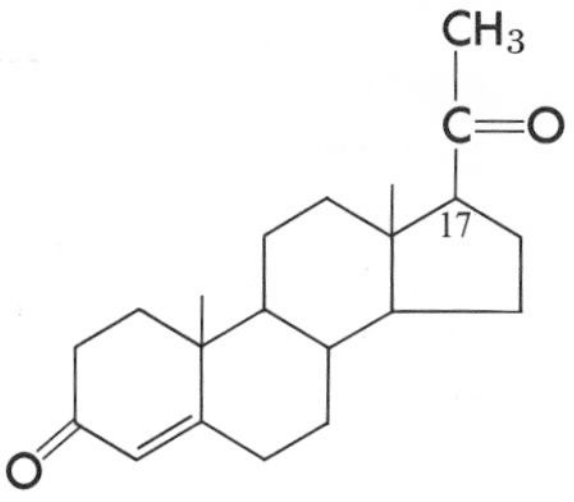

Progesterone

Numerous steroids have been isolated from the adrenal cortex. For purposes of nomenclature, the parent compound is corticosterone; among the various physiologically active modifications of this molecule found in the adrenal cortex is 17-hydroxycorticosterone.

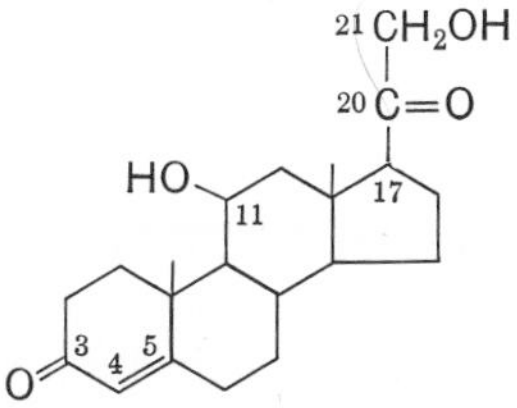

Corticosterone

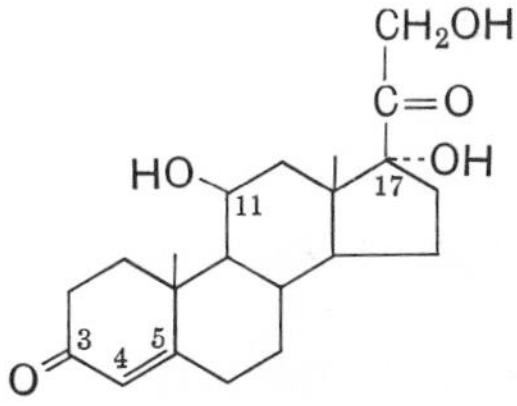

Cortisol
[17-hydroxycorticosterone (compound F)]

The important structural characteristics of these compounds include the system of conjugated double bonds at carbon atoms 3, 4, and 5, the so-called α, β-unsaturated ketone; the oxygenated substituent at position 11; and the state of oxidation of the side-chain carbon atoms 20 and 21.

ANDROGENS, ESTROGENS, AND RELATED STRUCTURAL TYPES— C_{19} AND C_{18} STEROIDS

The *androgens*, or male sex hormones, belong to the class of steroids devoid of a carbon side chain at position 17. The parent compound is testosterone, which is generated in the testis. Derived from testosterone, and from other steroids as well, is a group of compounds, occurring in urine, called 17-ketosteroids, some of which share, though to a lesser degree, the biological activity of testosterone. An important example of this group is androsterone.

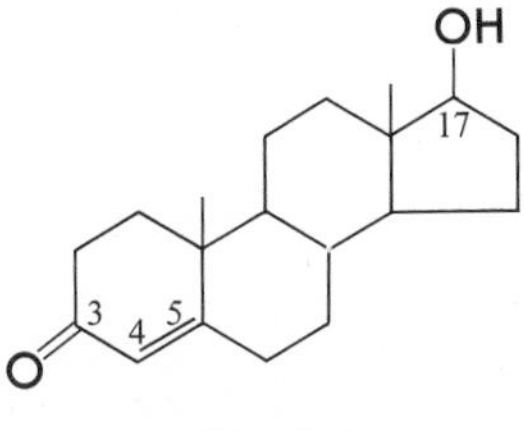

Testosterone

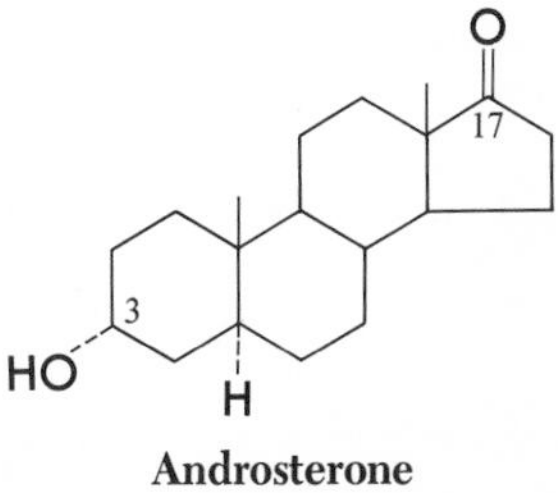

Androsterone

The *estrogens* differ from all the foregoing steroids in that ring A is aromatic. Consequently, there is no available valence for a methyl group at position 10 and the hydroxyl group at position 3 is phenolic rather than alcoholic in nature. Because of this latter fact, the estrogens behave as weak acids and are extractable from benzene solution with aqueous alkali. Two estrogens commonly encountered in natural sources are the following:

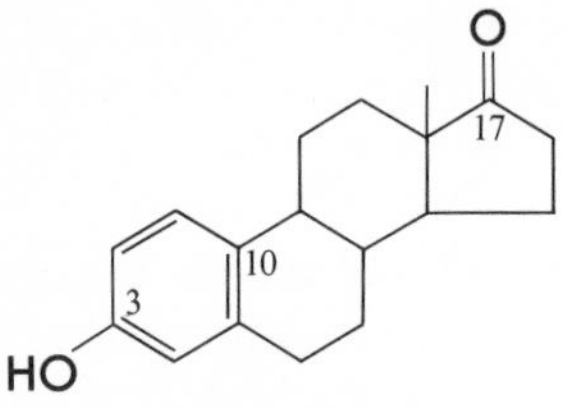

Estrone

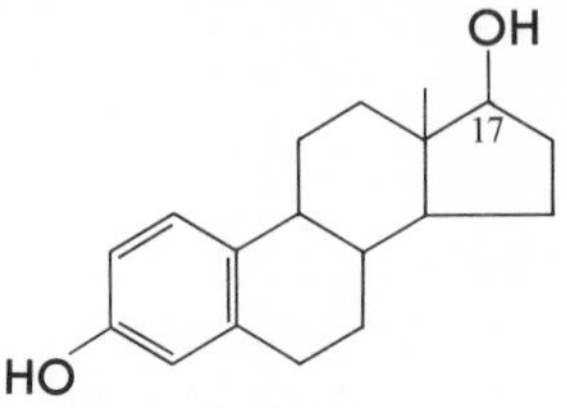

Estradiol-17β

It is noteworthy that estradiol-17β is precipitable by digitonin whereas the α-isomer is not.

MISCELLANEOUS STEROIDS

In addition to the several types already discussed, the steroids include many other compounds of interest. Among them are the cardiac-stimulating glycosides, drugs derived from the foxglove, squill, and other plants, which on hydrolysis yield a sugar moiety and a steroid aglycon, *e.g.*, digitoxigenin.

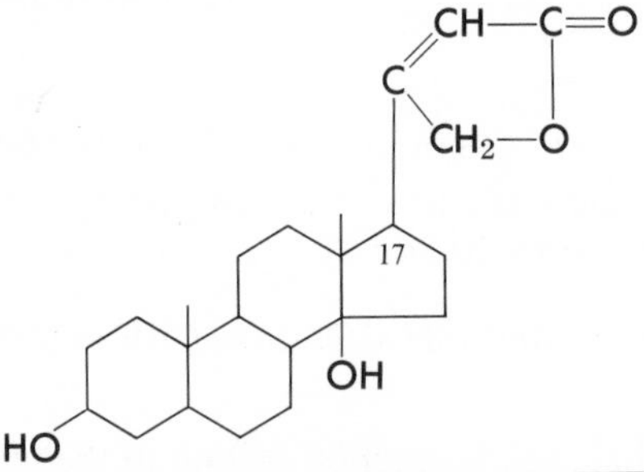

Digitoxigenin

The unusual structural characteristic of this group of compounds is the γ-lactone ring at position 17. The aglycon sapogenins of vegetable origin, as well as certain toad poisons, are also steroids. The complex between sapogenin and sugar is termed a *saponin*. All saponins lower the surface tension of water.

Aromatic compounds similar to steroids are often carcinogenic. A potent carcinogen is methylcholanthrene.

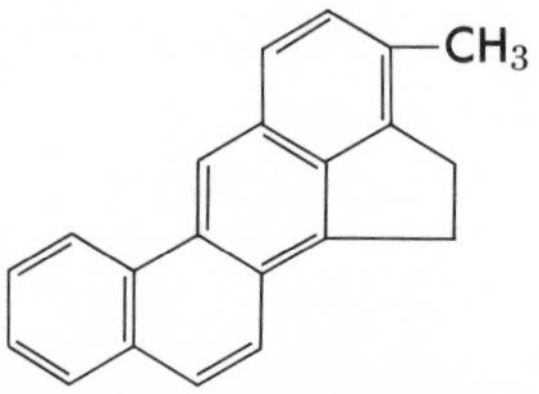

Methylcholanthrene

SPECIAL METHODS OF SEPARATION AND IDENTIFICATION OF STEROIDS

Steroids as a class may be separated from other lipids by virtue of their being nonsaponifiable. The bile acids are, of course, soluble in aqueous alkali, as are the estrogens. However, the estrogens, like other phenols, although extractable from organic solvents by aqueous NaOH or Na_2CO_3, are not extracted by weak bases such as aqueous $NaHCO_3$, whereas the fatty carboxylic acids are. Ketonic steroids may be extracted by treatment with the hydrazide of betaine chloride, Girard's reagent, yielding water-soluble salts of the resultant substituted hydrazones.

$$\text{C=O} + H_2N-NH-\overset{O}{\overset{||}{C}}-CH_2-\overset{+}{N}(CH_3)_3Cl^- \longrightarrow \text{C=N}-NH-\overset{O}{\overset{||}{C}}-CH_2-\overset{+}{N}(CH_3)_3Cl^-$$

Girard's reagent

Alcoholic steroids may be recovered as their hemisuccinates after treatment with succinic anhydride, thus yielding products soluble in aqueous alkali.

$$H-\overset{|}{\underset{|}{C}}-OH + \overset{O}{\overset{||}{C}}-CH_2-CH_2-\overset{O}{\overset{||}{C}} \longrightarrow H-\overset{|}{\underset{|}{C}}-O-\overset{O}{\overset{||}{C}}-CH_2-CH_2-COOH$$

Further separation of mixtures may be achieved by chromatographic and counter-current distribution procedures (Chap. 3). Paper, column, and gas-liquid chromatography are very useful for the separation and identification of steroids. Particularly applicable has been thin-layer chromatography (Chap. 3). The advantages of this procedure lie in the fact that a number of steroid mixtures may be resolved simultaneously, side by side, on the layered adsorbent. Also, after localization of substances on the plate with "developing" reagents (page 40), selected "strips" or areas of the plate's surface may be scraped off and the compounds isolated by extraction of the powder with suitable solvents, etc. It may be noted that thin-layer chromatography has also been useful for separation of classes of lipids, as well as separations among members of lipid groups other than steroids.

In addition to the conventional criteria employed in the identification of organic compounds, e.g., melting point, optical activity, etc., the steroid chemist utilizes optical rotatory dispersion and proton magnetic resonance spectroscopy, and has made special use of absorption spectroscopy, both in identification and as an aid in proof of structure. Although steroids are colorless compounds and do not absorb light in the visible portion of the spectrum, they do absorb in the ultraviolet and infrared portions. Absorption in the infrared portion of the spectrum is related to the vibrational energies of adjacent pairs of atoms, and the frequencies absorbed by a particular molecule therefore depend upon the occurrence in the substance of such atom pairs. Thus carbonyl groups absorb light maximally at a wavelength of about 5.8 μ†; hydroxyl groups, at 2.8 μ. The absorption due to a complex molecule in this portion of the spectrum is made up of numerous fine peaks, many of which can now be ascribed to certain specific atomic groupings. In

† A micron (μ) $= 10^{-6}$ m. A millimicron ($m\mu$) $= 10^{-3}$ $\mu = 10^{-9}$ m. An angstrom (Å.) $= 1 \times 10^{-8}$ cm. $= 10^{-10}$ m. $= 10^{-4}$ $\mu = 10^{-1}$ $m\mu$. The octave of visible light covers approximately 4,000 to 8,000 Å., 400 to 800 $m\mu$, or 0.4 to 0.8 μ in wavelengths.

the ultraviolet, broader bands of absorption are encountered for certain unsaturated steroids corresponding to specific electronic arrangements in the molecule. Thus many α,β-unsaturated ketones,

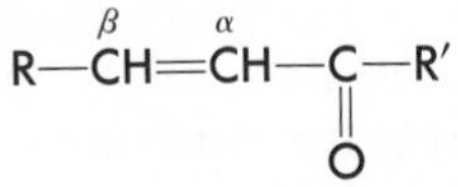

$$R—\overset{\beta}{C}H=\overset{\alpha}{C}H—\underset{\underset{O}{\|}}{C}—R'$$

exhibit absorption maxima in the region 230 to 260 mμ. Combined spectroscopic studies permit the unequivocal identification of steroids for which characteristic absorption spectra have been previously established.

REFERENCES

Books

Burchfield, H. P., and Storrs, E. E., "Biochemical Applications of Gas Chromatography," Academic Press, Inc., New York, 1962.

Cook, R. P., ed., "Cholesterol: Chemistry, Biochemistry, and Pathology," Academic Press, Inc., New York, 1958.

Deuel, H. J., Jr., "The Lipids: Their Chemistry and Biochemistry," vol. I, Interscience Publishers, Inc., New York, 1951.

Fieser, L. F., and Fieser, M., "Steroids," Reinhold Publishing Corporation, New York, 1959.

Florkin, M., and Mason, H. S., eds., "Comparative Biochemistry," vol. III, part A, chaps. 1 through 5, and 10; vol. IV, part B, chap. 14, Academic Press, Inc., New York, 1962.

Gunstone, F. D., "An Introduction to the Chemistry of Fats and Fatty Acids," John Wiley & Sons, Inc., New York, 1958.

Hanahan, D. J., Gurd, F. N., and Zabin, I., "Lipide Chemistry," John Wiley & Sons, Inc., New York, 1960.

Heftmann, E., and Mosettig, E., "Biochemistry of Steroids," Reinhold Publishing Corporation, New York, 1960.

Hilditch, T. P., "The Chemical Constitution of Natural Fats," 3d ed., John Wiley & Sons, Inc., New York, 1956.

Klyne, W., "The Chemistry of the Steroids," John Wiley & Sons, Inc., New York, 1957.

Kritchevsky, D., "Cholesterol," John Wiley & Sons, Inc., New York, 1958.

Lovern, J. A., "The Chemistry of Lipids of Biochemical Significance," Methuen & Co., Ltd., London, 1955.

Pecsok, R. L., ed., "Principles and Practice of Gas Chromatography," John Wiley & Sons, Inc., New York, 1959.

Ralston, A. W., "Fatty Acids and Their Derivatives," John Wiley & Sons, Inc., New York, 1948.

Shoppee, C. W., "Chemistry of the Steroids," Academic Press, Inc., New York, 1958.

Review Articles

Asselineau, J., and Lederer, E., Chemistry of Lipids, *Ann. Rev. Biochem.*, **30**, 71–92, 1961.

Celmer, W. D., and Carter, H. E., Chemistry of Phosphatides and Cerebrosides, *Physiol. Revs.*, **32**, 167–196, 1952.

Hanahan, D. J., and Thompson, G. A., Jr., Complex Lipids, *Ann. Rev. Biochem.*, **32**, 215–240, 1963.

Rapport, M. M., and Norton, W. T., Chemistry of the Lipids, *Ann. Rev. Biochem.*, **31**, 103–138, 1962.

7. The Proteins

Amino Acids and Peptides

The name protein (Gk., preeminent, or first) was suggested by Berzelius to Mulder and given by the latter in 1838 to the complex organic nitrogenous substances found in the cells of all animals and plants. Proteins occupy a central position in the architecture and functioning of living matter. They are intimately connected with all phases of chemical and physical activity that constitute the life of the cell. Some proteins serve as important structural elements of the body, for example, as hair, wool, and collagen, an important constituent of connective tissue; other proteins may be enzymes (Chap. 12), hormones (Part Six), or oxygen carriers (Chap. 34). Still other proteins participate in muscular contraction (Chap. 38), and some are associated with the genes, the hereditary factors (Chap. 29). The antibodies that are concerned with immunological defense mechanisms are proteins (Chap. 32). It is apparent that there is hardly an important physiological function in which proteins do not participate. Indeed, proteins are quantitatively the main material of animal tissue for they constitute approximately three-fourths of the dry substance (Table 1.1, page 4).

In essence, the objective of protein chemistry is to explain the special physiological functions of these large complex molecules in terms of their structure. The experimental approach consists largely in examination of the parts of the molecules, the probable arrangement of these parts in individual proteins, and the chemical and physical behavior of the intact proteins. These tasks are formidable and present considerable technical difficulties because of the great diversity and complexity of proteins.

GENERAL COMPOSITION

All proteins contain carbon, hydrogen, oxygen, nitrogen, and, with few exceptions, sulfur also. The elementary composition of proteins tells little of their intimate structure since these figures are very similar for most proteins. These approximate values are C = 45 to 55 per cent, H = 6 to 8 per cent, O = 19 to 25 per cent, N = 14 to 20 per cent, and S = 0 to 4 per cent. The average nitrogen content of proteins is frequently taken as 16 per cent for the estimation of the protein content of tissues and foodstuffs although it is recognized that this represents only an approximation. Most animal proteins contain from 0.5 to 2.0 per cent of sulfur. Insulin has one of the highest known contents of this element, 3.4 per cent.

Under conditions that hydrolyze amides and esters, proteins yield mainly a mixture of simpler substances, the amino acids. Hydrolysis of proteins may be effected by boiling with strong mineral acids or alkalies or by the action of certain proteolytic enzymes. Each of these methods has inherent limitations. The most common procedure is to boil the protein under reflux with five to ten times its weight of $6N$ hydrochloric or $8N$ sulfuric acid for 18 to 24 hr. This treatment usually results in complete destruction of one of the amino acids, tryptophan (page 94), and gives rise to brownish decomposition products (humins), especially when carbohydrate is present. Certain other amino acids may also be partially altered during acid hydrolysis of proteins. For special purposes, other acidic agents are also used for hydrolysis; these include formic, hydriodic, and certain long-chain sulfonic acids. Alkaline hydrolysis produces far more destruction of amino acids, notably cysteine, cystine, and arginine (pages 94 *ff.*), and racemization of all the amino acids occurs.

Hydrolysis of proteins with proteolytic enzymes does not destroy any amino acid; however, the process is slow and seldom liberates all amino acids.

The products of complete acidic hydrolysis of proteins are ammonia and free amino acids. Amino acids are the fundamental structural units of the proteins. The amino acids that have been isolated from protein hydrolysates are, with two exceptions, primary α-amino acids, *i.e.*, the carboxyl and amino groups are attached to the same carbon atom.

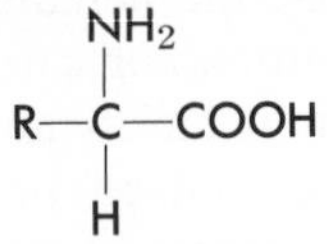

$$
\begin{array}{c}
NH_2 \\
| \\
R-C-COOH \\
| \\
H
\end{array}
$$

The various α-amino acids possess different R groups attached to the α-carbon. The usual classification of amino acids depends on the number of acidic and basic groups that are present. Thus, the neutral amino acids contain one amino and one carboxyl group. The acidic amino acids have an excess of carboxyl over amino groups. The basic amino acids possess an excess of basic groups. Two amino acids are secondary rather than primary α-amino acids.

NEUTRAL AMINO ACIDS

Aliphatic Amino Acids. *Glycine* is the simplest of the amino acids and one of the first to be isolated from proteins. It has a characteristic sweet taste.

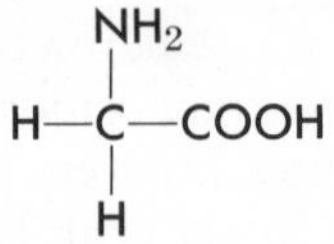

$$
\begin{array}{c}
NH_2 \\
| \\
H-C-COOH \\
| \\
H
\end{array}
$$

Alanine

$$
\begin{array}{c}
NH_2 \\
| \\
CH_3-C-COOH \\
| \\
H
\end{array}
$$

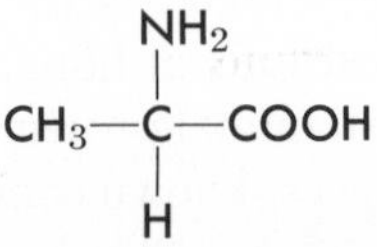

Valine

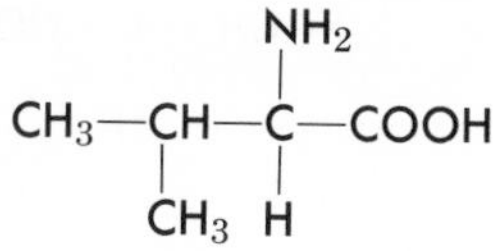

$$CH_3-\underset{\underset{CH_3}{|}}{CH}-\underset{\underset{H}{|}}{\overset{\overset{NH_2}{|}}{C}}-COOH$$

The isomeric straight-chain compound *norvaline* (α-amino-*n*-valeric acid) has not been found in proteins.

Leucine is one of the few amino acids that are sparingly soluble in water.

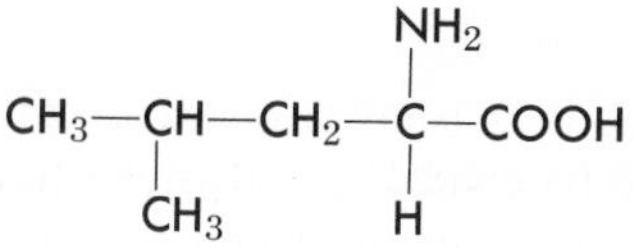

$$CH_3-\underset{\underset{CH_3}{|}}{CH}-CH_2-\underset{\underset{H}{|}}{\overset{\overset{NH_2}{|}}{C}}-COOH$$

Isoleucine

$$CH_3-CH_2-\underset{\underset{CH_3}{|}}{\overset{\overset{H}{|}}{C}}-\underset{\underset{H}{|}}{\overset{\overset{NH_2}{|}}{C}}-COOH$$

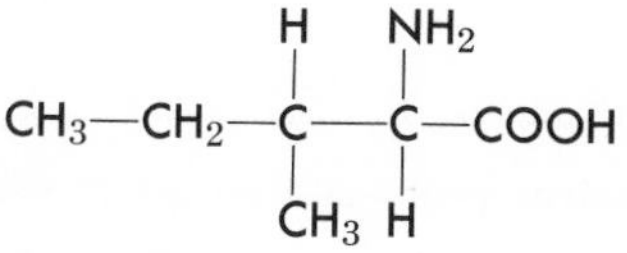

The straight-chain amino acid, *norleucine* (α-amino-*n*-caproic acid), which is isomeric with leucine and isoleucine, has not been found in proteins.

Serine was first obtained from the silk protein, sericin.

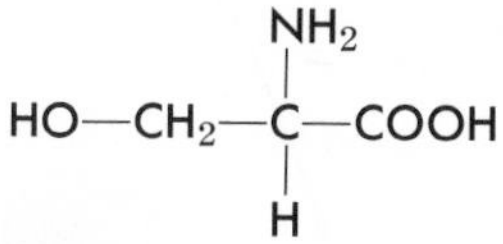

$$HO-CH_2-\underset{\underset{H}{|}}{\overset{\overset{NH_2}{|}}{C}}-COOH$$

Threonine was one of the last of the common amino acids to be discovered (Table 7.1, page 98).

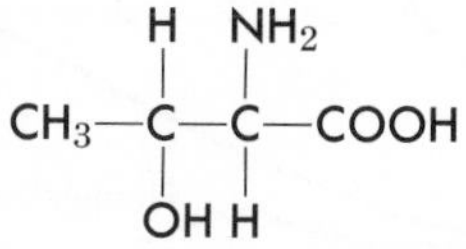

$$CH_3-\underset{\underset{OH}{|}}{\overset{\overset{H}{|}}{C}}-\underset{\underset{H}{|}}{\overset{\overset{NH_2}{|}}{C}}-COOH$$

Aromatic Amino Acids. The presence of these amino acids in proteins is responsible for their ultraviolet absorption maximum at about 275 to 280 mμ. The absorption spectra of these amino acids are shown in Fig. 7.1.

Phenylalanine

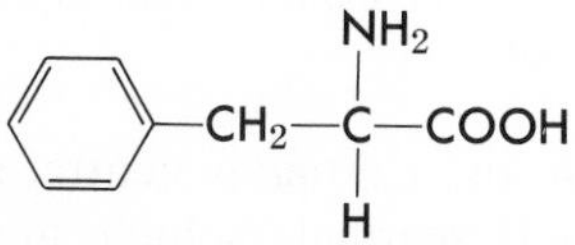

$$\text{C}_6\text{H}_5-CH_2-\underset{\underset{H}{|}}{\overset{\overset{NH_2}{|}}{C}}-COOH$$

Tyrosine is sparingly soluble in water. Proteins containing tyrosine all give characteristic reactions for the phenolic group present in this amino acid.

$$HO-\langle\ \rangle-CH_2-\overset{\overset{\displaystyle NH_2}{|}}{\underset{\underset{\displaystyle H}{|}}{C}}-COOH$$

Tryptophan

This heterocyclic amino acid is usually included with the aromatic compounds since it is similar to them in its general behavior, including absorption spectrum. It is destroyed during acidic hydrolysis of proteins but may be isolated after enzymic hydrolysis. Proteins that contain tryptophan react with reagents for the heterocyclic indole group.

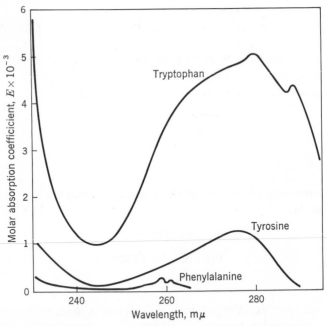

FIG. 7.1. The absorption spectra of tryptophan, tyrosine, and phenylalanine at pH 8. The spectrum for tyrosine undergoes a shift in position at alkaline pH values; this is completed above pH 12. The contribution of phenylalanine to protein absorption at 275 to 280 mμ is negligible. (*After J. S. Fruton and S. Simmonds, "General Biochemistry," 2d ed., p. 73, John Wiley & Sons, Inc., New York, 1958.*)

Sulfur-containing Amino Acids. *Cystine* is neutral since it contains two amino and two carboxyl groups; it is sparingly soluble in water. It was discovered in urinary calculi by Wollaston in 1810, but not until 1899 was it obtained from proteins.

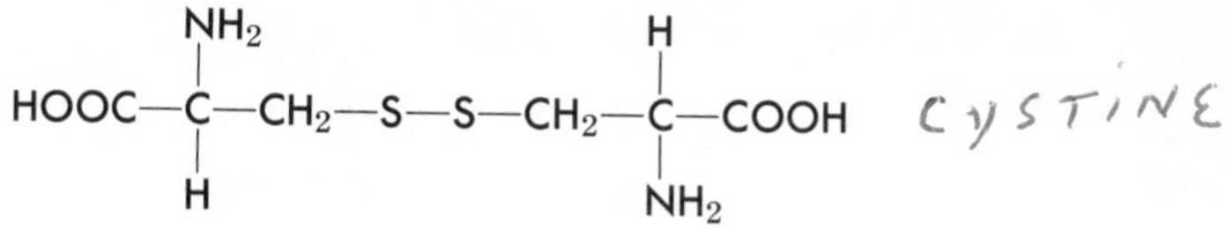

$$\underset{\substack{|\\H}}{\overset{\substack{NH_2\\|}}{HOOC-C}}-CH_2-S-S-CH_2-\underset{\substack{|\\NH_2}}{\overset{\substack{H\\|}}{C}}-COOH \quad \textit{CYSTINE}$$

Reduction of cystine gives the sulfhydryl-containing amino acid, cysteine.

Cysteine is present in many proteins, and these give a positive test for free sulfhydryl groups.

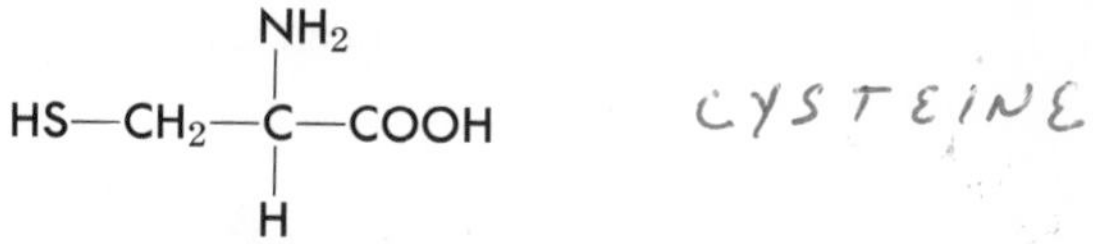

$$HS-CH_2-\underset{\substack{|\\H}}{\overset{\substack{NH_2\\|}}{C}}-COOH \qquad \textit{CYSTEINE}$$

Methionine contains sulfur in thioether linkage.

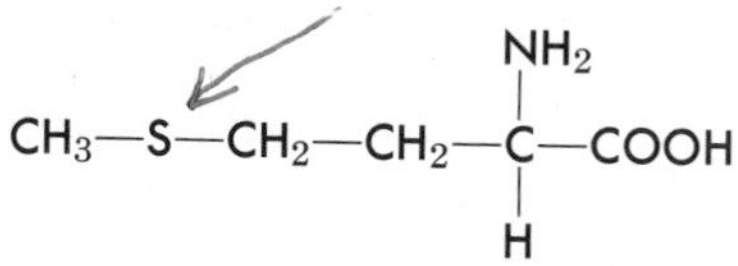

$$CH_3-S-CH_2-CH_2-\underset{\substack{|\\H}}{\overset{\substack{NH_2\\|}}{C}}-COOH$$

Secondary Amino Acids. There are two amino acids that contain a secondary rather than a primary amino group. The nitrogen is present in a pyrrolidine ring. Unlike other amino acids, proline is very soluble in alcohol and hydroxyproline is somewhat soluble.

Proline is present in all proteins that have been studied.

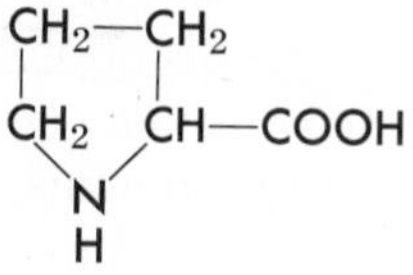

$$\begin{array}{c} CH_2-CH_2 \\ |\qquad\quad| \\ CH_2 \quad CH-COOH \\ \backslash\;\;/ \\ N \\ | \\ H \end{array}$$

Hydroxyproline (4-hydroxypyrrolidine-2-carboxylic acid, or 4-hydroxyproline) has been obtained only from collagen and gelatin.

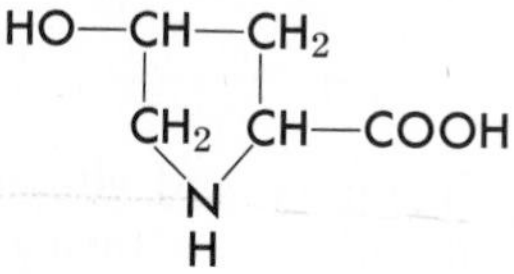

$$\begin{array}{c} HO-CH-CH_2 \\ |\qquad\quad| \\ CH_2 \quad CH-COOH \\ \backslash\;\;/ \\ N \\ | \\ H \end{array}$$

The isomeric 3-hydroxyproline has also been found in collagen.

DICARBOXYLIC AMINO ACIDS AND THEIR AMIDES

Aspartic acid

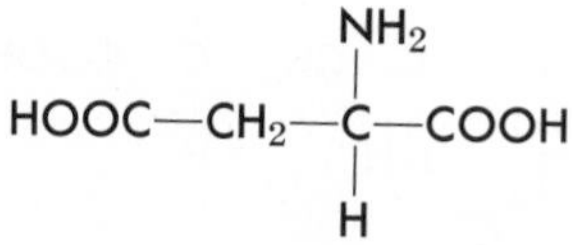

$$HOOC-CH_2-\underset{\substack{|\\H}}{\overset{\substack{NH_2\\|}}{C}}-COOH$$

The β-amide of aspartic acid, *asparagine,*

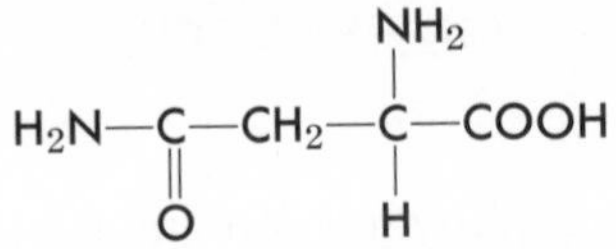

$$H_2N-\underset{\underset{O}{\|}}{C}-CH_2-\underset{\underset{H}{|}}{\overset{\overset{NH_2}{|}}{C}}-COOH$$

has been isolated from proteins after enzymic hydrolysis. Ammonia is produced from this substance during acidic or alkaline hydrolysis of proteins, giving rise to aspartic acid. Asparagine has long been known as a constituent of plant tissues.

Glutamic acid

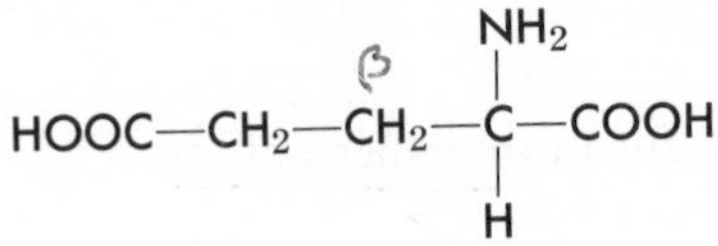

$$HOOC-CH_2-\overset{\beta}{CH_2}-\underset{\underset{H}{|}}{\overset{\overset{NH_2}{|}}{C}}-COOH$$

The monosodium salt of glutamic acid is widely used for artificial meat flavoring. *Glutamine,* the γ-amide of glutamic acid,

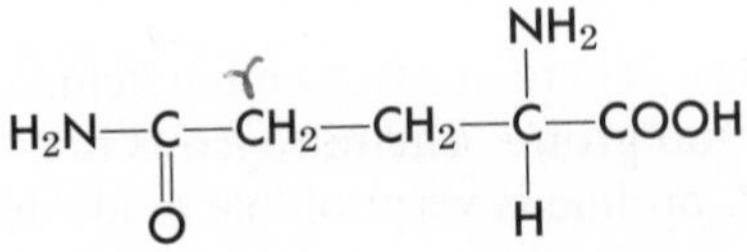

$$H_2N-\underset{\underset{O}{\|}}{C}-\overset{\gamma}{CH_2}-CH_2-\underset{\underset{H}{|}}{\overset{\overset{NH_2}{|}}{C}}-COOH$$

has been isolated from proteins after enzymic hydrolysis. Like asparagine it yields ammonia on acidic or alkaline hydrolysis. The two amides are responsible for the ammonia produced by chemical hydrolysis of proteins. Free glutamine is found in many animal and plant tissues. Under certain conditions, glutamine readily undergoes ring closure, with elimination of ammonia, to yield pyrrolidone carboxylic acid.

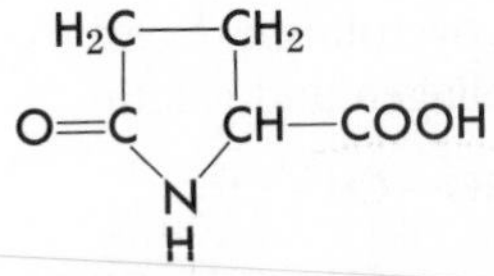

$$\begin{array}{ccc} H_2C & \!\!-\!\! & CH_2 \\ | & & | \\ O\!=\!C & & CH-COOH \\ & \diagdown\!\!\underset{|}{N}\!\!\diagup & \\ & H & \end{array}$$

It should be noted that asparagine and glutamine are *neutral* amino acids. They are listed here for convenience to show their relationship to the corresponding dicarboxylic acids.

BASIC AMINO ACIDS

Histidine

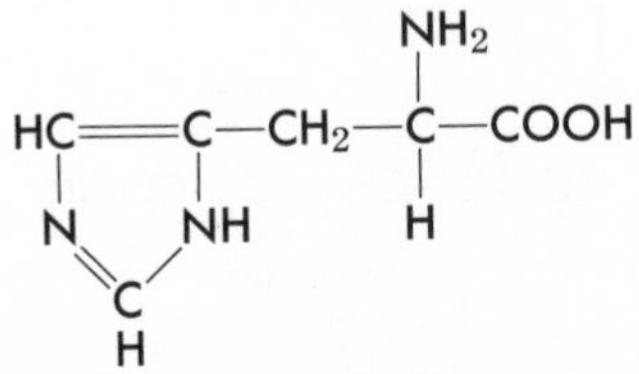

$$\begin{array}{c} HC\!=\!\!=\!C-CH_2-\underset{\underset{H}{|}}{\overset{\overset{NH_2}{|}}{C}}-COOH \\ \underset{N}{|} \quad \underset{NH}{|} \quad \\ \diagdown\!\underset{\underset{H}{|}}{C}\!\diagup \end{array}$$

The imidazole group is basic (see below).

Arginine

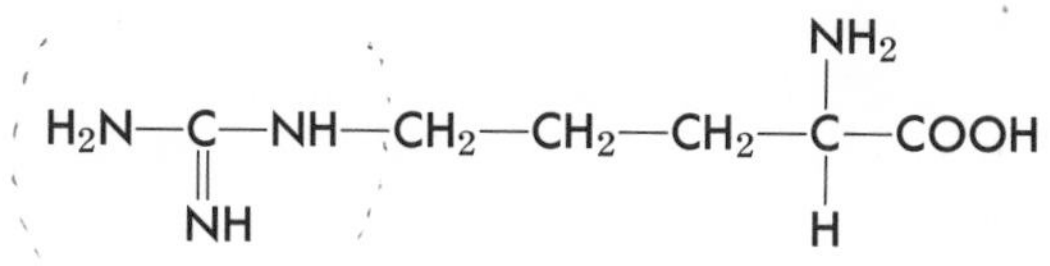

$$H_2N-\underset{\underset{NH}{\|}}{C}-NH-CH_2-CH_2-CH_2-\underset{\underset{H}{|}}{\overset{\overset{NH_2}{|}}{C}}-COOH$$

The guanido group is basic.

Lysine

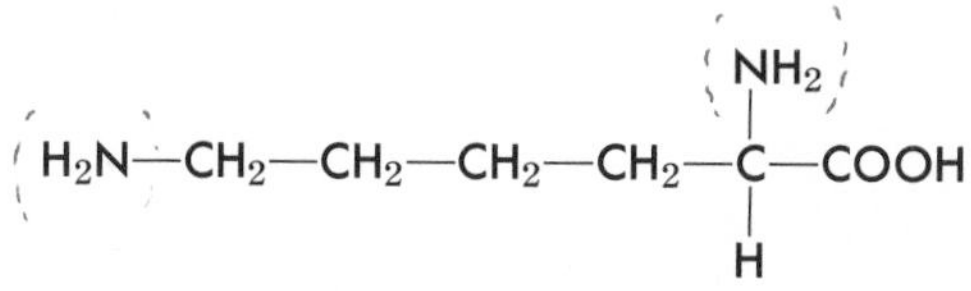

$$H_2N-CH_2-CH_2-CH_2-CH_2-\underset{\underset{H}{|}}{\overset{\overset{NH_2}{|}}{C}}-COOH$$

Hydroxylysine has been found, thus far, only in collagen and gelatin.

$$H_2N-CH_2-\underset{\underset{OH}{|}}{CH}-CH_2-CH_2-\underset{\underset{H}{|}}{\overset{\overset{NH_2}{|}}{C}}-COOH$$

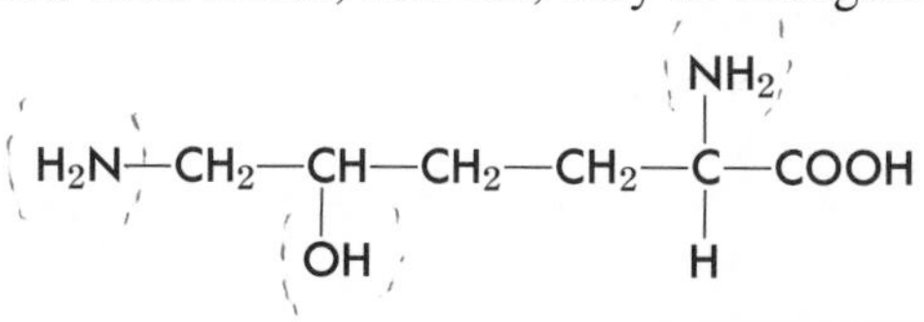

All the above amino acids have been demonstrated to occur in proteins. The hydroxyprolines and hydroxylysine appear to be of very limited distribution in proteins since they have been identified with certainty thus far only in collagen and gelatin.

In Table 7.1 are given the dates and the discoverers of the amino acids in proteins. The common types of protein have been thoroughly examined for new

Table 7.1: THE DISCOVERY OF THE AMINO ACIDS IN PROTEINS

Amino acid	Discoverer	Date
Leucine	Proust	1819
Glycine	Braconnot	1820
Tyrosine	Liebig; Bopp	1846; 1849
Serine	Cramer	1865
Glutamic acid	Ritthausen	1866
Aspartic acid	Ritthausen	1868
Alanine	Schützenberger and Bourgeois; Weyl	1875; 1888
Phenylalanine	Schulze and Barbieri	1879
Lysine	Drechsel	1889
Arginine	Hedin	1895
Histidine	Kossel; Hedin	1896
Cystine	Mörner	1899
Valine	Fischer	1901
Proline	Fischer	1901
Tryptophan	Hopkins and Cole	1901
4-Hydroxyproline	Fischer	1902
Isoleucine	Ehrlich	1904
Methionine	Mueller	1922
Threonine	Meyer and Rose	1936
Hydroxylysine	Schryver and associates; Van Slyke and associates	1925; 1938
3-Hydroxyproline	Ogle and associates; Irreverre and associates	1962

amino acids, and it is certain that the main ones are now known. This is also indicated by the fact that for many common proteins, summation of the individual known amino acids accounts for the nitrogen content of the protein. However, new amino acids of limited distribution may still remain to be discovered. It should be noted that since 1904 only four new amino acids have definitely been proved to be constituents of proteins.

SOME OTHER AMINO ACIDS

Many amino acids other than those commonly found in proteins occur in nature. Certain of these may be mentioned here.

β-Alanine is found in the important vitamin, pantothenic acid (Chap. 55), and in the naturally occurring peptides, carnosine and anserine (page 115).

$$H_2N-CH_2-CH_2-COOH$$

γ-Aminobutyric acid has been found in plants and in brain and other animal tissues.

$$H_2N-CH_2-CH_2-CH_2-COOH$$

The isomeric *α-aminobutyric acid* is found in certain animal and plant tissues.

Ornithine possesses one less carbon atom than its homologue, lysine.

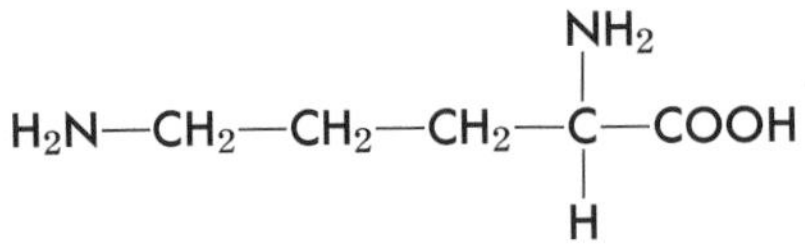

$$H_2N-CH_2-CH_2-CH_2-\underset{\underset{H}{|}}{\overset{\overset{NH_2}{|}}{C}}-COOH$$

This amino acid and citrulline are concerned in the formation of arginine. Ornithine also occurs in the urine of some birds as dibenzoylornithine, or ornithuric acid.

Citrulline was first isolated from the watermelon (*Citrullus vulgaris*).

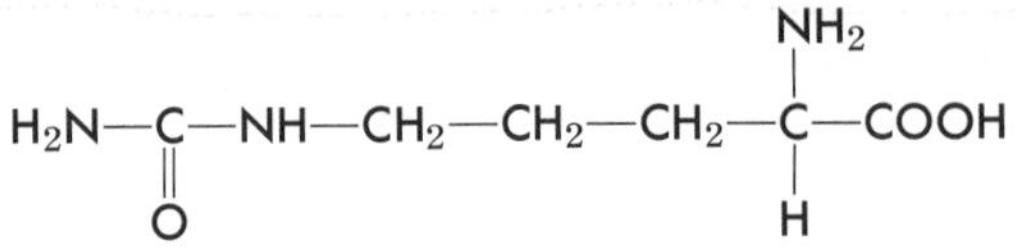

$$H_2N-\underset{\underset{O}{\|}}{C}-NH-CH_2-CH_2-CH_2-\underset{\underset{H}{|}}{\overset{\overset{NH_2}{|}}{C}}-COOH$$

Homoserine is an important intermediate in metabolism and is found in animal and plant tissues.

$$HO-CH_2-CH_2-\underset{\underset{H}{|}}{\overset{\overset{NH_2}{|}}{C}}-COOH$$

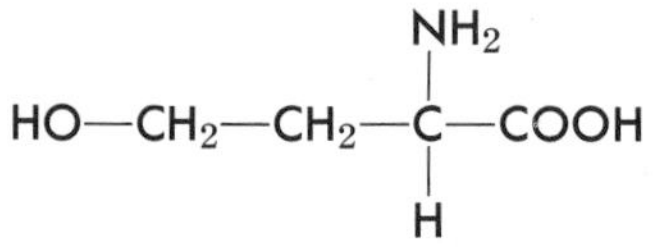

3,5,3′-*Triiodothyronine* is a constituent of the thyroid gland; its name is derived from the fact that the thyroxine nucleus (see formula below), devoid of its iodine atoms, is termed *thyronine*.

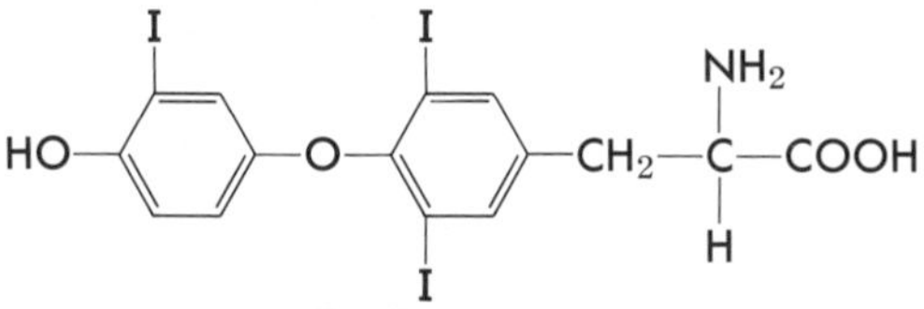

Thyroxine (3,5,3′,5′-tetraiodothyronine)

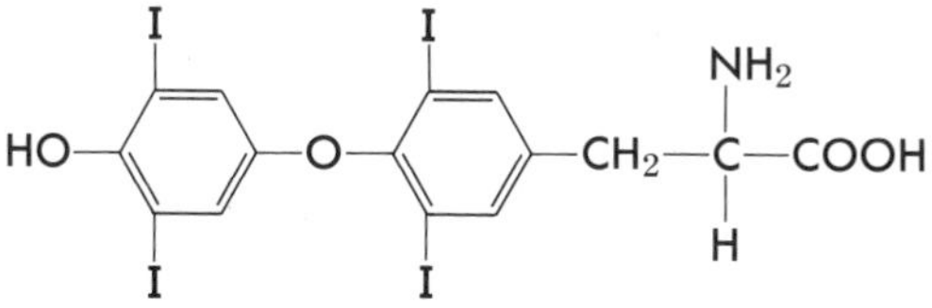

The iodinated compounds above are found in the thyroid gland (Chap. 46).

Dihydroxyphenylalanine (dopa) is found in the seedlings of velvet beans. It is important in mammalian metabolism as a precursor of dark pigments, the melanins (Chap. 44).

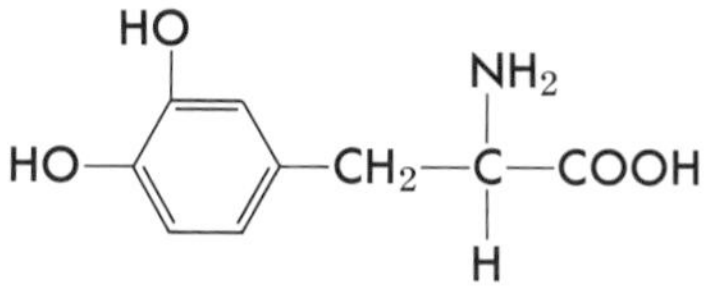

OPTICAL ACTIVITY OF AMINO ACIDS

With the exception of glycine, all naturally occurring α-amino acids are optically active since the α-carbon atom is a center of asymmetry, as indicated in the formula on page 92. The amino acids of proteins all belong to the same configurational series and possess the same configuration as L-alanine, which has been shown to be related to L-glyceraldehyde. It should be noted that the symbols, D or L, here as in the sugar series (page 13), do not refer to the sign of rotation but are used to indicate configurational relationships of similar compounds.

L-Glyceraldehyde **L-Lactic acid** **L-Alanine** **D-Alanine**

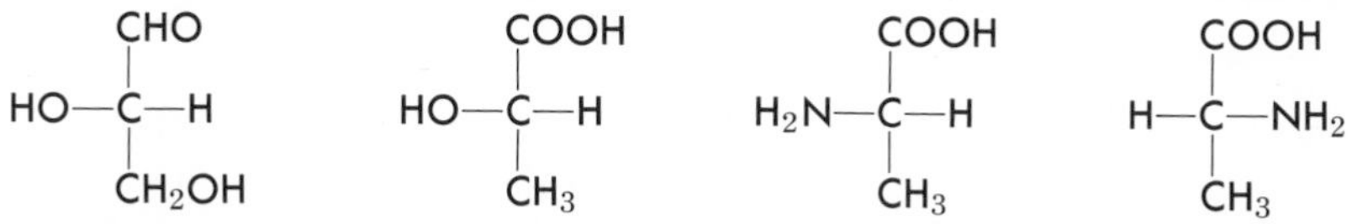

L-Alanine and L-lactic acid are actually dextrorotatory when examined in the polarimeter, but the present system of nomenclature indicates their structural relationship to L-glyceraldehyde. Only L-amino acids have been obtained from animal and plant proteins under conditions that do not produce racemization. It should be noted that among the common amino acids, threonine, hydroxylysine, cystine, isoleucine, and the two hydroxyprolines possess two optically active centers. Hence the synthetic compounds are mixtures of four diastereoisomers. Two are designated as L- and D-, respectively. The two additional diastereoisomeric forms are described as L-allo and D-allo; thus the terms allothreonine, alloisoleucine, etc.

The actual degree of rotation of an amino acid is strongly influenced by the acidity of the solution, and the configuration is therefore described by the chemical relationships rather than by the actual sign of rotation. In general, all amino acids of the L-configuration show positive shifts in the sign of the rotation as the acidity is increased, and amino acids of the D-configuration give the opposite change. This empirical rule is useful in determining the spatial structures of newly isolated amino acids.

Certain D-amino acids have been obtained from microorganisms. D-Glutamic acid is a constituent of the capsular material of *Bacillus anthracis* and some related organisms. D-Glutamic acid and D-alanine are abundant in material comprising the cell walls of many bacteria (page 58). Some D-amino acids have also been obtained from the hydrolytic products of polypeptide antibiotics, such as gramicidin and bacitracin.

SOME PHYSICOCHEMICAL PRINCIPLES

Before proceeding with a discussion of the properties and behavior of the amino acids in solution, it is necessary to review some aspects of the theory of weak electrolytes.

The simplest definition of an acid according to the Brønsted theory is that it is a substance, charged or uncharged, that liberates hydrogen ions (H^+) or protons in solution. A base is a substance that can bind hydrogen ions or protons and remove them from solution. It should be emphasized that in this terminology, ammonia, NH_3, acetate ion, CH_3COO^-, and sulfate ion, $SO_4^=$, are bases, whereas ammonium ion, NH_4^+, acetic acid, CH_3COOH, and bisulfate ion, HSO_4^-, are acids.

It is necessary to distinguish between strong and weak electrolytes. Strong electrolytes are essentially completely ionized in aqueous solution; these include almost all neutral salts, *e.g.*, $NaCl$, Na_2SO_4, KBr, etc., as well as strong acids, such as hydrochloric and nitric, and strong alkalies, such as $NaOH$, KOH, etc. Weak electrolytes are only partially ionized in aqueous solution and yield a mixture of the undissociated compound and ions. Many acids (HA) are weak electrolytes, and partially dissociate to produce hydrogen ions and the generalized anion A^-. It follows that a measurement of the hydrogen ion concentration, $[H^+]$, of a solution of a weak acid will not give a measure of the total concentration of the acid since there is a reservoir of the substance in the form of undissociated HA. However, if the free $[H^+]$ is titrated, additional HA will dissociate and titration will eventually give an estimate of the total acid since both the free H^+ and that derivable from the undissociated molecule will be titrated. Hence we distinguish between titratable acidity and actual acidity (hydrogen ion concentration) in dealing with weak acids. With strong acids at concentration levels at which they are completely dissociated, the titratable and actual acidity are the same.

A weak acid of the type HA dissociates reversibly in water to produce hydrogen ion H^+ and A^-.

$$HA \rightleftharpoons H^+ + A^- \tag{1}$$

Applying the mass law equation and expressing concentration in brackets, there is obtained the general equation

$$\frac{[H^+][A^-]}{[HA]} = K_a \tag{2}$$

where K_a is the ionization or dissociation constant of the acid. The equation indicates that K is a measure of the strength of the acid. The higher the value of K, the greater the number of hydrogen ions liberated per mole of acid in solution and hence the stronger the acid. Consequently, different acids may be compared in terms of their K values. It should be noted that the discussion here is of concentrations of H^+, A^-, and HA. More correctly, the equation applies rigidly only to *activity* values, and, throughout the discussion it must be understood that, in referring to concentrations, this is done only for convenience. In fact, most measurements of H^+ are measurements of activity rather than concentration, whether these are done by electrometric methods or by indicators. Equilibrium equations, such as (2), apply precisely only to activity values. The deviations from ideal behavior are due to interionic and other intermolecular forces. At low concentrations where such forces are negligible, differences between concentration and activity values are minimal.

The dissociation of BOH is represented in the same manner.

$$\frac{[B^+][OH^-]}{[BOH]} = K_b \tag{3}$$

Water, the usual solvent, dissociates into hydrogen and hydroxyl ions; the equation for the dissociation of water is

$$\frac{[H^+][OH^-]}{[H_2O]} = K \tag{4}$$

Inasmuch as the amount of undissociated water is large and remains essentially constant, this equation is usually simplified to

$$[H^+][OH^-] = K_w \tag{5}$$

where K_w, the ion product of water, is approximately 10^{-14} at 25°C.

It must be emphasized that in aqueous solution, equation (5) must be satisfied. Alteration in $[H^+]$ or $[OH^-]$ must always result in immediate compensatory change in the concentration of the other ion. Hence the dissociation constant of water is of fundamental importance in any consideration of the behavior of acids and bases in solution.

In biological work, it is customary to arrange the mass law equations into a common form that is convenient for both acids and bases. Equation (2) may be put into the form

$$[H^+] = \frac{K_a[HA]}{[A^-]} \tag{6}$$

and, taking logarithms of both sides of the equation,

$$\log [H^+] = \log K_a + \log [HA] - \log [A^-] \tag{7}$$

Now, multiplying by -1,

$$-\log [H^+] = -\log K_a - \log [HA] + \log [A^-]$$

The term $-\log [H^+]$ was defined by Sørensen as the pH and $-\log K_a$ as pK_a. In this manner there is obtained the important relationship

$$pH = pK_a + \log \frac{[A^-]}{[HA]} \tag{8}$$

It is important to note that equation (8) is applicable to conjugate acids like NH_4^+ and its base NH_3, as well as to substances ordinarily recognized as acids.

Equation (5) may be transformed to

$$\log [H^+] + \log [OH^-] = \log K_w \tag{9}$$

and by multiplying by -1

$$-\log [H^+] - \log [OH^-] = -\log K_w$$

and by substituting pH for $-\log [H^+]$, pOH for $-\log [OH^-]$, etc., there results

$$pH + pOH = pK_w \tag{10}$$

From these definitions, pH can be used to express either the acidity or the alkalinity of a solution. Since $pK_w = 14$, it is possible to obtain readily the pH of a solution from pOH. In practice, pOH is rarely used, and all acidic or basic solutions are expressed on the pH scale. Since pH is a logarithmic term, it must be handled in the same manner as other logarithmic quantities. For a neutral solution, pH = 7. Since $pK_w = 14$, pOH = 7, or $[H^+] = 10^{-7}M = [OH^-]$. It is obviously more convenient to employ the pH scale in place of awkward exponents. This should be apparent since, for a neutral solution where pH = 7.0, the $[H^+] = 0.0000001$, or $10^{-7}M$. For a solution at pH 6.0, the $[H^+] = 0.000001$ or $10^{-6}M$. The difference between the quantities involved is more easily appreciated and stated as the pH values of 7 and 6 than by giving the numerical values. The pH range ordinarily encountered encompasses 14 units, from solutions that contain $1.0N$ acid (pH = 0), through the neutral range to solutions of $1.0N$ alkali (pH = 14). This is particularly convenient in handling $[H^+]$ changes graphically.

To obtain the pH of a solution from the hydrogen ion concentration, it is merely necessary to take the logarithm of the $[H^+]$ and change the sign. For example, to calculate the pH of a solution that contains $2 \times 10^{-5}M$ hydrogen ion, take the logarithm of 2, which is 0.30, and add -5.00, which gives -4.70. The pH is 4.70. It must be kept in mind that a change of one pH unit is a tenfold change

Table 7.2: Approximate pH Values of Common Fluids, Biological Fluids, and Foods

	Material	pH		Material	pH
Acids.............	Acetic, 0.1N	2.9	Foods..	Beers	4–5
	Boric, 0.1N	5.2		Cider	2.8–3.3
	Citric, 0.1N	2.2		Eggs	7.6–8.0
	Hydrochloric, 0.1N	1.1		Grapefruit	3.0–3.3
	Sulfuric, 0.1N	1.2		Lemons	2.2–2.4
Bases..............	Ammonia, 0.1N	11.1		Limes	1.8–2.0
	Potassium hydroxide, 0.1N	13.0		Oranges	3.0–4.0
	Sodium bicarbonate, 0.1N	8.4		Pickles	3.0–3.6
	Sodium carbonate, 0.1N	11.6		Potatoes	5.6–6.0
	Sodium hydroxide, 0.1N	13.0		Sauerkraut	3.4–3.6
Biological fluids.......	Blood plasma	7.3–7.5		Soft drinks	2.0–4.0
	Gastric juice	1.2–3.0		Vinegar	2.4–3.4
	Milk, cow's	6.3–6.7		Wines	2.0–4.0
	Saliva	6.5–7.5			
	Urine	5–8			

in hydrogen ion concentration since decimal logarithms are used for the pH scale.

The pH values for a number of materials are given in Table 7.2 in order to illustrate the applicability to common materials as well as to biologically important media.

Buffer Action. Buffered solutions resist the changes in [H⁺] which would otherwise result from the addition of an acid or a base. In general, buffer action is exhibited by ions of weak acids or bases. Strong acids and bases are almost completely dissociated in water and have no reservoir of undissociated acid or base. Weak electrolytes that exhibit buffer action have extremely important practical properties and have great value for living systems since most cells can survive within only fairly narrow pH limits.

Practically, the best buffer action is exhibited by a mixture of a weak acid HA and its salt BA. Salts may be regarded as completely dissociated; hence BA exists in solution as B⁺ and A⁻. Let it be assumed that the weak acid HA, which has a pK_a of 5, contributes only 10^{-5} mole of H⁺ and A⁻ for each mole of acid and thus, as a first approximation, may be regarded as entirely undissociated. The contribution of the ion A⁻ by the acid is negligible compared with that of the salt BA, and the salt concentration may be used for [A⁻]. Equation (8) may thus be expressed in the form

$$pH = pK_a + \log \frac{[\text{salt}]}{[\text{acid}]} \tag{11}$$

where [salt] = [A⁻] and [acid] = [HA]. Equation (11) is generally known as the Henderson-Hasselbalch equation.

If the weak acid HA is present at 0.1M concentration and the salt BA is likewise present at 0.1M, then

$$pH = 5 + \log \frac{0.1}{0.1}$$

and the pH of the solution is 5. If 0.01 mole of BOH is added, there is now formed an additional 0.01 mole of BA and 0.01 mole of water; the latter may be neglected since its contribution to the total water is negligible. The pH of the solution may be again calculated from the increased salt concentration and decreased acid concentration.

$$pH = 5 + \log \frac{0.11}{0.09}$$

The pH is now 5.09, an increase of only 0.09 pH unit. A similar addition of 0.01 mole of a strong acid would decrease the pH by 0.09 pH unit, giving the solution a final pH of 4.91.

It is important to contrast this behavior with that of a strong acid like hydrochloric at the same pH, *viz.*, 5. The concentration of HCl would be 0.00001M, and addition of 0.01 mole of base would bring the solution almost to pH 12, a change of 7 pH units, since there is no reservoir of undissociated acid. Even at pH 2 (0.01M HCl), addition of 0.01 mole of base brings the solution to neutrality, a change of 5 pH units.

It must be emphasized that in the regions where weak acids and bases exert their buffer action, from about pH 2 to pH 12, this buffering capacity represents an important means of maintaining constant pH. In the region near neutrality, where most living cells function, certain buffers, *viz.*, those formed from carbonic and phosphoric acids, are of paramount importance.

Equations (8) and (11) have been derived in such a way that they apply to all weak electrolytes and hence describe the titration of all weak acids and bases. The titration curve of a monobasic weak acid is shown in Fig. 7.2. The pH at the midpoint of the titration curve, where 50 per cent of the acid or base has been used up, gives the value of pK since [salt]/[acid] is 1 and log [salt]/[acid] is zero. Buffer-

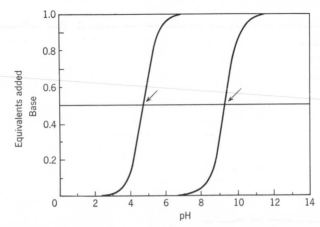

FIG. 7.2. The calculated titration curves for one equivalent of weak acid whose pK_a is 4.7 (acetic acid) and for ammonium ion whose pK_a is 9.3. The pH found when half an equivalent of base is added is the pK value. The shape of this curve is identical for all univalent acids or bases; the position of the curve is determined by the pK of the substance being titrated.

ing efficiency is at its greatest at the pH corresponding to the pK value and diminishes at more acid or more alkaline values. Thus, buffering efficiency is determined largely by the *ratio* of salt to acid. When the ratio is 1, the pH is at the pK value of the system and maximal buffering is found. This corresponds to the change in slope of the titration curve. The inflection point is the pK. It should be reemphasized that the salt of a weak acid alone, or a weak acid by itself, is not a complete buffer system.

For polybasic acids, each group has its characteristic pK value which may be described by equation (8). Table 7.3 gives the pK_a values for a number of compounds that are either useful or biologically important in buffers. It should be noted

Table 7.3: pK_a VALUES OF SOME IMPORTANT COMPOUNDS

Compound	pK_a	Compound	pK_a
Phosphoric acid (pK_1)	2.0	Citric acid (pK_3)	6.4
Citric acid (pK_1)	3.1	Phosphoric acid (pK_2)	6.7
Formic acid	3.8	Imidazole	7.0
Lactic acid	3.9	Diethylbarbituric acid	8.0
Benzoic acid	4.2	Tris(hydroxymethyl)aminomethane	8.1
Acetic acid	4.7	Boric acid	9.2
Citric acid (pK_2)	4.7	Ammonium ion	9.3
Pyridinium ion	5.3	Ethylammonium ion	9.8
Cacodylic acid	6.2	Triethylammonium ion	10.8
Maleic acid	6.2	Carbonic acid (pK_2)	10.4
Carbonic acid (pK_1)	6.3	Phosphoric acid (pK_3)	12.4

that the dissociation of a base represented by K_b in equation (3) is seldom used in biological work. It is more convenient to express all dissociation constants as pK_a values on the same scale: pK_a = pK_w − pK_b, where pK_b = −log K_b.

Indicators. Many substances that are themselves weak electrolytes exist in characteristically colored or colorless forms in different pH regions. These are useful as indicators of the pH of a solution. In general, the indicator is a weak electrolyte and may be written as the acid HIn, which can exist in two chromogenic forms:

$$HIn \text{ (color A)} \rightleftharpoons In^- \text{ (color B)} + H^+$$

From the Henderson-Hasselbalch equation

$$pH = pK + \log \frac{[In^-]}{[HIn]} \tag{12}$$

At any pH, [In$^-$]/[HIn] will give color B/color A. The mixture of color A and color B permits a visual comparison with color standards and hence a rapid determination of pH. Some commonly used indicators are listed in Table 7.4.

The applicability of indicator theory may be illustrated with bromocresol green as an example. In solutions more acid than about pH 3.9 this dye is yellow. In solutions more alkaline than approximately pH 5.3 it is blue. These are the two forms of this substance, each of which predominates at the extremes of its titration range. In solutions of pH 4.7, which corresponds to the pK value, the indicator is

Table 7.4: Useful pH Range of Some Indicators

Indicator	pK_a	Range of pH	Acid color	Alkaline color
Thymol blue (pK_1)	1.5	1.2–2.8	Red	Yellow
Bromophenol blue	4.0	3.0–4.6	Yellow	Blue
Bromocresol green	4.7	3.8–5.4	Yellow	Blue
Methyl red	5.1	4.4–6.0	Red	Yellow
Chlorophenol red	6.0	4.8–6.4	Yellow	Red
Bromothymol blue	7.0	6.0–7.6	Yellow	Blue
Phenol red	7.9	6.8–8.4	Yellow	Red
Thymol blue (pK_2)	8.9	8.0–9.6	Yellow	Blue
Phenolphthalein	9.7	8.4–10.5	Colorless	Red

Source: Adapted from W. M. Clark, "The Determination of Hydrogen Ions," 3d ed., The Williams & Wilkins Company, Baltimore, 1928.

present as equal quantities of the acid and of its salt. Hence, there are equal quantities of yellow and blue forms, and the solution is green. Changes in pH away from the pK value will alter the ratio of the two forms in accord with the Henderson-Hasselbalch equation. Thus, starting from the acid side the color of bromocresol green will change from yellow to yellow-green, then to green, to blue-green, and, finally, to blue. These characteristic color forms can be used as standards for the rapid determination of the pH of unknowns.

AMINO ACIDS AS ELECTROLYTES

Amino acids are ampholytes, *i.e.*, they behave as acids and as bases since they each contain at least one carboxyl group and one amino group. Each group has its characteristic pK value, and by convention these are designated pK_1, pK_2, etc., starting with the group titrated at the most acid region.

A monoamino monocarboxylic acid, like glycine, in aqueous solution exists as *dipolar ions,* also termed *zwitterions,* in which both the acidic and basic groups are ionized.

$$^+H_3N—CH_2—COO^-$$

However, the molecule is electrically neutral, since the number of positive charges is equal to the number of negative charges. In this condition, the molecule is termed isoelectric. The pH at which a dipolar ion does not migrate in an electrical field is called the *isoelectric point*. In water and in the absence of other solutes, this pH is also the *isoionic point*, *i.e.*, the pH at which the number of cations is equal to the number of anions. In salt solutions or in solutions containing ions other than those derived from the ampholyte, some of the ionizable groups of the ampholyte may be electrically neutralized by the other ions present. Under these circumstances, there will be differences between the value for the isoelectric point and that for the isoionic point. This is of significance for proteins particularly.

Addition of hydrogen ions to the isoelectric molecule, depicted above, produces a change in charge, since ionization of the carboxylate group is repressed and the molecule acquires a net positive charge.

$$^+H_3N—CH_2—COO^- + H^+ \rightleftharpoons {}^+H_3N—CH_2—COOH$$

The dipolar ion has accepted a proton, and the predominant form is now a positively charged molecule.

Correspondingly, addition of base to the dipolar ion removes a proton from the ammonium group, leaving the molecule with a net negative charge.

$$^+H_3N—CH_2—COO^- + OH^- \rightleftharpoons H_2N—CH_2—COO^- + H_2O$$

It is easier to regard the isoelectric amino acids as salts that are fully ionized and internally neutralized by their own amino and carboxyl groups than to look upon them as acids in the conventional sense.

The concept that under isoelectric conditions amino acids are ionized and possess no net charge is based upon evidence presented by Bjerrum in 1923. However, it was believed for many years earlier that the opposite was true, *viz.*, that an isoelectric amino acid, such as glycine, was undissociated and had the structure $H_2N—CH_2—COOH$ in aqueous solution. Evidence that amino acids are dipolar ions is now overwhelming and includes the following points:

1. In general, the isoelectric amino acids are soluble in water and other polar solvents, and insoluble in nonpolar solvents such as ether, chloroform, benzene, etc. Non-ionic compounds of similar structure are usually soluble in nonpolar solvents and sparingly soluble in water.

2. The α-amino acids melt with decomposition above 200°C., and many do so above 300°C. The great majority of structurally similar non-ionic organic compounds have much lower melting points. Amino acids are intermediate between the non-ionic compounds and the inorganic salts, which have very high melting points.

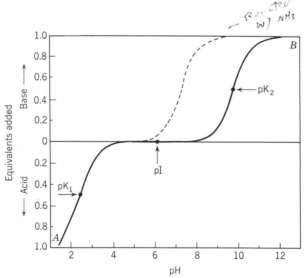

FIG. 7.3. Diagrammatic representation of the titration curve of a monoamino monocarboxylic acid such as glycine with pK_1 equal to 2.3 and pK_2 equal to 9.6. In the acid solution *A*, the substance present is glycine hydrochloride; in *B*, it is sodium glycinate. The dashed curve is obtained in the presence of formaldehyde. The isoelectric point, pI (page 110), is 6.

③ Formaldehyde combines with uncharged amino groups to form weakly basic derivatives. In the titration of amino acids with base in the presence of formaldehyde, only that pK is altered which may be ascribed to the amino group on the basis of dipolar ion structure. In the reaction of amino acids with formaldehyde in neutral or slightly basic solutions, one or two molecules of formaldehyde combine with the uncharged amino group to form a mono- or dimethylol derivative.

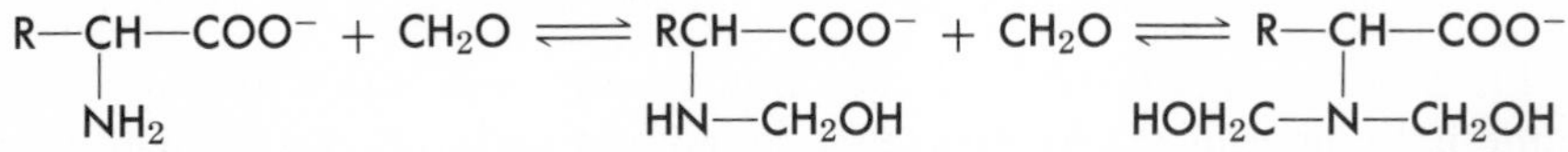

$$R-CH-COO^- + CH_2O \rightleftharpoons RCH-COO^- + CH_2O \rightleftharpoons R-CH-COO^-$$
$$\quad | \qquad\qquad\qquad\qquad | \qquad\qquad\qquad\qquad\qquad |$$
$$\quad NH_2 \qquad\qquad\qquad\qquad HN-CH_2OH \qquad\qquad HOH_2C-N-CH_2OH$$

The titration curve of a typical monoamino monocarboxylic acid is shown in Fig. 7.3. It is apparent that there are two titratable groups and that the more alkaline one is due to titration of the amino group as judged by the effect of formaldehyde in shifting the curve. The pK values for the titratable groups of amino acids that are known to be protein constituents are given in Table 7.5. The table includes values for the sulfhydryl group of cysteine and the phenolic group of tyrosine and for groups more obviously acidic or basic. It should be noted that amino acids, like other weak electrolytes, exert their maximal buffering effect at their pK and not at their pI values. As polyvalent electrolytes, therefore, each has several pH regions in which it can serve as a buffer. The pK values for the SH and NH_3^+ of cysteine overlap; values given are for the predominant form at the pK indicated.

It is of interest to examine the titration of some of the more complex amino acids. Glutamic acid in the isoelectric state has the structure shown in (II).

Table 7.5: APPARENT pK_a AND pI VALUES FOR AMINO ACIDS AT 25°C.

Amino acid	pK_1(COOH)	pK_2	pK_3	pI*
Alanine	2.34	9.69		6.00
Arginine	2.17	9.04 (NH_3^+)	12.48 (guanidinium)	10.76
Asparagine	2.02	8.80		5.41
Aspartic acid	1.88	3.65 (COOH)	9.60 (NH_3^+)	2.77
Cysteine (30°)	1.96	8.18 (SH)	10.28 (NH_3^+)	5.07
Cystine (30°)	<1.0	1.7 (COOH)	7.48 and 9.02 (NH_3^+)	4.60
Glutamic acid	2.19	4.25 (COOH)	9.67 (NH_3^+)	3.22
Glutamine	2.17	9.13		5.65
Glycine	2.34	9.60		5.97
Histidine	1.82	6.00 (imidazolium)	9.17 (NH_3^+)	7.59
Hydroxyproline	1.92	9.73		5.83
Isoleucine	2.36	9.68		6.02
Leucine	2.36	9.60		5.98
Lysine	2.18	8.95 (α-NH_3^+)	10.53 (ε-NH_3^+)	9.74
Phenylalanine	1.83	9.13		5.48
Proline	1.99	10.60		6.30
Serine	2.21	9.15		5.68
Tryptophan	2.38	9.39		5.89
Tyrosine	2.20	9.11 (NH_3^+)	10.07 (OH)	5.66
Valine	2.32	9.62		5.96

* pI = pH at the isoelectric point (page 110)

SOURCE: From E. J. Cohn and J. T. Edsall. "Proteins, Amino Acids and Peptides," Reinhold Publishing Corporation, New York, 1943.

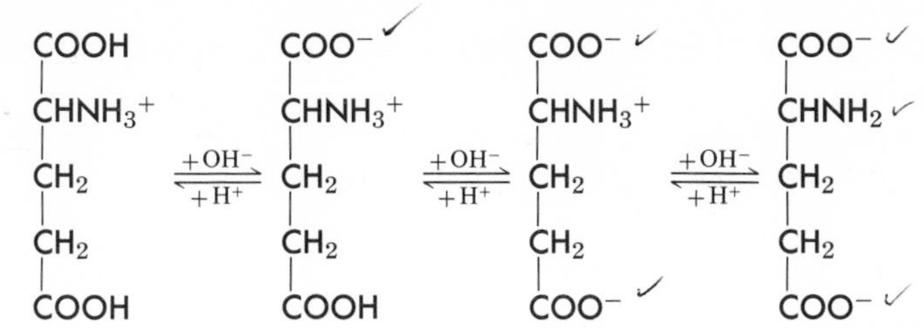

$$
\begin{array}{cccc}
\text{COOH} & \text{COO}^- & \text{COO}^- & \text{COO}^- \\
| & | & | & | \\
\text{CHNH}_3{}^+ & \text{CHNH}_3{}^+ & \text{CHNH}_3{}^+ & \text{CHNH}_2 \\
| & | & | & | \\
\text{CH}_2 & \text{CH}_2 & \text{CH}_2 & \text{CH}_2 \\
| & | & | & | \\
\text{CH}_2 & \text{CH}_2 & \text{CH}_2 & \text{CH}_2 \\
| & | & | & | \\
\text{COOH} & \text{COOH} & \text{COO}^- & \text{COO}^- \\
\text{(I)} & \text{(II)} & \text{(III)} & \text{(IV)}
\end{array}
$$

(arrows between structures: $\xrightleftharpoons[+H^+]{+OH^-}$)

Addition of one mole of acid produces (I). Addition of two moles of alkali to (II) gives rise successively to (III) and (IV). Aspartic acid behaves in the same manner as glutamic acid.

Formula (III) below represents the isoelectric state of lysine.

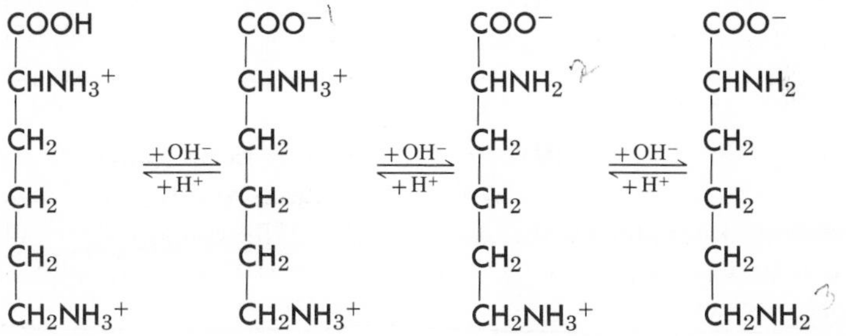

$$
\begin{array}{cccc}
\text{COOH} & \text{COO}^- & \text{COO}^- & \text{COO}^- \\
| & | & | & | \\
\text{CHNH}_3{}^+ & \text{CHNH}_3{}^+ & \text{CHNH}_2 & \text{CHNH}_2 \\
| & | & | & | \\
\text{CH}_2 & \text{CH}_2 & \text{CH}_2 & \text{CH}_2 \\
| & | & | & | \\
\text{CH}_2 & \text{CH}_2 & \text{CH}_2 & \text{CH}_2 \\
| & | & | & | \\
\text{CH}_2 & \text{CH}_2 & \text{CH}_2 & \text{CH}_2 \\
| & | & | & | \\
\text{CH}_2\text{NH}_3{}^+ & \text{CH}_2\text{NH}_3{}^+ & \text{CH}_2\text{NH}_3{}^+ & \text{CH}_2\text{NH}_2 \\
\text{(I)} & \text{(II)} & \text{(III)} & \text{(IV)}
\end{array}
$$

(arrows between structures: $\xrightleftharpoons[+H^+]{+OH^-}$)

(II) is a monoacid salt, such as lysine monohydrochloride; (I) is a diacid salt, such as lysine dihydrochloride; (IV) is a basic salt, such as sodium lysinate. In contrast to lysine, glutamic acid can form only a monohydrochloride but can yield mono- and disodium salts.

The various forms of histidine are shown below; (III) is the isoelectric form.

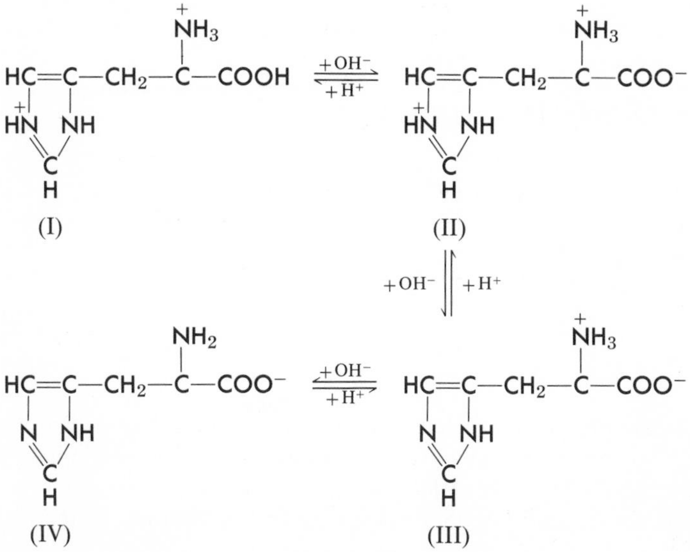

$$
\underset{\text{(I)}}{\overset{\overset{+}{N}H_3}{HC\!\!=\!\!\underset{\underset{HN\ \ NH}{|}}{C}\!\!-\!\!CH_2\!\!-\!\!\overset{|}{C}\!\!-\!\!COOH}} \quad \xrightleftharpoons[+H^+]{+OH^-} \quad \underset{\text{(II)}}{\overset{\overset{+}{N}H_3}{HC\!\!=\!\!\underset{\underset{HN\ \ NH}{|}}{C}\!\!-\!\!CH_2\!\!-\!\!\overset{|}{C}\!\!-\!\!COO^-}}
$$

with the imidazole ring closing at $\underset{H}{C}$.

$$+OH^- \updownarrow +H^+$$

$$
\underset{\text{(IV)}}{\overset{NH_2}{HC\!\!=\!\!\underset{\underset{N\ \ NH}{|}}{C}\!\!-\!\!CH_2\!\!-\!\!\overset{|}{C}\!\!-\!\!COO^-}} \quad \xrightleftharpoons[+H^+]{+OH^-} \quad \underset{\text{(III)}}{\overset{\overset{+}{N}H_3}{HC\!\!=\!\!\underset{\underset{N\ \ NH}{|}}{C}\!\!-\!\!CH_2\!\!-\!\!\overset{|}{C}\!\!-\!\!COO^-}}
$$

Note that the imidazolium group has a *lower* pK_a value than the ammonium group (Table 7.5).

In the case of arginine, the isoelectric form is (III). Observe that the guanidinium group has a very high pK_a value, 12.48 (Table 7.5).

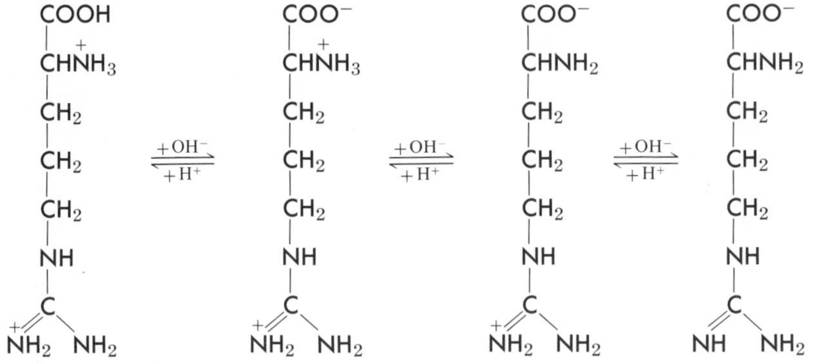

Structures (I), (II), (III), (IV)

Calculation of Isoelectric Point. The isoelectric point (page 106) of an ampholyte is determined by the magnitude of the dissociation constants, K_1 and K_2. The condition of the isoelectric point is that the net charge be equal to zero, or, expressed in other terms, that the number of cations A^+ be equal to the number of anions A^-. If A is the isoelectric molecule, then, at the isoelectric point, its dissociations as acid and as base are equal or

$$A + H^+ \rightleftharpoons A^+ \quad \text{and} \quad A \rightleftharpoons A^- + H^+$$

From the mass law,

$$K_1 = \frac{[H^+][A]}{[A^+]} \quad \text{and} \quad K_2 = \frac{[H^+][A^-]}{[A]} \tag{13}$$

At the isoelectric point $[A^+] = [A^-]$, or

$$[A^+] = \frac{[H^+][A]}{K_1} = [A^-] = \frac{K_2[A]}{[H^+]} \tag{14}$$

which yields

$$[H_I^+]^2 = K_1K_2 \quad \text{or} \quad pH_I = \frac{pK_1 + pK_2}{2} \tag{15}$$

where pH_I is the pH at the isoelectric point, or pI. The calculated pI values for the amino acids are given in Table 7.5. For those amino acids which contain more than two ionizable groups, the pI value may be calculated from the two pK values whose groups are titrated to either side of the isoelectric form of the amino acid.

CHEMICAL PROPERTIES OF THE AMINO ACIDS

The chemical reactions of the amino acids are relatively numerous because of the different reactive groups that are present in the same molecule. Aliphatic monoamino monocarboxylic acids give all the reactions expected for carboxyl and amino groups. The other amino acids give these same reactions and, in addition, those reactions characteristic of additional groups that may be present. For example, cysteine gives the reactions characteristic of the sulfhydryl (SH) group, tyrosine the reactions of a phenolic group, etc. Many of these reactions are also given by proteins because they contain these amino acids.

Reaction with Ninhydrin. Amino acids react with ninhydrin (triketohydrindene hydrate) to yield CO_2, ammonia, and an aldehyde containing one less carbon than the amino acid. The reaction also yields a blue or purple color, which is useful for the colorimetric quantitative estimation of amino acids. However, the colorimetric reaction is not entirely specific for amino acids since color with ninhydrin is produced by ammonia and by many amino compounds, including peptides and proteins, in circumstances in which CO_2 is not liberated in the reaction. Therefore, measurement of CO_2 production with ninhydrin is specific for the presence of a free carboxyl group adjacent to the amino group, *i.e.*, free α-amino carboxylic acid functions. Proline and hydroxyprolines give yellow products with ninhydrin.

The reaction of ninhydrin with α-amino acids is as follows:

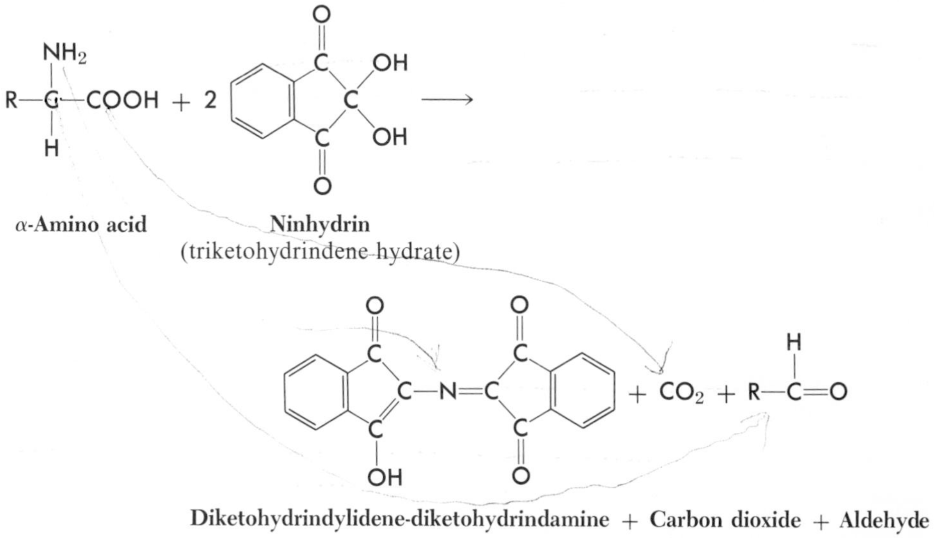

α-**Amino acid**   **Ninhydrin**
(triketohydrindene hydrate)

Diketohydrindylidene-diketohydrindamine + Carbon dioxide + Aldehyde

Reactions of Specific Amino Acids. Some of the color reactions given by particular amino acids are in such common use as analytical tools as to deserve mention. These reactions are also given by most proteins and thus aid in their determination or identification. Several of these reagents are used in sprays for the detection of specific amino acids on paper chromatograms (page 117).

Millon Reaction. A red color is obtained when phenolic compounds are heated with $Hg(NO_3)_2$ in nitric acid containing a trace of nitrous acid. Proteins containing tyrosine give this reaction.

Sakaguchi Reaction. Guanidines in alkaline solution give a red color with the reagent, which contains α-naphthol and sodium hypochlorite. The reaction is given by arginine and by proteins that contain this amino acid.

Nitroprusside Test. Cysteine and proteins that have free sulfhydryl groups give a red color with sodium nitroprusside [$Na_2(NO)Fe(CN)_5$—$2H_2O$] in dilute ammoniacal solution.

Aldehyde Reaction. Indole derivatives give strongly colored products with a number of aromatic aldehydes. With *p*-dimethylaminobenzaldehyde in sulfuric acid, a red-violet color is obtained with tryptophan (Ehrlich reaction). This test can be used for the quantitative estimation of tryptophan in proteins.

Folin's Reaction. In alkaline solution, amino acids give a deep red color with sodium 1,2-naphthoquinone-4-sulfonate. This method is used for rapid quantitative estimation of amino acids; it has been applied, for example, to blood.

Sullivan's Method for Cysteine. Cysteine (or cystine after reduction) gives a red color in alkaline solution with sodium 1,2-naphthoquinone-4-sulfonate in the presence of the strong reducing agent, sodium hydrosulfite ($Na_2S_2O_4$). This method can be used for the quantitative estimation of cysteine and cystine.

Pauly Reaction for Histidine and Tyrosine. Histidine and tyrosine couple with diazotized sulfanilic acid in alkaline solution, giving a red color.

PEPTIDES

Of the greatest importance in understanding the structure of proteins is the fact that amino acids can be linked together in amide bonds through the carboxyl group of one and the amino group of another to form a substituted amide bond, which is termed a peptide bond or linkage. The characteristic peptide bond structure is enclosed in the dotted area:

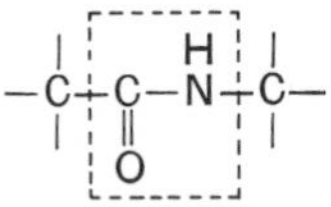

$$-\overset{|}{\underset{|}{C}} + \overset{|}{\underset{\underset{O}{\|}}{C}} - \overset{H}{\underset{|}{N}} + \overset{|}{\underset{|}{C}} -$$

Peptide nomenclature lists the amino acid residues as they occur in the chain starting from the *free* amino group, which is conventionally shown at the left hand part of the structure. The ending *-yl* is used for each of the residues except the terminal one, which bears the unsubstituted carboxyl group. Peptides containing two amino acid residues are dipeptides, those with three amino acid residues, tripeptides, etc. In general, peptides with more than two residues are termed polypeptides. The tetrapeptide alanylglycyltyrosylglutamic acid has the structure indicated on page 113.

The names of the amino acid radicals and their structures are given in Table 7.6 (page 114). The distinction between glutamyl and glutaminyl, as well as aspartyl and asparaginyl radicals, should be noted. It also should be emphasized that glutamyl derivatives may be of the γ type as well as the α variety.

Synthesis of complex peptides that contain optically active amino acids

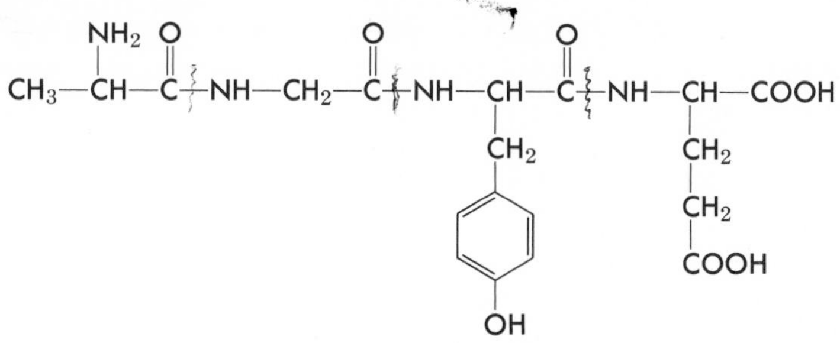

$$CH_3-\underset{\underset{NH_2}{|}}{CH}-\underset{\underset{O}{||}}{C}-NH-CH_2-\underset{\underset{O}{||}}{C}-NH-\underset{\underset{CH_2}{|}}{CH}-\underset{\underset{O}{||}}{C}-NH-\underset{\underset{CH_2}{|}}{CH}-COOH$$

Alanylglycyltyrosylglutamic acid

involves technically difficult problems in organic chemistry. Only a single example of how such syntheses may be achieved will be given here. One of the difficulties is the problem of limiting the reaction so that only desired products will be obtained.

The most important general method of peptide synthesis was devised by Bergmann and Zervas. The amino group is protected by the carbobenzoxy residue, which is easily removed later in the form of volatile products by catalytic hydrogenation. This method is suitable for synthesizing optically active di- and polypeptides, and many have been prepared. An example is the synthesis of glycyl-L-proline.

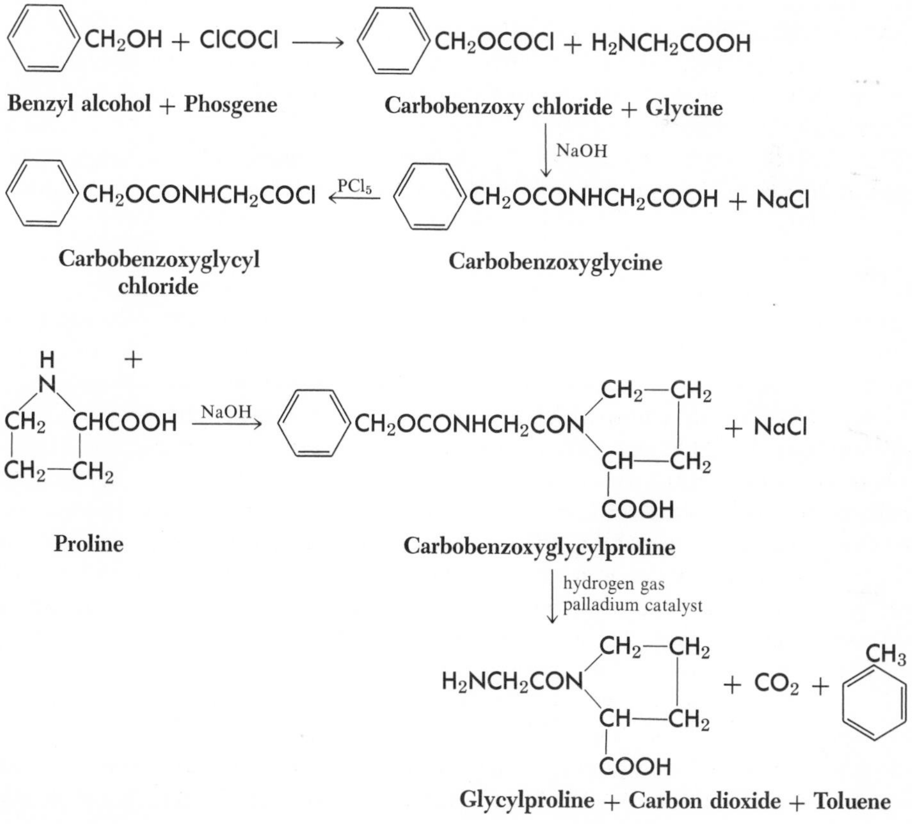

$$\text{⬡}CH_2OH + ClCOCl \longrightarrow \text{⬡}CH_2OCOCl + H_2NCH_2COOH$$

Benzyl alcohol + Phosgene   Carbobenzoxy chloride + Glycine

$$\downarrow NaOH$$

$$\text{⬡}CH_2OCONHCH_2COCl \xleftarrow{PCl_5} \text{⬡}CH_2OCONHCH_2COOH + NaCl$$

Carbobenzoxyglycyl   Carbobenzoxyglycine
chloride

$$\underset{\underset{CH_2-CH_2}{|}}{\underset{CH_2 \quad CHCOOH}{\overset{H \quad +}{\overset{N}{\diagup\diagdown}}}} \xrightarrow{NaOH} \text{⬡}CH_2OCONHCH_2CON\underset{CH-CH_2}{\overset{CH_2-CH_2}{\diagup\diagdown}} + NaCl$$
$$\underset{COOH}{|}$$

Proline   Carbobenzoxyglycylproline

$$\downarrow \begin{array}{l}\text{hydrogen gas}\\ \text{palladium catalyst}\end{array}$$

$$H_2NCH_2CON\underset{CH-CH_2}{\overset{CH_2-CH_2}{\diagup\diagdown}} + CO_2 + \text{⬡}CH_3$$
$$\underset{COOH}{|}$$

Glycylproline + Carbon dioxide + Toluene

Table 7.6: Amino Acid Radicals in Proteins

Radical name	Abbreviation	Radical name	Abbreviation
Alanyl	Ala	Isoleucyl	Ileu
Arginyl	Arg	Leucyl	Leu
Asparaginyl	AspNH$_2$	Lysyl	Lys
Aspartyl	Asp	Methionyl	Met
Cysteinyl	CySH	Phenylalanyl	Phe
Cystyl	CyS-SCy	Prolyl	Pro
Glutaminyl	GluNH$_2$	Seryl	Ser
Glutamyl	Glu	Threonyl	Thr
Glycyl	Gly	Tryptophanyl	Try
Histidyl	His	Tyrosyl	Tyr
Hydroxylysyl	Hylys	Valyl	Val
Hydroxyprolyl	Hypro		

THE PEPTIDE LINKAGE IN PROTEINS

In 1902 Hofmeister and Fischer proposed independently that the main type of linkage between the amino acids in proteins is the peptide bond. This hypothesis provided the foundation from which all advances in the chemistry of these complex substances have been made. A brief summary of some of the evidence that indicates the presence of peptide linkages in proteins follows:

1. Intact proteins show little free amino nitrogen, but large amounts are formed after hydrolysis. This is consistent with the view that the majority of the amino groups are linked in peptide bonds.

2. Acid or enzymic hydrolysis of proteins yields progressively increasing quantities of amino and carboxyl groups in equal amounts. This indicates that equivalent amounts of acidic and basic groups are simultaneously liberated.

3. Although complete hydrolysis of proteins yields a mixture of free amino acids, partial hydrolysis of proteins gives a mixture of amino acids and peptides. Many of these peptides have been isolated in pure form and shown to be identical with synthetic peptides. For example, partial hydrolysates of silk fibroin have yielded large amounts of glycyl-L-alanine and L-alanylglycine.

4. Proteolytic enzymes, which are very specific in hydrolyzing proteins, have also been found to split peptide bonds in synthetic peptides and in peptide derivatives of known structure. It is evident that these enzymes split the same or similar bonds in proteins and in synthetic substrates. The action of proteolytic enzymes on proteins yields a mixture of peptides of varying size and free amino acids.

5. Several antibiotics isolated from microorganisms have proved to be complex peptides. One of the most interesting is gramicidin S. Synge has shown that this compound is a complex cyclopeptide with the amino acids in the following order:

-L-valyl-L-ornithyl-L-leucyl-D-phenylalanyl-L-prolyl-

The peptide is a cyclodecapeptide in which the above unit occurs twice in a closed peptide chain. The presence of the unnatural D-phenylalanine should also be noted.

6. Biuret is obtained by heating urea to about 180°C.

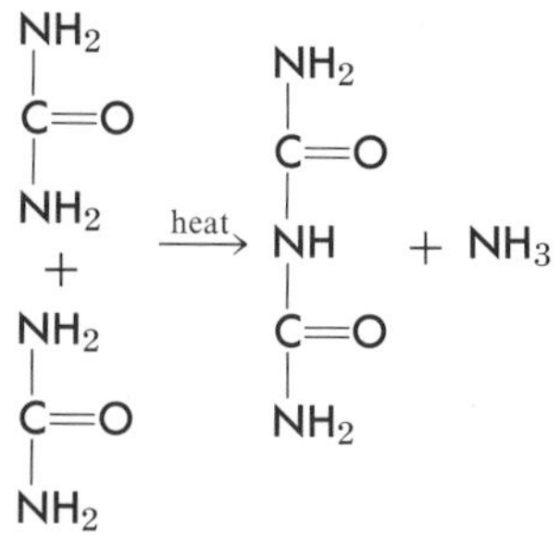

$$
\begin{array}{c}
\text{NH}_2 \\
| \\
\text{C}{=}\text{O} \\
| \\
\text{NH}_2 \\
+ \\
\text{NH}_2 \\
| \\
\text{C}{=}\text{O} \\
| \\
\text{NH}_2
\end{array}
\quad\xrightarrow{\text{heat}}\quad
\begin{array}{c}
\text{NH}_2 \\
| \\
\text{C}{=}\text{O} \\
| \\
\text{NH} \\
| \\
\text{C}{=}\text{O} \\
| \\
\text{NH}_2
\end{array}
\quad + \text{ NH}_3
$$

2 Urea ⟶ biuret + ammonia

In strongly alkaline solution, biuret gives a violet color with copper sulfate. This reaction, called the biuret reaction, is a general one, being given by all compounds with two amide or peptide bonds linked directly or through an intermediate carbon atom. Tripeptides and proteins possess the following structure and give the color reaction.

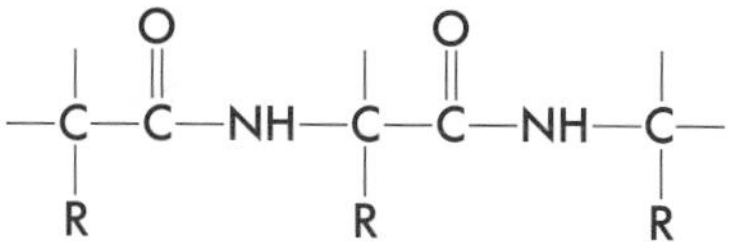

$$
\begin{array}{ccccc}
 & \text{O} & & \text{O} & \\
 & \| & & \| & \\
-\text{C}-\text{C}-\text{NH}-\text{C}-\text{C}-\text{NH}-\text{C}- \\
| & & | & & | \\
\text{R} & & \text{R} & & \text{R}
\end{array}
$$

Dipeptides and amino acids (with the exception of histidine, serine, and threonine) do not give this reaction. The biuret reaction is extensively used both as a qualitative test for the detection of proteins and as the basis for a quantitative colorimetric method for protein estimation.

Further evidence concerning the occurrence of peptide bonds in proteins will become apparent later. It should not be assumed that peptide linkages represent the sole method of holding the protein molecule in its specific conformation. There are many properties of proteins which show that protein molecules are far more complex than simple long polypeptides.

Of general interest in relation to the above consideration of peptides is the occurrence in animal tissues of some related compounds. Carnosine, β-alanyl-L-histidine, and anserine, which is β-alanyl-1-methyl-L-histidine, are found free in muscle tissue of vertebrates.

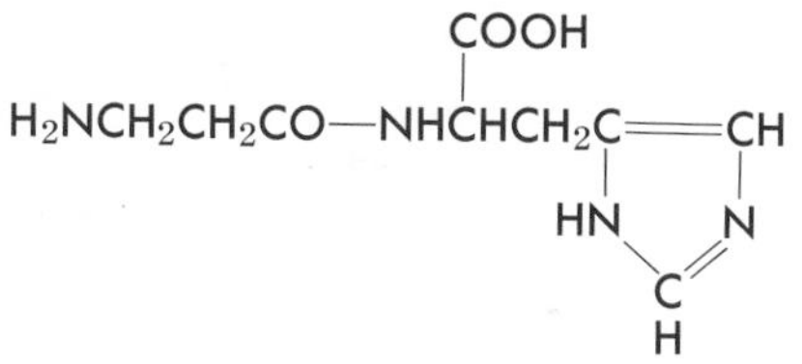

$$
\begin{array}{cc}
\text{COOH} & \text{COOH} \\
| & | \\
\text{H}_2\text{NCH}_2\text{CH}_2\text{CO}-\text{NHCHCH}_2\text{C}{=\!=}\text{CH} & \text{H}_2\text{NCH}_2\text{CH}_2\text{CO}-\text{NHCHCH}_2\text{C}{=\!=}\text{CH} \\
\text{HN}\quad\text{N} & \text{H}_3\text{CN}\quad\text{N} \\
\text{C} & \text{C} \\
\text{H} & \text{H}
\end{array}
$$

Carnosine (β-alanyl-L-histidine) 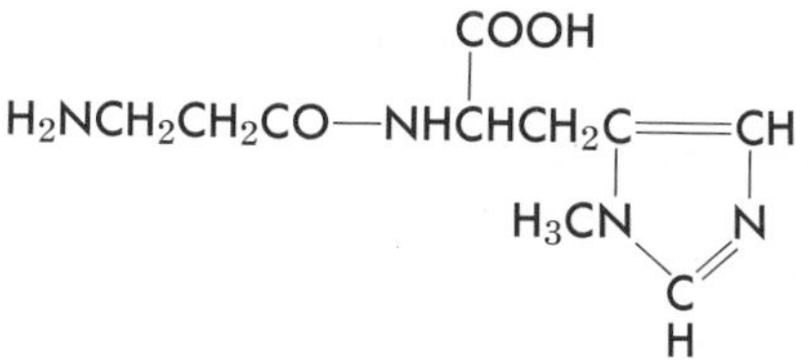   Anserine (β-alanyl-1-methyl-L-histidine)

Glutathione, a tripeptide, γ-L-glutamyl-L-cysteinylglycine, was isolated by Hopkins from yeast, muscle, and liver tissue and is widely distributed in nature.

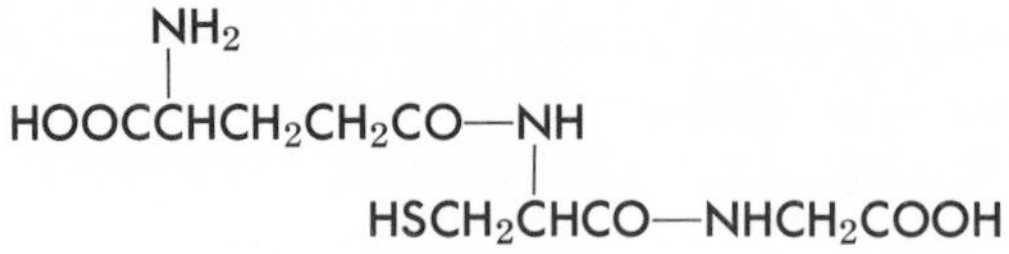

$$NH_2$$
$$|$$
$$HOOCCHCH_2CH_2CO—NH$$
$$|$$
$$HSCH_2CHCO—NHCH_2COOH$$

Glutathione

It should be noted that carnosine and anserine contain β-alanine, an amino acid that has not been found to occur in proteins, and that anserine also contains methylhistidine, which has not been identified in proteins, although it has been isolated from the urine of mammals. Glutathione likewise differs from the peptides commonly found in proteins in that the γ-carboxyl of glutamic acid is linked in peptide bond; however, the second bond is an α-peptide bond.

ESTIMATION AND SEPARATION OF AMINO ACIDS

Amino acid analysis is of prime importance in determining the composition and structure of proteins and polypeptides. These determinations are generally made after acidic hydrolysis. In addition, estimation of free amino acids in urine, tissue extracts, and body fluids is important in various types of physiological and clinical studies.

Amino Acid Analysis. As in all biological studies, the trend has been to develop rapid quantitative methods that are applicable to micro quantities of material. Some of these methods have already been discussed and will be mentioned again only briefly.

Gravimetric Methods. The general procedure of isolating and weighing substances finds rare application in quantitative amino acid analysis because of the general lack of reagents that will quantitatively precipitate a specific amino acid from a mixture. However, an example of a quantitative isolation technique is the precipitation of arginine as an insoluble flavianate. Such procedures are also useful for isolation of samples of optically active amino acids from protein hydrolysates.

Colorimetric Methods. Various amino acids give specific color reactions with certain reagents; several of these have been mentioned previously. Such methods are particularly applicable to amino acids which possess characteristic functional groups.

Microbiological Methods. Many microorganisms, such as bacteria and fungi, require complex mixtures of specific amino acids, vitamins, etc., for growth. If the nutritional requirements for growth of an organism are known, a medium may be prepared that lacks one essential nutrient. From the growth rate of the organism when some material, *e.g.*, a protein hydrolysate or tissue extract, is added, the amount of the limiting nutrient in the added material may be estimated. Many of the lactic acid bacteria are particularly suitable since determination of lactic acid liberated into the medium is readily made and serves as an index of bacterial growth.

Suitable bacterial species have been found for the estimation of practically all the amino acids found in proteins. Analyses made by microbiological assays are in reasonable agreement with those made by other methods.

Enzymic Methods. Specific enzymes may be used for estimation of certain amino acids and indeed for many other substances also. For example, the enzyme arginase acts only on arginine, yielding ornithine and urea. The urea is easily estimated by colorimetric methods and serves as an index of preexisting arginine.

$$H_2NCNHCH_2CH_2CH_2CHNH_2COOH + H_2O \xrightarrow{\text{arginase}}$$
$$\overset{\|}{NH}$$

$$H_2NCH_2CH_2CH_2CHNH_2COOH + H_2NCONH_2$$

Arginine + water $\longrightarrow$ ornithine + urea

The urea may be treated with the specific enzyme urease, yielding carbon dioxide and ammonia, as an application of another enzymic method.

$$H_2NCONH_2 + H_2O \xrightarrow{\text{urease}} 2NH_3 + CO_2$$

The ammonia or CO_2 may be estimated by a variety of methods. Other enzymes have also been applied to the estimation of amino acids, *e.g.*, specific bacterial decarboxylases that liberate CO_2; this gas is conveniently measured by manometric methods.

Chromatographic Methods. Some applications of chromatography to analysis have already been discussed (page 37). Partition chromatography on paper is

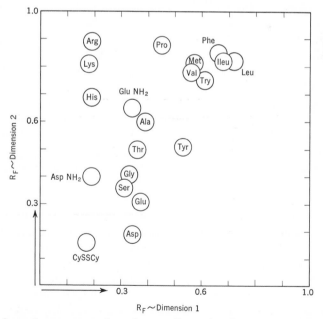

FIG. 7.4. A schematic representation of a two-dimensional paper chromatogram. The solvent for dimension 1 is *n*-butanol-acetic acid-water (250:60:250 vol. per vol.) and for dimension 2, phenol-water-ammonia (120:20:0.3 per cent). Each solvent front moves with an R_F equal to 1 in each dimension. The abbreviations used for amino acid radicals are given in Table 7.6 (page 114).

widely employed for detection of amino acids, and various methods are used for quantitative estimation. A ninhydrin spray is used for amino acids in general, and special reagents may be applied for the detection of particular functional groups, *e.g.*, the Pauly reagent (for histidine and tyrosine), the Ehrlich reagent (for tryptophan), the Sakaguchi reagent (for arginine), etc. (page 112).

A representative two-dimensional separation of amino acids is shown in Fig. 7.4. It should be noted that in the solvent system for dimension 1, the greatest movement is found for those amino acids which possess large nonpolar side chains since the stationary phase is the water phase of the solvent mixture. Hence those amino acids with the higher affinity for water, *i.e.*, the more polar compounds including those with additional ionic groups, have the lower R_F values.

Ion exchange chromatography is in wide use for the separation of amino acids; it employs synthetic resins, some being anionic and others cationic substances. Sulfonated polystyrene resin bears many $—SO_3H$ groups. When a column of this resin is treated with a buffer at pH 3 containing Na^+ ions, the resin is converted to the form $—SO_3Na$. Cationic amino acids introduced at the top of such a column will displace Na^+ and will be retarded or strongly adsorbed, the degree of retardation depending on the basicity of the individual amino acid. Thus, aspartic and glutamic acids emerge before most of the neutral amino acids, and well ahead of the basic amino acids. Even the neutral amino acids can be separated readily from one another since, despite their similar pK values, their side chains possess different affinities for the resin.

Figure 7.5 illustrates the separation achieved with a synthetic amino acid mixture. In this case the effluent from the column was mixed automatically with a ninhydrin reagent, the color developed by passage through a hot water bath, and the absorbancy recorded as the effluent passed through a light beam directed on a photocell. The change in photocurrent with volume of effluent was plotted automatically by a recorder. Integration of the area under each peak permits quantitative estimations. Identification of each amino acid is readily made, since, under controlled conditions, the position of emergence is constant for each amino acid. These principles have been utilized for construction of commercially available amino acid analyzers.

Various types of resins and buffer systems are in use for separation of amino acids, peptides, and proteins. The quantitative analysis of protein hydrolysates is discussed later (page 143).

Electrophoretic Methods. Inasmuch as amino acids are electrolytes, they migrate in an electric field at appropriate pH values. For example, at pH 5, glutamic and aspartic acids possess a net negative charge and migrate toward the anode; histidine, arginine, and lysine migrate toward the cathode; the "neutral" amino acids will remain stationary. Such electrophoretic methods may be applied on a single sheet or strip of paper to effect a group separation. At other pH values, *e.g.*, pH 3.0, even the neutral amino acids may be separated from one another to a considerable degree.

A widely used technique involves a two-dimension separation on paper, employing electrophoresis in one dimension and partition chromatography in the other. Such a system has a high resolving power and is used not only for separation

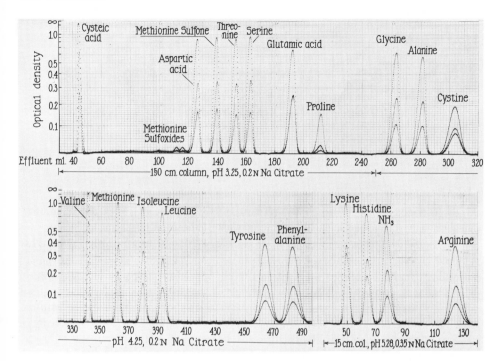

FIG. 7.5. Automatically recorded chromatographic analysis of a synthetic mixture of amino acids on a sulfonated polystyrene resin. (*From D. H. Spackman, W. H. Stein, and S. Moore, Anal. Chem.,* **30**, 1190, 1958.)

and identification of amino acids but also for peptides. Such methods are useful for critical estimation of purity since a pure substance will yield only a single spot when the entire sheet is sprayed with a general reagent, such as a ninhydrin solution.

REFERENCES

See list following Chap. 8.

8. The Proteins

Chemical and Physical Properties

Before discussing in detail the chemistry of the proteins, it is useful to summarize briefly a few of the main characteristics of these complex molecules.

1. Many of the proteins that have been crystallized or obtained in a highly purified state behave as homogeneous substances. These are large molecules with molecular weights ranging from approximately 6,000 to many millions. Because of their large size, proteins exhibit many properties that are called colloidal, *e.g.,* their diffusion rates are extremely slow as compared with those of small molecules, and although molecularly dispersed, they may produce considerable light scattering in solution. This may result in visible turbidity (Tyndall effect).

2. Proteins, like amino acids, are amphoteric dipolar ions (zwitterions) and contain both acidic and basic groups.

3. Many proteins are labile and readily modified in solution when subjected to alterations in pH, ultraviolet radiation, heat, organic solvents, etc. Aside from the information that such alterations may give concerning proteins, the lability of these compounds poses great technical difficulties and limits the tools and the conditions that may be used for their investigation.

4. Proteins are very reactive and highly specific in their behavior. This is in large part because of the side chains and active groups of the amino acids present in the proteins. Although almost all the α-carboxyl and α-amino groups are combined in peptide linkage, most of the other groupings appear to be free. These may include the γ- and β-carboxyl groups from glutamic and aspartic acids, respectively, amide groups from glutamine and asparagine, ϵ-amino groups from lysine, guanido groups from arginine, imidazole groups from histidine, sulfhydryl groups from cysteine, etc. Indeed, the specific properties of the proteins are conferred not only by highly reactive functional groups but also by the aliphatic and aromatic side chains.

CLASSIFICATION OF PROTEINS

No system of classifying the many thousands of proteins satisfactorily depicts their differences and similarities. Simpler compounds are generally grouped according to structure. The proteins are all similar in structure insofar as they contain amino acids, but since there is information regarding the structure of only a few individual proteins, other methods of classification must be used.

The classification given below is based upon three general properties of proteins, *viz.*, shape, solubility, and chemical composition. The classes of proteins listed, as well as the subgroups in each class, are designated by general names given to a group of proteins of similar physical and chemical properties. However, within each subgroup differences exist in the amino acid composition and, more significantly, in the order of arrangement of the individual amino acids in the polypeptide chains (page 153). Thus, serum albumin defines a group of proteins present in the blood serum of vertebrates. However, the serum albumin of the horse differs from the serum albumins of man, sheep, cow, dog, etc. Thus, most proteins are species-specific although very similar substances are generally found in closely related species.

Fibrous Proteins. These are insoluble animal proteins, highly resistant to digestion by proteolytic enzymes. Because of their insolubility, molecular weights cannot be determined. They include the proteins of silk, wool, skin, hair, horn, nails, hoofs, quills, connective tissue, and bone. This heterogeneous group may be subdivided into several distinct types of proteins. Collagens and elastins are of mesenchymal origin; keratins are derived from ectoderm.

1. *Collagens* are the major proteins of connective tissue. They are insoluble in water and resistant to animal digestive enzymes but are altered to easily digestible, soluble gelatins by boiling in water, dilute acids, or alkalies. More than half the total protein in the mammalian body is collagen. The collagens appear to be unique in their high content of hydroxyprolines and in containing hydroxylysine. They are poor in sulfur, since cysteine and cystine are absent, and contain no tryptophan.

2. *Elastins* are present in tendon, arteries, and other elastic tissues. Although similar to collagens in many respects, they cannot be converted to gelatins.

3. *Keratins* are the proteins of hair, wool, quills, hoofs, nails, etc. These proteins generally contain large amounts of sulfur as cystine. Human hair has about 14 per cent cystine.

Globular Proteins. These proteins are soluble in water or in aqueous media containing salts, acids, bases, or ethanol. This group includes all the enzymes, oxygen-carrying proteins, protein hormones, as well as others. As will become apparent in later chapters, the most significant description of these proteins is based on their functional properties, *e.g.*, enzymes are most readily recognized by their specific catalytic behavior.

A number of descriptive names that serve to categorize certain proteins are based on their solubility. Since these terms are in common use, they will be mentioned briefly. It should be understood that many of these names connote categories that are not mutually exclusive and that a single protein may be described in several ways.

Albumins are readily soluble in water and coagulable by heat. This is a large group, of which egg albumin and serum albumin are typical examples.

Globulins are insoluble or sparingly soluble in water, but their solubility is greatly increased by the addition of neutral salts such as sodium chloride. These proteins are coagulable by heat. Many globulins are easily prepared from animal or plant tissues since they are readily extracted by salt solutions (5 to 10 per cent

NaCl) and are precipitated from the saline solution by dilution with water. Examples are serum globulins, globulins of muscle and other tissues, and globulins of plant seeds.

Histones are basic proteins which are soluble in water and which yield, on hydrolysis, large amounts of the basic amino acids. Histones can be extracted in large amounts from certain glandular tissues, such as thymus and pancreas. Most histones are combined with nucleic acids (Chap. 10) within cells.

Protamines are strongly basic proteins of relatively low molecular weight. They are associated with nucleic acids and are obtained in large quantity from ripe sperm cells of fish. They contain no sulfur and have a high nitrogen content (25 to 30 per cent) because of the presence of large quantities of arginine. Tyrosine and tryptophan are absent. Typical protamines are salmine from salmon sperm, clupeine from herring, and sturine from sturgeon.

Conjugated Proteins. Conjugated proteins are combined with characteristic non-amino acid substances. The term *prosthetic group* is generally used to designate the non-amino acid moiety (see also page 210).

Nucleoproteins are combinations of proteins with nucleic acids. The latter will be discussed in Chap. 10.

The protein components of *mucoids or mucoproteins* are combined with large amounts (more than 4 per cent) of carbohydrate, measured as hexosamine. The carbohydrate portions of these conjugated proteins are complex polysaccharides containing N-acetylhexosamine in combination with uronic acids or other sugars. Many contain a sialic acid (page 36).

Well-defined soluble mucoproteins have been obtained from egg white (ovomucoid α), serum (Chap. 32), and human pregnancy urine; the product from the last-named source has gonadotropic activity (Chap. 51). Soluble mucoproteins are not readily denatured by heat, nor are they easily precipitated by common protein precipitants like trichloroacetic or picric acids.

The term *glycoprotein* is restricted to those proteins which contain small amounts of carbohydrate, less than 4 per cent hexosamine. This group includes many common albumins and globulins, *e.g.*, egg albumin, some serum albumins, and certain serum globulins.

Lipoproteins are water-soluble proteins conjugated with lecithin, cholesterol, cephalin, etc., such as the several lipoproteins of serum (Chap. 32). The *proteolipids* are distinguished from the *lipoproteins* by their solubility in organic solvents and insolubility in water. Brain and nerve tissue are rich sources of proteolipids and lipoproteins (Chap. 39).

Other types of conjugated proteins contain a variety of non-amino acid groups linked to the protein. These include hemoproteins (Chap. 11), flavoproteins, metalloproteins, phosphoproteins, etc.

PROPERTIES OF PROTEINS

Amphoteric Behavior. Like amino acids, proteins are ampholytes, *i.e.*, they act as both acids and bases. Since proteins are electrolytes, they migrate in an electric field and the direction of migration will be determined by the net charge of the molecule. The net charge is influenced by pH, and for each protein there is a pH value at which it will not move in an electric field; this pH value is the isoelectric point (pI). At pH values acid to the isoelectric point, the protein will have a net positive charge and as a cation will migrate to the negative pole (cathode). Correspondingly, at pH values alkaline to the isoelectric point the protein will possess a net negative charge and, as an anion, will migrate to the positive pole (anode). The isoelectric point of a given protein is a constant and aids in characterization of these substances. The isoelectric points for several proteins are given later (Table 8.3).

The quantitative behavior of proteins is strongly influenced by pH. Hence it is desirable to ascertain the amount and kind of charge possessed by a protein molecule and what determines the net charge at a particular pH value. Like amino acids, proteins are dipolar ions (zwitterions) at the isoelectric point, *i.e.*, the sum of the positive charges is equal to the sum of the negative charges and the net charge is zero. The total charge on the protein molecule, the sum of positive and negative charges together, may be at a maximum at the isoelectric point. For simplicity, the isoelectric protein molecule may be depicted as follows:

$$(H_3\overset{+}{N})_m\text{---}R\text{---}(COO^-)_n$$

The actual numbers of positive and negative charges can be measured by titration of the protein. The number of ionized groups in simple polyvalent acids like phosphoric or tartaric acids is determined by the number of equivalents of hydrogen ions that can be derived from each mole of acid. The same procedure may be employed for proteins. In titrating from the isoelectric point, the total base consumption is determined by the number of free carboxyl groups, and the total acid consumption, by the number of basic groups. Table 8.1 gives these values for several proteins, together with molecular weights of these proteins. It must be recognized that proteins possess a large number of ionic groups, *i.e.*, that these molecules are highly polyvalent, and that there are large differences among proteins.

The ionic groups of a protein are contributed by the side chains of the polyvalent amino acids. For example, a lysine residue in the interior of a peptide chain

Table 8.1: NUMBER OF TITRATABLE GROUPS OF SOME PROTEINS

Protein	Titratable basic groups	Titratable acidic groups	Molecular weight
Ovalbumin	91	82	40,000
Insulin	101	130	5,700
Zein	18–21	30	40,000
Casein	76–90	....	....
Edestin	127–134	....	310,000
Horse hemoglobin	148	113	68,000
Human serum albumin	144	135	69,000
Bovine serum albumin	147	134	69,000

Note: Data are given as equivalents of acid or base reacting with 100,000 g. of protein in order to compare the different proteins.

is combined in peptide linkage through its α-amino group and its α-carboxyl group, but the ε-amino group is free, as indicated by the fact that the ε-amino group of lysine in proteins may be deaminated with nitrous acid, and when proteins are benzoylated or benzenesulfonated, ε-benzoyllysine and ε-benzenesulfonyl-lysine can be isolated after hydrolysis. The guanido group of arginine and most of the imidazole groups of histidine are also free in proteins. Hence as a first approximation, the total acid-binding capacity should be equal to the sum of the number of arginine, histidine, and lysine residues in the protein.

Similarly, the anionic groups of proteins are the γ- and β-carboxylic groups contributed by glutamic and aspartic acids. However, some of these residues are present as glutamine and asparagine, the amides of these acids. The amide content of proteins is estimated by determining the amount of ammonia liberated by mild acid hydrolysis. The number of free carboxyl groups must then be equivalent to the sum of the aspartic and glutamic acids less the number of carboxyl groups combined with ammonia in amide linkage.

In general, the agreement between the computed and observed acid and base consumption is reasonably satisfactory. For some proteins, the observed acid and base consumption is significantly greater than the values calculated from the molecular weights, assuming a single free amino group and a single free carboxyl group at the two terminal ends of the polypeptide chains. To account for these additional ionic groups, it is necessary to assume the existence in these proteins of more than one peptide chain.

Titration data give valuable information concerning the structure of the protein. If it is assumed that the primary linkages between amino acids involve peptide bonds of α-amino and α-carboxyl groups, the other ionic groups are uncombined since they may be titrated. Thus, they must also be available for other chemical and physical interactions. As a corollary, it follows that other types of linkages involving ionic groups are either absent or present in small numbers. This excludes the presence of significant numbers of combined guanido, ε-amino, and other ionic groups, since these must be free to substantiate the agreement between data obtained by titration and by analysis.

Titration Curves. As would be expected from the large number and diversity

---

Table 8.2: CHARACTERISTIC pK VALUES FOR ACIDIC AND BASIC GROUPS IN PROTEINS

Group	pK_a at 25°
α-Carboxyl (terminal)	3.0–3.2
β-Carboxyl (aspartic)	3.0–4.7
γ-Carboxyl (glutamic)	Approx. 4.4
Imidazolium (histidine)	5.6–7.0
α-Amino (terminal)	7.6–8.4
ε-Amino (lysine)	9.4–10.6
Guanidinium (arginine)	11.6–12.6
Phenolic hydroxyl (tyrosine)	9.8–10.4
Sulfhydryl (cysteine)	Approx. 8–9

SOURCE: From E. J. Cohn and J. T. Edsall, "Proteins, Amino Acids, and Peptides as Ions and Dipolar Ions," Reinhold Publishing Corporation, New York, 1942.

of ionic groups, the titration curves of proteins are complex. Table 8.2 gives the characteristic pK values for the major ionic groups that can be titrated in proteins. These are the values that are found in proteins, and comparison with the data in Table 7.5 shows that the characteristic pK values are shifted somewhat from the constants found for the free amino acids.

It may be noted that sulfhydryl and phenolic hydroxyl groups are included in Table 8.2. However, since free sulfhydryl groups are usually present in only small amounts, their ionic contribution is usually neglected. The phenolic groups of tyrosine appear to contribute significantly in some proteins of high tyrosine content, such as insulin. Several major conclusions are apparent from Table 8.2. The presence in most proteins of nearly all the ionic groups listed in the table endows proteins with effective buffering capacity over the greater portion of the pH range.

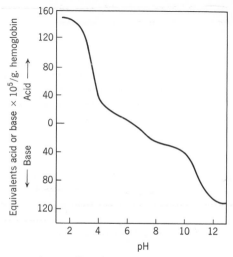

FIG. 8.1. The titration curve of crystalline horse hemoglobin. (*After E. J. Cohn, A. A. Green, and M. H. Blanchard, J. Am. Chem. Soc.,* **59**, 509, 1937.)

However, it should be emphasized that the only group which has significant buffering capacity at pH values near neutrality is the imidazolium group of histidine, since the number of terminal α-amino groups is usually small. Thus, histidine groups are of great physiological importance as buffer groups of proteins in tissues. The titration curve of horse hemoglobin, shown in Fig. 8.1, illustrates the complex titration curve characteristic of a protein.

Ion Binding of Proteins. As ampholytes, proteins can form salts of both types; *i.e.*, protein anions can bind with cations, and protein cations with anions. Indeed, a mixture of different proteins at a given pH will include both anions and cations if their isoelectric points fall on opposite sides of the pH value, and salts of protein-protein combinations will be formed. This will occur in tissues since both basic and acidic proteins are present. Specific combinations of small ions with proteins also play an important role in tissues and body fluids.

Many ions form insoluble salts with proteins and serve as excellent precipitating agents for proteins. Acids such as phosphotungstic, trichloroacetic, picric, sulfosalicylic, perchloric, etc., are commonly used for deproteinizing solutions, since the anions of these acids will form insoluble salts with proteins when the latter are in the form of cations (acid side of their isoelectric points). A standard method for determining the amount of protein nitrogen in a solution is to estimate the total nitrogen by the Kjeldahl method on an aliquot of the solution and to measure the nitrogen on an aliquot of the filtrate obtained after precipitating the proteins with one of the above acids, such as trichloroacetic. The difference between total nitrogen and nonprotein nitrogen gives the protein nitrogen. An average figure for the nitrogen content of proteins is 16 per cent. Hence multiplying the value for protein nitrogen by the factor 6.25 gives the amount of protein. Although this is only an approximation, it is useful in estimating the protein content of heterogeneous material, such as foodstuffs and tissues.

Heavy metal ions are used for precipitating proteins on the alkaline side of their isoelectric points, the proteins behaving as anions. Ions of mercury, copper, silver, zinc, barium, etc., are frequently employed for this purpose. Many acid dyes find practical use for coloring the insoluble proteins, wool and silk.

It should be noted that many of the ion combinations with proteins involve interactions other than simple salt formation. Ions such as Cu^{++}, Ni^{++}, etc., can form coordination complexes with imidazoles, substituted amines, and ammonia as in the familiar deeply blue cupric ammonia complex, $Cu(NH_3)_4^{++}$. Such complexes are also formed with peptides and proteins since free amino, imidazole, and other groups are present.

Electrophoresis. It has already been mentioned that proteins migrate in an electric field except at the pH of the isoelectric point. This was discovered by W. B. Hardy in 1899 and has been widely employed in the study of proteins because of its usefulness in ascertaining the properties of protein mixtures. The

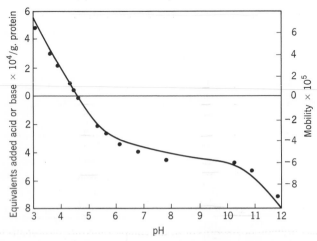

FIG. 8.2. The electrophoretic mobility in square centimeters per volt per second (shown as dots) and the titration curve of crystalline egg albumin. (*Mobility data from L. C. Longsworth, Ann. N.Y. Acad. Sci.,* **41**, 275, 1941; *titration data from R. K. Cannan, A. Kibrick, and A. H. Palmer, Ann. N.Y. Acad. Sci.,* **41**, 243, 1941.)

titration curve of a protein may be regarded as a measure of the charged state of the molecule at any pH value. The rate of migration of a molecule in an electric field is largely dependent on the net charge. Hence, the rate of electrophoretic migration will depend on pH in the same manner as does the degree of ionization. Figure 8.2 illustrates the electrophoretic migration and the titration curve of crystalline egg albumin. Although the shape and size of the molecule influence the absolute rate of migration, the major factor is the net charge.

Since proteins differ markedly in their isoelectric points and in their titration curves, they differ in electrophoretic mobility at any given pH value. Electrophoretic analysis is used to determine the purity of individual proteins and for quantitative analysis of complex mixtures.

In principle the technique of electrophoresis is simple. A protein solution containing a buffer at a definite pH is placed at the bottom of a U tube. Immediately above the protein solution, a layer of buffer solution is introduced without disturbing the boundary created between protein solution and buffer. Electrodes are inserted in the buffer solution. The whole U tube is immersed in a bath maintained at a constant temperature near 0°C. in order to minimize convection currents that may arise from the heat generated, and also to prevent heat coagulation of sensitive proteins. Modern electrophoretic technique, largely due to Tiselius, employs U tubes with optically flat surfaces and constructed so that the solutions may be

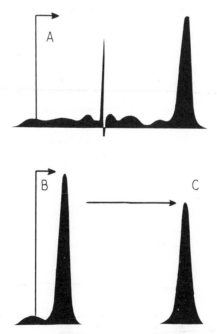

FIG. 8.3. The electrophoretic patterns of *A*, the complex mixture of proteins found in human plasma; *B*, the single peak found with crystalline carboxypeptidase; and *C*, the homogeneous peak found with crystalline bovine serum albumin. The vertical line indicates the starting point of the boundary. The peak at the initial position is due to the presence of the buffer salt.

introduced and equilibrated to temperature without boundary disturbance. The rate of migration of the protein in the electric field is measured by observing the movement of the boundary as a function of time. Migration of colored proteins, such as hemoglobin, is readily observed. Since most proteins are colorless, optical systems have been devised that permit visualization and measurement of variations in refractive index in the electrophoresis cell. These differences in refractive index of the various portions of the protein solution indicate alterations in concentration, i.e., refractive index gradients provide a measure of the distribution and quantity of the solute, in this case, protein.

Figure 8.3 shows the electrophoretic patterns of two highly purified proteins (B and C). The pattern obtained with a sample of normal human plasma (A) is also given in order to illustrate the result obtained with a complex mixture of dissolved proteins. With pure substances, only a single peak will be obtained which will be symmetrical and have the form of a probability curve. Multiple peaks and asymmetrical curves indicate mixtures. With mixtures it is possible to assess the proportion of the different components by measuring the fraction of the total area attributable to each component. Applications of electrophoretic analysis will be given later (Chaps. 32 and 37).

In addition to the applicability to charged compounds in solution, electrophoresis may also be performed by using a porous inert medium such as starch, silica gel, or moistened filter paper. The mixture of substances in solution is usually applied as a discrete spot or zone, and complete separation of components can be obtained. This process is known as zone electrophoresis and is useful both for analysis and for isolation of materials.

The method of immunoelectrophoresis is described in Chap. 32.

Solubility. Each homogeneous protein has a definite and characteristic solubility in a solution of fixed salt concentration and pH. Therefore, under definite conditions the amount of protein that may be dissolved to form a saturated solution at equilibrium is independent of the amount of excess solid phase suspended in the fluid. In fact, this provides a sensitive test for the purity of a protein. The hemoglobins prepared from several species are pure by this test. Since each protein has a characteristic solubility, this may be used as a means of distinguishing closely related proteins. Landsteiner and Heidelberger showed that a saturated solution of dog hemoglobin would still dissolve horse hemoglobin. In fact, as much horse hemoglobin was dissolved as in the pure solvent without dog hemoglobin. It was thus established that the two proteins were distinct molecules despite their similar function as oxygen carriers and general resemblance in other properties. This illustrates very simply the *species specificity* of the hemoglobins.

The solubility of proteins is markedly influenced by pH, as might be expected from their amphoteric behavior; solubility is at a minimum at the isoelectric point, and increases with increasing acidity or alkalinity. The explanation is as follows. In the isoelectric condition, electrostatic repulsive forces between solute molecules are at a minimum and crystal-lattice forces in the solid state will be at a maximum. When the ampholyte molecules exist predominantly as either anions or cations, repulsive forces between ions are high since all the molecules possess excess charges of the same sign and they will be more soluble than in the isoelectric state.

The solubility of β-lactoglobulin as a function of pH is shown in Fig. 8.4 for four different salt concentrations. Although the solubility is markedly enhanced by increased salt concentration, it is minimal in each case near the isoelectric point at pH 5.2 to 5.4.

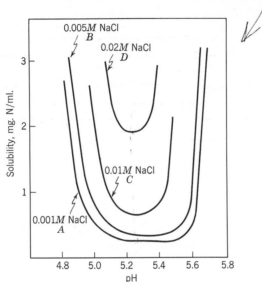

FIG. 8.4. The solubility of β-lactoglobulin as a function of pH at four different values of ionic strength (μ). Curve *A*, $\mu = 0.001$; curve *B*, $\mu = 0.005$; curve *C*, $\mu = 0.01$; curve *D*, $\mu = 0.02$.

It is apparent from previous comments (pages 121*ff.*) that various kinds of protein differ enormously in their solubility. Certain factors greatly influence protein solubility. These can be utilized for group separations, and, frequently, for purification of individual proteins. The major influences on solubility are considered below.

(1) Globulins are sparingly soluble in water, and their solubility is markedly increased by neutral salts. Globulins can often be precipitated by dilution of a saline tissue extract with distilled water or by removal of salts by *dialysis* against water of a protein solution contained in a bag made from a *semipermeable membrane,* such as collodion or cellophane. Semipermeable membranes permit free passage of water and small ions or molecules but not of the larger proteins.

The effect of neutral salts in increasing the solubility of globulins is called the "salting-in" effect. This is shown in Fig. 8.4 for β-lactoglobulin. The logarithm of the solubility is frequently a linear function of a term called the ionic strength, which is readily calculated from the molar concentrations of the ions and their charge, using the expression

$$\mu = \tfrac{1}{2}\Sigma m Z^2$$

where μ is the ionic strength, m the molarity, and Z the charge of the ion. The summation sign Σ denotes that the mZ^2 terms are added for each of the ions. For example, for a $0.1M$ solution of NaCl, the ionic strength $\mu = \tfrac{1}{2}(0.1 \times 1^2 +$

$0.1 \times 1^2) = 0.1$, or, for a salt of univalent ions, the ionic strength is equal to the molarity. For a $0.1M$ solution of Na_2SO_4, $\mu = \frac{1}{2}(0.2 \times 1^2 + 0.1 \times 2^2) = 0.3$.

The solubility of albumins in water is scarcely affected by addition of low concentrations of neutral salts. However, in mixtures of an organic solvent and water, solubility of albumins is increased by neutral salts.

The explanation of the "salting-in" phenomenon is as follows. Solubility of any substance depends on the relative affinity of solute molecules for each other (crystal-lattice formation) and for the solvent molecules. Any factor that decreases interaction of solute molecules will tend to increase solubility. The small ions of neutral salts will interact with the ionic groups of the protein molecules, diminishing protein molecule interactions and, therefore, increasing solubility.

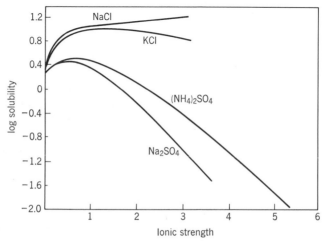

FIG. 8.5. The solubility of horse carboxyhemoglobin in salt solutions of different ionic strength. Both "salting in" and "salting out" are observed with this protein. (*From E. J. Cohn and J. T. Edsall, "Proteins, Amino Acids, and Peptides as Ions and Dipolar Ions," Reinhold Publishing Corporation, New York, 1942.*)

2. Proteins are precipitated from aqueous solution by high concentrations of neutral salts. This is the "salting-out" phenomenon. Di- and trivalent ions are more effective than univalent ions (Fig. 8.5). Commonly used salts are ammonium sulfate, sodium sulfate, magnesium salts, and phosphates. The most effective region of salting out is at the isoelectric point of the protein. The solubility of carboxyhemoglobin (carbon monoxide hemoglobin) as a function of ionic strength is shown in Fig. 8.5. Salting out occurs not only with proteins but with gases, uncharged molecules, and electrolytes.

The mechanism of salting out is complex. Hofmeister suggested that it was due to "dehydration" of the protein by the added salt. According to Debye, the salt ions attract around themselves the polarizable water molecules, making less water available for the proteins since, at high salt concentrations, the number of charged groups contributed by the salts is enormous compared with those of the proteins. Since solubility of proteins in water depends on clustering of water molecules around the hydrophilic ionic groups, removal of water molecules to other ions will decrease protein solubility. Qualitatively, the effect of salts on the solubility of proteins and of amino acids is very similar.

3. Proteins are precipitated from aqueous solutions by organic solvents that are miscible with water. Commonly used solvents are methanol, ethanol, and acetone. Protein solubilities in these solvents are markedly affected by neutral salts. Most satisfactory results are obtained by working at low temperatures at which proteins are most stable.

4. The effect of pH on protein solubility has already been noted, and this effect, *i.e.*, minimal solubility at or near the isoelectric point, applies regardless of the precipitating agent used: neutral salts, organic solvents, etc. Some proteins, such as casein of milk, are readily precipitated by adjusting the solution to the pH of the isoelectric point; hence the procedure is described as "isoelectric precipitation." The isoelectric points of some proteins are listed in Table 8.3; they vary from below pH 1.0 for pepsin to pH 10.6 for cytochrome c.

Molecular Weight. Most of the usual methods for determining the size of small molecules, such as alterations in freezing point, boiling point, vapor pressure, etc., are not applicable to proteins because of their high molecular weight and instability.

From Composition. The minimal molecular weight (M_{min}) of any substance may be computed from the content of any element present in small amount by making the assumption that the molecule contains only one atom of such an element. This computation has been applied to proteins for elements other than the abundant C, H, N, and O. The usual formula may be applied.

$$M_{min} = \frac{\text{atomic weight} \times 100}{\text{per cent of constituent}}$$

Table 8.3: MOLECULAR WEIGHTS AND ISOELECTRIC POINTS OF SOME PROTEINS

Protein	$M_{S,D}$	$M_{osmotic}$	pI
Cytochrome c................................	13,000	....	10.6
Ribonuclease................................	14,000	15,000	7.8
Myoglobin, horse..........................	17,000	....	7.0
Carboxypeptidase..........................	34,000	....	6.0
Pepsin..	35,500	36,000	Less than 1.0
Ovalbumin, hen............................	40,000	40,000–46,000	4.6
Growth hormone, ox.......................	49,000	44,300	6.9
Hemoglobin, horse.........................	68,000	67,000	6.9
Serum albumin, human....................	69,000	69,000	4.8
Diphtheria toxin............................	74,000		
Serum γ-globulins..........................	180,000	177,000	6.4–7.2
Catalase......................................	250,000	....	5.6
Fibrinogen...................................	450,000	580,000	5.5
Urease..	480,000	....	5.1
Thyroglobulin...............................	630,000	....	4.6
Hemocyanin, octopus......................	2,800,000		

Note: $M_{S,D}$ = molecular weight calculated from sedimentation and diffusion measurements (page 134); $M_{osmotic}$, from osmotic pressure measurements (page 132).

Mammalian hemoglobin contains 0.34 per cent iron (atomic weight = 55.8), and the computed M_{min} is 16,700. Actually the true molecular weight (M) of hemoglobin, found by other methods, is about 68,000, which indicates that a molecule of hemoglobin contains four atoms of iron.

In the same manner, minimal molecular weights may be computed from the content of amino acids present in small amounts. Bovine serum albumin has only 0.58 per cent tryptophan, which yields $M_{min} = 35,200$. M determined by other methods is almost twice this value, *viz.*, 69,000.

It is apparent that analytical data may be helpful in determining minimal values but do not indicate true molecular weights. In fact, most amino acids are present in such large amounts that minimal values are useless even for purposes of a rough estimate.

By Osmotic Pressure. For reasonable estimates of molecular weight, physical methods are most useful, and one of the first to be applied was that of osmotic pressure determinations. The general formula of the gas law is applicable to osmotic pressure,

$$\pi V = \frac{g}{M} RT$$

where π is the osmotic pressure in atmospheres (1 atmosphere = 760 mm. Hg), V the volume of solution in liters, g the weight of solute in grams, M the molecular weight, R the gas constant, and T the absolute temperature ($t°C. + 273.1$). R is known (0.082 liter-atmosphere per mole per degree); the other quantities can be measured experimentally, and M then computed. Many such determinations have been made for homogeneous proteins. Table 8.3 gives M values obtained for some proteins from osmotic pressure measurements.

The measurements are made by putting a solution of the protein in a rigid bag of a semipermeable membrane, such as collodion. The bag is placed in a buffer solution, and after equilibrium has been achieved, the increased pressure in the bag is measured by the height of the capillary above the solution (Fig. 8.6). There are a number of difficulties in making such measurements, and these may be mentioned briefly.

1. Equilibrium may be achieved only slowly, and readings must be made for days or weeks until no further change in pressure is recorded. Because of the time required, the measurements are generally made at a low, constant temperature to avoid bacterial growth and protein decomposition. However, osmometers have been devised which attain equilibrium in only a few hours; these are to be preferred.

2. The gas law equation given above is valid only at low concentrations of solute since osmotic pressure generally increases with protein concentration much more rapidly than is predicted by the simple equation. Measurements are usually made at several protein concentrations, and π is obtained by extrapolation to zero protein concentration.

3. The osmotic pressure of the protein must be obtained at the isoelectric point since higher values of π are found for the protein salts. The bound ions increase the osmotic pressure because of the Donnan equilibrium effect (see below).

4. The total osmotic pressure of a protein is small, and there are difficulties in

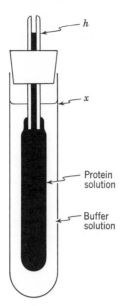

FIG. 8.6. A simple osmometer shown diagrammatically. The measured osmotic pressure is the difference in height between the level of the buffer solution (x) and the protein solution in the capillary (h).

obtaining precise readings. The equation also shows that the larger the protein, the smaller is the pressure for a given quantity of protein in solution. In practice, the method is not readily applicable to proteins with molecular weights greater than a few hundred thousand.

5. The observed osmotic pressure is recorded for all the proteins in the solution and therefore gives an average molecular weight. There is no way of determining from such measurements whether or not the system contains a mixture of molecules of different sizes.

Gibbs-Donnan Equilibrium. The measurement of osmotic pressure of a protein solution requires the use of a semipermeable membrane that prevents the migration of the large particles. For a system at equilibrium which contains protein ions bearing a net charge (such as P^-) and diffusible ions, we have the situation

$$Na_a^+, Cl_a^- \mid Na_b^+, Cl_b^-, P_b^-$$

where the subscripts a and b refer to the two sides of the membrane. In solution b, $[Na_b^+] = [Cl_b^-] + [P_b^-]$, and in solution a, $[Na_a^+] = [Cl_a^-]$ since electric neutrality must be maintained on each side of the membrane. The values for $[Na_a^+]$ and $[Na_b^+]$ must be different because P_b^- is present on only one side of the membrane. The concentrations of the diffusible ions bear the following relationship to one another, specifically for the example given, and generally for ions X^+ and Y^- in a system at equilibrium:

$$\frac{[Na_a^+]}{[Na_b^+]} = \frac{[Cl_b^-]}{[Cl_a^-]} = \frac{[X_a^+]}{[X_b^+]} = \frac{[Y_b^-]}{[Y_a^-]} \tag{1}$$

This relationship may be derived from the general equilibrium expression where the change in free energy ΔF is equal to zero and is given by the thermodynamic equation

$$\Delta F = 0 = RT \ln \frac{[\text{Na}_a^+]}{[\text{Na}_b^+]} + RT \ln \frac{[\text{Cl}_a^-]}{[\text{Cl}_b^-]}$$

which may be solved to give

$$[\text{Na}_a^+][\text{Cl}_a^-] = [\text{Na}_b^+][\text{Cl}_b^-]$$

which is the same as equation (1) at bottom of previous page. Similarly,

$$[\text{X}_a^+][\text{Y}_a^-] = [\text{X}_b^+][\text{Y}_b^-]$$

From these relationships, it is apparent that, at the isoelectric point of the protein at which its net charge is zero, the distribution of electrolytes will not be influenced by the amount of protein in solution and the osmotic pressure will be due only to the protein. Since the Gibbs-Donnan equilibrium effect leads only to small differences in diffusible electrolyte concentrations, it can be made negligible at pH values removed from the isoelectric points of proteins by adding high concentrations of neutral salts.

By Sedimentation. The rate at which a particle in solution is driven down a centrifuge tube under the action of centrifugal force depends (1) on the force applied, (2) on the size, shape, and density of the particle, and (3) on the density and viscosity of the solvent. Large molecules can be sedimented at high centrifugal forces whereas small molecules cannot be sedimented at forces presently attainable in the laboratory. Modern ultracentrifuges attain speeds as high as 75,000 r.p.m. and forces in excess of 400,000 times gravity. Several types of instruments have been devised for obtaining strong centrifugal fields. The first of these, devised by T. Svedberg and his collaborators, is a turbine driven by jets of oil. Others employ air jets or high-speed electrical motors. In all these instruments, the rotors are operated in high vacuum to minimize air resistance and consequent heating due to friction. These ultracentrifuges are equipped with suitable optical systems for recording the positions of the boundaries of the proteins during the sedimentation runs. The optical system generally used is similar to that employed in electrophoresis studies (page 127).

When the solution contains particles which are all of the same size and shape, they will move down the centrifuge tube at the same rate, giving a sharp boundary between the solute in solution and the clear solvent. A number of boundaries will be observed when the solution contains a mixture of substances of different particle size. It is thus possible to determine homogeneity with respect to particle size and, at the same time, to estimate characteristic sedimentation constants.

The fundamental equation derived by Svedberg for the molecular weight of a protein is

$$M = \frac{RTs}{D(1 - V\rho)}$$

where M is the molecular weight, T the absolute temperature, and R the gas constant as before (page 132). The sedimentation constant s, which has the dimensions of time per unit field of force, usually lies between 1×10^{-13} and 200×10^{-13} sec. The factor 1×10^{-13} is called the Svedberg unit (S). D is the diffusion constant in cm.^{2} per sec., V the partial specific volume of the protein, and ρ the density of the solvent.

The force exerted in the ultracentrifuge, which sediments the protein molecules, sets up an unequal distribution of the molecules. Diffusion, which is due to the thermal energy of the protein molecules, tends to oppose the sedimentation and to establish an equal distribution of the molecules. Molecular weight may be calculated from the observed sedimentation constant and from the diffusion constant (D) measured independently. D is measured by observing the spread of an initially sharp boundary, between the protein solution and a solvent, as the protein diffuses into the solvent layer.

V, the partial specific volume, is equal to the reciprocal of the density of the molecule. Rate of sedimentation depends on the difference in density of solute particles and the solvent. If the particles are of lower density than the solvent, they will rise to the top (as in a cream separator), and flotation will occur. Hence it is necessary for the equation to include the term V. For most proteins V has the value of 0.70 to 0.75. The exact value depends on the amino acid composition and can be calculated, when this is accurately known, or it can be determined experimentally.

Highly purified proteins show homogeneous boundaries in the ultracentrifuge; representative sedimentation curves obtained by a refractive-index method are shown in Fig. 8.7. The ultracentrifuge is a useful tool in studying the stability of proteins since under many conditions, *e.g.*, extremes of pH, temperature, etc., aggregation or dissociation may occur, and this can be detected by changes in sedimentation constants. Molecular weights of some proteins obtained by the sedimentation method are given in Table 8.3. Present methods estimate the molecular weight to within 5 or 10 per cent of the true value.

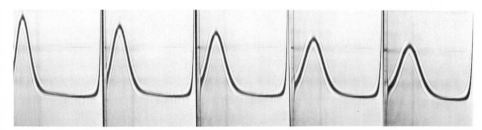

FIG. 8.7. Sedimentation of crystalline ribonuclease at 59,780 r.p.m. in the analytical ultracentrifuge. The direction of sedimentation is from left to right. The first picture was taken 1 hr. after attaining speed; subsequent exposures were made at 16-min. intervals. It will be noted that as the boundary moves down the cell, the height of the boundary decreases and its width increases. This is due to normal diffusion. The boundary at the bottom of the cell represents sedimented protein. When a preparation contains a mixture of proteins or other solutes of different sizes, multiple peaks are found.

One of the most remarkable facts of protein chemistry is that these large and complex molecules have definite and characteristic molecular weights, in contrast to polysaccharides, which are generally polydisperse. The size of many homogeneous proteins has been estimated by a variety of methods in addition to those given here, and in most instances there is satisfactory agreement among these different determinations.

By Sedimentation Equilibrium. Another technique for determining molecular weight in the ultracentrifuge depends on finding a low centrifugal force at which the protein boundary attains an equilibrium position. Under these conditions the boundary position and its spread will be determined by the opposing factors of sedimentation and diffusion. This obviates the necessity of independent measurements of the diffusion constant, thus providing more rapid determinations. A disadvantage of the method is that when the material is inhomogeneous an average value for all particle sizes is obtained.

Shape of Protein Molecules. From the sedimentation constant s and the diffusion constant D a frictional ratio f/f_o can be calculated from the formula

$$\frac{f}{f_o} = 10^{-8}\left(\frac{1 - V\rho}{D^2 s V}\right)^{1/3}$$

where the various terms have the same meaning as above (page 134). The molar frictional coefficient for a compact spherical and unhydrated sphere is f_o. When f/f_o is equal to 1.0, the molecule is essentially an unhydrated sphere. When f/f_o is greater than 1.0, the molecules may be asymmetrical or hydrated or both. In some instances, hydration may be estimated, and many globular proteins appear to be spherical or nearly spherical molecules. These proteins include ribonuclease, insulin, chymotrypsinogen, pepsin, and others. However, other proteins are highly asymmetrical and exist in solution as pronounced ellipsoids or rods. Fibrinogen, the plasma protein that is the precursor of fibrin of blood clots, and myosin, the main protein of muscle fibers, are examples of long ellipsoids. It is estimated that human fibrinogen has a cross-sectional diameter of 38 Å. and a length of 700 Å. Solutions of such molecules show pronounced light scattering, and the shape of molecules, as well as molecular weight, may be estimated from light-scattering measurements.

The *viscosity* of a solution depends on the molecular weight and shape of the solute molecules at a given solute concentration. Highly asymmetrical molecules show a high intrinsic viscosity as compared with spherical molecules of the same size. When M is known, the shape can be estimated from the variation of viscosity with solute concentration.

X-ray analysis has shown that insoluble fibrous proteins such as wool and silk exist as long fibers with extremely small cross sections. Thus proteins can range in shape from simple crystalloidal spherical structure to shapes which resemble those of synthetic, linear high polymers.

Stability of Proteins. It has been mentioned that proteins are sensitive to a variety of agents that do not hydrolyze the peptide bonds. Heating of proteins in neutral solutions causes alterations in properties, *e.g.*, decrease in solubility, loss of specific activity if the protein is a hormone, enzyme, etc., loss of crystallizability, etc. Collectively, these alterations are described by the term *denaturation*. In many instances, the distinct process of *coagulation* of the protein follows its denaturation. A number of native proteins do not contain the free sulfhydryl groups of cysteine as determined by the nitroprusside test; after denaturation, sulfhydryl groups are revealed.

Many native proteins, *e.g.*, egg albumin and serum γ-globulin, are resistant to digestion by the proteolytic enzyme, trypsin. In contrast, when denatured, these proteins are rapidly attacked by this enzyme.

Denaturation and coagulation are readily accomplished by heating. Ultraviolet radiation causes a denaturation similar to that produced by heat. The rate at which these processes occur is influenced by temperature, pH, and the concentration of electrolytes. Accompanying denaturation there may be large increases in viscosity and surface tension, and changes in optical rotation and in other characteristics.

High concentrations of urea and guanidine salts denature many proteins. In some instances, as with equine hemoglobin and edestin, the denaturation is accompanied by a reduction in molecular weight of the protein molecules. The denatured proteins are usually soluble in strong urea solutions but may precipitate on dilution or dialysis. Organic solvents of many types may also produce denaturation; these include alcohols, acetone, etc. Both anionic and cationic detergents cause denaturation of proteins; sodium dodecyl sulfate is a very effective denaturing agent. Shaking of protein solutions produces surface films of denatured proteins. An example is the beating of egg white in the formation of meringues.

In some instances, denaturation is reversible. Thus, cooling trypsin solutions that have been boiled for a short time may lead to a recovery of native trypsin which can be crystallized. For some proteins only little or no reversal of heat denaturation is possible, whereas reversal of urea denaturation is more readily demonstrated. Further discussion of the changes produced in proteins by denaturation is presented later.

Criteria of Purity. The ordinary criteria of purity of small molecules are not readily applicable to proteins. Such standards as sharpness of melting point cannot be used since dry proteins decompose on heating. Crystallization of proteins leads to purification in many cases but by itself is not a sufficient criterion of purity, since proteins readily form mixed crystals and repeated crystallization by the same method retains the mixture. The retention of constant composition and physical constants on recrystallization is useful, but if mixed crystals are formed, these criteria are useless. For these reasons special techniques have been devised for assessing the purity of proteins and other large molecules. Many of these techniques are applicable as well to small molecules, and thus have assumed great importance in the isolation and purification of natural products. Some of these procedures have already been mentioned, but it is useful to summarize them here. It should be understood that there are really no tests for purity, but only methods for the detection of impurities or inhomogeneity. It is assumed that a substance is pure only after all possible tests have failed to reveal inhomogeneity. The history of protein chemistry is replete with instances in which homogeneity has been thought to be established and the assumption has later been shown to be incorrect when new criteria have been applied.

Constant Solubility. Constant solubility, which is independent of the amount of solid phase present, is an important criterion of purity. Since this depends on the applicability of the phase rule, it may be employed for all substances. In practice, solubility tests should be made at a variety of pH and ionic strength conditions.

Homogeneity in Size as Determined in the Ultracentrifuge. The lower limit in size for this method, with presently available ultracentrifuges, is probably about 8,000 molecular weight (Fig. 8.7).

Homogeneity in Electrical Charge. As determined by electrophoretic mobility in different buffers at several pH values (Fig. 8.3), this criterion can be applied to small electrolytes as well as to proteins.

Homogeneity by Chromatography. Many proteins have been successfully chromatographed on columns of ion exchange resins or other adsorbents (page 117). Such methods have not only provided a critical evaluation of homogeneity but have permitted resolution of complex mixtures of proteins. In general basic proteins can be successfully chromatographed on carboxylic acid resins, *e.g.*, carboxymethyl cellulose or carboxylated polystyrene resins. Acidic proteins have been chromatographed on basic ion exchangers, such as diethylaminoethyl cellulose.

Partition chromatography and countercurrent distribution have been successfully employed with relatively few proteins because of the limited stability and solubility of most proteins in organic solvents. Nevertheless, such methods have been important for the study of insulins of various species, for the separation of polypeptides obtained from natural sources, and for the resolution of peptides obtained as degradation products of large proteins.

Separation on Molecular Sieves. Cross-linked dextrans (page 41), marketed as Sephadex, which possess pores of small but finite size permit the penetration of molecules up to a certain size limit but exclude larger molecules. This technique, termed "gel filtration," has permitted evaluation of purity by molecular size and has been used for separation of proteins of different molecular weights. The dextrans may be used in columns similar to those employed for chromatography. Peptides may also be separated on such dextrans. Resolution is aided by the fact that some adsorption may also occur.

Cross-linked dextrans of differing and relatively uniform pore size are available and permit study of molecules up to 100,000 molecular weight by this method.

Analytical Criteria. All chemical substances may be tested for purity by analytical criteria, *i.e.*, the atomic ratios should be constant after recrystallization from different solvents, and the elementary composition calculated from analytical data must yield whole numbers of atoms. For proteins, the amounts of the common elements are very similar and the number of atoms is so large that these criteria are seldom useful. For the elements present in lesser amounts, such as sulfur, or those found in only a few proteins, such as metals, phosphorus, iodine, etc., the analytical data may be useful. More fruitful is the consideration of amino acid content. Residues of amino acids must be present as an integral number of units per molecule of a pure protein. When only a few residues of a particular amino acid are found in a protein, valuable information as to homogeneity may be obtained. For example, human serum albumin contains 0.6 of a residue of tryptophan per mole of protein (molecular weight = 69,000). It is apparent that there are probably two very similar albumins present in such preparations, one that contains no tryptophan and the other with a single residue of tryptophan per mole.

Specific analysis may be used to detect other macromolecular substances that may be present. Tests for sugars can be used to estimate the content of various polysaccharides; however, sugars may be covalently bound to protein in glyco- and mucoproteins (page 122). Measurement of the absorption ratio at 280 mμ and 260 mμ is used to detect the presence of nucleic acids, which have a high absorption maximum at 260 mμ (page 170) in contrast to proteins, which possess a weak maximum near 280 mμ because of the presence of aromatic amino acid residues (page 94). The ratio of absorption of 280 to 260 mμ is near 1.75 for proteins, and near 0.5 for nucleic acids.

Specific Functional Properties. Many proteins have very specific functional properties, *i.e.,* they act as hormones, enzymes, oxygen carriers, etc. Tests for functional purity are extremely sensitive since minute quantities of these active substances can be detected by their physiological effects, catalytic behavior, etc. If a preparation has a number of catalytic or biological effects, and a single protein is responsible for these effects, then repeated fractionation or partial inactivation with respect to one type of activity should not alter the *relative* ratios to other effects. For example, if an enzyme preparation attacks *A* ten times more rapidly than it does *B* and reprecipitation alters the ratio from 10:1 to 100:1, it is evident that different enzymes must be responsible for the two catalytic effects and the original preparation must have been inhomogeneous.

The criterion of functional homogeneity is one of the most valuable in the study of the proteins because of the sensitivity of the tests. Frequently, an impurity present in as low a concentration as one part in many thousands or millions can be readily detected by a test of functional properties; this is a much greater sensitivity than can be obtained by presently available physical or chemical analytical methods.

Antigenic Properties. Most proteins and some polysaccharides are antigenic, *i.e.,* they stimulate the formation of specific antibodies when injected into a suitable test animal, *e.g.,* rabbit. Injection of a homogeneous substance will result in the formation of a single type of specific antibody, whereas a mixture of substances that are antigenic will produce several types of antibody. This biological method for ascertaining the homogeneity of protein preparations may be as sensitive as tests for enzymic or hormonal homogeneity, provided the impurities are antigenic.

The amount of a specific protein in solution can be estimated quantitatively by adding the specific antiserum (Chap. 32), separating the resulting precipitate, and determining the amount of precipitate by a variety of methods.

PURIFICATION OF PROTEINS

In order to follow the isolation of a single protein, some quantitative method of protein estimation is essential. Chemical methods include the determination of protein nitrogen (page 126), use of the biuret reagent (page 114), the ninhydrin reagent (page 111), the phenol reagent (page 111), and the Lowry method, which combines the use of the phenol and biuret methods. Physical methods include measurement of refractive index, estimation of dry weight of salt-free solutions, and measurement of light absorption at 280 mμ (page 94). Estimation of specific biological activity is used to follow the purification of enzymes (Part 2) or protein hormones (Part 6).

Procedures for Purification. A first and major requirement is that the protein be obtained in solution since many proteins are present in cellular structures which are particulate in character and proteins may be associated with materials, such as lipids, which render them insoluble in water. Tissues must be ground to rupture the cells and to permit access of the solvent to the entire mass of tissue. Proteins may frequently be dissolved by extraction with water or with salt solutions of low ionic strength. They may be solubilized by use of weak detergent solutions, by treatment with organic solvents, such as acetone and ether, to remove lipids, or by treatment with butanol, to disrupt cellular structures. These procedures also frequently denature and coagulate unwanted proteins. Similarly, brief heat treatment at temperatures from 40 to 60° is used to denature labile proteins, provided the desired protein is stable to such treatment.

Many of the procedures listed below have already been discussed and can be mentioned very briefly. The order in which they are listed is arbitrary, and in specific instances, some methods are more useful than others; the choices depend on the biological source and concentration of the protein.

1. *By differential solubility.* Factors that influence solubility—pH, ionic strength, and organic solvent concentration (alcohol, acetone, etc.)—have already been discussed (pages 127*ff.*).

2. *By specific precipitation.* Nucleic acids may be specifically precipitated with basic substances (*e.g.*, the small protein protamine, which is readily removed by dialysis) or by precipitation with a divalent cation, such as Mn^{++}. Many proteins can be specifically precipitated with other cations, Ag^+, Hg^{++}, Ba^{++}, Zn^{++}, etc. (page 126).

3. *By column chromatography.* This procedure (page 38) is applicable with anionic or cationic adsorbents, with inert media using partition methods with different solvents, with molecular sieves such as dextrans, with neutral adsorbents such as alumina, hydroxyapatite, etc.

4. *By preparative electrophoresis.* In order to perform electrophoretic separation on a reasonable scale, methods have been devised that permit use of inert supporting media such as starch or powdered cellulose. The high voltage is applied through a conducting buffer solution across the length of a vertical column or across a horizontal trough. An alternate method involves continuous flow of a solution through a high voltage field on a nonconducting, almost horizontal surface or on a vertical sheet of filter paper.

5. *By preparative ultracentrifugation.* With preparative ultracentrifuges, the proteins of higher molecular weight can be sedimented from solution, leaving smaller molecules behind in solution. The centrifugal force and the time of sedimentation will determine the partition that is effected.

6. *By enzymic digestion.* Some native proteins are more resistant to the action of proteinases than others. The digestion products, peptides and amino acids, are readily separated from resistant proteins. Digestion of other types of macromolecules may be accomplished with specific enzymes: nucleic acids by digestion with nucleases (page 171), glycogen and starch with amylases (page 49), hyaluronic acid with hyaluronidases (Chap. 40), etc.

Purification of proteins or of other natural products is an empirical procedure, and the various methods are largely "cut and try." In general, procedures 1 and 2 are most suitable for the first attempts since they are adaptable for handling large amounts of material. The methods of chromatography, electrophoresis, and ultracentrifugation are usually applied after considerable purification has already been achieved.

At each stage of purification, the preparation must be monitored for specific activity or by physical examination, *e.g.*, electrophoresis or ultracentrifugation. These last procedures may suggest the type of method that may effect further purification. The task is completed, *i.e.*, a pure protein is in hand, when all the criteria of purity, discussed above, have been satisfied to the necessary extent.

REFERENCES

Books

Bjerrum, N., "The Constitution of Ampholytes, Particularly That of Amino Acids, and Their Dissociation Constants," reprinted in Niels Bjerrum, "Selected Papers," Ejnar Munksgaards Forlag, Copenhagen, 1949.

Edsall, J. T., and Wyman, J., "Biophysical Chemistry, vol. I, Thermodynamics, Electrostatics, and the Biological Significance of the Properties of Matter," Academic Press, Inc., New York, 1958.

Greenstein, J. P., and Winitz, M., "Chemistry of the Amino Acids," 3 vols., John Wiley & Sons, Inc., New York, 1961.

Meister, A., "Biochemistry of the Amino Acids," Academic Press, Inc., New York, 1957.

Review Articles

Clarke, H. T., Natural Amino Acids, in H. Gilman, ed., "Organic Chemistry, An Advanced Treatise," 2d ed., vol. II, pp. 1079–1165, John Wiley & Sons, Inc., New York, 1943.

Dunn, M. S., and Rockland, L. B., The Preparation and Purity of the Amino Acids, *Advances in Protein Chem.*, **3**, 296–383, 1947.

Fruton, J. S., The Synthesis of Peptides, *Advances in Protein Chem.*, **5**, 1–82, 1949.

Goodman, M., and Kenner, G. W., The Synthesis of Peptides, *Advances in Protein Chem.*, **12**, 465–638, 1957.

Neuberger, A., Stereochemistry of Amino Acids, *Advances in Protein Chem.*, **4**, 298–383, 1948.

Tschiersch, B., and Mother, K., Amino Acids: Structure and Distribution, in M. Florkin and H. S. Mason, eds., "Comparative Biochemistry," vol. V, part C, pp. 1–90, Academic Press, Inc., New York, 1963.

Vickery, H. B., and Schmidt, C. L. A., The History of the Discovery of the Amino Acids, *Chem. Revs.*, **9**, 169–318, 1931.

See also list following Chap. 9.

9. The Proteins

Structure

The complex and specific chemical and biological properties of individual proteins should find explanation in terms of an exact description of their structure in the native state. In this chapter we shall consider primarily the methods being used to attack this problem, as well as some of the findings that pertain to proteins in general. First, the protein must satisfy the criteria of purity described in the previous chapter before structural studies can be undertaken. Second, the amino acid sequences obtained pertain only to the specific protein from a single species; homologous proteins may differ in structure if obtained from another tissue or another species. This problem is presented in Chap. 31. Specific properties of certain enzymes, protein hormones, antibodies, and other biologically active proteins are also described in later chapters.

For convenience, the structure of proteins may be considered under separate categories.

The main mode of linkage of the amino acids in proteins is the peptide bond which couples the α-carboxyl group of one amino acid residue to the α-amino group of another residue (pages 114ff.). Individual proteins may consist of one or more peptide chains. The complete amino acid sequences of several proteins have been established. This is sometimes called the *primary structure*.

If peptide bonds were the only structural linkage in proteins, these molecules would behave as randomly coiled long-chain polypeptides. However, the properties of native, globular proteins indicate an ordered structure in which the peptide chains are folded in a regular manner. Much of the folding is the result of linking the carbonyl and imide groups of the peptide chain backbone by means of hydrogen bonds.

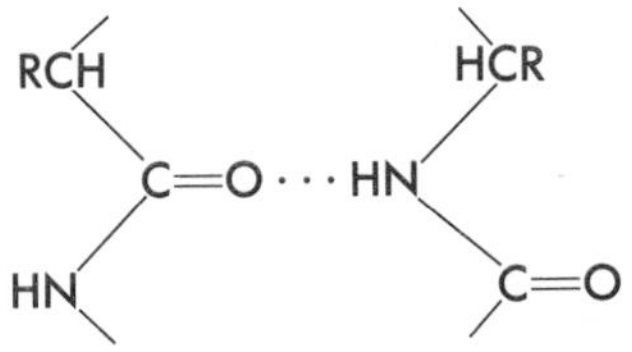

$$RCH \qquad HCR$$
$$C{=}O \cdots HN$$
$$HN \qquad C{=}O$$

Such folding, produced or maintained by hydrogen bonding, is frequently called the *secondary structure* of the protein. Present evidence suggests that in many proteins the hydrogen bonding produces a regular coiled arrangement, called the α-helix (described below).

142

If a globular protein consisted solely of a single helix, these molecules would be elongated structures with a large axial ratio (length to cross section); however, physical measurements reveal that many proteins are spherical or nearly so (page 136). Hence the helical arrangement must be periodically interrupted, permitting numerous bonds with additional folding. This spatial conformation in three dimensions must be maintained by covalent or other bonds. The covalent disulfide bond involving two half-cystine residues is one way in which this is achieved. However, this is not the only type of bonding. Indeed, many globular proteins are completely lacking in disulfide bonds, yet they are stable, globular molecules in solution. These additional types of bonds probably include hydrogen bonds, salt bonds, and hydrophobic or nonpolar bonds. This has been called the *tertiary structure.*

PRIMARY STRUCTURE OF PROTEINS

AMINO ACID COMPOSITION

As a preliminary to more detailed analysis of the amino acid sequence of a protein, it is essential to establish its amino acid composition. Various methods of analysis have been described (pages 116*ff*.); however, for the analysis of protein hydrolysates, the main quantitative method presently used involves ion exchange chromatography (page 117). For analysis of most of the amino acids the protein is usually hydrolyzed with 6N HCl at 110°C. for 20 hr. or longer in an anaerobic atmosphere. The time is usually varied, both to estimate the rate of destruction of labile amino acids, *e.g.*, serine, threonine, and tyrosine, and to ensure complete hydrolysis of more stable peptide bonds, particularly those involving isoleucine and valine residues. Acidic hydrolysis destroys tryptophan, which can be estimated by colorimetric or other methods. Glutamine and asparagine are converted to the respective dicarboxylic acids; however, the amides can be estimated after complete hydrolysis with proteolytic enzymes.

The data in Table 9.1 indicate that representative proteins differ greatly in composition. Insulin, a hormone, lacks tryptophan and methionine. The fibrous protein, collagen, contains hydroxylysine and hydroxyproline. Myoglobin does not contain cysteine or cystine.

It should be noted that the data in Table 9.1 are given as grams of amino acid per 100 g. of original protein and add up to approximately 118 g. of amino acids per 100 g. of protein, because of the addition of one molecule of water for each peptide bond hydrolyzed. If the recoveries of the amino acids are given as *residue weights* in grams rather than weights of free amino acids, the total recovery should be 100 per cent for a protein lacking non-amino acid constituents. For example, the hydrolysis of insulin yields 8.6 g. of free phenylalanine per 100 g. of protein (Table 9.1). If calculated as residue weight recovery, $8.6 \times 147/165 = 7.7$ g. per 100 g. of protein, since 165 is the molecular weight of phenylalanine and 147 is its residue weight in the polypeptides and proteins.

For an understanding of protein structure, another method of reporting amino acid analyses of proteins is more instructive. When the molecular weight of the protein is known, the numbers of amino acid residues per mole of protein may be

Table 9.1: AMINO ACID CONTENT OF PROTEINS, IN PER CENT

Constituent	Insulin (bovine)	Ribonuclease (bovine)	Cytochrome c (equine)	Hemoglobin (human)	Myoglobin (human)	Collagen (bovine)
Alanine	4.6	7.7	3.5	9.0	5.7	7.9
Amide NH$_3$	1.7	2.1	1.1	0.9	1.1	0.7
Arginine	3.1	4.9	2.7	3.3	2.7	8.0
Aspartic acid	6.7	15.0	7.6	9.6	9.2	5.8
Cysteine	0	0	1.7	1.0	0	0
Cystine	12.2	7.0	0	0	0	0
Glutamic acid	17.9	12.4	13.0	6.6	17.3	9.9
Glycine	5.2	1.6	5.6	4.2	6.3	20.3
Histidine	5.4	4.2	3.4	8.8	8.2	0.7
Hydroxyproline	0	0	0	0	0	10.9
Hydroxylysine	0	0	0	0	0	1.0
Isoleucine	2.3	2.7	5.4	0	5.0	1.3
Leucine	13.5	2.0	5.6	14.0	12.2	3.0
Lysine	2.6	10.5	19.7	9.6	16.1	3.4
Methionine	0	4.0	2.1	1.2	2.5	0.9
Phenylalanine	8.6	3.5	4.5	7.3	6.2	2.0
Proline	2.1	3.9	3.3	4.8	4.0	13.6
Serine	5.3	11.4	0	4.4	4.6	3.5
Threonine	2.0	8.9	8.4	5.2	2.9	1.8
Tryptophan	0	0	1.5	1.9	3.6	0
Tyrosine	12.6	7.6	4.9	2.9	2.4	0.8
Valine	9.7	7.5	2.4	10.3	5.3	2.0

calculated and should give whole numbers, since a fraction of a residue cannot be present. Table 9.2 gives the analysis calculated in this manner for the small protein, insulin.

AMINO ACID SEQUENCE OF PROTEINS

Knowledge of the amino acid composition of proteins represents the first step in attempts to understand the structure of these substances. The next is to obtain information concerning the sequence of the amino acids in the peptide chain(s). This presents many difficulties because of the possibilities of isomerism arising from the kinds of amino acid, the amount of each, and their positions relative to one another. As an illustration of the last type of isomerism, consider the dipeptides containing glycine and leucine in which there are two possible isomers, glycylleucine and leucylglycine. For a tripeptide with the same two amino acids and tyrosine, there are six possible isomers. It may be calculated that in a polypeptide containing 20 different amino acids in which each residue occurs only once, there is the possibility of factorial 20 (20!), or approximately 2×10^{18}, different compounds. Each of these contains the identical amino acids in the same proportions. Such a polypeptide of 20 amino acids would have a molecular weight of approximately 2,000.

When the proteins with their large molecular weights are contemplated, the magnitude of the problem becomes apparent. Synge has calculated that for a hypothetical protein with a molecular weight of 34,000, which contains only 12 different amino acids with 288 residues, there are 10^{300} isomers possible. If one molecule of each of these existed on earth, the total mass would be 10^{280} g. Fortunately, the total mass of the earth is only 10^{27} g., so the existence of all possible isomers need not be considered.

Protein Subunits. For many proteins, the minimal molecular weight calculated from amino acid analyses may be much smaller than the molecular weight obtained by physical determinations (page 132). In these instances the proteins may consist of a number of subunits, which may or may not be identical. When the subunits are held together by noncovalent forces, dissociation may be achieved by treatment with detergents or strong urea solutions.

Many other proteins may be dissociated by such methods, *e.g.*, hemoglobin, aldolase, muscle phosphorylase, and glutamic acid dehydrogenase. In general, the smaller proteins of molecular weight up to 30,000 are likely to consist of a single physical unit that cannot be dissociated, whereas many of the larger ones consist of subunits. Before attempting to determine the amino acid sequence of a protein, it is essential to determine the minimal physical unit as well as the minimal chemical unit. The latter is usually calculated from the amino acid composition and from end group determinations (see below).

The minimal molecular weight calculated for insulin from the amino acid composition in Table 9.2 is near 5,700. This value is in agreement with the smallest physical molecular weight estimate obtained in the presence of concentrated solutions of urea or guanidine salts.

Table 9.2: AMINO ACID RESIDUES OF BOVINE INSULIN

Amino acid	Residues	Amino acid	Residues
Alanine	3	Leucine	6
Arginine	1	Lysine	1
Aspartic acid	0	Methionine	0
Asparagine	3	Phenylalanine	3
Half-cystine	6	Proline	1
Glutamic acid	4	Serine	3
Glutamine	3	Threonine	1
Glycine	4	Tryptophan	0
Histidine	2	Tyrosine	4
Isoleucine	1	Valine	5
		Total	51

End Group Analysis. If a polypeptide or a protein consists of a single peptide chain, there should be only a single residue which bears a free α-amino group (amino-terminal residue) and a single residue with a free α-carboxyl group (carboxyl-terminal residue), as in the following example.

$$H_2NCHRCONH \cdots CONHCHRCOOH$$

Thus, quantitative determination of the number of such end groups (amino- or carboxyl-terminal) permits an evaluation of the number of peptide chains per mole of protein. End group analysis of this type is thus an essential first step to undertaking a study of the amino acid sequence. Furthermore, quantitative end group methods provide an additional assessment of the purity of the protein, since there must be a simple integral relationship between the number of end groups and the moles of protein present.

Amino End Group Methods. A technique of great value consists in the use of a reagent that binds strongly with the amino groups of proteins and is not removed by subsequent hydrolysis. Sanger has found that 1-fluoro-2,4-dinitrobenzene (FDNB) is a suitable reagent for estimating and identifying amino end groups. The reagent reacts with α- and ε-amino groups to give yellow dinitrophenyl (DNP) derivatives and with other amino acid side chains (imidazole, phenol, thiol) to yield colorless DNP compounds. The reaction of FDNB with an amino acid is illustrated below.

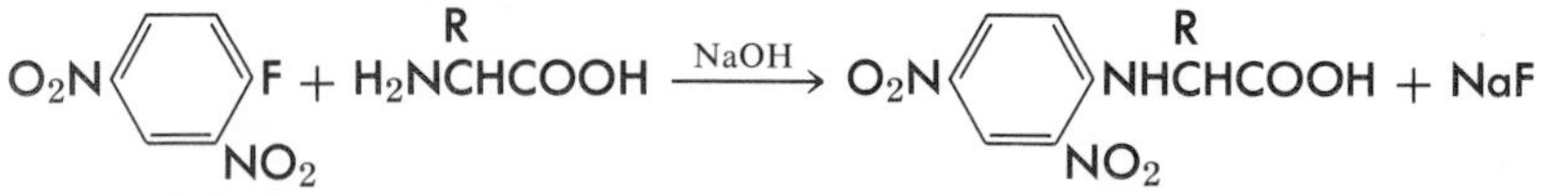

$$O_2N\langle\ \rangle F + H_2NCHCOOH \xrightarrow{NaOH} O_2N\langle\ \rangle NHCHCOOH + NaF$$

With a protein, the reagent is allowed to react under mildly alkaline conditions, the excess reagent is then removed, and the protein is hydrolyzed with $6N$ HCl. The yellow DNP-amino acids are extracted into an organic solvent such as ether or chloroform and separated by chromatographic procedures. Inasmuch as the ε-DNP lysine remains in the aqueous phase after extracting the α-DNP amino acids, a quantitative estimation of the ε-amino groups may also be made. In general, good agreement between such results and the lysine content of the protein is found, thus providing further evidence that ε-amino groups are unbound in proteins.

Some proteins have more than one free α-amino group per molecule, indicating that multiple peptide chains are present. Insulin has one N-terminal phenylalanine and one N-terminal glycine residue and therefore has two different peptide chains. Human hemoglobin has four polypeptide chains. Table 9.3 records some of the results that have been obtained by the DNP method of determining aminoterminal residues.

Table 9.3: Free α-Amino Groups of Some Proteins

Protein	Source	No. and nature of residues	Mol. wt.
Insulin	Beef, pig, sheep, etc.	1 Phenylalanine, 1 glycine	5,700
Ribonuclease	Beef	1 Lysine	14,000
Myoglobin	Human, horse	1 Glycine	17,000
Myoglobin	Whale	1 Valine	17,000
Chymotrypsin	Beef	1 Alanine; 1 isoleucine	21,000
Carboxypeptidase	Beef	1 Asparagine	34,000
Ovalbumin	Hen	None	40,000
Serum albumin	Human, beef, horse	1 Aspartic acid	69,000
Hemoglobin	Human, adult	4 Valine	68,000
Hemoglobin	Beef, sheep, goat	2 Valine; 2 methionine	68,000
Hemoglobin	Human, fetal	2 Valine; 2 glycine	68,000

Another type of approach to amino end group determination involves the use of a reagent that can be applied to the liberation of a derivative of the amino-terminal residue without hydrolysis of the remainder of the peptide chain. Edman's reagent, phenylisothiocyanate, has been successfully used in this way. The procedure is shown in the following reactions.

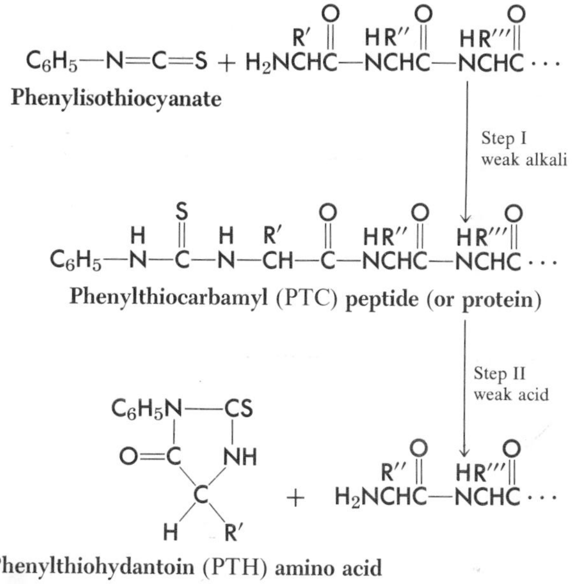

$$C_6H_5-N=C=S + H_2NCHC-NCHC-NCHC\cdots$$

Phenylisothiocyanate

Step I
weak alkali

$$C_6H_5-N-C-N-CH-C-NCHC-NCHC\cdots$$

Phenylthiocarbamyl (PTC) peptide (or protein)

Step II
weak acid

$$\begin{array}{c} C_6H_5N-CS \\ O=C \quad NH \\ C \\ H \quad R' \end{array} + H_2NCHC-NCHC\cdots$$

Phenylthiohydantoin (PTH) amino acid

In step I, the PTC peptide (or protein) is prepared. This derivative is then treated (step II) with weak acid at room temperature, thus liberating the *phenylthiohydantoin* (PTH) of the terminal amino acid and a peptide one residue shorter than the original. The PTH amino acid may be identified by its chromatographic behavior. The procedure may then be repeated with the shorter peptide. It is frequently possible to repeat the procedure five or six times for the identification of the amino-terminal peptide sequence. Such stepwise methods are of great value in the study of proteins and peptides.

In addition to chemical methods for determining amino end groups, an enzymic method is also used. The enzyme *leucine aminopeptidase* requires a terminal free α-amino group for its action. Therefore, in a peptide whose sequence is $H_2N-A \cdot B \cdot C \cdot D \cdot \cdots$ where A, B, C, and D are different residues, the action of the aminopeptidase will liberate sequentially the free amino acids. At any given time the amount of A liberated will be greater than that of B, and the amount of B greater than that of C, etc. Therefore, the sequence ABC can be deduced from rate measurements of amino acid liberation. The aminopeptidase acts most rapidly on terminal leucine residues but also liberates all others found in proteins, although its release of certain residues is very slow.

It should be emphasized that stepwise degradation of a protein by the Edman method or the use of the aminopeptidase can yield meaningful results only when applied to a single peptide chain.

For many proteins the number of free α-amino groups, as determined by the methods of Sanger or Edman, is in accord with the number of peptide chains. Nevertheless, there are proteins which do not possess free α-amino groups, *e.g.*, cytochrome c (page 200), ovalbumin, the protein of tobacco mosaic virus, and others. The single α-amino group is N-acetylated in these proteins. For other proteins which do not possess free α-amino groups, the nature of the blocking groups has not yet been determined, *e.g.*, catalase, phosphorylase.

Carboxyl End Group Methods. A chemical method for the identification of residues bearing α-carboxyl groups depends on the treatment of the protein (or peptide) with hydrazine under anhydrous conditions at 100°C. Cleavage of the peptide bonds by *hydrazinolysis* converts all amino acid residues to amino acid hydrazides except the carboxyl-terminal residue, which remains as the free amino acid and can be isolated and identified chromatographically.

$$\text{Protein} + n\text{H}_2\text{N}\text{—}\text{NH}_2 \longrightarrow n\text{-}1(\text{H}_2\text{NCHRCONHNH}_2) + \text{amino acid}$$

An enzymic method involves the use of pancreatic *carboxypeptidases. Carboxypeptidase A* liberates only the residue from a protein or peptide that bears a free α-carboxyl group. As in the case of the analogous aminopeptidase (page 147), information concerning the carboxyl-terminal sequence can be obtained by the rate of liberation of successive residues; *e.g.*, in a sequence $\text{H}_2\text{N}—A\cdot B\cdot C\cdot D\cdot \cdots W\cdot X\cdot Y\cdot Z—\text{COOH}$, after a given time of hydrolysis, the amount of Z liberated will be greater than that of Y, etc. Carboxypeptidase A has little or no action on carboxyl-terminal proline, arginine, or lysine residues. *Carboxypeptidase B,* a distinct enzyme, does liberate carboxyl-terminal basic amino acid residues.

When a protein consists of several peptide chains, the use of carboxypeptidases may yield equivocal results since there is no way of ascertaining whether the residues have been released by successive attack on one chain or simultaneous hydrolysis of more than one chain. In these instances, other information concerning the number of chains is needed to aid in interpreting the results.

DETERMINATION OF AMINO ACID SEQUENCE

Let us assume that we wish to determine the sequence of a protein consisting of a single peptide chain, whose molecular weight and amino acid composition are known, and whose sequence is as follows:

$$\text{H}_2\text{N}—A\cdot B\cdot C\cdot D\cdot E\cdot F\cdot \cdots T\cdot U\cdot V\cdot X\cdot Y\cdot Z—\text{COOH}$$

By the use of end group methods, the amino- and carboxyl-terminal residues, A and Z, respectively, have already been identified. Indeed, perhaps even the amino-terminal sequence, $A\cdot B\cdot C$, has been ascertained by the use of the stepwise Edman procedure and the sequence $X\cdot Y\cdot Z$ has been identified by the use of carboxypeptidases. The problem is now to elucidate the remainder of the sequence of the protein. The general method for accomplishing this is as follows: (1) partial hydrolysis of the protein, (2) isolation in pure form of the resulting peptides, (3) determination of the sequences of the smaller peptides, and finally, (4) the deduction of the complete sequence from the sequences of peptides of overlapping structures.

Partial Hydrolysis. Two general methods of partial hydrolysis of polypeptides and proteins are in use: (1) partial acidic hydrolysis, and (2) hydrolysis catalyzed by proteolytic enzymes.

Partial Acidic Hydrolysis. A partial cleavage of a polypeptide or protein can be obtained by limiting the time of hydrolysis, lowering the temperature, working with dilute acid or $12N$ HCl, the actions of which are slower than that of $6N$ HCl. These procedures yield a mixture of free amino acids and a large variety of small peptides. The technique is useful with smaller peptides but is seldom employed with larger peptides or proteins because of several inherent disadvantages as compared to the hydrolysis with enzymes (see below). These limitations are as follows: (1) the yield of peptides is low, (2) hydrolysis is essentially random, resulting in a mixture of many components that are difficult to isolate in pure form, and (3) larger peptides are seldom obtained in significant yield. To illustrate the problems, we may use as an example a tetrapeptide with the sequence $A \cdot B \cdot C \cdot D$. A partial acidic hydrolysate will yield the four amino acids as well as three dipeptides and two tripeptides, or nine components in all, excluding the original peptide. In contrast, it is frequently possible to hydrolyze a tetrapeptide with an enzyme, obtaining a theoretical yield of the dipeptides $A \cdot B$ and $C \cdot D$. Thus, only two components need be separated.

Action of Proteolytic Enzymes. The action of these enzymes produces only a limited cleavage, producing relatively large fragments in good yield. Since each peptide must be isolated in pure form, usually by chromatographic and ionophoretic methods, the smaller the number of fragments, the simpler is the problem of purification.

Each proteolytic enzyme will hydrolyze only certain types of peptide bonds. For example, crystalline trypsin catalyzes the hydrolysis of peptide bonds in which the carboxyl group of lysine or arginine residues participates. Thus, from a knowledge of the contents of these two amino acids in a given protein or polypeptide, the number of bonds susceptible to trypsin may be calculated. Each peptide resulting from tryptic action, with the possible exception of the original carboxyl-terminal one, should terminate in an arginine or lysine residue. For example, a protein containing 5 arginine and 10 lysine residues should yield, after tryptic hydrolysis, 16 peptides. If one of these lacks a basic residue, it will represent the carboxyl-terminal sequence of the protein.

Other proteinases, e.g., chymotrypsin, pepsin, papain, etc., can hydrolyze proteins or peptides at other loci in the peptide chain. The specificity of certain proteolytic enzymes, which are available in pure form and which are particularly useful for structural work on proteins, is indicated in Table 9.4.

The action of certain proteolytic enzymes on the oxidized B chain of bovine insulin is shown in Fig. 9.1. It is evident that the sites of action of the three enzymes are limited and relatively specific when compared with the random hydrolysis effected by acid.

For the complete sequence determination of a protein, at least two different forms of enzymic hydrolysis must be used in order to deduce the structure by the method of overlapping sequences. A hypothetical case is illustrated below in which the points of hydrolysis by trypsin are shown by the arrows, yielding peptides I through VI.

Table 9.4: SPECIFICITY OF SOME PROTEOLYTIC ENZYMES

Proteolytic enzyme	Source	Major sites of action*	Other sites of action
Trypsin.............	Pancreas	Arg, Lys	
Chymotrypsin........	Pancreas	Try, Phe, Tyr	Leu, Met, AspNH$_2$, His
Pepsin..............	Gastric mucosa	Try, Phe, Tyr, Met, Leu	Various; acidic, etc.
Carboxypeptidase A..	Pancreas	C-terminal bond of Tyr, Try, Phe, etc.	Does not act at Arg, Lys, Pro
Carboxypeptidase B...	Pancreas	Arg, Lys	None
Leucine aminopeptidase	Kidney, intestinal mucosa, etc.	N-terminal bond of various residues	Acts poorly at X-Pro bond†
Papain..............	Papaya	Arg, Lys, Gly, etc.	Wide specificity; does not act at acidic residues
Subtilisin...........	*Bacillus subtilis*	Neutral and acidic residues	
Elastase.............	Pancreas	Neutral residues	

* Except for the carboxypeptidases, the sites of action refer to the residues bearing the carbonyl group of the peptide bond, *e.g.*, trypsin catalyzed hydrolysis of arginyl and lysyl bonds.

† X = any other amino acid residue.

$$\text{H}_2\text{N}—A\cdot B\cdot C\cdot D\cdot E\cdot F\cdot G\cdot \cdots\cdots\cdots\cdots\cdots\cdots T\cdot U\cdot V\cdot W\cdot X\cdot Y\cdot Z—\text{COOH}$$

$$\begin{array}{ccccccc} & \uparrow & & \uparrow & \uparrow & \uparrow & \uparrow \\ & \text{I} & & \text{II} & \text{III} & \text{IV} & \text{V} & \text{VI} \end{array}$$

Peptides I and VI can be tentatively assigned positions if the amino- and carboxyl-terminal sequences are known. There is no way of positioning peptides II, III, IV, and V. If, however, hydrolysis of the protein is accomplished by chymotrypsin, a different series of peptides will be obtained since the action of this enzyme is mainly at aromatic amino acid residues (Table 9.4). Suppose a peptide is obtained having the sequence $C\cdot D\cdot E\cdot F\cdot G\cdot$, etc. It will overlap with the sequence of peptide I and peptide II, thus establishing this overlap. In similar fashion, the entire sequence can be deduced.

For small individual peptides, the sequence can be determined with the enzymic amino- and carboxyl-terminal methods, and with the stepwise phenylthiohydantoin method. For larger peptides, it may be necessary to hydrolyze first with other proteolytic enzymes. Thus a peptide is obtained from a tryptic digest, with the sequence $A\cdot B\cdot C\cdot\text{Tyr}\cdot E\cdot F\cdot G\cdot H\cdot\text{Lys}\cdot$, where A,B,C,E,F,G, and H are aliphatic residues of the type of glycine, alanine, serine, etc. Chymotrypsin can be used for hydrolysis at the tyrosine residue, liberating $A\cdot B\cdot C\cdot\text{Tyr}\cdot$ and $E\cdot F\cdot G\cdot H\cdot\text{Lys}\cdot$. Since the positioning of the two peptides relative to each other is already established, the one containing tyrosine being amino-terminal and the one containing lysine being carboxyl-terminal, further sequence work is relatively straightforward.

The Structure of Insulin. The work of Sanger and his associates on insulin was an important achievement because it was the first instance in which the structure of a protein was completely established. We shall consider briefly how this was accomplished since it illustrates the use of some of the methods described above as well as others.

Bovine insulin contains 51 amino acid residues (Table 9.2, page 145) and

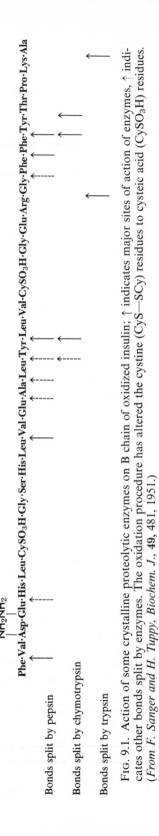

Fig. 9.1. Action of some crystalline proteolytic enzymes on B chain of oxidized insulin; ↑ indicates major sites of action of enzymes, ⫶ indicates other bonds split by enzymes. The oxidation procedure has altered the cystine (CyS—SCy) residues to cysteic acid (CySO₃H) residues. (*From F. Sanger and H. Tuppy, Biochem. J., 49, 481, 1951.*)

yields one amino-terminal glycine residue and one amino-terminal phenylalanine residue (Table 9.3, page 146). Therefore, insulin has at least two peptide chains which must be held together by other linkages; these are the S—S bonds of cystine. Oxidation of insulin with performic acid cleaved the S—S linkages and yielded a cysteic acid residue, $HO_3S—CH_2—CH(NH—)CO—$, in place of each half-cystine residue. This procedure produced two peptides which were separated electrophoretically. One was a peptide (B chain) possessing amino-terminal phenylalanine, and proved, on analysis, to contain 30 residues; the other, an acidic peptide (A chain) with amino-terminal glycine, contained 21 residues. Each chain was then studied separately.

From partial acidic hydrolysates of the DNP (page 146) derivative of the A peptide, Sanger isolated DNP glycine, DNP glycylisoleucine, DNP glycylisoleucylvaline, and DNP glycylisoleucylvalylglutamic acid. From this evidence, the A peptide chain has the initial sequence, glycylisoleucylvalylglutamyl $\cdots$. For the B chain, the initial sequence, derived by the same method, is phenylalanylvalylaspartylglutamyl $\cdots$. Thus, this approach succeeded in identifying a portion of the peptide structure of each chain of insulin.

With each chain, partial hydrolysates were then prepared, by both acidic and enzymic hydrolysis. The smaller peptides were separated by chromatographic procedures on columns and on paper, and by electrophoresis, and the structures were identified with the aid of the DNP method. Overlapping sequences were fitted together in the manner of a jigsaw puzzle.

As an example of how overlapping sequences were fitted together, the following di-, tri-, and tetrapeptides from partial acidic hydrolysates permitted deduction of a nonapeptide sequence in the A chain of insulin, with the information that only two tyrosine residues are present in this chain.

$$
\begin{array}{lll}
\text{Ser·Leu} & \text{Glu·Leu} & \text{Asp·Tyr} \\
\quad\text{Leu·Tyr} & \text{Leu·Glu} & \text{Tyr·CySO}_3\text{H} \\
\quad\quad\text{Tyr·Glu} & \text{Glu·Asp} & \\
\text{Ser·Leu·Tyr} & \text{Leu·Glu·Asp} & \\
\quad\text{Leu·Tyr·Glu} & \text{Glu·Asp·Tyr} & \\
\quad\quad\text{Glu·Leu·Glu} & & \\
\text{Ser·Leu·Tyr·Glu} & \text{Glu·Asp·Tyr·CySO}_3\text{H} &
\end{array}
$$

Sequence: Ser·Leu·Tyr·Glu·Leu·Glu·Asp·Tyr·CySO$_3$H

From such studies, the linear sequence of each oxidized chain, A and B, was established. However, the oxidized A chain contained four cysteic acid residues, and the B chain two cysteic acid residues, all present in native insulin in the form of half-cystine residues, cysteine being absent from this protein.

The arrangement of the two chains was established by digesting intact insulin with chymotrypsin and by partial acidic hydrolysis. Since the sequences of both chains were already known, it was necessary only to isolate peptides containing cystine which bridged the various half-cystine residues. It should be emphasized that methods must be used that preclude disulfide interchange, as in the following reversible reaction, resulting in a completely random distribution of disulfides.

$$R_1—S—S—R_2 + R_3—S—S—R_4 \xrightarrow[\text{alkaline pH}]{\text{strong acid or}} R_1—S—S—R_3 + R_2—S—S—R_4 + \text{etc.}$$

Since this occurs in strong acid as well as in neutral or alkaline solutions, the reaction must be inhibited to permit unequivocal identification of disulfide bridges. The complete structure of bovine insulin is shown in Fig. 9.2.

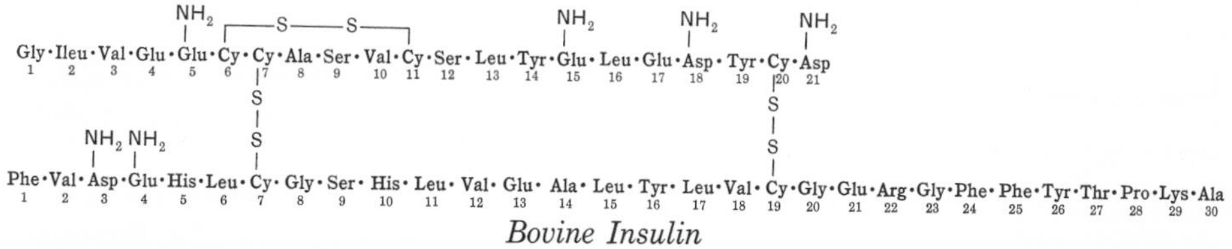

Bovine Insulin

FIG. 9.2. The structure of bovine insulin. The abbreviations used for the amino acid residues are given in Table 7.6. The NH_2 groups indicate the β- and γ-carboxamide groups of asparagine and glutamine, respectively. The presence of the internal disulfide bridge in the glycyl (A) chain of insulin between residues 6 and 11 is noteworthy. It should be noted that the standard convention is followed in which the amino-terminal residues are at the left of each chain.

Some Comments on Primary Structure. Since the elucidation of the complete structure of insulin in 1955, the structures of several other mammalian proteins have been established, *e.g.*, cytochrome c (page 200), hemoglobin (page 195), and ribonuclease (page 251), and the partial structures of others have been reported. Certain features of protein structure that have emerged from these studies should be emphasized, although some of these points have been mentioned earlier.

1. There is no apparent regularity or periodicity in the sequences established thus far. Each homogeneous protein is relatively unique and possesses a specific amino acid sequence; however, homologous proteins of different species do resemble one another (Chap. 31).

2. With respect to the presence and arrangement of disulfide bridges, all possible types of proteins have been found. Insulin contains an intrachain disulfide bridge (A chain) as well as two interchain disulfide bridges. There are other proteins with intrachain disulfide bridges (ribonuclease, page 251) and proteins lacking disulfide bridges—hemoglobin (page 195) and cytochrome c (page 200).

3. The distribution of glutamine and asparagine is independent of their relationship to glutamic and aspartic acids, respectively, and they must be regarded as individual amino acids.

4. Only amino acids of the L configuration, with the exception of the optically inactive glycine, have been found.

5. No covalent bonds between amino acids have been detected other than the α-peptide bond and the disulfide bridge. Thus, despite the wide range of composition, size, function, and other properties, the fundamental structure of the globular proteins follows the same relatively simple pattern.

THE CONFORMATION OF PROTEINS

The Hydrogen Bond. In 1936 Mirsky and Pauling suggested that a major factor in maintaining the folded structure of the peptide chain is the presence of hydrogen bonds. The formation of a hydrogen bond is due to the tendency of a hydrogen atom to share the electrons of an oxygen atom. For example, the carbonyl oxygen of one peptide bond shares its electrons with the hydrogen atom of another peptide bond.

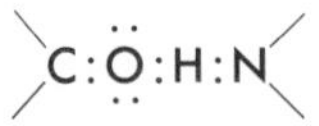

$$\diagup C:\overset{..}{\underset{..}{O}}:H:N\diagdown$$

Although individual hydrogen bonds of this type are relatively weak as compared with covalent bonds, they will reinforce each other if a molecule contains many such bonds.

Direct evidence for the presence of hydrogen bonds in proteins has come from the use of infrared spectroscopy. Strong absorption bands are found at the wavelengths characteristic of such hydrogen bonds.

Another type of evidence that indicates the existence of hydrogen bonds in proteins has been provided by Linderstrøm-Lang and his associates. When a substance is dissolved in a medium containing deuterium oxide (heavy water), an exchange takes place between dissociable hydrogens of the compound and the deuterium of the medium. Ionizable hydrogens and those present in peptide bonds (—CONH—), hydroxyl groups, and amide groups (—CONH$_2$) should be readily exchangeable, whereas carbon-bound hydrogens are not. In the small peptide, leucylglycylglycylglycine, there are six exchangeable hydrogen atoms, viz., three ammonium and three peptide hydrogens, which equilibrate rapidly with hydrogen from the medium. Similarly, in the oxidized A chain of insulin, the 41 exchangeable hydrogens equilibrate very rapidly. In contrast, native insulin contains 91 potentially exchangeable hydrogen atoms. However, only about two-thirds of these atoms exchange very rapidly; the others exchange more slowly, the rate of exchange being increased by raising the temperature from 0 to 38°C. or by adding urea or guanidine at 0°. These results are consistent with the view that the action of urea causes an unfolding of the structure of proteins and that hydrogen bonding may play a major role in maintaining this structure.

Pauling and Corey have proposed several structures for polypeptide chains in which maximal stability can be attained by extensive hydrogen bond formation when the known properties of peptide structures are taken into consideration. Since the C—N peptide bond is a partial double bond, the peptide bond group is planar and able to exist in cis and trans forms. The trans configuration (shown below) is preferred in most of the suggested structures of proteins since there is less steric hindrance from large R groups than in the cis form.

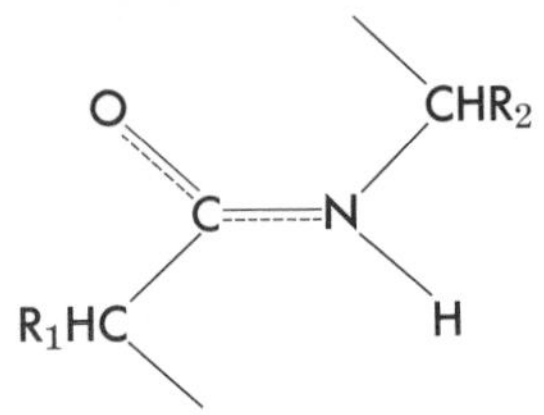

$$\underset{R_1HC\diagdown}{\overset{O\diagdown}{}}C\!=\!\!=\!\!N\overset{\diagup CHR_2}{\underset{\diagdown H}{}}$$

The most important of the regular structures proposed for proteins is the α-helix, in which 3.7 amino acid residues are present in each complete coil and the shape is maintained by hydrogen bonding between the CO and NH groups of adjacent coils. The right-handed helix is favored for L amino acids (Fig. 9.3). Direct evidence for the existence of the α-helix in proteins has come from x-ray diffraction studies, discussed below (page 157).

The Ionic Bond. The interaction of two ions leads to attraction or repulsion, depending on the charge of the ions. For a positive group, such as a substituted ammonium ion of lysine residues, and a negative group, such as a carboxylate ion, the attraction can become strong if these groups can come into juxtaposition. Similarly, the repulsive forces can be high for ionic groups possessing a similar charge.

Ionic bonds of the type between COO^- and ^+H_3NR are presumably stable only in the absence of water, inasmuch as both types of ion are strongly hydrated in the presence of water. In hydrophobic portions of protein molecules (see below), such ionic bonds would be stable and could contribute to the over-all stabilization of the native protein structure.

The Hydrophobic Bond. The side chains or R groups of alanine, valine, leucine, isoleucine, phenylalanine, tyrosine, methionine, and tryptophan are essentially

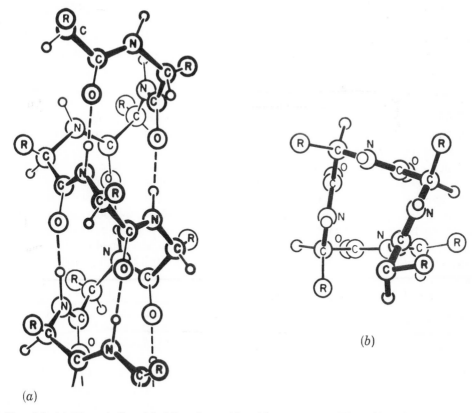

(a)

(b)

Fig. 9.3. (a) The α-helix with 3.7 amino acid residues per turn. The NH and CO of each peptide bond are linked by hydrogen bonds. (b) A cross section of the α-helix. (*From L. Pauling, R. B. Corey, and H. R. Branson, Proc. Nat. Acad. Sci.,* **37,** 205, 1951.)

hydrophobic, *i.e.*, they have little attraction for water molecules, as compared with the strong hydrogen bonding between water molecules. Such R groups can unite with each other, with exclusion of water, to form links of different parts of a peptide chain or to unite different chains. When large regions of peptide chains involve only hydrophobic residues, the exclusion of water will result in a very tightly bonded structure. The forces involved are similar to those involved in the coalescence of oil droplets suspended in water.

The formation of hydrophobic bonds in proteins also serves to bring together groups that can form hydrogen bonds or ionic bonds in the absence of water. Thus, there is a cooperative aspect to the proper folding of the peptide chain in the formation of the native globular protein. Each of the types of bonding aids in the formation of the others, with the hydrophobic bonds presumably playing a major part in this phenomenon. Hydrophobic bonds also play an important role in other protein interactions, *e.g.*, the formation of enzyme-substrate complexes (Chap. 14) and antibody-antigen interactions (Chap. 32).

Optical Rotation of Proteins. All protein solutions change the direction of the polarization of polarized light that passes through them. This is partly because of the presence of optically active amino acid residues present in these molecules. From our knowledge of small molecules, it is evident that the sign and magnitude of the optical rotation depend not only on the atoms and groups of atoms bonded to asymmetric carbon atoms but also on the relationships of the asymmetric carbons to one another. Thus any changes in the structure or conformation of the protein molecule will be reflected in the specific rotation (page 8).

The specific rotations of proteins are always negative and for globular proteins are usually in the range of -30 to $-60°$. For example, the specific rotation $[\alpha]_D$ for ovalbumin is near $-30°$ over the pH range 3.5 to 11, although the net charge per molecule changes from approximately $+20$ to -30. Clearly, the ionic state of the molecule has little or no effect on the rotation.

However, at higher or lower pH values the rotation becomes more negative, *e.g.*, at pH 13, $[\alpha]_D$ is near $-60°$. Similarly, in $8M$ urea solution, $[\alpha]_D = -88°$. Treatment of proteins at high temperatures produces similar increases in negative rotation. Inasmuch as these large increases in negative rotation are not accompanied by changes in primary structure, *i.e.*, rupture of peptide bonds, they must reflect drastic alterations in the conformation of the molecule, dependent upon those properties that are ascribed to secondary or tertiary structure. Such changes are generally described under the term "denaturation" (page 137).

It should be noted that the term "configuration" usually refers to the D and L forms in which four different groups are attached to a carbon atom. "Conformation" is used in protein chemistry to designate the over-all structure of a molecule in which asymmetry may be produced by a spiral arrangement (helix) or other special folding (see also page 154).

The nature of the changes responsible for the increased levorotation of proteins upon denaturation has been actively investigated. Doty and coworkers have studied model synthetic polypeptides. When such compounds in their α-helical form are transformed into a random coil arrangement they become more levorotatory. This has provided some evidence for the presence of helical arrangements in globular proteins.

Optical rotatory dispersion, i.e., the variation of optical rotation with the wavelength of monochromatic light, has provided some additional information concerning the structure of proteins. For synthetic polypeptides, such as poly-L-glutamic acid, the dispersion curves differ for the random-coil form and the helical form. Differences in dispersion curves are also found for native and denatured proteins. Various theoretical and empirical formulas have been applied to such data in attempts to calculate the amount of α-helix in proteins. For the present, it may be stated that such methods do not give absolute values; however, they do show that globular proteins vary in helical content, some containing perhaps as low as 10 to 20 per cent and others perhaps as high as 80 to 90 per cent of the amino acid residues in this form. Such methods are useful in following changes in conformation, but absolute determinations of conformation and helical content can be made at present only by the method of x-ray diffraction.

X-ray Analysis of Protein Structure. In crystals there is a regular three-dimensional lattice of unit cells, each unit cell having the same relationship to its neighbors and the contents of each cell being the same. The unit cell may be composed of one or a few atoms or molecules. In simple molecules composed of only a few atoms, much of the chemical behavior can be explained without taking into account exact dimensions and geometrical relationships. For complex molecules, particularly those as large and diverse as proteins, such relationships become of critical importance. At present, the only method available to obtain this information is the technique of x-ray analysis.

X-rays have very short wavelengths of the order of interatomic distances, *e.g.*, the x-ray beam of 1.542 Å., produced by electron bombardment of copper, is used for much of the work on protein structure. When x-rays strike an atom, they are diffracted (reflected) in proportion to the number of extranuclear electrons in the atom. Thus, heavier atoms, those of higher atomic number, produce more diffraction than lighter ones. The crystal may be regarded as a three-dimensional pattern of electron density, which has high values near the centers of atoms and low or zero values in between.

Figure 9.4 shows a typical roentgenogram of a single protein crystal. The spots form a regular two-dimensional lattice and, clearly, there is a marked symmetry in the pattern of spots in the four quarters of the photograph. Such a photograph has been obtained by mounting a small crystal in a known orientation in the path of a fine beam of monochromatic x-rays. The x-rays, scattered by the crystal, impinge on a photographic plate mounted behind the crystal. The picture in Fig. 9.4 is a two-dimensional lattice, since the photograph has been taken in a single plane, whereas the crystal is three-dimensional. From a series of electron-density photographs in different planes, the three dimensions of simple molecules can be constructed.

Such x-ray diffraction pictures permit measurement of the intensities (amplitudes) but not of the phases of the diffracted x-rays. There are several methods of attempting to determine the phases. The most important in the study of protein crystals is the technique of *isomorphous replacement*. This requires obtaining protein crystals that are identical except for the introduction of a heavy atom in the structure, for instance, replacing a hydrogen by a mercury atom. The diffraction patterns of the two crystals are similar except for the small changes in the intensi-

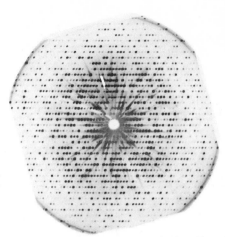

Fɪɢ. 9.4. A roentgenogram of crystalline whale myoglobin. The spots form a regular two-dimensional lattice in symmetry. Only a portion of the complete pattern is shown. (*Courtesy of Dr. John C. Kendrew.*)

ties of the diffracted rays that are caused by the different scattering power of the two atoms. These changes permit determination of the location of the heavy atom and then the calculation of approximate phase angles. This technique, introduced by Perutz for the study of hemoglobin, has been successfully applied in protein structure studies.

By measurement of a series of plates, such as shown in Fig. 9.4, with respect to both distance and intensity of the spots, it is possible to prepare by calculation electron-density maps which, at a relatively gross level, indicate the general conformation of a molecule and, at a highly refined level, may permit the assignment in space of each of the heavier atoms of a protein molecule. The most successful of these studies has been that on the structure of whale myoglobin by Kendrew and his associates.

Figure 9.5 shows the structure of a model of myoglobin. The tubes, shown at the left, are hollow, and the walls follow a spiral path which has the exact dimensions of the Pauling-Corey α-helix. The helical regions are shown at the right as double lines; the nonhelical corners or bends, as single lines. At presently available levels of resolution (2 Å.), it is possible to identify certain groups which are large and characteristic, such as the indole group and the imidazole group.

The information gleaned from the study of the myoglobin molecule has permitted for the first time direct verification of many of the major deductions concerning the general structure of globular proteins, as well as a precise picture of myoglobin itself. First, it is evident that the right-handed α-helix is a major feature of the secondary structure involving more than two-thirds of the 153 residues in myoglobin. Secondly, the remaining third of the residues are distributed over nonhelical regions with no regular pattern apparent. Proline residues do not fit an α-helix because the δ-carbon atom of the pyrrolidine ring occupies the position of the peptide (amide) hydrogen which for other amino acids functions to bond with the carbonyl in the next coil of the helix. The four proline residues of whale myoglobin are present in nonhelical regions; however, there are several such regions without

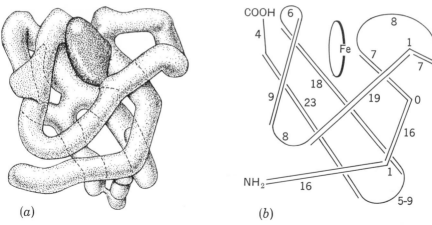

FIG. 9.5. The structure of whale myoglobin as deduced from x-ray crystallography. (*a*) The general conformation of the molecule. The plane of the heme group is not correct in this diagram. (*b*) A schematic representation of the molecule showing the numbers of amino acids in each of the α-helical segments (double lines) and the corners (single lines). (*Courtesy of Dr. John C. Kendrew.*)

proline. These nonhelical regions are stabilized by various types of interactions: hydrogen bonding involving the hydroxyl group of threonine, hydrophobic bonding between two parallel aromatic rings, etc. It may be noted that myoglobin is devoid of cysteine and cystine. The disulfide bonds of cystine contribute to the over-all conformation and stability of proteins containing such bonds.

Denaturation and Enzymic Activity. Study of the phenomenon of protein denaturation has contributed in many important ways to our understanding of protein structure. A few important examples of such studies will be cited.

Some of the physical and chemical agents that may denature proteins have already been mentioned (page 137). Changes in the reactivity of amino acid side chains in proteins may occur on denaturation; these alterations assist in assigning the role of such groups in maintaining native protein structure. An excellent example is the role of phenolic side chains of tyrosine residues. The titration of phenolic groups may be measured spectrophotometrically since there is a large shift in the ultraviolet absorption accompanying the change from the undissociated group to the phenolate ion. Ionization of phenolic groups should be complete near pH 12.0. However, in many proteins only a portion of such groups is instantaneously titrated. Heating, treatment with $6M$ urea, or bringing the protein solution to pH 13 or 14 may be required to titrate all phenolic groups. This has been interpreted as indicating that such groups are unavailable because they reside in a hydrophobic environment or because they are hydrogen-bonded to carboxylate ions, $-R-C_6H_4OH \cdots {}^-OOCR-$, or to both factors.

Similarly, a portion of other groups—imidazole, thiol, carboxyl, ε-amino, etc. —in certain native proteins is unavailable for titration. Evidently, the over-all conformation of a native protein, as indicated by the direct evidence for myoglobin and by much indirect evidence for other proteins, involves all the secondary forces discussed above—hydrophobic, ionic, and hydrogen bonding. This is also indicated by the types of agents that produce denaturation, which may now be defined as representing an alteration in the conformation of the protein. Hydrogen-bonding agents in high concentration—urea, guanidine salts, formamide, etc.—compete with the hydrogen bonds in the native protein and produce an unfolding. High concentrations of H^+ ion (pH 1 to 2) or OH^- ion (pH 12 to 14) disrupt ionic bonds. Agents, such as trichloroacetate ion, which bind strongly with cationic groups, also disrupt ionic bonds. Hydrophobic bonds are broken in the presence of detergents, agents which are water-soluble but which possess large hydrophobic groups, *e.g.*, dodecyl sulfonate, bile salts (page 86), etc.

All enzymically active proteins lose their catalytic activity on denaturation. This in itself suggests that the activity of such molecules is determined by the juxtaposition or interaction of amino acid side chains present in the native conformation and destroyed by denaturation. It has long been known that denaturation is in some cases a reversible phenomenon, indicating that the native form is, under proper conditions, a highly stable one, produced by specific interactions. Indeed, present views and understanding of protein biosynthesis (Chap. 31) suggest that protein structure is determined genetically by the synthesis of the linear polypeptide chain or chains and that the specific conformation is attained spontaneously. Another way of stating this is that under specific conditions of pH, ionic strength, temperature, etc., the native conformation is the most stable one.

The enzyme ribonuclease whose sequence is shown in Fig. 14.2 (page 251) contains four disulfide bridges. Reduction of these bonds, in the presence of $8M$ urea, produces a total loss of activity. After the urea has been removed by dialysis or other means, the enzyme remains inactive; however, reoxidation in air at neutral pH forms the original disulfide bonds, resulting in essentially complete regeneration of enzymic activity. Clearly, the over-all conformation is produced spontaneously, the correct disulfide bond formation occurring because the half-cystine residues are in proper juxtaposition within the single peptide chain of the molecule.

Hemoglobin lacks disulfide bonds and contains four peptide chains, two α and two β (pages 194*ff.*), each chain associated with a heme group (Chap. 11). At acid pH values in acetone, the heme is separated from the denatured globin. Nevertheless, at neutral pH values, native hemoglobin will be reformed from heme and globin. Thus, native conformation is reattained even in this complex molecule with four peptide chains, each with its heme group in the proper position. It can only be concluded that the secondary and tertiary structures are determined by the specific amino acid sequences of the linear polypeptide chains.

Other large proteins, including many enzymes, are dissociated into inactive subunits by various agents. Thus, although the active protein unit may be very large, of the order of several hundred thousand to millions in molecular weight, the primary peptide chains are relatively small. The forces involved in forming the active proteins by an aggregation of smaller units are the same as those involved in folding the individual peptide chain into its proper conformation.

Primary Structure and Biological Activity. Because proteolytic enzymes can cleave peptide bonds in a specific manner, they are used as reagents to degrade biologically active polypeptides and proteins in attempts to ascertain the parts of the molecule that are essential for activity. Among the first successful studies of this type was the demonstration that certain proteinases could hydrolyze specific antibodies to smaller molecules without loss of their antibody properties (Chap. 32).

By the same approach, studies have been made on a number of hormones. Carboxypeptidase can remove C-terminal alanine from the B chain of insulin without impairing the hormonal activity of this substance. Thus, the biological activity must reside elsewhere in the insulin molecule. A further example is the action of pepsin on adrenocorticotropic hormone (ACTH; see Chap. 51); a portion of the carboxyl-terminal end of the molecule can be removed without destroying the hormonal activity. In contrast to this, removal of a few residues from the amino-terminal end of the molecule by leucine aminopeptidase destroys the hormonal activity. Other examples of such studies are mentioned in Part Six.

Some enzymes can be degraded to smaller molecules without loss of activity. When pepsin is allowed to undergo autolysis (autodigestion), active fragments are produced that are small enough to dialyze through semipermeable membranes. Inasmuch as pepsin has a molecular weight of 34,000 and dialysis membranes generally allow passage only of molecules of about 10,000 or less, the degree of degradation is extensive. Another example is provided in the action of leucine aminopeptidase on the inactive mercury complex of papain. The aminopeptidase can liberate approximately two-thirds of the residues of papain, as free amino acids, by sequential hydrolysis from the amino-terminal end of the molecule. On removal of mercury, the fragment of the papain molecule retains the activity and specificity of the original molecule. In addition to the above two examples of extensive breakdown, other studies, particularly with carboxypeptidase, have shown that various enzymes, including ribonuclease and lysozyme, are unaffected by removal of one or a few residues from the carboxyl-terminal end of the molecules.

REFERENCES

Books

Anfinsen, C. B., Jr., Anson, M. L., Bailey, K., and Edsall, J. T., eds., "Advances in Protein Chemistry," Academic Press, Inc., New York. (An annual series beginning with vol. I in 1944.)

Cohn, E. J., and Edsall, J. T., "Proteins, Amino Acids, and Peptides as Ions and Dipolar Ions," Reinhold Publishing Corporation, New York, 1942.

Neuberger, A., ed., "Symposium on Protein Structure," Methuen & Co., Ltd., London, 1958.

Neurath, H., ed., "The Proteins: Composition, Structure and Function," 2d ed., vol. I, 1963; vol. II, 1964, Academic Press, Inc., New York.

Springall, H. D., "The Structural Chemistry of Proteins," Academic Press, Inc., New York, 1954.

Svedberg, T., and Pedersen, K. O., "The Ultracentrifuge," Oxford University Press, New York, 1940.

Tanford, C., "Physical Chemistry of Macromolecules," John Wiley & Sons, Inc., New York, 1961.

10. Nucleic Acids and Nucleoproteins

Present understanding of the architecture and functions of cells and of the hereditary determinants of living organisms assigns primary roles to the nucleic acids. This chapter presents the chemistry of these complex molecules, as well as some of the evidence for their role in inheritance. This latter role is considered further, and the significance of nucleic acids in metabolism and in the biosynthesis of proteins is discussed, in Chaps. 29, 30, and 31. Although the name suggests location of nucleic acids in the nuclei of cells, certain nucleic acids are also present in cytoplasm. Nucleic acids may naturally occur bound to proteins; hence the term nucleoprotein.

COMPONENTS OF NUCLEIC ACIDS

Elementary Composition. Nucleic acids contain carbon, hydrogen, oxygen, nitrogen, and, most strikingly, phosphorus. In almost all nucleic acids, there are approximately 15 to 16 per cent nitrogen and 9 to 10 per cent phosphorus.

Hydrolysis Products. Complete acid hydrolysis of a nucleic acid yields a mixture of basic substances called *purines* and *pyrimidines,* a *pentose* or *deoxypentose* sugar component, and phosphoric acid. After partial hydrolysis of nucleic acids, *nucleotides* and *nucleosides* can be isolated. Each nucleoside consists of a base and a sugar component; the nucleotides yield on hydrolysis the same components and, in addition, phosphoric acid. The successive degradation of the nucleoproteins is indicated in Fig. 10.1. Each of the components of nucleoproteins will be discussed separately.

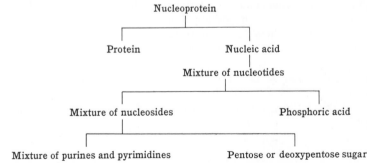

FIG. 10.1. Products arising in the successive hydrolytic degradation of nucleoproteins.

Pyrimidines. Substances of this type isolated from hydrolysates of nucleic acids are all derivatives of the parent heterocyclic compound *pyrimidine;* its structure and the convention of numbering the positions in the ring are indicated below. It may be noted that the numbering system now used for the pyrimidine ring is according to the International System, which replaces the traditional Fischer system, employed formerly. This point is made so that the student may not be confused, in referring to other sources of information on the pyrimidines, by the numbers assigned to substituents in the pyrimidine ring.

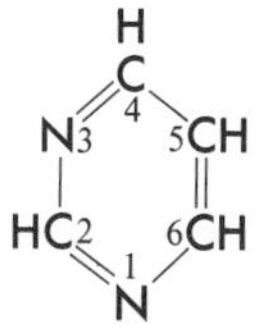

Pyrimidine

The prevalent pyrimidines found in nucleic acids are uracil, thymine, cytosine, and, of more limited distribution, 5-methylcytosine and 5-hydroxymethylcytosine (page 185). Pyrimidine itself has not been isolated from natural products.

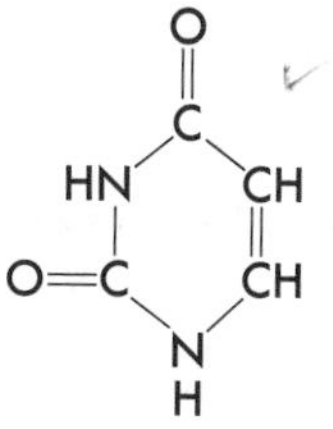

Uracil
(2,4-dioxypyrimidine)

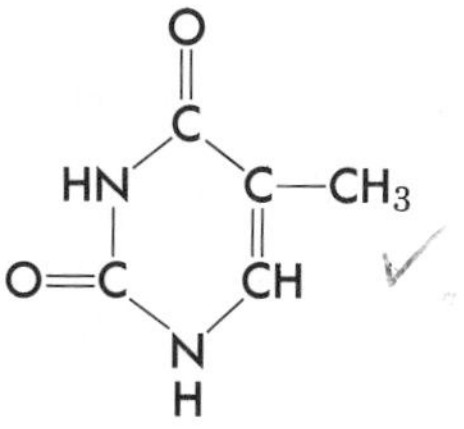

Thymine
(5-methyl-2,4-dioxypyrimidine)

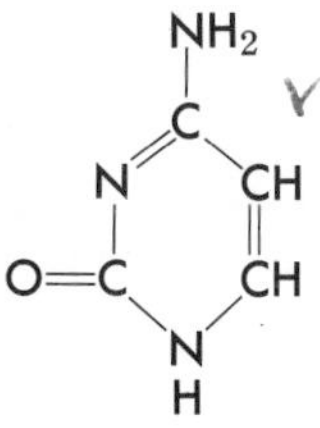

Cytosine
(2-oxy-4-aminopyrimidine)

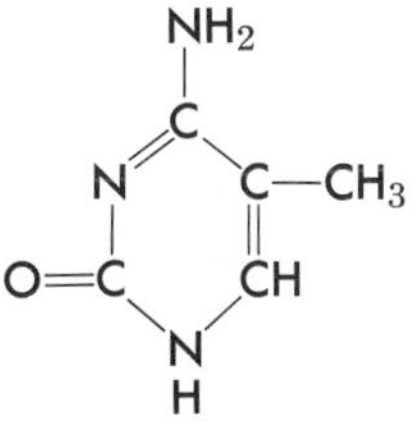

5-Methylcytosine
(5-methyl-2-oxy-4-aminopyrimidine)

The biological importance of pyrimidines is not restricted to nucleic acids. Several pyrimidine nucleotides play important roles in carbohydrate and lipid metabolism (Part Three). Vitamin B_1 (thiamine) is a pyrimidine derivative (Chap. 18). In recent years, certain synthetic pyrimidines have found important biological applications. Alloxan (2,4,5,6-tetraoxypyrimidine) produces experimental diabetes in animals (Chap. 21); this has proved fruitful in experimental investigations of this disease. Thiouracil and related compounds are employed for the treatment of hyperthyroidism (Chap. 46).

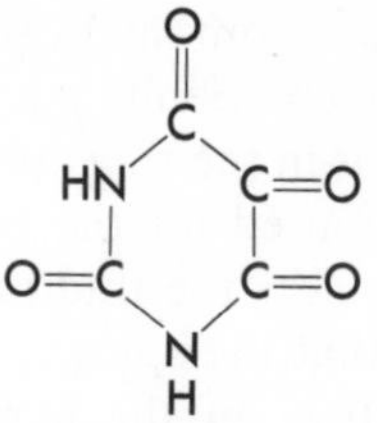

Alloxan

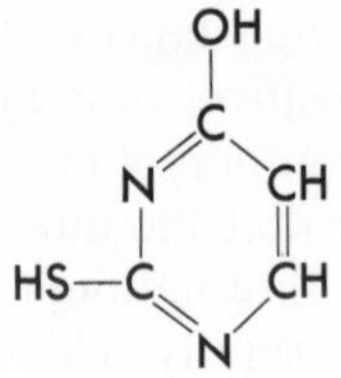

Thiouracil

The pyrimidines all show lactam-lactim tautomerism and may be written in either form illustrated for uracil. At neutral pH values, the lactam forms appear to predominate.

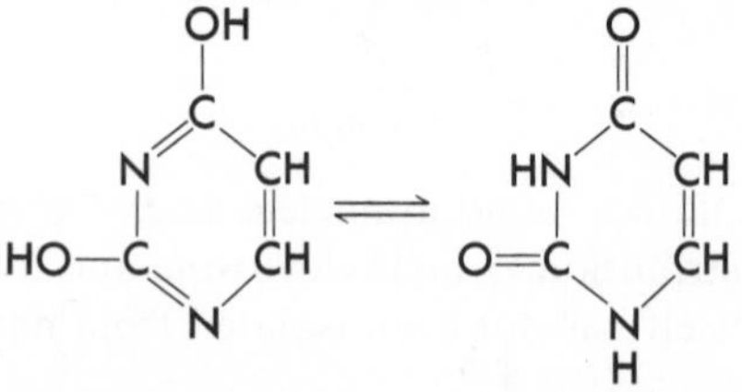

Lactim form of uracil　　　　**Lactam form of uracil**

Purines. The parent substance, purine, contains the six-membered pyrimidine ring fused to the five-membered imidazole ring. It should be recalled that the imidazole ring also occurs in the amino acid histidine.

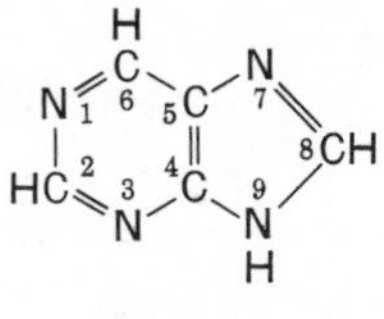

Purine

Adenine and guanine are the major purines that have been isolated from nucleic acids.

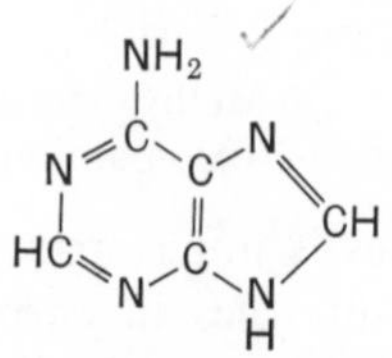

Adenine
(6-aminopurine)

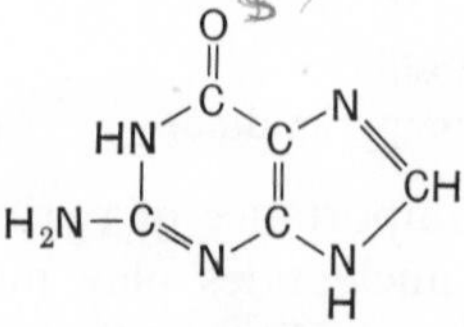

Guanine
(2-amino-6-oxypurine)

Of more limited distribution are various methylated derivatives of adenine and guanine (page 183).

A large number of other important purines occur in nature; these include hypoxanthine, xanthine, and uric acid.

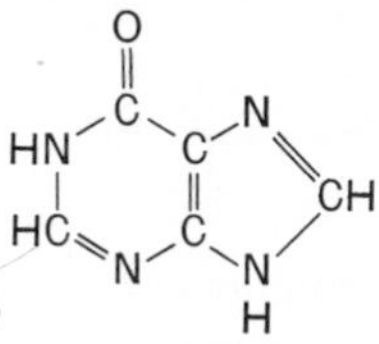

Hypoxanthine
(6-oxypurine)

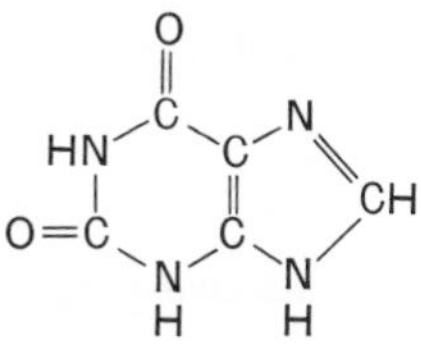

Xanthine
(2,6-dioxypurine)

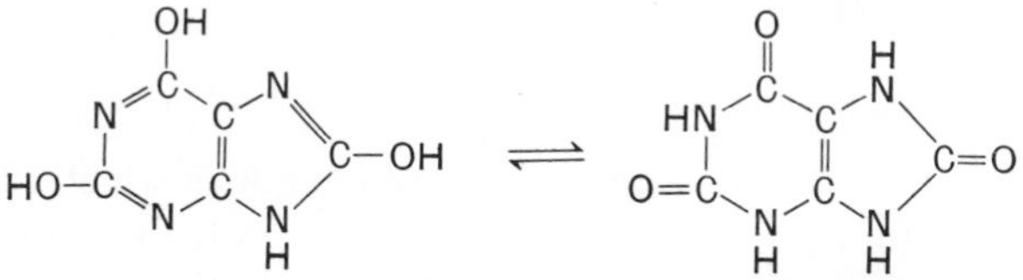

Uric acid (lactim form)

Uric acid (lactam form)
(2,6,8-trioxypurine)

Like the pyrimidines, purines show lactam-lactim tautomerism as illustrated above for uric acid. The lactim form of uric acid possesses weakly acidic properties ($pK' = 5.4, 10.3$) and forms salts such as mono- and disodium or potassium urates. Uric acid and its salts are sparingly soluble in water. This is reflected in the gradual precipitation of urates from urine that is allowed to stand (Chap. 37).

Caffeine (1,3,7-trimethylxanthine) is found in coffee, tea, and other plants; theobromine (3,7-dimethylxanthine) occurs in tea, cocoa, and chocolate. Other purines are also found in plants, and some of these, like caffeine and theobromine, have important pharmacological actions.

Sugars of the Nucleic Acids. The nucleic acids are classified into two large groups according to the type of sugar they contain. One type of nucleic acid yields the pentose, D-ribose; hence the name ribose nucleic acid, or ribonucleic acid, is applied to this class of substances. The abbreviated form RNA is commonly used. In nucleic acids, ribose occurs in the furanose form (page 18).

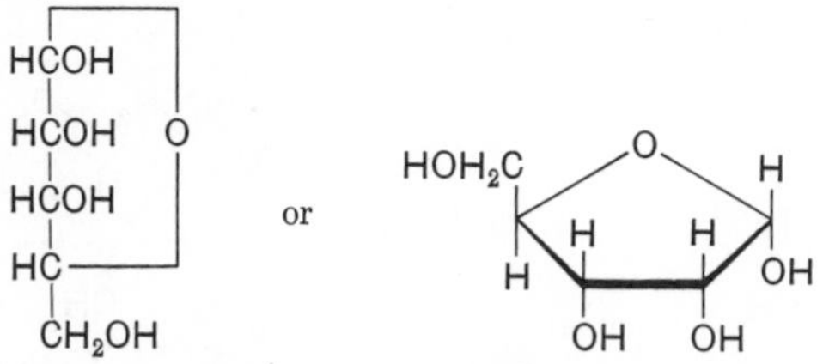

D-**Ribose** (α-D-ribofuranose)

The sugar in the other type of nucleic acid is D-2-deoxyribose; hence the name deoxyribose nucleic acid, or DNA.

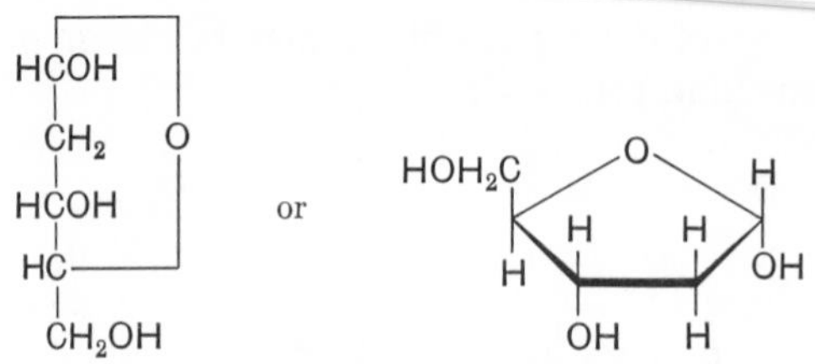

D-2-Deoxyribose (α-D-2-deoxyribofuranose)

Because of their presence in nucleic acids, both deoxyribose and ribose are universally present in animal and plant cells. Both sugars were unknown in nature until their isolation from nucleic acids, although Emil Fischer had prepared them synthetically much earlier.

NUCLEOSIDES

Partial hydrolysis of nucleic acids yields compounds in which ribose or deoxyribose is conjugated to a purine or pyrimidine base. Adenine linked to ribose is called adenosine, the guanine nucleoside is called guanosine, and, correspondingly, the pyrimidine nucleosides are cytidine and uridine. The analogous nucleosides formed with deoxyribose are called deoxyribonucleosides, as adenine deoxyribonucleoside or deoxyadenosine, deoxycytidine, etc. It should be noted, however, that the deoxyribonucleoside of thymine is called thymidine, not deoxythymidine, since this pyrimidine is primarily found in DNA. Thymine has also been found linked to ribose in a special type of RNA, so-called transfer RNA (page 182). In this specific instance, the name thymine ribonucleoside has been used. For the deoxyribonucleotide containing thymine as the base (see below), the name thymidylic acid generally suffices.

The purine nucleosides obtained from ribose nucleic acid have a β-glycosidic linkage from carbon-1 of the sugar to the nitrogen in position 9, as shown for adenosine. The pyrimidine nucleosides are N-1 glycosides, as shown for cytidine.

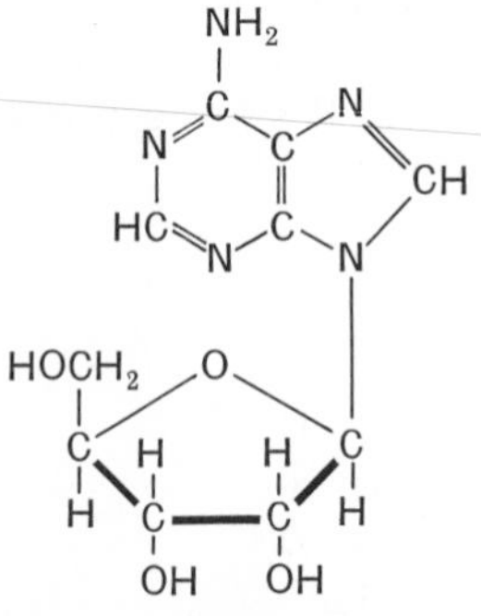

Adenosine
(9-β-D-ribofuranosyladenine)

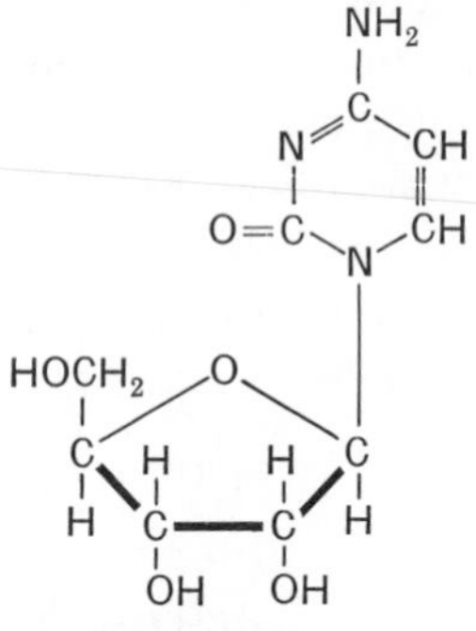

Cytidine
(1-β-D-ribofuranosylcytosine)

As in the case of O-glycosides, the nucleosides are stable in alkali. Purine nucleosides are readily hydrolyzed by acid whereas pyrimidine nucleosides hydrolyze only after relatively prolonged treatment with concentrated acid.

The nucleosides containing deoxyribose possess the same types of glycosidic linkages and are the 9-β-D-2'-deoxyribofuranosides of guanine and adenine and the 1-β-D-2'-deoxyribofuranosides of cytosine and thymine. It should be noted that in the nucleosides and their derivatives, the primed numbers refer to the positions in the sugar moiety.

From the mushroom *Agaricus nebularis,* a toxic, free nucleoside, named *nebularine,* has been identified as 9-β-D-ribofuranosylpurine. This is of some interest since it is the first reported biological occurrence of the purine nucleus substituted only in position 9; however, the free base, purine, has not been found in natural sources.

NUCLEOTIDES

These are phosphoric esters of the nucleosides and are strong acids. They are called adenylic acid, guanylic acid, thymidylic acid, cytidylic acid, and uridylic acid. The phosphate is always esterified to the sugar moiety.

For the nucleotides containing deoxyribose, phosphorylation of the sugar is possible only at C-3' and C-5', since C-1' and C-4' are involved in the furanose ring and C-2' does not bear a hydroxyl group. Both types of phosphate substitution have been found after appropriate conditions of hydrolysis of DNA. The structures of the two deoxyadenylic acids are shown.

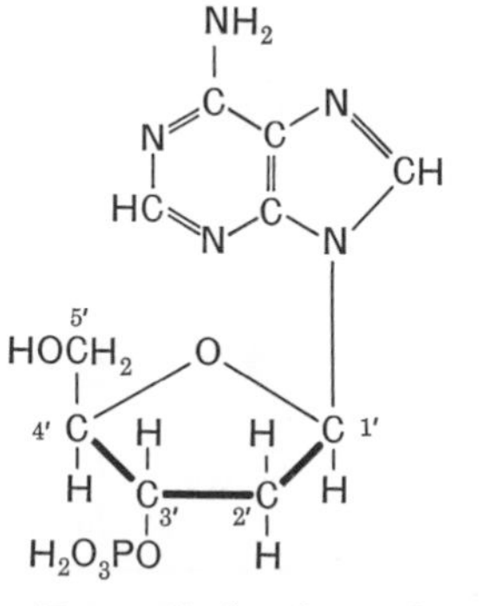

Deoxy-3'-adenylic acid
(deoxyadenosine 3'-phosphate)

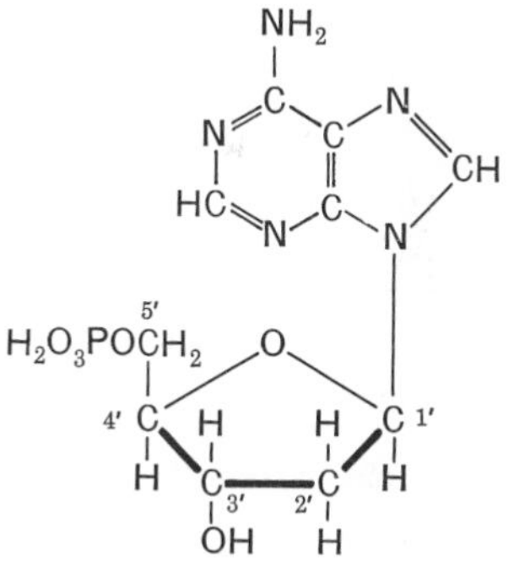

Deoxy-5'-adenylic acid
(deoxyadenosine 5'-phosphate)

Deoxyguanylic, thymidylic, and deoxycytidylic acids esterified at positions 3' and 5' are also found in hydrolysates of DNA.

The situation in the ribonucleic acids is more complex. Only positions 1' and 4' are unavailable for esterification, which leaves the possibility of substitution at C-2', C-3', and C-5'. Hydrolysis by alkali gives rise to isomeric nucleotides esterified at C-2' or C-3'.

The guanylic, cytidylic, and uridylic acids derived from alkaline hydrolysis of RNA are likewise mixtures of nucleoside 2'- and 3'-phosphates. Ribonucleic acid, degraded by digestion with the enzyme pancreatic *ribonuclease,* yields the nucleoside 3'-phosphates. Enzymic hydrolysis with snake venom *phosphodiesterase* yields the nucleoside 5'-phosphates. The significance of these different isomeric nucleotides will be considered later.

In muscle and other tissues, there is a free form of adenylic acid which contains ribose, adenosine 5'-phosphate; the latter is also found in compounds that are further phosphorylated, *e.g.*, adenosine diphosphate (ADP) and adenosine triphosphate (ATP). The di- and triphosphates do not occur in nucleic acids. Similar 5'-nucleoside di- and triphosphates of other purines and pyrimidines also occur in tissues, as both the ribose and deoxyribose derivatives. Some of these di- and triphosphates are listed in Table 10.1 with the commonly used abbreviations for their designation. The metabolic roles of these compounds will be developed later (Part Three).

Table 10.1: NOMENCLATURE AND ABBREVIATIONS FOR NUCLEOTIDES AND RELATED COMPOUNDS

Nucleotide	Abbreviations*	
Adenosine monophosphate (adenylic acid)...............	AMP	ARP
Adenosine diphosphate........................	ADP	ARPP
Adenosine triphosphate.......................	ATP	ARPPP
Guanosine monophosphate (guanylic acid)...............	GMP	GRP
Guanosine diphosphate.......................	GDP	GRPP
Guanosine triphosphate.......................	GTP	GRPPP
Cytidine monophosphate (cytidylic acid)..................	CMP	CRP
Cytidine diphosphate........................	CDP	CRPP
Cytidine triphosphate.......................	CTP	CRPPP
Uridine monophosphate (uridylic acid).................	UMP	URP
Uridine diphosphate........................	UDP	URPP
Uridine triphosphate........................	UTP	URPPP
Thymidine monophosphate (thymidylic acid)...............	TMP	TdRP
Thymidine diphosphate.......................	TDP	TdRPP
Thymidine triphosphate.......................	TTP	TdRPPP
Thymine ribonucleoside 5'-phosphate..................	TRP	
Deoxyadenosine monophosphate..................	dAMP	AdRP
Deoxyadenosine diphosphate....................	dADP	AdRPP
Deoxyadenosine triphosphate....................	dATP	AdRPPP
Deoxyguanosine monophosphate	dGMP	GdRP
etc.		

Note: The above nomenclature refers only to 5' substituents. Other monophosphates are 3'-AMP, 2'-AMP, 3'-GMP, etc. Note that, in the case of the thymidine derivatives, the commonly occurring deoxyribose derivatives are TMP, TDP, and TTP; the ribose derivatives must be specified.

* In each case the first abbreviation is more generally used.

The hydrolytic deamination product of adenylic acid is also found in muscle tissue but not in nucleic acids. This is inosinic acid, or 9-β-5'-phospho-D-ribosyl-hypoxanthine.

Although the first nucleotides studied were those obtained by partial hydrolysis of nucleic acids, there are other important nucleotides which are not found in nucleic acids and which contain substances other than the usual purines and pyrimidines. The more general definition describes a nucleotide as a compound containing a phosphorylated sugar glycosidically linked to a base. Some nucleotides contain a vitamin as a component of their structure and function as coenzymes (Table 12.1, page 212).

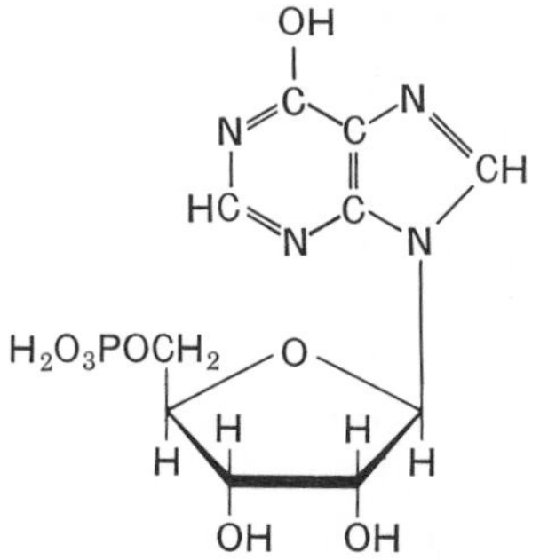

Inosinic acid (lactam form)

METHODS USED FOR THE STUDY OF NUCLEIC ACIDS AND THEIR COMPONENTS

Isolation of Nucleic Acids. Nucleic acids, present in tissues as nucleoproteins, may be prepared either by direct extraction or by first extracting the nucleoproteins, generally with $1M$ salt solution. The soluble nucleoprotein can be split by cautious addition of weak acid or alkali, or by saturating the solution with NaCl. Following scission of the nucleoprotein, the nucleic acid may be precipitated by careful addition of alcohol. Saturation with NaCl (above) precipitates the protein. The latter may also be first degraded with proteolytic enzymes, particularly trypsin, and the nucleic acid subsequently isolated. Proteins may also be separated from nucleic acids by a phenol extraction procedure. Extraction of tissues with hot trichloroacetic acid also removes nucleic acids.

It is also possible to prepare nucleic acids free of protein by procedures that denature proteins. Shaking a solution containing proteins and nucleic acids with chloroform and octanol produces a readily separable gel of denatured protein at the chloroform-water interface. It should be emphasized, however, that some procedures that denature proteins may also alter nucleic acids.

Identification of DNA and RNA. Recognition of the type of nucleic acid is usually accomplished by identification of the sugar component. Most of the currently used methods are colorimetric and can be employed for quantitative determinations of the sugars themselves, or in suitable modifications for estimation of nucleic acids, nucleotides, and other derivatives.

Some of the methods for pentose estimation depend on the liberation of furfural after heating with HCl (page 25). The furfural gives a red color with aniline acetate or a yellow color with p-bromophenylhydrazine. Ribose gives a distinctive color reaction with orcinol under suitable conditions (Table 3.1, page 30).

When DNA is heated with diphenylamine in acid solution (Dische reaction), a blue color is obtained. In the Feulgen reaction (page 30), deoxyribose, or DNA after partial acid hydrolysis, yields a blue-violet color. There are several other color reactions that have been described for estimation of deoxyribose or DNA: heating with cysteine and H_2SO_4, heating with tryptophan and perchloric acid, etc. (page 30).

Absorption Spectra. The presence of the conjugated ring systems of the purines and pyrimidines in nucleic acid results in marked absorption in the ultraviolet region of the spectrum, with absorption maxima near 260 mμ. Since proteins have a much weaker absorption in this region, one-fiftieth to one–one hundredth as much, the spectral properties of the nucleic acids have been useful in locating and estimating these substances in cells and tissues. The photography of cells by using ultraviolet light depends largely on the strong absorption of the nucleic acids and permits, for example, studies of chromosomal behavior in living cells without the necessity of staining. Much work of this character has been done, usually in conjunction with the use of highly purified enzymes that digest protein, permitting more precise location of nucleic acids. Conversely, nucleic acids may be removed by specific enzymic digestion, further establishing the intracellular localization of these substances. In addition, highly refined spectroscopic methods have permitted estimates of the amount of nucleic acids in cells under various physiological conditions (cf. Chap. 39).

Separation and Estimation of Nucleotides. The methods of ion exchange and paper chromatography have been applied for separation of the purine and pyrimidine bases, as well as the nucleosides and the nucleotides, from one another. Electrophoresis is also useful for separation of nucleotides. It is also possible by these techniques to separate ribose-containing compounds from deoxyribose-containing ones. When these methods are combined with measurements of ultraviolet absorption spectra, all the hydrolysis products can be identified and estimated from microgram quantities of nucleic acids.

The successful separation of the components of the nucleic acid by these methods depends on the presence of ionizable groups in the purines and pyrimidines: the enolic hydroxyl groups of uracil, cytosine, thymine, and guanine with pK' values in the range of 9 to 12.5, and the amino groups of adenine, guanine, and cytosine with pK' values between 2 and 4.5. Furthermore, the nucleotides all possess the two acidic groups of the substituted phosphoric acid, with a pK' value near 1 for the primary phosphate ionization and pK' near 6 for the secondary dissociation. By taking advantage of these properties, the complete and partial cleavage products of nucleic acids can be separated from one another.

STRUCTURE OF DEOXYRIBONUCLEIC ACIDS

Internucleotide Linkages. The fundamental units of the nucleic acids are the nucleotides. The deoxyribonucleic acids are polynucleotides in which the phosphate residues of each nucleotide act as bridges in forming diester linkages between the deoxyribose moieties. For DNA the internucleotide bonds are between C-3' and C-5'. Evidence for this has come from the study of partial hydrolysates of DNA; di- and trinucleotides have been isolated in which the nucleotides are linked only by 3',5'-phosphodiester bonds. Thus DNA is a long-chain polymer in which the internucleotide linkages are of the diester type between C-3' and C-5', in the manner illustrated in Fig. 10.2 for a portion of a DNA chain.

To show the DNA structure schematically, the type of diagram given at the right is used, in which the horizontal line represents the carbon chain of the sugar

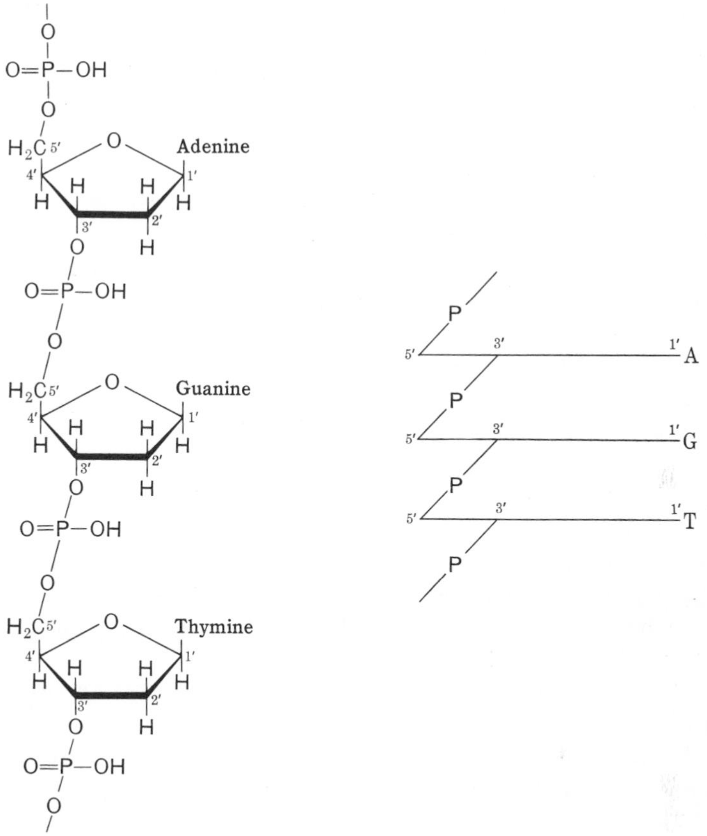

FIG. 10.2. Representation of a portion of a DNA chain, showing the position of the inter-nucleotide linkage between C-3′ and C-5′. Schematic representation is given at the right.

with the base attached at C-1′. The diagonal line indicates the C-3′ phosphate link-age at the middle of the horizontal line; that at the end of the horizontal line denotes the C-5′ phosphate linkage. This diagrammatic notation is used with both DNA and RNA.

For long sequences of polynucleotides, another shorthand system is also used. The letters A, G, C, U, and T represent the nucleosides, as in Table 10.1. The phosphate group is shown as p; when placed to the right of the nucleoside symbol, esterification is at C-3′; when placed to the left, esterification is at C-5′. Thus ApUp is a dinucleotide with a monoester at C-3′ of a uridine and a phosphodiester bond between C-5′ of U and C-3′ of A. Unless it is evident that deoxynucleotides are under discussion, it is useful to specify this, as in d-ApTpGpTp, etc., or as d-ATGT, etc., indicating that all the nucleosides contain deoxyribose.

Action of Nucleases and Other Enzymes. Certain enzymes that hydrolyze DNA are valuable tools in structural studies of these molecules. A pancreatic *deoxyribonuclease* degrades DNA mainly to a mixture of oligonucleotides. The few mono-nucleotides found are 5′-phosphates. When the action of this enzyme is followed

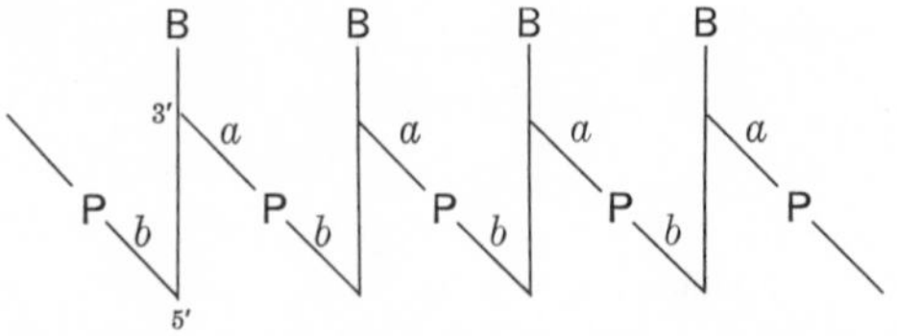

FIG. 10.3. Representation of hydrolysis of a section of DNA; B represents base. The points marked *a* represent the sites of hydrolysis of pancreatic deoxyribonuclease and venom diesterase. The points marked *b* are the sites of action of a deoxyribonuclease from spleen or from *Micrococcus* followed by the action of a spleen diesterase. Hydrolysis at *a* yields 5'-nucleotides; at *b*, 3'-nucleotides. An endonuclease (I) from *Escherichia coli* also acts at *a* with liberation of the 3'-hydroxyl groups, whereas a phosphatase from the same organism hydrolyzes the 5'-phosphates.

by the action of snake venom *diesterase,* essentially a quantitative yield of 5'-nucleotides is obtained.

In contrast, a deoxyribonuclease from spleen or from a species of *Micrococcus* hydrolyzes DNA to yield oligonucleotides and some mononucleotides in which the phosphate remains attached to the 3' position. When the action of this enzyme is followed by that of an enzyme from spleen (a diesterase), essentially a quantitative yield of 3'-mononucleotides is obtained. These actions are shown in Fig. 10.3 for a section of DNA.

Composition of DNA. Table 10.2 gives the base compositions of DNA from a number of sources. These analyses, as well as many others, show regularities of considerable importance, as first noted by Chargaff and his coworkers. In all cases, the amount of purines (Pu) is equal to the amount of pyrimidines (Py), *i.e.*, Pu/Py

Table 10.2: DNA COMPOSITION OF VARIOUS SPECIES

Species	Base proportions, moles %				$\dfrac{A+T}{G+C}$	A/T	G/C	Pu/Py
	G	A	C	T				
Sarcina lutea............	37.1	13.4	37.1	12.4	0.35	1.08	1.00	1.02
Alcaligenes faecalis.......	33.9	16.5	32.8	16.8	0.50	0.98	1.03	1.02
Brucella abortus..........	20.0	21.0	28.9	21.1	0.73	1.00	1.00	1.00
Escherichia coli K12	24.9	26.0	25.2	23.9	1.00	1.09	0.99	1.08
Salmonella paratyphi A....	24.9	24.8	25.0	25.3	1.00	0.98	1.00	0.99
Wheat germ.............	22.7	27.3	22.8*	27.1	1.19	1.01	1.00	1.00
Bovine thymus...........	21.5	28.2	22.5*	27.8	1.27	1.01	0.96	0.99
Staphylococcus aureus.....	21.0	30.8	19.0	29.2	1.50	1.05	1.11	1.07
Human thymus..........	19.9	30.9	19.8	29.4	1.52	1.05	1.01	1.03
Human liver.............	19.5	30.3	19.9	30.3	1.54	1.00	0.98	0.99
Saccharomyces cerevisiae..	18.3	31.7	17.4	32.6	1.80	0.97	1.05	1.00
Pasteurella tularensis......	17.6	32.4	17.1	32.9	1.88	0.98	1.03	1.00
Clostridium perfringens....	14.0	36.9	12.8	36.3	2.70	1.02	1.09	1.04

Note: G = guanine; A = adenine; C = cytosine; T = thymine; Pu/Py = purine/pyrimidine.
* Cytosine + methylcytosine.
SOURCE: Compiled from the work of several investigators.

is equal to 1. It is also striking that the ratio of adenine (A) to thymine (T) is equal to 1 and similarly that the ratio of guanine (G) to cytosine (C) (plus methylcyto-sine where it occurs) is equal to 1. Although the analyses are reported for the purines and pyrimidines per se, it should be emphasized that these are the ratios for the corresponding nucleotides, since for each base, purine or pyrimidine, there is one mole of deoxyribose and one mole of phosphate.

Such analyses have been performed on the DNA of a large number of species, and the same regularities have been found. Nevertheless, each species shows a characteristic composition that is unaffected by age, conditions of growth, various evironmental factors, etc. Indeed, in higher organisms, DNA from different organs or tissues of the same species are similar in composition, as indicated by the data in Table 10.2 for human liver and thymus. The characteristic composition of DNA from a given source can be indicated by the ratio of (A + T)/(G + C). In bacteria a wide range of compositions is encountered, some being high in A + T, others in G + C. In higher organisms the range is more limited; in most animals the ratio (A + T)/(G + C) is found to be from 1.3 to 2.2, and in higher plants from 1.1 to 1.7.

Only the two purines, adenine and guanine, and the two pyrimidines, cytosine and thymine, have been found in the DNA of a wide variety of microorganisms: bacteria, actinomycetes, fungi, algae, and protozoa. The presence of methylcytosine is a characteristic feature of the DNA of certain higher plants and animals, the DNA of plants being richer in this pyrimidine than the DNA of animals. Wheat germ, the richest source yet found, contains 6 moles of methylcytosine per 100 moles of bases. In all cases, however, it replaces an equivalent amount of cytosine. The base content of viruses is discussed below (page 184).

The analytical data presented in Table 10.2 were obtained on the total DNA of the various microorganisms or tissues. The DNA obtained from a single micro-organism behaves as though it were homogeneous, yielding a single sharp band on density gradient centrifugation (see below). The DNA of mammalian tissues is, however, inhomogeneous. Chargaff and coworkers were able to separate calf thymus into fractions with (A + T)/(G + C) ratios ranging from 1.0 to 1.8. Neverthe-less, it was found for each fraction that A/T = G/C = 1. Differential extraction procedures and chromatographic methods are being used in efforts to obtain further fractionation. As yet, no sample of DNA has been obtained from animal tissues that satisfies the criteria of molecular homogeneity.

Molecular Weight. Investigations on DNA prepared by relatively mild methods indicate values of the order of 6 to 12 million for the molecular weight of these substances. Since a nucleotide has a residue weight of the order of 300 to 350, it is evident that a molecule of DNA may contain more than 20,000 nucleotides. The physical behavior of DNA preparations indicates that these molecules are elongated polymers of threadlike character. For such large molecules, two procedures have been most useful for size determinations: sedimentation-diffusion (page 134) and light scattering.

The DNA from calf thymus shows sedimentation constants with values from 10 to 40 Svedberg units. As already noted, such preparations can be fractionated into preparations with different base composition (see above). In contrast to such DNA, bacterial and viral DNA is relatively homogeneous in size. Indeed, the

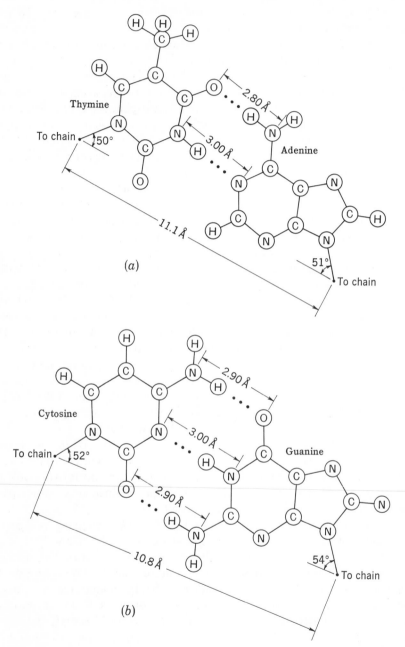

(a)

(b)

FIG. 10.4. Dimensions and hydrogen bonding of (a) thymine to adenine and (b) cytosine to guanine. (*From L. Pauling and R. B. Corey, Arch. Biochem. Biophys., **65**, 164, 1956.*)

total DNA of certain viruses and bacteria appears to behave as though it consisted of a single giant molecule, with the particle weight of some viral DNA being as large as 130 million. Such DNA preparations are also remarkably homogeneous in density, behaving as a single entity on density gradient centrifugation (page 178).

In view of the wide variations in composition of DNA from different species (Table 10.2), individual nucleic acids must differ greatly in nucleotide sequence, about which little is known. If one assumes, however, that the specificity of DNA depends on the different sequences of the four kinds of nucleotides, the potential isomerism can reach the same astronomical figures already noted for possible variations in protein structure due to different sequences of amino acids (page 144).

Double Helical Structure of DNA. Application of x-ray diffraction analysis to the problem of the native structure of DNA has proved exceedingly fruitful. From the data obtained by Wilkins and coworkers, Watson and Crick proposed that DNA is composed of two chains of polynucleotides which exist in a double helical structure. The main chain of each strand consists of deoxyribose residues joined by 3′,5′ phosphodiester bridges. The two chains are held together in part by hydrogen bonding, each amino group being joined to a keto group, *i.e.*, adenine to thymine, thymine to adenine, guanine to cytosine, etc. In each instance the pairing involves a pyrimidine and a purine base. The types of hydrogen bonding are shown in Fig. 10.4.

The two chains of the helix are coiled to permit the proper hydrogen bonding. Moreover, the chains are not identical but are complementary in terms of the appropriate base pairing, A to T and C to G, as shown for a hypothetical fragment of two chains of DNA, where the letters represent the deoxyribonucleotides.

It should be noted that the chains do not run in the same direction with respect to internucleotide linkages, *i.e.*, the chains are *antiparallel*. If, for example, the upper chain is linked 5′-3′ with respect to AG, GT, TC, etc., the lower chain is linked 3′-5′ with respect to TC, CA, AG, etc. Both chains follow right-handed helices, each coiled around the same axis. A schematic diagram of the coiling of the two chains is shown in Fig. 10.5.

An increasing body of evidence suggests that, in addition to hydrogen bonds, hydrophobic forces between the stacked purine and pyrimidine nuclei contribute significantly to maintenance of the rigid, two-stranded structure. Thus, reagents such as formamide and urea, which increase the solubility of the aromatic groups in the surrounding aqueous medium, also tend to denature DNA (see below).

The suggested base pairing is in accord with a content of G = C and A = T, as determined for a large number of DNA samples. The cross section of the helix ascertained from the x-ray diffraction measurements is consonant only with purine-pyrimidine hydrogen bonding, the planes of the bases being perpendicular to the fiber axis. The dimensions of the helix are such that there is insufficient space to

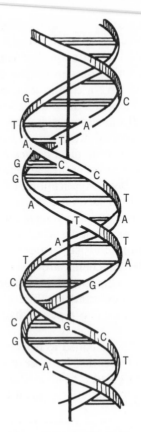

FIG. 10.5. A schematic representation of the double helix of DNA. The two ribbons represent the phosphate-sugar chains, and the horizontal rods represent the bonding between the pairs of bases. The vertical line indicates the fiber axis.

permit purine-purine pairing, and would allow too much space for hydrogen bonds to form between two pyrimidine residues on the individual strands.

Since Watson and Crick proposed the above structure in 1953, a great variety of supporting evidence has been obtained by the study of DNA and of model polynucleotides. The suggested structure depends on the hydrogen-bonding properties of the bases. As in the case of proteins (Chap. 9), individual hydrogen bonds of DNA are weak; it is the large number of such bonds which confers stability on the structure.

The effect of a variety of agents and conditions, *e.g.*, acid, alkali, heat, low ionic strength, on DNA structure can be explained on the basis that the DNA, initially in a firm, helical, two-stranded, native structure, can be converted to a "denatured" state which appears to be a single-stranded, flexible structure. The change from a native to a denatured form is usually very abrupt and is accelerated by reagents, *e.g.*, urea and formamide, which enhance the aqueous solubility of the purine and pyrimidine groups.

Several methods have proved to be of great utility in assessing the transition from the native to a denatured state, as well as in observing other properties of DNA. These methods can be described as follows:

1. *Ultraviolet absorption.* As noted above, all nucleic acids show a strong absorption in the ultraviolet with a maximum near 260 mμ. When native DNA is altered, there is a marked "*hyperchromic* effect," or increase in absorption. This change reflects a decrease in hydrogen bonding and is observed not only with DNA but with other nucleic acids, and with many synthetic polynucleotides which also possess a hydrogen bonded structure.

2. *Optical rotation.* Native DNA shows a strong positive rotation which is markedly decreased by procedures that produce denaturation. This change is analogous to the changes in rotation observed with the denaturation of proteins (page 156).

3. *Viscosity.* Solutions of native DNA posses a high viscosity because of the relatively rigid double helical structure and long, rodlike character of the DNA. Disruption of the hydrogen bonds produces a marked decrease in viscosity.

Effect of Temperature. Heating of a sample of DNA in a given ionic environment produces an increase in ultraviolet absorption and a decrease in optical rotation and viscosity at a critical temperature. The entire process is completed over a relatively narrow temperature range (Fig. 10.6).

The temperature midpoint (T_m) is analogous to the melting point of a crystal. DNA preparations from diverse sources possess different T_m values. Doty and coworkers observed that T_m depends on the absolute amounts of guanine (G) + cytosine (C) and adenine (A) + thymine (T); the higher the content of G-C, the higher the transition temperature between the native, two-stranded helix and the single-stranded form (Fig. 10.7). It will be noted (Fig. 10.5) that the G-C pair can form a triply hydrogen bonded structure whereas the A-T pair can form only a doubly hydrogen bonded structure. Indeed, it has been found that T_m determinations, using careful calibration with DNA preparations of known composition, permit estimations of the G + C and A + T content of an unknown DNA. Such studies must be performed at fixed ionic strength and pH, since these have a marked effect on the stability of DNA. T_m can be lowered by the addition of urea, an agent known to disrupt hydrogen bonds. In 8M urea, T_m is decreased by nearly 20°C. DNA in 95 per cent formamide is completely separated into single strands at room temperature.

Complete rupture of the two-stranded helix by heating is not a readily reversible process. However, if a solution of denatured DNA, prepared by heating, is returned slowly to room temperature, some renatured DNA is obtained. Maximal reversibility (50 to 60 per cent) is usually attained by "annealing" the denatured DNA, *i.e.*, holding the solution at a temperature about 25° below T_m and above a concentration of 0.4M Na$^+$ for several hours. Snake venom diesterase (page 172) does not attack native, two-stranded DNA but does hydrolyze the denatured, single-stranded form. When a preparation of partially renatured DNA is treated with the diesterase, the digestion products are readily removed from the renatured material; the latter exhibits all the properties—optical rotation, absorption, and viscosity—of the native form.

Effect of pH. Disruption of the double-stranded structure of DNA also occurs

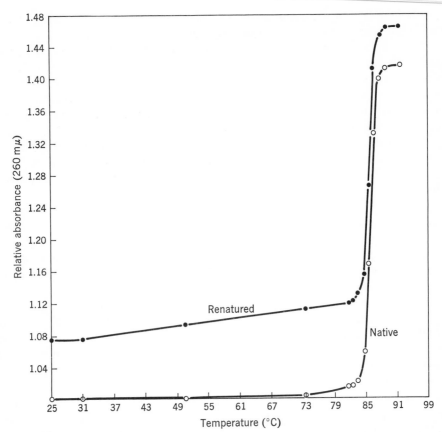

FIG. 10.6. Effect of temperature on the relative absorbance of native and renatured DNA. (*From P. Doty, in D. J. Bell and J. K. Grant, eds., "The Structure and Biosynthesis of Macromolecules," Biochemical Society Symposia; No. 21, p. 8, Cambridge University Press, New York, 1962.*)

at acid and alkaline pH values at which ionic changes of the substituents on the purine and pyrimidine bases can occur. Near pH 12, ionization of enolic hydroxyl groups occurs, preventing the keto-amino group hydrogen bonding. Similarly, in acid solutions near pH 2 to 3, at which amino groups bind protons, the helix is disrupted. Treatment of DNA at these extreme pH values produces single-stranded molecules of half the molecular weight of native DNA.

Density of DNA. When a concentrated solution of cesium chloride is centrifuged in the analytical ultracentrifuge at high speeds until equilibrium is attained, the opposing processes of sedimentation and diffusion (page 125) produce a stable concentration gradient of the CsCl, *i.e.*, there is a continuous increase in density along the direction of centrifugal force. If the CsCl solution contains a small amount of DNA, at equilibrium the molecules of DNA will be collected in bands at those zones of the centrifuge cell at which their density and the density of the medium are exactly equal. The position of the DNA in the cell can be established by ultraviolet absorption photography. Since the gradient of solution density can be precisely estimated throughout the cell, the density of the DNA sample can be established. The technique is termed *density gradient centrifugation.*

It is remarkable that samples of bacterial DNA from different species show very narrow density bands. Sueoka, Marmur, and Doty and Rolfe and Meselson showed independently that the density of a DNA preparation depends on the ratio of GC to AT pairs within the sample. The triply hydrogen bonded GC pairs produce a relatively more compact, higher-density structure than do the doubly bonded AT pairs. Thus, these findings are in accord with the Watson-Crick formulation of DNA structure inasmuch as the density depends on the relative amounts of the predicted types of hydrogen bonding between the base pairs.

Synthetic Polynucleotides. Considerable information concerning hydrogen bond-

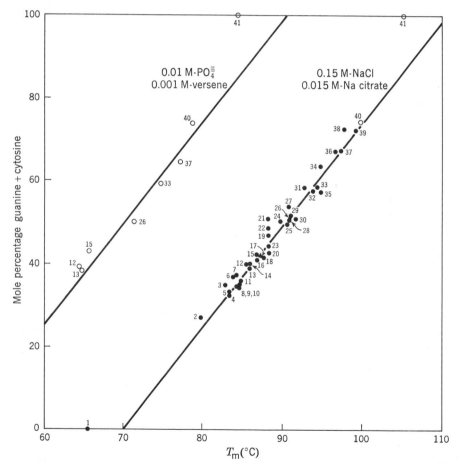

Fig. 10.7. Dependence of the temperature midpoint T_m on the content of guanine + cytosine. Numbers 2 through 40 represent points for samples of DNA from various sources. Number 1 is the value for dAT (page 180); No. 41, for d-poly G + d-poly C (page 180). (*From P. Doty, in D. J. Bell and J. K. Grant, eds., "The Structure and Biosynthesis of Macromolecules," Biochemical Society Symposia, No. 21, p. 8, Cambridge University Press, New York, 1962.*)

ing and base pairing has been obtained by studying polynucleotides synthesized enzymically with use of polynucleotide phosphorylase (Chap. 30) for preparation of RNA-like polymers, and of DNA polymerase (Chap. 29) for preparation of DNA-like polymers.

When polyadenylic acid (poly A) and polyuridylic acid (poly U) are mixed under appropriate conditions, a two-stranded helix is formed, in which, presumably, the hydrogen bonding is between A and U pairs. Heating such an equimolar mixture of the two homopolymers produces a considerable hyperchromic effect and other changes suggestive of the breakdown of a two-stranded helix. Similarly, d-poly G and d-poly C form a strongly hydrogen bonded structure with a very high T_m (Fig. 10.7). There is a strong hyperchromic effect on heating or on titration to pH 12. These effects are readily reversible, presumably because of the ease of base pairing, there being an exact fit of G to C along the entire length of the polymers.

A copolymer containing dAT has a structure in which each chain possesses a strictly alternating base sequence $\cdots$ ATATAT $\cdots$. Such a copolymer also forms a two-stranded structure resembling that of DNA. The T_m is low (Fig. 10.7), as expected for A-T hydrogen bonding. Changes in optical density and viscosity are produced by heating or alkaline titration, and these changes are readily reversible after quick cooling.

DEOXYRIBONUCLEOPROTEINS

DNA is found in the nuclei of cells as parts of the chromosome structure and has not been identified in cytoplasm. Basic proteins, either histones, or, in sperm cells, protamines, are associated with DNA, undoubtedly as a result of ionic linkages between anionic phosphate groups of DNA and cationic groups of the basic amino acids of histone and protamine.

The deoxyribonucleoproteins are viscous materials which are insoluble in 0.15 M sodium chloride (physiological concentration) but soluble in $1M$ salt solutions. These solubility characteristics are employed in the preparation of these nucleoproteins (page 168), which, when precipitated, are so viscous and sticky that they may be collected by winding on a stirring rod. The nucleoproteins are of high molecular weight; present estimates indicate values in excess of 10 million. These molecules are highly elongated and threadlike in shape. It has been estimated that 25 to 50 per cent of the dry weight of the deoxyribonucleoproteins is nucleic acid.

The amino acid composition of the nucleoproteins is distinctive. The histones of animal tissues are high molecular weight proteins that are rich in arginine or lysine or both, and deficient in tryptophan. Histones are usually obtained by extracting nuclei or nucleoproteins with dilute acids (0.2M HCl) and are then precipitated from the solution with alkali at about pH 10, or by salting-out techniques.

Protamines have been found only in the ripe sperm of certain families of fish and have never been obtained from somatic cell nuclei. These very basic proteins have usually been prepared by extraction with dilute mineral acids followed by precipitation with ethanol, or by dialysis of the nucleoprotamine in cellophane bags against $1M$ HCl; the protamines pass through the membrane. The protamines are relatively small proteins, lacking many amino acids but extremely rich in arginine.

The biological role of the deoxyribonucleoproteins will be considered in Chaps. 29, 30, and 31.

STRUCTURE OF RIBONUCLEIC ACIDS

In the period since 1950 abundant evidence has accumulated that there are several distinct types of RNA. These are distinguishable by their characteristic composition, size, and functional properties and by their location within the cell. These developments have made questionable much earlier work performed either on total cellular RNA or on fractions that were poorly defined. Some general aspects of the structure of RNA will be given first; this will be followed by a brief discussion of the properties of the presently recognized types of RNA. The special functions of these types will be considered later (Chaps. 30 and 31).

Internucleotide Linkage. In RNA, the hydroxyl groups at C-2′, C-3′, and C-5′ are available for esterification. However, present evidence indicates that, as in DNA, the internucleotide linkages are between C-3′ and C-5′.

When RNA is treated with a phosphodiesterase from snake venom, the main products are nucleoside 5′-phosphates. Crystalline ribonuclease of bovine pancreas hydrolyzes nucleotide linkages at a point distal to the phosphate of a pyrimidine nucleotide that is esterified at the 3′ position. The points of cleavage of this enzyme are shown by the vertical dotted lines.

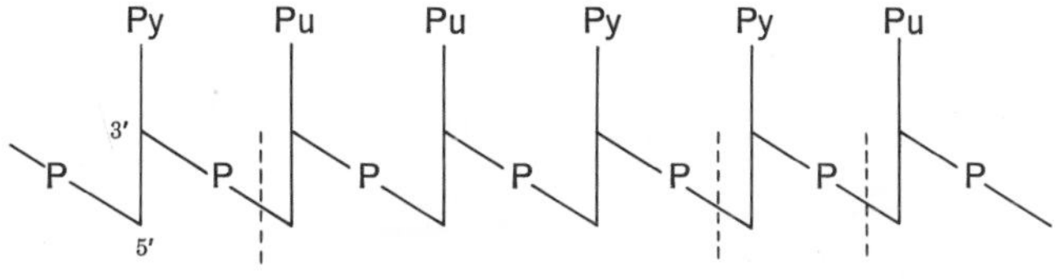

In this schematic structure, *Py* represents a pyrimidine; *Pu*, a purine; and *P*, orthophosphate in diester linkage. The action of the enzyme can be followed by the decrease in viscosity of the RNA preparation, appearance of dialyzable products, production of titratable acid groups, etc. The final products of ribonuclease action are pyrimidine-containing nucleoside 3′-phosphates and oligonucleotides terminating in a Py-3′-P, *i.e.,* ⋯ PupPupPupPyp.

Unlike DNA, RNA is hydrolyzed by weak alkali (pH 9 at 100°C.). This treatment leads to the intermediate formation of a phosphate triester followed by hydrolytic scission of one bond to leave a cyclic diester (Fig. 10.8). After such cleavage it has been possible to isolate 2′,3′ cyclic phosphates, of the type shown below, for each of the purine and pyrimidine mononucleotides present in RNA.

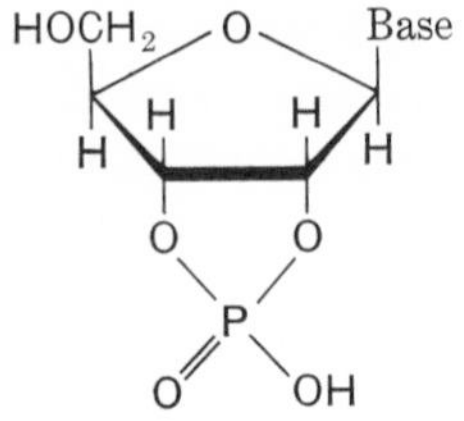

A 2′,3′ cyclic monophosphate nucleotide

The action of stronger alkali on the cyclic compounds produces a random hydrolytic cleavage giving a mixture of the isomeric 2′ and 3′ mononucleotides.

Thus the lability of RNA in alkali is due to formation of labile compounds in which phosphate is triply esterified; final cleavage of the internucleotide linkage gives a cyclic diester. The possibility of formation of such bonds exists only with RNA since in DNA there is no hydroxyl group at C-2′; this explains the relative stability of DNA in weak alkali.

It is noteworthy that pancreatic ribonuclease can hydrolyze the cyclic 2′,3′-phosphates of cytidine and uridine to yield the 3′-phosphates.

A cyclic nucleotide, adenosine 3′,5′-cyclic monophosphate, cyclic AMP, has proved to be of considerable importance in metabolism (Part Three).

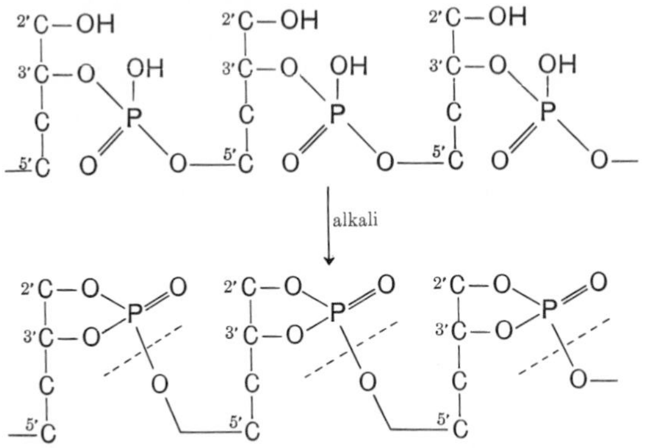

FIG. 10.8. Action of alkali on ribonucleic acid. The upper structure shows, diagrammatically, a trinucleotide unit linked 3′ to 5′; the lower diagram shows the intermediate triester formation. Cleavage at the points indicated (dashed lines) results in the formation of cyclic diesters of the mononucleotides. (*Adapted from D. M. Brown and A. R. Todd, J. Chem. Soc., p. 52, 1952.*)

Soluble or Transfer RNA. Soluble RNA (sRNA) is arbitrarily defined as that remaining in a broken cell suspension after centrifuging at 100,000 × gravity for several hours. Under this centrifugal force, nuclei, mitochondria, microsomes, and cellular debris are sedimented (Chap. 15). sRNA comprises approximately 10 to 20 per cent of the cellular RNA and is composed of relatively small molecules with a molecular weight of approximately 30,000. sRNA functions as a mediator in peptide bond synthesis, a specific sRNA serving for each amino acid. Thus, there are at least 20 different kinds of sRNA; this role of sRNA is presented in Chap. 30.

Alkaline digestion of sRNA releases the end group nucleoside and a mixture of nucleotides, thus providing a specific end group method. The major end group of sRNA is adenosine (over 90 per cent of the total), and it is released in a ratio of one residue per 70 nucleotides.

Although sRNA is composed largely of the four main types of ribonucleotides —adenylic, guanylic, cytidylic, and uridylic acids—there are, in addition, smaller quantities of other nucleotides. These include the nucleotides of pseudouridine (see below), various methylated adenines and guanines, methylated pyrimidines, such as thymine and 5-methylcytosine, and others. Not all these are present in any one source of sRNA, but pseudouridine appears to be the most abundant and universally distributed. The relative proportions of these additional components of RNA in the soluble fraction of rat liver are given in Table 10.3.

Table 10.3: RELATIVE PROPORTIONS OF ADDITIONAL COMPONENTS IN SOLUBLE RNA OF RAT LIVER

Component	Soluble RNA*
Pseudouridine	25
5-Methylcytosine	10
6-Methylaminopurine	8.1
6,6-Dimethylaminopurine	0.1
1-Methylguanine	3.3
2-Methylamino-6-hydroxypurine	2.3
2,2-Dimethylamino-6-hydroxypurine	3.0

* Values are in moles per 100 moles of uridine.

SOURCE: From D. B. Dunn, *Biochim. et Biophys. Acta,* **34**, 286, 1959.

Pseudouridine is of special interest in that the usual N-glycosidic bond is absent; the ribose is directly linked at C-1' to the 5 position of uracil by a carbon-to-carbon bond.

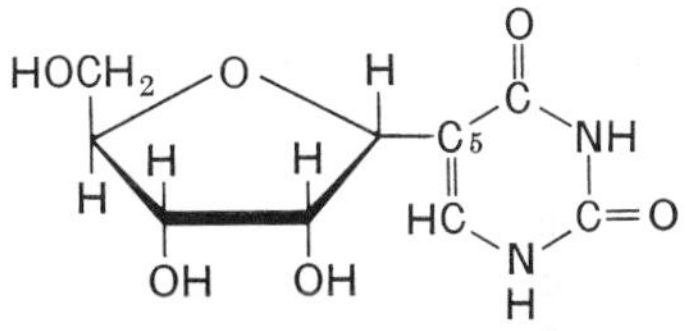

5-Ribosyluracil (pseudouridine)

The possible functional significance of the presence of pseudouridine and the other unusual bases is unknown.

Ribosomal RNA. Ribosomes (page 270) contain a large portion of the RNA of a cell, representing as much as 80 per cent of the total in some bacteria. This type of RNA is strongly associated with protein; RNA (of the ribosomal particles of mammalian cells) comprises about 40 to 50 per cent of the dry weight of these particles. The properties of these particles are best considered in connection with their biological role (Chap. 30).

Ribosomal RNA preparations from various sources, *e.g.*, rat liver or *Escherichia coli,* yield similar values for nucleotide content. Guanylic acid is invariably most abundant; uridylic and cytidylic acids are present in approximately equal amounts and are least abundant. Pseudouridine is present only in trace amounts, and the "unusual" bases appear to be present in negligible quantities. Indeed, it is likely that the presence of all these may be due to contamination by sRNA.

Messenger, Template, or "Information" RNA. The base composition of this type of RNA (mRNA) is similar to that of the DNA of the cell except that uracil occurs in place of thymine, and this RNA is single-stranded. Its biological role is presented later (Chaps. 30 and 31).

VIRUSES AS NUCLEOPROTEINS

In 1935, W. M. Stanley isolated the virus that causes tobacco mosaic disease, as a highly purified and apparently crystalline protein, and a year later it was shown by Bawden and Pirie that this substance was a nucleoprotein of the ribose type. Since that time, many additional plant viruses have been isolated as crystalline substances, and they are all ribonucleoproteins. All the presently available evidence indicates that the properties of the isolated nucleoproteins are consonant with the properties of the viruses themselves. Procedures that influence the chemical properties of the nucleoprotein, such as treatment by chemical or physical methods, digestion by enzymes, etc., also result in a loss of viral activity.

Table 10.4 gives the RNA content and particle weight (molecular weight) of certain plant and animal viruses; wide variation is evident. All these viruses contain only the usual four bases (A, G, U, C) of RNA.

Table 10.4: COMPOSITION AND SIZE OF SOME VIRUSES CONTAINING RNA

Virus	Percentage of RNA	Particle weight $\times 10^6$
Tobacco mosaic	6	40
Tomato bushy stunt	15	10.6
Tomato ring spot	44	1.5
Poliomyelitis	22–30	6.7
Equine encephalitis	4.4	50
Influenza, type A	0.7–1.0	280

Viruses can reproduce inside living cells but are incapable of doing so independently; this aids in distinguishing them as a group from bacteria and other small free-living organisms. What is so striking is that ability to reproduce, albeit in a host cell, a characteristic once regarded as reserved for "living cells," has been found to be possessed by nucleoproteins.

Preparations of tobacco mosaic virus have been treated by procedures that have permitted isolation of the specific RNA essentially free of protein. Isolated RNA of this type, although very labile, has proved to be infective in suitable host plants, leading to the formation of new tobacco mosaic virus. This evidence indicates that it is the RNA alone which possesses biological activity.

Bacteriophages may be regarded as viruses of bacteria insofar as they are infectious and can reproduce in specific host cells. The types of phage that have been obtained in highly purified form are rich in deoxyribonucleoproteins. With certain strains of phage it appears that the protein aids in penetrating the host bacterial cell but only the DNA actually enters the cell. After a brief period of time, the host cell breaks open (lysis) and many new phage particles are liberated. This evidence suggests that only the specific nucleic acid is concerned in the self-duplicating properties of the phage.

Certain bacteriophages contain 5-hydroxymethylcytosine in place of cytosine in their DNA. The hydroxymethyl group is linked glycosidically to glucose.

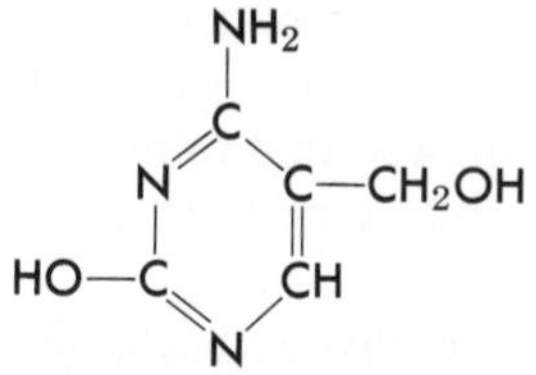

5-Hydroxymethylcytosine
(5-hydroxymethyl-2-oxy-4-aminopyrimidine)

Table 10.5 gives the base content of *E. coli* DNA in comparison with that of three different bacteriophages that can infect these cells. It is noteworthy that the glucosides may be of either the α or β configuration or the α-glucosyl-β-glucoside structure. In these DNA molecules, A = T and G = HMC. Other bacteriophages of *E. coli,* T1, T3, T5, T7, lack hydroxymethylcytosine; their base content reflects conventional base pairing of DNA, *i.e.,* A = T and G = C.

Table 10.5: BASE CONTENT OF DNA FROM *Escherichia coli* AND CERTAIN BACTERIOPHAGES

Source of DNA	Percentage of total bases							
	A	T	G	C	HMC	HMC-α-G	HMC-β-G	HMC-α-diG
Escherichia coli..........	25	25	24	26	0	0	0	0
T2.....................	32	32	18	0	4	12	0	1
T4.....................	32	33	18	0	0	12	5	0
T6.....................	32	33	18	0	4	1	0	12

Note: A, T, G, C = the usual four bases of DNA; HMC = 5-hydroxymethylcytosine; HMC-α-G = the α-glucoside; HMC-β-G = the β-glucoside; and HMC-α-diG = the α-glucosyl-β-glucoside.

SOURCE: D. S. Hogness, in "The Molecular Control of Cellular Activity," J. M. Allen, ed., p. 206, McGraw-Hill Book Company., Inc., New York, 1962.

An unusual base has been discovered in the DNA of a bacteriophage of *Bacillus subtilis.* This DNA contains guanine, adenine, cytosine, and, in place of thymine, 5-hydroxymethyluracil.

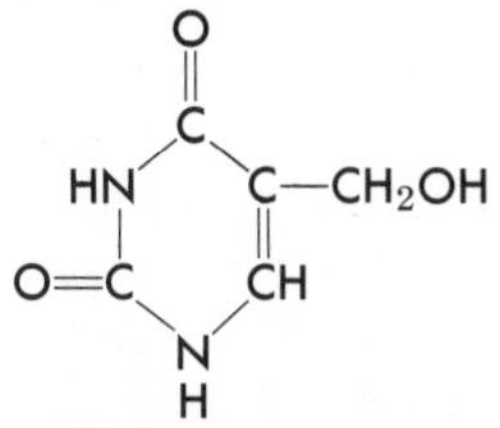

5-Hydroxymethyluracil
(5-hydroxymethyl-2,4-dioxypyrimidine)

NUCLEIC ACIDS AS TRANSFORMING FACTORS

An additional property of certain nucleic acids was first demonstrated with different strains of *Pneumococcus*. The various virulent strains of this organism have antigenically and chemically different capsular polysaccharides. Noncapsulated pneumococci (R cells) of one type may be transformed into capsular organisms (S cells) of another type by the introduction of a minute amount of the culture filtrate of a capsular-forming S organism. Avery, MacLeod, and McCarty isolated DNA from such filtrates and showed that minute quantities of DNA of a type III filtrate will induce the formation of type III polysaccharide in a type II, acapsular R strain.

In similar fashion, DNA from diverse bacterial species has been used to transform variant members of the same species with respect to such characteristics as resistance to various antibiotics or ability to synthesize a specific compound. One must conclude that the nucleic acid acts as a genetic transforming agent since the transformed or mutated strain will continue to reproduce as the induced type.

REFERENCES

Books

Chargaff, E., and Davidson, J. N., eds., "The Nucleic Acids. Chemistry and Biology," vols. I and II, 1955; vol. III, 1960, Academic Press, Inc., New York.

Davidson, J. N., "The Biochemistry of the Nucleic Acids," 4th ed., John Wiley & Sons, Inc., New York, 1960.

Michelson, A. M., "The Chemistry of Nucleosides and Nucleotides," Academic Press, Inc., New York, 1963.

Steiner, R. F., and Beers, R. J., Jr., "Polynucleotides. Natural and Synthetic Nucleic Acids," Elsevier Publishing Company, New York, 1961.

Review Articles

Doty, P., Inside Nucleic Acids, *Harvey Lectures,* **55,** 103–140, 1959–1960.

Doty, P., The Relationship of the Interaction of Polynucleotides to the Secondary Structure of Nucleic Acids, in D. J. Bell and J. K. Grant, eds., "The Structure and Biosynthesis of Macromolecules," Biochemical Society Symposia, No. 21, pp. 8–28, Cambridge University Press, New York, 1962.

11. Porphyrins, Hemoproteins, and Chlorophyll

The hemoproteins include the hemoglobins concerned in oxygen transport, the cytochromes, which are electron-transfer agents, and several enzymes such as catalase and peroxidase. In each instance the colorless protein is linked to an iron-porphyrin compound. Porphyrins are also found linked with other metals; the most important example is chlorophyll, a porphyrin derivative containing magnesium. The distribution of the hemoproteins embraces almost all living matter. The ability to synthesize porphyrins is possessed by almost all species; only a few species require exogenous porphyrins as growth factors.

The important place that porphyrins occupy in living organisms is also indicated by the findings that porphyrins derived from chlorophyll occur in petroleum, coals, oil shales, and asphalts. Porphyrins have also been found in fossilized excrements (coproliths) of crocodiles. Thus the geologist has provided evidence that essential biological compounds that functioned millions of years ago did not differ from those which function today.

THE PORPHYRINS

The naturally occurring porphyrins are derivatives of the fundamental substance *porphin,* which contains four pyrrole-like rings linked by four CH groups or methene bridges in a ring system.

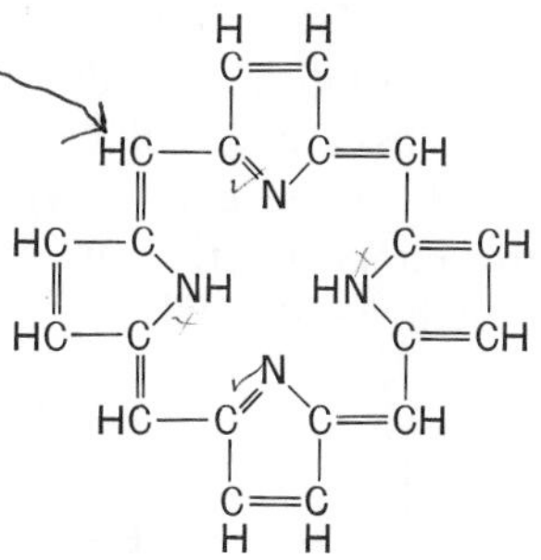

Porphin ($C_{20}H_{14}N_4$) 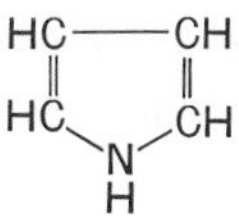   Pyrrole

The porphyrin structure contains a central 16-membered ring formed from 12 carbon and 4 nitrogen atoms contributed by 4 pyrrole rings. The positions assigned to the alternating double and single bonds of porphin are arbitrary because of resonance. Porphin was first synthesized by Hans Fischer and Gleim in 1935; the compound is not known to occur in nature.

It is convenient to use the formula shown below, in which the carbon atoms of the pyrrole rings are represented as the corners of pentagons, with the nitrogen shown and the hydrogen atoms omitted.

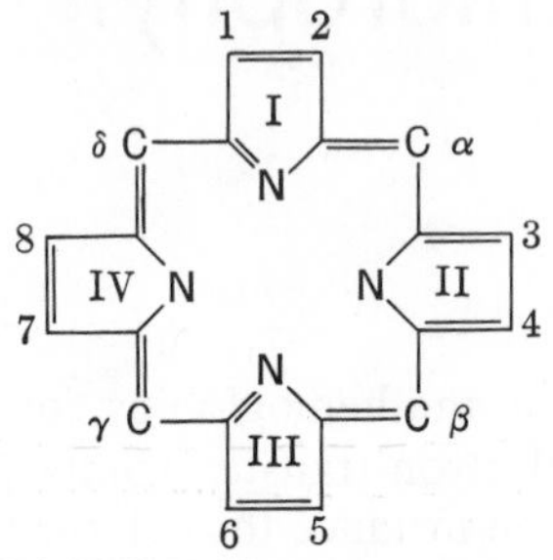

The porphyrins that are found in nature are all compounds in which side chains are substituted for the eight hydrogen atoms numbered in the pyrrole rings in porphin (formula above). For convenience in showing these substitutions, the simplified shorthand formula of Fischer is used for representing the porphyrin nucleus, with all the bridges and rings omitted:

The names of some of the important porphyrins are given in Table 11.1 with the types and positions of the side chains indicated.

Each formula listed in Table 11.1 actually represents a large group of substances, since considerable isomerism is possible. The simplest examples are etio-, copro-, and uroporphyrins, in which only two different kinds of groupings are found. For these porphyrins, four isomers are possible in each case. However, only two of these occur in nature, and these have been designated type I and type III by Fischer. The structures of the isomeric etioporphyrins are indicated in the formulas below, where M and E represent methyl and ethyl.

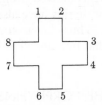

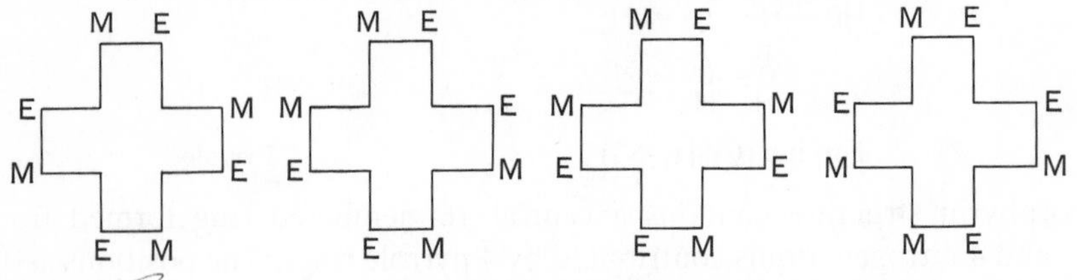

Isomeric etioporphyrins

Table 11.1: STRUCTURES OF PORPHYRIN TYPES I AND III

Porphyrin	Formula	Type I	Type III	Solubility in ether	Solubility in NaOH
Etioporphyrin	$C_{32}H_{38}N_4$	1,3,5,7-M,2,4,6,8-E	1,3,5,8-M,2,4,6,7-E	Soluble	Insoluble
Mesoporphyrin	$C_{34}H_{38}O_4N_4$	1,3,5,7-M,2,4-E,6,8-P	1,3,5,8-M,2,4-E,6,7-P	Soluble	Insoluble
Protoporphyrin	$C_{34}H_{34}O_4N_4$	1,3,5,7-M,2,4-V,6,8-P	1,3,5,8-M,2,4-V,6,7-P	Soluble	Insoluble
Coproporphyrin	$C_{36}H_{38}O_8N_4$	1,3,5,7-M,2,4,6,8-P	1,3,5,8-M,2,4,6,7-P	Soluble	Soluble
Uroporphyrin	$C_{40}H_{38}O_{16}N_4$	1,3,5,7-A,2,4,6,8-P	1,3,5,8-A,2,4,6,7-P	Insoluble	Soluble
Deuteroporphyrin	$C_{30}H_{30}O_4N_4$	1,3,5,7-M,2,4-H,6,8-P	1,3,5,8-M,2,4-H,6,7-P	Soluble	Insoluble
Hematoporphyrin	$C_{34}H_{38}O_6N_4$	1,3,5,7-M,2,4-EOH,6,8-P	1,3,5,8-M,2,4-EOH,6,7-P	Soluble	Soluble

Note: Symbols used for the side chains are as follows: M = methyl, E = ethyl, P = propionic acid, V = vinyl, EOH = hydroxyethyl, A = acetic acid, H = hydrogen. Numbers indicate the positions in the porphyrin nucleus at which these side chains are substituted.

189

It should be observed that type I represents alternating substitution, and type III, unsymmetrical substitution. Porphyrins derived from type III are the most important in nature.

When three types of side chain are present, as in protoporphyrin, the number of possible isomers is 15. Naturally occurring protoporphyrin and certain other compounds derived from it are all related to Fischer's type III etioporphyrin since the methyl groups occupy the same positions. Protoporphyrin is shown in the formula below, where M is methyl (—CH₃), V is vinyl (—CH=CH₂), and P is propionic acid (—CH₂—CH₂—COOH).

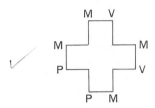

Protoporphyrin type III (No. IX)

This protoporphyrin is type III or, more commonly, No. IX, since it was the ninth in the series of isomers listed by Fischer. It should be noted that etio-, meso-, and deuteroporphyrin (Table 11.1) are not known to occur in nature.

Properties of Porphyrins. The porphyrins are all weak bases because of the tertiary nitrogens in the two *pyrrolene* nuclei in each porphyrin.

Pyrrolene nucleus

With the exception of the etioporphyrins, porphyrins are also acids, because of carboxyl groups in the side chains, and thus exhibit weakly amphoteric character. Porphyrins are easily precipitated from aqueous solutions in the isoelectric regions from about pH 3 to 4.5. The purification of the porphyrins is based largely on partition in organic solvents in the presence of acids.

The most striking physical property of the porphyrins is their color; they have sharply banded absorption spectra in the visible region. In organic solvents, they have four main bands in the visible and a strong band in the near ultraviolet near 400 mμ. For protoporphyrin in ether–acetic acid, the main bands are at 632.5, 576, 537, 502, and 395 mμ.

Solutions of porphyrins in organic solvents or mineral acids exhibit a strong red fluorescence when illuminated by ultraviolet light. The intense fluorescence is so characteristic that it is frequently used for the detection and estimation of small amounts of free porphyrins.

The strong absorption and fluorescence in visible light depends on the resonating character of the conjugated double bonds in the porphyrins. When the double bonds of the methene bridges are reduced by addition of hydrogen atoms, the porphyrins are converted to colorless porphyrinogens, which contain pyrrole nuclei linked by CH₂ groups.

Metal-Porphyrins. Porphyrins possess the ability to combine with almost all kinds of metals although the most important metalloporphyrins are those containing iron and magnesium. Other typical metal derivatives that can be formed include those with zinc, nickel, cobalt, copper, and silver. Although some of the complexes such as those with magnesium are labile in dilute acetic acid, stronger acids are required to remove iron or copper from their complexes.

The metal compounds of porphyrins are not salts, as shown by their solubility in organic solvents and by the fact that complexing occurs with both porphyrin esters and etioporphyrin, which do not contain carboxyl groups. It is now recognized that the metal replaces the two dissociable hydrogen atoms of two pyrrole rings and is simultaneously bound by coordinate valences to the tertiary nitrogen atoms of the pyrrole rings. Since resonance occurs, we do not distinguish among these valences but indicate that the central metal is bound equally to all four nitrogen atoms of the pyrrole rings, which lie in a plane.

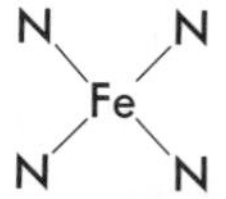

$$\begin{array}{ccc} N & & N \\ & \diagdown Fe \diagup & \\ N & & N \end{array}$$

For simplicity, only the central portion of the iron-porphyrin complex is shown.

This discussion will be restricted mainly to the iron compounds containing protoporphyrin since they have the greatest biological interest. Unfortunately, many important iron-porphyrin compounds were described before their chemistry was clearly understood, and the terminology has undergone a series of revisions as our knowledge has developed. The general types of compounds will be presented, designated in the terminology in most common use.

The iron compounds can exist in two forms depending on the valence of the iron, and these are distinguished by the prefixes *ferro-* for divalent iron and *ferri-* for trivalent iron. Ferroprotoporphyrin, or *heme,* contains divalent iron, but the

group possesses no net charge and may be written as $\left[\begin{array}{cc} N & N \\ & Fe \\ N & N \end{array}\right]^0$. Ferriproto-

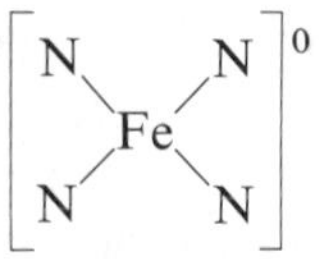

porphyrin, or *hemin,* has a net positive charge and forms salts. It is usually

obtained as the chloride; hence $\left[\begin{array}{cc} N & N \\ & Fe \\ N & N \end{array}\right]^+$ Cl⁻. The free heme is rather

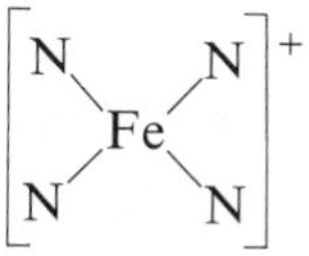

unstable and is rapidly oxidized to hemin. Crystalline hemin is easily obtained by heating a hemoglobin solution with acetic acid containing a little sodium chloride, a procedure frequently employed in legal medicine for the detection of blood.

In the presence of excess alkali, hemin gives rise to a divalent anion of ferriprotoporphyrin hydroxide in which two carboxyl groups of the propionic acid side chains are ionized and the iron is bound to the hydroxyl group of the base and to a mole of water.

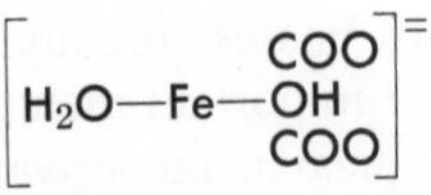

$$\left[\begin{array}{c} COO \\ H_2O-Fe-OH \\ COO \end{array} \right]^{=}$$

Hematin

If hemin is dissolved in excess alkali and then titrated with acid, the compound precipitates when two moles of acid have been added. The resulting neutral compound is known as *hematin, hydroxyhemin,* or ferriprotoporphyrin hydroxide. For simplicity the nitrogens are omitted in this and in the above formula.

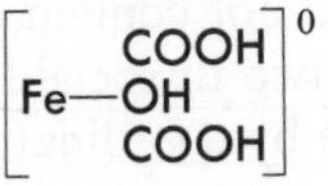

$$\left[\begin{array}{c} COOH \\ Fe-OH \\ COOH \end{array} \right]^{0}$$

An interesting copper-uroporphyrin III complex, *turacin,* is found as an ornamental red pigment in the feathers of certain South African birds of the genus *Turaco.*

Nitrogenous Compounds of Iron-Porphyrins. One mole of a ferro- or ferriporphyrin can combine with two moles of a nitrogenous base to form a complex compound. In the older terminology these compounds were known as *hemochromogens* (ferro) and parahematins (ferri). Here the terminology suggested by W. M. Clark and by Drabkin is adopted and these compounds are referred to as base ferro- (or ferri-) porphyrins. For example, the ferro compound with pyridine is pyridine ferroporphyrin. In these nitrogenous compounds, the nitrogen of the base is linked to the central iron atom, and hexacoordinate structures are formed.

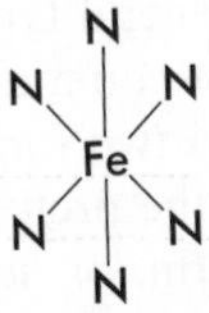

The atoms of N shown at the angles represent the porphyrin nitrogens, which lie in a plane; the vertical N atoms represent the nitrogens of the base, one of which lies above and the other below this plane. This type of complex is analogous to those of ferrous iron such as ferrocyanide ion, which may be pictured in a similar way.

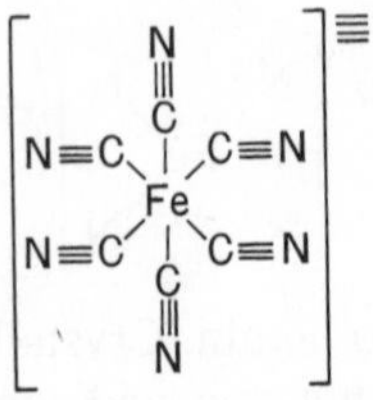

Ferroprotoporphyrin combines with other bases, *e.g.,* piperidine, nicotine, cyanide, and histidine. However, similar compounds are not formed with arginine or lysine. Denatured globin also combines readily with ferroporphyrin, giving globin ferroporphyrin. The base-ferroporphyrin compounds react readily with atmospheric oxygen, converting the divalent iron to the trivalent state. The cyanide ferroporphyrin and the pyridine ferroporphyrin complexes are shown as examples, which may be represented as follows:

Cyanide ferroporphyrin   Pyridine ferroporphyrin

Like the uncombined porphyrins, the metal derivatives as well as the nitrogenous compounds of the metal-porphyrins all possess characteristic absorption spectra which may be utilized both for identification and for quantitative estimation. Formation of pyridine ferroporphyrin has been extensively used for recogniton and measurement of ferroporphyrin both in tissues and in extracts.

HEMOGLOBIN

Among all the nitrogenous derivatives of ferroprotoporphyrin, hemoglobin is unique in its ability to bind molecular oxygen in a loose and easily reversible combination. In this combination, the iron remains in the ferrous state. The symbol Hb is used for unoxygenated or reduced hemoglobin and HbO_2 for oxyhemoglobin.

The hemoglobins are conjugated proteins containing the colorless basic proteins, the globins, and ferroprotoporphyrin, or heme. The hemoglobins of different species differ quantitatively in such properties as crystal form, solubility, amino acid content, affinity for oxygen, and absorption spectra. These differences are due entirely to the protein moiety since the same ferroprotoporphyrin is present in all vertebrate and in many invertebrate hemoglobins.

The two component portions of hemoglobin can be separated by treatment with acids or bases. In the presence of hydrochloric acid and acetone, the globin is precipitated, and the ferroprotoporphyrin remaining in solution is rapidly oxidized.

Hemoglobin + HCl ⟶ globin · HCl + ferroprotoporphyrin
2 Ferroprotoporphyrin + 2HCl + ½O_2 ⟶ 2 ferriprotoporphyrin chloride + H_2O
(heme)   (hemin)

In the presence of a strong reducing agent, such as $Na_2S_2O_4$, the ferroprotoporphyrin is not oxidized.

It was found by Hill and Holden that globin, at pH values near neutrality, recombines with ferroprotoporphyrin to give hemoglobin, or with ferriprotoporphyrin to yield methemoglobin (ferrihemoglobin).

Globin + ferroprotoporphyrin ⟶ hemoglobin
Globin + ferriprotoporphyrin ⟶ methemoglobin

Hemoglobin treated with oxidizing agents is directly converted to methemoglobin (see below), which can be cleaved by acids or bases to yield globin and ferriprotoporphyrin.

The globin from any one species may be combined with ferroprotoporphyrin of another species. The resulting hemoglobin always has the properties of the species from which the globin is derived. Globin can also combine with other ferroporphyrins to give synthetic hemoglobins which bind oxygen reversibly. Such artificial hemoglobins have been prepared with ferromesoporphyrin, ferrohemato-porphyrin, and others. From these findings it is evident that the vinyl groups present in protoporphyrin, but absent in the other compounds, are not essential for the combination with globin.

STRUCTURE OF HEMOGLOBIN

All mammalian hemoglobins have a molecular weight of approximately 67,000 and are essentially tetramers, consisting of four peptide chains, to each of which is bound a heme group. Each human being is capable, genetically, of synthesizing and incorporating into hemoglobin four distinct but related polypeptide chains, designated as α, β, γ, and δ, respectively. With but few exceptions, hemoglobin molecules are constructed by combining two α chains with two β, γ, or δ chains. Normal human adult hemoglobin, called Hb A, contains two α and two β chains; in short form this is designated as Hb A $= \alpha_2^A\beta_2^A$, to indicate that each chain is from Hb A and that there are two chains of each type. Correspondingly, normal human fetal hemoglobin is Hb F $= \alpha_2^A\gamma_2^F$.

The individual chains can be separated by removing the heme at an acid pH value, followed by ion exchange chromatography on a carboxylate resin, by countercurrent distribution or by electrophoresis. The complete amino acid sequence of the α, β, and γ chains has been elucidated by the work of three groups of investigators: Braunitzer and coworkers, R. J. Hill and colleagues, and Schroeder and associates. The sequences are shown in Fig. 11.1 with the structures aligned to permit comparison of the sequences. The α chain contains 141 residues, and the β and γ chains contain 146 residues; nevertheless, it is evident that there is close similarity among them.

By themselves the sequences in the three chains yield little information concerning the functional properties of hemoglobin; however, when they are considered in conjunction with x-ray crystallographic studies on the conformation of the chains, a wealth of information emerges. The work of Kendrew and coworkers on the structure of myoglobin has been discussed (page 158). Perutz and associates have demonstrated that each of the four chains in Hb A possesses an over-all conformation similar to that of myoglobin, and from the positions of the residues in myoglobin and the convolutions of the chains in hemoglobin, they assigned the positions of the residues in the helical and nonhelical regions of the α and β chains of the latter protein.

Figure 11.2 shows in a plane some of these relationships for the β chain only. The helical portions are labeled A, B, C, etc. Since the β and γ chains are of equal length and very similar in amino acid sequence, the relationships presumably apply to the γ chain also. The abbreviations for the residues that differ in the β and γ chains are shown in rectangles. The over-all structure of the α chain is also given by the structure in the figure, with a few differences. The interhelical region AB should be lengthened by two residues, and CD should be shortened by one;

α Val·Leu·Ser·Pro·Ala·Asp·Lys·Thr·Asg·Val·Lys·Ala·Ala·Try·Gly·Lys·Val·Gly·Ala·His·Ala·Gly·Glu·Tyr·

β Val·His·Leu·Thr·Pro·Glu·Glu·Lys·Ser·Ala·Val·Thr·Ala·Leu·Try·Gly·Lys·Val·Asg·Val· Asp·Glu·Val·

γ Gly·His·Phe·Thr·Glu·Glu·Asp·Lys·Ala·Thr·Ileu·Thr·Ser·Leu·Try·Gly·Lys·Val·Asg·Val· Glu·Asp·Ala·

10   20

α Gly·Ala·Glu·Ala·Leu·Glu·Arg·Met·Phe·Leu·Ser·Phe·Pro·Thr·Thr· Lys·Thr·Tyr·Phe·Pro·His·Phe·Asp·Leu·

β Gly·Gly·Glu·Ala·Leu·Gly·Arg·Leu·Leu·Val·Val·Tyr·Pro·Try·Thr·Glm·Arg·Phe·Phe·Glu·Ser·Phe·Gly·Asp·Leu·

γ Gly·Gly·Glu·Thr·Leu·Gly·Arg·Leu·Leu·Val·Val·Tyr·Pro·Try·Thr·Glm·Arg·Phe·Phe·Asp·Ser·Phe·Gly·Asg·Leu·

30   40

α Ser·His·Gly·Ser·Ala·   Glm·Val·Lys·Gly·His·Gly·Lys·Lys·Val·Ala·Asp·Ala·Leu·Thr·Asg·

β Ser·Thr·Pro·Asp·Ala·Val·Met·Gly·Asg·Pro·Lys·Val·Lys·Ala·His·Gly·Lys·Lys·Val·Leu·Gly·Ala·Phe·Ser·Asp·

γ Ser·Ser·Ala·Ser·Ala·Ileu·Met·Gly·Asg·Pro·Lys·Val·Lys·Ala·His·Gly·Lys·Lys·Val·Leu·Thr·Ser·Leu·Gly·Asp·

50   60   70   90

α Ala·Val·Ala·His·Val·Asp·Asp·Met·Pro·Asg·Ala·Leu·Ser·Ala·Leu·Ser·Asp·Leu·His·Ala·His·Lys·Leu·Arg·Val·

β Gly·Leu·Ala·His·Leu·Asp·Asp·Leu·Lys·Gly·Thr·Phe·Ala·Thr·Leu·Ser·Glm·Leu·His·Cys·Asp·Lys·Leu·His·Val·

γ Ala·Ileu·Lys·His·Leu·Asp·Asp·Leu·Lys·Gly·Thr·Phe·Ala·Glm·Leu·Ser·Glu·Leu·His·Cys·Asp·Lys·Leu·His·Val·

80   100   110

α Asp·Pro·Val·Asg·Phe·Lys·Leu·Leu·Ser·His·Cys·Leu·Leu·Val·Thr·Leu·Ala·Ala·His·Leu·Pro·Ala·Glu·Phe·Thr·

β Asp·Pro·Glm·Asp·Phe·Arg·Leu·Leu·Gly·Asg·Val·Leu·Val·Cys·Val·Leu·Ala·His·His·Phe·Gly·Lys·Glu·Phe·Thr·

γ Asp·Pro·Glu·Asg·Phe·Lys·Leu·Leu·Gly·Asg·Val·Leu·Val·Thr·Val·Leu·Ala·Ileu·His·Phe·Gly·Lys·Glu·Phe·Thr·

100   120

120   130

α Pro·Ala·Val·His·Ala·Ser·Leu·Asp·Lys·Phe·Leu·Ala·Ser·Val·Ser·Thr·Val·Leu·Thr·Ser·Lys·Tyr·Arg

β Pro·Pro·Val·Glm·Ala·Ala·Tyr·Glm·Lys·Val·Val·Ala·Gly·Val·Ala·Asp·Ala·Leu·Ala·His·Lys·Tyr·His

γ Pro·Glu·Val·Glm·Ala·Ser·Try·Glm·Lys·Met·Val·Thr·Gly·Val·Ala·Ser·Ala·Leu·Ser·Ser·Arg·Tyr·His

130   141

140   146

Fig. 11.1. Amino acid sequences in α, β, and γ chains derived from human hemoglobins; α and β from adult hemoglobin, and α and γ from fetal hemoglobin. Gaps are left in depicting the sequences only in order to emphasize sequence similarities in homologous portions of the three chains. In these sequences, *Asg* = asparagine and *Glm* = glutamine. The numbers at the top indicate every tenth residue position in the α chain; at the bottom the numbers refer to residues in the β and γ chains.

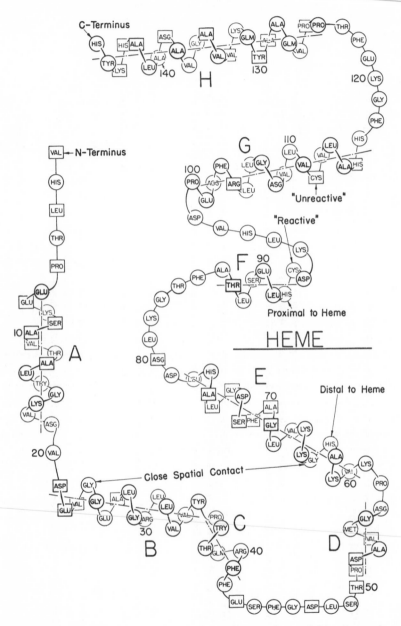

Fig. 11.2. The conformation of the β chain of human hemoglobin shown in a plane. Regions of α-helix are designated *A, B, C, D*, etc., with the bold face residues facing the same plane. Every tenth residue is numbered from the amino- or N-terminus. The heme residues are between regions *E* and *F*. Amino acid replacements in certain abnormal hemoglobins are indicated. The cysteine residue at position 93 is "reactive" with thiol reagents. (*From W. A. Schroeder, Ann. Rev. Biochem., 32, 301, 1963.*)

the helix D (residues 54 to 58) is absent since five residues in the β and γ chains have no counterpart in the α chain. It should be emphasized, however, that these differences between the α and β chains are not in the neighborhood of the heme group positions.

It is apparent that the heme group lies within a crevice. The hydrophobic vinyl groups of the porphyrin are surrounded by hydrophobic amino acid side chains. The two propionate side chains of each heme lie in juxtaposition to positively charged nitrogens of a lysine and an arginine. The iron component of the heme is closely coordinated to an imidazole side chain of histidine (residues No. 92 in β and γ, No. 87 in the α chain), as had been predicted by Wyman from the nature of the oxygen-binding curves (Chap. 34). The iron is somewhat more removed from and hence more loosely bound, if at all, to the histidine residue at position 58 in the α chain and position 63 in the β and γ chains. A molecule of water may normally lie between the iron atom and this histidine, and oxygen binding occurs at this site.

In the complete structure of hemoglobin, the four chains mesh together with little free space in the interior. The forces linking the four chains do not involve covalent bonding and presumably involve secondary forces, $i.e.$, hydrogen bonding, salt links, or hydrophobic bonds. Of interest is the hydrophobic interior of the molecule, with resultant low dielectric properties, whereas the exterior hydrophilic residues give the molecule its high solubility and charge characteristics.

It should be emphasized that the unique feature of hemoglobin is not its ability to bind oxygen per se. Ferroporphyrin and its other nitrogenous derivatives (base ferroporphyrins) can also bind oxygen, but, in these instances, the iron is rapidly oxidized to the ferric state. What is unique about hemoglobin is the formation of a stable oxygen complex in which the iron remains in the ferrous form. This special behavior is due to the fact that the heme moiety lies within a cover of hydrophobic groups of the globin. This is also suggested by the behavior of a model system. The hemochromogen of phenylethylimidazole and the diethyl ester of heme readily combine with O_2. In water this oxygenated iron is rapidly oxidized to the ferric state; if embedded in a film of polystyrene, the iron is readily oxygenated and deoxygenated with no change in valence. Globin provides a similar hydrophobic, low-dielectric environment for the heme moiety, as indicated by the x-ray analysis of both myoglobin and hemoglobin.

The structure of oxyhemoglobin may be represented in a simplified form, as shown below, with the four porphyrin nitrogens at the angles.

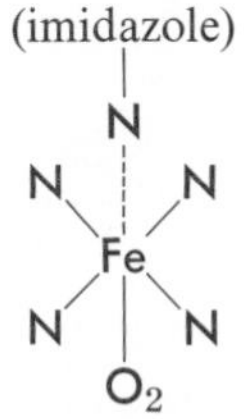

(imidazole)
|
N
|
N   N
\ | /
Fe
/ | \
N   N
|
O_2

Molecules that contain unpaired electrons are magnetic; those in which all the electrons are paired are diamagnetic—$i.e.$, there is no magnetic moment. Both Hb and O_2 possess magnetic moments. However, when these two molecules combine, the resulting HbO_2 is diamagnetic because all the unpaired electrons in both molecules have become paired. These magnetic changes probably represent the best available evidence that oxygen combines with the iron of the hemoglobin molecule. These changes are also in accord with the observed stoichiometry of the reaction, *i.e.*, each atom of iron can bind one molecule of oxygen.

As in the case of the base ferroporphyrins, hemoglobin and oxyhemoglobin have distinctive absorption spectra. Figure 11.3 shows the spectra for these two substances. Quantitative estimations of Hb and HbO_2 are frequently made by spectrophotometric methods. It may be noted that Hb has a single band at 552.5 mμ, whereas HbO_2 shows bands at 541.5 and 576 mμ in this part of the spectrum. The strong bands near 400 mμ of all hemoproteins are frequently called Soret bands after their discoverer. The absorption near 275 mμ is due to the presence of aromatic amino acids in the protein.

Carboxyhemoglobin (Carbon Monoxide Hemoglobin). Hemoglobin and the nitrogenous base derivatives of ferroprotoporphyrin bind carbon monoxide (CO). Car-

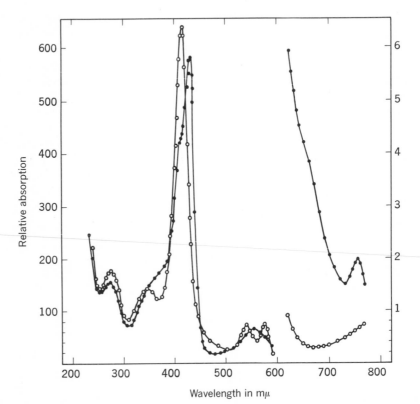

Fig. 11.3. Absorption spectra of human hemoglobin ($\bullet$) and oxyhemoglobin ($\circ$) given on the same relative basis. The scale on the right is multiplied 100 times in order to show the absorption curves above 600 mμ. (*After A. E. Sidwell, Jr., R. H. Munch, E. S. G. Barron, and T. R. Hogness, J. Biol. Chem.*, **123**, 335, 1938.)

boxyhemoglobin and other iron compounds with carbon monoxide are sensitive to light, and a photochemical dissociation is produced.

Methemoglobin. As already mentioned, when Hb is oxidized, methemoglobin (metHb), which contains ferric iron, is formed. MetHb cannot bind oxygen or carbon monoxide. Being positively charged, however, because of the additional charge on the ferric iron, it combines with hydroxide ion in alkaline solution, or with chloride and other anions in acidic solutions (cf. hemin). The brown color of metHb solutions changes on addition of ions, which form new compounds. The cyanide metHb complex is bright red. Spectroscopically distinctive derivatives are also formed with azide, sulfide, cyanate, nitric oxide, hydrogen peroxide, fluoride, and other substances.

The oxidation of hemoglobin to methemoglobin is readily accomplished by addition of any one of a large number of oxidizing agents such as peroxides, ferricyanide, quinones, etc. Treatment of oxyhemoglobin with ferricyanide or other oxidizing agents causes complete liberation of the bound oxygen and conversion to methemoglobin. In suitable gasometric apparatus, this provides a rapid method for the quantitative estimation of oxyhemoglobin. It may be noted that fully oxygenated hemoglobin is more resistant to oxidation by oxidizing agents than reduced hemoglobin.

OTHER IRON-PORPHYRIN PROTEINS

Cytochromes. In 1885, MacMunn observed spectroscopically that many tissues contain pigments that have absorption characteristics similar to those of hematin (ferriprotoporphyrin) and its derivatives; he named these pigments histohematins. In 1925, Keilin confirmed MacMunn's observations and pointed out the biological importance of these pigments. Keilin renamed them cytochromes (cell pigments) to avoid the earlier confusion of nomenclature. One of the cytochromes, cytochrome c, has been obtained in crystalline form; its chemistry will be considered here. The other cytochromes, as well as their important biological role, will be discussed later (Chap. 17).

Cytochrome c has a molecular weight of 12,400; it contains 0.45 per cent iron, or one atom of iron per molecule, and is relatively stable to heat and to acids. In contrast to hemoglobin, acid-acetone does not separate the iron-porphyrin from the protein. Cytochrome c may be represented as follows.

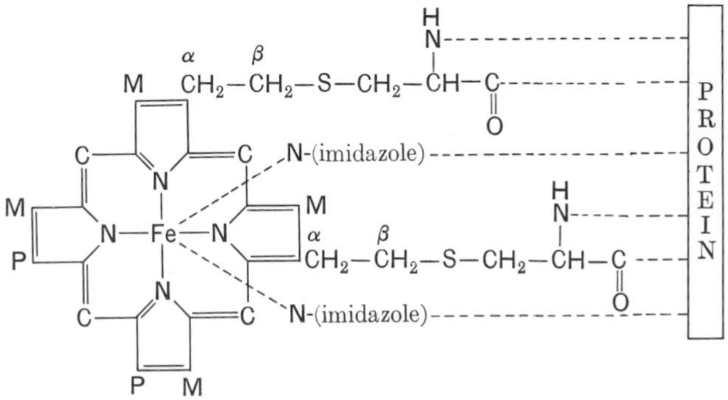

The iron-containing group is derived from protoporphyrin, but the two vinyl side chains are reduced and linked in thioether bonds with cysteine residues of the protein. Cleavage of the thioether bonds with silver salts gives rise to hematoporphyrin. The structure of cytochrome c is indicated with the cysteine side chains attached to the β-carbon atoms of the reduced vinyl groups, although it is still uncertain whether the sulfur atom is on the α- or β-carbon atom.

It has been suggested that two imidazole nitrogen atoms from histidine residues (as shown above) or that one imidazole of a histidine residue and one ϵ-amino nitrogen of a lysine residue are attached to the iron. Unlike hemoglobin, at physiological pH values, ferrocytochrome c does not combine with oxygen or carbon monoxide, and the ferri form combines only slowly with cyanide or azide.

The complete amino acid sequences of heart cytochrome c of a number of species have been elucidated. The protein consists of a single peptide chain of 104 residues (Fig. 11.4). The α-amino group at the amino-terminus is acetylated, a feature apparently common to all mammalian cytochromes. In all cytochromes of the c type that have been investigated, a histidine residue (position 18) is adjacent to a cysteine residue in a favorable position for binding to the iron. There are two amino acid residues between the cysteines which are linked to the porphyrin; however, these two residues may differ in various species. The differences in amino acid composition among the cytochromes c of various species are considered in Chap. 31.

A noteworthy feature of this basic protein is the bunching of the basic residues in Arg·Lys·, Lys·His·Lys·, Lys·Lys·Lys·, and three Lys·Lys· sequences. The absence of thiol groups and disulfide bonds is also striking.

Peroxidases. These enzymes (Chap. 19), in conjunction with hydrogen peroxide, catalyze the oxidation of certain organic compounds. Crystalline horseradish peroxidase is reversibly dissociated by acetone and hydrochloric acid to give an

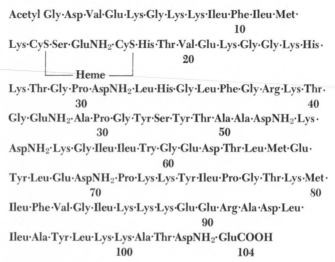

FIG. 11.4. The amino acid sequence of human heart cytochrome c. (*From H. Matsubara and E. L. Smith, J. Biol. Chem., 237, PC 3575, 1962.*)

inert colorless protein and ferriprotoporphyrin. In the intact enzyme, the iron is ferric and combined with one hydroxyl group. There also seems to be one carboxyl group combined with the iron; imidazole groups do not appear to play a role in this enzyme.

Peroxidase forms spectroscopically well-defined derivatives with various anions that can displace hydroxyl ion; these include cyanide, azide, fluoride, and the substrate, hydrogen peroxide. In its ability to bind such compounds, peroxidase resembles methemoglobin; however, methemoglobin possesses only weak peroxidatic activity. Reduction of peroxidase gives ferrous iron, which can combine with carbon monoxide. The ferrous compound does not bind oxygen. Further discussion of the enzymic behavior of peroxidase is given in Chap. 19.

Crystalline peroxidases have also been obtained from leukocytes (myeloperoxidase or verdoperoxidase) and from milk (lactoperoxidase). Both these enzymes contain greenish ferriporphyrins of unknown constitution. Neither can be split by acid-acetone, as can hemoglobin and horseradish peroxidase, or by silver salts, as can cytochrome c.

Catalases. These enzymes are present in all aerobic organisms and catalyze the decomposition of hydrogen peroxide and other reactions (Chap. 19). A number of catalases from different sources have been prepared in crystalline form. They contain ferriprotoporphyrin, which is easily removed by acid-acetone; recombination has not been achieved. The enzyme gives characteristic derivatives with cyanide, fluoride, azide, and other anions and with its substrate, hydrogen peroxide. The iron is not readily reduced to the divalent state.

Further discussion of certain of the enzymes which are hemoproteins is presented in Chap. 19.

CHLOROPHYLL

Present evidence suggests that chlorophyll is combined with protein in a lipoprotein complex that also contains carotenoids. The protein complex is broken by solvents like acetone or alcohol which also extract the pigments. In higher plants, two different forms of chlorophyll are found, a and b, which are present in a ratio of about 3:1. Chlorophylls c and d are found in certain algae and diatoms.

Chlorophyll a may be considered a model for this series of compounds. It is a magnesium-porphyrin derivative in which one pyrrole ring is partially reduced. The presence of a fifth isocyclic ring should be noted. The structure of chlorophyll a was determined largely by the work of Willstätter and his associates and by H. Fischer and his coworkers (see following page for structure). In view of the possibilities of resonance, other formulations with different positions of the double bonds are possible. It should be observed that both acid side chains are esterified, one as a methyl ester and the other as a phytyl ester. The structure of phytol has been presented (page 80). The non-ionic magnesium atom is held by two covalent and two coordinate linkages. In chlorophyll b, the methyl group at position 3 (above formula, in ring at upper right) is replaced by a formyl group, —CHO.

Treatment of chlorophyll with weak acid readily removes the magnesium atom

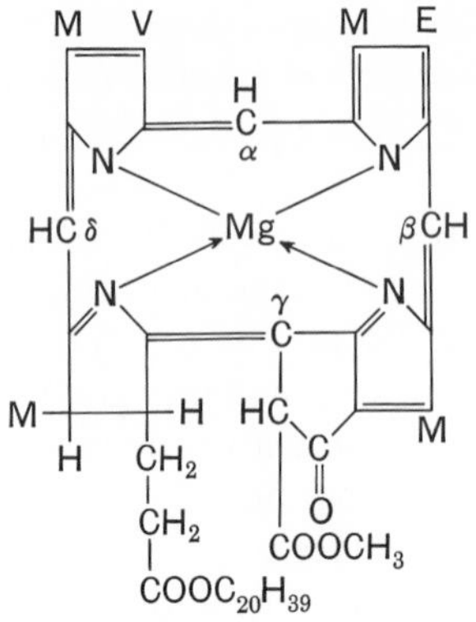

Chlorophyll a (according to H. Fischer)

to give *pheophytin.* Saponification with alkali gives rise to *chlorophyllides,* salts of the liberated carboxyl groups. Hydrolysis of chlorophyll by the enzyme *chlorophyllase* removes the phytyl group.

Drastic degradation of the chlorophylls gives pyrroetioporphyrin.

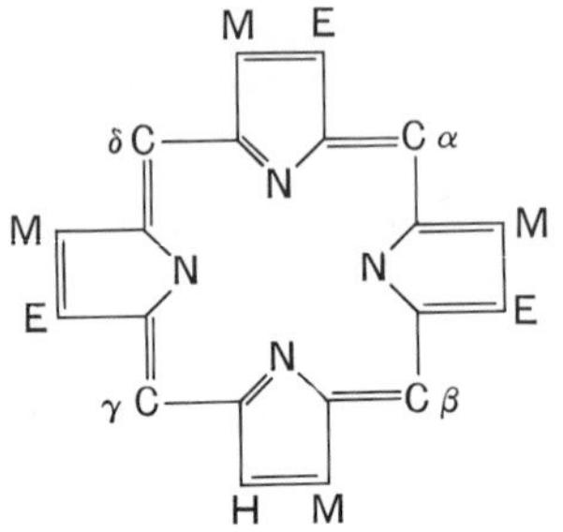

Pyrroetioporphyrin

This compound differs from etioporphyrin in containing a hydrogen atom in place of an ethyl group at position 6. The arrangement of the other groupings is identical with that in etioporphyrin III derived from protoporphyrin, indicating the close biological relationship of all these compounds.

REFERENCES

Books

Falk, J. E., Lemberg, R., and Morton, R. K., eds., "Hematin Enzymes," Pergamon Press, New York, 1961.

Fischer, H., and Orth, H., "Die Chemie des Pyrrols," Bd. I, Akademische Verlagsgesellschaft, M.b.H., Leipzig, 1934.

Fischer, H., and Orth, H., "Die Chemie des Pyrrols," Bd. II, 1 Hälfte, Akademische Verlagsgesellschaft, M.b.H., Leipzig, 1937.

Fischer, H., and Stern, A., "Die Chemie des Pyrrols," Bd. II, 2 Hälfte, Akademische Verlagsgesellschaft, M.b.H., Leipzig, 1940.

Ingram, V. M., "Hemoglobin and Its Abnormalities," Charles C Thomas, Publisher, Springfield, Ill., 1961.

Lemberg, R., and Legge, J. W., "Hematin Compounds and Bile Pigments, Their Constitution, Metabolism and Function," Interscience Publishers, Inc., New York, 1949.
Rabinowitch, E. I., "Photosynthesis," vol. I, Interscience Publishers, Inc., New York, 1945.

Review Articles

Corwin, A. H., The Chemistry of the Porphyrins, in H. Gilman, ed., "Organic Chemistry," vol. II, pp. 1259–1292, John Wiley & Sons, Inc., New York, 1943.
Schroeder, W. A., The Hemoglobins, *Ann. Rev. Biochem.*, **32**, 301–320, 1963.
Steele, C. C., Chlorophyll, in H. Gilman, ed., "Organic Chemistry," vol II, pp. 1293–1314, John Wiley & Sons, Inc., New York, 1943.

12. Enzymes

Nature and Classification

The outstanding characteristic of nearly all biochemical reactions is that they occur with great rapidity through the mediation of natural catalysts called *enzymes*. It is the high degree of specificity and the great efficiency of enzymes which direct biochemical reactions rapidly through defined pathways. Enzymes are universally present in living organisms, and the occurrence of metabolic reactions common to all cells reflects the specificity of the responsible enzymes.

Enzymic reactions were used by man long before written history. The discovery of fermentation to produce wines was attributed by the Greeks to Bacchus. The making of cheese, the leavening of bread, the manufacture of vinegar are enzymic processes which stem from antiquity. These practical aspects of enzyme chemistry have occupied an important place in the history of enzymology. The breweries and their research laboratories have provided much information concerning the processes by which living cells utilize sugar, for the fundamental reactions of fermentation in a yeast culture are much the same as in the tissues of mammals. Indeed, the name enzyme, coined by W. Kühne, means "in yeast," but the word is now used to connote a biological catalyst, regardless of origin.

The recognition that living cells are responsible for alcoholic and other types of fermentation was one of the great achievements of the nineteenth century. The work of Louis Pasteur and others destroyed the ancient beliefs that fermentation and putrefaction could spontaneously generate life and established that these chemical processes were caused by microscopic living organisms. However, Pasteur concluded that these processes could be performed only by intact living cells. Enzymology received a great impetus when the Büchner brothers showed that yeast cells, ground with sand and squeezed under high pressures, gave a cell-free juice capable of fermenting sugar with the production of alcohol and carbon dioxide. It is now apparent that yeast juice contains a complex mixture of enzymes which can catalyze these transformations and that enzymes can function extra- as well as intracellularly.

A substantial part of the study of the chemistry of living cells is today devoted to the enzymes, for it is now understood that all physiological functions, *e.g.*, muscular contraction, nerve conduction, excretion by the kidney, etc., are inextricably linked to the activity of enzymes. A complex process, such as muscular contraction, which requires the utilization of energy, may be dissected into a series of enzyme-catalyzed reactions. Many of these reactions have now been studied in vitro as isolated systems with pure, crystalline enzymes.

Even relatively simple reactions that occur in living cells may be catalyzed by enzymes when the noncatalyzed reaction is too slow for physiological needs. An example is the reversible combination of carbon dioxide and water to form carbonic acid, which in blood is catalyzed by the specific enzyme, carbonic anhydrase. The noncatalyzed reaction would not permit CO_2 interchange between the blood and the tissues, and between the blood and the lungs, at rates sufficient for physiological requirements.

NATURE OF CATALYSIS

Enzymes are catalysts peculiar to living matter, but catalysis itself is a familiar chemical phenomenon. A *catalyst* is defined as a substance that accelerates a chemical reaction but is not consumed in the over-all process. The use of platinum to catalyze the union of the elements of water is a familiar example from inorganic chemistry. The hydrolysis of sucrose is catalyzed by acid. The important characteristic of such reactions is that the amount of catalyst bears no stoichiometric relationship to the quantity of substance altered. The efficiency of a catalyst can be expressed as the moles of substrate transformed per mole of catalyst in unit time. The catalytic efficiency of enzymes is extremely high; this can be seen from the fact that pure enzymes may catalyze the transformation of as many as 10,000 to 1,000,000 moles of substrate per minute per mole of enzyme.

Another important aspect of catalysis is the directed nature of the reaction. It is a common experience in organic chemistry to perform reactions at a high temperature or pressure and find that the desired compound is obtained in small yield with a mixture of other products. In general, catalyzed reactions give a more uniform reaction, *i.e.*, the yield of products is high, and this is usually true of enzymic reactions.

Thermodynamic Principles. In order to discuss the nature of enzymic catalysis, it is necessary first to introduce some thermodynamic principles. Whereas chemistry generally is concerned with molecular transformations, the occurrence and extent of such phenomena are governed by the flow of energy. This is the subject matter of the science of thermodynamics, the major concepts of which can be stated in two unifying principles, the first and second laws of thermodynamics. These laws permit one to understand the direction of chemical events, *i.e.*, whether a reversible reaction will proceed from left to right or from right to left as it is written, whether the progress of such reactions will permit the accomplishment of useful work or whether, in order for the reaction to proceed, energy must be delivered from an external source. The principles of thermodynamics are stated in terms of parameters which were originally invented so as to permit description of energy transformation in physical and chemical systems: enthalpy, entropy, and free energy. Of these, the last has proved to be most useful in understanding biochemical events.

The first law of thermodynamics is essentially the law of conservation of energy. Even in dealing with a finite system of molecules within a container, it is generally impossible to ascertain the magnitude of U, the total energy of that system. But if, to the system, energy is added as heat Q, then

$$Q = \Delta U + W \tag{1}$$

where ΔU is the change in total energy, and W is the total work, if any, that has been accomplished.

In many instances the addition of energy as heat Q to the system may result in a change of volume, the pressure remaining constant. This change, $P\Delta V$, is in effect a form of work and, hence, is a component of the term W in equation (1). However, this is rarely a useful form of work and hence it has been found convenient to combine this component of W with the change in U, thereby defining a new term, H, *enthalpy* or heat content. The change in enthalpy in any process, at constant pressure, is:

$$\Delta H = \Delta U + P\Delta V \tag{2}$$

The first law can then be restated as

$$Q = \Delta H + W' \tag{3}$$

where W' is, therefore, *useful* work accomplished by input of the quantity of heat Q.

The first law, stated above, constitutes an adequate description of an ideal, reversible system, *i.e.*, one in which the energy utilized to alter the system is released as an exactly equal amount of energy, available to perform yet other work, when the system reverts to its original state. In fact, however, such instances of perfect reversibility do not occur. Some fraction of the increase in enthalpy resulting from adding energy to the system is not available to do useful work when the reverse process is allowed to proceed. Thus, it is common experience that most physical and chemical processes occur spontaneously in only one direction, *e.g.*, water runs downhill, protons and hydroxyl ions react, giving off heat. However, heating water does not drive it uphill, nor does it result in a net redissociation of water to a mixture of protons and hydroxyl ions. All such processes can be described in terms of the concept of equilibrium. Spontaneous changes tend toward the equilibrium state, not away from it; this is a manner of stating the second law of thermodynamics. The simplest description of the second law of thermodynamics is in terms of another thermodynamic quantity, the *entropy*, S, that fraction of the enthalpy which may not be utilized for the performance of useful work since, in most cases, it has increased the random motions of the molecules in the system. Hence, more generally, entropy is a measure of randomness or disorder. The product $T \times S$, in which T is the absolute temperature, represents energy that is wasted in the form of random molecular motions. In terms of S, the second law of thermodynamics states that given the opportunity, any system will undergo spontaneous change in that direction which results in an increase in entropy. Equilibrium is attained when entropy has reached a maximum; no further change may occur spontaneously unless additional energy is supplied from outside the system.

Let us now consider the consequence of adding heat to a system. Since heat represents the kinetic energy of random molecular motion, the addition of heat increases the entropy. If the system is at equilibrium, it follows that

$$Q = T\Delta S \tag{4}$$

If the system is not at equilibrium, however, change in the system may spontaneously increase the entropy even without addition of heat. Thus, in general for systems not at equilibrium,

$$T\Delta S > Q \tag{5}$$

If we combine equations (3) and (4), *i.e.*, combine the first and second laws, for a system at equilibrium we find that

$$\Delta H = T\Delta S - W' \tag{6}$$

However, in biochemistry we are rarely interested in the equilibrium state. Rather, interest is in reactions proceeding, as they must, in the direction which approaches toward equilibrium and at a single temperature. For such systems, equation (5) modifies the statement of equation (6) so that

$$\Delta H < T\Delta S - W' \tag{7}$$

This permits introduction of the thermodynamic parameter of greatest general utility in biochemistry, the quantity called "free energy," F. It is defined as

$$F = H - TS \tag{8}$$

In general, the change in free energy ΔF is the energy that becomes available to be utilized for the accomplishment of work, if there are appropriate means, as a system proceeds toward equilibrium. For a process at a single temperature,

$$\Delta F = \Delta H - T\Delta S \tag{9}$$

This is the form in which the laws of thermodynamics are most readily expressed for description of biochemical systems. For a system that is not at equilibrium,

$$\Delta F = -W' \tag{10}$$

Hence, systems not at equilibrium proceed spontaneously only in the direction of *negative* free energy change. When equilibrium has been attained, no further change in free energy can occur spontaneously. Once the system is at equilibrium, the *available* free energy content is zero. Conversely, a system already at equilibrium can be brought to a state remote from equilibrium only if, by some means, free energy can be made available to it. Utilization of free energy in this manner constitutes the performance of work.

Chemical Equilibria. The phenomenon of diffusion demonstrates that the free energy of a solute in solution increases with its concentration. Solutes in a concentrated solution placed in contact with a dilute solution diffuse into the latter until a uniform concentration is achieved. Since this occurs spontaneously, the free energy change for dilution by such diffusion must be negative. The variation of free energy with concentration is logarithmic,

$$F = F° + RT \ln [C] \tag{11}$$

where R is the gas constant, T is absolute temperature, $[C]$ is the molar concentration of solute, and $F°$ is the "standard free energy," *i.e.*, the free energy at a concentration of one mole per liter. Our interest, however, is not in such absolute values, but in the changes associated with chemical reactions.

For any chemical reaction,

$$A + B \rightleftharpoons C + D$$

and

$$\Delta F = \Delta F^\circ + RT \ln \frac{[C][D]}{[A][B]} \tag{12}$$

where $\Delta F^\circ = F_C^\circ + F_D^\circ - F_A^\circ - F_B^\circ$. Equation (12) is applicable under all conditions. At equilibrium, however, ΔF must be zero. Hence, if $\dfrac{[C][D]}{[A][B]} = K$, where K is the equilibrium constant, then

$$\Delta F^\circ = -RT \ln K \tag{13}$$

or at 37°,

$$\Delta F^\circ = -1{,}420 \log_{10} K \tag{14}$$

Thus, the standard free energy of a chemical reaction, *i.e.*, the free energy made available by reaction of a mole of each reactant to form a mole of each product under standard conditions, can be calculated from measurement of the equilibrium constant. If ΔF° is negative, the process may proceed spontaneously; if it is positive, the reaction can be made to proceed only if, by some means, external free energy is made available.

Rates of Chemical Reactions. For the same chemical reaction, $A + B \rightleftharpoons C + D$, proceeding by the simplest reaction mechanisms, the velocity of the forward reaction v_1 is proportional to the concentration of A and B, or

$$v_1 = k_1[A][B] \tag{15}$$

For the reverse reaction,

$$v_2 = k_2[C][D] \tag{16}$$

where k_1 and k_2 are the individual velocity constants.

At equilibrium, $v_1 = v_2$; hence

$$k_1[A][B] = k_2[C][D]$$

or

$$K = \frac{k_1}{k_2} = \frac{[C][D]}{[A][B]} \tag{17}$$

Thus K, the thermodynamic equilibrium constant, is also the relationship between the velocity constants. As we have seen, the actual net direction in which reaction will proceed is determined by the initial concentration of each reactant and the value of K; spontaneous reaction always proceeds in the direction of negative free energy change, *i.e.*, toward equilibrium.

If the initial system is not at equilibrium, reaction proceeds at a rate determined by the velocity constants, k_1 and k_2. Frequently, however, in common experience, a system of components remote from equilibrium appears to be in a *metastable* state. It should proceed by increase in entropy and/or decrease in free energy to the equilibrium state, yet fails to do so. This is obviously true of flammable organic compounds exposed to air; a spark may be required for ignition. Or a boulder, lying in a trough on a hillside, will roll downhill only if lifted over the barrier that holds it in check. Many chemical systems behave similarly. For reaction to proceed, energy must first be delivered that increases the incidence of excited or reactive molecules in the system. It is precisely for this reason that the chemist must frequently heat a reaction mixture in order to initiate the reaction. As shown in Fig. 12.1, as reaction then proceeds, the energy of activation E_a reemerges and the total energy change resulting from the reaction is the calculated ΔH and E_a. Further consideration of energy of activation is given later (page 229).

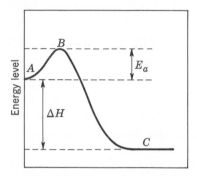

FIG. 12.1. The chemical compound A is in a metastable state. Energy of activation E_a is required for transition from A to B before the reaction liberates energy. In the change from B to C, E_a is recovered, and energy is made available according to the difference in state ΔH between A and C. At C, the new compound has reached an equilibrium state.

Living organisms usually do not influence the rate of metabolic reactions by invoking changes in temperature, nor can most survive at high temperatures. Hence a catalyzed reaction is necessary to make the process go fast enough at the temperature of the organism. Moreover, if important biological reactions proceeded without catalysts, no control could be exercised over their rates. If the organism loses control of the rates of important reactions, the maintenance of normal structure and function becomes impossible and the organism dies.

NATURE OF ENZYMES

Knowledge of the role of enzymes as catalysts has grown with knowledge of catalysis in general. Berzelius, who was one of the first to define and recognize the nature of catalysis, proposed in 1837 that "ferments" were catalysts produced by living cells. Nevertheless, little was known concerning the chemical nature of enzymes until the beginning of this century, when there was a growing conviction that enzymes were probably protein in nature. The announcement by J. B. Sumner in 1926 of the isolation of the enzyme urease as a crystalline protein was greeted with some skepticism, but in the next few years Northrop and Kunitz reported the isolation of crystalline pepsin, trypsin, and chymotrypsin. Since that time, several hundred enzymes have been obtained in highly purified form and about 100 of these in the crystalline state; they have all proved to be proteins.

Until 1926, much of the effort in studying enzymes was concerned with the nature of the process, *i.e.*, enzymes were characterized by the chemical reactions that they catalyzed. With the availability of crystalline enzymes, they have also been investigated from the viewpoint of protein chemistry. Indeed, a great deal of our present knowledge of the chemistry of proteins has come from study of crystalline enzymes and from attempts to understand the nature and mode of action of these catalysts. For the chemical and physical properties of enzymes, we may refer to the general chemistry of the proteins already presented. Many enzyme proteins have been cited as examples in the discussion of the properties of proteins.

It has been noted in an earlier chapter that the largest part of the dry weight of the tissues is protein. Since it is now recognized that the tissue enzymes are proteins, it is appropriate to inquire as to the relationship of the tissue proteins to the enzymes. Indeed, it has been suggested by some investigators that most of the proteins of actively functioning tissues such as liver and kidney, with the exception of some structural elements like collagen and elastin, are really enzymes. Regardless of the exact fraction of total body protein that possesses enzymic functions, it is clear that there must be a large number of different protein enzymes in the tissues in order to account for the myriad of known metabolic reactions.

Nomenclature. Enzymes are usually named in terms of the reactions that are catalyzed. A customary practice is to add the suffix *-ase* to a major part of the name of the substrate. The enzyme that attacks urea is urease, arginine is acted upon by arginase, tyrosine by tyrosinase, uric acid by uricase, etc. In addition, an older nomenclature has persisted, and we find such names as pepsin, trypsin, rennin, etc. Enzymes may also be classified by groups that catalyze similar chemical reactions, such as proteinases, lipases, oxidases, etc. An International Commission on Enzymes has devised a complete but rather complex system of nomenclature for enzymes. However, since this has not yet gained wide acceptance or general usage, it is not employed in this book.

As knowledge of the chemistry of the enzymes has developed, it has become apparent that many of them possess chemical groups that are non-amino acid in nature. These conjugated proteins (*holoenzymes*) may also be classified chemically in terms of these special groupings or prosthetic groups (page 122). Thus, an enzyme may frequently be dissociated into a protein component, termed the *apoenzyme,* and a nonprotein organic *prosthetic* portion. As an example, reddish-brown catalase (Chap. 11) dissociates in acid to yield a colorless protein and ferri-protoporphyrin. In other instances, an enzyme may contain only amino acids and a metal. For example, there are several enzymes known which are copper proteins; ascorbic acid oxidase is one of these. In this enzyme, the copper is tightly bound and is not separated readily from the protein. Many other enzymes require the addition of metal ions in order to activate the enzyme. In some instances these metal ions, frequently called *activators,* function in combination with the protein; in others, the metal ion forms a compound with the substrate, and it is the metal-substrate complex that reacts with the enzyme. Arginase, certain phosphatases, and some peptidases are examples of enzymes that require the presence of certain metal ions for their activity.

Many enzymes require the presence of certain organic substances as cofactors in order to function. The *cofactors,* or *coenzymes,* generally act as acceptors or donors of a grouping or of atoms that are removed from or contributed to the substrate. These organic cofactors may be regarded as easily dissociable moieties of conjugated proteins. The type of coenzyme concerned in the enzymic process aids in classification. Some of the organic cofactors and prosthetic groups whose presence has been definitely established in purified enzymes are listed in Table 12.1. Several of these cofactors are derived from components that cannot be synthesized by mammals and are essential nutritive factors, or vitamins. Other vitamins may also function in a similar manner, but their specific role in enzymic reactions has yet to be determined.

Specificity. Urease is a highly specific enzyme; its only known substrate is urea. In contradistinction, other enzymes can attack many related substrates of similar structure, *e.g.,* some esterases can act upon the esters of different fatty acids with a variety of alcohols. Nevertheless, the esterases are specific in their esterase action; they do not catalyze other hydrolytic reactions, nor do they function as oxidases, decarboxylases, etc. Specificity is evident in the type of reaction that is catalyzed. Almost all enzymes show a high degree of spatial specificity. Arginase acts only on L-arginine; it does not attack D-arginine. D-Amino acid oxidase has no action on L-amino acids, whereas D-amino acids are rapidly oxidized to the corresponding keto acids. The specificity of enzymes is one of their most fundamental and important properties and will be discussed in some detail later (Chap. 14).

The specificity of enzymes is of practical utility in preparative chemistry, particularly in the resolution of racemic compounds. Since D-amino acid oxidase acts only on D-amino acids, the action of the enzyme on a DL-amino acid mixture yields the L-amino acid and the keto acid. In view of the solubility of the keto acid in organic solvents, the two compounds are readily separated from each other. The spatial specificity of hydrolytic enzymes may also be used to advantage when both isomers are desired. For example, enzymes in extracts of kidney or pancreas will cleave only the natural or L form of chloroacetyl-DL-phenylalanine, resulting in a mixture containing the readily separable water-soluble L-phenylalanine and the chloroform-soluble chloroacetyl-D-phenylalanine; D-phenylalanine is obtained by acid hydrolysis of the latter compound. The stereochemical specificity of individual enzymes is frequently demonstrated by the whole organism. As long ago as 1858 Pasteur (who discovered the optical activity of the natural amino acids) showed that a green mold would ferment dextrorotatory tartaric acid but not levorotatory tartaric acid. Since that time, molds, bacteria, and yeasts as well as highly purified enzymes have been utilized for the destruction of one or the other isomer of various amino acids, sugars, and other compounds.

Enzymes are widely used as chemical reagents for analytical determinations. Some examples of enzymic reactions have been mentioned as used for the estimation of amino acids (page 117). It is obviously a great advantage to use rapid methods of analysis, *e.g.,* those involving the pH meter, colorimeter, spectrophotometer, or change in gas volume. The following examples illustrate some of these methods. Esterases liberate an acid that will lower the pH of an unbuffered solution. By adding sufficient alkali to maintain constant pH, the extent of reaction can be estimated by alkali consumption. Appearance of amino groups as a result

Table 12.1: SOME ORGANIC COENZYMES AND PROSTHETIC GROUPS OF ENZYMES

Coenzyme or prosthetic group	Structure given on page	Enzymic and other functions	Essential nutritional factor or vitamin*
Diphosphopyridine nucleotide (DPN)	312	As hydrogen acceptor of dehydrogenases	Nicotinic acid
Triphosphopyridine nucleotide (TPN)	338	As hydrogen acceptor of dehydrogenases	Nicotinic acid
Adenosine triphosphate (ATP)	305	Transphosphorylation	None
Pyridoxal phosphate	494	Transaminases, amino acid decarboxylases, racemases, etc.	Pyridoxine
Thiamine pyrophosphate	321	Oxidative decarboxylation	Thiamine or vitamin B_1
Flavin mononucleotide (FMN)	344	As hydrogen acceptor of dehydrogenases	Riboflavin
Flavin adenine dinucleotide (FAD)	313	As hydrogen acceptor of dehydrogenases	Riboflavin
Coenzyme A (CoA)	316	Acetyl or other acyl group transfer; fatty acid synthesis and oxidation	Pantothenic acid
Iron-protoporphyrin	190	In catalase, peroxidase, cytochromes, hemoglobin	None
6,8-Dithio-n-octanoic acid (lipoic acid)	318	Oxidative decarboxylation; as hydrogen and acyl acceptor	Required by some microorganisms
Tetrahydrofolic acid	502	One carbon transfer	Folic acid
Biotin	962	CO_2 transfer	Biotin
Cobamide	968	Group transfer	Cobalamine

* See also Chaps. 55 and 56.

of proteolysis can be measured by the ninhydrin reaction (page 111), with quantitative estimations made in a colorimeter. A change in light absorption in the ultraviolet region of the spectrum accompanies enzymic alteration in the saturation of organic compounds; this can be quantitatively evaluated at a specific wavelength in the spectrophotometer.

Purified enzymes are used to convert a substance that may be difficult to estimate to another product that is easily measured quantitatively by readily available apparatus. It is frequently possible to use several purified enzymes that can catalyze the alteration of a substance by several steps to a product that can be estimated conveniently. It should be reemphasized that it is only because of the great specificity manifested by enzymes that such methods are possible. Many types of compounds present in only minute quantities can be estimated by such methods.

Other practical uses of enzymes are in the degradation of complex molecules in order to study the structure of whole molecules and of their constituent parts. Examples have already been cited that illustrate the use of enzymes for analysis of the structure of polysaccharides, proteins, and nucleic acids. Isolation of L-tryptophan, glutamine, and asparagine from proteins can be accomplished only after enzymic digestion of proteins. Other examples of such procedures will be described later. The coming together of classical chemical procedures and the enzymic methods of the biochemist is permitting rapid progress in the study of complex molecules generally.

CLASSIFICATION OF ENZYMES

It has been noted (under Nomenclature) that enzymes may be described in chemical terms, as conjugated proteins, and by the reaction catalyzed. The usual schemes of classification are grossly inadequate to deal with the many types of reactions, and most of these catalyzed reactions are understood best in relation to metabolic processes. Here it will suffice to indicate, with a few illustrations, some of the main types of reactions catalyzed by enzymes. It should be emphasized that most enzymic reactions have their counterparts in familiar types of chemical reactions, but many novel reactions have been discovered first in biological systems. Many of the more specialized types of reactions are best presented later in the chapters that deal with details of processes of metabolism.

HYDROLYTIC ENZYMES

Hydrolytic enzymes act by catalyzing introduction of the elements of water at a specific bond of the substrate. These reactions are frequently reversible, and the classification of these enzymes as hydrolytic rather than synthetic is arbitrary, based on the more easily measurable phenomenon and on the fact that in aqueous solution, equilibrium favors a predominance of hydrolytic products.

Esterases. These are enzymes that catalyze hydrolysis of ester linkages. More specific classification depends on both the type of acid and the type of alcohol comprising the ester. Some of these enzymes effect hydrolysis of a variety of compounds of similar structure; others are highly specific.

Simple esterases such as liver esterase catalyze reversibly the scission and synthesis of esters of lower alcohols and fatty acids. An example is the reversible hydrolysis of ethyl butyrate to give ethanol and butyric acid.

$$CH_3CH_2CH_2COOC_2H_5 + H_2O \rightleftharpoons CH_3CH_2CH_2COOH + C_2H_5OH$$

The true lipases hydrolyze fats into long-chain fatty acids and glycerol. Examples are *pancreatic lipase* and many plant lipases. The action of the simple esterases and lipases is reversible, and synthesis or hydrolysis proceeds to equilibrium in solution.

Phosphatases hydrolyze esters of phosphoric acid. This is a large and complex group of enzymes, some of which appear to be highly specific. The *monoesterases* hydrolyze monophosphoric esters according to the following general reaction.

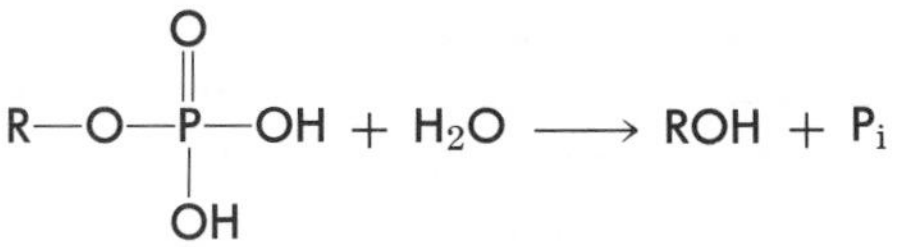

$$R-O-\overset{\overset{\displaystyle O}{\|}}{\underset{\underset{\displaystyle OH}{|}}{P}}-OH + H_2O \longrightarrow ROH + P_i \quad (H_2PO_4^- \ \text{?} \ HPO_4^=)$$

The symbol P_i, employed in the equation above, will be encountered frequently in this textbook and in the biochemical literature. It is an abbreviation for inorganic orthophosphate and implies the mixture of $H_2PO_4^-$ and $HPO_4^=$ which would exist at the specific pH of the reaction medium, calculated from the Henderson-Hasselbalch equation (page 103). Similarly, the abbreviation PP_i will indicate inorganic pyrophosphate, which at pH 7.4 is largely

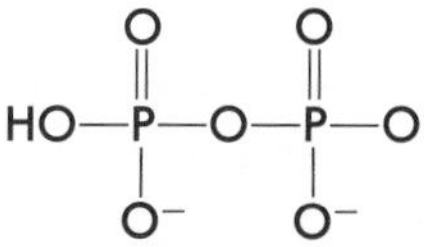

$$HO-\overset{\overset{\displaystyle O}{\|}}{\underset{\underset{\displaystyle O^-}{|}}{P}}-O-\overset{\overset{\displaystyle O}{\|}}{\underset{\underset{\displaystyle O^-}{|}}{P}}-O^-$$

Pyrophosphatases are enzymes that split pyrophosphate linkages, liberating orthophosphate. A crystalline pyrophosphatase from baker's yeast splits inorganic pyrophosphate to orthophosphate.

Nucleases cause a depolymerization of nucleic acids, liberating oligo- or mononucleotides. These enzymes are *diesterases* of a special type which split the linkages that bind the individual nucleotides.

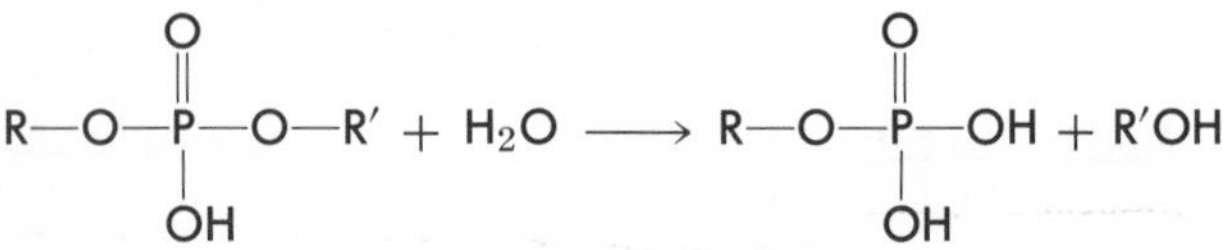

$$R-O-\overset{\overset{\displaystyle O}{\|}}{\underset{\underset{\displaystyle OH}{|}}{P}}-O-R' + H_2O \longrightarrow R-O-\overset{\overset{\displaystyle O}{\|}}{\underset{\underset{\displaystyle OH}{|}}{P}}-OH + R'OH$$

Two specific nucleases have been obtained in crystalline form from mammalian pancreas. *Ribonuclease* hydrolyzes nucleic acids of the ribose type, and the site of action appears to be at diester linkages involving pyrimidine nucleotides (page 181). *Deoxyribonuclease* acts in the presence of Mg^{++} ions, causing the depolymerization of deoxyribonucleic acids.

Carbohydrases. These enzymes hydrolyze the glycosidic linkages of simple glycosides, oligosaccharides, and polysaccharides.

Glycosidases hydrolyze simple glycosides and oligosaccharides. An example is yeast *invertase*, which hydrolyzes sucrose to glucose and fructose.

Polysaccharidases act on the complex polysaccharides. α-1,4-Glucan maltohydrolases (*β-amylases*) hydrolyze starch and glycogen to maltose and to residual polysaccharides. Their action has been described (Chap. 4). The polysaccharidases of wheat, barley, soybeans, and other plants are of this type.

α-1,4-Glucan 4-glucanohydrolases (*α-amylases*) can hydrolyze glycogen and starch and the residual polysaccharides of starch (amylodextrins) to give glucose, maltose, and products that no longer give a color with iodine (page 52). These enzymes are widely distributed in plants. Animal amylases of this type have been obtained in crystalline form from pancreas and saliva and are also found in blood and urine.

Proteases (Proteolytic Enzymes). These are enzymes which attack the peptide bonds of proteins and peptides. It is customary to distinguish between the proteinases (endopeptidases) and the peptidases (exopeptidases).

The *peptidases* (*exopeptidases*) act on peptide bonds adjacent to a free amino or carboxyl group. Among the principal types of peptidases are the following.

Carboxypeptidases require the presence of a free carboxyl group in the substrate and split the peptide bond adjacent to this group, liberating a free amino acid. Examples are the carboxypeptidase of mammalian pancreas and carboxypeptidases of kidney, spleen, etc.

$$R---\underset{\underset{O}{\|}}{C}-\underset{\underset{H}{|}}{N}-CHR'-COOH + H_2O \longrightarrow R---COOH + H_2NCHR'COOH$$

Aminopeptidases act on the peptide bond adjacent to the essential free amino group of simple peptides. An example is an *aminotripeptidase* found in many animal tissues which splits tripeptides such as L-alanylglycylglycine to L-alanine and glycylglycine.

Dipeptidases specifically act only on certain dipeptides; an example is *glycylglycine dipeptidase*, which requires Co^{++} or Mn^{++} for its action.

Proteinases (*endopeptidases*) act on the interior peptide bonds of proteins; they can, however, also split peptide bonds in suitable simple peptides and their derivatives. Examples are *pepsin, trypsin,* and *chymotrypsin* from animals (Chap. 24).

Cathepsins are intracellular proteinases found in most animal tissues. The richest sources are liver, kidney, and spleen. Many of these enzymes are active only in the presence of certain reducing substances such as cysteine, glutathione, HCN, H_2S, and ascorbic acid.

Plant Proteinases. Papain is obtained from the unripe fruit of the papaya, or papaw tree. Similar enzymes are *bromelin,* found in pineapples, and *ficin,* in the milky sap of the fig tree. Ficin has long been used for the clotting of milk in areas of the Near East. Some of the plant proteinases are used commercially for tenderizing meat.

PHOSPHORYLASES

Polysaccharide phosphorylases catalyze reversibly the phosphorolytic cleavage of the α-glucosidic 1,4 linkages of glycogen and starch to α-glucose 1-phosphate.

This degradation is not a hydrolysis such as that carried out by the amylases since it involves the elements not of water but of phosphoric acid. The reaction may be written

$$\text{Glycogen} + n \text{ phosphate} \rightleftharpoons n \text{ glucose 1-phosphate}$$

Polynucleotide phosphorylases catalyze the reversible formation of polynucleotides, as in the following example.

$$\text{Polynucleotide} + n \text{ phosphate} \rightleftharpoons n \text{ nucleoside diphosphates}$$

OXIDATION-REDUCTION ENZYMES

Enzymes concerned with *oxidation-reduction* processes play an extremely important role in metabolism and will be considered in detail elsewhere (Chaps. 18 and 19). Here it is desirable to indicate a few of the main types since the study of some of these enzymes has had a major influence on knowledge of enzymes in general.

Dehydrogenases. Oxidation of organic compounds is generally a dehydrogenation process, and there are many *dehydrogenases,* enzymes catalyzing dehydrogenation, which are highly specific. The over-all process for dehydrogenation may be represented as follows.

$$XH_2 + A \longrightarrow X + AH_2$$

An example is the action of *ethanol dehydrogenase,* in which diphosphopyridine nucleotide (DPN, page 312) is the hydrogen acceptor.

$$\text{Ethanol} + DPN^+ \rightleftharpoons \text{acetaldehyde} + DPNH + H^+$$

Oxidases. There are a number of *aerobic oxidases* which can utilize oxygen directly.

Cytochrome oxidase, an iron-porphyrin enzyme, is one of the most important of this group (Chap. 18). The iron of the prosthetic group undergoes reversible oxidation-reduction from the ferrous to the ferric state, accepting electrons which are transferred subsequently to oxygen.

Flavin Enzymes. These enzymes have prosthetic groups that are mono- or dinucleotides containing riboflavin (page 313). This moiety functions in accepting hydrogen atoms and some are subsequently oxidized by molecular oxygen (Chap. 18). An example is *xanthine oxidase,* found in liver and milk; the enzyme contains flavin adenine dinucleotide, iron, and molybdenum, and catalyzes the oxidation of hypoxanthine to xanthine and the latter to uric acid. This enzyme also catalyzes oxidation of a variety of aldehydes.

Copper Enzymes. The *phenol oxidases* are copper-containing proteins that catalyze the oxidation of phenol derivatives to quinones. Examples are the *polyphenol oxidases* of mushrooms and potatoes.

Tyrosinase, another copper enzyme widely distributed in animals and plants, catalyzes the oxidation of tyrosine to the orthoquinone; subsequent oxidation steps, some of which appear to be spontaneous, lead to the formation of the dark pigment *melanin* (Chap. 44).

TRANSFERRING ENZYMES (TRANSFERASES)

There are many types of enzyme which catalyze the transfer of a group from one substance to another. The *transaminases* (Chap. 24) catalyze transfer of an amino group of an amino acid to an α-keto acid. Such a reaction is shown below for *glutamic-aspartic transaminase,* also termed glutamic-oxaloacetic transaminase.

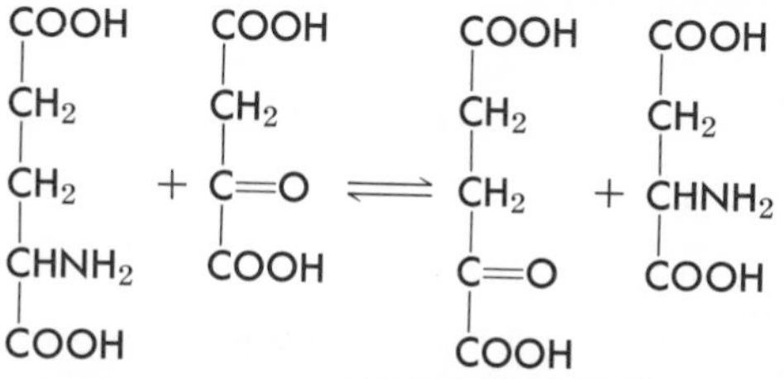

$$
\begin{array}{ccccccc}
\text{COOH} & \text{COOH} & & \text{COOH} & \text{COOH} \\
| & | & & | & | \\
\text{CH}_2 & \text{CH}_2 & & \text{CH}_2 & \text{CH}_2 \\
| & | & & | & | \\
\text{CH}_2 & + \;\text{C}{=}\text{O} & \rightleftharpoons & \text{CH}_2 & + \;\text{CHNH}_2 \\
| & | & & | & | \\
\text{CHNH}_2 & \text{COOH} & & \text{C}{=}\text{O} & \text{COOH} \\
| & & & | \\
\text{COOH} & & & \text{COOH}
\end{array}
$$

Glutamic acid + oxaloacetic acid $\rightleftharpoons$ α-ketoglutaric acid + aspartic acid

There are many different types of transfer reactions, involving transfer of phosphate groups, methyl groups, amide groups, etc. It may be noted that transfer reactions are also catalyzed by many so-called hydrolytic enzymes such as the *carbohydrases, phosphatases, esterases,* and *proteinases.*

DECARBOXYLASES

The decarboxylases remove CO_2 without oxidation from various carboxylic acids.

Amino acid decarboxylases of microorganisms are very widespread. These enzymes are responsible for the formation of amines. An example is lysine decarboxylase.

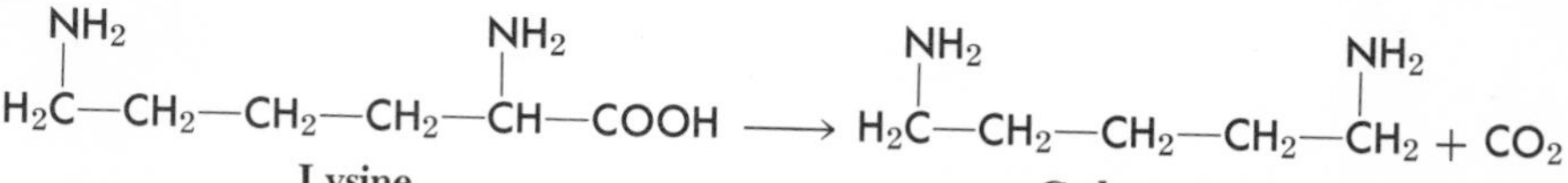

$$
\underset{\text{Lysine}}{\overset{\text{NH}_2}{\underset{|}{\text{H}_2\text{C}}}-\text{CH}_2-\text{CH}_2-\text{CH}_2-\overset{\text{NH}_2}{\underset{|}{\text{CH}}}-\text{COOH}} \longrightarrow \underset{\text{Cadaverine}}{\overset{\text{NH}_2}{\underset{|}{\text{H}_2\text{C}}}-\text{CH}_2-\text{CH}_2-\text{CH}_2-\overset{\text{NH}_2}{\underset{|}{\text{CH}_2}}} + CO_2
$$

Keto acid decarboxylases are important in the liberation of CO_2. An example is the catalyzed decarboxylation of oxaloacetate to pyruvate and CO_2.

HYDRASES

These enzymes catalyze addition to or removal of water from their specific substrates. *Fumarase* catalyzes the interconversion of malic and fumaric acids.

$$
\text{HOOC}-\text{CH}_2-\text{CHOH}-\text{COOH} \rightleftharpoons \text{HOOC}-\text{CH}{=}\text{CH}-\text{COOH} + H_2O
$$

ISOMERASES

The term *isomerase* has been used to denote those enzymes which catalyze an intramolecular rearrangement, *e.g.,* the interconversion of aldose and ketose sugars. For example, *phosphohexose isomerase* catalyzes the following interconversion.

Glucose 6-phosphate $\rightleftharpoons$ fructose 6-phosphate

In this group of enzymes may also be included the *epimerases, e.g., uridine diphosphate galactose 4-epimerase,* which catalyzes a Walden inversion in which the configuration about carbon-4 of the galactosyl residue is transformed to that of a glucosyl residue (page 405):

$$\text{Uridine diphosphate galactose} \rightleftharpoons \text{uridine diphosphate glucose}$$

Uridine diphosphate glucose plays an important role in several aspects of carbohydrate metabolism (Chap. 21).

REFERENCES

Books

Boyer, P. D., Lardy, H., and Myrbäck, K., eds., "The Enzymes," 2d ed., 8 vols., Academic Press, Inc., New York, 1958–1963.

Colowick, S. P., and Kaplan, N. O., eds., "Methods in Enzymology," 6 vols., Academic Press, Inc., New York, 1954–1963.

Dixon, M., and Webb, E. C., "Enzymes," 2d ed., Academic Press, Inc., New York, 1963.

"Report of the Commission on Enzymes of the International Union of Biochemistry," Pergamon Press, New York, 1961.

13. Enzymes

Kinetics, Inhibition, and Metabolic Inhibitors

There are three general ways in which the problem of mechanism of enzyme action is being attacked. One is by a study of the chemical nature of the enzyme itself; this is essentially a special problem in protein chemistry. The second method is to study the mechanism of action of simpler catalysts on the same reaction; the investigation of such model reactions has been exceedingly fruitful. The third approach is to determine how various factors influence the rate of enzymic reactions. We shall first consider this last type of study.

The view that has dominated all attempts to explain mechanisms of enzymic catalysis is that the enzyme forms an intermediate complex with the substrate or substrates. Before proceeding to a more detailed examination of the evidence in support of this concept, it is desirable to summarize briefly some of the early experiments that led to this view.

1. In 1880, Wurtz noted that after addition of the soluble proteinase, *papain,* to the insoluble protein, fibrin, repeated washing of the fibrin did not stop the proteolysis. He concluded that the papain had formed a compound with the fibrin.

2. O'Sullivan and Tompson, in 1890, observed that the enzyme, *invertase,* could withstand higher temperatures in the presence of the substrate, sucrose, than in its absence. To explain this observation they suggested that the enzyme invertase had combined with its substrate, sucrose.

3. The experiments of Emil Fischer in the 1890s indicated that certain *glycosidases* were highly stereospecific with respect to their substrates. He suggested a similar specificity in the structure of the enzymes since these results could be explained only if enzyme and substrate reacted. His remarks have been widely quoted.

Inasmuch as the enzymes are in all probability proteins, . . . it is probable that their molecules also have an asymmetrical structure, and one whose asymmetry is, on the whole, comparable to that of the hexoses. Only if enzyme and fermentable substance have a similar geometrical shape can the two molecules approach each other close enough for the production of a chemical reaction. Metaphorically, we may say that enzyme and glucoside must fit into each other like lock and key.

4. Many investigators observed that rates of substrate conversion did not follow the rate laws of a simple reaction. A. Brown (1892) and V. Henri (1903) both suggested that product formation depended on the rate of decomposition of an enzyme-substrate complex. However, it remained for Michaelis and Menten in 1913 to offer rigorous proof in support of this view and to supply an acceptable mathematical formulation.

We shall consider first the study of rates of enzymic reactions before proceeding to other aspects of enzymology.

RATE OF ENZYMIC REACTIONS

For the biochemist, the problem of rate studies is of paramount importance. It is insufficient to know that a synthetic reaction takes place in living tissue; the reaction must occur rapidly enough to supply the needs of the organism for the products of the reaction. For the removal of a toxic metabolic product, the substance must be eliminated at sufficient velocity to prevent its accumulation to injurious levels. When a needed substance is not supplied or a product is not removed at sufficient speed, derangements may result that are described as metabolic disorders or disease processes. Correspondingly, metabolic derangements also occur when a physiological process is uncontrolled and the rate is much greater than normal. Thus, there is a dual purpose in considering rates of enzymic processes, viz., to understand the normal and abnormal metabolism of the organism as a whole, and to attempt to elucidate the intimate nature of the enzymic process itself.

The rates of chemical reactions are generally estimated as the change in concentration c of substrate or product per unit of time t. Customary units are moles per liter and seconds. Thus, if c is the initial concentration which decreases with time, the reaction velocity is $-dc/dt$. This rate may depend upon the instantaneous value of c in various ways. It may be independent of c:

$$-\frac{dc}{dt} = k_0 = k_0 c^0 \quad \text{(zero-order reaction)}$$

It may be proportional to c:

$$-\frac{dc}{dt} = k_1 c = k_1 c^1 \quad \text{(first-order reaction)}$$

Or it may be proportional to the second, or rarely a higher power of c:

$$-\frac{dc}{dt} = k_2 (c \times c) = k_2 c^2 \quad \text{(second-order reaction)}$$

In each case, k is known as the *reaction velocity constant* or *rate constant*. It should be noted that the dimensions of k depend on the order of the reaction. Thus k_0 has dimensions of (ct^{-1}); k_1 of (t^{-1}); k_2 of $(c^{-1}t^{-1})$. From this it follows that velocity constants for reactions of different orders may not be added or subtracted. Also, only in first-order reactions is the velocity constant devoid of the dimension of concentration. Thus only for first-order reactions is the half-time, *i.e.*, the time for the initial concentration to be halved, a constant at all concentrations.

For enzymic reactions in which the molecular weight of the enzyme is known, rate constants are given in terms of moles of enzyme. When the molecular weight of the enzyme is unknown or the enzyme preparation is impure, the velocity is frequently expressed per milligram of protein per milliliter or in rate per milligram of protein nitrogen per milliliter.

For all enzymic processes, other conditions being constant, the rate of the reaction depends on the concentration of the enzyme and of its substrate. The rates vary in a characteristic way and yield information of considerable importance. When the enzyme concentration is constant, the initial velocity of the reaction increases, as the substrate concentration is increased, in a hyperbolic manner toward a maximum velocity. It should be emphasized that *initial* velocity is specified since substrate will be consumed as the reaction proceeds. In practice, this means that sensitive methods must be used so that the velocity can be estimated accurately before the substrate concentration changes appreciably.

Figure 13.1 shows the rate of hydrolysis of sucrose to glucose and fructose, as a function of the sucrose concentration. Similar curves are found for all enzymic reactions. One of the noteworthy features is the limiting velocity found at high substrate concentrations. It should be emphasized that the rate does not increase linearly with increase in substrate concentration, as might be anticipated for a purely physical phenomenon. Instead, the rate approaches a limiting velocity at high substrate concentrations. Here we shall use the explanation of these findings offered in 1913 by Michaelis and Menten.

The Michaelis-Menten Hypothesis. The most important feature of this theory is the assumption that an intermediate enzyme-substrate complex is formed. It is further assumed that the rate of conversion of the substrate to the products of the

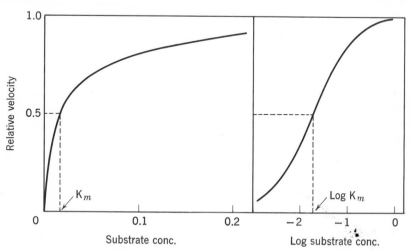

Fig. 13.1. Relative initial velocity as a function of substrate concentration (*left*) and as a function of the logarithm of the substrate concentration (*right*) for the action of yeast invertase on sucrose. The value of the substrate concentration for half the maximal velocity is $0.017M$, which is equal to K_m; for the semilogarithmic plot, at half-maximal velocity, log substrate concentration is -1.77, which is equal to log K_m.

reaction is determined by the rate of conversion of the enzyme-substrate complex to reaction products and the enzyme. The following scheme may be written to illustrate this concept:

Enzyme (E) + substrate (S) $\rightleftharpoons$ enzyme-substrate complex (ES)

$$\downarrow$$

Enzyme + products (P)

Thus, the rate of product formation depends on the concentration of ES. If the rate of formation of P depended directly on [S], then at constant [E] a linear relationship could be expected between velocity and the concentration of S. Since this is not obtained, Michaelis and Menten proposed the following explanation, which is given in a somewhat simplified form, it being assumed that only a single substrate and a single product are formed. It is also assumed that the process proceeds essentially to completion and that the concentration of the substrate is much greater than that of the enzyme in the system.

$$E + S \underset{k_2}{\overset{k_1}{\rightleftharpoons}} ES \xrightarrow{k_3} P + E \tag{1}$$

where k_1, k_2, and k_3 are the respective velocity constants of the three assumed processes. For the rate of formation of ES we may write

$$\frac{d[ES]}{dt} = k_1([E] - [ES])[S] \tag{2}$$

where [E] − [ES] is the concentration of uncombined enzyme. This simply states that the rate of formation of ES, which is $d[ES]/dt$, is proportional to the concentration of uncombined enzyme and substrate. The rate of disappearance of ES is then

$$\frac{d[ES]}{dt} = k_2[ES] + k_3[ES] \tag{3}$$

since ES can disappear to give the initial reactants (k_2) or by the formation of products (k_3) [see equation (1)].

When the rate of formation and disappearance of ES are equal, i.e., when $d[ES]/dt$ [equation (2)] equals $-d[ES]/dt$ [equation (3)], then equation (4) describes the steady state.

$$k_1([E] - [ES])[S] = k_2[ES] + k_3[ES] \tag{4}$$

The terms may be rearranged to give

$$\frac{[S]([E] - [ES])}{[ES]} = \frac{k_2 + k_3}{k_1} = K_m \tag{5}$$

The term containing the three velocity constants is usually called K_m, the Michaelis constant.

The relationships among the substrate concentration, the enzyme concentration, and the velocity of the enzyme-catalyzed reaction can be developed in the following manner. From equation (5), by rearrangement to solve for [ES], the steady state concentration of the enzyme-substrate complex is

$$[ES] = \frac{[E][S]}{K_m + [S]} \tag{6}$$

Inasmuch as it is desirable to obtain a measure of K_m, i.e., the Michaelis-Menten constant, it is necessary to derive an expression that relates K_m, E, and S. Because it is not generally convenient to measure the concentration of ES, advantage is taken of the relationship,

$$V = k_3[ES] \tag{7}$$

where V is the observed *initial* velocity. When the substrate concentration is made so high in relation to the enzyme concentration that essentially all the enzyme is present as ES, then the velocity of the reaction is maximal, and this velocity, V_{max}, has the value

$$V_{max} = k_3[E] \tag{8}$$

By substituting for ES in equation (7) its value in equation (6), and dividing equation (7) by equation (8), there is obtained the desired expression:

$$V = \frac{V_{max}[S]}{K_m + [S]} \quad \text{or} \quad K_m = [S]\left(\frac{V_{max}}{V} - 1\right) \tag{9}$$

This is the Michaelis-Menten equation.

For experimental determination of K_m, the velocity of the reaction (relative activity of the enzyme) is measured as a function of substrate concentration. These experimentally determined values may be plotted against one another as indicated in Fig. 13.1.

When $V = \frac{1}{2}V_{max}$, it will be seen from equation (9) that K_m is numerically equal to the substrate concentration, or K_m is equal to the concentration (expressed in moles per liter) of the substrate which gives half the numerical maximal velocity, V_{max}. Thus, from the data of Fig. 13.1 it is possible to ascertain K_m.

The K_m shown in Fig. 13.1 is indicated to be 0.017M. It is important to note that for any enzyme-substrate system, K_m has a characteristic value which is independent of the enzyme concentration. If the same enzyme can attack several substrates, the K_m values frequently give a useful comparison of the affinity for different substrates. Such information has been of value in assessing the specificity and binding groups in various enzymes (Chap. 14). In addition K_m values for the several enzymes in a metabolic series of consecutive reactions can occasionally indicate the rate-limiting step in the pathway.

There are many alternative methods of determining K_m. One of the most commonly used, suggested by Lineweaver and Burk, depends on rearrangement of equation (9) to give the following form:

$$\frac{[S]}{V} = \frac{[S]}{V_{max}} + \frac{K_m}{V_{max}} \tag{10}$$

A plot of $[S]/V$ vs. $[S]$ gives a straight line. The intercept of the line on the $[S]/V$ axis is K_m/V_{max} and the slope is $1/V_{max}$ (Fig. 13.2A). Thus, K_m can be calculated from the slope and the intercept. When a pure enzyme is used at known concentration, $V_{max} = k_3[E]$ [equation (8)], as on page 223, and k_3 may be calculated from the slope and the molecular weight of the enzyme. It should be noted that measurements at high values of $[S]$ which approach V_{max} are unnecessary since V_{max} can be evaluated from the slope.

Two additional methods of plotting kinetic data are also shown in Fig. 13.2. The equation for the linear form of plot B (Fig. 13.2) is given later [equation (27), page 235].

K_m is a complex constant since $K_m = (k_2 + k_3)/k_1$. Three conditions are possible. (1) If k_2 is very much greater than k_3, we may neglect k_3, and $K_m = k_2/k_1$.

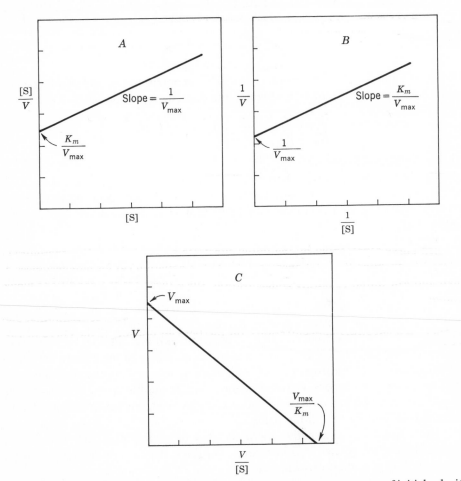

FIG. 13.2. Three methods of obtaining linear plots involving measurements of initial velocity V and substrate concentration $[S]$. For plots A and B, V_{max} and K_m can be obtained from the intercept on the abscissa and the slope. For plot C, the values at the two intercepts yield values of V_{max} and K_m.

K_m is then the thermodynamic equilibrium constant for the reversible formation of ES. (2) If k_3 is very much greater than k_2, then $K_m = k_3/k_1$, and K_m is a steady state constant containing two independent velocity constants. (3) When k_2 and k_3 are of the same order of magnitude, all three reaction constants determine the value of K_m.

It has frequently been assumed that condition (1) represents the usual situation, and K_m has been treated as a thermodynamic constant. There are now many indications that all three conditions are possible, depending on the particular enzyme-substrate system that is studied.

It may be noted that the condition represented by equation (1) is seldom achieved since most reactions are readily reversible. More generally,

$$E + S \underset{k_2}{\overset{k_1}{\rightleftharpoons}} ES \underset{k_4}{\overset{k_3}{\rightleftharpoons}} P + E \tag{11}$$

Equation (9) is still applicable inasmuch as [P] is zero when the *initial velocity* is measured. However, for equation (11) the equilibrium constant may be shown to be related to the four velocity constants and to the K_m and V_{max} values

$$K_{eq} = \frac{[P]_{eq}}{[S]_{eq}} = \frac{k_1 k_3}{k_2 k_4} = \frac{V_{max}^S K_m^P}{V_{max}^P K_m^S} \tag{12}$$

where the superscript S pertains to the substrate S and P to the product P. K_m and V_{max}^P are measured for the reverse reaction in the same manner as already described above for the substrate S.

Measurements for the reversible system of equation (11) offer a useful check on the kinetic constants, particularly since K_{eq} can be determined from concentrations alone.

Kinetics of Enzymic Reactions. It has already been indicated that the rate of an enzymic reaction will depend on the substrate concentration [equation (9)]. The course of the reaction with time will be determined by the region of the Michaelis-Menten curve represented by the initial substrate concentration. It is therefore of interest to examine the relationships indicated in equation (9) for circumstances of high and low initial substrate concentration, since these are the conditions which obtain at the beginning and at the end, respectively, of an enzyme-catalyzed reaction. When [S] is much greater than K_m, i.e., at constant enzyme concentration and at very high substrate concentrations, on the plateau portion of the curve of Fig. 13.3,

$$-\frac{d[S]}{dt} = V = V_{max} = k_3[E] \tag{13}$$

The rate of the reaction is constant for a given enzyme concentration, E. Under these conditions, the enzyme is saturated with substrate and the reaction is proceeding at maximal velocity. In other words, a further increase in [S] will not alter the velocity.

With a fall of the substrate concentration to values much less than K_m, at the bottom portion of the curve in Fig. 13.3,

$$-\frac{d[S]}{dt} = V = \frac{V_{max}[S]}{K_m} = \frac{k_3[E][S]}{K_m} \tag{14}$$

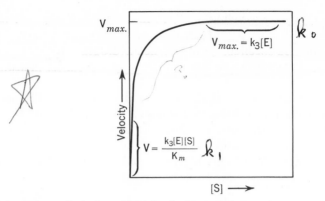

FIG. 13.3. A theoretical plot of initial velocity vs. substrate concentration. When $V = V_{max}$, the rate is independent of substrate concentration (zero-order reaction). When the substrate concentration is small compared with K_m, the rate is proportional to the substrate concentration and a first-order expression is obtained.

That is, the velocity of the reaction is directly proportional to the substrate concentration for a given enzyme concentration, E.

The reaction in which the rate is independent of the substrate concentration is a zero-order reaction with respect to substrate. In terms of the *total amount* of substrate transformed in a given time, zero-order reactions characteristically show a linear relationship between the amount of substrate altered and the time. This follows from the fact that at constant [E], integration of equation (13) yields

$$[S] = k_3[E]t \tag{15}$$

where [S] is the *amount* of substrate, in moles per liter, transformed to products in time t, measured from $t = 0$.

The dependence of the reaction velocity on the substrate concentration, at constant enzyme concentration, is a first-order relationship as in equation (14). Integration of equation (14) gives

$$k[E] = \frac{1}{t} \ln \frac{[S_0]}{[S]} \tag{16}$$

where [S] is substrate concentration at time t, starting with a substrate concentration $[S_0]$, and where $k = k_3/K_m$. Equation (16) describes enzymic reactions when the initial substrate concentration is much smaller than the value of K_m.

At intermediate substrate concentrations, when [S] is approximately equal to K_m, the expression becomes more complicated since both first-order and zero-order terms are present.

The Enzyme-Substrate Complex. The assumptions involved in the Michaelis-Menten kinetic scheme were accepted long before any direct chemical proof was available. Many of the reasons for this will be discussed later, in the sections on the inhibition of enzymes and enzymic specificity.

In 1937 Keilin and Mann found direct evidence that peroxidase forms a definite chemical compound with its substrate, hydrogen peroxide. In common with methemoglobin, catalase, and the cytochromes, which are also iron-protoporphyrin proteins, peroxidase in solution is reddish brown and shows characteristic absorption bands when examined spectroscopically. When hydrogen peroxide is added to the enzyme, there is an immediate shift of the absorption bands, indicating the formation of a new chemical compound.

$$\text{Peroxidase} + H_2O_2 \underset{k_2}{\overset{k_1}{\rightleftharpoons}} [\text{peroxidase} \cdot H_2O_2] \tag{17}$$

In the presence of a suitable hydrogen donor, such as an oxidizable dye or ascorbic acid, which may be designated simply as H_2A, a further reaction occurs:

$$[\text{Peroxidase} \cdot H_2O_2] + H_2A \xrightarrow{k_3} \text{peroxidase} + 2H_2O + A \tag{18}$$

That reactions (17) and (18) can be observed directly through the spectroscope constitutes convincing proof of the correctness of the assumption that an ES compound is formed. Although there is evidence which indicates that the product in equation (17) represents a change in valence of the peroxidase iron, the over-all kinetic picture remains the same, the nature of the complex, [peroxidase $\cdot$ H_2O_2], being unspecified.

Chance has utilized the spectroscopic changes to measure the kinetics of reactions (17) and (18). For these rapid reactions it was necessary to devise special equipment. The equipment permits rapid mixing of the solution of the enzyme and of the substrate as they are forced in a continuous flow past a photocell, with the continuous formation of the enzyme-substrate complex occurring in front of the photocell. The latter measures the change in the amount of light transmitted through the reaction vessel, at a wavelength at which a large change in light absorption occurs. The current from the photocell is conducted to a sensitive amplifier, and the recordings are made photographically.

At 25°C. with leukomalachite green, an oxidizable dye, as the hydrogen donor H_2A, k_1 is 1.2×10^7 liter per mole per second, k_2 is 0.2 per second, and k_3 is 5.2 per second. K_m measured from the effect of substrate concentration on the initial velocity by the method of Michaelis is 0.41×10^{-6}. It is apparent that k_3 is twenty-six times larger than k_2; hence,

$$K_m = \frac{k_3}{k_1} = 0.44 \times 10^{-6}$$

which is in excellent agreement with the direct measurement of 0.41×10^{-6}.

$$K_{eq} = \frac{k_2}{k_1} = 2 \times 10^{-8}$$

which is much smaller than K_m. For peroxidase, K_m is not an equilibrium constant, and Chance later found this to be true also for catalase, where the reaction constants k_1, k_2, and k_3 can be estimated directly by the same technique. Later experiments by Theorell and Chance with crystalline alcohol dehydrogenase of liver have shown that the change in ultraviolet absorption that occurs when reduced DPN (page 341) interacts with the protein may also be utilized for direct kinetic measurements. Direct kinetic measurement of the formation and decomposition of the enzyme-substrate complex, in the case of some dehydrogenases which utilize pyridine nucleotides (page 340), has also been achieved by measurements of alterations in fluorescence spectra, which occur when the reduced coenzyme is bound to the apoenzyme (page 341). These and many other experiments have provided definitive evidence of the correctness of the Michaelis-Menten concept of an enzyme-substrate complex and the consequent kinetic theory of enzymic action.

For catalase and peroxidase, $K_m = k_3/k_1$, and this is apparently true for other enzymes, as shown by indirect methods. However, the situation where $K_m = k_2/k_1$ appears to be valid for yeast invertase, chymotrypsin, and for other enzymes.

Effect of Temperature. The rate of most chemical reactions depends strongly on temperature, and reactions catalyzed by enzymes are no exception to this rule. The general formulation of the effect of temperature on reaction rate was given by Arrhenius. He postulated that not all the molecules in a system are capable of reaction; only those molecules which have sufficient energy of activation are capable of reacting.

If there is an equilibrium between the inactive and active molecules, we may write

$$\text{Inactive} \underset{k_2}{\overset{k_1}{\rightleftharpoons}} \text{active} \tag{19}$$

and the constant K for this process may be treated as an equilibrium constant.

The effect of temperature on an equilibrium constant for a chemical reaction is given by the van't Hoff equation,

$$2.3 \log K = C - \frac{\Delta H}{RT} \tag{20}$$

where ΔH is the heat of the reaction in calories per mole, R is the gas constant equal to 1.98 cal. per mole per degree, and T is the absolute temperature. C is an integration constant. It follows from this equation that graphs of log K plotted against the reciprocal of the absolute temperature $(1/T)$ should give a straight line. The slope of the line is $\Delta H/2.3R$.

Arrhenius assumed that the energy of activation E_a could be obtained for rate processes in the same manner as ΔH for equilibrium processes. Since an increase in temperature will increase the rate of a chemical reaction, the effect of temperature on the equilibrium depicted in equation (19) can be assumed to be one of determining the rate of formation of active molecules. Thus the effect of temperature will be on K, the equilibrium constant, as described in equation (20), where ΔH for this reaction is the heat of activation.

The Arrhenius equation relating a velocity constant k to absolute temperature is

$$2.3 \log k = B - \frac{E_a}{RT} \tag{21}$$

where B is a constant which is a qualitative expression of the frequency of collisions and of the requirement for specific orientation between the colliding molecules. For two temperatures

$$2.3 \log \frac{k'}{k''} = -\frac{E_a}{R}\left(\frac{1}{T''} - \frac{1}{T'}\right) \qquad (22)$$

where E_a is the energy of activation. As a rule, this equation describes the data for ordinary chemical reactions in a satisfactory manner. The plots of $\log k$ vs. $1/T$ may not give straight lines, suggesting that for these reactions the equation is not an adequate description of what is taking place. In general, increased temperatures favor the formation of active molecules, *i.e.*, those with sufficient energy of activation to react, and this process is satisfactorily described by the Arrhenius equation. In modern terms we usually think of the "active" molecules as being the molecules having sufficient energy of activation (page 209) to permit them to form an activated complex from which state a spontaneous conversion to the reaction products or to the original reactants may occur.

The effect of temperature on *enzymic* reactions usually is twofold: (1) an increase in rate with temperature until a maximal rate is achieved and (2) a region at high temperatures in which the rate decreases with increase in temperature. The decreased rate at high temperatures has been demonstrated to be due to thermal inactivation of the enzyme itself, a phenomenon discussed below. In the region in which the enzyme itself is not destroyed by heat, the Arrhenius equation describes the data. Figure 13.4 shows the effect of temperature on the velocity constant k_3 for the hydrolysis of two substrates by carboxypeptidase in the range from 5 to 25°C.

Energy of Activation. The energy of activation is a measure of the energy needed for the conversion of molecules to the reactive state (page 209). A catalyst lowers the necessary activation energy for a reaction that can proceed without a

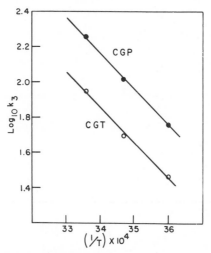

FIG. 13.4. Effect of temperature on the rate of hydrolysis k_3 of carbobenzoxyglycylphenylalanine (CGP) and carbobenzoxyglycyltryptophan (CGT) by crystalline carboxypeptidase. The data are plotted as $\log_{10} k_3$ vs. the reciprocal of the absolute temperature. The apparent activation energies E_a are 9900 cal. per mole for CGT and 9600 cal. per mole for CGP. (*Data from R. Lumry, E. L. Smith, and R. R. Glantz, J. Am. Chem. Soc., 73, 4330, 1951.*)

Table 13.1: ENERGY OF ACTIVATION FOR ENZYMIC AND NONENZYMIC CATALYSES

Process	Catalyst	E_a, cal./mole
Decomposition of hydrogen peroxide....................	None	18,000
	Colloidal platinum	11,700
	Catalase	$<$2,000
Hydrolysis of ethyl butyrate...........................	Hydrogen ion	16,800
	Hydroxyl ion	10,200
	Pancreatic lipase	4,500
Hydrolysis of casein..................................	Hydrogen ion	20,600
	Trypsin	12,000
Hydrolysis of sucrose.................................	Hydrogen ion	25,600
	Yeast invertase	8,000–10,000
Hydrolysis of β-methylglucoside.......................	Hydrogen ion	32,600
	β-Glucosidase	12,200

SOURCE: These data have been compiled from the work of several investigators.

catalyst. Table 13.1 shows the activation energies for a number of processes. The decomposition of hydrogen peroxide requires 18,000 cal. per mole; this is lowered to 11,700 when colloidal platinum is the catalyst, and is much lower for the enzymic reaction. It is obvious that catalase is far more efficient than the inorganic catalyst of this reaction. In fact, catalase is so efficient that only a small activation energy is required in the process. This is consistent with the knowledge that the decomposition of hydrogen peroxide by catalase proceeds at a higher rate than any other known enzymic reaction.

Inspection of the other data in Table 13.1 shows that the same relationship holds, *viz.*, that a catalyst lowers activation energy and that an enzyme decreases E_a more than an inorganic catalyst does. It must be emphasized that the effectiveness of enzymes as catalysts is indicated by the high reaction velocities at physiological temperatures. In other words, the decreased E_a permits rapid reaction rates at temperatures much lower than for the uncatalyzed reaction. This may be shown in a very simple way by comparing the relative values of the velocity constants for the same reaction at a given temperature (37°C.) when the activation energies are different. The data given in Table 13.1 for the hydrolysis of sucrose by yeast invertase and by hydrogen ion may be taken as an example. Equation (21) may be written for the enzyme (*e*) as

$$\log k_e = \frac{B_e}{2.3} - \frac{8,000}{2.3RT} \tag{23}$$

and for the hydrogen ion (*h*) as

$$\log k_h = \frac{B_h}{2.3} - \frac{25,600}{2.3RT} \tag{24}$$

Let us assume that the values for B_e and B_h are approximately the same. In order to calculate the relative rates of the enzyme-catalyzed and of the hydrogen ion-catalyzed reactions, *i.e.*, the ratio of the two rate constants, equation (24) is subtracted from equation (23), with the values for $R(1.98)$ and $T(37 + 273 = 310)$ substituted. This gives

$$\log \frac{k_e}{k_h} = \frac{25,600 - 8,000}{2.3 \times 1.98 \times 310} = \frac{17,600}{1,415} = 12.4 \tag{25}$$

and

$$\frac{k_e}{k_h} = 2.5 \times 10^{12} \tag{26}$$

In other words, the rate constant for the enzymic reaction may be expected to be approximately a trillion times greater than for the hydrogen ion–catalyzed reaction at the same temperature.

Inactivation of Enzymes. Like other proteins, enzymes are subject to denaturation at elevated temperatures. The thermal inactivation of an enzyme is readily measured since it can be estimated by the loss of catalytic ability. For ordinary chemical reactions, including catalytic ones, E_a values range from a few thousand up to approximately 40,000 cal. per mole, with the majority in the neighborhood of 15,000 to 25,000 cal. per mole. The remarkable fact is that the apparent E_a values for the inactivation of enzymes and the denaturation of proteins are all extremely high, from about 40,000 up to 100,000 cal. per mole and, in some cases, even higher. The similarity between enzymes and ordinary proteins in this respect has long been known and was used as an indication of the protein nature of enzymes many years before any enzyme had been obtained in a highly purified state.

The high E_a values for enzyme inactivation depend greatly on the conditions of measurement, such as pH, presence of substrate, ionic strength, etc. Nevertheless, the high values are almost unique among chemical reactions and point to the complexity of the denaturation or inactivation process. The interpretation is that the protein molecules undergo a complex rearrangement of the structure in which many weak bonds (such as hydrogen bonds, hydrophobic bonds, etc., see Chap. 9) are altered. Enzyme inactivation, or protein denaturation in general, at high temperatures is usually a first-order process, *i.e.*, the rate of inactivation is dependent on the first power of the enzyme concentration.

Effect of pH. The pH has a marked influence on the rate of enzymic reactions. Characteristically, each enzyme has a pH value at which the rate is optimal, and on each side of this optimum the rate is lower. Figure 13.5 shows the influence of pH on the action of several enzymes. Table 13.2 gives the optimal pH values for some representative enzymes. It is obvious from these data that there is a great spread from the optimal action of pepsin at acid pH values to that of alkaline phosphatase at very alkaline values. Practically, it is necessary in all enzymic studies to control the pH by the addition of suitable buffers, although it should be mentioned that the type of buffer may influence the optimal pH (Fig. 13.5C). It is interesting to note that the original definition of pH arose from Sørensen's studies of enzymic action in 1908.

The influence of pH on enzymic reactions is not clearly understood in all instances; it is apparent that several different types of effect may be involved. Enzymes, like other proteins, are ampholytes and possess many ionic groups. If the enzymic function depends on certain special groupings, these may have to be present in some instances in the un-ionized state and, in others, as charged ions. The latter is the more likely situation since many nonenzymic catalytic reactions clearly depend on ionic mechanisms. Inspection of the descending limbs of the pH curves in Fig. 13.5B and D shows that they have a shape similar to that of an ordinary titration curve. The requirement of ionic groups for the functioning of enzymes is also suggested by the fact that the ionic strength of the solution has been shown to affect the rate of some enzymic reactions, notably for carboxypeptidase and urease. This type of effect is usual for nonenzymic ionic catalysis.

In many cases, the substrates of enzymes are themselves electrolytes, and the reaction may depend on a particular ionic or non-ionic form of the substrate. Such

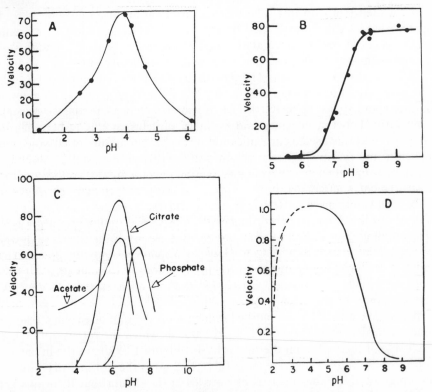

FIG. 13.5. The influence of pH on the action of several enzymes. *A* indicates the pH effect on the splitting of carbobenzoxy-L-glutamyl-L-tyrosine by pepsin. (*Data from J. S. Fruton and M. Bergmann, J. Biol. Chem.,* **127**, 627, 1939.) The optimal pH of pepsin action varies with the substrate (see Table 13.2). *B* shows the influence of pH on the hydrolysis of L-leucinamide by Mn^{++}-activated leucine aminopeptidase. At the optimal pH region, the substrate is uncharged; the pH effect appears to be primarily on the enzyme. (*Data from E. L. Smith, D. H. Spackman, and W. J. Polglase, J. Biol. Chem.,* **199**, 801, 1952.) *C* illustrates the effect of pH on the scission of urea by urease. (*Data from S. F. Howell and J. B. Sumner, J. Biol. Chem.,* **104**, 619, 1934.) The nature of the buffer has a marked influence on the activity and pH relationships. *D* shows the effect of pH on the hydrolysis of sucrose by yeast invertase. The dotted line indicates the region of enzyme instability. Since the substrate (sucrose) is not an electrolyte, the effect of pH is on the enzyme.

Table 13.2: OPTIMAL pH VALUES FOR SOME HYDROLYTIC ENZYMES

Enzyme	Substrate	Optimal pH
Pepsin	Egg albumin	1.5
Pepsin	Casein	1.8
Pepsin	Hemoglobin	2.2
Pepsin	Carbobenzoxyglutamyltyrosine	4.0
α-Glucosidase	α-Methylglucoside	5.4
α-Glucosidase	Maltose	7.0
Urease	Urea	6.4–6.9
Trypsin	Proteins	7.8
Pancreatic amylase	Starch	6.7–7.2
Malt amylase	Starch	4.5
Carboxypeptidase	Various substrates	7.5
Plasma alkaline phosphatase	β-Glycerophosphate	9–10
Plasma acid phosphatase	β-Glycerophosphate	4.5–5.0
Arginase	Arginine	9.5–9.9

an influence is undoubtedly present in the action of pepsin on different proteins; as shown in Table 13.2, the substrate has a marked influence on the pH optimum.

The pH may influence the rate of enzymic action indirectly insofar as many enzymes, like proteins in general, are stable only within a relatively limited pH range, most often near neutrality. Nevertheless, there are many exceptions, and pepsin exhibits the most unusual properties since it is stable at acid pH values and is rapidly inactivated in neutral and alkaline solutions.

Many enzymes are conjugated proteins in which the nonprotein portion is loosely bound to the protein. Since both moieties are essential for activity, conditions that influence the conjugation will destroy the enzymic activity, although this dissociation is frequently reversible. It has already been noted that peroxidase is a heme-protein. This enzyme is split into its two component inactive portions at acid pH values; readjustment of the solution to pH 7 restores the activity. Such effects are frequently encountered with the metal-enzymes.

INHIBITION OF ENZYMES

The concept of enzymic action already developed is that an enzyme reacts with its substrate to form an intermediate complex. Although the entire enzyme molecule may be necessary for its catalytic behavior, there must be a small but definite locus on the surface of the enzyme where the substrate can combine. In those instances in which the enzyme is a conjugated protein, the non-amino acid portion, or prosthetic group, is one place where the substrate may combine or react. Even for those enzymes which are simple proteins, there must be an "active center" or "active site." That this must be so is evident from size considerations alone. The smallest enzymes are proteins of about 12,000 molecular weight, and most enzymes are ten or more times larger than this. In contrast, most substrates are small molecules with molecular weights that are but a tiny fraction of those of the enzymes.

The combination of catalase (molecular weight of 250,000) with hydrogen peroxide (molecular weight of 34) illustrates this point.

Perhaps the strongest evidence for the localization of active centers comes from studies with specific inhibitors of enzymes. By specific inhibitors are meant compounds that can combine with an enzyme in such a manner as to prevent the normal substrate-enzyme combination and the catalytic reaction. It is necessary to distinguish these inhibitors from agents that denature proteins.

Competitive Inhibition. The simple scheme for the formation of the enzyme-substrate complex may again be stated as

$$E + S \rightleftharpoons ES \longrightarrow E + P$$

The formation of an enzyme-inhibitor complex may be given as

$$E + I \rightleftharpoons EI$$

where I is the inhibitor and EI is the enzyme-inhibitor complex.

If formation of EI is reversible and there is continuing competition between the substrate and the inhibitor for the same locus on the enzyme, the situation is designated as "competitive inhibition." The actual rate of the catalyzed reaction is then strictly dependent on the relative concentrations of substrate and inhibitor.

This type of inhibition was noted by Quastel and Wooldridge for the enzyme succinic acid dehydrogenase, which catalyzes the following reaction in the presence of a suitable hydrogen acceptor (A):

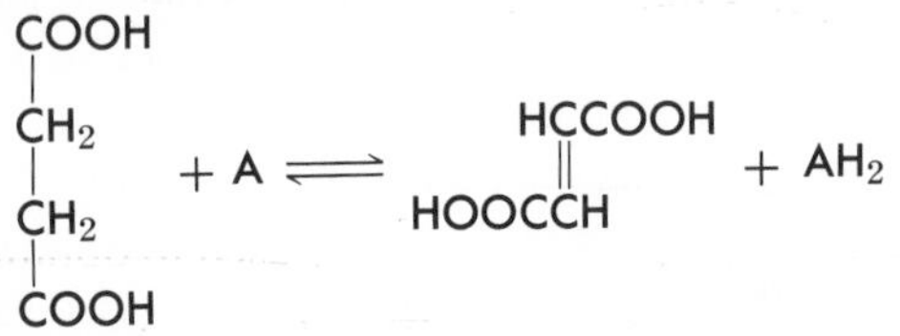

Succinic acid + acceptor $\rightleftharpoons$ fumaric acid + hydrogenated acceptor

Many compounds which are structurally similar to succinic acid but which are not dehydrogenated can combine with the enzyme. Since the enzyme has no effect on these substances, the inhibition is due to the blocking of the active centers. Several compounds that inhibit succinic acid dehydrogenase are shown below.

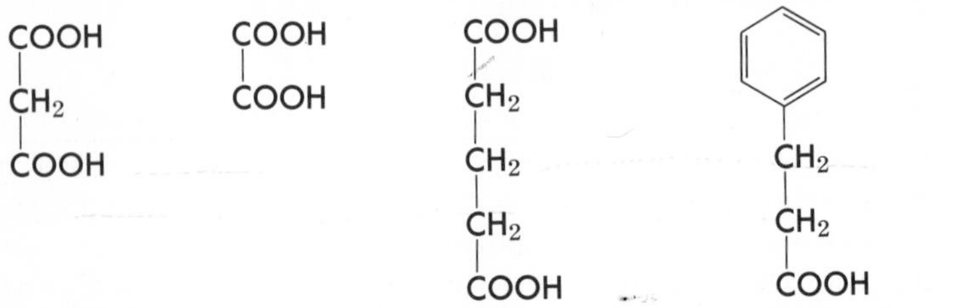

Malonic acid   Oxalic acid   Glutaric acid   Phenylpropionic acid

The most potent of these inhibitors is malonic acid. When the concentration ratio of inhibitor to substrate is 1:50, the enzyme is inhibited 50 per cent. Increasing the concentration of substrate but maintaining the concentration of inhibitor decreases the amount of inhibition, and, conversely, decreasing the substrate concentration increases the inhibition over a considerable range of absolute concentrations. If succinic and malonic acids were bound at different sites on the enzyme, it would be difficult to explain why they should compete with one another. Since they do compete, it must be concluded that they combine with the enzyme at the same locus. The phenomenon of competitive inhibition gives further proof for the concept that the combination of substrate and enzyme is highly specific and that this interaction occurs at a specific place in the structure of the enzyme. Competitive inhibitors have been found for many enzymes, and other examples will be cited later.

Competitive inhibition can be recognized by the effect of inhibitor concentration on the relationship between V and [S]. The linear plot, shown in Fig. 13.2B, is given by equation (27).

$$\frac{1}{V} = \frac{[S] + K_m}{V_{max}[S]} = \frac{K_m}{V_{max}} \cdot \frac{1}{[S]} + \frac{1}{V_{max}} \tag{27}$$

A plot of $1/V$ vs. $1/[S]$ gives a straight line in which the ordinate intercept equals $1/V_{max}$ and the slope is K_m/V_{max}.

For the action of a competitive inhibitor, an equation may be derived incorporating the inhibitor concentration [I] and the dissociation constant of the enzyme-inhibitor complex, K_i, in a manner similar to that used in obtaining equation (9). The following equation gives the relationship among these terms:

$$V = \frac{V_{max}[S]K_i}{K_mK_i + K_m[I] + K_i[S]} \tag{28}$$

Rearrangement of equation (28) in the same way used to obtain equation (27) yields

$$\frac{1}{V} = \frac{K_m}{V_{max}} \left(1 + \frac{[I]}{K_i}\right) \frac{1}{[S]} + \frac{1}{V_{max}} \tag{29}$$

When a plot of $1/V$ against $1/[S]$ is made, it is found, for competitive inhibition, that the ordinate intercept, $1/V_{max}$, is the same as in the uninhibited reaction, but that the slope, which is now $\left(\frac{K_m}{V_{max}}\right)\left(1 + \frac{[I]}{K_i}\right)$, is increased by the factor $\left(1 + \frac{[I]}{K_i}\right)$. This is shown graphically in Fig. 13.6. Thus, by using a sufficiently high substrate concentration, the effect of the competitive inhibitor can be overcome and V_{max} can be reached. For noncompetitive inhibition (discussed below) both the slope and the intercept are altered, which readily permits distinguishing between these two types of inhibition, as also shown in Fig. 13.6.

Noncompetitive Inhibition. In this instance, there is no relationship between the degree of inhibition and the concentration of substrate. Inhibition depends only on the concentration of the inhibitor. In contrast to the competitive type, it may be assumed that the formation of EI occurs at a locus on the enzyme that is not attacked by the substrate.

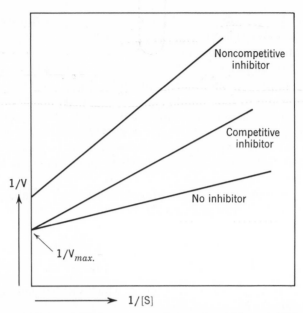

FIG. 13.6. A plot of $1/V$ vs. $1/[S]$ for an enzymic reaction with no inhibitor, a competitive inhibitor, and a noncompetitive inhibitor. For competitive inhibition, the slope is changed and the intercept remains the same; for noncompetitive inhibition, both the slope and the intercept are increased.

and
$$E + I \rightleftharpoons EI$$
$$ES + I \rightleftharpoons ESI$$

where EI and ESI are inactive.

Examples of noncompetitive inhibition may be found in the inhibition of many enzymes by heavy metal ions such as Ag^+, Hg^{++}, Pb^{++}, etc. Urease is extremely sensitive to traces of these ions.

Many instances of noncompetitive inhibition are actually examples of combination of inhibitor and enzyme to form chemical derivatives in which the combination is essentially irreversible. This inhibition may be a result either of irreversible combination of the inhibitor with the same site on the enzyme at which the substrate would combine, or of combination of the inhibitor with some portion of the enzyme molecule not immediately involved in enzyme-substrate combination but which may result in a conformational change so that catalytic activity is lost. This may also be essentially irreversible.

When irreversible combination occurs, it cannot always be easily determined whether the active locus is involved or not. However, such inhibitions give valuable information concerning the chemical nature of the enzyme. Sulfhydryl groups are present in some enzymes, and these groups are, in many instances, essential for the enzymic activity. A widely used agent for the detection of sulfhydryl groups is iodoacetamide, which reacts chemically in the manner illustrated.

$$RSH + ICH_2CONH_2 \longrightarrow RS{-}CH_2CONH_2 + HI$$

Various organic mercury derivatives such as *p*-mercuribenzoate, certain arsenicals, and N-ethylmaleimide also react with SH groups.

Those enzymes which contain essential metal ions are specifically inhibited by compounds that form complexes with the metal. Cyanide and hydrogen sulfide produce strong inhibition of iron-containing enzymes such as peroxidase and catalase. Fluoride and oxalate inhibit enzymes that need magnesium, calcium, or similar ions. Table 13.3 lists some of the reagents commonly employed as inhibitors in enzymic studies.

Table 13.3: SOME COMMONLY USED ENZYME INHIBITORS

Inhibitor	Enzyme group that combines with inhibitor
Cyanide	Fe^{+++}, Cu, Zn, certain other metals
Sulfide	Various metals
Fluoride	Mg, Ca, other metals
Oxalate	Ca, Mg
Carbon monoxide	Fe^{++}, Cu
Diethyldithiocarbamate	Cu
Pyrophosphate	Mg, Mn, Zn, other metals
α,α'-Dipyridyl	Fe
Azide	Fe^{+++}-protoporphyrin enzymes
o-Phenanthroline	Fe, Co, Zn, other metals
Ethylenediaminetetraacetate	Various metal ions
Cysteine and other sulfhydryl compounds	Fe, Cu, and other metals; may also produce reduction
Heavy metals (Ag^+, Hg^{++}, Pb^{++}, etc.)	Sulfhydryl; may also cause nonspecific protein precipitation
Iodoacetamide	Sulfhydryl
p-Mercuribenzoate	Sulfhydryl
Various arsenicals	Sulfhydryl
N-Ethylmaleimide	Sulfhydryl
Diisopropylphosphofluoridate	Serine hydroxyl

Certain enzyme inhibitors already mentioned, such as cyanide, carbon monoxide, oxalic acid, etc., are poisonous for many living organisms. Since their toxicity is due to their ability to inhibit enzymic reactions, it is apparent that a substantial part of what is called toxicology must be understood in terms of the specific inhibition of enzymes that are vital to the organism. In normal metabolism it is likely that the rates of most processes are regulated through the inhibition or release of inhibition of enzymes.

METABOLIC INHIBITORS—ANTIMETABOLITES

The recognition that an enzyme may be inhibited by compounds possessing a structure related to the natural substrate is of great importance, and this concept is not limited to applications involving individually known enzymic reactions. Indeed, the pharmacologist has long recognized that substances having related structures may compete with physiologically active substances. Although knowledge of the enzymes concerned is, in most cases, lacking, there is evidence suggesting that many pharmacologically active substances alter metabolic processes by virtue of their action on enzymes or enzymic systems.

All higher animals and many microorganisms lack the ability to synthesize certain organic compounds that are essential for survival. Requirements vary for different species and may include certain amino acids, fatty acids, the heterogeneous group of substances known as vitamins, certain purines and pyrimidines, etc. The essential substances needed for survival or for growth are used by the organism for incorporation into the functioning tissue structures, proteins, nucleic acids, etc., or they are transformed into other substances that are required by the cells or tissues. Obviously, the utilization of the required *metabolites* is dependent on enzymes, and these enzymes may be inhibited by substances whose structures are related to those of the metabolites. Although, in most cases, the nature of the essential enzymic step is unknown, the term *antimetabolites* is used to describe these inhibitors.

Antimetabolites may also block the utilization of metabolites that are synthesized by the organism itself. This provides an important tool in studying metabolic pathways since, in many instances, the inhibition of growth can be overcome by the addition of the necessary metabolite. Thus, study of antimetabolites has a two-fold interest, *i.e.*, the discovery of essential metabolites and growth factors necessary for different species and the search for potent inhibitors of the growth of pathogenic microorganisms and neoplasms. The antimetabolites that have been obtained from living organisms, such as bacteria, fungi, actinomycetes, etc., are commonly called antibiotics.

Although synthetic antibacterial agents such as arsphenamine and the sulfonamides were discovered earlier by empirical search, the rational investigation of antimetabolites may be said to have had its beginning with the observation of D. D. Woods in 1940 that the inhibition of bacterial growth produced in certain organisms by sulfanilamide is competitively overcome by *p*-aminobenzoic acid, whose role as a growth factor was first recognized in this way. The structural similarity of the two substances is obvious, and the phenomenon is akin to that of competitive inhibition of an isolated enzyme.

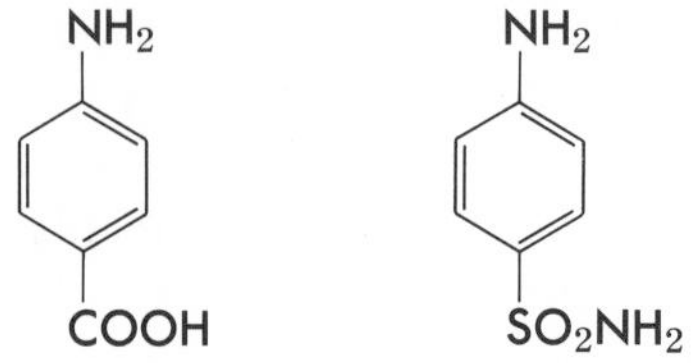

p-Aminobenzoic acid	Sulfanilamide

Indeed, *p*-aminobenzoic acid will competitively overcome the inhibition of all sulfonamides of the structure $NH_2-C_6H_4-SO_2NHR$, *e.g.*, sulfaguanidine, sulfathiazole, sulfapyridine, and sulfadiazine.

Those organisms which require *p*-aminobenzoic acid for growth utilize it for the synthesis of folic acid.

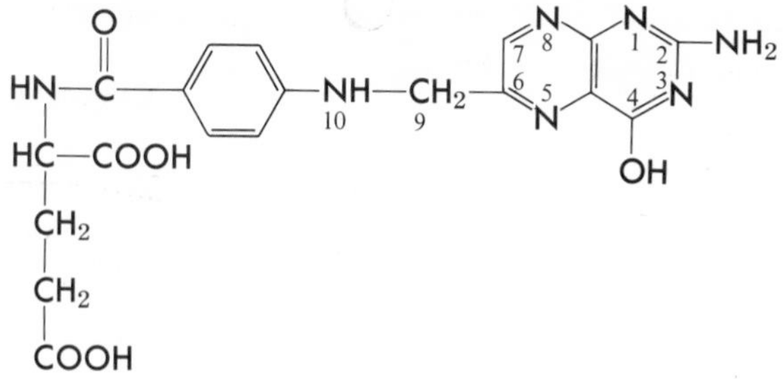

Folic acid (pteroylglutamic acid)

The linkage coupling the *p*-aminobenzoic acid (PABA) and glutamic acid is a peptide bond. Hydrolysis of this bond gives pteroic acid and glutamic acid.

Growth of those organisms which require PABA can be inhibited by sulfonamides, and this inhibition can be reversed by PABA. Those organisms which need folic acid for growth and cannot utilize PABA are not inhibited by sulfonamides. It thus appears that the sulfonamides inhibit the enzymic step or steps involved in the synthesis of folic acid from *p*-aminobenzoic acid and other metabolic precursors. This simplified picture illustrates how the sulfonamides have been useful in elucidating some aspects of the role of PABA in bacterial metabolism. The effective utilization of the sulfonamides in combating bacterial infections in man probably depends on the fact that man requires folic acid and cannot synthesize it from PABA. Thus, the sulfonamides block a metabolic reaction essential for certain bacteria without influencing the metabolism of the host who does not derive his folic acid from PABA.

Many thousands of compounds have been synthesized in attempts to discover new antimetabolites. Some of the considerations involved in the search for effective inhibitors may be illustrated by listing a few representative synthetic antimetabolites used in the study of metabolically important compounds.

Metabolite

Antimetabolite

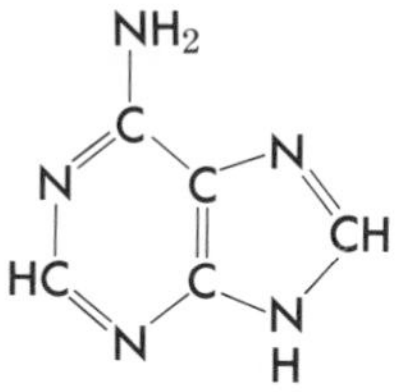

Adenine

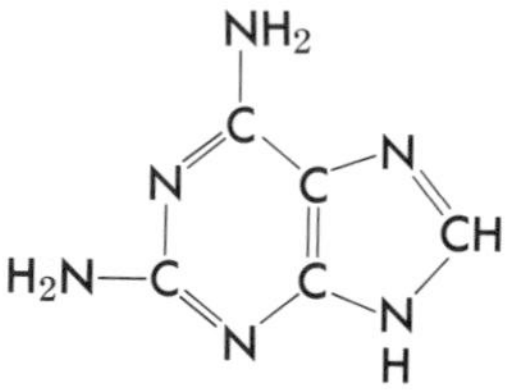

2,6-Diaminopurine
(2-aminoadenine)

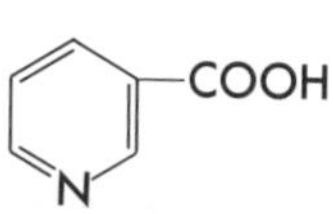

Nicotinic acid

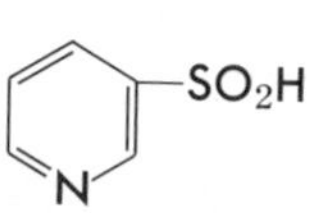

Pyridine-3-sulfonic acid

Metabolite

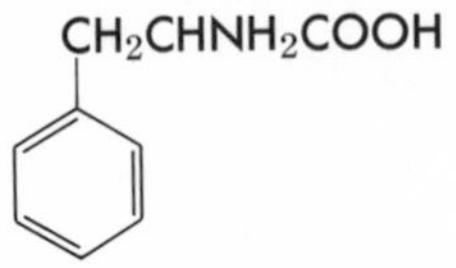

CH$_2$CHNH$_2$COOH

Phenylalanine

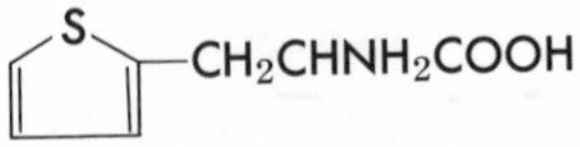

Antimetabolite

S—CH$_2$CHNH$_2$COOH

β-2-Thienylalanine

Certain of the folic acid antagonists have been used experimentally and, to some extent, clinically in the treatment of leukemia and other neoplastic diseases. Thus 4-aminopteroylglutamic acid (aminopterin) has been shown to produce considerable inhibition of growth of certain types of tumors. This has stimulated a wide search for other potential inhibitors of neoplasms; many of these studies are based upon the antimetabolite concept.

REFERENCES

See list following Chap. 14.

14. Enzymes

Specificity and Mechanism of Action

The two most remarkable properties of enzymes are their specificity and their catalytic efficiency, and it is in these properties that enzymes differ most strikingly from simple catalysts. Consideration has already been given to the efficiency of enzymes in reducing the activation energies of chemical reactions. It should be clear that, at any given temperature, it is not possible to lower the activation energy for a specific, defined chemical reaction. If activation energy for an over-all process appears to have been lowered, as is true for all catalyzed processes, it follows that the over-all reaction must be accomplished by a mechanism, or via a series of intermediates, different from that of the spontaneous, uncatalyzed event. This chapter will examine the mechanisms of enzymic catalysis in order to provide an understanding of the manner in which the enzymic surface modifies the requirement for the needed energy of activation. The subjects of enzymic specificity and mechanism of action are too extensive to allow full discussion here. Certain examples have been selected to illustrate the more general considerations and the methods employed. Further examples are mentioned in succeeding chapters in Part 3.

BINDING FORCES IN ENZYME-SUBSTRATE INTERACTION

Evidence has been presented that enzymes combine with their substrates. This is indicated by consideration of kinetics, by the phenomenon of competitive inhibition, and by the few instances in which more direct spectroscopic evidence of the existence of the intermediary compound has been obtained. As previously noted, studies of enzymic specificity have contributed most strikingly to this concept. Experimentally, enzymic specificity is tested by utilizing a number of compounds in which the structure is varied systematically. When the enzyme has *absolute specificity* with respect to a single substrate, limited information can be gained, and some enzymes show this type of specificity. Two examples, already mentioned, are the action of urease on urea and that of carbonic anhydrase on carbonic acid.

When the enzyme reacts with a variety of compounds, it is said to show *relative specificity*. An example is D-amino acid oxidase, which reacts with many D-amino acids but at different rates (Table 14.1).

Table 14.1: RATE OF OXIDATION OF D-AMINO ACIDS AND OTHER
SUBSTRATES BY D-AMINO ACID OXIDASE

Substrate	Oxygen uptake*	Substrate	Oxygen uptake*
D-Tyrosine	190	D-Histidine	6.2
D-Proline	148	D-Threonine	2.1
D-Methionine	80	D-Cystine	1.9
D-Alanine	64	D-Aspartic acid	1.4
D-Serine	42	D-Lysine	0.6
D-Tryptophan	37	D-Glutamic acid	0
D-Valine	35	L-Amino acids	0
D-Phenylalanine	26	D-Peptides	0
D-Isoleucine	22	N-Acetylalanine	0
D-Leucine	14	β-Pyridyl-4-alanine	95

* Crude extract of acetone-dried sheep kidney cortex at pH 8.3 used as source of enzyme. Rate of oxygen consumption is calculated from uptake in 10 min., and results are given as microliter per milligram of enzyme preparation per hour.

SOURCE: After H. A. Krebs, chap. 58, in J. B. Sumner and K. Myrbäck, eds., "The Enzymes," vol. II, part I, Academic Press, Inc., New York, 1951.

The general equation for the action of the oxidase is the following.

$$R—CH—COOH + \tfrac{1}{2}O_2 \longrightarrow R—C—COOH + R'NH_2$$

with HNR' below the first carbon and O (double-bonded) below the second carbon.

R' is an alkyl or substituted alkyl group or an H atom. R is the side chain of the amino acid. Peptides containing D-amino acids or N-acyl-α-amino acids are not attacked. Dehydrogenation can occur only if there is at least one H atom on the α-carbon and one on the N of the amino group. The enzyme can catalyze oxidation of compounds with large variations in R, many of which do not occur biologically, *e.g.*, β-pyridyl-4-alanine. It is noteworthy that compounds with ionic side chains, *e.g.*, glutamic acid, lysine, histidine, etc., are poorly attacked.

Understanding of enzymic specificity must be sought in the nature of the binding forces involved in the formation of the enzyme-substrate compound, and in the nature of the groups in the enzyme responsible for the catalytic action. In essence, these groups in the enzyme must be the side chains of the amino acids that are linked in the peptide chains and the organic cofactor or metal ion present in many enzymes.

The first clear formulation that interaction involves more than one group of the substrate, and hence of the enzyme also, emerged from studies of the hydrolysis of simple peptides by certain exopeptidases. In 1926, von Euler and Josephson observed that benzoylglycylglycine was resistant to the action of enzyme preparations that rapidly hydrolyzed glycylglycine. From this observation they concluded that a free amino group was required for the action of the enzyme (now called *glycylglycine dipeptidase*) and proposed the "diaffinity theory," which postulates that the enzyme combines with the substrate at the amino group and at the peptide linkage to be hydrolyzed.

The peptide, L-leucylglycine, is rapidly hydrolyzed by *leucine aminopeptidase* of mammalian tissues, yet the antipodal compound, D-leucylglycine, is completely resistant. Bergmann and his coworkers noted in 1935 that in order to explain such *spatial specificity*, it was necessary to postulate a minimum of three points of attachment of the substrate to the enzyme. If only two points of attachment were necessary, the stereoisomeric peptide, D-leucylglycine, could combine with the enzyme just as easily as the L compound. This "polyaffinity" concept has played an important role in our understanding of enzymic action, for the spatial specificity manifested by most enzymes can be explained only in terms of multipoint attachment.

Leucine aminopeptidase hydrolyzes di- and polypeptides at the bond adjacent to the free amino group and also acts on L-amino acid amides. The rate of hydrolysis of amides, $R—CH(NH_2)CONH_2$, depends on the nature and size of the substituent R, increasing from $H < CH_3 < C_2H_5 < C_3H_7 < C_4H_9$. The presence of polar or *hydrophilic* groups in R, such as COO^-, NH_3^+, $CONH_2$, CH_2OH, etc., decreases the rate. It has been concluded that nonpolar *hydrophobic* forces (page 155) are involved in the interaction between the R group of the substrate and similar hydrophobic groups in the protein. This view is supported by observations that aliphatic alcohols are inhibitors of this enzyme, presumably because their R groups compete for the protein-binding sites. Such hydrophobic binding is also apparently involved in the action of D-amino acid oxidase.

Similar considerations apply to other proteolytic enzymes, *e.g.*, chymotrypsin and carboxypeptidase, which preferentially hydrolyze peptide bonds involving aromatic or large aliphatic amino acid side chains (Table 9.4, page 150), as well as to various lipases whose affinity for the aliphatic hydrocarbon chains of the substrates is very great, and to a large number of other enzymes that act on various types of compounds which may entirely lack polar or ionic groups or may contain only a limited number of them. In all such instances, the complementary shapes of enzyme and substrate must permit a precise fit and the major binding forces are of the hydrophobic type. This appears to be the case for all enzymes that interact with neutral fats, fatty acids, sterols, steroids, terpenes, carotenoids, etc. However, the examples of the aminopeptidase and D-amino acid oxidase, cited above, show that hydrophobic interactions are not limited to nonpolar substances.

Enzymes that react specifically with individual amino acids, purines, nucleotides, etc., must "recognize" the geometry of the side chain, bind with this grouping, and exclude substrates that do not bind with sufficient energy of interaction. The data presented in Table 14.1 for the action of D-amino acid oxidase indicate not only that hydrophobic forces are involved but that the shape of the R group is also an important factor (cf. leucine and isoleucine).

Water-soluble substances, such as the hexoses, with a multiplicity of hydrophilic groups, do not possess groupings that would permit interaction with an enzyme by hydrophobic forces. With such compounds, the enzyme-substrate fit must involve complementary structures and binding must be achieved by the reactive carbonyl group and the hydroxyl groups of the substrate. These hydroxyl groups can form hydrogen bonds with suitable oxygen atoms, *e.g.*, those in peptide carbonyl groups or others.

Ionic forces also play a major role in enzyme-substrate interactions. This is probably so for *succinic acid dehydrogenase* (page 234), which catalyzes reversibly the dehydrogenation of succinate or hydrogenation of fumarate. These substrates must possess free carboxylate ions. Moreover, all the competitive inhibitors of this enzyme (page 234) possess at least one carboxyl group. Presumably, enzymic specificity involves reaction with the two carboxylate ions in succinate or fumarate, or with those of the potent inhibitor malonate, for which the binding constant with the enzyme is greater than that of either substrate. Although no information is available concerning the groups in the enzyme that react with the carboxylate ions, presumably they are cationic side chains of amino acid residues in the protein, *e.g.,* guanidinium, ammonium, or imidazolium.

Similar considerations apply to the proteolytic enzyme *trypsin,* which acts only at peptide, amide, or ester bonds involving arginine or lysine residues (Table 9.4, page 150). The synthetic compounds, α-benzoyl-L-argininamide or α-benzoyl-L-lysinamide, serve as suitable model substrates. The specificity for reaction of the cationic group of the substrate, presumably with an anionic group of the enzyme, is so exact that deamidation will not occur with compounds in which the cationic group is displaced by one CH_2 group from the sensitive amide bond. Neither the longer chain of α-benzoyl-L-homoargininamide nor the shorter chain of α-benzoyl-L-ornithinamide provides a suitable structure for reaction with trypsin.

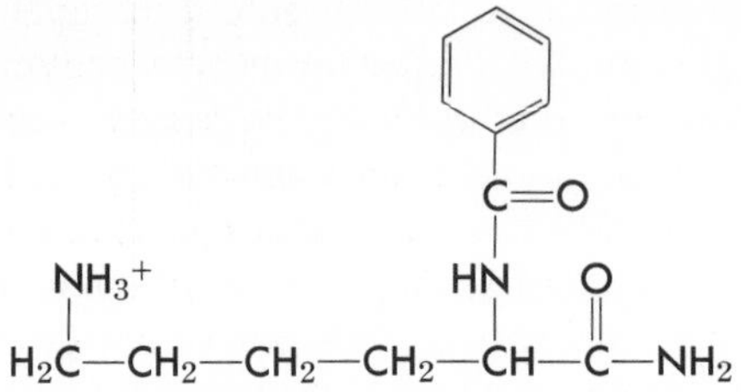

α-Benzoyl-L-lysinamide

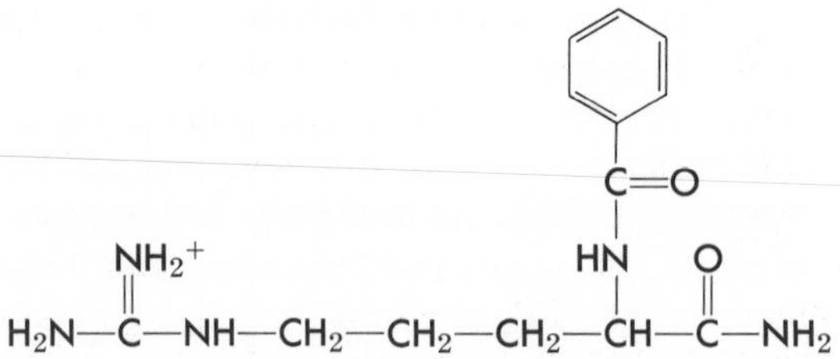

α-Benzoyl-L-argininamide

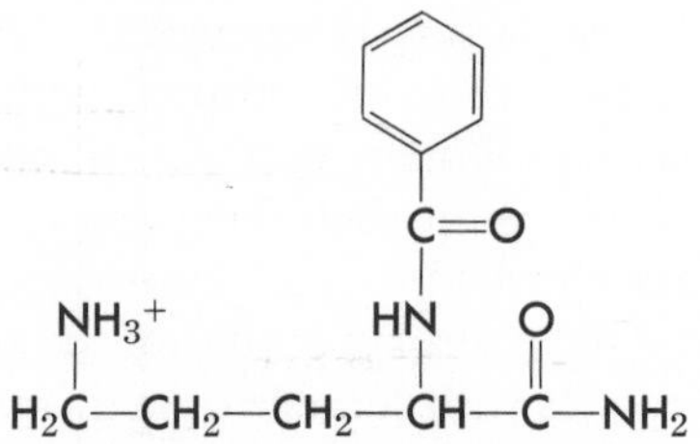

α-Benzoyl-L-ornithinamide

$$
\begin{array}{c}
\text{C}{=}\text{O} \\
\end{array}
$$

α-Benzoyl-L-homoargininamide

From the foregoing it is evident that some of the factors already implicated in maintaining protein structure itself, *viz.*, hydrophobic forces, ionic interaction, and hydrogen bonding, are involved in enzyme-substrate interactions. Obviously, a side chain of an amino acid residue in an enzyme can serve either function and in a similar manner.

Conformation and Enzymic Activity. It is apparent that catalytic activity is dependent on the appropriate conformation of each enzyme. It must not be assumed that this conformation is absolute. Indeed, the active site, in the sense of both binding forces and participating groups, may not preexist in the form required until the approach of the substrate. Koshland has suggested that the surface conformation may then be altered, resulting in an "induced fit." Evidence suggestive of a change in enzymic conformation as a consequence of substrate binding has been noted in several instances. Examples include failure to combine with antibody to the native enzyme in the presence of substrates—*adenylic acid deaminase* (page 260) and *creatine kinase* (page 308); stabilization against heat denaturation by substrates (many enzymes); changes in optical rotation—*creatine kinase, triose phosphate dehydrogenase* (page 372); reversal by substrate of inactivation at low temperature—*Neurospora glutamic acid dehydrogenase* (page 488); changes in sedimentation behavior—*acetyl CoA carboxylase* (page 446) and D-*amino acid oxidase* (page 345); and dissociation into discrete subunits—*glutamic acid dehydrogenase.*

A similar conclusion may be drawn from the fact that for several enzymes that catalyze reaction between two substrates, kinetic data suggest a compulsory order of binding. Thus, *lactic acid dehydrogenase,* which catalyzes reduction of pyruvic acid by reduced diphosphopyridine nucleotide (page 375), appears to offer no binding site for pyruvate until the nucleotide is fixed in place. It is noteworthy also that x-ray crystallographic data indicate a rather dramatic change in conformation when hemoglobin is oxygenated; similarly, oxidized cytochrome c is considerably less susceptible to hydrolysis by certain proteases than is the reduced form. In sum, these diverse observations indicate that although, generally speaking, the "lock-and-key" theory originally proposed by Emil Fischer remains valid, to some extent the "lock" tailors itself to fit the "key" as the latter approaches and is bound.

Enzymic Recognition of *meso*-Carbon Atoms. The multipoint attachment of substrate and enzyme affords a means of discriminating among the four substituent groups about a given carbon atom. Historically, this recognition derives from the observation that the two —CH_2COOH groups of citric acid behave, biologically, in nonidentical manner (page 318). Since the citric acid molecule possesses a plane of symmetry and, hence, exhibits no optical rotation, it had been considered that the two —CH₂COOH groups were intrinsically identical and should not be differentiated in chemical reactions. This dilemma was initially solved by Ogston, who indicated that, if the molecule were to be affixed to an enzymic surface at three points ("three-point attachment"), there could be only one manner of binding, resulting in discrimination between the two identical groups.

A stereochemical solution of the problem was provided by Carter and Schwartz, who showed that in a molecule in which there is a carbon atom that can be represented as C_{aabd}, the two a groups are not geometrically equivalent but bear a mirror-image relationship to each other, as shown below.

In citric acid these groups are, respectively, $a_1 = $ —CH₂COOH, $a_2 = $ —CH₂COOH, $b = $ —OH, $d = $ —COOH. The behavioral asymmetry of citric acid in biological systems, therefore, is not the consequence of attachment to an enzymic surface; rather, the asymmetric enzymic surface distinguishes between the two intrinsically, geometrically nonequivalent —CH₂COOH groups. The carbon atom with its valence bonds linked to groups a,a,b,d has been termed a "*meso*-carbon" (page 10).

Meso-carbon atoms occur in many substances of biological interest. Some of these are shown in bold type in the structures below.

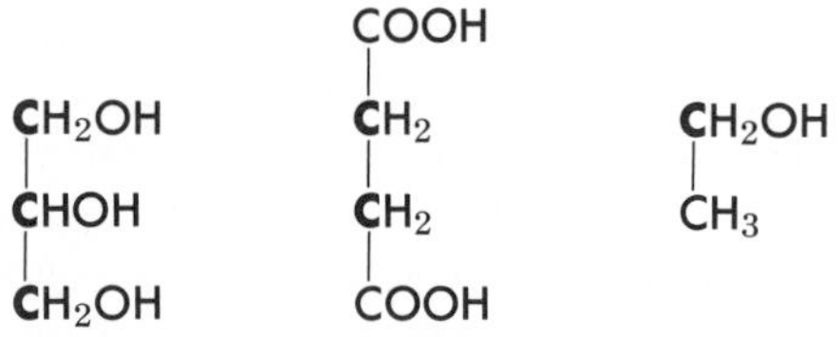

$$
\begin{array}{ccc}
 & \text{COOH} & \\
 & | & \\
\textbf{CH}_2\textbf{OH} & \textbf{CH}_2 & \textbf{CH}_2\textbf{OH} \\
| & | & | \\
\textbf{CHOH} & \textbf{CH}_2 & \text{CH}_3 \\
| & | & \\
\textbf{CH}_2\textbf{OH} & \text{COOH} & \\
\text{Glycerol} & \text{Succinic acid} & \text{Ethanol}
\end{array}
$$

As in the case of citric acid, enzymes that catalyze reactions involving compounds bearing *meso*-carbon atoms invariably discriminate between the two nonequivalent like groups. For example, phosphorylation of glycerol, catalyzed by *glycerokinase,* results exclusively in the formation of L-α-glycerophosphate rather than the DL mixture that would otherwise result.

NATURE OF ENZYMIC ACTIVE SITES

Up to this point we have been concerned chiefly with the factors involved in the formation of the enzyme-substrate complex. Some success has attended efforts to recognize and identify those amino acid residues in a given enzyme which are present at that locus at which substrate binding occurs and which may also participate in the catalytic reaction mechanism. Some of these groups have been identified in several instances. Examples of studies on a few enzymes will serve to illustrate the approaches that have been employed to attack these problems.

Chymotrypsin. The specificity of *chymotrypsin* has previously been noted (Table

9.4, page 150), its most sensitive substrates being those which contain aromatic or large aliphatic side chains. Clearly, hydrophobic forces are implicated in the R group interactions. In addition, chymotrypsin exhibits strong esterase action with substrates analogous to peptide derivatives, *e.g.*, acetyl-L-tyrosine ethyl ester as well as acetyl-L-tyrosinamide.

Chymotrypsin and other animal proteinases that are active in the gastrointestinal tract, *e.g. trypsin, pepsin, elastase,* etc., do not contain a prosthetic group or require a cofactor for their action. Nevertheless, chymotrypsin is synthesized in the pancreas in a completely inactive form as its *proenzyme* or *zymogen, chymotrypsinogen.* Inactive chymotrypsinogen consists of a single peptide chain cross-linked by five disulfide bridges. Hydrolysis by trypsin of a single peptide bond converts chymotrypsinogen to the active *π-chymotrypsin.* This is followed by liberation of the dipeptide, Ser·Arg, yielding δ-*chymotrypsin.* Another dipeptide, Thr·AspNH$_2$, is then released, yielding the more stable α-*chymotrypsin.* The process is shown schematically in Fig. 14.1, together with the alternate route of α-chymotrypsin formation.

Several features of the activation process should be noted: (1) there are 4 arginine and 11 lysine residues in chymotrypsinogen, yet only a single bond involving arginine is selectively attacked by trypsin; (2) the single peptide chain of the inactive zymogen is converted to the three-chain active chymotrypsin; (3) as a result of the removal of one or two dipeptides, there is a profound conformational change in the structure, as shown by a large decrease in levorotation (page 56). This suggests that the conformation of the active enzyme produces a juxtaposition of amino acid side chains that are remote from one another in the inactive zymogen. The novel interaction of groups in the enzyme results in a high degree of reactivity of certain groups, as shown below.

Chymotrypsin is irreversibly inactivated by a stoichiometric reaction with certain reactive phosphorus derivatives, *e.g.*, diisopropylphosphofluoridate (DIPF), and forms a diisopropylphosphoryl derivative with a single, specific serine residue of the enzyme.

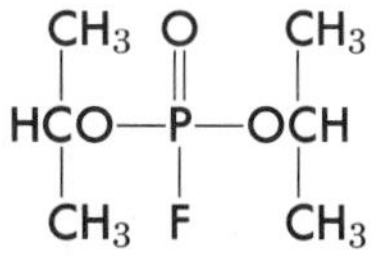

$$
\begin{array}{ccc}
CH_3 & O & CH_3 \\
| & \| & | \\
HCO\!-\!P\!-\!OCH \\
| & | & | \\
CH_3 & F & CH_3
\end{array}
$$

Diisopropylphosphofluoridate

It should be emphasized that neither chymotrypsinogen nor denatured chymotrypsin reacts with DIPF and that although chymotrypsin contains approximately 30 serine residues, only a single specific one can combine with the reagent. Clearly, the formation of inactive protein by such a specific combination with an inhibitor indicates that only a small well-defined part of chymotrypsin is responsible for its activity and that the reactive serine probably forms a part of the "active site" of the enzyme. Table 14.2 presents the amino acid sequence near the reactive serine of chymotrypsin and other enzymes that are inhibited by DIPF or similar reagents. Furthermore, the special reactivity of the serine residues of the enzymes listed is indicated by the findings that free serine does not react with DIPF or similar reagents, nor do small serine peptides.

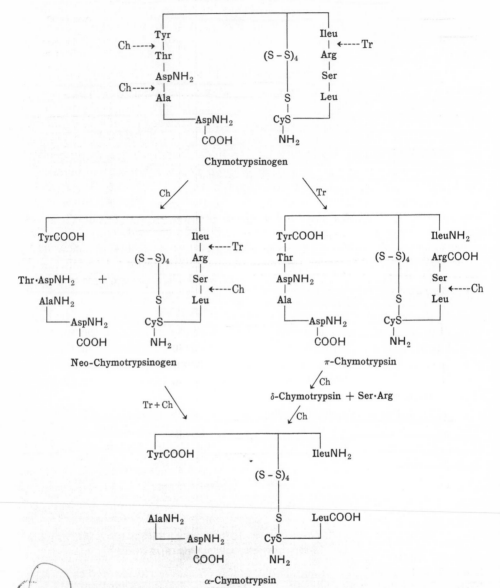

FIG. 14.1 Scheme for activation of chymotrypsinogen A. Hydrolysis of the Ileu-Arg bond produces π-chymotrypsin. This is followed by liberation of the dipeptide, Ser·Arg, producing δ-chymotrypsin, which is then converted to α-chymotrypsin by liberation of Thr·AspNH₂. Alternatively, inactive neo-chymotrypsinogen is formed as an intermediate; tryptic action on this protein yields active α-chymotrypsin. Chymotrypsinogen possesses a single peptide chain, whereas α-chymotrypsin contains three chains held together by five disulfide bridges, arbitrarily shown in the diagrams. *Tr* = trypsin; *Ch* = chymotrypsin. (*From the work of Neurath and of Desnuelle and their associates.*)

Table 14.2: Sequences Adjacent to the Reactive Serine in Enzymes

Enzyme	*Sequence**
Chymotrypsin	Gly·Asp·Ser·Gly·
Trypsin	Gly·Asp·Ser·Gly·
Elastase	Gly·Asp·Ser·Gly·
Subtilisin	Thr·Ser·Met·Ala·
Aliesterase	Gly·Glu·Ser·Ala·
Pseudocholinesterase	Gly·Glu·Ser·Ala·
Phosphoglucomutase	Thr·Ala·Ser·His·Asp·

* The serine residue in each of these sequences is the one that reacts with DIPF or accepts phosphate from phosphorylated substrates.

Much indirect and direct evidence also implicates a histidine residue in the catalytic activity of chymotrypsin. The effect of pH on the value of the kinetic constant k_3 (page 222) suggests the participation of a grouping with a pK value similar to that of the imidazole of histidine, the active form being the uncharged N of this ring structure. Moreover, treatment of chymotrypsin with L-1-(*p*-toluenesulfonyl) amido-2-phenylethylchloromethyl ketone results in a parallel loss of activity and of one histidine residue.

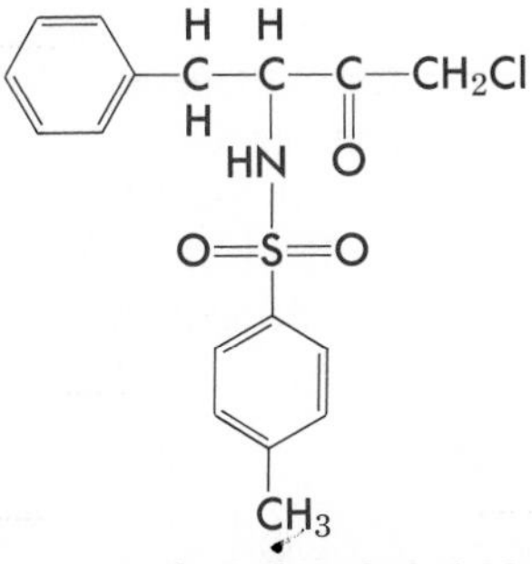

L-1-(*p*-Toluenesulfonyl)amido-2-phenylethylchloromethyl ketone

It should be noted that the above compound reacts with chymotrypsin because of a resemblance to substrates, such as an acylphenylalanine amide or ester, in which the $-NH_2$ or $-OCH_3$ is present in place of the nonhydrolyzable $-CH_2Cl$.

Although the complete amino acid sequence of chymotrypsin has not yet been elucidated, the studies of Hartley and of Sorm, Keil, and their associates have shown that the reactive serine and the two histidine residues of the protein are remote from one another in the sequence. However, the two histidine residues are near each other as a result of linking by adjacent half-cystine residues in a disulfide bridge. As is the case with all other enzymes, denaturation, *i.e.*, unfolding of the protein, results in complete inactivation of chymotrypsin. Again, this implies that the active form of the enzyme depends on the native conformation, which somehow brings together the specific side chains of the amino acid residues essential for determining the specificity and catalytic reactivity of the protein.

As indicated in Table 14.2, there is a large class of enzymes—esterases and proteinases (which are also esterases)—that possesses a reactive serine residue.

This group of enzymes obviously must possess structural and catalytic features in common; however, in view of their great differences in specificity, other parts of their "active sites" must differ profoundly.

Ribonuclease. The action of pancreatic *ribonuclease* on RNA has already been presented (pages 181 *ff.*). Ribonuclease (bovine) is a protein containing 124 amino acid residues; its composition is given in Table 9.1 (page 144). The work of Moore and Stein and their coworkers and of Anfinsen and collaborators led to the elucidation of the complete sequence of the single peptide chain and the positions of the disulfide bridges, as shown in Fig. 14.2.

Under conditions of limited digestion by the bacterial proteinase *subtilisin,* Richards found that ribonuclease (RNase) is hydrolyzed at the peptide bond between residues 20 and 21. The two fragments, S-peptide and S-protein, may be separated at acid pH, but neither is active. These fragments recombine at neutral pH, and enzymic activity is restored. Although the peptide bond is not re-formed, it is noteworthy that the 20-residue S-peptide binds strongly to the 104-residue S-protein, presumably by secondary valence forces. Hofmann and coworkers have shown that a synthetic peptide containing the amino-terminal 13 residues of the S-peptide will regenerate approximately 70 per cent of the enzymic activity with the S-protein, thus demonstrating that residues 14 to 20 play no essential *catalytic* role. Furthermore, the undecapeptide, lacking histidine and methionine (residues 12 and 13, respectively), is inactive.

Treatment of ribonuclease with iodoacetate at pH 5.5 produces two inactive monocarboxymethylhistidine derivatives of the enzyme. Crestfield, Stein, and Moore have demonstrated that one of these is 1-carboxymethylhistidine ribonuclease substituted at position 119; the other is the 3-carboxymethylhistidine derivative substituted at position 12 in the peptide sequence (Fig. 14.2); these are formed in a ratio of 8:1. The structures of these isomeric derivatives are shown.

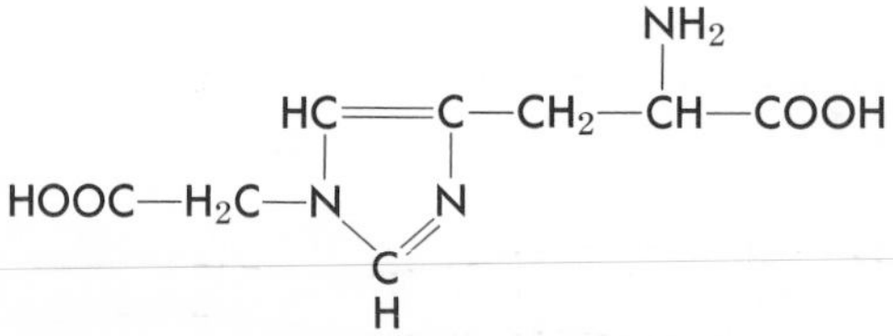

3-Carboxymethylhistidine 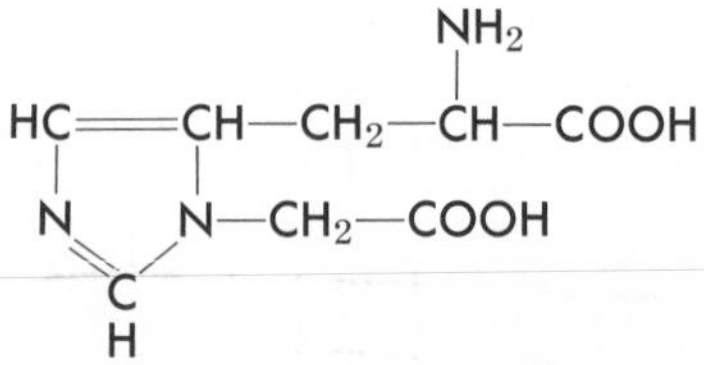   1-Carboxymethylhistidine

Inasmuch as both derivatives of RNase are essentially inactive, it is evident that both histidine residues must be essential for enzymic activity. Moreover, alkylation of one histidine residue prevents alkylation of the other. Aggregates of RNase (dimers, trimers, etc.) are formed by lyophilization from 50 per cent acetic acid. When such aggregates are formed with a mixture of the two inactive RNase derivatives, the resulting hybrids manifest about half the activity of an equivalent weight of native enzyme treated in the same fashion. These results indicate that histidine-12 and histidine-119 are both at the active site which can be formed from parts of two different molecules. This activity disappears when the aggregates are broken up by heating at 67°C. for 10 min., conditions which do not denature untreated RNase.

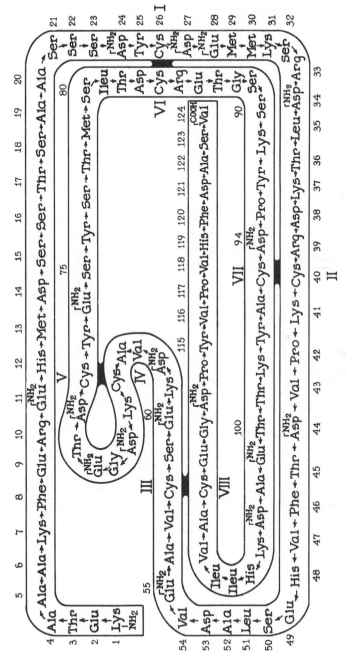

Fig. 14.2. The amino acid sequence of bovine pancreatic ribonuclease. (*From D. G. Smyth, W. H. Stein, and S. Moore, J. Biol. Chem.,* **238**, 227, 1963).

These findings indicate once again that the enzymic activity is a consequence of specific folding or conformation of the peptide chain, *viz.*, active sites are formed by the juxtaposition of amino acid side chains that may be remote from one another in the sequence; however, the folding is a consequence of linear amino acid sequence (Chaps. 9 and 29). Moreover, as in the case of the reactive serine of chymotrypsin, trypsin, and other enzymes described above, the histidine residues of RNase are uniquely reactive with iodoacetate or bromoacetate at pH 5.5. Histidine itself, the other two histidine residues of RNase, and histidine residues of other proteins do not react with these reagents at this pH value. Obviously, it is the special conformation which confers this unique reactivity.

MECHANISM OF ENZYMIC ACTION

A major goal of biochemistry is to provide a detailed account of the mechanisms by which enzymes catalyze specific reactions. It must be admitted, at the outset, that this goal has not yet been realized in a single instance. The simplest concept of the action of an enzyme is that its surface serves to gather together, in favorable proximity, the various reactants involved, *i.e.*, the substrates and cofactors. In effect, this would accomplish a marked local increase in concentration of reactants, as achieved, for example, by platinum black for H_2 and O_2. This could also assure appropriate orientation of the reacting groups in space so that collision must occur and in a manner leading to a specific reaction. If this concept were adequate, only the specific binding capacity of the protein would be involved. However, for most of the reactions studied, this concept appears to offer only a partial solution to the remarkable catalytic efficiency of enzymes generally. Thus, many enzymes increase by a factor of 10^6 to 10^{10} the rate at which the same reaction would occur were all the reactants present in $1M$ aqueous solution in the absence of the enzyme. Indeed, this is even true of hydrolytic reactions; enzymically catalyzed hydrolyses proceed about 10^3 times as fast as do the same reactions even when catalyzed by acid or base.

Activation by Strain or Bond Distortion. A relatively old hypothesis to account for enzymic catalysis suggested that specific attachment to the enzymic surface induces "strain" or "deformation" in the bonds that are to be broken. Although the concept of strain has been poorly defined, the idea is not without merit, if it be interpreted to mean the intermediate formation of a compound or complex which, kinetically, will rapidly be converted to the desired reaction products, *i.e.*, which is inherently less stable than the original reactants. An example of strain in this sense is afforded by the fact that the base-catalyzed hydrolysis of ethylene phosphate occurs 10^7 times more rapidly than does that of dimethylphosphate.

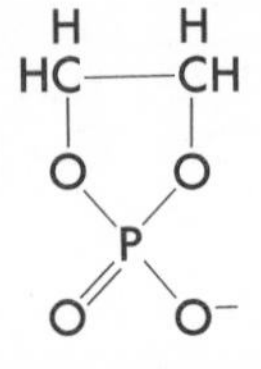

Ethylene phosphate 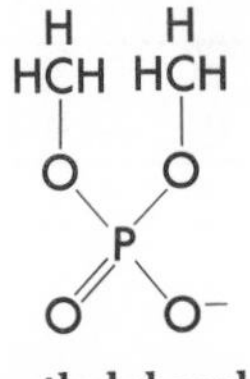   Dimethylphosphate

The strain hypothesis has seemed an attractive explanation for enzymic catalysis. An actual example appears to be reflected in the behavior of horse liver esterase. In studying the hydrolysis of a series of esters of *m*-hydroxybenzoic acid,

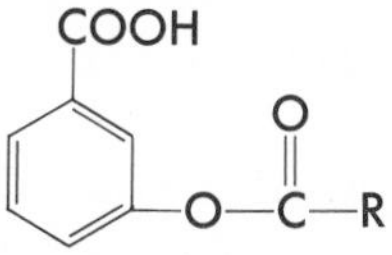

Hofstee found that K_m was almost independent of the chain length of R, whereas V_{max} increased by several orders of magnitude as the chain length increased. Since the bond to be hydrolyzed is the same in each instance, it can be inferred that the increased binding energy of the longer-chain esters reduced the activation energy for the reaction, *i.e.*, the energy of the tighter bonding of the hydrocarbon moiety is offset by the strain energy induced in the acyl portion of the molecule.

Functional Groups at the Catalytic Site. The most likely explanation of enzymic catalytic efficiency that has gained general acceptance is the presence at the "active site" of amino acid residues or other groupings, such as metal ions, which can serve as acids or bases or as nucleophilic (electron-donating) or electrophilic (electron-attracting) agents and, thus, actually participate in the reaction mechanism. In the case of enzymes containing metal ions, the metal ion itself can bind with groupings, in the substrate and act as a strain-producing agent by forming a chelated intermediary compound. At the same time, the metal ion, because of its positive charge, is a strong electrophilic agent which can act as an effective participant in the reaction. As already noted (page 210), many enzymes contain bound metal ions which do not alter their valence state during the enzymic reaction, *e.g.*, Mg^{++}, Mn^{++}, Zn^{++}, and which probably function as electrophilic groups. This has been suggested for certain hydrolytic enzymes, notably the peptidases.

There are many enzymes that lack metal ions or other non-amino acid groups. In these instances, the groupings at the "active sites" have been sought by other methods. As described previously, it is possible to demonstrate by various procedures the essentiality of an unaltered form of several amino acid residues for the functioning of a given enzyme. Methionine residues can be oxidized to the corresponding sulfoxide, $CH_3S—CH_2—$, histidine residues may be destroyed by photo-

$$\overset{\|}{O}$$

oxidation, sulfhydryl groups may be caused to react with heavy metals or with iodoacetate. Enz— below connotes the remainder of the enzyme.

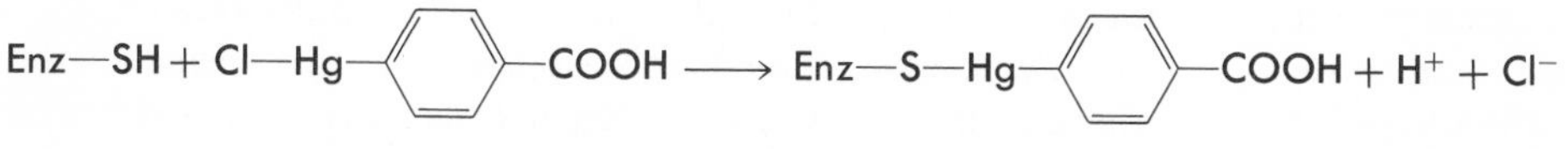

$$Enz—SH + Cl—Hg—\bigcirc—COOH \longrightarrow Enz—S—Hg—\bigcirc—COOH + H^+ + Cl^-$$

$$Enz—SH + ICH_2COO^- \longrightarrow Enz—S—CH_2—COO^- + H^+ + I^-$$

Histidine residues also react with iodoacetate, as in the case of ribonuclease (page 250). Lysine residues can react with fluorodinitrobenzene (page 146) or with various acylating agents and can be converted to homoarginine by reaction with isothiourea.

$$\text{Enz}-(CH_2)_4-NH_2 + HS-\overset{\overset{\displaystyle NH}{\|}}{C}-NH_2 \longrightarrow \text{Enz}-(CH_2)_4-\underset{\underset{\displaystyle H}{|}}{N}-\overset{\overset{\displaystyle }{\|}}{\underset{\underset{\displaystyle NH}{}}{C}}-NH_2 + H_2S$$

Another useful procedure is examination of the titration curve of the enzyme in the region of its optimal pH. The presence of titratable amino acid residues in this region suggests that these groups may participate in the enzymic reaction mechanism and are required in either the protonated or the unprotonated form. Since most enzymes exhibit pH optima in the region 6.5 to 7.5, and since the imidazole group of histidine is the only residue titratable in this range, there is now an almost embarrassingly long list of enzymes for which it has been suggested that histidine has a specific function.

Evidence of the types described above does not adequately establish the participation of these various amino acid residues in the catalytic event. Titration of histidine, binding of a sulfhydryl group, or oxidation of methionine could have altered the conformation of the protein, thereby influencing the catalytic site. In each instance it is necessary to demonstrate that the amino acid residues in question are indeed at the active site. This information can be provided only through knowledge of the complete, three-dimensional structure of the enzyme as it might be reconstructed from x-ray crystallographic analysis. Data of this type are not presently available for any enzyme. Moreover, demonstration of the presence of a specific residue at the active site does not necessarily indicate that it participates as a *reactant* in the catalytic process.

More acceptable as evidence is a demonstration that a specific residue can react with substrate, or a suitable model compound, to form a stable, covalently bonded derivative. Evidence of this type is available in several instances. As noted previously, several hydrolytic enzymes containing individual serine residues that react with DIPF also have reactive histidine residues. In the case of chymotrypsin, this has been shown by formation of a histidine derivative when the enzyme was exposed to a substance of a character similar to that of a model synthetic substrate. Hypotheses regarding the mechanism of action of these enzymes, therefore, are based on the nucleophilic character of the seroxide group, $-OC-CHNHR-CH_2O^-$, and the ease with which the imidazolium group can serve as proton donor. A serine residue has also been implicated in the functioning of *phosphoglucomutase* (page 403); the phosphate ester of one serine residue can be isolated following treatment of the enzyme with the substrate, glucose 1,6-diphosphate. It is of interest that there is a histidine residue immediately adjacent to this serine in the primary structure of the enzyme. However, evidence is lacking that this serine residue is phosphorylated and dephosphorylated at a rate commensurate with the over-all catalysis.

The sulfhydryl groups of cysteine residues have been implicated as participating in the catalytic mechanisms of a variety of enzymes. Thus, it has been suggested that proteolysis by *papain* and *ficin* entails intermediate formation of an enzyme-bound thioester of the carboxyl group of the ruptured peptide bond.

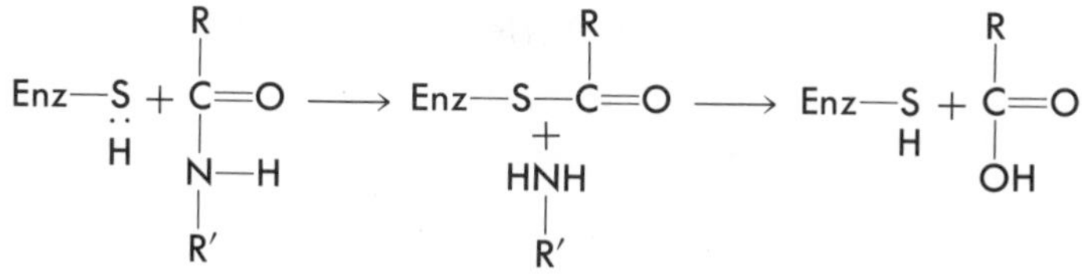

$$\text{Enz—S} \overset{\cdot\cdot}{} + \overset{R}{\underset{N—H}{\overset{|}{C}}}\!=\!O \longrightarrow \text{Enz—S—}\overset{R}{\underset{HNH}{\overset{|}{C}}}\!=\!O \longrightarrow \text{Enz—S} + \overset{R}{\underset{OH}{\overset{|}{C}}}\!=\!O$$

In the diagram, (a) has Enz—S with H below and the carbonyl carbon bearing R above, $=O$, and $N—H$ below with R'; (b) the central structure with $+$ and HNH, R'; (c) Enz—S with H.

$$\quad\quad\quad(a)\quad\quad\quad\quad\quad\quad(b)\quad\quad\quad\quad\quad\quad(c)$$

Enzyme sulfhydryl groups are thought to participate in electron transfer in several oxidative enzymes such as *lipoyl dehydrogenase* (page 347) and by addition to the aldehyde function of 3-phosphoglyceraldehyde so that the first oxidation product is the 3-phosphoglyceryl thioester of the enzyme (page 372), similar in general structure to that shown in (*b*) above.

In yet another instance, phosphate has been shown to be covalently bound to the imidazole nitrogen of a histidine residue of a protein during "oxidative phosphorylation" in mitochondria (page 331).

Another form of covalent bonding of substrates is apparent in the formation of Schiff bases (aldimines) between carbonyl compounds and the ε-amino group of lysine in some enzymes. Thus when dihydroxyacetone phosphate is incubated with *aldolase* (page 371) in the absence of 3-phosphoglyceraldehyde (its normal partner in the reaction catalyzed by this enzyme), the following reaction appears to take place.

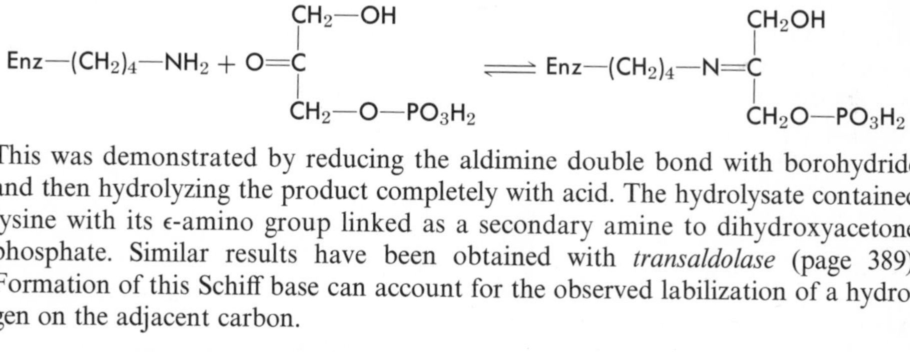

$$\text{Enz—(CH}_2)_4\text{—NH}_2 + O\!=\!\overset{\overset{\displaystyle CH_2—OH}{|}}{\underset{\underset{\displaystyle CH_2—O—PO_3H_2}{|}}{C}} \rightleftharpoons \text{Enz—(CH}_2)_4\text{—N}\!=\!\overset{\overset{\displaystyle CH_2OH}{|}}{\underset{\underset{\displaystyle CH_2O—PO_3H_2}{|}}{C}}$$

This was demonstrated by reducing the aldimine double bond with borohydride and then hydrolyzing the product completely with acid. The hydrolysate contained lysine with its ε-amino group linked as a secondary amine to dihydroxyacetone phosphate. Similar results have been obtained with *transaldolase* (page 389). Formation of this Schiff base can account for the observed labilization of a hydrogen on the adjacent carbon.

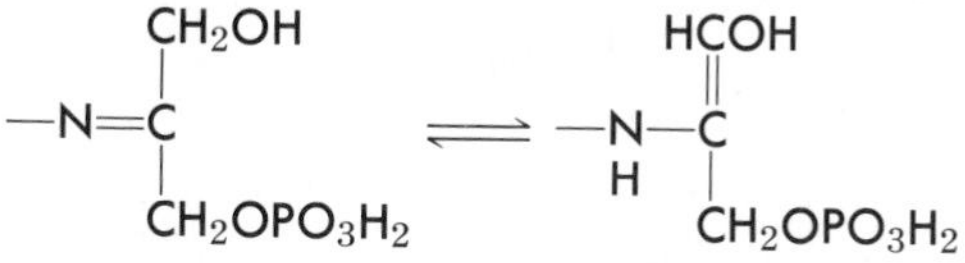

$$-\text{N}\!=\!\overset{\overset{\displaystyle CH_2OH}{|}}{\underset{\underset{\displaystyle CH_2OPO_3H_2}{|}}{C}} \rightleftharpoons -\overset{}{\underset{\underset{\displaystyle H}{|}}{N}}\!-\!\overset{\overset{\displaystyle HCOH}{||}}{\underset{\underset{\displaystyle CH_2OPO_3H_2}{|}}{C}}$$

Of interest in this regard is the manner in which pyridoxal phosphate functions in transaminases. This mechanism is discussed in detail elsewhere (page 494). It need only be noted here that in transamination the aldehyde function of pyridoxal phosphate initially participates in formation of a Schiff base with a lysine ε-amino group of the apoenzyme. This also occurs in muscle phosphorylase. This is not merely a means of binding the pyridoxal phosphate to the enzyme; this is accomplished elsewhere on the pyridoxal phosphate molecule. The initial binding serves rather to accelerate the enzymic reaction since *transaldimination* is much more rapid than is initial formation of the Schiff base. Thus the initial step in this reaction may be visualized as in Fig. 14.3.

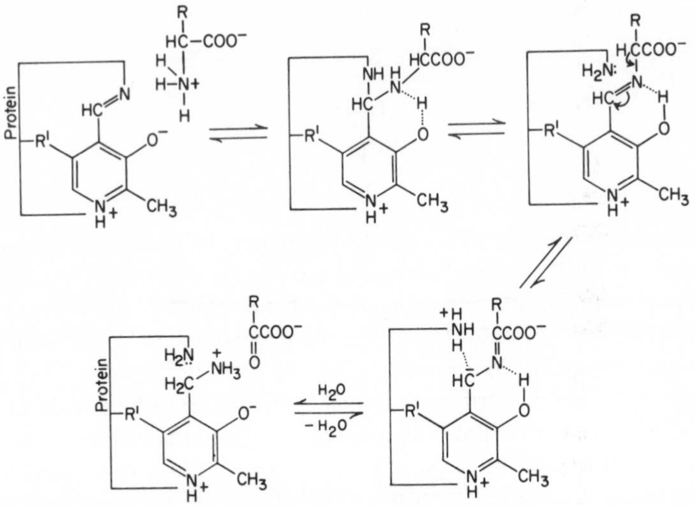

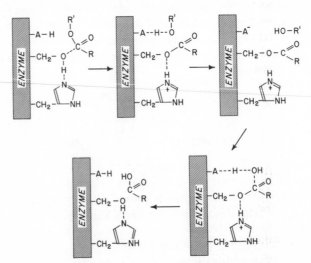

FIG. 14.3. Speculative scheme for catalysis of a half-reaction of enzymic transamination illustrating how the nonhydrogen-bonded aldimine structure facilitates interaction with the amino acid substrate, and how the liberated ε-amino group of lysine might act as a general acid-base catalyst for the electron shifts initiated by pyridoxal. (*From E. E. Snell, Brookhaven Symposia in Biology, No. 15, Brookhaven National Laboratory, Upton, N.Y., p.* 39, *1962.*)

Studies such as those cited above have led to the postulation of reaction mechanisms for a variety of enzymes. The total evidence available for chymotrypsin and ribonuclease is greater than that for other enzymes; the most generally accepted hypotheses are depicted in Figs. 14.4 and 14.5. The mechanism shown for ribonuclease rests, among other observations, on the isolation of cyclic phosphate

FIG. 14.4. A suggested mechanism for hydrolysis of an ester catalyzed by chymotrypsin. As shown, catalysis requires concerted operation of a serine residue, a histidine imidazole group, and an unidentified acid function (—A—H). (*Modified from F. M. Westheimer, Advances in Enzymol.,* **24,** 464, *1962.*)

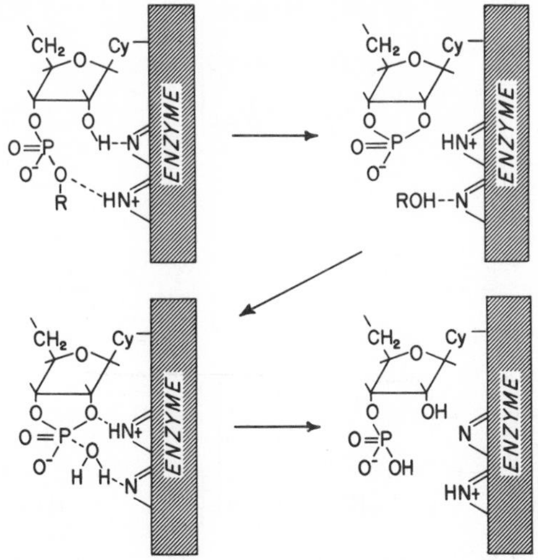

FIG. 14.5. Generalized representation of cooperative function of two histidine residues in catalyzing hydrolysis of an internucleotide linkage of ribonucleic acid by ribonuclease. *Cy* indicates the cytosine residue. Note the postulated formation of the cyclic phosphate nucleotide, on the enzymic surface, as an intermediate.

esters from the reaction mixture and the fact that hydrolysis of cytidine 3',5'-cyclic phosphate by ribonuclease is exceedingly rapid.

In general, two types of phenomena, *transfer* and *exchange*, have suggested formation in the catalytic process of an intermediate in which a group from one of the reactants is covalently linked to a site on the enzyme. Many hydrolytic enzymes can be shown to catalyze not only the hydrolysis for which each is regarded as specific, but group transfer reactions as well. This was originally observed as the process of *transpeptidation*, as shown below.

1. Hydrolysis:

$$\underset{\substack{\| \\ \text{O}}}{\text{R—C}}\text{—NH—}\underset{\substack{| \\ \text{R}'}}{\text{CO}}\text{—NH—Y} \xrightarrow{\text{HOH}} \underset{\substack{\| \\ \text{O}}}{\text{R—C}}\text{—NH—}\underset{\substack{| \\ \text{R}'}}{\text{COOH}} + \text{H}_2\text{N—Y}$$

2. Transpeptidation:

$$\underset{\substack{\| \\ \text{O}}}{\text{R—C}}\text{—NH—}\underset{\substack{| \\ \text{R}'}}{\text{CO}}\text{—NH—Y} + \text{H}_2\text{N—X} \longrightarrow \underset{\substack{\| \\ \text{O}}}{\text{R—C}}\text{—NH—}\underset{\substack{| \\ \text{R}'}}{\text{CO}}\text{—NH—X} + \text{H}_2\text{N—Y}$$

Similar reactions have been observed with amylases, in which, instead of hydrolysis, a new glycoside results when the medium contains an appropriate alcohol, which displaces the group leaving. Esterases normally catalyze hydrolysis of esters, but in the presence of an alcohol in the medium can catalyze transesterification.

$$\text{R—CO—OA} + \text{BOH} \rightleftharpoons \text{R—CO—OB} + \text{AOH}$$

On the basis of such transfers, it has been suggested that the actual mechanism might be as follows.

$$\text{Enz} \underset{N:}{\overset{OH}{\diagdown}} + \underset{O-A}{\overset{R}{\underset{|}{C}}} =O \longrightarrow \left[\text{Enz} \underset{N^+:H}{\overset{O\cdots\cdots C=O}{\diagdown}} \overset{R}{\underset{|}{O-A}} \right] \longrightarrow \left[\text{Enz} \underset{N:HO-A}{\overset{O-C=O}{\diagdown}} \overset{R}{\underset{|}{}} \right] \longrightarrow$$

$$\text{Enz} \underset{N:}{\overset{O-\overset{R}{\underset{|}{C}}=O}{\diagdown}} + HO-A \longrightarrow \text{Enz} \underset{N:}{\overset{O-\overset{R}{\underset{|}{C}}=O}{\diagdown}} + HO-B \longrightarrow$$

$$\left[\text{Enz} \underset{N:HO-B}{\overset{O-\overset{R}{\underset{|}{C}}=O}{\diagdown}} \right] \longrightarrow \left[\text{Enz} \underset{N^+:H\ O-B}{\overset{O\cdots\cdots\overset{R}{\underset{|}{C}}=O}{\diagdown}} \right] \longrightarrow \text{Enz} \underset{N:}{\overset{OH}{\diagdown}} + \underset{O-B}{\overset{R}{\underset{|}{C}}} =O$$

The —OH and N= groups could be those of serine and histidine, respectively.

A similar mechanism has been invoked to explain the frequently observed exchange reactions. Thus, for an esterase such as that above, the use of C^{14}†-labeled compounds has demonstrated that the enzyme catalyzes the following exchange.

$$CH_3COO-CH_3 + C^{14}H_3OH \rightleftharpoons CH_3-COOC^{14}H_3 + CH_3OH$$

On the other hand, if the same enzyme is incubated with unlabeled ester and labeled acid $C^{14}H_3C^{14}OOH$, no exchange into the ester occurs, in accord with the proposed mechanism. This is a general phenomenon; enzymes that catalyze such exchanges, *viz.*,

$$A-B + B^* \rightleftharpoons A-B^* + B$$

fail to catalyze exchange with the other component of the system (A); *i.e.*, A*—B is not formed when enzyme is incubated with A—B and A*. From this it follows that there must be formation of an intermediate in which A is covalently bonded to the enzyme in a manner that retains the bond energy of A—B.

$$Enz-H + A-B \rightleftharpoons Enz-A + BH$$

It is this reaction which is observed as an "exchange." Since it occurs reversibly at a velocity equal to that of normal hydrolytic catalysis, and Enz—A retains much of the bond energy of A—B, ΔF for this process must be small. Hydrolysis, then, represents the subsequent hydrolytic rupture of Enz—A to Enz—H + AOH, and it is this step which must proceed with a favorable negative change in free energy.

It should be understood that observation of an exchange process such as that discussed above, of itself, does not constitute proof of participation of the enzyme in the manner indicated. It is entirely conceivable that on an enzymic surface, binding of an ester might occur in a manner which makes it susceptible to direct attack by the exchanging group, *i.e.*, the alcohol in the series above. Additional

† Superscript numbers of atoms indicate their mass numbers. Thus, C^{12} designates naturally occurring carbon and C^{14} a radioactive isotope of carbon with mass 14 (see page 273).

evidence of a more direct nature is required before these exchange studies may be accepted as an indication of participation of the enzyme as a reactant.

Covalent bonding of intermediates to group(s) on the enzyme is not limited to hydrolytic enzymes. Indeed, the first convincing evidence for this was provided by *sucrose phosphorylase* (page 409). This enzyme was originally observed to catalyze the following reaction.

(a) $\qquad$ Sucrose + P_i $\rightleftharpoons$ α-D-glucose 1-phosphate + fructose

The enzyme also catalyzes each of the following reactions.

(b) $\qquad$ Glucose 1-phosphate + P_i^{32} $\rightleftharpoons$ glucose-1-$P^{32}O_4$ + P_i
(c) $\qquad$ Sucrose + sorbose $\rightleftharpoons$ glucose-sorboside + fructose

These observations are best reconciled by the following reaction mechanism.

(d) $\qquad$ Enz—OH + glucose—O—R $\rightleftharpoons$ Enz—O—glucose + HOR
(e) $\qquad$ Enz—O—glucose + HO—Y $\rightleftharpoons$ Enz—OH + glucose—O—Y

No evidence is available to suggest the nature of the group on the enzyme which functions as described. The best evidence for this scheme is the fact that in both sucrose and the glucose 1-phosphate which is formed in reaction (a), the glucose is in the α configuration. Were the phosphorolysis of sucrose a normal metathetical reaction, simply occurring on the enzyme surface, it would proceed as a "back-sided attack" and sucrose, an α-glucoside, should yield β-glucose 1-phosphate.

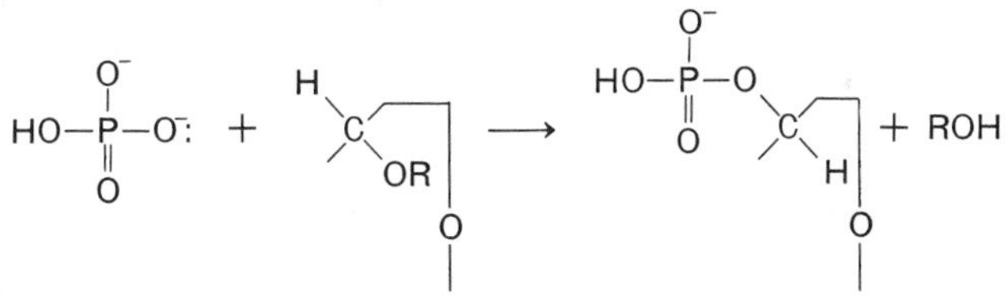

Since the actual product is the α form, it is believed that the mechanism consists of two consecutive double displacements, the first of which involves a group on the enzyme, represented below as an oxygen function for convenience since the actual group is unknown.

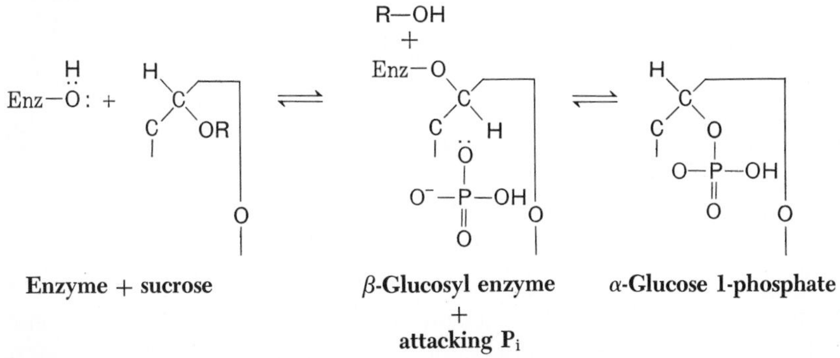

Enzyme + sucrose $\qquad$ β-Glucosyl enzyme + attacking P_i $\qquad$ α-Glucose 1-phosphate

The combination of exchange data and the observed stereochemical events led Rose to postulate the scheme shown in Fig. 14.6 for the mechanism of action of

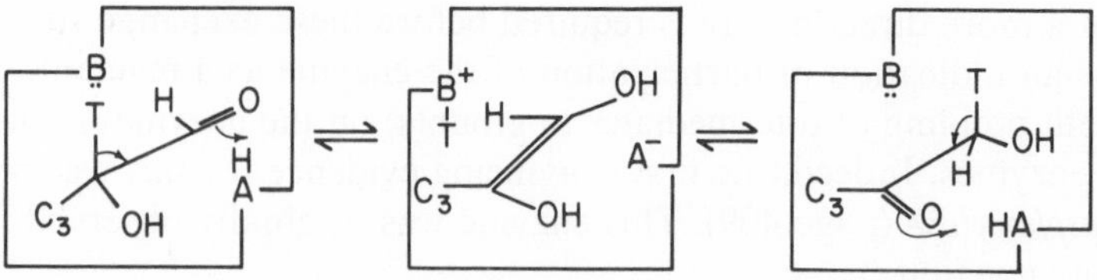

FIG. 14.6. Generalized mechanism by which an enzyme may catalyze formation of a *cis*-enediol from an aldose or ketose. *B* and *HA* are not specifically defined but represent a base and an acid, respectively, on the enzymic surface. This scheme indicates the manner in which a base, fixed in position with relation to the substrate, assures stereospecific migration of a proton, indicated in the figure as *T* (tritium) for labeling purposes.

phosphoglucose isomerase (page 370). In this and many other reactions in carbohydrate metabolism, the hydrogen atom α to a carbonyl group is labilized and removed. In this instance, it was shown by the use of tritium labeling that the hydrogen atom is removed in a specific stereochemical manner and is not diluted by the protons of the water. In the conversion of glucose 6-phosphate to fructose 6-phosphate, a reaction shown to involve intermediate formation of a *cis*-enediol, the tritium label behaves as shown below (T = tritium, H³).

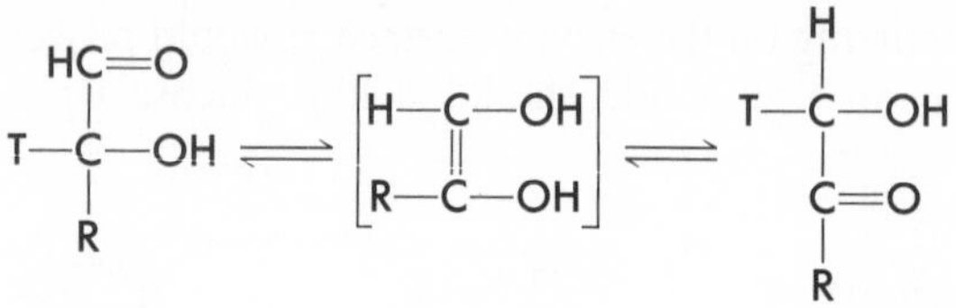

| Glucose | Postulated *cis*- | Fructose |
| 6-phosphate | enediol | 6-phosphate |

Although the actual enzymic groups were not identified, the absolute steric specificity and the failure of the migrating proton to dilute with the medium require postulation of an arrangement involving a nucleophilic agent and an acid, such as that depicted in Fig. 14.6.

Although group transfer reactions, such as transpeptidation and transglycosylation discussed above, proceed by transient formation of an intermediate in which the group to be transferred is covalently bound to the enzyme, many transfer reactions seem to occur as metathetical reactions between the substrates at an appropriate locus on the enzymic surface. Thus, *kinases,* each of which catalyzes transfer of a phosphate group from ATP to a specific acceptor, do not appear to form intermediate phosphate-enzyme compounds. *Creatine kinase* (page 750) which catalyzes the reaction

$$\text{ATP} + \text{creatine} \rightleftharpoons \text{ADP} + \text{creatine phosphate}$$

will not catalyze exchange of creatine-C^{14} with creatine phosphate or of ADP^{32} with ATP, as might be expected if an intermediate phosphate-enzyme compound were formed. Nevertheless, catalysis of the reaction entails more than merely binding both substrates in such a manner that they can react. A series of observations strongly suggest the concerted participation of both a histidine residue and a sulfhydryl group of the enzyme, as well as a Mg^{++} ion, as depicted in Fig. 14.7.

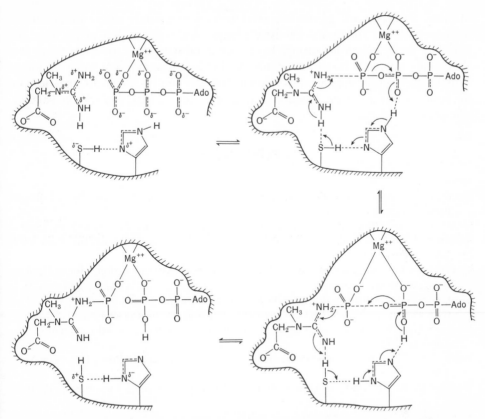

FIG. 14.7. Schematic representation of the transfer of a phosphate group from ATP to creatine, catalyzed by muscle creatine kinase. *Ado* represents the adenosine portion of ATP. The
upper left diagram shows the disposition of all groups at the instant of binding of creatine
and ATP. The lower left diagram represents completion of the reaction just prior to
departure of creatine phosphate and ADP from the enzymic surface.

Thus, a substantial body of both direct and circumstantial evidence indicates
that enzymes do not merely offer convenient surfaces on which defined reactions
may occur. It seems quite clear that, in addition, functional groups on enzymic surfaces also directly participate in the reaction mechanism. This may take the form
of acid or base catalysis, or nucleophilic or electrophilic attack. The substrate may
be altered through abortive complexes or defined transition states or may become
covalently linked to the enzyme during the course of the reaction. As these suggestions have arisen it has seemed possible that the proposed mechanisms might be
examined experimentally by use of model systems, *e.g.*, study of the possible catalytic influence of histidine or histidyl·seryl peptides on the hydrolysis of esters or
amides. Perhaps the most striking conclusion from such studies is that in these
model systems, catalysis is most effective if the presumed catalytic group is appropriately located within the very molecule to be hydrolyzed. Thus, regardless of the
absolute concentration of the molecule, the catalytic activity of a histidine residue
within a synthetic peptide is equivalent to that which might be exhibited by a 5 or
$10M$ solution of histidine. In a sense, this is precisely what is accomplished by

enzymes; the forces and groups that bind the substrate ensure almost instantaneous reaction with the functional catalytic groups. Although studies of the role and nature of these functional groups have been conducted only for a few years, it is abundantly apparent that these groups do, indeed, exist and that when combined with those aspects of enzymic structure which confer binding specificity, they account for both the nature of the reaction that is catalyzed and the remarkable catalytic efficiency of enzymes.

REFERENCES

Books

Brookhaven Symposia in Biology, "Enzyme Models and Enzyme Structure," No. 15, Brookhaven National Laboratory, Upton, N.Y., 1962.

Ingraham, L. L., "Biochemical Mechanisms," John Wiley & Sons, Inc., New York, 1962.

Kosower, E. M., "Molecular Biochemistry," McGraw-Hill Book Company, Inc., New York, 1962.

McElroy, W. D., and Glass, B., eds., "The Mechanism of Enzyme Action," Johns Hopkins Press, Baltimore, 1954.

Nord, F. F., ed., "Advances in Enzymology," Interscience Publishers, Inc., New York. (This is an annual series since 1941 and contains numerous review articles.)

Waley, S. G., "Mechanisms of Organic and Enzymic Reactions," Oxford University Press, London, 1962.

Webb, J. L., "Enzyme and Metabolic Inhibitors," vol. I, Academic Press, Inc., New York, 1963.

Woolley, D. W., "A Study of Antimetabolites," John Wiley & Sons, Inc., New York, 1952.

Review Articles

Bender, M. L., Mechanisms of Catalysis: Nucleophilic Reactions of Carboxylic.Acid Derivatives, *Chem. Revs.* **60**, 53–113, 1960.

Bender, M. L., and Breslow, R., Mechanisms of Organic Reactions, in M. Florkin and E. H. Stotz, eds., "Comprehensive Biochemistry," vol. II, pp. 1–218, Elsevier Publishing Company, Amsterdam, 1962.

Chance, B., Enzyme-substrate Compounds, *Advances in Enzymol.,* **12**, 153–190, 1951.

Eigen, M., and Hammes, G., Elementary Steps in Enzyme Reactions, *Advances in Enzymol.,* **25**, 1–38, 1963.

Jencks, W. P., Mechanism of Enzyme Action, *Ann. Rev. Biochem.,* **32**, 639–676, 1963.

Neurath, H., The Activation of Zymogens, *Advances in Protein Chem.,* **12**, 319–386, 1957.

Smith, E. L., and Hill, R. L., Leucine Aminopeptidase, in P. D. Boyer, H. Lardy, and K. Myrbäck, eds., "The Enzymes," 2d ed., vol. IV, pp. 37–62, Academic Press, Inc., New York, 1960.

Westheimer, F. H., Mechanisms Related to Enzyme Catalysis, *Advances in Enzymol.,* **24**, 441–482, 1962.

15. Introduction to Metabolism

All the chemical changes that take place in an organism constitute its *metabolism*, a term encompassing all the numerous processes that occur within living organisms. *Anabolism* is the sum of those processes in which the structural and functional compounds of the body are synthesized from materials available in the diet or in the internal environment. *Catabolism* implies degradative processes, with the products generally being of smaller molecular size than the starting material. Thus the biosynthesis of protein from amino acids is an anabolic process, whereas the breakdown of glycogen to glucose and of glucose to CO_2 are catabolic processes. In many cases, the distinction becomes meaningless, however, either because there is no change in size of molecules in the reaction or, as will be seen in subsequent discussion, because during the course of a catabolic sequence of reactions condensations may occur, with temporary increase in molecular size of the materials involved. During catabolism, the energy derived from degradation of organic materials may be transferred temporarily to specific "high-energy compounds" (page 304); during anabolism, this energy is drawn upon for biosynthetic processes.

As understanding of metabolism has increased, attention has become focused upon certain small molecules or radicals, limited in number, and containing one, two, or three carbon atoms. These fragments derive from many areas of metabolism and are the common units providing for integrations among diverse metabolic processes.

EXPERIMENTAL APPROACHES TO THE STUDY OF METABOLISM

Many diverse techniques have been developed in order to determine what chemical reactions are occurring in living systems, to measure the effects of assorted variables upon these reactions, and to determine the rates at which these reactions occur in health and in disease. In all experimental science, in contrast to purely observational science, it is necessary to apply some disturbing condition to the system under observation and to measure the effect of that disturbance. In biochemistry, this means that one must experimentally modify or alter the organism or tissue being studied. Present understanding of metabolism has been obtained from experiments in which the applied disturbance has ranged from the addition of a minute amount of an isotopically labeled nutrient to the diet of an intact animal to experiments in which the animal was sacrificed, an organ removed, an enzyme isolated from the organ, and the kinetics of the reaction catalyzed by the enzyme studied.

LEVELS OF ORGANIZATION

In *the intact organism* the constituent substrates and enzymes bear definite geometrical and chemical relationships to each other. The rates at which materials are delivered to and removed from a given tissue are determined by the activities of other tissues. Many processes are regulated by products discharged into the blood stream at remote points. The various membranes of the body serve to compartmentalize materials and to limit the rates at which substrates enter or leave certain compartments. Hence, one may anticipate that the rate at which the normal liver *in situ* performs various reactions differs from the rate at which the same organ, isolated and perfused, sliced or minced, will conduct these processes. The intact animal offers many experimental difficulties, chiefly because many processes are occurring simultaneously. There are, however, several profitable techniques for exploring what is happening in the intact animal. These include administration of diets deficient in one or another normal nutrient, addition by dietary or parenteral route of either an abnormal material or an excess of a normal material, or introduction into the animal of some metabolite labeled in such a fashion that the consequent distribution of the label can be studied. A variety of surgical procedures have also been employed which give the experimenter access to some previously inaccessible tissue or body fluid. These include the establishment of fistulas from various segments of the gastrointestinal tract, the biliary tract, or the lymphatic system, as well as procedures that permit sampling of blood at various points in the circulatory system. Study of the effects of partial or complete excision of one or another organ is also a useful tool, although here the magnitude of the derangement is somewhat greater.

The next level of organization is the perfused, isolated organ or extremity. In such studies, one is apt to lose certain of the regulatory mechanisms, *e.g.*, hormonal and/or nervous control, which operate upon the organ or the extremity in its normal locus. However, such experiments have been widely employed to determine the organ in which a particular reaction occurs and in the study of products that may be formed by an organ after a given precursor is added to the perfusing fluid.

The next level of organization is the sliced organ. Liver, kidney, brain, and other tissues may be cut into slices approximately 50μ in thickness; in this condition a sufficient surface is offered to the bathing fluid to permit adequate exchange of nutrients and waste products so that viability is maintained for several hours. Although a fraction of cell membranes must be incised in the slicing operation, most cellular constituents are still contained within cells. Although reaction rates within the cell of a sliced liver, shaken in a crudely simulated extracellular fluid, may deviate from normal rates, this technique has proved extremely useful because of the simplicity of subsequent experimental operations. There is complete control, not only of the organ and the previous nutritional status of the animal, but also of the composition of the bath fluid and of the gas phase with which it is equilibrated. By judicious addition of precursors to the bath fluid, detailed pathways of metabolism may be delineated.

A yet lower level of organization remains after mincing the tissue in some type of mechanical mill. In this operation, cell membranes are generally ruptured, and many relationships which obtained between parts in the normal cell no longer exist. This procedure has proved particularly useful in studies designed to determine the location of chemical processes within the cell. From such a minced preparation, it is possible to separate various particulate structures of the cell—nuclei, mitochondria, and microsomes (page 268)—by differential centrifugation. By addition of suitable substrates, one may then determine the presence or absence of a given enzymic activity in these cellular fractions.

The lowest level of organization is the enzyme in solution. The enzyme may be present as a component of a crude mixture, or, as the result of previous fractionation, it may be in a homogeneous state. A purified enzyme is in general a prerequisite to a complete understanding of the reaction which it catalyzes, and detailed knowledge of any particular biochemical transformation will therefore depend ultimately upon purification of the appropriate enzyme. By use of such materials, studies may be conducted of the kinetic and thermodynamic characteristics of a metabolic reaction and the equilibrium and reaction constants established. It must, however, be borne in mind that in the intact organism, enzymes do not exist by themselves in a pure state, and that in the organized system they may be subject to inhibitory or stimulatory influences which are absent in the pure system. Furthermore, study of the behavior of purified enzymes is limited by depletion of substrates or accumulation of end products, whereas in the intact animal, substrate is more or less continuously being supplied, and products of reaction are constantly being removed either by the circulating fluid or by the occurrence of secondary chemical reactions. As a consequence, reactions that occur inside the normal cell may never reach the equilibria that are attainable with the purified enzymic system.

It is from the synthesis of information obtained by all these techniques that existing knowledge of reactions of metabolism has been obtained. Information has been procured from biological material at each level of organization and has been integrated with data secured from other types of experiments. It is the ultimate object of this field of research to obtain as complete an understanding as possible of the individual chemical reactions occurring in the body, their rates, the factors controlling these rates, and those deviations from these rates which are termed *disease.*

TECHNIQUES USED IN STUDIES OF METABOLISM

BALANCE STUDIES

Determination of the amount of a substance ingested and the quantity of the same compound or of its metabolic products excreted has long been used to study metabolic processes in vivo. This permits construction of a balance sheet between intake and output and makes possible inferences regarding the level and nature of the metabolic activity involving one or another dietary constituent. The balance technique has been particularly informative, albeit limited, in studies of a variety of substances, *e.g.*, proteins, minerals, etc.

LABORATORY ANIMALS

The mouse and the rat have probably been used most frequently for investigations of metabolism, although valuable data, particularly in nutrition, have been derived from studies with the guinea pig, chicken, and dog. Mice and rats have the advantage that they breed well under laboratory conditions, have a rapid rate of growth and development, and relatively short life spans, *viz.*, under 3 years. This last fact makes it possible to study several generations of animals; inbreeding is readily possible in these species, and establishment of pure strains and examination of the significance of genetic factors are feasible. Growth studies with the rat have provided much of the data on which the modern science of nutrition is based (Part Seven).

NATURALLY OCCURRING AND INDUCED METABOLIC ALTERATIONS

Surgical extirpation of or severe damage to an organ *in situ* is one of the oldest approaches to studies of metabolism. For example, the role of the pancreas in the etiology of diabetes mellitus was discovered as a result of studies of the surgically depancreatized dog. Similarly, much has been learned of the metabolic role of the liver from observation of hepatectomized dogs and of human beings with various liver disorders.

Several metabolic disorders were termed by Garrod "inborn errors of metabolism" because the metabolic aberration is present throughout life and is hereditary. The inborn errors of metabolism listed by Garrod in 1908 were cystinuria, alkaptonuria, congenital porphyria, pentosuria, congenital steatorrhea, and albinism. Many additional metabolic alterations of man have been described which have a genetic basis (Chap. 31). Individuals with such conditions have provided experimental approach to problems of metabolism, particularly with regard to elucidation of metabolic pathways.

It may be noted that the hereditary nature, and therefore the genetic basis, of certain of these errors of metabolism indicates that they arise as a consequence of the development of mutant strains. Thus the human mutants resemble microorganisms in which existence of a mutation can be discerned as a consequence of the organism's inability to conduct a particular metabolic transformation or group of transformations (Chap. 29). Such bacterial mutants have been singularly useful in elucidating biosynthetic pathways.

Most abnormalities in metabolism, whether induced by abnormal diets, by drug, by poison, or by disease, are reflections of changes in the specific rates of one or more body processes. These changes in rates may in turn result in changes in body composition, but it is only from a study of rates that changes in composition can be fully understood. For example, the concentration of glucose of the blood in the normal animal is relatively constant. It is, however, subject to a rapid turnover, and the constancy of its concentration is the result of a complex series of mechanisms which serve to balance the rate of glucose production against the rate of glucose destruction. Under various abnormal circumstances, the concentration of glucose in the blood is found to rise, and indeed such a rise is a cardinal manifestation of diabetes mellitus. Clearly this rise in concentration might result from an abnormal decrease in the rate of glucose utilization or from an increase in the rate of glucose production. By appropriate application of the isotopic technique (page 272), problems of this kind may be analyzed in terms of individual rates and a better insight gained into the nature of the pathological processes.

EXPERIMENTAL FISTULAS

Application of surgical techniques can provide experimental animals with suitable fistulas which permit sampling of blood or lymph entering and leaving particular organs, as well as making accessible the secretions of the various segments of the gastrointestinal and biliary tracts. The use of fistulas affords an in vivo approach to the study of reactions conducted by a particular organ or tissue.

CATHETERIZATION OF BLOOD VESSELS

The contribution of various tissues and organs to metabolism can often be evaluated by comparison of the chemical composition of the arterial supply and venous drainage of a particular structure. Intravascular catheterization also provides a possibility not only of withdrawing a blood sample but also of adding specific substances to the arterial flow. Thus, an in vivo approach to the study of metabolic transformations effected by a particular organ becomes available. This is, in most respects, the in vivo counterpart of the isolated organ perfusion approach described below and complements the fistula technique.

ORGAN PERFUSION

By perfusion of an isolated organ in vitro it is possible to introduce into an organ, via the perfusion fluid, a known substance and, by analysis of the fluid emerging from the organ, to gain insight into metabolic transformations occurring in that organ with respect to the particular compound or substance being perfused.

In practice, after removal from the experimental animal, the organ is placed in a closed system designed to allow circulation of a suitable oxygenated fluid under positive pressure provided either by a pump or by gravity. The circulating medium may be defibrinated blood or whole blood containing a suitable anticoagulant (Chap. 33), or erythrocytes suspended in solutions of physiologically isotonic mixtures of salts designed to simulate normal plasma in pH, ionic strength, and ionic composition. Analyses of the perfusate yield data regarding the metabolic effects of the organ on the compounds being studied. This approach has been extensively used with the liver, heart, kidney, and small intestine, and has contributed significantly to our knowledge of the metabolic roles of these organs. Inferences drawn from the data are obviously tempered by the artificial conditions under which the tissue is operating.

HISTOCHEMISTRY

The procedures of histochemistry are designed to map the histological distribution of compounds, enzymes, and metabolic systems. This is achieved by treating a suitably prepared tissue section with a solution containing a reagent which reacts specifically with the tissue component being studied. The colored reaction product remains at its site of formation, thus providing a direct visualization of the location of the substance in question. In this manner it has been possible to determine the histological distribution of various important metabolites and enzymes and to study variations in the relative quantity and distribution of these substances under diverse experimentally produced alterations in metabolism. The techniques of histochemistry also have been applied to separated cellular components, *e.g.*, nuclei and mitochondria, obtained by differential centrifugation (see below).

METABOLISM OF TISSUE SLICES, MINCES, AND BROKEN CELL PREPARATIONS

In 1912, Warburg initiated studies of the metabolism of tissue slices, using the manometric technique. The apparatus, invented 10 years earlier by Barcroft and Haldane, measures quantitatively changes in gas volume or pressure. The Warburg procedure permits study of the metabolism of small segments of a particular tissue or organ by determining manometrically the rate of oxygen utilization and carbon dioxide production (the respiratory quotient, page 283). In addition, it is possible to examine the rate of utilization of a foodstuff or substrate added to the medium in which the tissue has been placed, and to determine the nature and amount of metabolites produced during the experimental period. This technique has been extended to minces of tissues and to broken cell or cell-free preparations of tissues (see below), as well as to tissue slices.

BIOCHEMICAL CYTOLOGY

The diverse chemical mechanisms upon which cellular functions are based are not randomly dispersed within the cytological units, *e.g.*, nucleus, cytoplasm, etc., of cells, but are specifically localized in discrete compartments. This results in characteristic cellular patterns of distribution both of cell constituents and of chemical processes. This intracellular organization of structural and chemical units permits sequences and cycles of reactions to occur coupled to one another in a manner that could not be achieved if participants and catalysts were randomly distributed throughout the cell. Biochemical cytology, particularly of mammalian liver, has begun to provide explanation for the special biological functions of discrete structural units. Knowledge has derived from use of light, phase contrast, and electron microscopy, from application of histochemical techniques (see above), and from disruption and fractionation of cells, with physical and chemical examination of the components obtained.

The *cytoplasmic membrane* of certain specialized cells, *e.g.*, the erythrocyte (Chap. 32), has been studied most extensively. It appears to be a three-layered mosaic of complexes between proteins and lipids, particularly phosphatides, and also includes complex carbohydrates, such as neuraminic acids and glycolipids. The cytoplasmic membrane exhibits a significant degree of selective permeability. In general, large or multiply charged molecules penetrate the membrane with difficulty. The passage of some ions and solutes occurs readily, while that of others is restricted; this selectivity is manifested among ions and molecules of similar charge and volumes. These characteristics, together with quantitative differences in ion concentrations within and without cells, are ascribed to specific, active metabolic processes (Chap. 35) rather than to the physical properties of cell membranes.

Within many cell types is found a system of membrane-bound channels, the *endoplasmic reticulum.* This may consist of tubules, tubules and vesicles, or connected vesicles (*cisternae*); the membranes may be "smooth" or fringed with particles of ribonucleoprotein, the *ribosomes* (Chap. 30). The term *ergastoplasm* has been applied to the endoplasmic reticulum studded with ribosomes.

The largest structure within cells in general is the *nucleus,* visible under the light microscope without staining because its density and refractility differ from those of the surrounding cytoplasm. Within the nucleus are chromatin granules, dense aggregates of deoxyribonucleic acid (Chap. 10); lesser quantities of ribonucleic acid (Chap. 10) are also present. The nucleus usually contains a distinct body, the *nucleolus,* which is rich in ribonucleic acid and devoid of deoxyribonucleic acid. In the electron microscope, the nucleus is seen to have two membranes whose nature is unknown. The inner one may be considered the true nuclear membrane; the intermembrane space appears frequently to be continuous with the channels of the endoplasmic reticulum.

Within the cytoplasm are particles or organelles of varying sizes; the largest and most dense of these are the *mitochondria,* which by electron microscopy appear as minute spheres, rods, or filaments enclosed by a double membrane. A number of highly important integrated enzymic systems, *e.g.*, the oxidative and respiratory enzymic systems (Chap. 18), are concentrated in cell mitochondria. The inner membrane of the mitochondrion is folded into villi or crests (*cristae*). A correlation appears to exist between the complexity of mitochondrial structure, *i.e.*, the number of cristae, and the level of oxidative activity of the cell, *e.g.*, kidney cells compared to fibroblasts. Within differentiated cells, mitochondria are frequently aggregated within that area in which the demand for energy is maximal, *e.g.*, in muscle as rings around the contractile myofibrils; in nerves at the synapse; in sperm at the neck of the cell at the point at which the head joins the whiplash tail; and in cells of the renal tubule, in the folds of the absorbing cell surface.

The *Golgi apparatus* is a cytoplasmic organelle revealed in the electron microscope as an irregularly arranged, interlacing network of fibrils and of small and large vesicles. This structure appears to play an important but unknown role in the secretory activities of cells; secretory products may be seen aggregated as granules within Golgi vesicles for transport to the cell surface. Other inclusions visible in the phase contrast or electron microscope may be present in cytoplasm. For example, *pigment granules* are found in specialized cells.

CENTRIFUGAL SEPARATION OF SUBCELLULAR STRUCTURES

The application of histochemical methods (page 267), combined with light microscopy, has yielded additional descriptive information regarding the structural characteristics of cells. However, in order to characterize submicroscopic structural elements, and to describe more specifically the composition and function of the diverse cellular particles, the biochemist has attempted to separate them by physical means. Cell membranes may be disrupted by subjecting a suspension of cells, in a suitable isotonic medium, *e.g.*, 0.25M sucrose, to ultrasonic vibration, or by utilization of a mechanical blendor, such as a Waring blendor or a hand- or motor-driven pestle rotating in a mortar in which the tissue, in suitable medium, is subjected to a shearing force that effectively disrupts cells and yields broken cell preparations, loosely termed "homogenates." These have few unbroken cells and are suspensions of nuclei, mitochondria, microsomes, other cellular organelles and disrupted cellular membranes, as well as the soluble phase of the cytoplasm. The broken cell suspension can then be subjected to differential centrifugation at low temperatures to achieve separation of the individual particulate fractions of the suspension. Table 15.1 indicates the usual fractions obtained by this technique, as well as the distribution of several important enzymic systems and reaction pathways in these fractions. It should be strongly emphasized that the fractionation procedure and the description of the fractions obtained are often arbitrary and have operational rather than anatomical significance. For example, the terms "particle" or "particulate fraction" merely indicate a water-insoluble complex that is sedimented in a suitable gravitational field. A continuum is often found between particles and soluble proteins; indeed, the same complex may behave as a particle under one set of conditions and as soluble protein under another. Moreover, the particulate state need not be an expression of molecular size; it may be a reflection of a preponderance of water-repelling groups in the molecular unit.

Table 15.1: Usual Distribution of Typical Cellular Components Achieved by Fractional Centrifugation of a Broken Cell Preparation of Liver

Fraction	Centrifugal field for separation, × gravity	Time of centrifugation, min.	Enzymic or other activities
Cellular debris; nuclei; membranes	1,000–6,000	10	
Mitochondria; lysosomes	10,000–15,000	30	Electron transport; oxidative phosphorylation; citric acid cycle; fatty acid oxidation; amino acid oxidation; urea synthesis; hydrolases
Microsomes; ribosomes	100,000	60	Protein synthesis; hydroxylating systems; cytochrome b_5; hydrolases; glucuronyl transferases; steroid reductases; phosphatases
"Soluble fraction," or supernate	. . . .	. .	Glycolytic system; hexose monophosphate pathway; glycogen synthesis; glycogenolysis; fatty acid synthesis; purine and pyrimidine catabolism; peptidases; transaminases

The arbitrary nature of the fractionation procedure is seen in the heterogeneity of the fractions obtained. Thus, the mitochondrial fraction contains, in addition to the mitochondria proper, particles termed *lysosomes,* intermediate in size between the mitochondria and the microsomes. The heterogeneity of the microsomes, derived from fragmentation of the endoplasmic reticulum, is also indicated from studies utilizing density gradient centrifugation (page 179); this technique permits recognition of microsomes of varying RNA content. Microsomes that are high in RNA concentration are concerned exclusively with protein synthesis (Chap. 30) and have been designated as *ribosomes.* The term microsome includes the ribosomes and the remainder of the sedimented "particles," including the membranous structure to which ribosomes are attached and with which they sediment under conditions described above.

Despite the above limitations, fractionation of broken cell preparations has proved to be an invaluable and powerful technique. As centrifugal procedures become more refined, and as the electron microscope is used to define more rigorously the composition of fractions obtained by centrifugation, knowledge of the intracellular localization of enzymic reactions becomes increasingly precise.

STUDY OF TISSUE CULTURE

Although cells and tissues have been grown in vitro in suitable flasks or vessels for many decades, it is only relatively recently that notable success has been achieved in the development of accurately defined media. This success is in large measure due to the isolation and identification of essential growth factors, *e.g.*, vitamins and amino acids, required for cellular proliferation.

In vitro tissue culture techniques permit the study of the metabolism of resting or proliferating cells under rigidly controlled experimental conditions. Homogeneous cell populations can be utilized to provide a greater degree of experimental uniformity and duplicability. It is also possible, by serial analysis of the tissue culture medium and the cellular population, to determine the nature and amounts of metabolic products elaborated by the growing cells. A number of different types of cells, both normal and malignant, of several mammalian species, including the human, have been grown in vitro by tissue culture techniques in media containing either entirely or almost entirely pure ingredients of known quantity and composition. Tissue culture techniques have also provided another experimental approach to the mechanism of virus propagation in cells, making it possible to examine chemical alterations induced in the host cells in vitro by the viral agent. In theory, this technique affords all the advantages of metabolic studies with microorganisms (see below) in liquid culture. The tissue culture technique has provided insight into selected metabolic phenomena in vitro under these experimental conditions. The significance of data obtained from tissue culture studies for phenomena in vivo may well be limited, and caution must be exercised in their interpretation. Perhaps the most serious difficulty encountered in such studies is the tendency of animal cells to dedifferentiate during multiplication; a culture derived from liver cells cannot be considered identical to liver cells in vivo.

STUDIES WITH MICROORGANISMS

Application of biochemical knowledge and techniques to the discipline of microbiology has led to significant advances in understanding of bacterial metabolism. In turn, use of microorganisms has provided the biochemist with useful living forms for laboratory studies. These lower forms have relatively simple requirements for growth and development, reproduce rapidly, can be provided in large quantities, and not infrequently perform chemical transformations that the organic chemist finds difficult to duplicate. In addition, mutant strains of microorganisms can readily be produced experimentally and have contributed not only to the understanding of genetic influences in metabolic phenomena (Chap. 29), but also, by generating diverse, specific metabolic "blocks," to the delineating of normal metabolic pathways. Also of significance for biochemical genetic studies is the experimental use of microorganisms for exploration of the phenomenon of microbial transformation, induced in vitro under certain conditions by specific preparations of DNA (page 186).

Studies with microorganisms have also contributed analytical tools for the quantitative determination of one or more substances that a particular strain may require for growth. For example, growth or failure of growth of microorganisms requiring a particular amino acid or vitamin in the culture medium may serve as the basis for quantitative estimation of that amino acid (page 116) or vitamin in biological materials.

Microorganisms have also been of value in studying the influence of metabolic inhibitors (antimetabolites) and antibiotics on metabolic phenomena (page 237) and in studies of the mechanism of adaptation, since they can be influenced markedly in their metabolic characteristics by alterations in the nutritive medium in which they grow. This last phenomenon has made possible the study of the mechanism of adaptive enzyme formation in response to the presence of a new constituent in the medium.

APPLICATION OF ISOTOPIC TRACERS

Biochemists have long recognized the desirability of labeling or tagging molecules in order to permit the experimenter to follow the fate of the label, and consequently of the molecule, in its metabolic transformations. This is particularly desirable for normal body constituents which, when administered, are impossible to trace because they become indistinguishable from molecules of the same substance already present in body tissues and fluids. Early attempts in this direction involved the replacement of a carbon-bound hydrogen atom by halogen or by a phenyl group. However, it was recognized that these labeled molecules were different chemically from the metabolites that occurred normally and consequently that the distribution and fate of the labeled metabolite might differ from those of its normal analogue.

The availability of isotopes of the common elements obviated these difficulties, since, for most purposes, the chemical differences between isotopic siblings of any given element are negligible. Isotopes of the common elements of organic compounds, viz., hydrogen, nitrogen, carbon, sulfur, phosphorus, and oxygen, together with those of iodine, sodium, potassium, iron, and calcium are now commonly employed in what are termed *tracer* experiments. The contributions of Schoenheimer and his collaborators were particularly noteworthy in pioneering applications of isotopes to problems of metabolism.

Definitions and Characteristics of Isotopes. The nucleus of each of the approximately 100 elementary species is characterized by an atomic number, Z, which is equal to the number of protons contained in the nucleus and is also equal to the number of planetary electrons about the nucleus when the atom exists in an electrically neutral state. All atoms of a particular element have the same atomic number. Each nucleus is also characterized by a second number, A, which is the mass number and is equal to the number of nucleons, the sum of the neutrons and protons contained therein. The quantity $A - Z$ is therefore the number of neutrons contained in the nucleus, and isotopic siblings of a given element differ from each other in this quantity. A convention has been adopted in which the subscript that precedes the elementary symbol is the atomic number Z and, being implicit in the symbol, is sometimes not included. The superscript that follows the symbol is the mass number A and distinguishes one isotope from another. Thus, for example,

$$_2He^4, \, _{11}Na^{23}, \, _{17}Cl^{35}, \, _{17}Cl^{37}, \, _7N^{14}, \, _7N^{15}$$

Of the element hydrogen, three isotopes are recognized:

$$_1H^1, \, _1H^2, \, _1H^3$$

to which trivial names of *protium, deuterium,* and *tritium* have been given.

Of the isotopes commonly used in biochemistry, some occur in nature, as minor constituents, and some are prepared by nuclear reactions in which atoms are subjected to bombardment by protons ($_1p^1$ or $_1H^1$), neutrons ($_0n^1$), deuterons ($_1d^2$ or $_1H^2$), or α particles ($_2\alpha^4$ or $_2He^4$). Still other isotopes are derived from the products of fission of certain heavy elements.

Another distinguishing characteristic of isotopes is that, whereas the nuclei of certain isotopes are completely stable, those of other isotopes are unstable and exhibit radioactivity. In the course of radioactive decay, nuclei emit electrons, either positive or negative (β^+ or β^-), sometimes accompanied by electromagnetic radiation of very high frequency, γ-rays or x-rays. Among the elements of high atomic weight, radioactive isotopes that emit α particles are also encountered. It should be noted that an individual atom of a radioactive isotope is indeed stable until the moment of its decay, at which time it undergoes transmutation to a second more stable atom of different A and Z.

The designation of the concentration of *stable isotopes* is usually in the units of *atoms per cent excess, i.e.,* the number of isotopic atoms in 100 atoms of that element over and above the natural abundance. For radioactive elements, which emit one or another type of radiation that results in ionization of the surrounding gases, the quantity of radioactive material is measured and defined in terms of the rate at which atomic disintegrations are occurring. The *curie* is defined as that quantity of radioactive material which undergoes the same number of disintegrations per second as does 1 g. of radium, *viz.,* 3.7×10^{10} disintegrations per second. The *millicurie* is consequently that quantity of material which undergoes 3.7×10^7 disintegrations per second. Units most frequently encountered in practice are *specific activity* or *relative specific activity.* The usefulness of these terms results from the fact that most laboratories are not equipped to measure radioactivity in terms of the primary radium standard. For most purposes it is sufficient to know the radioactivity of a particular sample of the element with reference to some other sample of the same element. Since radioactivity is measured with a suitable counting device, which, other things being equal, records a constant fraction of all the radioactive decays occurring in the sample, it is convenient to report specific activity in units such as *counts per minute per milligram* or *counts per minute per millimole.* These numbers are proportional to the units of *atoms per cent excess* employed with stable isotopes, but the proportionality factor varies with experimental conditions.

Measurement of Isotope Abundance. The primary instrument for the determination of abundance of a stable isotope is the mass spectrometer. The element, or a volatile derivative thereof, is introduced into a chamber at low pressure, where it is subjected to the ionizing influence of an electron beam. The positive ions are driven down a tube by the application of an electrostatic field and are then diffracted and focused by a magnetic prism so designed that the path of the particles of greatest mass is bent least and the paths of the lighter particles are bent most. By suitable adjustment of the electrostatic and magnetic forces, particles of any desired mass may be brought to focus upon a collector electrode, whence their positive electricity leaks to ground through a high resistance. The voltage across this resistance is measured and is proportional to the relative abundance of that mass species. From the successive or simultaneous collection of two or more masses of a given ion and measurement of the resultant voltages, one may calculate the relative abundance of each isotopic variety of the sample under consideration.

The mass spectrometer is used for analyzing mixtures of stable isotopes of carbon, oxygen, or nitrogen, as well as hydrogen. However, in the case of hydrogen, where the mass ratio of deuterium to hydrogen is relatively large, other methods have also been employed, e.g., measurements of density or refractive index of water containing the hydrogen under study. Mass spectrometric techniques for estimating stable isotopes are less sensitive and more tedious than are techniques for measuring radioactive isotopes. However, since no useful radioactive isotopes of oxygen or nitrogen exist, the mass spectrometer remains an essential tool for studies involving the fate of these elements.

Radioactive isotopes are measured by detecting the radiations they emit. In the case of the lighter elements, these are generally β particles of varying energy and in some cases γ radiation. Alpha particles are emitted only by the heavier elements. The electroscope and the ionization chamber may be used, but in most biological work other instruments are more common. The Geiger-Müller and the proportional counters are devices filled with gases and containing an anode, which is generally centrally placed, and a peripheral cathode. A large voltage difference is applied across these electrodes, and the voltage, as well as the gas filling, is so adjusted that normally no current flows. When ionizing radiation enters such a vessel, it produces ionizations which rapidly multiply and the tube becomes momentarily conductive. The resultant electrical pulse is collected in an electronic computing machine called a scaler, which records the number of such pulses in a predetermined time. The sample to be counted is in some instances a gas and is actually included in the filling of the counter tube. More frequently the sample is a solid and is placed exterior to the counting tube in front of an appropriate window. Since certain of the important biologically useful isotopes, such as C^{14} and S^{35}, emit β particles of relatively low energy, which are efficiently absorbed by any solids that they encounter, very thin windows must be employed in the detectors. Increase in sensitivity may be achieved by placement of the solid to be counted within the sensitive volume of the tube. Loss due to absorption by the window is thereby avoided; however, upper layers of samples may absorb radiation from lower layers, necessitating correction for "self-absorption" which varies with sample thickness.

An alternative method, which is rapidly replacing the Geiger-Müller technique, is termed *scintillation counting*. It involves transformation of β or γ radiation into ultraviolet or visible light by use of a phosphor, often a highly aromatic substance such as *p*-terphenyl. The flashes of light, *scintillations,* which result from radioactive decay are detected by a sensitive photomultiplier, and the resultant electrical pulses are collected in a scaler. Scintillation counting has proved particularly useful for tritium (H_3), C^{14}, and other isotopes which emit low energy β particles. Under certain circumstances, the material to be assayed and the phosphor may be dissolved in a single solvent. This continuous close contact between isotope and phosphor makes unnecessary the self-absorption corrections required with solid samples.

The Half-life of Radioactive Elements and Its Mathematical Relationships. Radioactive decay is a true first-order phenomenon. The probability of decay of any particular atom is an intrinsic property of that atom and independent of the size of the sample in which it resides, the temperature, the pressure, and other variables. Given an initial homogeneous population of radioactive atoms, a constant fraction will undergo decay in each succeeding time interval. This relationship is expressed in the differential equation,

$$- \frac{dN}{dt} = kN \tag{1}$$

where N is the number of atoms, $-dN/dt$ is the rate of decay, and k is the first-order decay constant, the fraction of all atoms undergoing decay per unit time.

Whereas the total life of a sample of radioactive material is a useless number, since it may approximate infinity, the half-life ($t_{1/2}$) is a very useful characteristic of each species of radioactive isotope. It may be defined as the time elapsed when the initial number of radioactive atoms, N_0, shall have been halved. Upon integration, equation (1) becomes

$$\ln \frac{N_0}{N} = kt$$

Since $N = \frac{1}{2}N_0$ when $t = t_{1/2}$, then

$$\ln \frac{N_0}{\frac{1}{2}N_0} = kt_{1/2}$$

$$kt_{1/2} = \ln 2 = 0.693 \tag{2}$$

$$t_{1/2} = \frac{0.693}{k} \tag{3}$$

The term, half-life, is a useful constant not only for radioactive decay but for all first-order (page 220) phenomena.

The half-lives of various radioactive elements range from fractions of a second to millennia. In Table 15.2 are given representative examples. From these numbers and other physical constants, one may calculate the relationship between the primary unit of radioactivity, the *curie,* and the primary unit of mass, the *gram.* As an example, let us consider C^{14}, the half-life of which is approximately 5,700 years.

Table 15.2: Some Isotopes of Importance in Biochemical Research
(Natural abundances, half-lives, and radiation characteristics are included.)

Isotope	Natural abundance, per cent	Half-life, $t_{1/2}$*	Radiation characteristics	
			Radiation	Energy, mev†
$_1H^2$	0.0154	∞		
$_1H^3$	.....	12.5 y	β^-	0.018
$_6C^{11}$	.....	20.4 m	β^+	0.97
$_6C^{13}$	1.108	∞		
$_6C^{14}$	Trace	5,760 y	β^-	0.155
$_7N^{15}$	0.365	∞		
$_8O^{18}$	0.204	∞		
$_{11}Na^{24}$	.....	15.01 h	β^-	1.39
			γ	2.753
$_{15}P^{32}$	.....	14.3 d	β^-	1.712
$_{16}S^{35}$	.....	87.1 d	β^-	0.167
$_{17}Cl^{36}$	.....	3.1×10^5 y	β^-	0.714
$_{19}K^{40}$	0.0119	1.25×10^9 y	β^-	1.33
			$\gamma(EC)$‡	1.46; 1.5
$_{19}K^{42}$	.....	12.5 h	β^-	3.55; 1.99; 1.53
$_{20}Ca^{45}$	.....	152 d	β^-	0.255
$_{26}Fe^{55}$	.....	2.94 y	X-rays	
$_{26}Fe^{59}$	.....	45 d	β^-	0.46; 0.27
			γ	1.29; 1.10
$_{27}Co^{60}$	.....	5.2 y	β^-	0.31
			γ	1.17; 1.33
$_{53}I^{125}$	.....	60 d	γ	0.035
$_{53}I^{130}$	.....	12.6 h	β^-	1.03; 0.61
			γ	0.74; 0.67; 0.54; 0.42
$_{53}I^{131}$	.....	8.07 d	β^-	0.61; 0.34
			γ	0.28; 0.36; 0.64

* y = years; d = days; h = hours; m = minutes.

† mev = million electronvolts; instances where more than one value appears are examples of multi-step decay processes with radiation energy of each step.

‡ electron capture forming excited state of $_{18}A^{40}$ with γ emission following.

$$t_{1/2} = 5,700 \text{ years} = 1.8 \times 10^{11} \text{ sec.}$$

From equation (3)

$$k = \frac{0.693}{t_{1/2}} = \frac{0.693}{1.8 \times 10^{11}} = 3.9 \times 10^{-12}/\text{sec.}$$

Since 1 mole of C^{14} contains 6×10^{23} atoms (Avogadro's number),

$$3.9 \times 10^{-12} \times 6 \times 10^{23} = 2.3 \times 10^{12} \text{ decays/sec./mole}$$

One curie is defined as 3.7×10^{10} decays per second; hence

$$1 \text{ curie of } C^{14} = \frac{3.7 \times 10^{10}}{2.3 \times 10^{12}} = 1.6 \times 10^{-2} \text{ mole}$$

Each mole of C^{14} weighs 14 g., hence

$$1 \text{ curie of } C^{14} = 1.6 \times 10^{-2} \times 14 = 0.22 \text{ g.}$$
$$1 \text{ millicurie of } C^{14} = 0.22 \text{ mg.}$$

A similar calculation for P^{32}, which has a half-life of only 14.3 days, shows that one millicurie of P^{32} consists of only 3.5×10^{-6} mg. of phosphorus. Thus, particularly for short-lived isotopes, measurement of radioactivity provides a remarkably sensitive, as well as convenient, method of analysis.

BIOLOGICAL APPLICATIONS OF ISOTOPES

In the application of the isotopic tracer technique to biological problems, the first consideration is the form in which the isotope is administered. In many experiments, the isotopic atom may be a constituent of a simple molecule:

$$C^{14}O_2, \ D_2O, \ T_2O, \ Na^{24}Cl, \ NaH_2P^{32}O_4, \ KI^{131}$$

In other experiments, organic compounds of greater or lesser complexity labeled in one or more constituent atoms must first be prepared. Often this is done by application of classical methods of organic syntheses; many of the compounds useful in biological research and isotopically labeled are now available commercially. In some cases the biosynthetic route is either the best or the only available method. Thus isotopic serum albumin may be prepared by inclusion of a labeled amino acid in the diet of an animal and subsequent isolation of albumin from the animal's serum. Similarly, C^{14} may be incorporated into glucose by allowing photosynthesis (Chap. 20) to proceed in an atmosphere of $C^{14}O_2$, with subsequent hydrolysis of the starch that accumulates in the leaves. Not infrequently, it is desirable to include more than one isotopic label in the same substance. Thus if it is desired to study the fate of both the carbon skeleton and the nitrogen atom of the amino acid glycine, one may synthesize glycine-C^{14} and glycine-N^{15} separately and by simply mixing the two products obtain what is, in effect, a doubly labeled material. Compounds with more than one isotopic label may also be synthesized by methods that permit incorporation of more than one isotope into a single molecule.

Certain types of problem lend themselves particularly to the isotopic approach. The simplest of these is the analysis of a mixture by the so-called *isotope dilution technique.* Consider a mixture in which material A occurs in unknown abundance and for which a satisfactory analytical method is not available. A sample of material A containing isotope is prepared, and a known weight of pure isotopic A is added to the mixture. Material A is now isolated from the mixture without regard to yield but is carefully purified. The isotope concentration in this product will be determined by the quantity of nonisotopic A initially present in the mixture, the quantity of isotopic A added, and the isotope concentration of the latter material. These relationships are expressed mathematically as follows:

Let a = grams of isotopic material A added
a_0 = grams of nonisotopic material A initially present
b = isotope concentration in material added
c = isotope concentration in material isolated

Then
$$a \times b = c(a + a_0)$$
$$a_0 = a\left(\frac{b}{c} - 1\right)$$

A second application of isotopes relates to the problem of *anatomical distribution*. The isotopic material may be administered and, from subsequent analyses for the appropriate isotope in various tissues or products derived from them, the distribution of the isotopic atom may be ascertained. In the case of radioactive isotopes an additional tool is available, *viz.*, radioautography. In this procedure photographic film is applied to a cut section of a tissue, and, after adequate exposure and development, those portions of the film which were close to radioactive areas in the tissue will be found to have darkened. With isotopes of satisfactory radiation characteristics this technique can be refined to permit resolution at a histological level.

Isotopes have been widely used in the study of the *precursor-product relationship*. The purpose of such experiments is to determine whether compound *A* is converted into *B* in the organism. Isotopic compound *A* is administered; compound *B* is isolated, carefully purified, and then analyzed for isotope. Application of this technique has been particularly useful in the demonstration in the animal of reactions that had previously been susceptible of study only in a simpler system. By degradation of the product and determination of the distribution of isotope among its atoms, one may often procure further information as to the mechanism of the transformation observed.

The isotopic technique has been extremely important in the *analysis of rates of processes,* particularly in the intact animal. The quantity of any tissue constituent may be reasonably constant in the adult animal in balance, but this constancy of quantity may result from a balance between rate of synthesis and rate of degradation. Prior to the advent of the isotopic technique, no satisfactory method was available for measurement of these rates. With isotopes, two approaches have been used in studies of this kind. The body store of a given compound may be labeled in a preliminary period by administration of the labeled material, and the subsequent disappearance of isotope followed. Alternatively, an isotopically labeled precursor of the material may be administered and a study made of the appearance of isotope in the product. From the rates of change in isotope concentration, the rates of synthesis and destruction may be calculated. From studies of this type, the concept of continuous *turnover* (synthesis, degradation, and replacement) of certain body constituents, even at constant composition, has been evolved. This concept of a dynamic steady state was dramatically emphasized in the work of Schoenheimer and his collaborators.

REFERENCES

Books

Brachet, J., "Biochemical Cytology," Academic Press, Inc., New York, 1957.

Calvin, M., Heidelberger, C., Reid, J. C., Tolbert, B. M., and Yankwich, P. E., "Isotopic Carbon," John Wiley & Sons, Inc., New York, 1949.

Dixon, M., "Manometric Methods," Cambridge University Press, London, 1951.

Extermann, R. C., ed., "Radioisotopes in Scientific Research," vol. III, Pergamon Press, New York, 1958.

Garrod, A. E., "Inborn Errors of Metabolism," 2d ed., Henry Frowde and Hodder & Stoughton, Ltd., London, 1923.

Glasser, O., ed., "Medical Physics," Year Book Publishers, Inc., Chicago, vol. I, 1944, vol. II, 1950.

Kamen, M. D., "Radioactive Tracers in Biology: An Introduction to Tracer Methodology," 3d ed., Academic Press, Inc., New York, 1957.

Umbreit, W. W., Burris, R. H., and Stauffer, J. F., "Manometric Techniques and Related Methods for the Study of Tissue Metabolism," rev. ed., Burgess Publishing Company, Minneapolis, 1957.

Review Articles

Anderson, N. G., Techniques for Mass Isolation of Cellular Components, in G. Oster and A. W. Pollister, eds., "Physical Techniques in Biological Research," vol. III, pp. 229–352, Academic Press, Inc., New York, 1956.

Eagle, H., Metabolic Studies with Normal and Malignant Cells in Culture, *Harvey Lectures,* **54,** 156–175, 1958–1959.

Hogeboom, G. H., Fractionation of Cell Components of Animal Tissues, in S. P. Colowick and N. O. Kaplan, eds., "Methods in Enzymology," vol. I, pp. 16–19, Academic Press, Inc., New York, 1955.

Porter, K. R., The Endoplasmic Reticulum, in T. W. Goodwin and O. Lindberg, eds., "Biological Structure and Function," vol. I, pp. 127–155, Academic Press, Inc., New York, 1961.

Puck, T. T., Quantitative Growth of Mammalian Cells, *Harvey Lectures,* **55,** 1–12, 1959–1960.

16. General Metabolism

Energy Considerations

Transformation of energy necessarily accompanies the variety of chemical reactions that make possible the characteristic properties, *e.g.*, movement, respiration, reproduction, growth, and irritability, which distinguish living cells from non-living structures. The terms *metabolism, anabolism,* and *catabolism* have been defined in the preceding chapter. Studies of total metabolism in the intact animal mark the beginning of modern knowledge of metabolism. The total metabolism which is manifest as the energy released by all chemical transformations in the animal and must derive ultimately from the oxidation of foodstuffs may appear as heat or as external mechanical work. Even during muscular activity, the major portion of the energy appears as heat because of the relative inefficiency of the muscles as mechanical devices. During rest, practically all this energy appears as heat.

Since all cellular activity is based on chemical transformations, it should be possible to estimate the energy production, provided that the nature and quantity of reacting substances and end products of these reactions are known. In the latter part of the eighteenth century, Lavoisier demonstrated that production of heat by the animal organism, as by a lighted candle, is dependent upon consumption of oxygen, with production of carbon dioxide from the oxidation of carbon. The quantity of carbon dioxide produced by a guinea pig during a fixed period of study was equal to that produced by combustion of 3.3 g. of pure carbon in air. With the physicist Laplace, Lavoisier constructed an ice calorimeter, and, from the amount of ice melted when the guinea pig was in the instrument, calculated the heat produced by the animal. When 3.3 g. of carbon were burned in the calorimeter, an amount of heat was obtained comparable with that liberated by the animal. There was thus established a correlation between the heat produced in the animal organism and the quantity of expired carbon dioxide. This demonstration of the conversion of one form of energy to another was the forerunner of the law of conservation of energy, enunciated by Mayer and Helmholtz almost 70 years later, and was the earliest recognition that living organisms obey the laws of thermodynamics.

As will be developed in detail in subsequent chapters, biological oxidations normally proceed only at the rate at which the free energy (ΔF) liberated is required for the performance of useful work. The latter takes many forms. Living cells are effective transducers of chemical potential energy into other forms of energy, *viz.*, chemical, mechanical, electrical, and osmotic, and in some organisms, even into electromagnetic light. Thus, the energy derived from the oxidation of glucose can be utilized for the synthesis of proteins, fatty acids, nucleic acids, or steroids; for the contraction of muscles, conduction of the nervous impulse or, in the electric eel, generation of an electrical charge; for secretion of hypertonic urine or maintenance of a large concentration gradient for Na^+ and K^+ within and outside of cells; and in the "lightning bug," for production of light. Of the total energy, ΔH, released during glucose oxidation, only the free-energy component, ΔF, can be so utilized in processes indicated above, whereas the entropic component, $T\Delta S$, must appear as heat. However, the transfer of energy occurs in quanta, and if a chemical reaction which yields, for example, -8000 cal./mole is coupled to a process which requires $+5000$ cal./mole (as the synthesis of the peptide bond), the difference, 3000 cal./mole, cannot be saved for future use but must immediately appear as heat. In the subsequent fate of the molecule which had been synthesized, $e.g.$, hydrolysis of that peptide bond, again only the free energy thus released may be utilized for performance of some task if the means be available. The entropy must again appear as heat, and if no mode is available to take advantage of the free energy change, it, too, will appear as heat. If all such processes are summed, each 24 hr., in a 70-kg. adult, about 2000 Cal. will have been generated and released. Since neither his weight, structure, nor composition will have changed significantly over this period, all this energy will have appeared as heat, regardless of any intermediary transformations, except for that work which was done upon the environment, such as lifting weights, etc. Since the energy loss, as heat, is also irretrievably dissipated to the environment, there is engendered a requirement for daily provision of new, external sources of energy, $viz.$, foodstuffs which can be oxidized. The total process, which incidentally provides the heat necessary for the maintenance of body temperature in an external environment cooler than 37°C., is not, as might appear, wasteful. It is the sum of these activities, made possible by transient use of the free energy of oxidation, that makes possible the highly ordered structures and vital activities of the living organism.

CALORIC VALUES OF FOODSTUFFS

The Calorie referred to in metabolic studies is the kilo-calorie (1000 calories), the amount of heat required to raise the temperature of 1,000 g. of water from 15 to 16°C. The energy that may be derived from oxidation of compounds, including those of food, can be measured in a bomb calorimeter. The over-all energy release accompanying a chemical reaction, ΔH (page 206), is independent of the reaction mechanism. Much evidence demonstrates that ΔH for the reaction

$$\text{Glucose} + 6O_2 \longrightarrow 6CO_2 + 6H_2O$$

is identical whether it occurs in a bomb calorimeter or in man. Inasmuch as the prime source of energy of the mammalian organism is food, it is of importance to determine the heat of combustion of various foodstuffs.

The first measurements of the heat that can be produced by oxidation of foodstuffs outside the body were conducted by Rubner, who compared the values obtained in the bomb calorimeter with those given by direct measurement of heat production by a dog placed in a calorimeter and then fed a known quantity of carbohydrate, protein, or lipid. For carbohydrate and lipid, the values were similar whether the foodstuff was burned inside or outside the body. However, the in vivo value for protein (4.1 Cal. per g.) was less than that obtained in the bomb calorimeter (5.3 Cal. per. g.). This discrepancy is due to the fact that under physiological conditions, the nitrogen of proteins is not oxidized.

Since the carbohydrates, lipids, and proteins of the natural foodstuffs include mono- and polysaccharides, short- and long-chain fatty acids, saturated and unsaturated fatty acids, etc., the caloric values of individual members of each of these major classes are variable. Thus, glucose yields 3.75 Cal. per g., whereas glycogen gives 4.3 Cal. per g. Again, animal proteins appear to yield higher values than do plant proteins; and most animal lipids liberate 9.5 Cal. per g., although butter and lard give 9.2 Cal. per g. Therefore, the caloric values given for the three classes of foodstuff represent averages. The average caloric values of the three major foodstuffs are given in Table 16.1. If additional allowance is made for the possibility of incomplete digestion and/or absorption, the values can be rounded off to 4, 9, and 4 for carbohydrate, lipid, and protein, respectively.

Table 16.1: Average Metabolic Energy Derived from the Three
Major Foodstuffs

Foodstuff	*Cal./g.*
Carbohydrate	4.1
Lipid	9.3
Protein	4.1

DIRECT CALORIMETRY

As indicated previously, Rubner measured the heat production of a dog placed in a calorimeter. Measurement of heat production of a human subject in a calorimeter by recording the temperature change produced in a known weight of water is theoretically simple. However, its practical achievement presents a number of problems. Most of these, such as heat loss through avenues other than the water insulating medium, and possible heat storage in the apparatus or in the subject, have been circumvented by elaborate construction. The cost and nature of the apparatus prevent its being used widely for laboratory or clinical studies. However, the relatively few of these instruments that have been constructed have made possible extensive studies of energy metabolism.

The apparatus that has generally been used consists of an insulated chamber large enough to accommodate an animal or a man. The heat generated by the subject is absorbed by water which circulates through copper pipes. The difference in temperature between water entering and leaving the chamber, together with the quantity of water in kilograms, permits calculation of heat production. More recently devised apparatus relies on lining the chamber with thousands of thermocouples instead of with a water jacket. The apparatus provides also for measurement of the quantity of water vapor given up by the lungs and skin of the subject, to the circulating air in the chamber, by absorption of this water in sulfuric acid.

This permits calculation of the heat used to vaporize the water that is produced, since 0.59 Cal. is the latent heat of 1 g. of water evaporated at 20°C. The heat utilized for water vaporization during the experiment must be added to the heat production calculated from the temperature change of the circulating water.

The heat produced by the subject may be transmitted to the circulating water within the copper coils in the chamber or to the circulating air (including its water vapor) within the chamber. Also, the heat may be stored within the chamber, including the subject. However, if the rate of flow and temperature of the water are adjusted carefully to the rate of heat production, the subject's total heat production will then equal total heat loss. The latter can be calculated, as indicated above, from the measurements made upon the circulating water and the air within the chamber.

Measurements of this type, which comprise *direct calorimetry,* yield values of approximately 1500 to 1800 Cal. per day for the average total heat production of an adult, postabsorptive (after absorption of food from the intestine has ceased), resting male subject. This technique permits the study of effects of activity or exercise, food consumption, various occupations, and environmental temperature on heat production, inasmuch as the large size of the chamber permits a moderate degree of normal activities.

THE RESPIRATORY QUOTIENT

Metabolic heat production is the consequence of the oxidation of foodstuffs by atmospheric oxygen with attendant production of carbon dioxide. The magnitude and nature of this gaseous exchange vary with the type of foodstuff, or the mixture of foodstuffs, undergoing oxidation since the relative proportions of carbon and oxygen differ in carbohydrates, lipids, and proteins. The theoretical relationship between oxygen consumption and carbon dioxide production can be calculated from the stoichiometry of the equations for the oxidation of carbohydrate, lipid, and protein, respectively.

The complete oxidation of glucose, a typical carbohydrate, may be represented as

$$C_6H_{12}O_6 + 6O_2 \longrightarrow 6CO_2 + 6H_2O$$

The molar ratio of carbon dioxide produced to oxygen utilized is one. This ratio, *viz.,* the volume of carbon dioxide produced divided by the volume of oxygen consumed, is defined as the respiratory quotient, frequently abbreviated as R.Q. For all carbohydrates its value is 1.

The theoretical equation for the oxidation of a typical triglyceride, tripalmitin, may be represented as

$$C_{51}H_{98}O_6 + 72.5O_2 \longrightarrow 51CO_2 + 49H_2O$$

The calculated value for the R.Q. is $51/72.5 = 0.703$. The fact that the value is less than 1 is a reflection of the highly reduced nature of fatty acids as compared to carbohydrates. Therefore, more oxygen proportionately must be consumed in the oxidation of lipid than is the case with carbohydrate. It is evident that the R.Q.

for oxidation of tripalmitin will differ somewhat from that for other triglycerides, *e.g.*, triolein (0.713), tristearin (0.699). However, the average R.Q. for either mixed dietary or body lipids is 0.71. Therefore, during fasting, when energy production is derived almost entirely from reserve calories in the form of depot lipids, the R.Q. approaches 0.71. Conversely, when a marked degree of conversion of carbohydrate to lipid occurs as in animals force-fed carbohydrate (fattening of geese), the R.Q. may even exceed 1.0. Under these circumstances, an oxygen-rich foodstuff (carbohydrate) is transformed into an oxygen-poor material (lipid). Thus, carbon dioxide production exceeds oxygen consumption, and the R.Q. is greater than unity. This may be seen from the following equation:

$$4C_6H_{12}O_6 + O_2 \longrightarrow C_{16}H_{32}O_2 + 8CO_2 + 8H_2O$$
$$\text{Glucose} \qquad\qquad \text{Palmitic acid}$$

The R.Q. for this synthesis of fatty acid from carbohydrate (lipogenesis, see Chap. 22) is 8.0, and values approaching 2.0 have been obtained experimentally in young hogs fed a mixture of starch and glucose. Under normal circumstances, however, the R.Q. seldom exceeds 1.0 and the extent to which the R.Q. approaches 1 at any time during the metabolism of mammals reflects the degree to which carbohydrate oxidation predominates in the metabolic mixture.

Calculation of a theoretical R.Q. for oxidation of protein is complicated inasmuch as oxidation of proteins is not carried completely to carbon dioxide and water and the nitrogenous end products of protein oxidation are for the most part excreted in the urine. However, calculations by Loewy in 1910 provided a basis for establishing the R.Q. for proteins. Loewy found that 100 g. of meat protein contained 52.4 g. of carbon, 7.3 g. of hydrogen, 22.7 g. of oxygen, 16.7 g. of nitrogen, and 1.0 g. of sulfur. Of this quantity of ingested meat protein, Loewy estimated that urine and feces contained 10.9 g. of carbon, 2.9 g. of hydrogen, 15.0 g. of oxygen, 16.7 g. of nitrogen, and 1.0 g. of sulfur. The urinary and fecal excretion of these elements, subtracted from the quantities contained in 100 g. of meat protein, left 41.5 g. of carbon, 4.4 g. of hydrogen, and 7.7 g. of oxygen for complete oxidation to carbon dioxide and water. Calculation reveals that this would require 138.2 g. of oxygen from extraneous sources, with production of 152.2 g. of carbon dioxide. One gram of oxygen at 0°C. and 760 mm. Hg (standard conditions of temperature and pressure) occupies 0.6997 liter, whereas 1 g. of carbon dioxide, under standard conditions, occupies 0.5089 liter. Therefore, $138.2 \times 0.6997 = 96.68$ liters of oxygen would be required to produce $152.2 \times 0.5089 = 77.45$ liters of carbon dioxide from the complete oxidation of that portion of those elements, derived from 100 g. of protein, which are not excreted in the urine or feces but are completely oxidized. Thus, the R.Q. for protein would be 77.45/96.68, or 0.801.

INDIRECT CALORIMETRY

Since the total energy released as heat during any period of time results from the oxidation of a mixture of protein, carbohydrate, and lipid, estimation of the actual amounts oxidized of each of these major components permits calculation of the necessarily associated heat production while obviating the need for the complex apparatus required for direct calorimetry. This approach is termed *indirect calorimetry*. In practice, protein oxidation is estimated from urinary nitrogen excretion while the extent of oxidation of lipid and carbohydrate is calculated from measurement of the total oxygen consumption and R.Q., after applying corrections for the oxygen utilized and the CO_2 produced by the oxidation of the protein metabolized during the same period.

The heat production associated with a given amount of oxygen consumed and carbon dioxide produced varies with the type of food being oxidized. For example, a liter of oxygen consumed during combustion of carbohydrate results in a greater liberation of heat (5.0 to 5.4 Cal.) than when lipid (4.5 to 4.7 Cal.) or protein (4.3 to 4.7 Cal.) is oxidized.

It is rare, however, that a single foodstuff is being oxidized. Hence, the nature of the mixture of foodstuffs burned, as indicated by the R.Q., must be considered. This can be calculated in the following manner. The amount of protein catabolized is obtained from measurement of urinary nitrogen during the period under study. Each gram of urinary nitrogen is equivalent to 6.25 g. of protein ($100/16 = 6.25$, 16 being the average percentage of nitrogen in proteins) and represents the production of 4.76 liters of carbon dioxide and the consumption of 5.94 liters of oxygen.

Subtraction of the volumes of oxygen and carbon dioxide exchanged in the catabolism of protein from the total oxygen consumption and carbon dioxide production yields a ratio for these two gases which is termed the *nonprotein respiratory quotient*. In Table 16.2 are given the percentages of lipid and carbohydrate undergoing combustion, per liter of oxygen consumed, as calculated for nonprotein

Table 16.2: RELATION OF NONPROTEIN RESPIRATORY QUOTIENTS TO CALORIES PER LITER OF OXYGEN USED AND TO PERCENTAGES OF CARBOHYDRATE AND LIPID METABOLIZED

Nonprotein respiratory quotient	Cal./ liter O_2	Calories derived from	
		Carbohydrate, per cent	Lipid, per cent
0.707	4.686	0	100
0.72	4.702	4.8	95.2
0.74	4.727	12.0	88.0
0.76	4.751	19.2	80.8
0.78	4.776	26.3	73.7
0.80	4.801	33.4	66.6
0.82	4.825	40.3	59.7
0.84	4.850	47.2	52.8
0.86	4.875	54.1	45.9
0.88	4.899	60.8	39.2
0.90	4.924	67.5	32.5
0.92	4.948	74.1	25.9
0.94	4.973	80.7	19.3
0.96	4.998	87.2	12.8
0.98	5.022	93.6	6.4
1.00	5.047	100	0

respiratory quotients ranging from 0.707 to 1.0, and the relation of these quotients to heat production.

Therefore, from knowledge of nitrogen excretion, oxygen consumption, and carbon dioxide production during a given period, the quantity of protein, carbohydrate, and lipid catabolized can be estimated, and the heat production calculated.

In clinical practice, the heat production is determined under resting, postabsorptive conditions (see below, Basal Metabolism). In these circumstances, urinary nitrogen is not measured, the R.Q. of the postabsorptive state is assumed to be 0.82, and heat production can be calculated directly from the oxygen consumption on the basis that, at this R.Q., 1 liter of oxygen is equivalent to 4.825 Cal. (Table 16.2). Fortunately, only minor errors are incurred as a result of these assumptions.

BASAL METABOLISM

It is not possible to access the relative significance at a specified time in metabolism of the energy relationships among foodstuffs, heat production, metabolic energy, and stored energy. However, one can limit the significance of food and of heat produced as a result of work. This is accomplished by measurement of energy exchange in a postabsorptive period and in the resting state, thus minimizing energy utilization due to work on the environment. Under these controlled conditions, heat production becomes the major means of energy loss from the body, and stored energy can be the only source of this heat. Since energy cannot be created or destroyed, the decrease in stored energy becomes equal to the heat loss, and measurements of the latter afford an estimate of the total metabolism. Since this measurement is done under resting, postabsorptive conditions, it estimates the *basal metabolism*. The basal metabolism reflects the energy requirements for maintenance and conduct of those cellular and tissue processes which are fundamental to the continuing activities of the organism, *e.g.*, the metabolic activity of muscle, brain, renal, liver, and other cells, plus the heat released as a result of the mechanical work represented by contraction of the muscles involved in respiration, circulation, and peristalsis. The total energy requirement of these processes, the basal metabolism, comprises approximately 50 per cent of the total energy expenditure required for the diverse activities of a normal 24-hr. day. The *basal metabolic rate*, abbreviated B.M.R., is not the minimal metabolism necessary for mere maintenance of life, since there are circumstances, *e.g.*, during sleep, when the metabolic rate may be lower than the basal rate.

The apparatus commonly employed for measurements of basal metabolism by indirect calorimetry is the Benedict-Roth apparatus (Fig. 16.1). The subject is in the reclining position, at least 12 to 14 hr. following the last meal; the flow of air is controlled by a mouthpiece. The regular breathing of the subject through the inhalation and exhalation tubes provides continuous free circulation of air through the oxygen-containing system, which includes a spirometer. The carbon dioxide produced is absorbed by passage through soda lime and therefore does not influence the volume of gas in the system. From the volume of oxygen consumed, corrected to dry oxygen at standard temperature and pressure, it is possible to

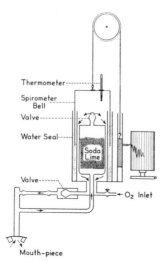

Thermometer

Spirometer
Bell

Valve

Water Seal

Soda
Lime

Valve

O₂ Inlet

Mouth-piece

FIG. 16.1. Sectional view of Benedict-Roth closed-circuit apparatus.

calculate heat production by use of the value 4.825, the caloric equivalent of 1 liter of oxygen for an R.Q. of 0.82 (Table 16.2).

The basal metabolism is usually given in terms of *Calories per hour.* In practice the basal metabolic rate is determined over a 10- to 15-min. period and expressed per square meter of body surface or as a percentage above or below certain standard values (see below).

Factors Affecting the Basal Metabolism. The basal metabolism is quite constant in a given individual and in similar individuals of the same species. Many factors may, however, affect basal metabolism, *e.g.*, body size, age, sex, climatic conditions, diet, physical training, drugs, etc. The basal metabolism may deviate from normal values in a variety of pathological states, and in certain of these its measurement provides a useful diagnostic tool.

Influence of Body Size on Basal Metabolism. There are four important factors in heat loss from the organism: (1) the temperature difference between the environment and the organism, (2) the nature of the surface that radiates the heat, (3) the area of that surface, and (4) the thermal conductance of the environment. Under the conditions of determination of the basal metabolism, surface area appears to be the most important of these factors, and, under similar physiological conditions, the basal metabolism of various mammals is roughly proportional to the surface area. The relation of heat production to body weight and to surface area is seen in Table 16.3. It is evident from the table that, although the *heat production per kilogram* may vary widely among various species and is *inversely* related to *body weight,* the *heat production per square meter of body surface is essentially constant.* The relationship of basal metabolism to surface area was first demonstrated clearly by Rubner in 1883, although suggestions of this relationship had been made earlier. Thus, knowledge of the surface area of the subject was required in establishing the standards of basal metabolism, since heat production in the postabsorptive, resting state is a function of the total surface area.

Table 16.3: RELATION OF DAILY BASAL HEAT PRODUCTION TO BODY WEIGHT AND SURFACE AREA

	Body weight, kg.	Metabolism per kg. of body weight per day, Cal.	Metabolism per m.² of body surface per day, Cal.
Horse........................	441.0	11.3	948
Pig...........................	128.0	19.1	1078
Man..........................	64.3	32.1	1042
Dog..........................	15.2	51.5	1039
Goose........................	3.5	66.7	969
Fowl.........................	2.0	71.0	943
Mouse........................	0.018	212.0	1188

SOURCE: After G. Lusk, "The Elements of the Science of Nutrition," 4th ed, W. B. Saunders Company, Philadelphia, 1928.

The pioneer work of determining total surface area in man was conducted by E. F. Du Bois and D. Du Bois. Initially, measurements of the surface area of an individual were made by means of flexible but inelastic paper molds. The laborious nature of this method led to a search for a formula for surface area that was accurate but fairly simple and resulted in an expression based on the height and weight of the subject. This expression is

$$A = W^{0.425} \times H^{0.725} \times C$$

where A is the surface area in square centimeters; W, the weight in kilograms; H, the height in centimeters; and C, a constant with a value of 71.84. The formula can also be expressed as follows:

$$\log A = 0.425 \log W + 0.725 \log H + 1.8564$$

In order to avoid this calculation, nomograms have been constructed so that approximate surface area can be ascertained, the height and weight of the subject being known.

A somewhat simpler expression of metabolic rate, independent of surface area, has been derived from a relatively consistent general relation of the metabolic rate and the body mass of homeotherms. This is expressed by the approximation $B = 3W^{3/4}$, where B is the hourly metabolic rate in Calories and W is the body weight in kilograms.

Influence of Age and Sex on Basal Metabolism. Both age and sex affect the basal metabolism, the values being higher in childhood than in adult life, and uniformly higher in the male as compared with the female in the same age group. The heat production of premature babies is extremely low, and the basal metabolism of the newborn is significantly lower (25 Cal.) than that of infants a few weeks of age (55 Cal.). Heat production gradually declines with advancing age from 45 to 50 Cal. per m.² per hr. in the ten-year-old male to approximately 35 Cal. at the age of sixty-five. Table 16.4 shows some values of basal heat production in relation to age and sex. One of the pioneer investigators in the field of energy metabolism, Magnus-Levy, determined his basal metabolism at the beginning and end of a 50-

Table 16.4: BASAL HEAT PRODUCTION IN RELATION TO AGE AND SEX

Age, yr.	Average Cal./hr./m.² body surface		Age, yr.	Average Cal./hr./m.² body surface	
	Males	Females		Males	Females
5	53.0	51.6	20–24	41.0	36.9
6	52.7	50.7	25–29	40.3	36.6
7	52.0	49.3			
8	51.2	48.1	30–34	39.8	36.2
9	50.4	46.9	35–39	39.2	35.8
10	49.5	45.8	40–44	38.3	35.3
11	48.6	44.6	45–49	37.8	35.0
12	47.8	43.4			
13	47.1	42.0	50–54	37.2	34.5
14	46.2	41.0	55–59	36.6	34.1
15	45.3	39.6			
16	44.7	38.5	60–64	36.0	33.8
17	43.7	37.4	65–69	35.5	33.4
18	42.9	37.3	70–74	34.8	32.8
19	42.1	37.2	75–79	34.2	32.3

year interval during his life. His data in Table 16.5 illustrate the influence of age on basal metabolism in a single individual.

Other Factors Affecting the Basal Metabolism. The environmental temperature appears to influence the basal metabolic rate. The basal metabolism of individuals living in a tropical climate is usually lower than that for similar individuals in temperate or colder climates. A minimum basal metabolic rate is observed at normal environmental temperature, *i.e.*, 20 to 25°C. Environmental temperatures above 30°C. cause a slight rise in the metabolic rate and in body temperature. When the temperature falls below 15°C., muscular tone increases, shivering may ensue, and heat production increases. However, elevation of the basal metabolic rate in colder climates is apparently independent of the increased heat production caused by shivering and is related to an actual augmentation of the basal oxygen consumption.

Muscular training, as in athletes, may be reflected in a slightly elevated basal metabolic rate.

Table 16.5: INFLUENCE OF AGE ON THE BASAL METABOLISM OF THE SAME PERSON AS SEEN FROM MEASUREMENTS AT THE BEGINNING AND AT THE END OF A 50-YEAR PERIOD

Year	Age, yr.	Height, cm.	Weight, kg.	Surface area, m.²	Cal./hr.	Cal./m.²/hr.
1891	26	167.0	67.5	1.76	67	38.1
1941	76	165.5	60.0	1.65	52	31.5
Differences	50	. . . . .	−11%	−6%	−22%	−17%

SOURCE: From A. Magnus-Levy, *J.A.M.A.*, **118**, 1369, 1942.

Certain drugs, e.g., epinephrine and thyroxine, cause an increase in the basal metabolic rate.

Pathological Alterations in Basal Metabolic Rate. As suggested above, determination of the basal metabolic rate may be of value as an aid in diagnosis of disease and in following the response to therapeutic measures. In 1897, Magnus-Levy described the alterations in basal oxygen consumption that occur in thyroid disease. Since that time, the basal metabolic rate has been a useful criterion for assessing aberrations in thyroid activity. In *hyperthyroidism,* the basal metabolic rate may be increased 50 to 75 per cent above normal standards; in *hypothyroidism,* the rate may be as much as 40 per cent lower than normal (Chap. 46). *Fever* causes an increase in heat production of approximately 13 per cent of the basal metabolic rate for each degree centigrade increase in body temperature, and, indeed, this is probably the most frequently encountered reason for increased basal metabolic rate. The augmenting effects of temperature increments on rates of metabolic processes, *e.g.,* enzymic reactions, have been described (page 228). Table 16.6 lists a few of the circumstances in which the basal metabolic rate may be above or below normal.

Table 16.6: Some Circumstances in Which Basal Metabolic Rate May Vary

Below normal	Above normal
During sleep	Athletic training
Malnutrition	Latter half of pregnancy
Hypothyroidism	Hyperthyroidism
Hypophyseal insufficiency	Fever
Addison's disease	Cardiorenal disease with dyspnea
Drug administration, *e.g.,* anesthetics	Leukemia
Elevated environmental temperature, *e.g.,*	Polycythemia
in tropical climates	Drug administration, *e.g.,* epinephrine,
	caffeine, thyroid, or thyroxine

FACTORS AFFECTING THE TOTAL METABOLISM

It has been indicated previously that conditions for determining the basal metabolism are defined so that the variables of food and voluntary muscular activity are eliminated. The extent to which food and muscular work may alter metabolism from the basal level will be considered briefly.

Effect of Food. Caloric restriction may be accompanied by a considerable decline in total metabolism. Conversely, ingestion of food is followed by an increase in heat production above normal basal level. This occurs immediately after eating and can be related to the digestion and absorption of foodstuffs. Additional elevation of metabolism may then result as a consequence of subsequent metabolic transformations of absorbed products.

Of the three major foodstuffs, the ingestion of protein causes the greatest elevation in the total metabolism. The stimulating effect of food on the heat production of the organism was called by Rubner the *specific dynamic action,* which is the extra heat produced by the organism, over and above the basal heat production, as a result of food ingestion. In the case of protein, the specific dynamic effect amounts to approximately 30 per cent, for carbohydrate 6 per cent, and for lipid 4 per cent, respectively, of the energy value of the food ingested. Thus, ingestion of 25 g. of protein, equivalent to 100 Cal., leads to 30 Cal. of extra heat production over the basal metabolic rate. These calories are wasted as heat, and therefore only 70 Cal. of potentially useful energy can be derived from the 25 g. of protein. Thus it is essential, in calculating the caloric value or equivalent of a diet, to make provision for the calories dissipated as heat as a result of the specific dynamic effect.

The specific dynamic effect of foodstuffs is a consequence of the extra energy released incident to metabolism of the food. In the dog, removal of the liver diminished significantly the specific dynamic effect of individual amino acids. Therefore, it appears that reactions in the metabolism of foodstuffs in the liver are responsible in part for the specific dynamic action of these substances.

Effect of Muscular Work. Muscles are capable of utilizing the energy of oxidation for the performance of mechanical work with an efficiency of approximately 30 per cent. Moreover, when engaged in hard work, the total energy required for performing this work may be many times that reflected by the basal metabolic rate. Table 16.7 indicates the influence of muscular activity on the degree of caloric expenditure.

Table 16.7: APPROXIMATE CALORIC EXPENDITURE OF MAN AS AFFECTED BY MUSCULAR ACTIVITY

Type of muscular activity	Cal./hr.
Sleeping	65
Awake, lying still	77
Awake, sitting up, at rest	100
Reading aloud	105
Standing relaxed	105
Standing at attention	115
Light to extreme muscular exercise	170–600

Effect of Mental Effort. Mental effort, in contrast to muscular effort, produces little increase in metabolism. The mental effort associated with the preparation for examinations or solution of a mathematical problem led to an increase of only 3 or 4 per cent in the metabolism.

Intense emotion may elevate the metabolism 5 to 10 per cent above the basal level. The metabolism may fall *below* the basal level during *sleep*, since the muscles are more completely relaxed than when the individual is awake, provided the sleep is undisturbed.

DAILY CALORIC REQUIREMENT

It is apparent from previous considerations that the total caloric requirement of man varies considerably with age, sex, diet, and daily activity and is not the same at all periods of life of a given individual. Therefore, it is not possible to establish standard caloric requirements; instead the range of values under various circumstances is indicated. To prevent loss or wasting of body tissues, the caloric intake of the food ingested must be at least equivalent to the total heat production during the same period. This heat production is equal to the basal metabolic rate plus the energy expended in performing the day's activities, including work. Table 16.8 indicates the average caloric expenditure of normal individuals in various types of activity.

Table 16.8: APPROXIMATE CALORIC EXPENDITURE IN VARIOUS OCCUPATIONS

Activity or occupation	*Cal./hr.*
Seamstress	110
Typist	140
Housemaid	150
Bookbinder	170
Shoemaker	180
Carpenter, metalworker, industrial painter	240
Stonemason	400
Lumberman, in cold environment	500

Inasmuch as the first law of thermodynamics is obeyed by living organisms, the balance that obtains between caloric intake and energy expenditure is the prime factor, under normal circumstances, that determines whether weight gain or weight loss occurs over a period of time. Weight gain in relation to lipid metabolism is discussed in Chap. 22.

REFERENCES

Books

Brody, S., "Bioenergetics and Growth," Reinhold Publishing Corporation, New York, 1945.
Consolazio, C. F., Johnson, R. E., and Pecora, L. J., "Physiological Measurements of Metabolic Functions in Man," McGraw-Hill Book Company, Inc., Blakiston Division, New York, 1963.
Kleiber, M., "The Fire of Life: An Introduction to Animal Energetics," John Wiley & Sons, Inc., New York, 1961.

Review Articles

Hardy, J. D., Physiology of Temperature Regulation, *Physiol. Revs.*, **41**, 521–606, 1961.
Keys, A., Energy Requirements of Adults, in "Handbook of Nutrition," American Medical Association, pp. 259–274, McGraw-Hill Book Company, Inc., Blakiston Division, New York, 1951.
Keys, A., Undernutrition, in G. G. Duncan, ed., "Diseases of Metabolism," 4th ed., pp. 501–528, W. B. Saunders Company, Philadelphia, 1959.
Kleiber, M., Body Size and Metabolic Rate, *Physiol. Revs.*, **27**, 511–541, 1947.
Kleiber, M., and Rogers, T. A., Energy Metabolism, *Ann. Rev. Physiol.*, **23**, 15–36, 1961.
Sadhu, D. P., The Specific Dynamic Action of Nutrients, with Special Reference to the Effects of Vitamins and Hormones, *Missouri Univ. Agr. Expt. Sta. Res. Bull.* 408, pp. 3–64, 1947.
Strang, J. M., Obesity, in G. G. Duncan, ed., "Diseases of Metabolism," 4th ed., pp. 529–633, W. B. Saunders Company, Philadelphia, 1959.
Symposium on Energy Balance, *Am. J. Clin. Nutr.*, **8**, 527–774, 1960.

17. Biological Oxidations

Oxidation-Reduction Reactions. Phosphate Bond Energy

Oxidation in living cells serves two chief functions: (1) to provide energy for endergonic cellular processes, and (2) to transform dietary materials into cellular constituents. Many of the problems involved in biological oxidations may be introduced by considering the oxidation of glucose, which may be represented as follows.

$$C_6H_{12}O_6 + 6O_2 \longrightarrow 6CO_2 + 6H_2O + \text{energy}$$

The complete oxidation of a mole of glucose according to the above equation would result in a free-energy release, under standard conditions, of 686,000 cal. Were this energy released instantaneously, in the manner of the heat released in a bunsen flame, oxidation of a few molecules of glucose would suffice to disrupt cellular structure. Moreover, the equation above provides no information concerning the means by which the cell may utilize for its functions the energy arising from oxidation. In man-made machines the energy derived from the oxidation of fuel is released as heat which is used to expand a gas in a manner that permits useful work to be accomplished. Within cells, however, a large fraction of the free energy available from oxidations is trapped as chemical energy rather than released as an equivalent amount of heat. Indeed, since the temperature of mammalian cells is rather constant, heat, *of itself,* could not even in theory be employed for useful work (page 207). Work can be derived from heat only in a device that operates with a temperature differential, *e.g.*, a steam engine. However, mammalian cells operate isothermally and rather efficiently employ the energy derived from oxidations to perform useful work. This work, therefore, is not accomplished by using the *heat* released by oxidation of glucose or other foodstuffs.

In the course of many biological oxidations, the free energy released is used to synthesize a compound whose chemical energy is, in turn, available for doing work. Further, whether the material being oxidized is carbohydrate, lipid, or amino acid, the free energy available from each oxidative step is immediately employed, with but few exceptions, to synthesize one compound, *adenosine triphosphate* (ATP) (page 305); the energy of ATP is then available for the manifold endergonic processes of the body. The standard free energy required to synthesize ATP from adenosine diphosphate and inorganic phosphate is approximately $+7000$ cal. per mole. For the synthesis of ATP at 37°C., pH 7.4, and at prevailing biological concentrations of phosphate and adenosine diphosphate, ΔF is of the order of $+8000$

cal. per mole. To obtain maximal benefit from the oxidation of a given metabolite, its complete oxidation should, therefore, be subdivided into the largest possible number of steps, each of which will yield slightly more than 8000 cal. Thus, the living organism differs from man-made, fuel-consuming engines in the important fact that a portion of the loss of energy as heat is eliminated; the metabolic apparatus operates with incomplete heat loss, and much of the free energy of oxidation is trapped directly as another form of potential chemical energy.

It is implicit in these concepts that, unless released as heat, energy *may* be transferred repeatedly under isothermal conditions. Thus, energy supplied to the organism as glucose may next appear locked into a molecule of ATP, may then appear in a newly synthesized protein molecule, and may finally emerge as heat when the protein undergoes hydrolysis to component amino acids. Despite the numerous steps in such transformations, which are here oversimplified, the overall energy change is identical with that which may be observed, as heat production, in a bomb calorimeter as described in the previous chapter. To the extent that each of the consecutive transfers of energy involves the production of heat and of unavailable energy as entropy, metabolic transformations are inefficient, insofar as the energy economy of the organism is concerned. However, it is this very "inefficiency" which gives *direction* to metabolic events. For example, in the reaction series,

$$A \rightleftharpoons B \rightleftharpoons C \rightleftharpoons D \rightleftharpoons E$$

if ΔF for each step were zero, A would be transformed into an equal mixture of A, B, C, D, and E. If, however, ΔF for each step were large and negative, particularly that for $D \rightleftharpoons E$, then A would be converted almost entirely to E.

At this point one may ask why an animal requires a source of energy, apart from that required to do work on the environment such as exercise, etc. This question is particularly pointed in respect to the adult who remains at constant weight and fixed body composition in an isothermal environment. In general, *the energy derived from biological oxidations is employed to maintain the body in a state remote from equilibrium.* Thus, cells contain large quantities of polysaccharides, proteins, lipids, and nucleic acids in the presence of relatively small concentrations of their constituents, *i.e.*, glucose, amino acids, etc. Yet, at equilibrium, in the presence of appropriate enzymes, quite the opposite situation would prevail. Again, the ionic composition of the solution bathing body cells is remarkably different from that within the cell, despite permeability of the cell membrane to the ions on both sides. Free energy from the oxidation of glucose is employed to synthesize polysaccharides, proteins, etc., at a rate equal to that at which they are degraded as they tend toward equilibrium. Similarly, energy is employed to expel various ions from within the cell in opposition to the tendency to attain equilibrium across the cell membrane. As large molecules are hydrolyzed, or as ions return to the cell, energy is lost as a consequence of both entropy change and lack of means of utilizing the resultant free-energy release. Over a period of time, therefore, since the rates in both directions are equal, all the energy supplied appears ultimately as heat, but the disequilibrium has been maintained. Thus, the "order" of the foodstuffs is altered, through oxidation, to maintain the high degree of "order" of the cell. The sum of such processes in the organism may be presumed to comprise a major fraction of the basal metabolic rate (page 286). If the supply of food or oxygen ceases, the tendency toward equilibrium is not counterbalanced, and the expected equilibria are attained. This is post-mortem autolysis.

It is the purpose of these chapters to describe biological oxidations and particularly the means by which the oxidation of foodstuffs by molecular oxygen may occur at 37°C. without disrupting cellular structure while the free energy of oxidation is utilized for the endergonic processes of living cells.

OXIDATION-REDUCTION REACTIONS

The term oxidation is restricted to those reactions between molecules which involve electron transfer. Loss of an electron is oxidation; acquisition of an electron is reduction.

$$Fe^{++} \rightleftharpoons Fe^{+++} + e$$
$$Co^{++} \rightleftharpoons Co^{+++} + e$$
$$Na \rightleftharpoons Na^{+} + e$$

The above equations describe oxidation of metals at an electrode. In solution, oxidation of a metal ion occurs by transfer of an electron directly to an acceptor ion or molecule. Many factors affect the ease of electron transfer to or from metal ions. In general, the process is facilitated (1) by bridging groups that can combine with both reacting species, $i.e.$,

$$A + X^{-}B^{+} \longrightarrow AX^{-}B^{+} \longrightarrow A^{+}X^{-}B \longrightarrow A^{+}X^{-} + B$$

or (2) by coordination of the metal ion to ligands, particularly to ligand groups with relatively large, highly resonant structures.

That loss of an electron is an "oxidation" is readily understood for most inorganic substances but may not be quite so obvious for the reaction $H_2 + \frac{1}{2}O_2 \rightleftharpoons H_2O$, since the H—O bond is covalent and a pair of electrons is shared between the oxygen and hydrogen atoms. Even here, however, since the pair of electrons is somewhat closer to the oxygen nucleus than it is to the hydrogen nucleus, it can be stated that the hydrogen is oxidized since it has partially lost an electron while the oxygen has partially gained electrons. The polarity of water and the electrolysis of water by an electric current are further evidence that the reaction between H_2 and O_2 is primarily an electron transfer from one atom to another.

A more complex problem arises in the case of organic compounds for which oxidation is generally synonymous with dehydrogenation. Consider the oxidation of hydroquinone, which may be represented as:

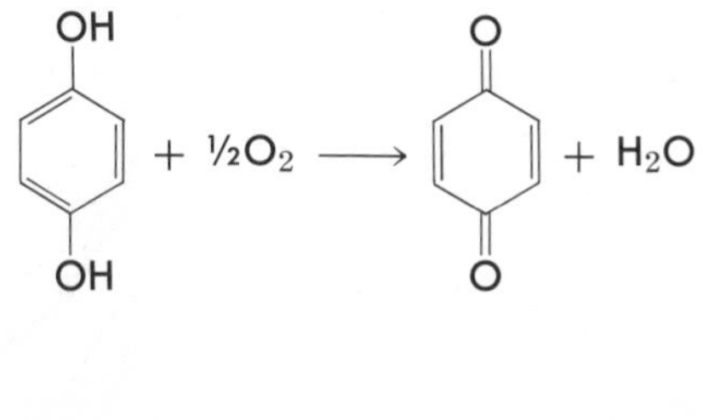

The reaction may also be regarded as proceeding in steps, the first being an acidic dissociation, and the second, withdrawal of electrons.

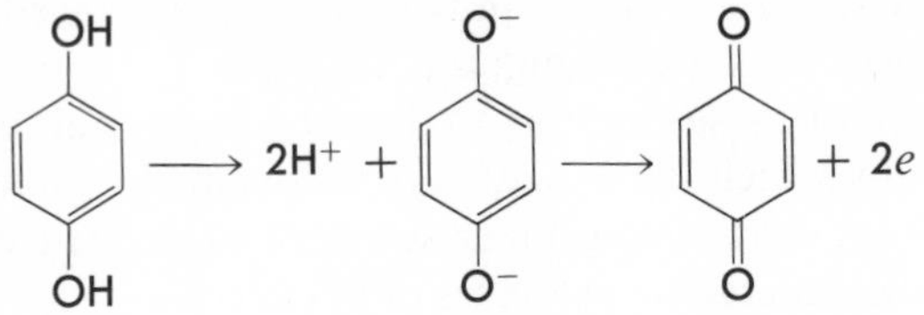

If the oxidant were ferric ion, for example, the over-all reaction would be

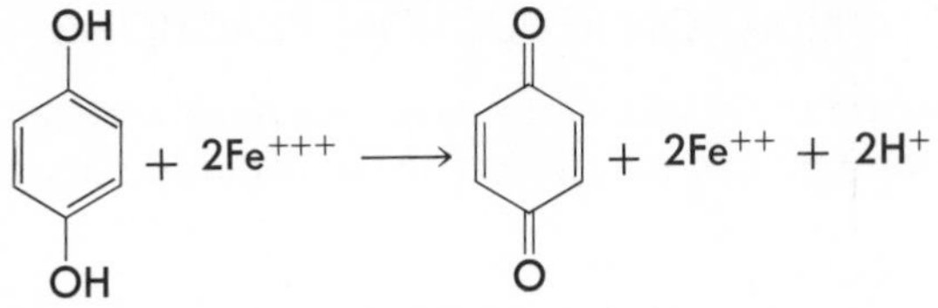

In the example given, protons and electrons depart independently from the molecule being oxidized. In other instances the departing group may be an intact hydrogen atom H°, whereas in many biological systems, oxidation occurs by transfer of a hydride ion, H:⁻, to the acceptor molecule.

One-electron Transfer: Free Radicals. In the example above, two hydrogen atoms and two electrons were removed from the hydroquinone molecule. However, the ferric ion, Fe^{+++}, like several biological oxidants, can accept but one electron. Since the likelihood of a ternary collision, involving simultaneously two 1-electron acceptor ions and one 2-electron donor, is remote, it appears that the mechanism shown above is inadequate and that electron transfer can occur in successive 1-electron steps, even from organic molecules. Such a process may again be illustrated by the oxidation of hydroquinone.

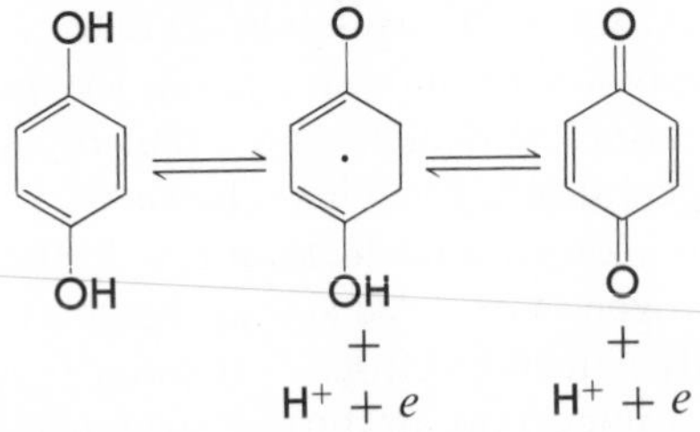

Hydroquinone   Semiquinone   Quinone

Since the intermediate *semiquinone* is formed by loss of a proton and an electron, it is a free radical, *i.e.*, distributed through the molecule is an odd or unpaired electron. Such free radicals vary widely in their stability. Some, *e.g.*, $CH_3 \cdot$, exist for no more than millimicroseconds; others, with large resonant structures, and particularly those with complex conjugated double-bond systems, are relatively stable and, hence, readily detected. The latter group is of interest and significance in biological oxidations.

The odd electron does not confer a negative charge upon the semiquinone molecule; rather, it represents an unfilled valence bond. However, it does confer other distinctive properties. The two members of an electron pair spin in opposite directions so that their magnetic moments cancel. Since the spin of an odd electron is unopposed, the entire molecule has a net magnetic moment equal to that of one unpaired electron, *viz.*, one Bohr magneton, and the molecule is said to be para-magnetic (page 197). Molecules with no magnetic moment are termed diamagnetic. Hence, these can be distinguished by devices which measure magnetic susceptibility.

A more sensitive and useful technique for detection and estimation of such free radicals is *electron spin resonance spectrometry.* When a population of free-radical molecules is in zero magnetic field, the spins and magnetic moments of their unpaired electrons are randomly oriented and all have equal energy. When placed in a magnetic field, however, the unpaired electrons must align themselves with their spins and magnetic moments either parallel or antiparallel to the applied field. Those aligned with the field have energies $\frac{1}{2}g\beta H$ less than the zero-field value, and those arranged antiparallel have energies $\frac{1}{2}g\beta H$ greater than the zero-field value. Thus, the difference in energy between these two groups of unpaired electrons is $g\beta H$, where β is a constant, the Bohr magneton, H is the magnetic field strength in gauss, and g, the spectroscopic splitting factor, is a function characteristic of the unpaired electrons of a particular organic free radical or paramagnetic metal. The precise value of g is determined by electron spin resonance spectrometry in the following manner. If electromagnetic radiation is applied to a solution of free radicals in a magnetic field, some of the antiparallel (lower-energy) electrons absorb the incident radiant energy, "flopover," and jump to the higher-energy level. In a given magnetic field H this is possible only at that frequency, ν, at which the energy of the absorbed quanta, $h\nu$, exactly equals the difference in energy levels between the two classes of unpaired electrons, *viz.*, when $h\nu = g\beta H$. Thus, the value of the "spectroscopic splitting factor" becomes

$$g = \frac{h\nu}{\beta H}$$

In principle, electron resonance absorption can occur at any frequency of applied radiation if the strength of the magnetic field is adjusted to satisfy the equation above. In practice, it is convenient to use a generator of fixed frequency output, vary the magnetic field strength, and measure the absorption of the radiant energy by the sample.

For an electron spinning freely, g is 2.0023. Since organic free radicals yield g values very close to 2.00, the remainder of these molecules exerts relatively little influence on the unpaired electron.

Organic free radicals are generally intensely colored, *i.e.*, they absorb light energy in the visible portion of the spectrum. This has permitted their detection and estimation by spectrophotometry, although this procedure is not so sensitive as electron spin resonance spectrometry.

The occurrence of oxidation-reduction reactions demonstrates that molecules and atoms vary in their affinity for electrons. A familiar expression of this varying affinity is to be found in the electromotive series of the elements. It will be recalled that metals high in the series will displace any metal below from its salts. Thus for

$$2Na + Cu^{++} \longrightarrow 2Na^+ + Cu$$

the Na is oxidized and Cu^{++} is reduced. Further, the more remote two metals are from each other in the series, the greater the relative oxidizing and reducing powers. A similar series can also be compiled for organic substances, expressing their relative affinities for electrons. A few systems of interest are presented in Table 17.1 (page 302). From this table, oxygen should oxidize ethyl alcohol; yet at room temperature this reaction does not occur readily. Again, many substances should be capable of reducing acetaldehyde to ethanol, whereas relatively few such reactions do occur. Rather, in order to oxidize alcohol, vigorous conditions may be required, *e.g.*, chromic acid at elevated temperature, and to reduce acetaldehyde, a strong reducing agent such as sodium amalgam may be needed. A pair of substances that should interact, yet do not, is termed a *sluggish system.* This failure is due to a relatively high activation energy, E_a (page 229), for the reacting molecules, so that the expected reaction proceeds too slowly to be observed. In contrast are compounds that are readily oxidized and reduced in reversible manner. A useful example of such systems is the following reaction.

$$\text{Methylene blue} + 2e + 2H^+ \rightleftharpoons \text{leukomethylene blue}$$

A compound is said to be *autoxidizable* if the reduced form is readily reoxidized by atmospheric oxygen in the absence of a catalyst. Michaelis suggested that solutions of compounds, which are readily oxidized and reduced in reversible systems, contain both oxidized and reduced forms and also have significant amounts of intermediary semiquinone, whereas sluggish systems such as ethanol/acetaldehyde contain relatively little of the free radical.

Quantitative Aspects of Oxidation-Reduction Reactions. When a metal strip, *e.g.*, zinc, here termed an electrode, is placed in an aqueous solution, some of the zinc atoms in the metal surface give up electrons and form zinc ions (Zn^{++}) which enter the solution at the metal surface. The electrons remain on the metal and give it a negative charge, thus building up an electrical double layer. The potential difference across this layer is the *electrode potential.* The process is reversible and, after a short time, zinc ions in solution begin to recombine with electrons on the surface of the metal to form zinc atoms. At equilibrium, the rate at which ions from the solution combine with electrons on the metal surface to form atoms is equal to the rate at which zinc atoms lose electrons to form ions in the solution, and the electrode exhibits its reversible potential.

The ionization of molecular hydrogen is also an oxidation.

$$\tfrac{1}{2}H_2 \rightleftharpoons H^+ + e$$

For this reaction the dissociation constant may be formulated as

$$K = \frac{[H^+][e]}{[H_2]^{1/2}}$$

where $[e]$ represents the *electron pressure* at the place where ionization occurs. This electron pressure must be closely related to what is measured as an "electrode potential."

Inasmuch as hydrogen is a gas, it cannot be used directly as an electrode. However, an inert metal, *e.g.*, platinum, covered with finely divided platinum

(platinum black) adsorbs hydrogen; reversible dissociation of this hydrogen occurs on the surface, and the arrangement then functions as a hydrogen electrode. The potential of this electrode, from the formulation above, is a function of the ratio $[H^+]/[H_2]^{1/2}$, *i.e.*, of the oxidized and reduced forms of hydrogen. The potential can be determined by comparison with a second electrode and measurement of the potential difference between the two electrodes. If the potential of one electrode is arbitrarily designated as zero, all other electrode potentials can be referred to it and their potentials expressed numerically in volts. This reference electrode is the *normal hydrogen electrode, i.e.,* a platinum wire immersed in $1N$ H^+ equilibrated with hydrogen gas at 1 atmosphere.

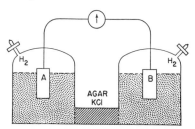

FIG. 17.1. An electrolytic cell consisting of two hydrogen electrodes.

Consider a cell consisting of two hydrogen electrodes, as depicted in Fig. 17.1, in which the two solutions are initially of equal $[H^+]$, but the hydrogen pressure in half-cell B is less than 1 atmosphere. If now the two electrodes are connected by a conducting wire, electrons will move through the wire from electrode A to electrode B. The following reactions occur.

$$\text{At A:} \quad \tfrac{1}{2}H_2 \longrightarrow H^+ + e$$
$$\text{At B:} \quad H^+ + e \longrightarrow \tfrac{1}{2}H_2$$

Effectively, the net result is transfer of hydrogen ions from B to A; current flows until, in both vessels, the *ratio* $[H^+]/[H_2]^{1/2}$ is identical. To maintain electrical neutrality, anions, *e.g.*, Cl^-, must flow through the salt bridge from B to A. If a potentiometer is interposed between B and A, the tendency of electrons to flow from A to B may be measured. This is the potential difference, E, which is expressed in volts. In this instance electrode A would be negative with respect to B in the exterior circuit since electrons are entering B and leaving A.

Ions in dilute solution obey the gas laws, and from these laws a quantitative expression can be derived for the potential difference between the electrodes A and B.

$$-E = \frac{RT}{F} \ln [H_2]_B^{1/2} \quad \text{or} \quad -E = \frac{RT}{2F} \ln [H_2]_B \tag{1}$$

where R is the molar gas constant, 8.315 joules per degree, T is the absolute temperature, and F is the faraday, 96,500 coulombs. At 30°C, substituting in (1) and converting to $\log_{10}$,

$$\frac{8.315 \times 303 \times 2.303}{2 \times 96,500} = 0.03$$

hence
$$-E = 0.03 \log [H_2]_B \quad \text{volts} \tag{2}$$

This expression is valid when A is the normal hydrogen electrode and the $[H^+]$ in B is unity ($1N$). If the H_2 pressure in B had been 1 atmosphere but the $[H^+]$ less than $1N$, electrons would have flowed from electrode B to electrode A, the electrode reactions would have been reversed, and the electrode potential at B would be expressed

$$E = \frac{RT}{F} \ln [H^+]_B$$

Substituting as above and converting to $\log_{10}$,

$$E = 0.06 \log [H^+]_B$$

or
$$-E = 0.06 \, pH_B \tag{3}$$

By combining both expressions, a statement is obtained for the potential difference between the normal hydrogen electrode and a hydrogen electrode in any other dilute aqueous solution.

$$E = \frac{RT}{F} \ln \frac{[H^+]}{[H_2]^{1/2}} \tag{4}$$

$$E = \frac{RT}{F} \ln [H^+] - \frac{RT}{2F} \ln [H_2] \tag{5}$$

At 30°,

$$E = 0.03 \log \frac{1}{[H_2]} - 0.06 \, pH \tag{6}$$

If $[H_2]$ is maintained at some known pressure, one can perform potentiometric pH measurements. If the pH is known, the hydrogen pressure can be determined.

Since the oxidation of an organic compound occurs by dehydrogenation, a solution of such a compound may be thought of as exerting an infinitesimal hydrogen pressure. Various autoxidizable dyes can be reduced by gaseous hydrogen in the presence of a suitable catalyst, e.g., platinum black; with the reduced form of methylene blue (MbH_2) as an example, the reaction is

$$MbH_2 \rightleftharpoons Mb + H_2$$

A solution of the reduced dye, by this formulation, exerts a small but real hydrogen pressure which can be measured with an inert electrode or used to reduce some other autoxidizable substance. For this reaction

$$K = \frac{[Mb][H_2]}{[MbH_2]}$$

and
$$[H_2] = \frac{K[MbH_2]}{[Mb]}$$

The hydrogen pressure in equilibrium with this system thus depends on the *ratio* of reduced to oxidized form of the dye; the potential of an inert electrode in this system is that of a hydrogen electrode at this hydrogen pressure and varies with pH as does any hydrogen electrode.

We may, therefore, substitute for $[H_2]$ in equation (5),

$$[H_2] = K\frac{[\text{reductant}]}{[\text{oxidant}]}$$

so that

$$E = \frac{RT}{F}\ln[H^+] - \frac{RT}{2F}\ln K\frac{[\text{reductant}]}{[\text{oxidant}]} \tag{7}$$

or

$$E = \frac{RT}{F}\ln[H^+] - \frac{RT}{2F}\ln K + \frac{RT}{2F}\ln\frac{[\text{oxidant}]}{[\text{reductant}]} \tag{8}$$

For any system $(RT/2F)\ln K$ must be a constant, and if measurements are made in well-buffered media so that $(RT/F)\ln[H^+]$ is constant, these may be combined as a new constant E_0'. Since for reactions in general one or more electrons may be involved per molecule, the term n is introduced for the number of electrons transferred per mole. The new expression may be formulated as

$$E = E_0' + \frac{RT}{nF}\ln\frac{[\text{oxidant}]}{[\text{reductant}]} \tag{9}$$

At 30° this simplifies to

$$E = E_0' + \frac{0.06}{n}\log\frac{[\text{oxidant}]}{[\text{reductant}]} \tag{10}$$

It may be seen that E_0' is the potential of the half-reduced system at some stipulated pH and temperature since, with a ratio value of 1, the second term is then zero.

The *redox* (oxidation-reduction) *potential, E*, of a given solution in expression (10) is, then, the "electron pressure" that this solution exerts on an inert electrode and can be measured with appropriate apparatus and a potentiometer. Returning to the simplest example, the dissociation of hydrogen to protons and electrons, it is apparent that such a solution must also exert a "proton pressure." Protons do not readily "flow" over wires, and no simple *instrumental* arrangement permits a *direct* measurement of proton pressure. The electrometric measurement of pH described above is, rather, a measurement of the effects of variation in proton pressure on electron pressure, and it is the latter which is measured, thereby permitting calculation of the pH. Thus, the pH of a solution represents its proton pressure, exactly as E measures the electron pressure. Just as a system composed of an acid and its salt resists changes in pH, or buffers a given solution, a system composed of oxidant and reductant also resists changes in redox potential E, or *poises* the solution.

Table 17.1 includes E_0' values for some systems of biological interest. The word "system" is used here in the sense of a mixture of the oxidized and reduced forms of a given substance, *e.g.*, quinone-hydroquinone, pyruvate-lactate, etc. The values shown are for electrode potentials. It may be remarked that many handbooks and reference works use a different convention for designating the electron pressure of an oxidation-reduction system, *viz.*, the "electrode E.M.F." (electromotive force). The latter is particularly convenient in considerations of the behavior of

Table 17.1: ELECTRODE POTENTIALS OF SOME REDUCTION-OXIDATION SYSTEMS

System	E_0', volts*	pH
$H_2O/\frac{1}{2}O_2$..........	0.82	7.0
NO_2^-/NO_3^-..........	0.42	7.0
Phenylalanine/dihydroxyphenylalanine..........	0.37	7.0
Ferrocyanide/ferricyanide..........	0.36	0.0
$H_2O_2/\frac{1}{2}O_2 + H_2O$..........	0.30	7.0
Cytochrome a Fe^{++}/Fe^{+++}..........	0.29	7.0
Cytochrome c Fe^{++}/Fe^{+++}..........	0.22	7.0
2,6-Dichlorophenolindophenol red/ox†	0.22	7.0
Butyryl CoA/crotonyl CoA..........	0.19	7.0
Hemoglobin/methemoglobin..........	0.17	7.0
Cytochrome b_2 Fe^{++}/Fe^{+++}..........	0.12	7.4
Ubiquinone red/ox..........	0.10	7.4
Ascorbic acid/dehydroascorbic acid..........	0.08	6.4
Cytochrome b Fe^{++}/Fe^{+++}..........	0.07	7.4
Succinic acid/fumaric acid..........	0.03	7.0
Methylene blue red/ox..........	0.01	7.0
"Old" yellow enzyme $FMNH_2/FMN$..........	−0.12	7.0
Alanine/pyruvic acid + NH_4^+..........	−0.13	7.0
Glutamic acid/α-ketoglutaric acid + NH_4^+..........	−0.14	7.0
Malic acid/oxaloacetic acid..........	−0.17	7.0
Lactic acid/pyruvic acid..........	−0.19	7.0
Ethanol/acetaldehyde..........	−0.20	7.0
β-Hydroxybutyric acid/acetoacetic acid..........	−0.27	7.0
3-Phosphoglyceraldehyde + P_i‡/1,3-diphosphoglyceric acid..........	−0.29	7.0
$DPNH + H^+/DPN^+$..........	−0.32	7.0
Malic acid/pyruvic acid + CO_2..........	−0.33	7.0
Glutathione red/ox..........	−0.34	7.0
Xanthine/uric acid..........	−0.36	7.0
Acetaldehyde + CoA/acetyl CoA..........	−0.41	7.0
$\frac{1}{2}H_2/H^+$..........	−0.42	7.0
Acetaldehyde/acetic acid..........	−0.60	7.0
α-Ketoglutaric acid/succinic acid + CO_2..........	−0.67	7.0
Pyruvic acid/acetic acid + CO_2..........	−0.70	7.0

* The values shown for E_0' are the potentials that would be exhibited by a potentiometer interposed between a standard hydrogen electrode and an inert electrode in a solution containing equimolar amounts, at the pH specified, of the oxidized and reduced member of each pair, were the latter electroactive. Circuit closure is effected by a salt bridge between the hydrogen electrode and the solution under study.

† red/ox = reduced form/oxidized form.

‡ P_i = inorganic orthophosphate (see page 214).

metallic electrodes. Since electrode potential = −electrode E.M.F., the convention with respect to sign, + or −, is reversed in such tables.

From equation (6) it will be seen that of two systems at the same pH, the one with the more negative potential is the stronger reducing agent inasmuch as it is in equilibrium with a greater hydrogen pressure.

The oxidized member of a system is inherently capable of being reduced by the reduced member of a system with a more negative E_0'. According to equation (6), a solution which is 0.03 volt more negative than another has ten times the hydrogen pressure of the second. When two solutions of different potentials are mixed, reaction may proceed until equilibrium is attained; the final solution has a potential between that of the two original solutions. Thus, were a solution containing A and its reduced form, AH_2, mixed with a solution of B and BH_2, reaction would proceed until both systems attained the same potential. At that point,

$$E'_{0(B)} + \frac{RT}{nF} \ln \frac{[B]}{[BH_2]} = E'_{0(A)} + \frac{RT}{nF} \ln \frac{[A]}{[AH_2]}$$

and

$$E'_{0(B)} - E'_{0(A)} = \frac{RT}{nF} \ln \frac{[A]}{[AH_2]} - \frac{RT}{nF} \ln \frac{[B]}{[BH_2]}$$

from which

$$\Delta E'_0 = \frac{RT}{nF} \ln \frac{[A][BH_2]}{[B][AH_2]} \tag{11}$$

Hence the difference in potential between the original solutions determines the relative amount of each reactant at equilibrium or, stated in another way, the extent to which reaction proceeds. The course of such a reaction may be followed by titration, analogous to acidimetric procedures. Instead of an indicator whose color changes with acidic dissociation, e.g., phenolphthalein, a small amount of dye whose color is dependent on its state of oxidation may be used, e.g., methylene blue. Or the same potentiometer and electrode may be employed for either type of titration. For acidimetry, potential changes are followed as the $[H^+]$ changes; during oxidation-reduction reactions, the potential changes with the "hydrogen pressure" or "electron pressure." Typical electrometric titration curves are shown in Fig. 17.2. Note the resemblance to the curves obtained by plotting pH changes in acidimetric titrations, as expected from the similarity in form of expression (10) and the Henderson-Hasselbalch equation (page 103).

Energy Relations in Oxidative Reactions. Since interest in oxidative reactions derives in large measure from the fact that they yield energy, let us consider some quantitative aspects of oxidative changes in relation to energy production.

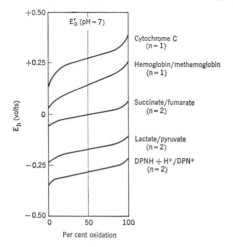

FIG. 17.2. Potentiometric titration curves. E_h = observed potential difference (in volts); n = number of electrons transferred per mole oxidized.

If the reduced form of one system is mixed with the oxidized form of another, reaction proceeds according to the equation

$$AH_2 + B \rightleftharpoons A + BH_2$$

For this reaction, the standard free-energy change, in calories per mole, may be calculated from equilibrium data in the usual manner. K is the equilibrium constant.

$$K = \frac{[A][BH_2]}{[AH_2][B]} \tag{12}$$

Actual determination of K, therefore, depends on the availability of adequate analytical methods for the various components. When the difference in potential, $\Delta E_0'$, between the two reacting systems is large, equilibrium may lie so far in one direction that accurate determination of the final concentration of AH_2 and B may be impossible. The free-energy change associated with the reaction may, however, be calculated from knowledge of the potentials of the two reacting systems. By substitution of the expression for K of equation (12) in equation (11) one obtains:

$$\Delta E_0' = \frac{RT}{n\mathsf{F}} \ln K \tag{13}$$

or $\qquad\qquad n\mathsf{F}\,\Delta E_0' = RT \ln K$

Since $\qquad\quad -\Delta F^\circ = RT \ln K \qquad$ (page 208)

then $\qquad\qquad -\Delta F^\circ = n\mathsf{F}\,\Delta E_0' \tag{14}$

where ΔF° is the standard free energy of the reaction, n is the number of electrons (or hydrogens) involved, F is the faraday (96,500 coulombs), and $\Delta E_0'$ is the difference between the E_0' values of the two systems. The units of $\mathsf{F}\,\Delta E_0'$ are coulomb-volts or joules, which are readily converted to the usual units of free energy since 4.18 joules equal 1 g.-cal. The value obtained for ΔF° is that for the oxidation of one mole of reductant. Consider as an example the oxidation of malic acid to oxaloacetic acid by cytochrome c under circumstances such that equimolar concentrations always exist of each of the reactants of the two systems. Since the E_0' values are -0.17 volt and 0.2 volt, respectively (Table 17.1), then

$$\Delta F^\circ = -n\mathsf{F}\,\Delta E_0' = \frac{-2 \times 96,500 \times [0.2 - (-0.17)]}{4.18} = -18,246 \text{ cal.}$$

The oxidation of one mole of malic acid by cytochrome c, under these circumstances, results in the release of 18,246 cal., which could then be available under physiological circumstances for doing useful work. Were the malic acid oxidized by molecular oxygen, 45,715 cal. would be released, since E_0' for the reduction of oxygen is $+0.82$ volt.

"HIGH-ENERGY COMPOUNDS"

Earlier in this chapter it was stated that within cells a mechanism exists by means of which the free energy available from oxidative reactions may be utilized to drive endergonic processes. This is accomplished largely by trapping this energy through the formation of a special class of phosphate compounds. The significance of phosphates in energy metabolism was elucidated over a period of about 40 years. Present concepts are due largely to Meyerhof, Lipmann, and Kalckar.

As the intermediate phosphate esters in alcoholic fermentation and in the anaerobic glycolysis of muscle (Chap. 20) were identified, Meyerhof and his colleagues determined the equilibrium for the hydrolysis of each compound.

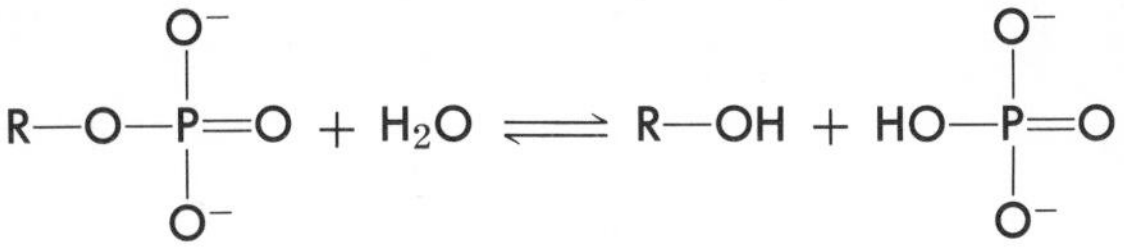

$$\text{R}-\text{O}-\overset{\overset{\displaystyle O^-}{|}}{\underset{\underset{\displaystyle O^-}{|}}{P}}=O + H_2O \rightleftharpoons \text{R}-\text{OH} + \text{HO}-\overset{\overset{\displaystyle O^-}{|}}{\underset{\underset{\displaystyle O^-}{|}}{P}}=O$$

$$K = \frac{[\text{ROH}][\text{HPO}_4^=]}{[\text{ROPO}_3^=]}$$

As stated previously (page 304), from equilibrium data it is possible to calculate the free-energy change in such hydrolyses.

In general, two classes of organic phosphates were found to occur in metabolism. One group consists of simple esters of which α-glycerophosphate and glucose 6-phosphate are typical. These are stable and, in the laboratory, can be hydrolyzed only by prolonged digestion with hot acid.

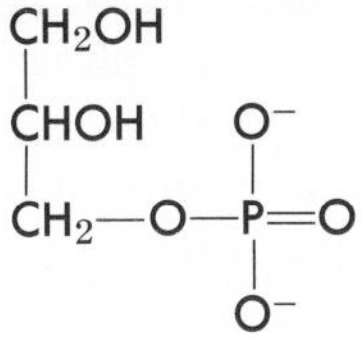

α-Glycerophosphate 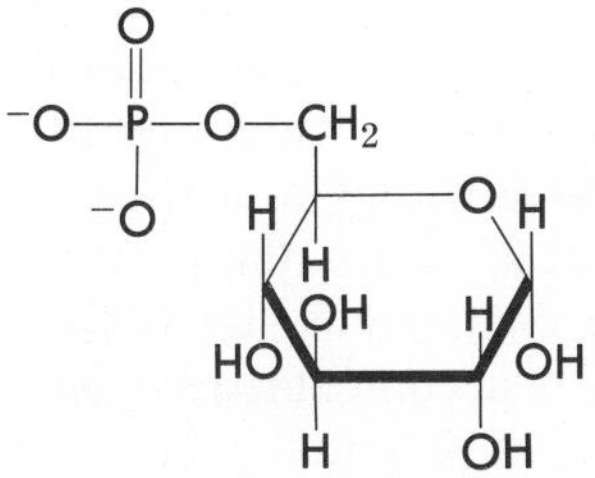   Glucose 6-phosphate

For the hydrolysis of these esters, $\Delta F°$ is -1000 to -4000 cal. per mole. Numerous esters of this type occur in intermediary metabolism. The second class contains fewer representatives and consists of those organic phosphates whose hydrolysis occurs with a $\Delta F°$ between $-5,000$ and $-11,000$ cal. per mole. These are relatively unstable and may be quantitatively hydrolyzed by $1N$ H^+ in a few minutes. Examples of such "high-energy phosphate-containing compounds" are the following:

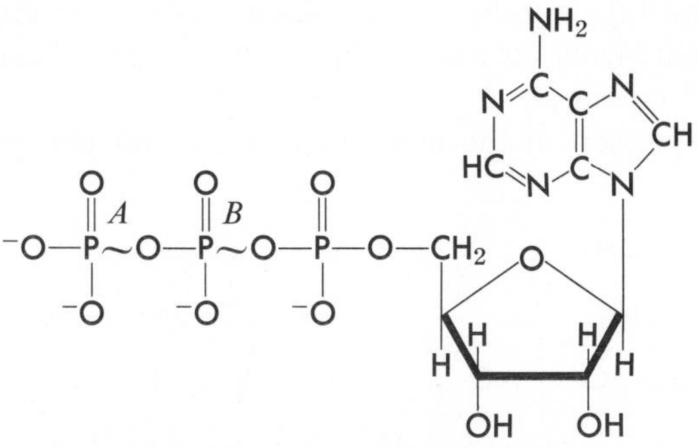

Adenosine triphosphate (ATP)

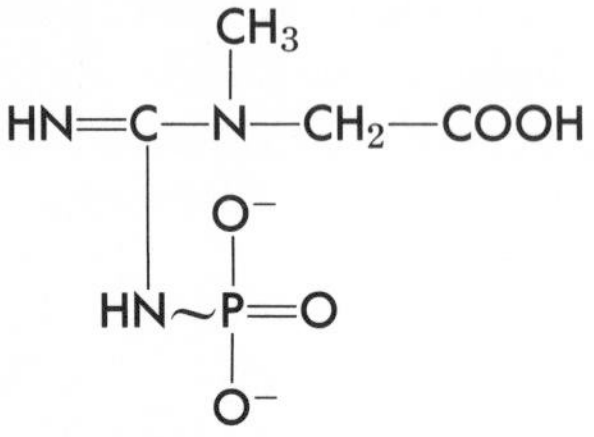

$$HN{=}C{-}N{-}CH_2{-}COOH$$

with CH₃ on the carbon and $HN{\sim}P{=}O$ group (with O^- and O^-)

Creatine phosphate

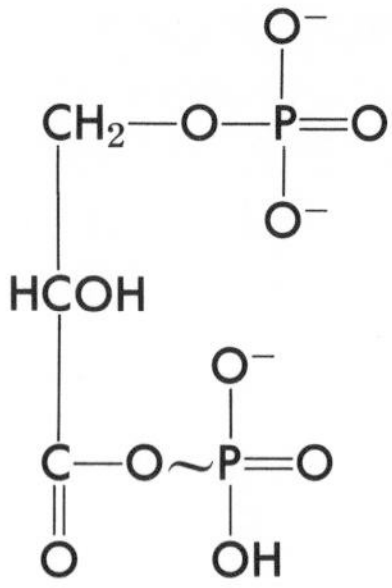

$$CH_2{-}O{-}P{=}O$$ (with O^-, O^-)

$$HCOH$$

$$C{-}O{\sim}P{=}O$$ (with O^-, OH, and O)

1,3-Diphosphoglyceric acid

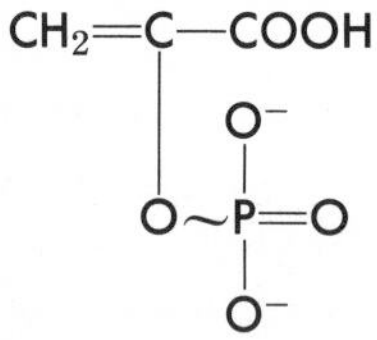

$$CH_2{=}C{-}COOH$$

$$O{\sim}P{=}O$$ (with O^-, O^-)

Phosphoenolpyruvic acid

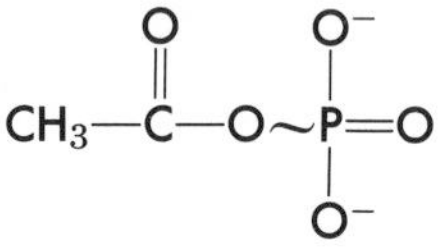

$$CH_3{-}C{-}O{\sim}P{=}O$$ (with O, O^-, O^-)

Acetyl phosphate

All known high-energy phosphate compounds fall into one of three classes: acid anhydrides, phosphate esters of enols, or derivatives of phosphamic acid $R{-}NH{-}PO_3H$. It will be recalled that acid anhydrides, *e.g.*, P_2O_5, acetylchloride, etc., are unstable in water and hydrolyze rapidly, with liberation of considerable heat. The free energy of hydrolysis, $\Delta F°$, for phosphoenolpyruvate ($-11,000$ cal. per mole at 25°C.) is the greatest of all known naturally occurring high-energy phosphate compounds. By convention, the symbol $\sim$ denotes the bond whose hydrolysis is accompanied by the release of a large amount of free energy. The relatively high potential energy that is made available on hydrolysis is a property of the structure of the phosphate compound as a whole and does not merely reside in the P—O bond which is ruptured by hydrolysis. Indeed, there is no single adequate explanation for the relatively large values for $\Delta F°$ for the hydrolysis of the diverse high-energy phosphate compounds in biological systems. Two pertinent factors appear significant in most instances. (1) The formation of creatine phosphate markedly reduces the total number of resonant forms of both the creatine and phosphate moieties. Since, of two possible states, that exhibiting the greater number of resonant forms is the more stable, energy must be supplied if a reaction is to proceed in which the number of resonating forms is minimized, *i.e.*, formation of creatine phosphate from creatine $+ P_i$. (2) Hydrolysis of many of the "energy-rich" phosphate compounds, at pH 7, results in an increase of charge. This is illustrated by comparison of the hydrolysis of glycerol phosphate and of acetyl phosphate.

(*a*)
$$CH_2OH$$
$$CHOH$$
$$CH_2{-}O{-}P{=}O \text{ (with } O^-, O^-) + H_2O \rightleftharpoons$$
$$CH_2OH$$
$$CHOH + HO{-}P{=}O \text{ (with } O^-, O^-)$$
$$CH_2OH$$

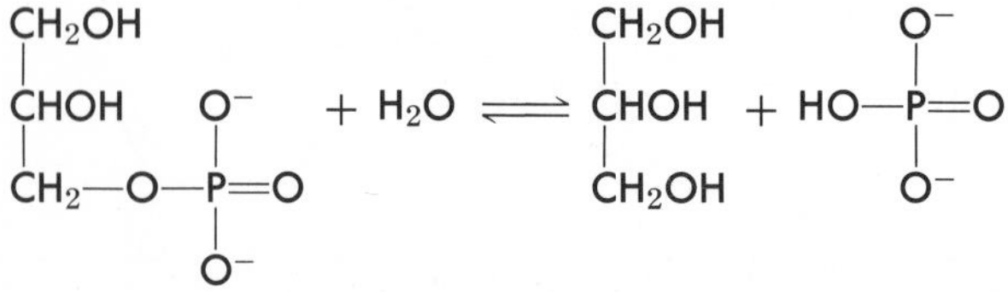

(b)
$$CH_3-\overset{\overset{\displaystyle O}{\|}}{C}-O\sim\overset{\overset{\displaystyle O^-}{|}}{\underset{\underset{\displaystyle O^-}{|}}{P}}=O + H_2O \rightleftharpoons CH_3-\overset{\overset{\displaystyle O}{\|}}{C} + HO-\overset{\overset{\displaystyle O^-}{|}}{\underset{\underset{\displaystyle O^-}{|}}{P}}=O + H^+$$

It will be seen that hydrolysis of a mole of acetyl phosphate results in formation of a proton. Removal of the latter by the buffered medium makes a large contribution to the total change in free energy, driving the reaction, as represented above, to the right. Thus, the relative instability of the energy-rich phosphate compounds appears in large measure to be due to the restriction imposed on the possible number of resonating forms by formation of the phosphate bond and the relative unlikelihood of its formation from similarly charged molecules.

Other instances of high-energy compounds, in the sense that the free-energy change accompanying their hydrolysis is in the range $-6,000$ to $-11,000$ cal. per mole, are found in living systems. Particularly noteworthy are acyl thioesters, i.e., compounds of the general structure $R-CO-S-R'$ such as the fatty acyl esters of coenzyme A (page 440) and amino acyl esters of the ribose moiety of nucleic acids (page 308), as well as sulfonium compounds of the general structure $R-\overset{+}{\underset{\underset{\displaystyle R''}{|}}{S}}-R'$ (page 504).

Phosphate Transfer. The intervention of phosphate in metabolic processes was established by Harden and Young (page 370) in their classical studies of fermentation by yeast extracts. Many studies of metabolism in contracting muscle demonstrated that the energy for contraction, under anaerobic conditions, is in some manner supplied by the glycolytic process converting glycogen to lactic acid. This process is described in detail in Chap. 20. Lundsgaard, however, observed that contraction also proceeded in muscles poisoned with iodoacetate, an inhibitor which prevents glycolysis. Further, these muscles continued to contract until their supply of creatine phosphate was exhausted by conversion to creatine and P_i. Lohmann then demonstrated that muscle does not possess an enzyme system for catalysis of this reaction unless adenine nucleotides are present; he formulated the process as follows:

(a) Creatine $\sim$ phosphate + ADP $\longrightarrow$ creatine + ATP $\Delta F° = -1500$ cal.
(b) ATP $\longrightarrow$ ADP + phosphate $\Delta F° = -7000$ cal.

Net: Creatine $\sim$ phosphate $\longrightarrow$ creatine + phosphate $\Delta F° = -8500$ cal.

Thus, the reaction in which ATP is "hydrolyzed" seemed to be the immediate source of energy for the contractile process. This concept has since been expanded: *ATP is the immediate source of energy for a great number of endergonic biological systems.*

The mechanism by which an exergonic reaction can drive an endergonic process may now be stated. Consider the synthesis of an ester and the simultaneous apparent hydrolysis of ATP to AMP + PP_i.

(a) RCOOH + HO—R' $\rightleftharpoons$ RCOOR' + H_2O $\Delta F° = +4000$ cal.
(b) ATP + H_2O $\rightleftharpoons$ AMP + PP_i $\Delta F° = -6000$ cal.

Net: RCOOH + HO—R' + ATP $\longrightarrow$ RCOOR' + AMP + PP_i $\Delta F° = -2000$ cal.

Reaction (*b*) can be utilized to drive (*a*) *only* if they are coupled by way of a common intermediate, as in the following hypothetical case:

(*c*) **RCOOH + ATP $\rightleftharpoons$ RCOO—AMP + PP$_i$** $\Delta F° = 0$
(*d*) **RCOO—AMP + HO—R′ $\rightleftharpoons$ RCOOR′ + AMP** $\Delta F° = -2000$ cal.

Net: RCOOH + HO—R′ + ATP $\longrightarrow$ RCOOR′ + AMP + PP$_i$ $\Delta F° = -2000$ cal.

The intermediate, RCOO—AMP, is an anhydride of the carboxylic acid and the phosphate of adenylic acid.

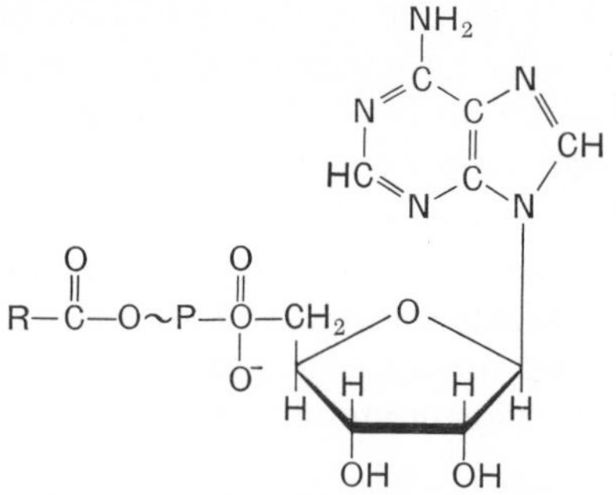

An acyl adenylate (RCOO—AMP)

There are numerous instances of such reactions in metabolism (*e.g.*, pages 316 and 440).

In the formation of an acyl adenylate, it is the bond between the pyrophosphate and adenylate moieties of ATP which is ruptured (bond *B*, shown on page 305), with pyrophosphate, rather than orthophosphate, appearing as the final product. $\Delta F°$ for hydrolytic cleavage of this bond appears to be significantly lower than that for hydrolysis of the other high-energy bond of ATP (bond *A*, page 305). From the relatively small change in ΔF, it will be recognized that synthesis of the organic ester by this mechanism can proceed but is not strongly favored. Pyrophosphate appears to have relatively few metabolic fates; most prominent among these is hydrolysis to orthophosphate catalyzed by *pyrophosphatases* present in all cells. The $\Delta F°$ for pyrophosphate hydrolysis is -7000 cal.; therefore, the immediate hydrolysis of the pyrophosphate formed in the reaction sequence involved in ester synthesis effectively renders the latter irreversible. Instances of processes in which pyrophosphate hydrolysis renders irreversible an otherwise reversible process are nucleotide (page 566), polynucleotide (page 604), and peptide bond (page 599) syntheses and fatty acid activation (page 440).

Enzymes that catalyze transfer of phosphate from ATP to an acceptor are designated *kinases* and may be considered in two categories. Since ΔF for the hydrolysis of each of the various high-energy compounds is of the same magnitude, kinases catalyzing transfer among these compounds may operate readily in both directions and actually do so in metabolism, *e.g.*,

ADP + creatine phosphate $\rightleftharpoons$ ATP + creatine $\Delta F° = -1500$ cal., $K = 10$

In contrast, transfer with formation of low-energy compounds may be expected to proceed significantly in the forward direction only.

ATP + glucose $\longrightarrow$ ADP + glucose 6-phosphate $\Delta F° = -4500$ cal., $K = 4000$

Lipmann suggested that the unique merit of phosphate esters, aside from requirements of enzymic specificity, resides in the fact that phosphate confers kinetic stability on thermodynamically labile molecules. Thus, while $\Delta F°$ for the hydrolysis of acetic anhydride, acetyl phosphate, and inorganic pyrophosphate are all of the same magnitude, they are stable in water for a few seconds, several hours, and years, respectively. Since the energy of oxidation is employed to synthesize an energy-rich molecule whose function is to drive endergonic reactions, it is of a considerable advantage that this intermediate, ATP, is stable in water, since its simple hydrolysis would be wasteful and pointless in the biological economy.

It should be noted that the various values for free-energy changes cited above have been for $\Delta F°$, the free-energy change when each of the reactants is in the standard equimolar state. Since the actual free-energy change is defined by

$$-\Delta F = RT \ln K - RT \ln \frac{[c][d]}{[a][b]}$$

then, if the reactants in a biological system are maintained in a steady state remote from equilibrium, the true value for ΔF may be significantly greater or less than $\Delta F°$.

From these facts a basic concept emerges: to supply energy for endergonic biological processes, the respiratory process must, in some manner, be coupled with the synthesis of energy-rich phosphate compounds, specifically ATP. The latter is the "unit of currency" in metabolic energy transformations. The equation describing the over-all oxidation of glucose may now be stated as

$C_6H_{12}O_6 + xP_i + xADP \longrightarrow 6CO_2 + 6H_2O + xATP +$ unavailable energy

The fraction of the total ΔF for the oxidation of glucose, or any other metabolic fuel, which is employed for ATP synthesis represents the true efficiency of the cellular respiration process, insofar as its objective is to supply energy for endergonic processes. $\Delta F°$ for ATP synthesis is about $+7000$ cal. per mole. Under physiological conditions, the true ΔF is about $+8000$ cal. per mole. Since $\Delta F°$ for complete oxidation of one mole of glucose is $-686,000$ cal., this could *potentially* provide energy for the synthesis of about 85 moles of ATP from ADP and P_i. However, simultaneous collisions between many molecules are unlikely, and it is apparent that if the combustion of a molecule of glucose is to result in the formation of a large number of ATP molecules, the total oxidation process must be accomplished by the summation of many individual oxidations. The manner in which this is achieved by coupling ATP synthesis with oxidations occurring in steps is considered in the following chapter.

REFERENCES

Books

Bray, H. G., and White, K., "Kinetics and Thermodynamics in Biochemistry," Academic Press, Inc., New York, 1957.

Clark, W. M., "Topics in Physical Chemistry," 2d ed., The Williams and Wilkins Company, Baltimore, 1951.

Howett, L. F., "Oxidation-Reduction Potentials in Bacteriology and Biochemistry," 6th ed., E. and S. Livingston, Ltd., Edinburgh, 1950.

Ingram, D. J. E., "Free Radicals as Studied by Electron Spin Resonance," Academic Press, Inc., New York, 1958.

Krebs,, H. A., and Kornberg, H. L., "Energy Transformations in Living Matter," Springer-Verlag OHG, Berlin, 1957.

Review Articles

Axelrod, B., Enzymatic Phosphate Transfer, *Advances in Enzymol.,* **17,** 159–188, 1956.

Bock, R. M., Adenine Nucleotides and Properties of Pyrophosphate Compounds, in P. D. Boyer, H. Lardy, and K. Myrbäck, eds., "The Enzymes," vol. II, pp. 3–38, Academic Press, Inc., New York, 1960.

Ennor, A. H., and Morrison, J. F., Biochemistry of the Phosphagens and Related Guanidines, *Physiol. Revs.,* **38,** 631–674, 1958.

George, P., and Griffith, S. J., Electron Transfer and Enzyme Catalysis, in P. D. Boyer, H. Lardy, and K. Myrbäck, eds. "The Enzymes," vol. I, pp. 347–390, Academic Press, Inc., New York, 1959.

George, P., and Rutman, R. J., The 'High Energy Phosphate Bond' Concept, in J. A. V. Butler and B. Katz, eds., "Progress in Biophysics and Biophysical Chemistry," vol. X, pp. 1–53, Pergamon Press, New York, 1960.

Huennekens, F. M., and Whiteley, H. R., Phosphoric Acid Anhydrides and Other Energy-rich Compounds, in M. Florkin and H. S. Mason, eds., "Comparative Biochemistry," vol. I, pp. 107–180, Academic Press, Inc., New York, 1960.

Leach, S. J., The Mechanism of Enzymic Oxidoreduction, *Advances in Enzymol.,* **15,** 1–48, 1954.

Lipmann, F., Biosynthetic Mechanisms, *Harvey Lectures,* **44,** 99–123, 1948–1949.

Michaelis, L., Fundamentals of Oxidation and Reduction, in D. E. Green, ed., "Currents in Biochemical Research," pp. 207–227, Interscience Publishers, Inc., New York, 1946.

Pardee, A. B., and Ingraham, L. L., Free Energy and Entropy in Metabolism, in D. M. Greenberg, ed., "Metabolic Pathways," vol. I, pp. 1–40, Academic Press, Inc., New York, 1960.

Pullman, B., and Pullman, A., Electronic Structure of Energy-rich Phosphates, *Radiation Research,* Suppl. **2,** pp. 160–181, 1960.

18. Biological Oxidations

Citric Acid Cycle. The Mitochondrion. Electron Transport. Oxidative Phosphorylation

The energy needs of living cells are met by the process of *respiration*, with oxidation of organic compounds by molecular oxygen and liberation of free energy. Respiration is accomplished by a highly ordered array of enzymes, organized in *mitochondria*. The mitochondria receive from the cytoplasm oxidizable substrates, such as pyruvic or fatty acids. An appropriate group of enzymes catalyzes a series of consecutive transformations, including dehydrogenations, of these substrates, resulting in their complete oxidation to CO_2 and H_2O. The electrons removed from the substrates during these oxidations flow through an organized arrangement of electron carriers, from the lowest to the highest potential, and thence to oxygen. In the course of this electron flow, much of the free energy thus made available is trapped by concurrent synthesis of ATP, the common form of energy utilizable in the endergonic processes of living cells. Thus, substrates, oxygen, ADP, and P_i enter the mitochondrion, and CO_2, H_2O, and ATP leave this structure. In this chapter we shall consider the enzymes and coenzymes required for dehydrogenation of the organic substrates, the major reaction sequence in which these dehydrogenations occur (the citric acid cycle), the organized array of electron carriers which convey electrons from the dehydrogenated substrates to O_2, and the means by which the free energy of this process is harnessed to the synthesis of ATP.

OXIDATIVE ENZYMES, COENZYMES, AND RESPIRATORY CARRIERS

Biological oxidations are catalyzed by enzymes which function in conjunction with a group of coenzymes and electron carriers. These substances and their properties and mechanism of action are presented, in some detail, in the following chapter. For appreciation of the subject matter of the present chapter, the following summary may suffice.

Each oxidative enzyme consists of a specific protein which functions in conjunction with a coenzyme or prosthetic group. The protein moiety confers substrate specificity on the system, activates both substrate and prosthetic group, and, frequently, alters the redox potential of the latter, which invariably participates in the reaction. Although there is a great variety of these proteins, there are only a few coenzymes, and each enzyme is specific not only for its substrate but for its coenzyme as well. Only rarely does this type of system catalyze a direct reaction in which the metabolite (MH_2) reacts with O_2, as would appear from the over-all reaction,

$$MH_2 + \tfrac{1}{2}O_2 \longrightarrow M + H_2O$$

Rather, a transfer of electrons occurs from substrate to coenzyme

$$MH_2 + Co \longrightarrow M + CoH_2$$

with subsequent oxidation of the reduced coenzyme.

Coenzymes of Respiration. The coenzyme most frequently employed as acceptor of electrons from the substrate is *diphosphopyridine nucleotide* (DPN^+).

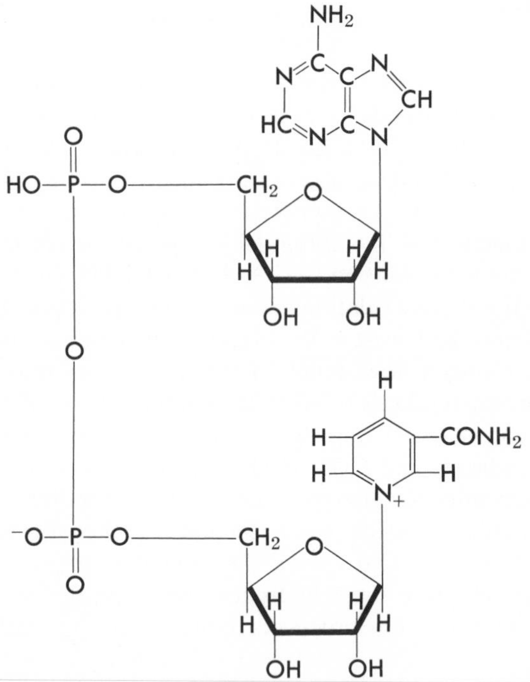

Diphosphopyridine nucleotide (DPN)

When bound to the appropriate site on a dehydrogenase protein, a hydride ion is transferred to the nicotinamide moiety and a proton is liberated into the medium.

$$MH_2 + DPN^+ \rightleftharpoons M + DPNH + H^+$$

The details of this process are described in the following chapter. Less frequently, the coenzyme may be a phosphorylated derivative of DPN^+, *triphosphopyridine nucleotide* (TPN^+) (page 338), which functions in the same manner. In either case, the reduced coenzyme is not metabolized further on the same enzymic surface. Both the oxidized substrate and the reduced pyridine nucleotide (DPNH or TPNH) must then dissociate from the dehydrogenase. DPNH and TPNH are not autoxidizable in the presence of O_2; reoxidation to DPN^+ or TPN^+ requires the participation of a second group of enzymes, to be described below.

It may be noted that the above-described pyridine nucleotides have been abbreviated as DPN⁺ and TPN⁺, respectively, since their discovery. Because DPN⁺ is not a nucleotide of "diphosphopyridine," because this name does not indicate the presence either of nicotinamide or of adenine, and because this nomenclature is not in keeping with that used for many related compounds, an International Commission, in 1961, suggested that these two coenzymes be designated as *nicotinamide adenine dinucleotide* (NAD) and *nicotinamide adenine dinucleotide phosphate* (NADP). Their reduced forms, in this convention, are denoted as $NADH_2$ and $NADPH_2$, respectively. Both groups of terms are in current use. Until it is determined which terminology achieves general acceptance, it has seemed appropriate to continue the use of DPN and TPN in this textbook.

A second, large group of oxidative enzymes employ as cofactor either of two derivatives of the vitamin riboflavin (Chap. 55). These are flavin mononucleotide (FMN) and flavin adenine dinucleotide (FAD), respectively. In contrast to the ready dissociation of pyridine nucleotides from dehydrogenases, the two flavin nucleotides are invariably rather tightly bound, the combination being termed a *flavoprotein*. Many flavoproteins function by transfer of electrons from an organic substrate to the riboflavin component of a flavin coenzyme. Of particular interest is mitochondrial *DPNH dehydrogenase,* which catalyzes reduction of its flavin coenzyme by a reduced pyridine nucleotide, as shown below.

$H^+ + DPNH +$

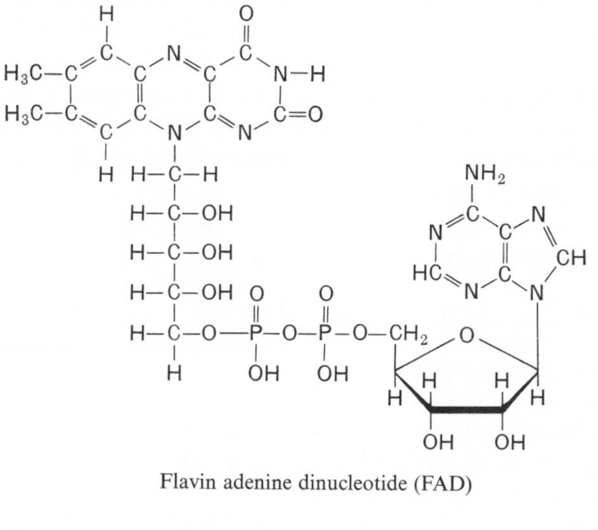

Flavin adenine dinucleotide (FAD)

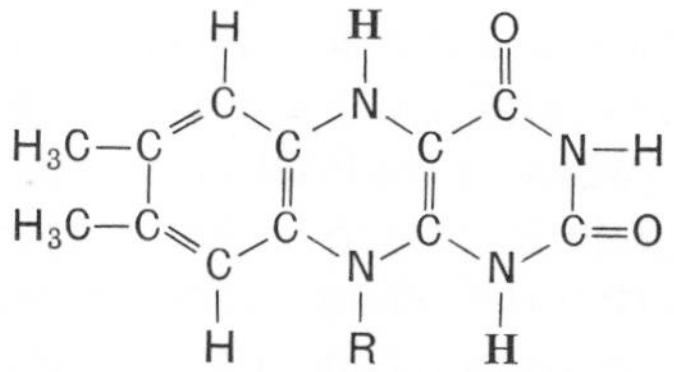

$+ DPN^+$

(R = remainder of molecule, above)

FADH₂

The fate of the reduced flavoprotein will be considered later in this chapter. It may be noted in the above structure that the riboflavin moiety is a derivative of D-ribitol whereas the adenosine moiety is a β-ribofuranoside.

Of great significance in respiration is a group of electron carriers which, properly speaking, are not enzymes. One of these is the extremely hydrophobic compound called *ubiquinone* or coenzyme Q (page 326).

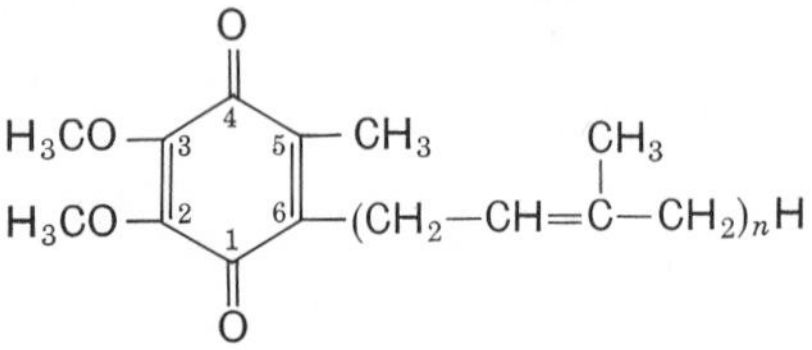

Ubiquinone

As obtained from diverse biological sources, n in the above formula varies from 6 in some yeasts to 10 in mammalian liver. Ubiquinone forms a relatively stable semi-quinone on partial reduction and hence could participate in both 1- or 2-electron transfers.

All the other known electron carriers in mammalian cells are members of the group of *cytochromes*. These are hemoproteins (page 199) varying in their proteins, the exact nature of the side chains of the metalloporphyrin, and the mode of attachment of the heme-like group to the protein. The cytochromes are most conveniently recognized by the absorption spectra of their reduced forms. Of the group, cytochrome b is the member of lowest potential, which increases through c_1 and c to cytochrome oxidase. The latter is, itself, a hemoprotein which, like the other members, undergoes alternate reduction and reoxidation of the iron constituent during normal function. Uniquely, the ferrous form of this cytochrome can reduce molecular oxygen. Indeed, it is the only component of mitochondria that can do this readily, and reoxidation of this cytochrome is the predominant mechanism for reduction of oxygen in mammalian tissues.

CITRIC ACID CYCLE—GENERAL CONSIDERATIONS

Although many organic compounds are oxidized by respiring tissues, one group of reactions may be set apart as the major reaction sequence which provides electrons to the transport system that accomplishes reduction of oxygen while generating ATP. This series of reactions is known as the *citric acid cycle,* the *tricarboxylic acid cycle,* or the *Krebs cycle.*

Figure 18.1 presents the major intermediates of the citric acid cycle. The reaction sequence may be pictured as commencing (reaction 1) by condensation of a 2-carbon acetyl residue with oxaloacetic acid to yield the 6-carbon tricarboxylic acid, citric acid. By successive loss and recapture of water, this compound is rearranged into isocitric acid, which is oxidized to oxalosuccinic acid; this, in turn, is decarboxylated to α-ketoglutaric acid. Succinic acid is formed from this last compound by oxidative decarboxylation, and then, by an oxidation, a hydration, and a second oxidation, a molecule of oxaloacetic acid is again formed.

For each revolution of the cycle, one mole of acetyl is consumed and two moles of CO_2 are evolved. Oxaloacetic acid, which is utilized in the initial conden-

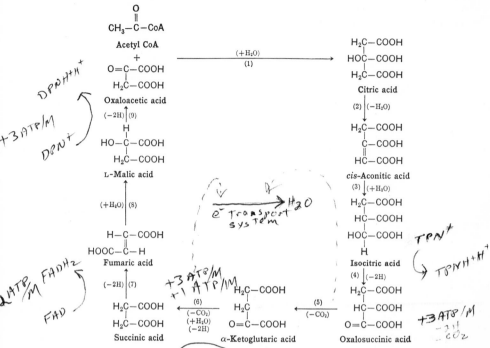

FIG. 18.1. Major intermediates of the citric acid cycle. The numbers in parentheses are for reference to identify these reactions in the text.

sation, is regenerated, permitting the process to operate in a continuous manner as long as acetyl continues to enter the cycle and hydrogen atoms and CO_2 are removed. Four of the individual reactions are dehydrogenations; the net accomplishment of the cycle, per revolution, may be represented as follows.

$$CH_3COOH + 2O_2 \longrightarrow 2CO_2 + 2H_2O + \text{energy}$$

Some aspects of the individual reactions may now be considered.

CITRIC ACID CYCLE—INDIVIDUAL REACTIONS

Acetyl Coenzyme A. Much of the succeeding chapters dealing with the metabolism of carbohydrates, lipids, and amino acids will relate to their transformation into products that can enter the tricarboxylic acid cycle. The most important of these products, quantitatively, is "active acetyl," the acetyl thioester of coenzyme A. This coenzyme is composed of adenosine 3'-phosphate-5'-pyrophosphate, bound in ester linkage to the vitamin pantothenic acid, which, in turn, is attached in amide linkage to β-mercaptoethylamine. The acetyl group considered here is linked to the sulfur of coenzyme A as a thioester. In this text, coenzyme A is frequently abbreviated as either CoA or CoA—SH. The —SH shown in the latter abbreviation refers to the sulfhydryl group of coenzyme A and is not intended to represent an additional sulfhydryl group.

Acetate in the reactive form of acetyl CoA is utilized in a variety of biological processes. As will be seen subsequently, acetyl CoA is the precursor for biosynthe-

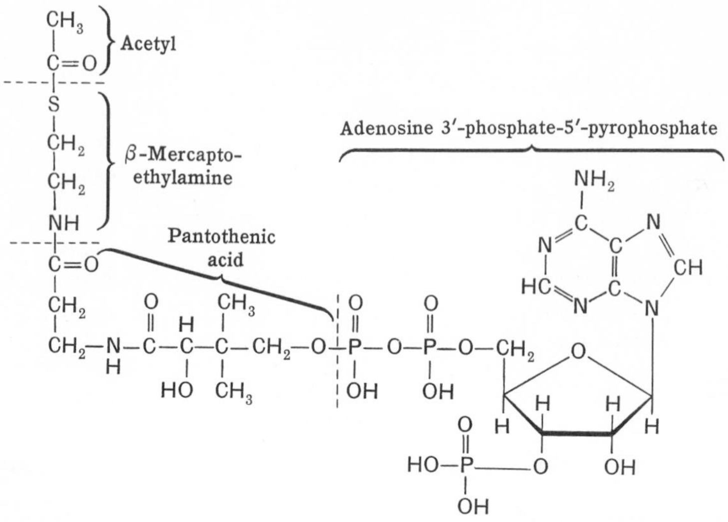

Acetyl coenzyme A (acetyl CoA)

sis of fatty acids and sterols, can give rise to acetoacetic acid, and is the biological acetylating agent in the synthesis of such compounds as acetylcholine, acetyl-sulfanilamide, etc.

Acetyl CoA may be synthesized by organisms from acetic acid itself. In view of the relatively small quantities of acetic acid normally available to mammalian tissues, this may be, quantitatively, a relatively unimportant process. However, by virtue of this activation of acetate, biochemists have had experimental access to studies of the many fates of acetyl CoA. The activation requires adenosine triphosphate (ATP) and yields adenylic acid (AMP) and inorganic pyrophosphate (PP_i). Although catalyzed by a single enzyme, the reaction appears to proceed in two steps.

(a)	ATP + acetate $\rightleftharpoons$ acetyl-AMP + PP_i
(b)	Acetyl-AMP + CoA $\rightleftharpoons$ AMP + acetyl CoA
Sum:	ATP + acetate + CoA $\rightleftharpoons$ AMP + PP_i + acetyl CoA

Acetyladenylate is the mixed anhydride of the carboxyl of acetic acid and the phosphate of adenylic acid. Its structure is that shown on page 308 for the general form of an acyl adenylate. No *free* acetyladenylate (acetyl-AMP) appears during the reaction. This is an invariant property of all systems in which there is an acyl adenylate as intermediate. It is bound tightly to the locus on the enzyme where it is formed, and the subsequent reaction occurs with this enzyme-bound intermediate. This reaction sequence seems likely since reaction (b) is catalyzed by the enzyme with CoA and synthetic AMP-acetate as substrates and since the enzyme catalyzes exchange of $PP_i{}^{32}$ with ATP, *i.e.*, reversal of reaction (a), but only in the presence of acetate. Similar enzyme-bound acyl adenylates are formed as intermediates in the activation of long-chain fatty acids (Chap. 22) and of amino acids (Chap. 30).

It is noteworthy that, as an acyl thioester, acetyl CoA is a "high-energy compound" since its simple hydrolysis at pH 7

$$CH_3CO\!-\!SCoA + HOH \rightleftharpoons CH_3COO^- + HS\!-\!CoA + H^+$$

proceeds with a free-energy change, $\Delta F°$, of approximately $-10,000$ cal. per mole. This is the energy which permits the functioning of acetyl CoA in biological acetylations and which drives the formation of citric acid.

Origin of Acetyl Coenzyme A. As seen in Fig. 18.1, the source of acetyl CoA is essentially irrelevant to the cyclic process here considered, but because acetyl CoA is the fuel that is oxidized by this process, it is appropriate to examine its origin. The two major sources derive from the metabolism of glucose (Chap. 20) and fatty acids (Chap. 22). The process of glycolysis (Chap. 20) consists of a series of transformations by which each glucose molecule is transformed, in the cell cytoplasm, into two molecules of *pyruvic acid.* The latter may then enter a mitochondrion, where it is oxidized according to the following over-all equation.

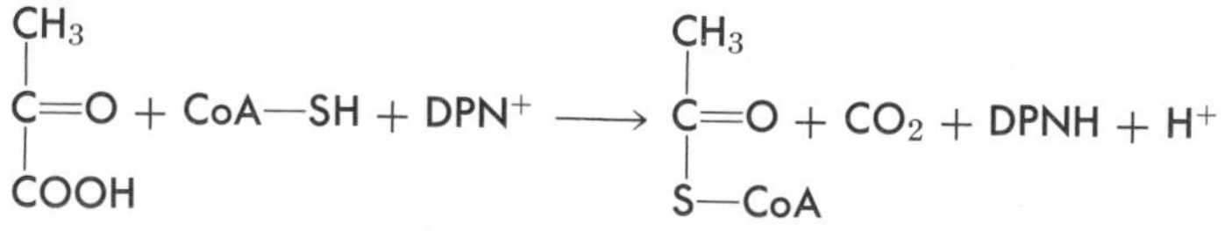

$$
\begin{array}{l}
CH_3 \\
|\\
C\!=\!O + CoA\!-\!SH + DPN^+ \longrightarrow \\
|\\
COOH
\end{array}
\qquad
\begin{array}{l}
CH_3 \\
|\\
C\!=\!O + CO_2 + DPNH + H^+ \\
|\\
S\!-\!CoA
\end{array}
$$

This process requires the cooperation of several enzymes and four cofactors present in a tightly knit complex, the sum of which constitutes *pyruvic acid dehydrogenase.* The entire process proceeds with a favorable free-energy change; ΔF for formation of acetyl CoA and DPNH in the manner shown is about -8000 cal.

The initial event is a reaction between pyruvic acid and *thiamine pyrophosphate*† (ThPP), the pyrophosphate ester of vitamin B_1, resulting in evolution of CO_2 and formation of a compound that serves as "active acetaldehyde," *α-hydroxyethyl thiamine pyrophosphate.*

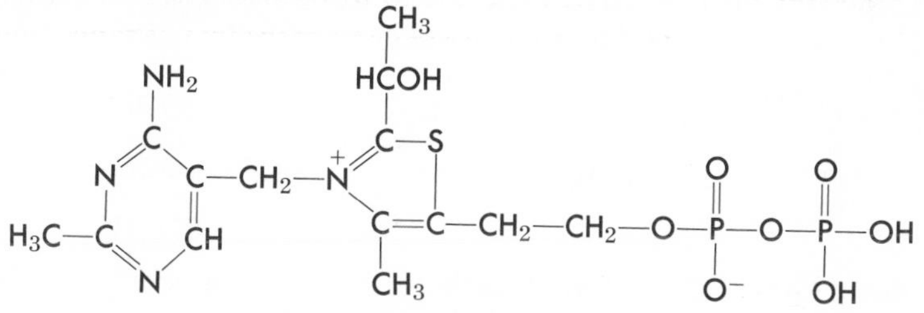

α-Hydroxyethyl thiamine pyrophosphate

On the same enzymic surface, the "active acetaldehyde" is transferred to *lipoic acid.* The latter is present as an amide, apparently linked to the ε-amino group of a lysine residue of the enzyme. Schematically, the reaction is as shown on the next page. Effectively, the aldehyde is oxidized to acetic acid while the lipoamide disulfide is reduced to a disulfhydryl compound. Still on the same enzymic surface, the

† Because thiamine pyrophosphate was originally encountered as the coenzyme of the yeast enzyme which catalyzes decarboxylation of pyruvic acid to acetaldehyde and CO_2, it was designated "cocarboxylase" and this term was used in the biochemical literature for many years. However, since pyridoxal phosphate is the coenzyme for enzymes which catalyze decarboxylation of amino acids, and biotin is the coenzyme for many enzymes catalyzing carboxylation reactions, the term cocarboxylase is not used in this text.

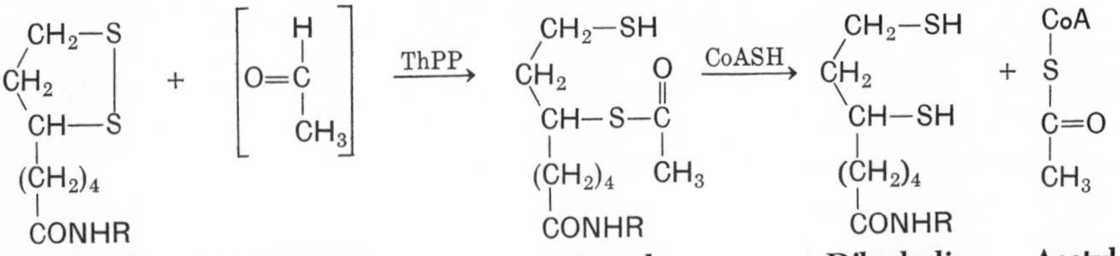

$$\underset{\substack{\text{Lipoamide}}}{\begin{array}{l}\text{CH}_2\text{--S}\\|\\\text{CH}_2\\|\\\text{CH--S}\\|\\(\text{CH}_2)_4\\|\\\text{CONHR}\end{array}} + \underset{\substack{\text{"Active}\\\text{acetaldehyde"}}}{\left[\begin{array}{c}\text{H}\\|\\\text{O}=\text{C}\\|\\\text{CH}_3\end{array}\right]} \xrightarrow{\text{ThPP}} \underset{\substack{\text{Acetyl-}\\\text{lipoamide}}}{\begin{array}{l}\text{CH}_2\text{--SH}\\|\\\text{CH}_2\quad\ \ \text{O}\\|\qquad\ \|\\\text{CH--S--C}\\|\qquad\ \ |\\(\text{CH}_2)_4\ \ \text{CH}_3\\|\\\text{CONHR}\end{array}} \xrightarrow{\text{CoASH}} \underset{\substack{\text{Dihydrolip-}\\\text{oamide}}}{\begin{array}{l}\text{CH}_2\text{--SH}\\|\\\text{CH}_2\\|\\\text{CH--SH}\\|\\(\text{CH}_2)_4\\|\\\text{CONHR}\end{array}} + \underset{\substack{\text{Acetyl}\\\text{CoA}}}{\begin{array}{l}\text{CoA}\\|\\\text{S}\\|\\\text{C}=\text{O}\\|\\\text{CH}_3\end{array}}$$

acetyllipoamide is attacked by the sulfhydryl group of coenzyme A; the acetyl group is transferred to the thiol group of coenzyme A, liberating the disulfhydryl form of lipoamide.

At this stage, with respect to the pyruvic acid, the reaction is complete; it has been oxidized to acetyl CoA + CO_2. The thiamine pyrophosphate has also completed its catalytic cycle but the lipoamide, originally a disulfide, is in the disulfhydryl form. It is reoxidized, within the same complex, by a flavoprotein *lipoyl dehydrogenase* (page 347), which catalyzes the following reaction.

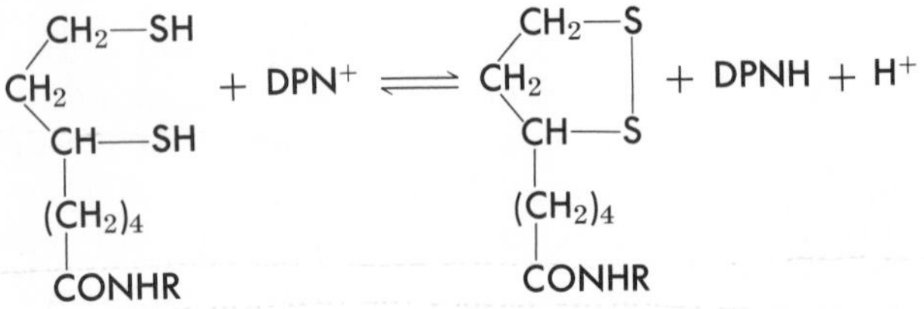

$$\begin{array}{l}\text{CH}_2\text{--SH}\\|\\\text{CH}_2\\|\\\text{CH--SH}\\|\\(\text{CH}_2)_4\\|\\\text{CONHR}\end{array} + \text{DPN}^+ \rightleftharpoons \begin{array}{l}\text{CH}_2\text{--S}\\|\qquad\ |\\\text{CH}_2\\|\\\text{CH--S}\\|\\(\text{CH}_2)_4\\|\\\text{CONHR}\end{array} + \text{DPNH} + \text{H}^+$$

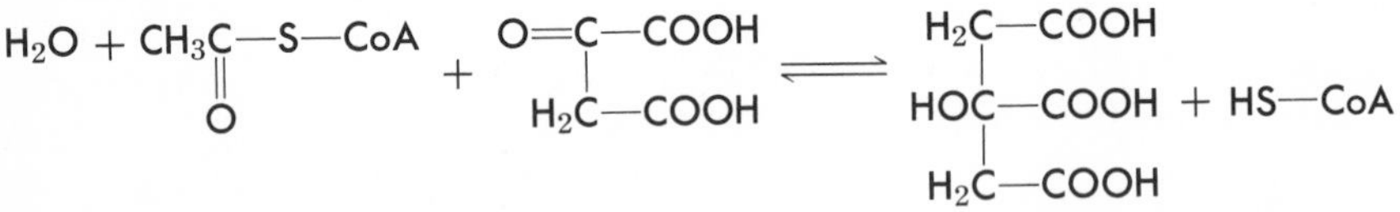

Acetyl CoA + Oxaloacetic Acid (Reaction 1, Fig. 18.1). The "condensing enzyme" catalyzing the formation of citric acid was isolated as a crystalline protein from pig heart by Ochoa and Stern. The equilibrium for the reaction

$$H_2O + \underset{\substack{\text{Acetyl CoA}}}{\text{CH}_3\text{C}\underset{\displaystyle\|\atop\displaystyle O}{}\text{--S--CoA}} + \underset{\substack{\text{Oxaloacetic}\\\text{acid}}}{\begin{array}{l}\text{O}=\text{C--COOH}\\|\\\text{H}_2\text{C--COOH}\end{array}} \rightleftharpoons \underset{\substack{\text{Citric acid}}}{\begin{array}{l}\text{H}_2\text{C--COOH}\\|\\\text{HOC--COOH}\\|\\\text{H}_2\text{C--COOH}\end{array}} + \underset{\substack{\text{CoA}}}{\text{HS--CoA}}$$

lies far to the right; under physiological conditions, $K = 5 \times 10^5$, $\Delta F = -7800$ cal.

In forming citric acid, acetyl CoA behaves as though the methyl rather than the carboxyl carbon of acetic acid is being activated. This is true of a number of reactions of acetyl CoA and is in contrast to such transacylating fates of acetyl CoA as the formation of acetylcholine, acetylsulfanilamide, and acetyl phosphate.

Biological Asymmetry of Citric Acid. Citric acid does not have an asymmetrically substituted carbon atom and is thus devoid of optical activity. It might therefore be anticipated, with reference to the reactions depicted in Fig. 18.1, that introduction of acetyl-1-C^{14} CoA into the sequence should give rise to α-ketoglutaric acid equally labeled in both carboxyl groups. The product actually recovered in such experiments proved to be labeled exclusively in the γ-carboxyl carbon.

$$CH_3C^{14}OOH$$
$$+$$
$$O=\overset{|}{C}-COOH \xrightarrow[1-5]{\text{reactions}}$$
$$H_2\overset{|}{C}-COOH$$

$$H_2\overset{\gamma}{C}-C^{14}OOH$$
$$H_2\overset{|}{C}\beta$$
$$O=\underset{\alpha}{\overset{|}{C}}-COOH$$

It was this observation which led Ogston to suggest that, as shown in Fig. 18.2, the two —CH₂COOH groups of citric acid are not truly geometrically equivalent and that this nonequivalence becomes apparent upon three-point attachment to an enzymic surface. This problem is considered in greater detail on page 245.

Citric, cis-Aconitic, and Isocitric Acids (Reactions 2 and 3, Fig. 18.1). The reversible interconversions of these three acids, involving only dehydration and hydration reactions, are catalyzed by one enzyme, *aconitase*. For maximal activity, the enzyme requires reduced glutathione or cysteine, and Fe^{++}.

$$\begin{array}{ccc}
H_2C-COOH & H_2C-COOH & H_2C-COOH \\
HOC-COOH & C-COOH & HC-COOH \\
H_2C-COOH & HC-COOH & HOC-COOH \\
& & H
\end{array}$$

$$\xrightarrow[(+H_2O)]{(-H_2O)} \qquad \xrightarrow[(-H_2O)]{(+H_2O)}$$

Citric acid   ***cis*-Aconitic acid**   **Isocitric acid**

At equilibrium the relative abundances of the three products are citric acid, 90 per cent; *cis*-aconitic acid, 4 per cent; isocitric acid, 6 per cent. Although citric acid is favored at equilibrium, in respiring tissues the reaction sequence proceeds to the right as isocitric acid is oxidized by isocitric acid dehydrogenase in the subsequent reaction. On the basis of steric considerations outlined above, it is likely that the attachment of citric acid to aconitase occurs at three points prior to dehydration to *cis*-aconitic acid.

Respiration is inhibited by the presence of fluoroacetic acid, with resultant accumulation of citric acid. Fluoroacetic acid condenses with oxaloacetic acid to give a fluoroanalogue of citric acid which competitively inhibits citric acid utiliza-

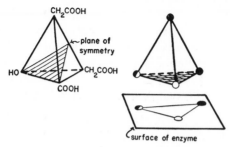

FIG. 18.2. Asymmetry apparent upon three-point attachment of citric acid to an enzymic surface. The central carbon atom of citric acid is in the center of the equilateral tetrahedron. Because of the plane of symmetry, the molecule in free solution is optically inactive. If the surface of the enzyme is asymmetric and forces attachment by —OH, —COOH, and —CH₂COOH groups in the manner shown, only one face of the tetrahedron (cross-hatched) can be accommodated on the enzymic surface. Hence, the two —CH₂OOH groups are not equivalent and only one attaches to the enzymic surface.

tion. The constitution of the fluorotricarboxylic acid that arises is not known, but it appears to differ from that of synthetic fluorocitric acid.

Formation of α-Ketoglutaric Acid (Reactions 4 and 5, Fig. 18.1). Isocitric acid is oxidized by transfer of electrons to a pyridine nucleotide. Animal tissues contain two *isocitric acid dehydrogenases,* specific, respectively, for transfer to TPN^+ and DPN^+. The DPN-dependent enzyme is present exclusively in mitochondria; the enzyme in cytoplasm is TPN-specific. However, it appears that mitochondria from some cells may also contain a TPN-specific enzyme. The fate of intra- and extra-mitochondrial TPNH will be considered later (page 327).

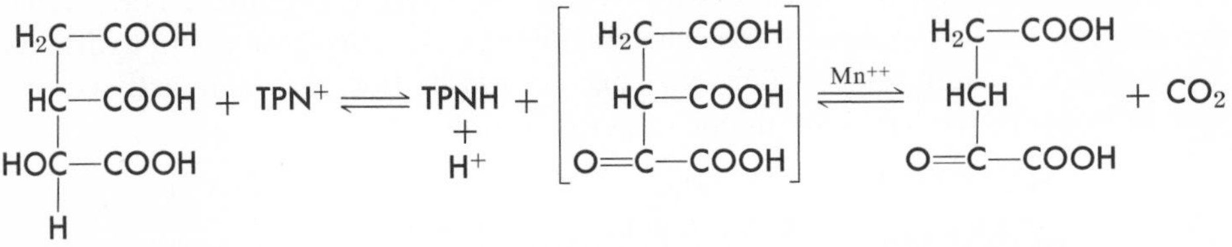

$$
\begin{array}{c}
H_2C—COOH \\
| \\
HC—COOH \\
| \\
HOC—COOH \\
| \\
H
\end{array}
+ TPN^+ \rightleftharpoons TPNH + \underset{H^+}{+}
\left[
\begin{array}{c}
H_2C—COOH \\
| \\
HC—COOH \\
| \\
O=C—COOH
\end{array}
\right]
\overset{Mn^{++}}{\rightleftharpoons}
\begin{array}{c}
H_2C—COOH \\
| \\
HCH \\
| \\
O=C—COOH
\end{array}
+ CO_2
$$

Isocitric acid   **Oxalosuccinic acid**   **α-Ketoglutaric acid**

The isocitric acid dehydrogenases are typical of a group of β-hydroxy acid dehydrogenases. In no instance does the β-keto acid formed in the initial dehydrogenation actually leave the enzymic surface; the second step, decarboxylation, follows immediately but is slow and rate-limiting in the absence of Mn^{++}. If, however, free β-keto acid (oxalosuccinic acid in this instance) is added to the enzyme, decarboxylation occurs readily if Mn^{++} is present. Decarboxylation is catalyzed by formation of an unstable, enzyme-bound chelate of Mn^{++} and the β-keto acid. Similar enzymes include "malic enzyme" (page 380) and 6-phosphogluconic acid dehydrogenase (page 387).

The equilibrium position of the net reaction favors α-ketoglutaric acid formation; under physiological conditions, $\Delta F =$ about -5000 cal.

α-Ketoglutaric acid represents a point of convergence in the metabolic pathways of carbohydrates and lipids and that of certain amino acids. Glutamic acid can by transamination or oxidation yield α-ketoglutaric acid; this appears to be a significant source of the latter acid in mammalian metabolism (Chap. 24). Moreover, all amino acids that can yield glutamic acid in the course of their metabolism are also potential precursors of α-ketoglutaric acid; these include ornithine, proline, glutamine, and histidine (Chap. 27). Conversely, glutamic acid and its derivatives are formed from α-ketoglutaric acid, which is produced by the citric acid cycle.

α-Ketoglutaric Acid → Succinic Acid (Reaction 6, Fig. 18.1). The oxidation of α-

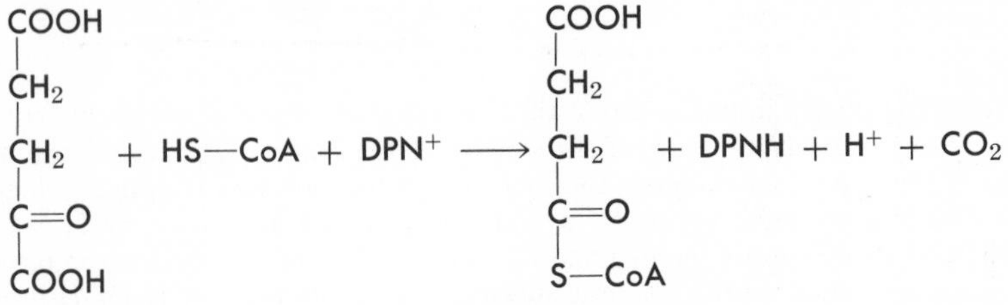

$$
\begin{array}{c}
COOH \\
| \\
CH_2 \\
| \\
CH_2 \\
| \\
C=O \\
| \\
COOH
\end{array}
+ HS—CoA + DPN^+ \longrightarrow
\begin{array}{c}
COOH \\
| \\
CH_2 \\
| \\
CH_2 \\
| \\
C=O \\
| \\
S—CoA
\end{array}
+ DPNH + H^+ + CO_2
$$

α-Ketoglutaric acid   **Succinyl CoA**

ketoglutaric acid is analogous to that of pyruvic acid (page 317). The responsible enzyme exists as part of a high molecular weight complex that catalyzes the over-all reaction, for which $\Delta F = -8000$ cal. In the initial event, α-ketoglutaric acid reacts, on the enzyme surface, with thiamine pyrophosphate, to form an "active succinic semialdehyde." By analogy with the mechanism for pyruvic acid oxidation, the intermediate is inferred to be α-*hydroxy-γ-carboxypropyl thiamine pyrophosphate.*

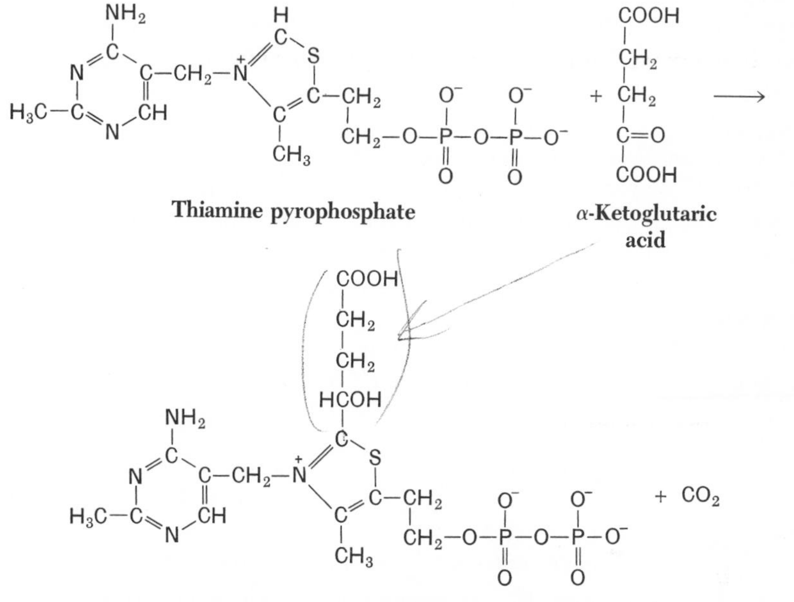

Thiamine pyrophosphate α-**Ketoglutaric acid**

α-**Hydroxy-γ-carboxypropyl thiamine pyrophosphate**

The derivative of thiamine pyrophosphate formed during the decarboxylation reaction is, in effect, the succinic semialdehyde addition compound of the coenzyme.

On the surface of the same protein, the 4-carbon chain is transferred to enzyme-bound lipoic acid, forming a succinyl lipoamide compound. The succinyl group is then transferred to coenzyme A and the dihydrolipoamide is reoxidized by DPN^+, as in the case of pyruvic acid oxidation (page 318). The thioester energy of succinyl CoA may be utilized to initiate fatty acid oxidation (page 440), for acylation reactions, and, by condensation with glycine, to initiate porphyrin synthesis (page 533). However, the energy of most of the succinyl CoA formed by operation of the citric acid cycle is utilized for additional ATP synthesis. The initial reaction in this sequence is

$$\text{Succinyl CoA} + \text{GDP} + \text{P}_i \longrightarrow \text{succinate} + \text{GTP} + \text{CoA}$$

where GDP and GTP are guanosine di- and triphosphate (page 169), respectively. Little is known of the mechanism of this reaction, which is catalyzed by *succinic acid thiokinase*. A *nucleoside diphosphokinase* then catalyzes phosphate transfer from GTP to ADP.

$$\text{GTP} + \text{ADP} \rightleftharpoons \text{GDP} + \text{ATP}$$

Dehydrogenation of Succinic Acid (Reaction 7, Fig. 18.1). The oxidation of succinic acid to fumaric acid is catalyzed by *succinic acid dehydrogenase* and is the only dehydrogenation in the citric acid cycle in which pyridine nucleotides do not participate.

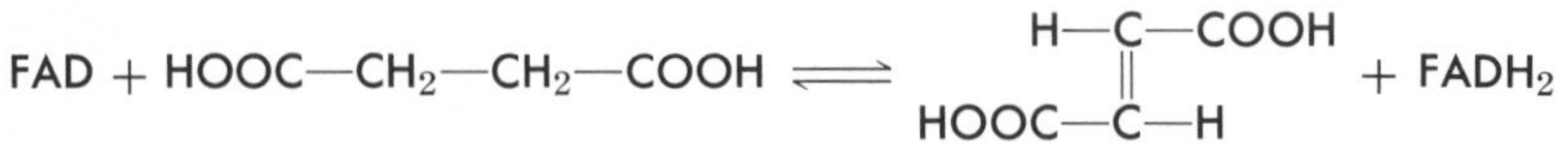

$$FAD + HOOC—CH_2—CH_2—COOH \rightleftharpoons \begin{matrix} H—C—COOH \\ \| \\ HOOC—C—H \end{matrix} + FADH_2$$

Succinic acid   Fumaric acid

Succinic acid dehydrogenase obtained from heart muscle contains four atoms of iron and one mole of flavin per mole of protein, molecular weight 200,000. The flavin appears to be FAD but, unlike other flavoproteins, the flavin component cannot be removed except by extensive proteolysis. The reaction is specific for the *trans* form; maleic acid, the *cis*-isomer, is not produced by this enzyme. Malonic acid is a specific competitive inhibitor of the oxidation of succinic acid (page 234). In consequence, when present in sufficiently high concentration, malonate can be employed to interrupt the citric acid cycle at this point with resultant accumulation of succinate.

Malic Acid Formation (Reaction 8, Fig. 18.1). The reversible hydration of fumaric acid to yield L-malic acid is catalyzed by *fumarase*.

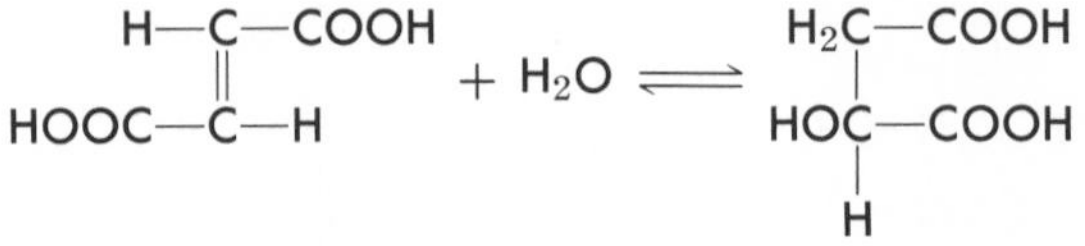

$$\begin{matrix} H—C—COOH \\ \| \\ HOOC—C—H \end{matrix} + H_2O \rightleftharpoons \begin{matrix} H_2C—COOH \\ | \\ HOC—COOH \\ | \\ H \end{matrix}$$

Fumaric acid   L-Malic acid

For the reaction, as written, $K = 4$; thus it is freely reversible. The absolute steric specificity, *viz.*, for the *trans*-unsaturated acid and the L-hydroxy acid, is noteworthy. It may also be noted that of all members of the citric acid cycle, fumarate is most abundant in mammalian tissues.

Regeneration of Oxaloacetic Acid (Reaction 9, Fig. 18.1). Malic acid is oxidized in the presence of *malic acid dehydrogenase* and DPN$^+$, to yield oxaloacetic acid.

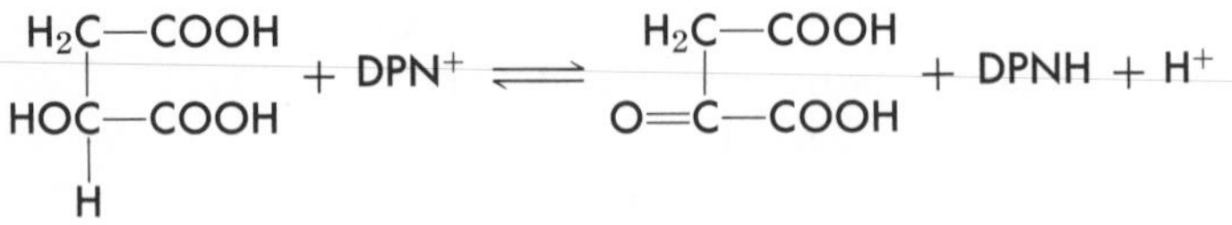

$$\begin{matrix} H_2C—COOH \\ | \\ HOC—COOH \\ | \\ H \end{matrix} + DPN^+ \rightleftharpoons \begin{matrix} H_2C—COOH \\ | \\ O{=}C—COOH \end{matrix} + DPNH + H^+$$

Malic acid   Oxaloacetic acid

By this reaction, the cycle is completed and the generated oxaloacetic acid made available for condensation with another mole of acetyl CoA and repetition of the process.

CITRIC ACID CYCLE—FATE OF INDIVIDUAL CARBON ATOMS

In Fig. 18.3 are represented the fates of the methyl (·) and the carboxyl (x) carbon atoms of acetic acid as they enter into and pass through the citric acid cycle. As a consequence of the asymmetric attachment of citrate to aconitase, no

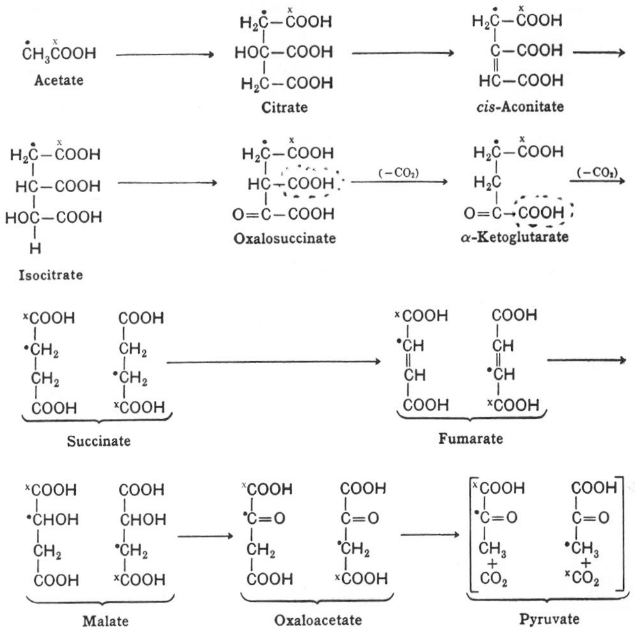

Fig. 18.3. Fate of the carbon atoms introduced as acetyl coenzyme A in a single turn of the citric acid cycle.

randomization of this molecule occurs about its center of symmetry. Whereas two moles of CO_2 are produced as one mole of acetyl CoA is consumed, neither of the carbon atoms lost as CO_2 actually is derived from that acetyl CoA on the first turn of the cycle. At the level of free succinic acid, randomization does occur and isotope will be symmetrically distributed about the plane of symmetry. On subsequent revolutions of the cycle, with reappearance and reutilization of oxaloacetic acid, acetyl carbon will be eliminated as CO_2.

MITOCHONDRIAL ELECTRON TRANSPORT

Within mitochondria are localized the enzymes of the citric acid cycle, the electron transport arrangements that deliver the electrons abstracted from intermediates of the citric cycle to oxygen, and the means by which the energy of this process is conserved by linking it to formation of ATP. In addition, mitochondria from various tissues contain varying amounts of other enzymes, including dehydrogenases for glutamic, pyruvic, β-hydroxybutyric, and fatty acids as well as for proline, choline, and α-glycerol phosphate, enzymes for activation of fatty acids, for synthesis of phosphatides, hippuric acid, urea, and fatty acids, and hydrolytic enzymes such as glutaminase. All the dehydrogenases function with electron transport arrangements similar to, or identical with, those which serve the enzymes of the Krebs cycle.

Individual cells may contain dozens or hundreds of mitochondria, which are cigar-shaped bodies with lengths of 0.5 to 3μ and widths that vary from 0.1 to

0.6μ. The most prominent aspects of their substructure are a limiting membrane and a system of *cristae,* closed vesicles stacked on one another like saucers. Both the membrane and the cristae reveal double layers by electron microscopy; it is uncertain whether the cristae are extensions of the membrane itself. Liver mitochondria, which contain many enzymes not immediately related to the citric acid cycle or electron transport, show loosely packed cristae. In contrast, heart muscle mitochondria, which are almost entirely concerned with the citric acid cycle, fatty acid oxidation, and electron transport, exhibit extremely tightly packed cristae.

When mitochondria are disrupted by mechanical means such as ultrasound or freezing and thawing, or by chemical treatment, *e.g.*, with dilute ethanol or concentrated salt solutions, insoluble particles much smaller than mitochondria are formed. Generally, these processes render soluble many of the ancillary enzymes of mitochondria, the enzymes of the citric acid cycle, with the exception of succinic acid dehydrogenase, and the intramitochondrial pyridine nucleotides. The remaining insoluble particles are rich in lipid and contain all the cytochromes of the parent mitochondria, except for some loss into the medium of cytochrome c. The activities exhibited by these submitochondrial particles depend on their structure and, hence, on their manner of preparation.

For example, by treatment of mitochondria with digitonin, Lehninger prepared particles which had lost all the enzymes of the citric acid cycle but which retained the ability to oxidize succinic and β-hydroxybutyric acids and DPNH with attendant formation of ATP. In Green's laboratory, particles that can oxidize DPNH and succinic acid, with or without conservation of ATP synthesis, have been prepared from mitochondria by treatment with various detergents. It is of interest that those particles which conduct oxidative phosphorylation appear to retain the double-layered structure of mitochondria, whereas those which cannot are singly layered.

Chemical Composition of Mitochondria. Approximately one-third of the dry weight of mitochondria is lipid. Phosphatides containing choline and ethanolamine are predominant, but lesser amounts of phosphatidyl serine, inositol, and glycerol (Chap. 5) are also present. About 25 per cent of the fatty acid chains are present as plasmalogens (page 75), and the total lipid is rich in polyunsaturated fatty acids. The full significance of these lipids remains uncertain. Their structural role is apparent from the fact that the only means for further dispersal of mitochondrial particles is treatment with detergents, *e.g.*, bile salts, or with acetone, amyl alcohol, etc. Significant also is a "structural protein" of high isoelectric point and large molecular weight. Because of its high content of basic amino acids, this protein at neutral pH is capable of binding significant quantities of cytochromes a, b, and c_1, as well as phosphatides, but does not bind cytochrome c, which is also a basic protein (page 199).

With respect to the electron transport components, mitochondria contain a DPNH dehydrogenase that is a high molecular weight iron-containing flavoprotein, and succinic acid dehydrogenase, which is also an iron-flavoprotein (page 348). Spectroscopic evidence indicates the presence of cytochromes b, c_1, c, a, and a_3. The possible identity of the last and the function of cytochrome a as cytochrome c oxidase are discussed elsewhere (page 349). In addition there are substantial quantities of ubiquinone. Of these, only cytochrome c and ubiquinone may be relatively easily extracted from the insoluble lipid-protein complex; the other components are firmly bound. The relative amounts of each of these components appear to be fixed, but they are not equimolar. Thus, it has been reported that for each molecule of DPNH dehydrogenase there are 1 molecule each of succinic acid dehydrogenase, cytochrome c, and cytochrome c_1, 3 molecules of cytochrome b, 6 molecules of cytochrome oxidase, and 15 molecules of ubiquinone.

The Electron Transport Chain. If mitochondria or submitochondrial particles are incubated anaerobically with intermediates of the citric acid cycle, all the above-cited components—DPN^+, flavin, nonheme iron, ubiquinone, and cytochromes b, c_1, c, a, and a_3—undergo reduction. Most studies of this type have relied on absorption spectrophotometry, as illustrated in Fig. 18.4. Attempts to establish the

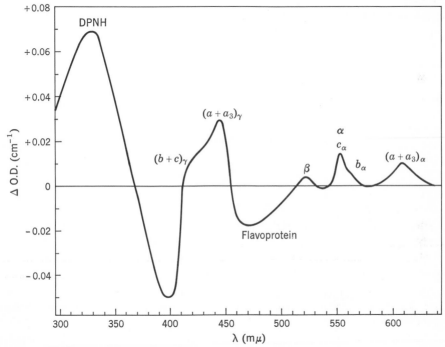

FIG. 18.4. Difference absorption spectrum between anaerobic and aerobic guinea pig liver mitochondria. The curve traces the *change* in optical density of a mitochondrial suspension, over the range of wavelength shown, caused by complete lack of oxygen. (*Courtesy, Dr. Britton Chance and Dr. Ronald W. Estabrook.*)

order of electron transport among these components have relied on several strata-gems. (1) Are the various components equally reduced when succinic acid or DPNH is the initial reductant? Such studies have suggested that cytochrome b may be more significant in the succinate $\rightarrow O_2$ than in the DPNH $\rightarrow O_2$ electron pathway. (2) Inhibitors may interrupt electron flow. Thus, barbiturates, *e.g.*, amytal, prevent reduction of ubiquinone and the cytochromes, whereas antimycin A (an antibiotic from *Streptomyces griseus*) permits reduction of the flavin, nonheme iron, and ubiquinone components while blocking reduction of cytochrome c_1, c, and a_3. Cyanide, which combines with the oxidized form of cytochrome oxidase (page 351), prevents reduction of cytochromes $a + a_3$, but not of any other components of the system. (3) Fractionation of submitochondrial particles by detergents in one laboratory has been reported to yield four types of particles, which catalyze the following processes: (i) DPNH → ubiquinone; (ii) succinate → ubiquinone; (iii) ubiquinone → cytochrome c; (iv) cytochrome c → O_2. A summary of the results of these diverse procedures permits assignment of the order of electron transport shown in Fig. 18.5. Although the details remain to be firmly established, the picture that emerges is one of a highly organized solid-state arrangement. Presumably, each of the electron carriers is rather rigidly in place and located in a manner to permit it to accept electrons from its reductant and yield these to its oxidant without need for migration from its fixed position. Seemingly, also, the entire arrangement exists in a lipid, hydrophobic milieu so that only at the binding sites for the metabolic substrates, *e.g.*, pyruvate or succinate, and, perhaps, at the oxygen-binding sites, are the electron transport units exposed to an aqueous environment.

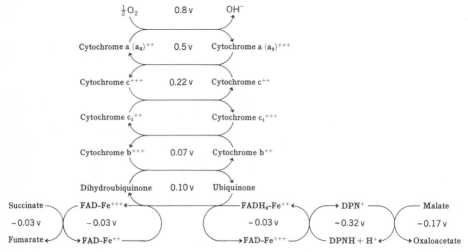

FIG. 18.5. Apparent organization and electron flow in the mitochondrial electron transport chains. Approximate values for E_0' are shown. The relative positions of cytochrome b and ubiquinone are not certain.

If this view of electron transport is correct, the water formed in biological oxidations arises as follows: From the substrate, hydrogen atoms are transferred, via the flavoproteins, to ubiquinone (coenzyme Q). As the latter is oxidized by cytochrome b, protons are added to the medium. Further along the chain, oxygen is reduced by cytochrome oxidase, with formation of hydroxyl ions. Combination of the latter with the previously generated protons is the immediate means of metabolic formation of water. This may be depicted as follows.

(a) $\qquad CoQH_2 + 2Fe^{+++} \longrightarrow CoQ + 2H^+ + 2Fe^{++}$
(b) $\qquad \dfrac{\frac{1}{2}O_2 + H_2O + 2Fe^{++} \longrightarrow 2OH^- + 2Fe^{+++}}{}$
Sum: $\qquad CoQH_2 + \frac{1}{2}O_2 \longrightarrow CoQ + H_2O$

Although by no means definitely established, available data suggest that for each dehydrogenase molecule or complex there may be an individual electron transport unit to which other dehydrogenases may not have ready access. In any case, within the mitochondrion each electron transport unit must lie within easy access of a dehydrogenating complex which accepts, from its substrate, electrons to be transferred to the unit, *i.e.*, the dehydrogenases of the citric acid cycle, pyruvic acid, β-hydroxybutyric acid, choline, proline, glutamic acid, sarcosine and glycerol phosphate dehydrogenases, the fatty acyl CoA dehydrogenase (page 441), and the β-hydroxy acyl CoA dehydrogenase (page 441). Of these, fatty acyl dehydrogenase has been found to have only indirect access to the transport unit; electrons must be transferred from its flavin moiety to that of an "electron-transferring flavoprotein" (page 347) and thence to some component of the transport system, *e.g.*, nonheme iron, coenzyme Q, or cytochrome b.

Oxidation of Extramitochondrial Pyridine Nucleotides. Mitochondria contain a larger molar concentration of bound pyridine nucleotides than of bound cytochromes (DPN/cytochrome c = 40/1). Moreover, external (cytoplasmic) pyridine nucleotides penetrate the intact mitochondrion with great difficulty. Hence, it is intramitochondrial DPN which is reduced by the mitochondrial dehydrogenases.

Accordingly, DPNH produced by reactions in the cell cytoplasm cannot, of itself, be oxidized by mitochondria. If mitochondria are treated so that their permeability characteristics are altered, *e.g.*, in hypotonic media, then external DPNH can be oxidized, but the mitochondria no longer generate ATP incident to this process. However, this difficulty is circumvented in the living cell by at least two devices, in each of which an enzyme capable of utilizing a specific substrate occurs both inside and outside the mitochondrion. Cytoplasm contains an *α-glycerol phosphate dehydrogenase* which catalyzes reduction of dihydroxyacetone phosphate to α-glycerol phosphate by DPNH. Mitochondria, particularly from muscle, most notably from insect flight muscle, contain another glycerol phosphate dehydrogenase which is a flavoprotein. Their coupled action accomplishes the mitochondrial oxidation of cytoplasmic DPNH.

(a) H^+ + DPNH + dihydroxyacetone-P $\longrightarrow$ DPN$^+$ + glycerol-P (cytoplasm)
(b)   Glycerol-P + FAD $\longrightarrow$ dihydroxyacetone-P + FADH$_2$ (mitochondrion)
Sum: H^+ + DPNH + FAD $\longrightarrow$ DPN$^+$ + FADH$_2$ (cell)

This device functions with the movement of α-glycerol phosphate from cytoplasm into mitochondria, and a transfer of dihydroxyacetone phosphate in the reverse direction.

The couple β-hydroxybutyric acid/acetoacetic acid may possibly play a similar role in liver. Tightly bound to the mitochondrial lipid-protein structure is a DPN-dependent β-hydroxybutyric acid dehydrogenase that loses activity when separated from this structure and freed of lipid. The organization of liver mitochondria allows this enzyme, or groups of enzymes, to function with both extramitochondrial and intramitochondrial DPN. This permits operation of the following sequence.

Acetoacetate + DPNH + H^+ $\longrightarrow$ β-hydroxybutyrate + DPN$^+$ (extramitochondrial)
β-Hydroxybutyrate + DPN$^+$ $\longrightarrow$ acetoacetate + DPNH + H^+ (intramitochondrial)

The intramitochondrial DPNH is then available to the electron transport system, while the acetoacetate returns to the cytoplasm to be utilized again.

The quantitative significance of these two devices for the metabolism of extra-mitochondrial DPNH has not been evaluated.

Oxidation of TPNH. Although there appears to be a TPN-dependent isocitric acid dehydrogenase in mitochondria from some tissues, there is no transport system for direct oxidation of TPNH. Oxidation of the latter, to the extent that this may occur, is therefore dependent on the operation of *transhydrogenases*. These are of two types. Within liver mitochondria, as within chloroplasts of green plants, there are transhydrogenases that catalyze the following reaction.

$$\text{TPNH} + \text{DPN}^+ \longrightarrow \text{TPN}^+ + \text{DPNH}$$

Transfer of electrons from TPNH to DPN$^+$ within the mitochondrion would thus permit oxidation via the electron transport system.

A second category of transhydrogenase comprises all the cytoplasmic dehydrogenases which exhibit dual specificity, *i.e.*, which can catalyze reduction of both TPN$^+$ and DPN$^+$ by their substrates. If K_m for the substrate is very low, and if DPN$^+$ and TPN$^+$ can be utilized equally well, a transhydrogenase system is thus provided. By donating electrons from TPNH to the oxidized substrate and then returning them to DPN$^+$, the over-all reaction is identical with that of the simple transhydrogenases cited above. However, there is no evidence that TPNH, generated in the living cell, is actually oxidized by these means. It seems more likely that most of the TPN reduced in cytoplasm is reoxidized by serving as reductant in cellular synthetic processes, *viz.*,

$$\text{AH}_2 + \text{TPN}^+ \longrightarrow \text{A} + \text{TPNH} + \text{H}^+$$
$$\text{TPNH} + \text{H}^+ + \text{X} \longrightarrow \text{XH}_2 + \text{TPN}^+$$

where A and X are metabolites. The significance of this process will become evident when considering coupling of the hexose phosphate pathway for glucose oxidation (page 387) with fatty acid synthesis (page 449).

OXIDATIVE PHOSPHORYLATION

The physiological objective of the oxidation of carbohydrates and lipids is the conservation of the free energy thus made available in physiologically utilizable form, *viz.*, ATP. It has been demonstrated repeatedly that oxidation of intermediates of the citric acid cycle by carefully prepared mitochondria is accompanied by the formation of ATP from ADP and P_i. Oxidation of DPNH occurs with net formation of three molecules of ATP per molecule of DPNH or per atom of oxygen consumed; this is conventionally expressed as a *P/O ratio* of 3. Since oxidation of β-hydroxybutyric or malic acids proceeds with a similar P/O ratio, it is apparent that ATP is generated incident to the reoxidation of the DPNH formed by oxidation of the substrate and that, with the exception of the oxidation of α-ketoglutaric acid (page 320), the immediate step in which substrate is oxidized serves only as a means of providing electrons to the electron transport units.

The immediate mechanisms by which the oxidation of DPNH is coupled to the generation of ATP remain uncertain, but some general features are apparent. The studies of Chance, Lehninger, Slater, and Lardy have established the approximate sites of energy conservation along the path of electron transport from each molecule of DPNH to oxygen. One of these sites is at the point of transport from DPNH to the flavin moiety of DPNH dehydrogenase; a second is associated with the passage of electrons from ubiquinone or ferrocytochrome b to ferricytochrome c; and the third is in the course of oxidation of ferrocytochrome c by O_2.

Whereas E_0' for DPNH/DPN$^+$ is -0.32 volt, that for succinate/fumarate is 0.03 volt (Table 17.1). Hence, succinate cannot be expected to reduce DPN$^+$ directly. Moreover, $\Delta E_0'$ between succinate/fumarate and FADH$_2$/FAD is too small to permit ATP formation from this process. A minimum difference in potential, $\Delta E_0'$, of 0.18 volt is required to provide the 8000 cal. per mole necessary to form ATP from ADP + P_i. Hence, the oxidation of succinic acid occasions formation of only two moles of ATP per mole of succinic acid and the two sites of ATP formation correspond to the last two (see above) which operate during DPNH oxidation.

It is generally agreed that associated with each of these discrete oxidative steps, there must be formation of an energy-rich intermediate compound that reacts with inorganic phosphate to form an energy-rich phosphate compound, which, in turn, may react with ADP to form ATP. A tentative formulation of this hypothesis for the synthesis of ATP at the first site is the following.

(a)	$DPNH + H^+ + FAD + X \rightleftharpoons X^* + DPN^+ + FADH_2$
(b)	$X^* + Y \rightleftharpoons X \sim Y$
(c)	$X \sim Y + P_i \rightleftharpoons Y \sim P + X$
(d)	$Y \sim P + ADP \rightleftharpoons ATP + Y$

This formulation is in accord with a large body of experimental evidence. The postulated carriers X and Y are unknown, but certain characteristics should be noted. (1) X* is a proposed high-energy compound occasionally designated as DPN$^+ \sim X$, but its formation may utilize only the proton or hydride ion which is involved in reaction (a) so that X* may equally well be a "high-energy" form of X which is not linked, covalently, to DPN. (2) $X \sim Y$ is a second high-energy compound. If X* is not DPN$^+ \sim X$, there is no basis for postulating the existence of two intermediate carriers. In that case the coupling mechanism, formally, would simplify to the following.

(e)	$DPNH + H^+ + FAD + X \rightleftharpoons X^* + DPN^+ + FADH_2$
(f)	$X^* + P_i \rightleftharpoons X \sim P$
(g)	$X \sim P + ADP \rightleftharpoons X + ATP$

Formation of a high-energy compound, DPN$^+ \sim X$, would permit conservation of a large fraction of the free energy that otherwise would appear as heat when DPNH is oxidized by the FAD of DPNH dehydrogenase. Some evidence is available that such a compound does exist. Pinchot, using respiratory particles from *Alcaligenes faecalis*, found that DPNH was oxidized to form an intermediate that was stably linked to a soluble protein. Addition of P_i and ADP then resulted in formation of ATP and release of DPN$^+$. In this instance the protein component was bound to the phosphorylating particle by a specific polynucleotide, and was dissociated during oxidation of DPNH. Further elucidation of this system may resolve the problem as to whether, at each of the three sites, the high-energy compound initially formed is generated during oxidation or reduction.

There is somewhat greater difficulty in formulating a mechanism for ATP generation at the second two sites. If, indeed, coenzyme Q (ubiquinone) is obligatorily reduced in electron transport, its reoxidation by the transport segment cytochrome b–cytochrome c_1–cytochrome c is the locus of the second phosphorylation. However, it is not clear how two consecutive 1-electron transfers can be utilized to generate a single molecule of ATP, although this appears to be the case. This problem arises again as the two electrons from DPNH pass, one at a time, from cytochrome c to oxygen via cytochrome oxidase.

"Coupling Factors" and the Mechanism of Oxidative Phosphorylation. Although X and Y have not been identified, presumably related "coupling factors" have been obtained from mitochondria in several laboratories. These are proteins which restore phosphorylating ability to mitochondria or submitochondrial particles which have been "uncoupled" by various means, i.e., which can conduct electron transport but do not generate ATP concomitantly. Current evidence suggests that independent coupling factors may be operative at each of the three sites of energy conservation along the electron transport chain. When partially purified, these factors catalyze exchange of P_i^{32} with ATP and of ADP^{32} with ATP, as suggested by reactions $(c + d)$ or $(f + g)$ above, as do intact, phosphorylating particles. Thus, the properties of these proteins are compatible with their serving as X or Y in the formulation above. One further exchange is of interest, that of H_2O^{18} with P_i, promoted by mitochondria in the presence of ATP. When coupled with Boyer's observation that the bridge oxygen between the terminal phosphate residues of ATP is furnished by ADP rather than by P_i, it becomes clear that oxidative phosphorylation must entail formation of a covalently bonded, high-energy phosphate intermediate, viz., $X \sim P$ or $Y \sim P$.

Recent observations of Boyer suggest the possible nature of X^* and of $X \sim P$ in these formulations. A soluble coupling-factor protein, isolated from mitochondria that had been incubated with succinate and P_i^{32} but no ADP, was shown, by proteolysis, to contain histidine phosphate. Addition of ADP to the isolated protein resulted in formation of ATP^{32}. When substrate but neither P_i nor ADP was included in the previous incubation, the isolated protein then reacted with P_i, binding it as phosphohistidine, and the phosphate could be transferred to ADP. Finally, if isolated from mitochondria that had not been incubated with substrate, the protein did not react with P_i but in the presence of ATP^{32}, P^{32}-labeled phosphohistidine was formed. From these observations, Boyer postulated the mechanism shown in Fig. 18.6. The over-all validity of this proposal remains to be established; since the function of the isolated protein is uncertain, it is not clear either whether this mechanism is applicable at all three sites of energy conservation or how formation of the activated compound is accomplished by electron transport. Thus, it remains to be demonstrated whether histidine phosphate does indeed serve as $X \sim P$ in the general formulation above.

"Uncouplers" of Oxidative Phosphorylation. Numerous types of compounds have been found to interfere with oxidative phosphorylation; the mechanisms of action of three of these are especially noteworthy as they afford evidence for the validity of the general scheme above. Dinitrophenol, pentachlorophenol, and other highly substituted lipid-soluble phenols are uncouplers of oxidative phosphorylation. In

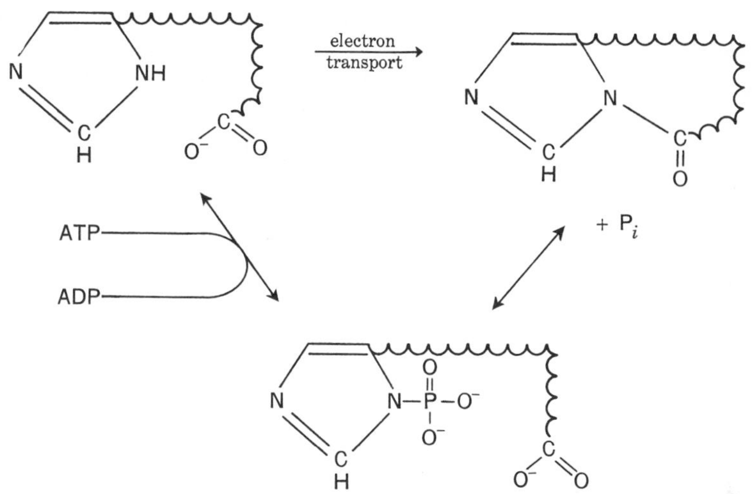

FIG. 18.6. A hypothetical scheme for participation of histidine phosphate in oxidative phosphorylation. The wavy line indicates protein molecule. The —COOH group involved in these transformations is thought *not* to be the —COOH of the histidine molecule which furnishes the imidazole residue. It is not certain which of the two N atoms of the imidazole residue is involved.

their presence, electron transport proceeds at a maximal rate without formation of ATP, suggesting reaction of the substituted phenol with some intermediate to form a highly unstable compound which immediately hydrolyzes. This is consonant also with the enhanced ATPase activity both of mitochondria and of several isolated coupling factors in the presence of dinitrophenol. Arsenate also uncouples, but apparently by substituting for P_i in reaction (c) (page 329) again yielding an unstable intermediate which hydrolyzes. Of particular interest is oligomycin, an antibiotic that is an inhibitor rather than an uncoupler of oxidative phosphorylation, since in its presence, neither respiration nor ATP formation occurs. Dinitrophenol overcomes this inhibition of respiration, but oligomycin blocks the ATPase activity elicited by dinitrophenol in nonrespiring mitochondria. However, oligomycin is without influence on arsenate-induced ATPase activity. Examination of the hypothetical scheme of oxidative phosphorylation above (in the light of these observations) suggests that oligomycin is operative in the middle of the scheme, *e.g.*, inhibiting further utilization of X ~ Y. This is in accord with the finding that the antibiotic inhibits exchange of $P_i{}^{32}$ into ATP by the particles obtained by treatment of mitochondria with digitonin, but is difficult to reconcile with inhibition of ADP^{32}-ATP exchange by the same preparation.

Reversal of Mitochondrial Electron Flow. A striking illustration of the operation of the electron transport system is the finding that in the presence of ATP, mitochondria can catalyze the following reaction.

$$\text{Succinate} + \text{DPN}^+ \longrightarrow \text{fumarate} + \text{DPNH} + \text{H}^+$$

As noted earlier (page 329), from the redox potentials of these components reaction in the reverse direction is strongly favored. Although the amount of ATP utilized during the reaction is unknown, it is apparent that by utilizing the energy of ATP, for example, for formation of $DPN^+ \sim X$ in the scheme shown above, reduction to DPNH does occur, thereby demonstrating the equivalence of "reducing power" and "phosphate bond energy" in the operation of the mitochondrial respiratory mechanism. In studying this system, Griffiths demonstrated the formation of a "DPNH-phosphate" of unknown structure when mitochondria were incubated with succinic acid, ATP, and DPN^+. No evidence for formation of this compound during oxidation of DPNH or of substrates that are oxidized by DPN-utilizing dehydrogenases has yet been obtained. Hence, its physiological role remains to be elucidated.

Respiratory Control. It is inherent in the formulation of oxidative phosphorylation presented above that if mitochondria are "tightly coupled," so that respiration proceeds almost exclusively over phosphorylating pathways, then respiration can proceed no more rapidly than is permitted by the availability of inorganic phosphate and ADP for ATP formation. This has been amply demonstrated. The inhibition of both respiration and phosphorylation by oligomycin strongly supports this concept. Further, Lardy found that a supply of ADP and P_i is essential for maximal respiration with any substrate oxidized by a mitochondrial DPN-linked dehydrogenase. Chance utilized this observation to determine, by spectrophotometric means, the effect of ADP concentration on the state of reduction of the various electron carriers and was able to ascertain the sites of energy conservation in the electron transport scheme. Some results of these studies are summarized in Table 18.1.

Table 18.1: Oxidation-Reduction Levels of Members of the Respiratory Chain in Various Metabolic Circumstances

Substrate level	O_2 level	ADP level	Respiration rate	Rate-limiting factor	Steady-state percentage reduction of				
					DPN	Flavins	Cytochromes		
							b	c	a
High.......	0	High	0	O_2	100	100	100	100	100
0..........	+	High	Slow	Substrate	0	0	0	0	0
Low.......	+	Low	Slow	ADP	90	21	17	7	0
High.......	+	Low	Slow	ADP	99	40	35	14	0
High.......	+	High	Fast	Respiratory chain	53	20	16	6	4

Source: Adapted from B. Chance and G. R. Williams, *Advances in Enzymol.,* **17,** 65, 1956.

The tight coupling of oxidation to phosphorylation, evident in normal mitochondria, provides a means by which the rate at which foodstuffs may be oxidized is regulated by the requirements of the cell for useful energy. The utilization of ATP to drive the diverse energy-requiring processes of the cell automatically increases the available supply of ADP and inorganic phosphate, which in turn become available to react in the coupling mechanism and permit respiration to proceed.

Mitochondrial Structure and Function. The continuing operation of oxidative phosphorylation is clearly dependent on preservation of some basic aspect of mitochondrial structure, perhaps the doubly layered membrane. Only those submito-chondrial fragments which retain this structure can couple ATP synthesis to electron transport. Any treatment that results in imbibition of water by mito-chondria, such as a hypotonic medium, high concentrations of reduced glutathione, thyroxine, Ca^{++}, fatty acids, or simply aging the mitochondria, results in lowered P/O ratios. In each instance, water uptake is associated with concurrent electron transport, and inhibitors of the latter process, such as antimycin A, prevent imbi-bition of water but cannot restore phosphorylation. Added ATP can, however, induce contraction of mitochondria in most instances. A protein termed "C factor" can restore phosphorylation and simultaneously cause extrusion of water from mitochondria that have been swollen under the influence of glutathione; the latter causes release of C factor into the medium. Those circumstances which lead to swelling also lead to passive translocation of ions into the mitochondria, and normal intramitochondrial Na^+ and K^+ concentrations are restored during oxida-tive phosphorylation. Of interest also is the accumulation of large amounts of insoluble magnesium phosphate if both these ions are abundant in the medium of actively respiring mitochondria. The fact that this process is not sensitive to oligo-mycin suggests that ion transport in place of net ATP formation may be an alter-native means of utilizing the energy derived from electron transport, even though the mechanism is entirely obscure. Although it is abundantly evident that electron transport, and formation of X*, occurs in a lipid, nonaqueous milieu, the under-lying significance of this arrangement is not understood. It is also not clear whether ATP formation occurs in the lipid or aqueous phase.

Of wide biological significance is the fact that the process of oxidative phos-phorylation is accomplished in a membranous structure which is a protein-lipid complex and which also effects the translocation of ions. All cell membranes are protein-lipid complexes. Since membranes isolated from mammalian erythrocytes appear to generate ATP by glycolysis and the cell membranes of bacteria are the site of oxidative phosphorylation, it would appear that the ability both to conserve metabolic energy and to operate "active transport" devices for ions and organic molecules may be universal in biological membranes. Some evidence suggests that ion translocation may be an alternative to ATP formation in mitochondria and that an earlier intermediate may be common to both processes. It will be obvious that progress in understanding of the mechanism of oxidative phosphorylation is necessarily intimately related to increased understanding of mitochondrial struc-ture and the mechanisms of ion translocation.

Energy Yield of the Citric Acid Cycle. The operation of the citric acid cycle includes three steps in which DPNH arises. These are isocitrate $\rightarrow \alpha$-ketoglutarate; α-ketoglutarate $\rightarrow$ succinyl CoA; and malate $\rightarrow$ oxaloacetate. Accordingly, each of these steps provides the opportunity for formation of three moles of ATP. An addi-tional mole of ATP is derived from succinyl CoA (page 321). The oxidation of succinate to fumarate circumvents the usual pyridine nucleotide step and yields two rather than three moles of ATP. The yields of ATP for the individual steps in the cycle are summarized in Table 18.2. It will be seen that per mole of acetyl con-sumed, 12 moles of inorganic phosphate are utilized and 12 moles of ATP are gen-erated. Considering ΔF for synthesis of ATP from ADP and P_i as approximately

Table 18.2: ENERGY YIELD OF THE CITRIC ACID CYCLE

Reaction	Coenzyme	ATP yield/mole
Isocitrate $\longrightarrow$ α-ketoglutarate + CO_2........................	DPN	3
α-Ketoglutarate $\longrightarrow$ succinyl CoA + CO_2...................	DPN	3
Succinyl CoA + ADP + P_i $\longrightarrow$ succinate + ATP............	GDP	1
Succinate $\longrightarrow$ fumarate...	FAD	2
Malate $\longrightarrow$ oxaloacetate...............................	DPN	3
Total...	....	12

+8000 cal. per mole under physiological conditions, this represents a net energy yield, as ATP synthesized, of 96,000 cal. per mole of acetate utilized.

The total oxidation of acetic acid to CO_2 and H_2O,

$$CH_3COOH + 2O_2 \longrightarrow 2CO_2 + 2H_2O$$

has a gross energy yield of 209,000 cal. per mole. Thus, $\dfrac{96,000}{209,000} \times 100$, or about 45 per cent of the gross energy yield, is conserved in energy-rich phosphate compounds. The oxidation of acetyl CoA via the citric acid cycle, coupled to phosphorylation, may be represented as follows.

$$CH_2CO\!-\!SCoA + 2O_2 + 12ADP + 12P_i \longrightarrow 2CO_2 + CoASH + 12ATP$$

This equation disregards the water released in formation of the pyrophosphate bond of ATP and the one mole of water required for hydrolysis of the thioester.

Tissue Respiration. The oxygen consumption (microliters of gas at standard pressure and temperature) per milligram of tissue is denoted as the Q_{O_2}. As shown in Table 18.3, considerable variation is apparent among animal tissues. It is not possible to define, precisely, the factors that determine the respiratory rate of a

Table 18.3: RESPIRATION OF VARIOUS TISSUES

Tissue	$-Q_{O_2}$	Tissue	$-Q_{O_2}$
Retina.................................	31	Lung.................................	8
Kidney................................	21	Placenta..............................	7
Liver (fasted animal).....................	17	Myeloid bone marrow.....................	6
Liver (fed animal)........................	12	Thymus...............................	6
Jejunal mucosa..........................	15	Pancreas..............................	6
Thyroid................................	13	Diaphragm............................	6
Testis..................................	12	Heart................................	5
Cerebral cortex..........................	12	Ileal mucosa...........................	5
Hypophysis.............................	12	Lymph node...........................	4
Spleen.................................	12	Skeletal muscle.........................	3
Adrenal gland...........................	10	Cornea...............................	2
Erythroid bone marrow....................	9	Skin.................................	0.8
Duodenal mucosa........................	9	Lens.................................	0.5

(Q_{O_2} = microliters O_2 per milligram dry weight per hour. All values are for rat tissue slices in Ringer's phosphate + glucose.)

given tissue. Since, however, the bulk of this respiration in all tissues appears to occur over the cytochrome chain and, presumably, is phosphate-linked, it may be assumed that it is the demand for energy-rich phosphate which conditions the particular respiratory rate of each tissue. Oxidations catalyzed by aerobic dehydrogenases, copper-containing oxidases, and the peroxidases are not phosphate-linked. Consequently, the rate at which these particular oxidations may proceed depends only on the usual factors that influence enzymic activity. If, then, any substance whose oxidation is catalyzed in this manner is administered to an intact animal or incubated with an isolated tissue preparation, its oxidation may be expected to occur readily, thereby increasing the rate of oxygen consumption. In contrast, administration of a substance whose oxidation is coupled obligatorily with phosphorylation, *e.g.*, feeding of excess carbohydrate, does not stimulate respiration. The superfluous calories are stored in tissues as glycogen or lipid until the demand for ATP initiates oxidation of these reserve sources of energy.

REFERENCES

Books

Chance, B., ed., "Energy-linked Functions of Mitochondria," Academic Press, Inc., New York, 1963.

Dixon, M., "Manometric Methods," 3d ed., Cambridge University Press, London, 1951.

Lehninger, A. L., "The Mitochondrion: Structure and Function," W. A. Benjamin, Inc., New York, 1964.

Umbreit, W. W., Burris, R. H., and Stauffer, J. F., "Manometric Techniques and Related Methods for the Study of Tissue Metabolism," rev. ed., Burgess Publishing Company, Minneapolis, 1957.

Warburg, O., "The Metabolism of Tumours," translated by F. Dickens, Constable and Co., Ltd., London, 1930.

Review Articles

Baddiley, J., The Structure of Coenzyme A, *Advances in Enzymol.*, **16**, 1–22, 1955.

Chance, B., Techniques for Assay of the Respiratory Enzymes, in S. P. Colowick and N. O. Kaplan, eds., "Methods in Enzymology," vol. IV, pp. 273–338, Academic Press, Inc., New York, 1957.

Chance, B., and Williams, G. R., The Respiratory Chain and Oxidative Phosphorylation, *Advances in Enzymol.*, **17**, 65–134, 1956.

Green, D. E., and Fleischer, S., Mitochondrial System of Enzymes, in D. M. Greenberg, ed., "Chemical Pathways in Metabolism," 2d ed., vol. I, pp. 41–96, Academic Press, Inc., New York, 1960.

Green, D. E., and Fleischer, S., On the Molecular Organization of Biological Transducing Systems, in M. Kasha and D. Pullman, eds., "Horizons in Biochemistry," pp. 381–420, Academic Press, Inc., New York, 1962.

Krebs, H. A., and Lowenstein, J. M., The Tricarboxylic Acid Cycle, in D. M. Greenberg, ed., "Chemical Pathways of Metabolism," 2d ed., vol. I, pp. 129–203, Academic Press, Inc., New York, 1960.

Lehninger, A. L., Water Uptake and Extrusion by Mitochondria in Relation to Oxidative Phosphorylation, *Physiol. Revs.*, **42**, 467–517, 1962.

Lehninger, A. L., and Wadkins, C. L., Oxidative Phosphorylation, *Ann. Rev. Biochem.*, **31**, 47–78, 1962.

Lipmann, F., Metabolic Generation and Utilization of Phosphate Bond Energy, *Advances in Enzymol.*, **1**, 99–162, 1941.

Massey, V., and Veeger, C., Biological Oxidations, *Ann. Rev. Biochem.,* **32**, 579–638, 1963.

Newton, J. W., and Kamen, M. D., Cytochrome Systems in Anaerobic Electron Transport, in I. C. Gunsalus and R. Y. Stanier, eds., "The Bacteria," vol. II, pp. 397–424, Academic Press, Inc., New York, 1961.

Ochoa, S., Enzymic Mechanisms in the Citric Acid Cycle, *Advances in Enzymol.*, **15**, 183–270, 1954.

Racker, E., Mechanisms of Synthesis of Adenosine Triphosphate, *Advances in Enzymol.*, **23**, 323–399, 1961.

Slater, E. C., The Constitution of the Respiratory Chain in Animal Tissues, *Advances in Enzymol.*, **20**, 147–199, 1958.

Smith, L., Cytochrome Systems in Aerobic Electron Transport, in I. C. Gunsalus and R. Y. Stanier, eds., "The Bacteria," vol. II, pp. 365–396, Academic Press, Inc., New York, 1961.

19. Biological Oxidations

Oxidative Enzymes, Coenzymes, and Carriers

The preceding chapter introduced briefly the enzymes and coenzymes that participate in biological oxidations. Patently, few substances oxidized within the mammalian organism are spontaneously oxidized by oxygen at 37°C. and pH 7. Such reactions are all thermodynamically possible, *i.e.*, the E_0' values of the substances to be oxidized are lower than that of the O_2/OH^- couple. It is the function of the enzymes that catalyze oxidations to provide a reaction pathway or mechanism which, effectively, lowers the activation energy so that the reaction can proceed. Whether oxidative enzymes thus affect oxygen or the substrates was long debated. Warburg supported the concept of an "oxygen-activating" enzyme; Wieland suggested that enzymes activated the substrate, thus loosening the hydrogen atoms. The demonstrations by Thunberg and by Battelli and Stern that animal tissues contain enzymes that make possible the anaerobic reduction of methylene blue by naturally occurring compounds, such as lactic, isocitric, glutamic, and β-hydroxybutyric acids, lent great weight to the concept of Wieland. Eventually it was evident that both schools were correct to some degree.

PYRIDINE NUCLEOTIDES

The existence of diphosphopyridine nucleotide (DPN), the most abundant of the respiratory coenzymes, was noted by Harden and Young during their studies of yeast fermentation; it was isolated in the laboratory of von Euler, and its structure (page 312) was established in 1936. Triphosphopyridine nucleotide (TPN) was first described by Warburg and Christian as the coenzyme for oxidation, in erythrocytes, of glucose 6-phosphate to 6-phosphogluconic acid; its general structure was established in 1935. This nucleotide differs from DPN in that TPN contains a third molecule of phosphate esterified at C-2' of the ribose moiety of the adenosine portion of the molecule, as shown on the following page.

Molecular models indicate that these compounds can exist in an extended form, with the adenine moiety remote from the nicotinamide, or, as depicted above, with the plane of the adenine ring lying above the plane of the nicotinamide portion of the molecule. Present evidence does not decisively indicate which form participates in enzymic reactions.

Whereas DPN is present in concentrations of 0.4 to 2.0 mg. per g. of tissue, TPN varies from 0.01 to 0.1 mg. per g. In liver, their concentrations are approxi-

337

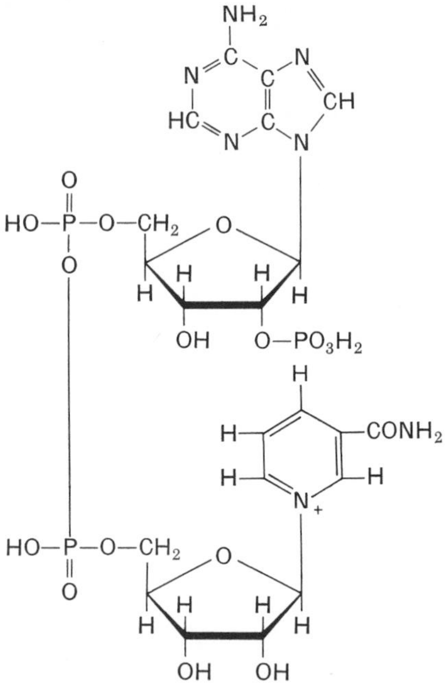

Triphosphopyridine nucleotide (TPN$^+$)

mately equal. Most of the DPN in the cell is present in the oxidized form; the TPN is present chiefly in the reduced state. Both nucleotides are synthesized from their components in the cells in which they occur. The biogenesis and fate of the pyridine nucleotides are presented in Chap. 28.

The abbreviated structures shown in Fig. 19.1 indicate that when DPN$^+$ is reduced by 2-electron transfer in an enzymic reaction, the DPN$^+$ accepts the equivalent of a hydride ion (H:$^-$) from the oxidized substrate while a proton is liberated to the medium. The quinonoid reduced compound bears no charge on the ring nitrogen and contains one hydrogen derived from the substrate; hence the abbreviation for reduced DPN$^+$ is DPNH. Colowick demonstrated that the newly introduced hydrogen is fixed to the pyridine ring at the 4 or *para* position.

Since the pyridine ring of DPNH is planar, the two hydrogen atoms at carbon-4 project on either side of the plane. The stereospecificity of the formation and reoxidation of DPNH was shown by the following observations of Vennesland and

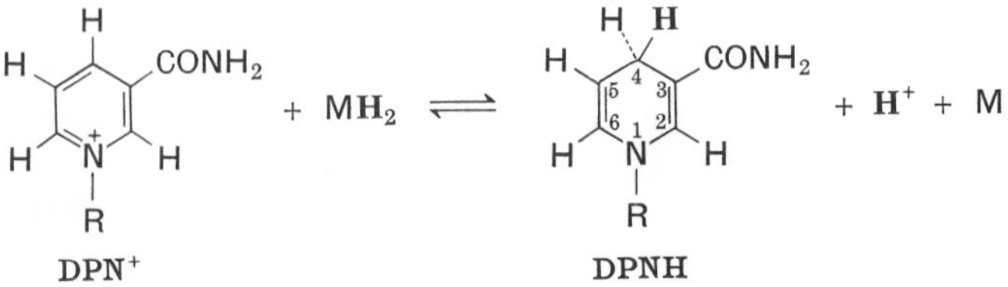

FIG. 19.1. The stereospecific reduction of diphosphopyridine nucleotide by a dehydrogenase of the α series. R represents the remainder of the structure (page 312).

Westheimer. DPND was formed nonenzymically by reduction of DPN$^+$ with dithionite in D_2O, and then used, with alcohol dehydrogenase, to reduce acetaldehyde. The resulting ethanol and DPN$^+$ each contained one-half an equivalent atom of deuterium per mole. However, when DPN$^+$ was reduced by synthetic CH_3CD_2OH in the presence of yeast alcohol dehydrogenase, DPND containing one atom of deuterium per molecule was formed. When this DPND was incubated with acetaldehyde and alcohol dehydrogenase, or with pyruvate and lactic acid dehydrogenase, the deuterium was quantitatively retransferred, with formation of deuteroethanol or deuterolactate, respectively. Thus, transfer of hydrogen atoms by these dehydrogenases is stereospecific with respect to the plane of the pyridine ring. Yeast alcohol dehydrogenase and heart lactic acid dehydrogenase exhibit the same stereospecificity, *i.e.*, they catalyze transfer of hydrogen to and from the same side of the pyridine ring. These are termed dehydrogenases of the α type. As shown in Table 19.1, a somewhat larger group of enzymes is presently known to exhibit stereospecific transfer to and from the opposite side of the pyridine ring. These are dehydrogenases of the β type. It has been possible to establish the absolute configuration of the two series. The hydrogen atom added by dehydrogenases of the α series projects toward the reader from the plane of the pyridine ring when that ring is oriented as in Fig. 19.1.

Table 19.1: STEREOSPECIFICITY OF PYRIDINE NUCLEOTIDE DEHYDROGENASES

Substrate	Nucleotide	Source	Stereospecificity
Isocitrate	TPN	Heart	α
Ethanol	DPN	Yeast	α
Lactate	DPN	Heart	α
Malate	DPN	Heart	α
Farnesyl pyrophosphate	TPN	Liver	β
Glucose	DPN	Liver	β
Glucose 6-phosphate	TPN	Yeast	β
Glutamate	TPN	Muscle	β
Glutathione	TPN	Yeast	β
3α-Hydroxysteroids	DPN	Liver	β
β-Hydroxysteroids	DPN	*Pseudomonas*	β
17β-Hydroxysteroids	DPN, TPN	Liver	β
6-Phosphogluconate	TPN	Liver	β
3-Phosphoglyceraldehyde	DPN	Yeast, muscle	β
Transhydrogenase	TPN, DPN	*Pseudomonas, Escherichia coli*	β

The pyridine nucleotides participate as coenzymes in a wide variety of biological oxidations. Only a few of these known enzymes are listed in Table 19.2. No relationship is obvious between the nature of the substrate and enzyme preference for TPN or DPN. Thus, there are dehydrogenases that exhibit activity only with one of the two nucleotides, a few that catalyze reaction with either at almost equal rates, and, more frequently, dehydrogenases that exhibit catalytic activity with one coenzyme at a rate many times greater than with the other. This behavior may also vary with the species from which an enzyme is obtained. Thus, glucose 6-phosphate dehydrogenase from yeast has an absolute specificity for TPN whereas that from mammalian liver uses DPN at about 7 per cent of the rate with TPN at equivalent concentration. *In general, enzymes responsible for oxidations that supply energy to the organism utilize DPN*[+], *while those which catalyze reductive biosyntheses employ*

Table 19.2: SOME DEHYDROGENASES EMPLOYING PYRIDINE NUCLEOTIDES

Substrate	Products	Coenzyme	Preparative source
Acyclic polyols.............	Ketoses	DPN	Rat liver, *Aerobacter*
Aldehydes.................	Carboxylic acids	DPN	Liver
Aspartic β-semialdehyde......	β-Aspartyl phosphate	DPN	Liver
Betaine aldehyde...........	Betaine	DPN	Rat liver
Ethanol...................	Acetaldehyde	DPN	Liver, kidney, yeast
D-Glycerate...............	Hydroxypyruvate	DPN	Liver
α-Glycerophosphate.........	Phosphodihydroxy-acetone	DPN	Yeast, muscle, liver
L-Gulonate...............	Xylulose + CO_2	DPN	Kidney
ω-Hydroxy acids...........	ω-Aldehyde acids	DPN	Liver
D($-$)-β-Hydroxybutyrate	Acetoacetate	DPN	Liver
L($-$)-β-Hydroxybutyryl CoA..	Acetoacetyl CoA	DPN	Liver
3β-Hydroxysteroids........	3-Ketosteroids	DPN	*Pseudomonas*
17β-Hydroxysteroids........	17-Ketosteroids	DPN	*Pseudomonas*
Isocitrate.................	α-Ketoglutarate + CO_2	DPN	Beef heart, rat liver, yeast
Lactate...................	Pyruvate	DPN	Muscle, other animal tissues
Malate.................	Oxaloacetate	DPN	Muscle, other animal tissues
Malonic semialdehyde........	Malonate	DPN	*Pseudomonas*
3-Phosphoglyceraldehyde.....	1,3-Diphosphoglycerate	DPN	All animal tissues, yeast, bacteria
Ribitol...................	Ribulose	DPN	Liver
Succinic semialdehyde........	Succinate	DPN	Brain, bacteria
Tartronic semialdehyde.......	Glycerate	DPN	*Pseudomonas*
Glycerol..................	Dihydroxyacetone	DPN or TPN	Pig liver, rat liver, *Escherichia coli*, *Aerobacter aerogenes*, *Penicillium*, *Candida*
Glutamate.................	α-Ketoglutarate + NH_4^+	DPN or TPN	Muscle, liver, yeast
3β-Hydroxysteroids..........	3-Ketosteroids	DPN or TPN	Liver
21-Hydroxysteroids..........	21-Dehydrosteroids	DPN or TPN	Liver, adrenal
Dihydrofolate..............	Tetrahydrofolate	TPN	Liver
Glucose 6-phosphate........	6-Phosphogluconate	TPN	Liver, erythrocytes, yeast
L-Gulonate................	D-Glucuronate	TPN	Kidney
Isocitrate.................	α-Ketoglutarate + CO_2	TPN	Various animal tissues, yeast
Malate..................	Pyruvate + CO_2	TPN	Heart
Reduced glutathione (G-SH)..	Glutathione (G-SS-G)	TPN	Yeast, liver
Shikimate.................	Dehydroshikimate	TPN	Peas, *Escherichia coli*

TPN^+. However, it will be apparent in later discussions that there are many exceptions to this generalization.

The terms "prosthetic group" and "coenzyme" are rather misnomers when applied to the pyridine nucleotides. The K_m for DPN^+ and TPN^+ varies from 10^{-4} to $10^{-6}M$, whereas K_m for the "substrates" of these enzymes varies from 10^{-3} to $10^{-5}M$. In general, DPNH is bound about ten times as firmly as DPN^+ by each specific dehydrogenase. The pyridine nucleotides readily dissociate from the dehydrogenases and are really cosubstrates, which serve as coenzymes only in that, physiologically, there exist *other* enzymes that catalyze reoxidation of the reduced forms, thus permitting reutilization of the nucleotides. Also, by virtue of this ease of dissociation, pyridine nucleotides, uniquely among oxidative coenzymes, may participate in dismutations, *i.e.*, reduction of one metabolite by another.

(a) $\qquad$ $AH_2 + DPN^+ \longrightarrow A + DPNH + H^+$

(b) $\qquad$ $B + DPNH + H^+ \longrightarrow BH_2 + DPN^+$

Sum: $\qquad$ $AH_2 + B \longrightarrow A + BH_2$

Such a dismutation requires, therefore, that the DPN shuttle between the surfaces of the two substrate specific dehydrogenases. The classical example of this process is the participation of DPN in glycolysis (page 375).

Formally, the reduction of DPN^+ to DPNH by MH_2 (Fig. 19.1) represents acceptance by DPN^+ of a hydride ion ($H:^-$) as a proton enters the medium. This seems a likely mechanism but has not been established unequivocally. It has been suggested that on the enzymic surface, DPN^+ and the substrate may be brought into such close proximity that a "charge transfer complex" may be formed. In such complexes, two organic nuclei approach each other and the reductant transfers an electron to the acceptor. This electron, which is generally distributed through the acceptor molecule, gives it a negative charge. The donor molecule is relatively positively charged, and the charges then serve to maintain the two molecules in an intermolecular complex.

$$A + BH_2 \longrightarrow [A^- BH_2^+] \longrightarrow AH_2 + B$$

Such complexes are highly colored and, in some instances, may be detected spectrophotometrically, but this technique has not been successful for establishing charge transfer complex formation in the reduction of DPN^+ or in the reoxidation of DPNH. Subsequent transfer of a hydrogen atom completes the reduction of the acceptor molecule.

In contrast to their oxidized forms, DPNH and TPNH both strongly absorb light at 340 mμ; this is the basis of most analytical procedures for following reactions in which these coenzymes participate. In addition, both exhibit fluorescence when activated by light at 340 mμ; the maximal emission is at about 465 mμ. The binding of DPNH or TPNH to the apoprotein of a dehydrogenase is accompanied by a shift of the absorption maximum to a lower wavelength (330 to 335 mμ) and a corresponding shift in the maximum of the emitted fluorescent light to about 440 mμ. Under these conditions, there also occurs a considerable intensification of the emitted light (an increase in quantum yield) which renders such fluorescence measurements particularly sensitive as detectors of enzyme-coenzyme complex formation.

An additional technique, *fluorescence polarization,* has provided information concerning the nature of the enzyme-coenzyme complex. When polarized light, of the proper wavelength, is used to activate small molecules, the resultant fluorescence is generally unpolarized. Light quanta can be absorbed only by those molecules appropriately oriented to the exciting wave. The subsequent fluorescence emitted also emerges parallel to the same orientation, *i.e.,* the emitted light from each molecule is polarized. However, brownian motion of small molecules is very rapid, and in the time between absorption and reemission (10^{-8} to 10^{-7} sec.), the molecules in a sample randomly redistribute their positions so that, *in sum,* the emitted light is unpolarized. In contrast, large molecules like proteins exhibit much slower brownian motion. Thus, proteins fluoresce when activated with light at 280 mμ, the absorption maximum of their tryptophan residues, and if the exciting light is plane-polarized, the emitted light is only slightly less polarized. When a dehydrogenase, *e.g.,* lactic acid dehydrogenase, to which DPNH is bound is excited by plane-polarized light at 340 mμ, the emitted fluorescent light is also strongly polarized. Hence, the coenzyme must be tightly bound to the enzyme in a rigid conformation. Such data, however, must be interpreted with caution, since they do not discriminate between binding of DPNH at the catalytic site of a dehydrogenase protein and nonspecific binding elsewhere on the molecule.

The mechanism by which these dehydrogenases catalyze hydrogen transfer remains to be established. Kinetic evidence strongly suggests that transfer requires the transient existence of a ternary complex, *e.g.,* enzyme-lactate-DPN$^+$ which becomes enzyme-pyruvate-DPNH and then dissociates. In those instances which have been carefully studied, there appears to be a compulsory order of binding. Thus, pyruvate cannot bind to lactic acid dehydrogenase until after formation of the enzyme-DPNH complex. This suggests that the enzymic surface, of itself, presents no pyruvate binding site and that the latter results from changes in conformation and/or charge, etc., consequent to formation of the enzyme-DPNH complex. The mode of coenzyme binding is not clear, but for alcohol, lactic acid, and several other dehydrogenases there is evidence that a sulfhydryl group of the protein mediates attachment to the coenzyme.

Several DPN-dependent dehydrogenases are zinc-proteins. Beef liver glutamic acid dehydrogenase and the alcohol dehydrogenases of yeast, horse liver, and human liver contain 4, 4, 2, and 2 gram-atoms of zinc per mole of protein, respectively. Although it is possible that the zinc serves only a structural function, it appears likely that the metal participates in coenzyme and/or substrate binding since the three alcohol dehydrogenases bind 4, 2, and 2 moles of DPNH per mole of protein, respectively. It is of interest that the turnover number of the yeast enzyme is 100 times greater than that of the horse and 1,000 times greater than that of man.

The pyridine nucleotides exhibit marked specificity in structural requirements. For binding to a dehydrogenase, the adenine, carboxamide, pyrophosphate, and ribose portions are all required. Alteration in any aspect of the molecule that affects its normal spatial conformation reduces or destroys its function as a coenzyme. However, Kaplan has prepared several analogues of DPN which can substitute for DPN with various dehydrogenases. Among these are analogues in which, for the —CONH$_2$ group on the pyridine ring, has been substituted $-\overset{\displaystyle \|}{\underset{\displaystyle O}{C}}-CH_3$ or

$-\overset{\displaystyle \|}{\underset{\displaystyle O}{C}}-CH_2-CH_3$ or $-\overset{\displaystyle \|}{\underset{\displaystyle S}{C}}-NH_2$, etc. Each analogue exhibits a higher K_m than

does DPN itself with any particular dehydrogenase, but their relative values differ from one dehydrogenase to another. They also differ somewhat in potential from that of DPN$^+$/DPNH; hence the equilibrium position of the reaction is also altered.

The binding of substrates and coenzymes to the dehydrogenases may alter markedly their redox potentials, usually bringing them closer together. The binding sites are in such proximity and so oriented that appropriate group migration, *e.g.*, a hydride ion, is facilitated. These properties combine to lower E_a for the over-all reaction. In some instances, a group on the protein may itself participate in the reaction mechanism. (See discussion of phosphoglyceraldehyde dehydrogenase, page 372.)

The character of the binding sites for coenzyme and substrate on the enzymic surface confers specificity to the reaction. These binding sites usually exist on a specific polymeric form of the enzyme. Thus, glutamic acid dehydrogenase (molecular weight $= 1 \times 10^6$) can be dissociated into subunits (molecular weight $=$ 250,000) which no longer exhibit enzymic activity. Similarly, yeast alcohol dehydrogenase can be deaggregated into subunits that are inert enzymically. Binding of the specific coenzyme appears to maintain both the conformation and the specific polymeric nature of several dehydrogenases.

The polymeric nature of some dehydrogenases results in the presence of different but related forms of the same enzyme in animal tissues. Lactic acid dehydrogenase of mammalian tissues, molecular weight 135,000, is a tetramer, apparently composed of four chains. Two electrophoretically distinguishable polypeptide chains, α and β, can be equally well bound in such tetramers. Hence, it is possible to observe the presence, in different tissues, of five lactic dehydrogenases which apparently may be composed of 4α, 4β, $1\alpha + 3\beta$, $2\alpha + 2\beta$, or $3\alpha + 1\beta$ chains. These electrophoretically distinct forms of an enzyme with identical function have been termed *isozymes*. Each exhibits different K_m values for DPN and its analogues. The physiological and genetic factors that determine the mixture of the various lactic acid dehydrogenase isozymes characteristic of a given tissue or individual are not known.

In some instances, cells have more than one enzyme that can catalyze the same reaction, yet these are not isozymic forms. Thus, mammalian cells contain malic acid and isocitric acid dehydrogenases in both cytoplasm and mitochondria. The intra- and extramitochondrial forms of each may be distinguished by differing molecular weights, amino acid composition, and electrophoretic and immunochemical behavior.

FLAVOPROTEINS

In 1932 Warburg and Christian obtained from yeast a "yellow ferment" capable of catalyzing the oxidation of TPNH. After the structure of riboflavin had been established, the prosthetic group of this enzyme was recognized as riboflavin 5′-phosphate (flavin mononucleotide, FMN) in 1936. In 1938, Warburg and Christian isolated the coenzyme of renal D-amino acid oxidase and demonstrated it to be flavin adenine dinucleotide, FAD (page 313). Many riboflavin-containing enzymes have been identified subsequently; FAD is the prosthetic group in most instances. Flavoproteins serve as electron transport agents by catalyzing the consecutive reactions shown below.

(a) $MH_2 + flavin \longrightarrow M + reduced\ flavin$
(b) $Reduced\ flavin + X \longrightarrow flavin + XH_2$

MH_2 of reaction (a) may be a metabolite or the reduced form of one of the pyridine nucleotides as illustrated previously (page 341); X may be a metabolite, a pyridine nucleotide, a metal ion, a heme derivative, or O_2. For all flavoproteins, the natural acceptor, X, may be replaced in the laboratory by an appropriate reducible dye such as methylene blue, 2,6-dichlorophenol indophenol, or phenazine methosulfate.

The mode of binding of the flavin moiety to the apoprotein has not been established, but the binding is considerably stronger than that of pyridine nucleotides to their dehydrogenases. The equilibrium constant for the dissociation,

$$Protein\text{-}flavin \rightleftharpoons protein + flavin$$

is generally of the order of 10^{-8} or 10^{-9}; effectively, therefore, the flavin component remains permanently attached to the enzymic protein. In at least one instance, succinic acid dehydrogenase, there is a covalent bond, of unknown nature, between FAD and a group on the protein; hence, the FAD can be removed only by proteolysis. In most other cases the flavin may be separated from the protein by treatment with ammonium sulfate in an acidic medium. The intense fluorescence characteristic of riboflavin is slightly diminished in FMN; the fluorescence of FAD solutions is only 15 per cent that of riboflavin. Binding of either flavin to an apoprotein results in complete quenching of fluorescence.

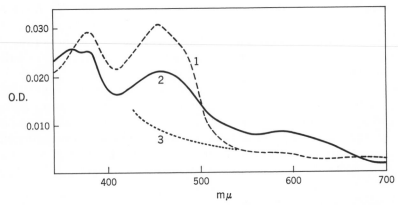

FIG. 19.2. The absorption spectrum of a flavoprotein in the fully oxidized (FAD) (1), semiquinone (FADH·) (2), and fully reduced (FADH₂) (3) forms. The spectrum shown is that of microsomal TPNH–cytochrome c reductase (1), reduced by its substrate (2), and by dithionite (3). (*Courtesy of Dr. H. Kamin and Dr. B. S. Masters.*)

Table 19.3: SOME FLAVOPROTEINS

Substrate	Physiological electron acceptor	Other functional components	Source
D-Amino acids	O_2	...	Liver, kidney
L-Amino acids	O_2	...	Kidney, snake venoms
Diamines	O_2	...	Liver, kidney, brain, plasma
Glucose	O_2	...	Molds, liver
Monoamines	O_2	...	Liver, kidney, brain, plasma
Acyl CoA (C_6–C_{12})	ETF*	...	Liver and heart mitochondria
Butyryl CoA	ETF*	...	Liver and heart mitochondria
Dihydrolipoic acid	DPN^+	...	Heart, liver, *Escherichia coli*
DPNH	Cytochrome b_5	...	Liver microsomes
Reduced glutathione	TPN^+	...	Liver, yeast, *E. coli*
Sarcosine	ETF*	...	Liver and kidney mitochondria
TPNH	Cytochrome c	...	Liver microsomes
TPNH	?	...	Yeast
TPNH	O_2	...	Yeast
TPNH	?	...	Erythrocytes
Choline	Respiratory chain	Fe	Liver mitochondria
Dihydroorotic acid	DPN^+	Fe	*Zymobacterium oroticum*
DPNH	Respiratory chain	Fe	Heart mitochondria
DPNH, TPNH	Menadione	?	Heart mitochondria and cytoplasm
α-Glycerophosphate	Respiratory chain	Fe	Liver mitochondria
L-Gulono-γ-lactone	?	?	Rat liver microsomes
H_2	DPN^+	?	*Clostridium kluyverii*
Purines	O_2	Mo, Fe	Milk
Purines	O_2, DPN	Mo, Fe	Chicken liver
Succinic acid	Respiratory chain	Fe	Heart mitochondria
TPNH	NO_3^-	Mo	*Neurospora*
Aldehydes	O_2	Fe, Mo, ubiquinone	Liver
DPNH	NO_3^-	Heme	*E. coli, Mycobacterium tuberculosis*
DPNH	NO_3^-	Mo, Fe, heme(?)	*Pseudomonas aeruginosa*
DPNH	NO_2^-	Cu, Fe, heme(?)	*P. aeruginosa*
Formic acid	NO_3^-	Vitamin K_3, cytochrome b_1	*E. coli*
D-α-Hydroxyacids	?	Zn^{++}	Yeast
D-Lactic acid	Cytochrome c	Zn^{++}	Yeast
L-Lactic acid	Cytochrome c	Heme	Yeast
Sulfite	O_2, cytochrome c	Heme	Liver microsomes

* ETF, Electron-transferring flavoprotein (page 327).

Flavoproteins exhibit characteristic absorption spectra with maxima at about 280, 380, and 450 mμ. Complete reduction is accompanied by a diminution in the absorption at 280 and 380 mμ and by complete bleaching of the band at 450 mμ, as shown in Fig. 19.2. Formation of the half-reduced form, *i.e.*, the flavin semi-quinone, is evidenced by a decrease of about 50 per cent in absorbancy at 450 mμ and by the appearance of a small but broad absorption band at longer wavelengths (550 to 620 mμ).

Although E_0' for FAD and FMN in solution is readily measurable, E_0' for flavoproteins varies over a wide range, the redox potential being markedly affected by the mode of binding of the coenzyme to the apoprotein.

As evident in Table 19.3, flavoproteins vary in complexity from relatively low molecular weight proteins with a single, easily dissociable FAD or FMN to enzymes that are miniature electron transport systems and may include one or more metal ions, a heme group, or an additional reducible organic group such as ubiquinone (page 314). These types will be discussed in order of increasing complexity.

Among the simplest flavoproteins are the *glucose oxidase* of *Penicillium notatum* (*notatin*) and the "old yellow enzyme" of yeast (page 343), which catalyzes oxidation of TPNH; these contain one FAD and one FMN, respectively. Glucose oxidase is an *aerobic dehydrogenase, i.e.*, it oxidizes an organic substrate and is itself autoxidizable by oxygen. The latter process, as does the oxidation of all autoxidizable flavoproteins, results in peroxide formation.

(*a*) $\text{Glucose} + \text{FAD} \longrightarrow \text{gluconic acid} + \text{FADH}_2$

(*b*) $\text{FADH}_2 + \text{O}_2 \longrightarrow \text{FAD} + \text{H}_2\text{O}_2$

A much larger group of flavoproteins are those which bind two molecules of FAD per molecule of protein. Among them are the L-*amino acid oxidases* of liver, kidney, and snake venoms and the D-*amino acid oxidase* of liver and kidney. In each instance there is evidence of the catalytic participation of a semiquinone intermediate. These enzymes may exist in several forms, indicated as follows.

$$
\text{Enz}\!\!\begin{array}{c}\text{FAD} \\ \\ \text{FAD}\end{array} \qquad \text{Enz}\!\!\begin{array}{c}\text{FADH}_2 \\ \\ \text{FAD}\end{array} \qquad \text{Enz}\!\!\begin{array}{c}\text{FADH}\cdot \\ \\ \text{FADH}\cdot\end{array} \qquad \text{Enz}\!\!\begin{array}{c}\text{FADH}_2 \\ \\ \text{FADH}_2\end{array}
$$

$$
\text{(1)} \qquad\qquad \text{(2)} \qquad\qquad \text{(3)} \qquad\qquad \text{(4)}
$$

The fully oxidized form (1), and the semiquinone form (3) definitely participate in the normal steady-state operation of the enzyme, but the role of forms (2) and (4) is less certain. Reoxidation of the reduced enzyme results in formation of H_2O_2, but it is not known whether form (2) or (3) or a complex between the half oxidized substrate and the flavin semiquinone reacts directly with O_2.

In this regard, microsomal *TPNH–cytochrome c reductase* is of interest since it forms an unusually stable semiquinone which does not react with O_2 whereas the fully reduced enzyme is readily oxidized by O_2 to the semiquinone form.

Many flavoproteins, largely of mitochondrial origin, bind FAD in a manner that prevents its reduced forms from reacting with O_2. Among these flavoproteins are the *acyl coenzyme A* (page 441) and *sarcosine* (page 531) *dehydrogenases,* for which the normal electron acceptor is the flavin moiety of yet another flavoprotein, the *electron-transferring flavoprotein,* ETF, which in turn is capable of directing electrons to the cytochrome system (page 327).

Lipoyl dehydrogenase (page 318), with two FAD molecules per mole and two sulfhydryl groups which become apparent only upon reduction of the enzyme by substrate, is of interest because it catalyzes a reaction between two reactants with E_0' values at least 0.3 volt below that of free FAD.

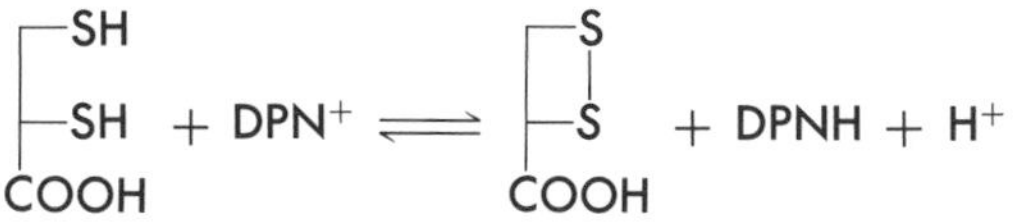

$$\left[\begin{array}{l}-SH \\ -SH \\ COOH\end{array}\right. + DPN^+ \rightleftharpoons \left[\begin{array}{l}-S \\ -S \\ COOH\end{array}\right. + DPNH + H^+$$

A series of experimental observations led Massey to formulate the reaction mechanism shown in Fig. 19.3. A similar mechanism for *glutathione reductase* of *Escherichia coli* seems likely.

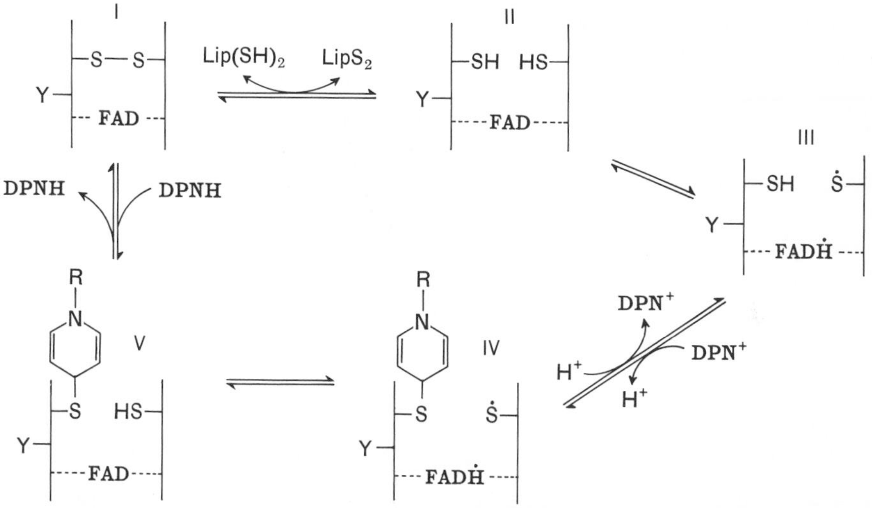

FIG. 19.3. Mechanism of action of lipoyl dehydrogenase. The oxidized enzyme is shown as I. Reduction of the enzyme disulfide by the reduced (sulfhydryl) form of lipoamide results in the disulfhydryl form (II), which transfers one electron to the enzyme-bound FAD (III). This free radical form reacts with DPN^+ to form the transient intermediates IV and V. Departure of DPNH leaves the enzyme in the oxidized form I. R indicates the remainder of the DPN molecule (page 312).

Metal Flavoproteins. Several flavoproteins include firmly bound ferric iron or hexavalent molybdenum. Their mode of action appears to involve full reduction of the flavin moiety by the substrate, followed by successive 1-electron transfers to the metal component and thence to the natural acceptor. Such a scheme appears reasonable for the molybdenum-containing *TPNH–nitrate reductases of Neurospora crassa* and *E. coli.* It is noteworthy that the iron-flavoproteins invariably contain an even number of iron atoms, *e.g.,* dihydroorotic acid (page 574), succinic acid, and DPNH dehydrogenases (page 348). Upon reduction by substrate, these yield a characteristic asymmetric electron spin resonance signal at $g = 1.94$, which is attributed to a pair of very closely situated ferrous atoms. Electron transport is thought to proceed from substrate to flavin to iron to the natural acceptor.

"Cytochrome Reductases." Before recognition of the possible role of ubiquinone in mitochondrial electron transport (page 326), many investigators sought "cytochrome reductases." Indeed, microsomes do contain the *TPNH–cytochrome c reductase* mentioned above (page 345) and another flavoprotein which serves as a *DPNH–cytochrome b_5 reductase* (page 352). The metabolic significance of microsomal electron transport remains obscure. In seeking similar enzymes in mitochondria, a series of flavoproteins that were termed *diaphorases* were found. They catalyze the reduction of dyes, *e.g.*, methylene blue, by DPNH.

$$H^+ + DPNH + \text{methylene blue} \longrightarrow DPN^+ + \text{leukomethylene blue}$$

In view of the variety of flavoproteins that catalyze reduction of metabolites by DPNH and the ease of reduction of diverse dyes by $FADH_2$ and $FMNH_2$, it will be apparent that "diaphorase" activity need not indicate a protein that normally functions between DPNH and the cytochromes. Thus, the diaphorase initially reported has proved to be the lipoyl dehydrogenase described above; its diaphorase activity, therefore, is entirely artifactual. Carefully prepared mitochondrial DPNH dehydrogenase, which appears to contain as many as 16 iron atoms per FAD, does not directly reduce cytochrome c, and its physiological acceptor is uncertain, although it may be ubiquinone. If less care is taken in the preparation of the mitochondria, a protein is obtained that contains FMN rather than FAD and can reduce cytochrome c. However, this activity, again, appears to be artifactual. If, indeed, ubiquinone or some other carrier is interposed between the dehydrogenase and the cytochrome of lowest potential in mitochondrial electron transport, there is no basis for seeking a DPNH– or a succinic acid–cytochrome c reductase.

Iron-Flavoproteins. In view of their common relation to the remainder of the mitochondrial electron transport sequence, it is noteworthy that both succinic acid and DPNH dehydrogenases are iron-flavoproteins that are nonautoxidizable. Both may be isolated as lipid complexes, capable of reducing dyes and ferricyanide, but not cytochrome c or O_2. In contrast, at least three iron-flavoproteins are autoxidizable. These are *dihydroorotic acid dehydrogenase* (page 574), milk *xanthine oxidase* (page 216), and liver *aldehyde oxidase*. In each instance, evidence indicates that the reduction of oxygen is accomplished by the iron atoms in an arrangement similar to that suggested below.

$$\begin{bmatrix} Fe^{++} \\ Fe^{++} \end{bmatrix} + \begin{matrix} O \\ O \end{matrix} \longrightarrow \begin{bmatrix} Fe^{+++} \\ Fe^{+++} \end{bmatrix} + \begin{matrix} O^- \\ O^- \end{matrix}$$

Xanthine and aldehyde oxidases contain molybdenum as well as iron, and it has been suggested that the molybdenum is involved in the initial hydroxylating attack upon the substrate, being the first component of the enzyme to be reduced. Aldehyde oxidase also contains ubiquinone (coenzyme Q_{10}, page 314), and electron transport in this enzyme has been postulated to occur as follows.

$$\text{Substrate} \longrightarrow Mo^{+6} \longrightarrow FAD \longrightarrow \text{ubiquinone} \longrightarrow Fe^{+++} \longrightarrow O_2$$

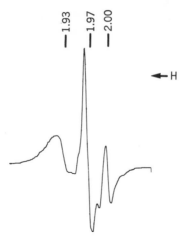

FIG. 19.4. Electron paramagnetic resonance spectrum of the reduced form of rabbit liver aldehyde oxidase. The curve traces the first derivative of the actual signal tracing. The signals at $g = 2.00$, 1.97, and 1.93 indicate the presence of an organic free radical, Mo^{+5}, and an unusual, enzyme-bound form of Fe^{++}, respectively.

Electron spin resonance spectrometry has shown (Fig. 19.4) that the iron and molybdenum are reduced by the substrate and that the semiquinone form of one (or both) of the organic constituents participates in the reaction sequence. The mode of binding of the iron in these diverse enzymes has not been established. Since, however, they exhibit similar absorption spectra with a maximum at 430 mμ and a shoulder at 500 to 550 mμ, and each, upon acidification, releases sulfide in an amount stoichiometric to the iron, it is apparent that the mode of iron binding is common to all members of the group.

Hemoflavoproteins. Several enzymes are known to possess at their catalytic sites a molecule of FAD (or FMN) and a heme group. All these enzymes are bound within the lipid structure of mitochondria or the respiratory particles of microorganisms. Best known is the L (+)-*lactic acid dehydrogenase* of yeast, which has one FMN and one iron-protoporphyrin IX per molecule. This protein is also known as *cytochrome b_2*. A cytochrome such as cytochrome c serves normally as final electron acceptor. Electron transport appears to occur in the following sequence.

$$\text{Lactate} \longrightarrow \text{FMN} \longrightarrow \text{heme-Fe}^{+++} \longrightarrow \text{cytochrome c}$$

Other hemoflavoproteins are listed in Table 19.3. Thus, "flavoproteins" vary from relatively small proteins, with a single flavin prosthetic group, to large proteins, on the surface of which is a multiple-component electron transport system.

CYTOCHROMES

The discovery of the cytochromes and their general identification by Keilin has been described earlier (page 199). It is now evident that cytochromes occur in the cells of virtually all aerobic organisms. In general, the cytochrome content of tissues parallels their respiratory activity; the highest concentrations are found in heart and other actively working muscles, such as the flight muscles of birds and insects. Lesser quantities occur in liver, kidney, brain, and nonstriated muscle; the lowest values are in skin and lung. Tumors and embryonic tissue are unusually low in cytochrome content, consistent with the fact that these tissues derive energy largely by anaerobic pathways of metabolism.

Keilin's early studies of the cytochromes demonstrated that in the presence of oxidizable substrates, and in the absence of oxygen, a series of sharp absorption bands was visible upon spectroscopic examination of a tissue suspension. Admission of oxygen resulted in disappearance of these bands, which were replaced by a group of less intense and more diffuse bands. This permitted Keilin to distinguish three cytochromes, which he designated as a, b, and c. In reduced form, each was characterized by a series of absorption maxima, summarized in Table 19.4. Of this group, Keilin demonstrated that it is cytochrome a which is autoxidizable, *i.e.*, it is reduced cytochrome a which effects the reduction of molecular oxygen. Hence, cytochrome a, which was shown to be reduced by cytochrome c, has been termed *cytochrome oxidase*. In subsequent years it has become apparent that there are numerous cytochromes. As each has been identified, it has been designated according to which of the original cytochromes it most closely resembles by these spectroscopic criteria: thus, cytochrome b_1, b_2, b_3, b_4, etc. This nomenclature should not be interpreted as indicating that their structures are *necessarily* closely related, that their E_0' values are of the same magnitude, or that they serve equivalent roles in electron transport.

Table 19.4: PROPERTIES OF MAMMALIAN CYTOCHROMES

Cytochrome	Absorption maxima of reduced forms			E_0' , volts
	α, mμ	β, mμ	γ, mμ	
a_3	600	...	445	
a	605	517	414	+0.29
c	550	521	416	+0.25
c_1	554	523	418	+0.22
b	563	530	430	+0.07
b_5	557	527	423	+0.03

Addition of intermediates of the citric acid cycle to tissue suspensions, under anaerobic conditions, results in rapid reduction of the cytochromes in the order b, c_1, c, and a; admission of oxygen rapidly reoxidizes all components. However, reoxidation can be prevented by cyanide, azide, sulfide, and carbon monoxide. The respiration of most animal tissues is reduced 60 to 90 per cent by these inhibitors, presumably indicating that at least this fraction of the respiration of animal cells normally occurs over the electron chain leading to cytochrome oxidase.

Except for cytochrome b_5, all the cytochromes of animal cells are associated with the mitochondrial protein-lipid complex. Only cytochrome c is readily obtained as a homogeneous, water-soluble protein by extraction with aqueous solvents; the other cytochromes remain fixed to the insoluble particulate matter of the mitochondria. However, treatment of mitochondria or mitochondrial fragments with detergents, *e.g.*, deoxycholate or dodecylsulfate, permits isolation of each of the mitochondrial cytochromes in relatively pure form. It must be cautioned, however, that their properties in aqueous solution may differ markedly from those which obtain in their native hydrophobic milieu.

The *cytochromes b* are those of lowest potential; E_0' for isolated heart cytochrome b in aqueous solution is -0.34 volt, whereas in mitochondria it behaves as if E_0' were about $+0.07$ volt. In the absence of a cationic detergent, this protein (with molecular weight of 28,000) readily aggregates to a polymeric form. The structure of the prosthetic group is not known with certainty, but it appears to be heme (iron-protoporphyrin IX, page 190). The reduced form does not autoxidize, nor does the oxidized form react with cyanide.

Cytochrome c has been obtained in crystalline form from a large variety of animal tissues. The complete amino acid sequences of the cytochrome c proteins obtained from the hearts of human, horse, and other species have been elucidated (pages 200, 616). At neutral pH, ferrocytochrome c does not react with CO or O_2 nor can the ferric form react with CN^-. Thus, the fully coordinated iron atom must lie in a crevice, probably bound to two imidazole groups defined by the location of the two histidine residues of tuna cytochrome c (page 615), and is prevented from reacting with the afore-mentioned reagents. A similar behavior is seen with cytochromes b and c_1. Thus, apparently only an electron can enter or leave these molecules; the sites of this activity are unknown.

Treatment of the purified protein with the mixed lipids of mitochondria or with purified phosphatidyl ethanolamine yields a lipid-soluble complex of which only 15 per cent is cytochrome c. In this form, cytochrome c readily serves as substrate for cytochrome oxidase, and this may resemble the manner in which cytochrome c functions in mitochondria.

Cytochrome c_1 is the most recently recognized of the mitochondrial cytochromes; its spectroscopic properties closely resemble those of cytochrome c (Table 19.4). Their prosthetic groups and mode of attachment to the proteins are identical. Cytochrome c_1 is obtained as a polymer of a unit that has a molecular weight of 38,000. The ferrous form of neither the latter nor its polymer can react directly with cytochrome oxidase. Addition of a small amount of cytochrome c permits rapid oxidation, by the oxidase, of substrate amounts of cytochrome c_1. Thus, cytochromes c and c_1 react readily together, but only the former is a substrate for cytochrome oxidase. The advantage to the cell of the presence of both cytochrome c and cytochrome c_1 is not apparent.

Cytochrome oxidase is the terminal member of the cytochrome chain inasmuch as it is the only member capable of reducing oxygen. From the absorption spectra of yeast and heart muscle preparations treated with CO or cyanide and reduced by substrate, it had been concluded that two cytochromes, a and a_3, were present as terminal members of the chain. Of these, a_3 was thought to be autoxidizable at low O_2 tension and to combine with CO and CN^- whereas cytochrome a does not. Hence, a_3 was considered to be the actual oxidase. However, purified preparations of cytochrome oxidase exhibit only the spectral properties of cytochrome a, yet readily autoxidize and react with CO and cyanide. No adequate explanation of this discrepancy is available. Considerable evidence indicates that cytochrome oxidase is readily autoxidizable only in the presence of cytochrome c. Thus in effect cytochrome oxidase is a cytochrome c–cytochrome a complex and the appearance of a cytochrome a_3 in intact mitochondria may relate to this fact. Cytochrome oxidase is a polymer of subunits of molecular weight about 72,000, each of which contains one heme as well as one atom of copper, and is active only in the polymeric form complexed with mitochondrial lipid. The prosthetic group of cytochrome oxidase, termed heme$_a$ and porphyrin "a," is a derivative of deuteroheme (Table 11.1, page 189), with the following structure.

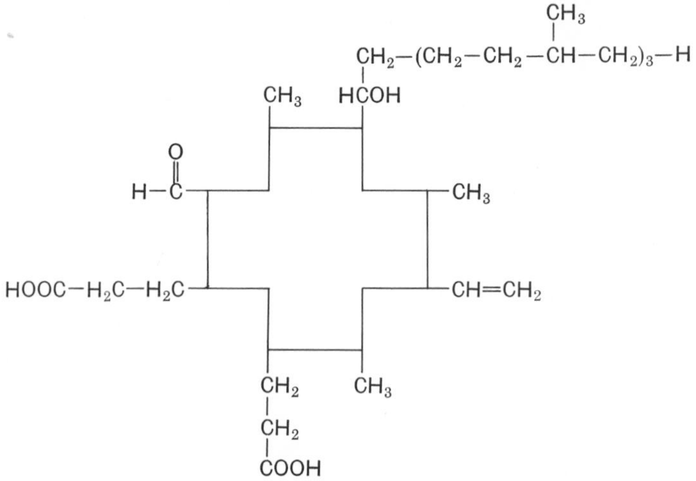

$$CH_2-(CH_2-CH_2-\underset{\underset{CH_3}{|}}{CH}-CH_2)_3-H$$

The oxidized ferric form of the enzyme combines avidly with CN^- at low concentration and cannot then be reduced; this provides explanation for the high toxicity of cyanide. Reaction of the ferrous form with CO and O_2 reveals a competition reminiscent of that observed with hemoglobin. The presence of one copper atom per heme and the demonstration that the copper can be reversibly reduced in the presence of cytochrome c and reoxidized in the presence of oxygen led to the suggestion that the copper atom may be the immediate site of oxygen binding and reduction. Resolution of this problem may permit insight into the actual mechanism of oxygen reduction. This reaction can at present only be described by the following equation.

$$O_2 + 2H^+ + 4e \longrightarrow 2OH^-$$

No intermediates have been detected, despite the fact that if the O_2 is attached at either the ferrous or cuprous atom of the reduced cytochrome oxidase, four consecutive 1-electron transfers would appear to be required.

   Cytochrome b_5 is present in microsomes from liver and other animal tissues and is a protein of molecular weight 13,000 with iron-protoporphyrin IX as its prosthetic group. The physiological role of this material is puzzling. These microsomes also contain a flavoprotein which catalyzes reduction of cytochrome b_5 by DPNH. Ferrocytochrome b_5 is not autoxidizable; in vitro it may be oxidized by cytochrome c, but the normal mode of reoxidation is not clear since microsomal cytochrome b_5 does not have access to the mitochondrial electron transport system. This protein is of particular interest since it is the only cytochrome that has been resolved into its heme and apoprotein constituents and successfully reconstituted. This study revealed that binding of heme is effected by one imidazole group and one amino group of the protein. It should be noted that microsomes also contain a specific *TPNH–cytochrome c reductase;* as in the case of cytochrome b_5 reductase, the physiological role of this enzyme is not understood.

BACTERIAL CYTOCHROMES AND ELECTRON TRANSPORT

The cells of higher plants respire in a manner similar to that of animals. Respiration is conducted in mitochondria which contain enzymes of the citric acid cycle, an organized electron transport system with cytochromes resembling those of animals, and an associated phosphorylating system. However, in bacterial cells, organelles resembling mitochondria are not apparent. The respiratory systems of bacteria may be obtained from broken cell preparations as small lipid-rich insoluble particles of varying size which appear to be fragments of the cell membrane. These particles contain dehydrogenases and cytochromes and conduct oxidative phosphorylation. The dehydrogenases are similar to those of mammalian cells. The cytochromes of bacteria may be classified on the basis of their absorption spectra as cytochromes a, b, and c, but these designations do not necessarily connote electron transport relationships similar to those in animal mitochondria. Cytochromes of the c type are most widely distributed and, in aerobes, generally resemble those of mammals. Several bacteria appear to possess more than one autoxidizable cytochrome of the a class, and widely distributed among bacteria is a heme-protein that has been designated cytochrome o. The latter, which has a prosthetic group resembling that of cytochrome c, seems to serve as the terminal oxidase in those cells in which it is found.

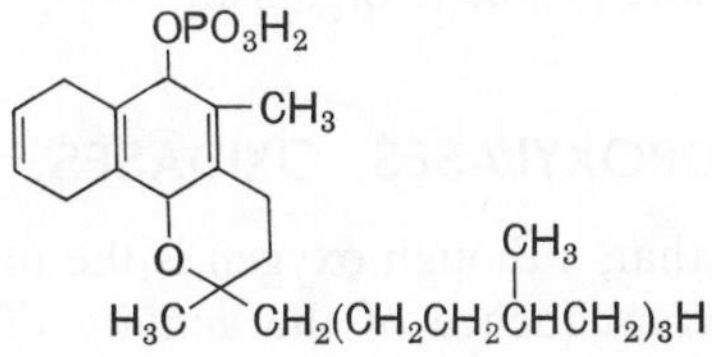

The character of oxidative phosphorylation in bacteria differs markedly from that of mammalian mitochondria. In no instance is there evidence of "respiratory control"; absence of ADP or P_i does not limit the rate of respiration. With the exception of *Mycobacterium phlei,* bacterial systems are insensitive to the uncoupling action of dinitrophenol, and in *M. phlei,* dinitrophenol not only uncouples phosphorylation incident to electron transport, but also abolishes the substrate level phosphorylation associated with the oxidation of α-ketoglutaric acid. Of interest is the suggestion that a derivative of *vitamin K_1* may participate in the respiratory chain of several bacteria, notably *M. phlei.* Thus, when incubated with respiratory particles of *M. phlei,* the α-chromanyl phosphate derivative of reduced vitamin K_1 reduces cytochrome c with concomitant ATP formation. This derivative of vitamin K (Chap. 56) accumulates when *M. phlei* particles are incubated anaerobically with substrate. These findings are of interest in view of repeated reports that abnormally low P/O ratios are obtained with mitochondria from vitamin K–deficient animals, although significant quantities of vitamin K are not known to be present in animal mitochondria.

Cytochromes are entirely absent from the cells of such obligate anaerobes as clostridia and from such facultative aerobes as pneumococci and staphylococci. Oxygen consumption in the latter species reflects the activity of autoxidizable flavoproteins. Extensive studies have been conducted of the cytochromes of "oxidative anaerobes," *viz.*, the photosynthetic bacteria that live anaerobically and generate both reducing and oxidizing power by photolysis of water, and the chemosynthetic bacteria, organisms for which N_2, $SO_4^=$, NO_3^-, or Fe^{+++} serves as ultimate oxidant. All such organisms contain cytochromes which mediate reduction of the oxidant. It must be emphasized that the presence of a cytochrome c is postulated on the basis of spectroscopic evidence, *viz.*, absorption bands for the reduced compound at 550, 525, and 415 mμ. This spectrum is characteristic of the prosthetic group, whereas the redox potential appears to reflect also the mode of attachment to the protein as well as the size, conformation, and composition of the protein.

The lowest potential recorded is that of cytochrome c_3 from *Desulfovibrio desulfuricans,* with an E_0' of -0.20 volt, 0.5 volt lower than that of horse heart cytochrome c, but appropriate for functioning in the reduction of $SO_4^=$ to $SO_3^=$ ($E_0' = -0.19$ volt) by H_2 at pH 7.0 ($E_0' = -0.4$ volt). This unusual cytochrome contains two heme groups per molecule and has a molecular weight of only 12,000. Nitrate-reducing organisms, such as *Pseudomonas denitrificans,* contain cytochromes of more conventional redox potential, satisfactory for reduction of NO_3^- to NO_2^- ($E_0' = +0.5$ volt). It is not known whether ATP may be generated in the course of these reactions. Cytochromes c from photosynthetic bacteria exhibit E_0' values ranging from 0 to $+0.35$ volt. Of the many cytochromes c isolated from bacteria, only a few can serve as substrate for mammalian cytochrome oxidase, whereas cytochromes c from aerobes can be oxidized by the cytochrome oxidases of the same species. It will be recognized that only a beginning has been made in characterizing the bacterial cytochromes. Spectroscopic classification may be seriously misleading with regard to function. In an organism such as *Hemophilus parainfluenzae,* which has several cytochromes c, the cytochromes c can operate as an electron transport chain by virtue of their differences in potential, whereas the cytochrome component of *Pseudomonas aeruginosa,* apparently consisting of two cytochrome prosthetic groups, may well employ consecutive transfer from the heme of its cytochrome c–like group to that of the cytochrome a_2 group on the surface of the same protein. Despite the apparent diversity among the dozens of different bacterial cytochromes, the principles of electron transfer in mammalian mitochondria are equally evident in these more primitive organisms.

OXYGENASES, HYDROXYLASES, OXIDASES, AND PEROXIDASES

Earlier it was noted that, although oxygen is the ultimate biological oxidant, most respiration is the consequence of the activity of enzymes which catalyze reaction between substrate and a coenzyme (DPN or FAD); thereafter electrons are transported from the reduced coenzyme to oxygen via a cytochrome-containing transport system. It is this arrangement which permits conservation of energy and ATP synthesis. A large number of enzymes, however, do in fact catalyze a direct reaction between a substrate and molecular oxygen. These reactions are seen in a wide variety of biosynthetic and degradative pathways, particularly of aromatic compounds and steroids. The chemical energy thus released is wasted since there is no associated means of energy conservation. Many of these enzymes will be encountered in subsequent chapters of this textbook. Accordingly, only a general survey is provided here. It may also be noted that the contribution of reactions of this type to the total oxygen consumption of the organism is small.

Oxidases. Two major classes of oxidases have been encountered previously. Autoxidizable flavoproteins, such as the D- and L-*amino acid oxidases,* reduce oxygen to the level of peroxide (Chap. 24), which must be decomposed by catalase or utilized by a peroxidase (page 357). Cytochrome oxidase provides a means for reduction of oxygen to water by electrons from the metal(s) of the enzyme plus protons from the medium. In principle, the copper-containing enzymes, *ascorbic acid oxidase* (page 360) and *laccase* (see below), are of the same type. Both the latter, like hemocyanin (Chap. 34) and ceruloplasmin (Chap. 32), are blue in the native state, contain bound cupric ions, and can be bleached by their substrates. Laccase, from the lacquer tree, catalyzes oxidation of a large group of *o-* and *p*-dihydroxyphenols to the corresponding quinones. Presumably in each instance, the substrate reduces the metal to the cuprous state, and, in some manner, the enzyme then effects the 4-electron reduction of O_2. In contrast, however, *phenolase,* from mushroom or potato, catalyzes a similar oxidation of *o*-phenols to *o*-quinones, e.g.,

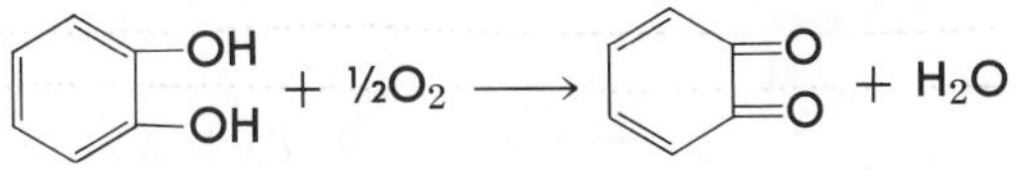

$$\text{(catechol)} \quad + \tfrac{1}{2}O_2 \longrightarrow \text{(o-quinone)} + H_2O$$

but the mechanism is unclear since, in this enzyme, the four to six copper atoms per molecule appear at all times to be in the cuprous condition. Phenolase also exhibits phenol hydroxylase activity.

Oxygenases may be defined as that group of enzymes which utilize oxygen for oxidation of the substrate by a mechanism resulting in incorporation of both atoms of the oxygen molecule into the product. An example is the *pyrocatechase* of bacterial origin, discovered by Hayaishi, which catalyzes oxidation of catechol to *cis, cis*-muconic acid.

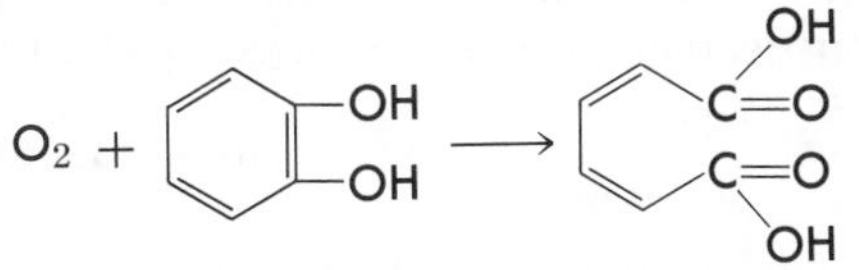

$$O_2 + \text{(Catechol)} \longrightarrow \text{(cis,cis-Muconic acid)}$$

Catechol   *cis,cis*-Muconic acid

Other similar oxygenases are listed in Table 19.5. Each of these enzymes contains ferrous iron; it is presumed that oxygen binding and reaction occur at this site on

Table 19.5: Some Oxygenases and Their Distribution

Enzyme	Substrate	Product	Source
Pyrocatechase.....................	Catechol	*cis, cis*-Muconic acid	*Pseudomonas*
Tryptophan pyrrolase................	L-Tryptophan	L-Formylkynurenine	Rat liver
Homogentisic acid oxygenase.........	Homogentisic acid	Maleylacetoacetic acid	Rat liver
Hydroxyanthranilic acid oxygenase.....	3-Hydroxy-anthranilic acid	Picolinic acid	Rat liver
Protocatechuic acid oxygenase........	Protocatechuic acid	*cis, cis*-β-Carboxy-muconic acid	*Neurospora*
Inositol oxygenase.................	Inositol	Glucuronic acid	Liver

the enzyme, but the mechanism is not known. No intermediates, such as the hypothetical peroxy compound, have been found.

Hydroxylases. Many instances of hydroxylation of an organic substrate, usually an aromatic nucleus, have been recognized, *i.e.*,

$$R\text{—}H \longrightarrow R\text{—}OH$$

The newly introduced oxygen atom derives from water rather than from oxygen in at least three instances studied. These include the oxidation of purines by milk xanthine oxidase (pages 216 and 348), of N^1-methylnicotinamide by liver "aldehyde oxidase" (Chap. 55), and of nicotinic acid by various bacteria. The first two enzymes are molybdoflavoproteins, and the mechanism proposed is removal of a hydride ion, which is accepted by the flavin, and replacement by a hydroxyl ion from the medium.

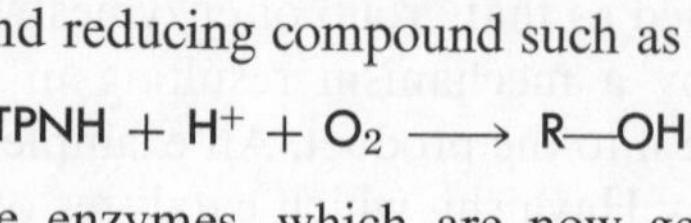

However, studies with O_2^{18} have demonstrated that most hydroxylation reactions involve incorporation of an atom of oxygen from atmospheric O_2 into the product, while the other atom is reduced to the level of water. The reaction requires participation of a second reducing compound such as TPNH.

$$R\text{—}H + TPNH + H^+ + O_2 \longrightarrow R\text{—}OH + TPN^+ + H_2O$$

Hence, the responsible enzymes, which are now generally termed *hydroxylases,* were originally described as "mixed-function oxidases" by Mason, who discovered this general class of reactions. Typical of reactions of this type is the hydroxylation of acetanilide by the nonspecific "aromatic hydroxylase" of rat liver microsomes.

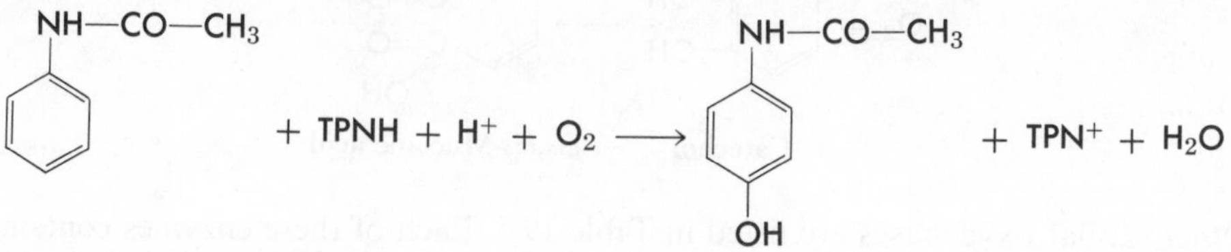

TPNH is the reducing cosubstrate for most hydroxylations, particularly in mammalian liver. However, as indicated in Table 19.6 (page 358), other substrates such as DPNH, ascorbic acid, and dihydroxyfumaric acid have been found to function in this capacity, particularly in bacterial systems. An important enzyme in mammalian metabolism, phenylalanine hydroxylase (page 500), utilizes as coelectron donor a tetrahydropteridine (page 500).

One final member of this enzyme group is of interest. The *lactic acid oxidative decarboxylase* of mycobacteria, which utilizes FMN as prosthetic group, is a "mixed-function oxidase." The reaction catalyzed is the following.

$$CH_3CHOHCOOH + O_2 \longrightarrow CH_3COOH + CO_2 + H_2O$$

In this reaction an atom of oxygen is introduced into the acetic acid formed. Simultaneously, a pair of electrons is withdrawn from the *same substrate* and transferred via the flavin to the second oxygen atom, which is reduced to water. The detailed mechanism has not been elucidated.

Catalases and Peroxidases. Thénard, who discovered hydrogen peroxide, observed in 1818 that this substance was decomposed by animal tissues, with the liberation of gaseous oxygen.

$$2H_2O_2 \longrightarrow 2H_2O + O_2$$

Seventy-five years later it was established that this effect was due to a specific enzyme, named *catalase* by Loew in 1901. Recognition of the possible metabolic significance of this enzyme and of the closely allied *peroxidases* awaited the observation that aerobic autoxidation of flavoproteins results in peroxide formation (page 345). The earliest observation of peroxidase activity was made by Schönbein, in 1855, who found that plant and animal tissues were able to "activate" hydrogen peroxide so that tincture of guaiac was oxidized and colored blue in its presence. Since then, many polyphenols have been observed to be oxidized by tissue extracts.

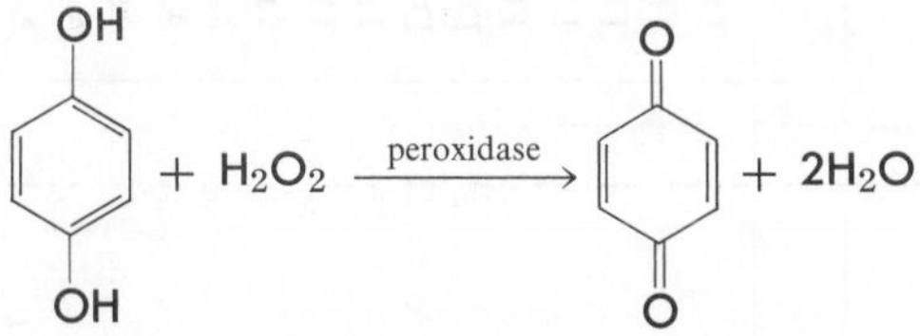

Catalase activity is present in nearly all animal cells and organs; liver, erythrocytes, and kidney are rich sources. This activity is also present in all plant materials studied and in all microorganisms other than obligate anaerobes. In each instance, catalase is believed to prevent accumulation of noxious peroxide under circumstances otherwise favoring such an event.

Peroxidases are relatively rare in the animal world. Liver and kidney exhibit weak peroxidase activity, and a peroxidase has been isolated from milk; leukocytes contain a "verdoperoxidase," which is responsible for the peroxidase activity of pus. All higher plants, on the other hand, are rich in peroxidase activity. Horseradish and turnip have been extensively employed in investigations of the peroxidases. Some peroxidases exhibit specificity for a substrate other than phenols. Thus, erythrocytes contain a peroxidase specific for oxidation of reduced glutathione

Table 19.6: SOME HYDROXYLASES

Enzyme	Reductant	Substrate	Product	Source
Aromatic hydroxylase.	TPNH	Acetanilide	p-Hydroxyacetanilide	Liver
Kynurenine hydroxylase.	TPNH	L-Kynurenine	L-3-Hydroxykynurenine	Liver
Steroid 11-hydroxylase.	TPNH	Deoxycorticosterone	Corticosterone	Adrenal
Steroid 17-hydroxylase.	TPNH	Progesterone	17 α-Hydroxyprogesterone	Adrenal
Squalene oxidocyclase	TPNH	Squalene	Lanosterol	Liver
Imidazoleacetic acid hydroxylase	DPNH	Imidazoleacetic acid	Imidazoloneacetic acid	Pseudomonas
Kynurenic acid hydroxylase. . . .	DPNH	Kynurenic acid	Kynurenic acid 7,8-dihydrol	Pseudomonas
Cholesterol 20-hydroxylase. . . .	TPNH	Cholesterol	20-Hydroxycholesterol	Adrenal
Steroid 21-hydroxylase.	TPNH or DPNH	Progesterone	Deoxycorticosterone	Adrenal
Fatty acid hydroxylase.	TPNH or DPNH	Fatty acids	ω-Hydroxy fatty acids	Liver
Fatty acyl CoA hydroxylase	?	Fatty acyl CoA	9:10-Fatty acyl CoA	Yeast
Phenolase.	Ascorbic acid	3,4-Dimethylphenol	4,5-Dimethylcatechol	Mushroom
Hydroxyphenylpyruvic acid oxidase. . .	Ascorbic acid	p-Hydroxyphenylpyruvic acid	Homogentisic acid	Liver
Dopamine hydroxylase.	Ascorbic acid	3,4-Dihydroxyphenylethylamine	Norepinephrine	Adrenal
Phenylalanine hydroxylase.	A pteridine	Phenylalanine	Tyrosine	Liver

(Chap. 42); yeast and placenta contain peroxidases for ferrocytochrome c, and some bacteria possess peroxidases that oxidize DPNH. Advantage is taken of the peroxidase activity of all hemoproteins in the usual laboratory procedures for the detection of occult blood in feces, urine, etc. Minute amounts of blood, in the presence of peroxide, catalyze the oxidation of benzidine, gum guaiac, and other substances to colored products.

If the catalatic reaction is written as

$$\begin{matrix} HO \\ | \\ HO \end{matrix} \;+\; \begin{matrix} HO \\ \diagup \\ HO \end{matrix} \;\longrightarrow\; 2H_2O \;+\; \begin{matrix} O \\ \| \\ O \end{matrix}$$

and the peroxidatic reaction as

$$\begin{matrix} HO \\ | \\ HO \end{matrix} \;+\; \begin{matrix} HO \\ \diagup \\ HO \end{matrix}\, R \;\longrightarrow\; 2H_2O \;+\; \begin{matrix} O \\ \| \\ R \\ \| \\ O \end{matrix}$$

the analogy between the two reactions becomes more apparent. In this sense, the catalatic splitting of hydrogen peroxide to water and oxygen becomes merely a special case of a peroxidatic reaction in which hydrogen peroxide serves both as substrate and as acceptor. This analogy becomes more real on noting that at high concentrations of low molecular weight alcohols or formaldehyde and low peroxide concentration, catalase also exhibits peroxidatic activity. This, therefore, represents a competition between two acceptors for the "activated peroxide." Under the conditions ordinarily used to study these reactions, peroxide is the favored acceptor for catalase activity. However, since physiologically there may exist high concentrations of other acceptors and very low concentration of peroxide, it is conceivable that catalase serves almost exclusively as a peroxidase in animal tissues. This has cast doubt upon the existence of an independent peroxidase in animal tissues. Theorell has proposed that both classes of enzymes be given the common name *hydroperoxidases,* indicating that their common substrate is hydrogen peroxide.

Ferriprotoprophyrin IX (page 191) is the prosthetic group of both mammalian catalases and horseradish peroxidase. Beef liver catalase of molecular weight 248,000 has four heme groups per enzyme molecule. It may be dissociated into smaller subunits, but they lack enzymic activity. The turnover rate for catalase is higher than that of any other known enzyme; one molecule of catalase can decompose 44,000 molecules of hydrogen peroxide per second. Catalase reacts with H_2O_2 to form a relatively stable enzyme-substrate complex (page 227) of uncertain structure. It is in this form only that catalase may react with the specific inhibitor 3-amino-1,2,4-triazole.

Horseradish peroxidase has a molecular weight of about 44,000 and one heme group per molecule. It reacts with peroxide to give a series of consecutive complexes, which have been designated compounds I, II, and III respectively, and characterized by their absorption spectra. It is uncertain whether compound I is a "complex" with H_2O_2 or an oxidized form of the enzyme containing ferryl ($Fe^{++}O$) iron. In any case this is converted to compound II and back to the original enzyme

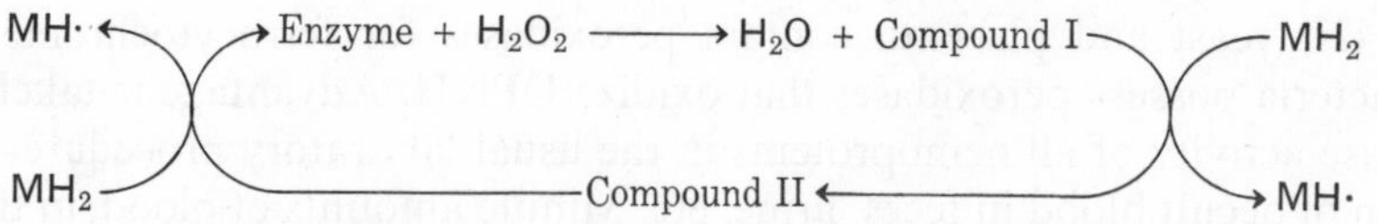

FIG. 19.5. Proposed mechanism of action of peroxidase (see text).

in consecutive reactions, in each of which the substrate appears to be oxidized to a free radical (Fig. 19.5).

OTHER ELECTRON CARRIERS

Ubiquinone. Crane and his colleagues demonstrated the presence in mitochondria of a group of related quinones that were reduced when mitochondria were incubated anaerobically with various substrates. Accordingly, they were designated as coenzyme Q (for quinone) before their structure was established by Folkers and coworkers. The type of structure has been given previously (page 314), and their postulated role in electron transport has been presented (page 326).

Glutathione, γ-glutamylcysteinylglycine (GSH), is a ubiquitous component of animal tissues. Since free cysteine is present in only trivial quantities, glutathione is the most abundant sulfhydryl compound in cells and appears to function in maintaining many enzymes in their active conformation. Spontaneous oxidation of these enzymes may lead to disulfide formation. Consecutive disulfide exchange reactions with glutathione can serve to restore the active sulfhydryl forms, thus:

$$2Enz—SH + O_2 \longrightarrow Enz—S—S—Enz$$
$$Enz—S—S—Enz + GSH \longrightarrow EnzSH + Enz—S—S—G$$
$$Enz—S—S—G + GSH \longrightarrow EnzSH + G—S—S—G$$

The oxidized glutathione can then be reduced by the widely distributed flavoprotein *glutathione reductase* which utilizes reduced TPN.

$$TPNH + H^+ + GSSG \longrightarrow TPN^+ + 2GSH$$

Glutathione functions as the specific coenzyme for *glyoxalase* activity. Methylglyoxal undergoes an intramolecular oxidation-reduction to lactate in liver and muscle, although the metabolic origin of methylglyoxal is unknown. Lohmann demonstrated that glutathione is necessary for this dismutation; Quastel postulated formation of a glutathione-methylglyoxal complex which was later isolated by Racker, who also found that the consecutive action of two enzymes is required for glyoxalase activity.

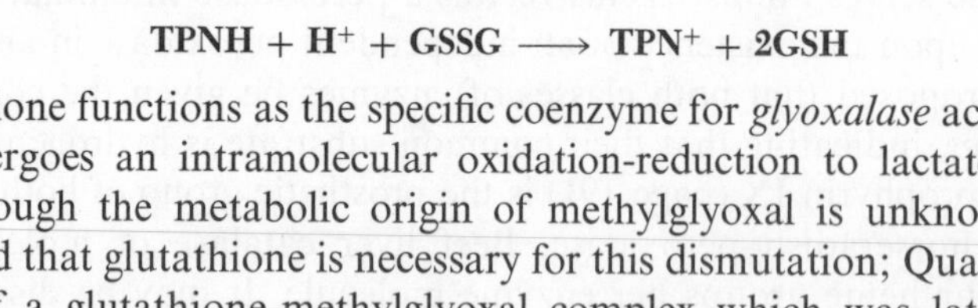

Ascorbic Acid. Ascorbic acid is reversibly oxidized by many oxidants and tissues, particularly those of plants, to dehydroascorbic acid. This reaction is catalyzed by *ascorbic acid oxidase,* a copper protein that resembles laccase in its action and reduces oxygen to water. Some plant tissues appear to maintain a respiratory

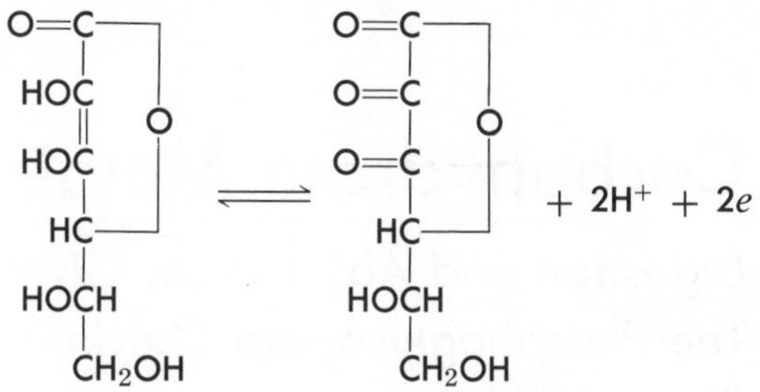

Ascorbic acid   Dehydroascorbic acid

pathway in which the electron flow is

$$MH_2 \longrightarrow TPN^+ \longrightarrow GSSG \longrightarrow \text{dehydroascorbate} \longrightarrow O_2$$

but the physiological role of this process is not clear.

REFERENCES

Books

Falk, J. E., Lemberg, R., and Morton, R. E., eds., "Haematin Enzymes," Pergamon Press, New York, 1961.

Hayaishi, O., "The Oxygenases," Academic Press, Inc., New York, 1962.

Kosower, E. M., "Molecular Biochemistry," McGraw-Hill Book Company, Inc., New York, 1962.

Lardy, H. A., "Respiratory Enzymes," Burgess Publishing Company, Minneapolis, 1949.

Udenfriend, S., "Fluorescence Assay in Biology and Medicine," Academic Press, Inc., New York, 1962.

Wolstenholme, G. E. W., and O'Connor, C. M., eds., "Quinones in Electron Transport," Little, Brown and Company, Boston, 1961.

Review Articles

Beinert, H., Flavin Coenzymes, in P. D. Boyer, H. Lardy, and K. Myrbäck, eds., "The Enzymes," vol. II, pp. 339–416, Academic Press, Inc., New York, 1960.

Hatefi, Y., Coenzyme Q (ubiquinone), *Advances in Enzymol.*, **25**, 275–328, 1963.

Kaplan, N. O., The Pyridine Coenzymes, in P. D. Boyer, H. Lardy, and K. Myrbäck, eds., "The Enzymes," vol. III, pp. 105–170, Academic Press, Inc., New York, 1960.

Lemberg, R., Cytochromes of Group A and Their Prosthetic Groups, *Advances in Enzymol.*, **23**, 265–322, 1961.

Mahler, H. R., Nature and Function of Metalloflavoproteins, *Advances in Enzymol.*, **17**, 233–292, 1956.

Mason, H. S., Mechanisms of Oxygen Metabolism, *Advances in Enzymol.*, **19**, 79–233, 1957.

Paul, K. G., Heme Compounds in Enzyme Catalysis, in P. D. Boyer, H. Lardy, and K. Myrbäck, eds., "The Enzymes," vol. III, pp. 277–328, Academic Press, Inc., New York, 1960.

Racker, E., Action and Properties of Pyridine Nucleotide-linked Enzymes, *Physiol. Revs.*, **35**, 1–56, 1955.

Shifrin, S., and Kaplan, N. O., Coenzyme Binding, *Advances in Enzymol.*, **22**, 337–415, 1960.

Singer, T. P., and Kearney, E. B., Chemistry, Metabolism, and Scope of Action of the Pyridine Nucleotide Coenzymes, *Advances in Enzymol.*, **15**, 79–140, 1954.

Theorell, H., Kinetics and Equilibria in the Liver Alcohol Dehydrogenase System, *Advances in Enzymol.*, **20**, 31–49, 1958.

20. Carbohydrate Metabolism

Digestion and Absorption. Glycolysis.
The Phosphogluconate Oxidative Pathway.
Photosynthesis

Many processes essential to life are *endergonic*. In animals, the energy demands of these processes must be met by chemical energy derived from the diet. Ultimately, however, this energy is derived from the sun; as will be discussed subsequently, chlorophyll-containing plants can absorb solar energy and utilize it for synthesis of organic compounds. These compounds in turn serve as energy sources for other transformations of radiant energy into chemical bond energy.

For mammals, energy in the form of dietary carbohydrate is provided by a relatively few substances. Of the total food ingested, as much as 60 per cent may be carbohydrate, and most of this is in the form of starches, amylose and amylopectin; glycogen may be present in small amount. Other polysaccharides in the diet, but of little nutritional significance in most animal species, are cellulose and the pentosans. The disaccharide sucrose is widely distributed in the vegetable world and is added in variable amounts in the preparation and seasoning of foods. Of special importance in infant nutrition is the disaccharide lactose. Except for small amounts of glucose and fructose, monosaccharides are not present in significant quantities in the normal diet.

DIGESTION OF DIETARY CARBOHYDRATES

The mucosa of the gastrointestinal tract acts as a barrier against the entry into the body proper of large molecules, which, if absorbed, are not well utilized. *Digestion* is the sum of the enzymic hydrolyses of large molecules—polysaccharides, proteins, lipids, nucleic acids—to smaller components which can be absorbed and then metabolized.

Salivary Digestion of Polysaccharides. When saliva is incubated with starch and the mixture tested at intervals with iodine, the color test, initially blue, changes successively to purple, then to red-brown, and finally disappears as the *salivary α-amylase* (page 50) disrupts the starch molecules. The role of saliva in digestion of starch in the intact mammal is uncertain owing to variable duration of contact of enzyme and substrate. The mixing of the bolus of food with the acidic gastric

362

juice undoubtedly terminates the action of salivary amylase, which is inactivated at low pH values. Only in individuals deficient in secretion of gastric HCl may salivary digestion be presumed to continue in the stomach.

Pancreatic Amylase. There are no known amylolytic enzymes in gastric juice, and the only expected effects upon starch during its passage through the stomach are those of possible residual amylase activity and, perhaps, some hydrolysis catalyzed by H^+ ions. The major locus of starch digestion is in the small intestine, and the most important enzyme involved in this process is *pancreatic amylase.*

In view of the embryological and histological similarity of the pancreas to the salivary glands, it is of interest that pancreatic amylase is indistinguishable from salivary amylase. It is also an α-amylase with an absolute requirement for Cl^- ion, is stimulated by Ca^{++}, and has an optimal pH at about 7.1. This optimum is probably often approached in the small intestine as a consequence of the mixing of acidic gastric chyme with alkaline pancreatic and biliary secretions. The mode of action of α-amylase (α-1,4-glucan 4-glucanohydrolase) is shown in Fig. 4.1 (page 50). The α-amylases can apparently effect digestion of the intact starch granule, and do not require preliminary rupture of the granule, *e.g.,* by cooking. Hence undigested starch granules are infrequent in feces of normal individuals on normal diets but do occur abundantly in the feces when pancreatic amylase is not entering the intestinal lumen at a normal rate.

Oligosaccharases of the Intestine. The final digestion of carbohydrates to the monosaccharide level is effected by several little-studied enzymes of the intestine. *Maltase,* capable of catalyzing hydrolysis to glucose of the maltose arising from amylase digestion, is supposed to be formed throughout the length of the mucosa of the small intestine. An *oligo-1,6-glucosidase* hydrolyzes oligosaccharides, *e.g.,* isomaltose (page 49), containing an α,1,6 bond. A specific disaccharase for lactose (*lactase*) occurs in the intestine, particularly abundantly in infancy. Also present is a *sucrase* that is an α-glucosidase with a high affinity for sucrose but also catalyzing hydrolysis of maltose and isomaltose. These enzymes, with apparent pH optima between 5 and 7, are present and function within the brush border of the mucosal cells lining the intestine; they are not secreted into the intestinal juice.

Digestible and Nondigestible Polysaccharides. The polysaccharides digestible by the human gastrointestinal tract include amylose, amylopectin, and glycogen, *viz.,* anhydropolymers of glucose in which the glucosidic bond is either α,1,4 or α,1,6. The disaccharides maltose, sucrose, and lactose are also digested.

However, the gastrointestinal tract is deficient in enzymes capable of attacking many other types of glycosidic bonds. Thus the cellobiose bond of cellulose (β,1,4, page 45) is not affected by any known mammalian enzyme. There are bacterial *cellulases* that can effect hydrolysis of cellulose, and in certain mammals, especially those having a rumen or large cecum, bacterial digestion of cellulose in the gastrointestinal tract makes a considerable contribution to the nutritional economy. In man the nutritional significance of dietary cellulose is negligible, and undigested vegetable fibers are demonstrable in the feces. Similarly, the vegetable pentosans are not affected by the enzymes of the mammalian gastrointestinal tract. However, some pentosans and other polysaccharides are hydrolyzed and partially degraded by bacteria in the large intestine, with formation of CO_2, alcohols, and organic acids. These acids stimulate peristalsis, while the unchanged cellulose serves as bulk or roughage, so that these plant polysaccharides are occasionally employed as mild cathartics.

INTESTINAL ABSORPTION OF CARBOHYDRATES

In the normal gastrointestinal tract, carbohydrate is converted to monosaccharides prior to transport across the intestinal mucosa. Intestinal absorption of some undigested disaccharides may occur to a limited extent. Sucrose enters the blood stream when fed in large amounts; it is treated as a foreign substance, appearing unchanged in the urine, and consequently is devoid of nutritional significance. Except for a small portion of the mixture of glucose, fructose, and galactose that is consumed by the metabolism of the intestinal bacteria, these monosaccharides are efficiently transported across the intestinal barrier into the portal blood.

It has long been recognized that absorption of simple sugars across the intestinal mucosa does not occur only by simple diffusion. The rapid absorption of certain hexoses is not critically dependent on the concentration gradient, as would be expected if simple diffusion occurs. The several hexoses, which diffuse physically at similar rates, are absorbed from the intestinal lumen at widely differing rates. Pentoses, lower in molecular weight, hence diffusing more rapidly, have been found to be absorbed more slowly than several hexoses. In order of decreasing rate of absorption, the data show galactose > glucose > fructose > mannose > xylose > arabinose. Isolated preparations of intestine have been shown to transfer sugars from the mucosal to the serosal side against a concentration gradient.

Summarizing the work of several investigators, Crane has delineated the minimal structural features of sugars that are subjected to such active transport as the following:

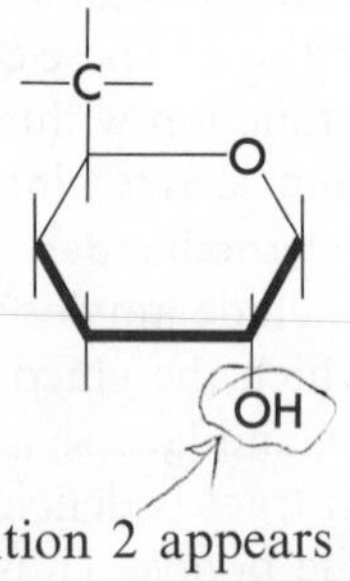

Only the hydroxyl group at position 2 appears to be essential. The transporting mechanism, which requires simultaneous movement of Na^+ in the same direction, is localized in the brush border of mucosal cells. The mechanism of action of this "pump" and the manner in which it utilizes metabolically derived energy are uncertain. It seems likely, however, that it may be a modification of the mechanisms found in cells at all phylogenetic levels for concentrating in their interiors specific sugars present in their external environment. The device in *Escherichia coli* for concentration of galactosides and other sugars has been called a *permease,* but except that one inducible protein, or more, is required for its operation, the mechanism is obscure.

Absorptive Hyperglycemia. As a result of the rapid absorption of glucose, its oral administration is followed by a prompt rise in the glucose concentration in peripheral blood. This rise may result in a maximum glucose concentration after about 1 hr. and is normally followed by a decline to fasting levels or below after 2 hr. The feeding of 1 g. glucose per kg. of body weight will generally not result in glucosuria, *i.e.*, the level of glucose in the blood will not exceed the renal tubular reabsorptive capacity (Chap. 37), since several mechanisms, to be discussed subsequently, can remove glucose from the blood under these circumstances as rapidly as it can be absorbed. The initial rise in blood glucose, however, is characteristically manifest after ingestion of a carbohydrate meal (cf. Glucose Tolerance, page 425).

In the disease sprue, hyperglycemia does not follow oral administration of glucose although intravenous injection of glucose produces a normal rise. The locus of the defect in this disease is therefore thought to be at the intestinal barrier. A similar condition results when the intestinal tract is poisoned with phlorhizin or iodoacetate. It may be mentioned that in sprue, not only glucose but also lipid fails to leave the intestinal canal at a normal rate.

GLUCOSE METABOLISM

If an attempt is made to record on a single chart all the known biochemical fates of glucose and all the compounds derived therefrom, the result is a complex network. A study of this network reveals numerous possible "pathways" whereby carbon atoms, initially contained in glucose, may ultimately appear in CO_2, other hexoses, pentoses, lipids, amino acids, purines, pyrimidines, etc. However, glucose itself suffers only one major fate in mammalian cells—phosphorylation to glucose 6-phosphate.

Phosphorylation of Glucose; Hexokinases. *Hexokinases,* which catalyze phosphorylation of hexoses, occur almost universally in living cells. The hexokinases of yeast and brain are relatively nonspecific, catalyzing phosphorylation of glucose, fructose, and mannose to give the corresponding 6-phosphates.

$$\text{Glucose} + \text{ATP} \xrightarrow{\text{Mg}^{++}} \text{glucose 6-phosphate} + \text{ADP}$$

α-D-Glucose 6-phosphate

In contrast, in muscle, and probably in liver, glucose and fructose phosphorylation are catalyzed by distinct and apparently specific enzymes called *glucokinase* and *fructokinase,* respectively. Like the general hexokinases, glucokinase activity results in formation of glucose 6-phosphate. However, the actions of the fructokinases of intestine, muscle, and perhaps liver seem to result in formation of fructose 1-phosphate. Similarly, the galactokinases of liver, yeast, and *E. coli* catalyze phosphorylation in the 1 position, forming galactose 1-phosphate.

In the phosphorylation of glucose, an energy-rich phosphate is utilized and a relatively energy-poor phosphoric acid ester is formed. The reaction is therefore decidedly exergonic, $\Delta F° = -5000$ cal., hence essentially irreversible. The glucose 6-phosphate which is formed shares with other phosphate esters a limited ability to cross cell walls. Whereas glucose is capable of crossing cell membranes, at least in limited degree, and occurs intra- as well as extracellularly, glucose 6-phosphate is an intracellular substance. Hence, it has been suggested that the hexokinase reaction serves as a mechanism for the "capture" of glucose, locking otherwise diffusible glucose in the intracellular compartment.

Alternate Fates of Glucose. A few reactions of glucose other than phosphorylation are known in mammalian metabolism. A hepatic *glucose dehydrogenase* has been demonstrated to catalyze the following reaction.

$$\text{Glucose} + \text{DPN}^+ \longrightarrow \text{gluconic acid} + \text{DPNH} + \text{H}^+$$

Further metabolism of gluconic acid in mammals entails phosphorylation catalyzed by a *gluconokinase;* the product, 6-phosphogluconic acid, enters the direct oxidative pathway of glucose metabolism (page 387). Direct oxidation of glucose to the level of gluconic acid occurs in various microorganisms; the enzyme that is responsible for such an oxidation in *Penicillium notatum* is the antibiotic *notatin,* a flavoprotein.

Another fate of glucose is reduction to sorbitol, catalyzed by *aldose reductase,* and oxidation of the sorbitol, catalyzed by *ketose reductase,* to yield fructose.

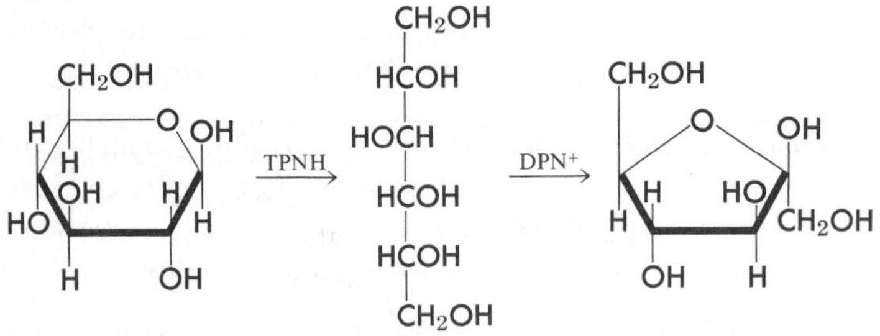

β-D-Glucose   Sorbitol β-D-Fructose

This reaction sequence has been proposed as providing the fructose that abounds in seminal plasma.

FATES OF GLUCOSE 6-PHOSPHATE

Effectively, carbohydrate metabolism may be regarded as commencing with glucose 6-phosphate, rather than with glucose itself, since it is from this ester that the important "pathways" of carbohydrate metabolism stem. These pathways are summarized in outline form in Fig. 20.1, which indicates the four prime metabolic fates possible for glucose 6-phosphate. (1) In the cells of liver, intestine, and kidney only, glucose 6-phosphate may be hydrolyzed, releasing glucose to the environment. In liver, this hydrolysis is catalyzed by a specific microsomal enzyme, *glucose 6-phosphatase.* It should be emphasized that this reaction, which is essentially irreversible, is *not* the reversal of the hexokinase reaction. Indeed, the sum of

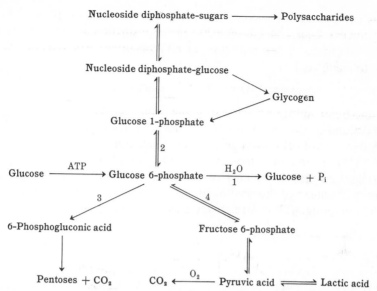

FIG. 20.1. Alternate metabolic fates of glucose 6-phosphate. The numbers adjacent to some of the arrows indicate the prime metabolic fates of glucose 6-phosphate (page 366).

the hexokinase reaction plus the glucose 6-phosphatase reaction is equivalent to the hydrolysis of ATP to ADP + P_i. (2) Conversion to glucose 1-phosphate is the initial step in the synthesis of various nucleoside (adenosine, guanosine, uridine, thymidine) diphosphate esters of glucose which, in turn, are utilized for synthesis of the diphosphate esters of such sugars as galactose, galactosamine, glucuronic acid, iduronic acid, rhamnose, and fucose; these nucleoside diphosphate esters are then used for synthesis of a wide variety of heteropolysaccharides. (3) Oxidation at C-1 yields 6-phosphogluconic acid; this is the initial step in the formation of pentose and of a special oxidative pathway by which glucose may be consumed and TPNH generated for use in biosynthetic processes. (4) Perhaps the most prominent fate of glucose 6-phosphate is its conversion to fructose 6-phosphate. This is the initial event in *glycolysis*, the process by which some of the energy of the glucose molecule is made available to the cell as ATP and which is preparatory to the complete oxidation of glucose via the citric acid cycle.

GLYCOLYSIS

The predominant metabolic fate of glucose in mammalian cells is the process by which the potential chemical energy of glucose is utilized for synthesis of the ATP required to drive essential endergonic processes. The maximum yield of the energy derived from complete oxidation of glucose to CO_2 is obtained by converting glucose to pyruvic acid in the cell cytoplasm, and then oxidizing the pyruvic acid via acetyl CoA to CO_2 in mitochondria by means of the tricarboxylic acid cycle and its associated oxidative phosphorylation (Chap. 18). In addition, however, virtually all cells possess a means for obtaining from glucose a more limited amount of energy without a requirement for molecular oxygen. In mammalian tissues this process, *anaerobic glycolysis,* is accomplished by a series of reactions in which a net synthesis of two molecules of ATP occurs as each glucose molecule is converted to lactic acid.

$$\text{Glucose} + 2\text{ADP} + 2\text{P}_i \rightleftharpoons 2 \text{ lactic acid} + 2\text{ATP}$$

The intermediates in this process are shown in Fig. 20.2. Table 20.1 gives the names and some of the characteristics of the enzymes participating in glycolysis. Although the yield of ATP from glycolysis is small compared to the net yield of 38 moles of ATP per mole of glucose available by complete oxidation (page 379), it will be recognized that the balance of this energy is still available to the organism from later metabolism of the accumulated lactic acid. Glycolysis provides a means for rapidly obtaining ATP in a relatively anaerobic organ, such as a muscle, that is

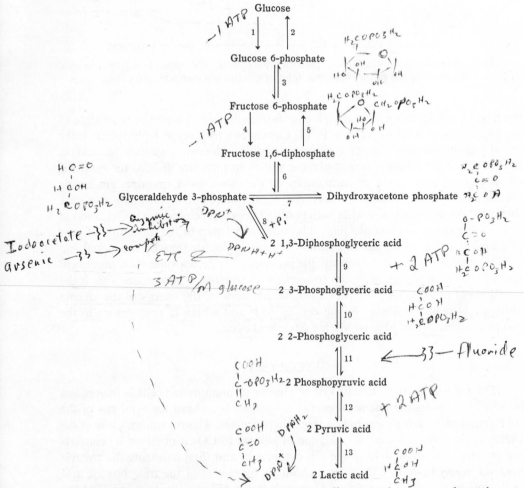

FIG. 20.2. The reactions of glycolysis. The numbers adjacent to the arrows refer to the participating enzymes, which are listed in Table 20.1.

Table 20.1: ENZYMES OF GLYCOLYSIS

Enzyme*	Coenzyme or activators	Inhibitors	Equilibrium constant (approx.) at pH 7.4
1. Hexokinase	Mg++		$\dfrac{\text{Glucose 6-phosphate} \times \text{ADP}}{\text{Glucose} \times \text{ATP}} = 6{,}300$
2. Glucose 6-phosphatase	Mg++		Hydrolysis strongly favored
3. Phosphohexose isomerase			$\dfrac{\text{Glucose 6-phosphate}}{\text{Fructose 6-phosphate}} = 2.3$
4. Phosphofructokinase	Mg++, ADP, AMP	ATP, O_2	
5. Diphosphofructose phosphatase	Mg++	F⁻	Hydrolysis strongly favored
6. Aldolase	None for muscle; yeast enzyme activated by Zn++, Co++, Fe++, Cu++	None for muscle; yeast enzyme inactivated by PP_i, cysteine	$\dfrac{\text{Fructose 1,6-diphosphate}}{\text{Glyceraldehyde 3-phosphate} \times \text{dihydroxyacetone phosphate}} = 10^5$
7. Phosphotriose isomerase			$\dfrac{\text{Dihydroxyacetone phosphate}}{\text{Glyceraldehyde 3-phosphate}} = 25$
8. Phosphoglyceraldehyde dehydrogenase	DPN	Iodoacetate	$\dfrac{\text{Glyceraldehyde 3-phosphate} \times \text{DPN}^+ \times \text{P}_i}{\text{1,3-Diphosphoglycerate} \times \text{DPNH}} = 1$
9. Phosphoglyceric acid kinase	Mg++		$\dfrac{\text{3-Phosphoglycerate} \times \text{ATP}}{\text{1,3-Diphosphoglycerate} \times \text{ADP}} = 3{,}000$
10. Phosphoglyceromutase	Mg++; 2,3-diphosphoglycerate		$\dfrac{\text{3-Phosphoglycerate}}{\text{2-Phosphoglycerate}} = 4$
11. Enolase	Mg++, Mn++	F⁻, PP_i	$\dfrac{\text{2-Phosphoglycerate}}{\text{Phosphoenolpyruvate}} = 1.4$
12. Pyruvic acid kinase	Mg++, K+	Ca++	$\dfrac{\text{Pyruvate} \times \text{ATP}}{\text{Phosphoenolpyruvate} \times \text{ADP}} = 2{,}000$
13. Lactic acid dehydrogenase	DPN	Oxamate	$\dfrac{\text{Lactate} \times \text{DPN}^+}{\text{Pyruvate} \times \text{DPNH}} = 3 \times 10^5$

* The numbers in this column correspond to the reaction numbers of Fig. 20.2.

suddenly required to contract vigorously, or in microbial cells that normally live in a relatively anaerobic environment. Thus, bacteria, such as those responsible for souring of milk or fermentation of cabbage to sauerkraut, also derive their energy by transformation of glucose to lactic acid. However, lactic acid is not universally the end product of anaerobic glucose metabolism. Other microorganisms anaerobically ferment glucose by pathways that also result in ATP formation but yield products such as ethanol, CO_2, acetoin, propionic acid, etc.

Study of the mechanism of alcoholic fermentation by brewer's yeast began early in the nineteenth century, attracting the attention of Lavoisier, Gay-Lussac, Berzelius, Liebig, and Pasteur. The accidental observation, in 1890, by the brothers Büchner, that a cell-free extract of yeast could catalyze alcoholic fermentation removed the last traces of "vitalism" in biological thinking and set the stage for the beginnings of modern biochemistry in the subsequent studies of Harden and Young. The latter investigators observed the following properties of alcoholic fermentation by Büchner extracts of brewer's yeast.

1. Inorganic phosphate was essential to fermentation, which ceased when the supply of phosphate was exhausted.

2. As fermentation proceeded, a hexose diphosphate accumulated. The overall process could be summarized by the following equation.

$$2 \text{ Glucose} + 2P_i \longrightarrow 1 \text{ hexose diphosphate} + 2 \text{ ethanol} + 2CO_2$$

3. When arsenate was substituted for phosphate, no hexose diphosphate accumulated and fermentation continued until all the glucose was converted to ethanol plus CO_2.

4. The extract could be separated into a heat-labile protein fraction and a dialyzable fraction; the latter contained, as essential components, Mg^{++}, P_i, and an organic substance called *cozymase.*

After the studies of A. V. Hill indicated that the conversion of glycogen to lactic acid is closely related to the process of muscular contraction, Meyerhof prepared soluble extracts of muscle which catalyzed glycolysis and later demonstrated that, except for the final steps, glycolysis and alcoholic fermentation are essentially similar. These processes and their component enzymes have been intensively studied by Meyerhof, Embden, Parnas, Neuberg, and Cori, who have provided explanation of the phenomena observed by Harden and Young.

Initiation of Glycolysis. Although a consequence of glycolysis is the synthesis of ATP, this process commences with the utilization of ATP in the hexokinase reaction to form glucose 6-phosphate. Hence, the total synthesis of ATP in the course of glycolysis must exceed the amount invested in this initial reaction if there is to be a net gain of ATP.

The Fructose Phosphates. Operation of the glycolytic sequence requires transformation of the aldohexose phosphate into the corresponding ketose, fructose 6-phosphate. This readily reversible reaction is catalyzed by *phosphohexose isomerase,* equilibrium favoring the glucose over the fructose derivative in a ratio of 70:30. This isomerization of the 6-phosphates of glucose and fructose is reminiscent of the alkali-catalyzed isomerization of glucose into fructose and mannose (page 26), and appears to involve an enzyme-bound enediol intermediate (page 260).

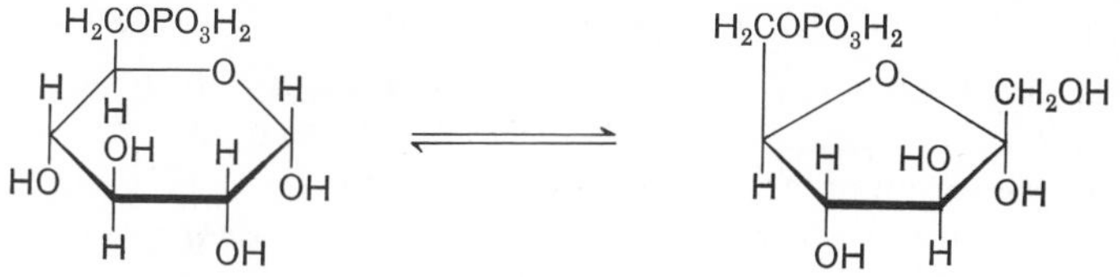

Glucose 6-phosphate   Fructose 6-phosphate

The further phosphorylation of fructose 6-phosphate by a second molecule of ATP to yield fructose 1,6-diphosphate is catalyzed by *phosphofructokinase.*

Fructose 6-phosphate + ATP $\longrightarrow$ fructose 1,6-diphosphate + ADP

Like the hexokinase reaction, this exergonic reaction is not reversible to any significant extent. Fructose 1,6-diphosphate is the "hexose diphosphate" that accumulated in the experiments of Harden and Young (see above).

The Aldolase Reaction. The enzyme *aldolase* catalyzes the reversible cleavage of fructose 1,6-diphosphate between C-3 and C-4 to yield dihydroxyacetone phosphate and the phosphate ester of the isomeric aldotriose, glyceraldehyde. Equilibrium strongly favors the reverse reaction, formation of fructose diphosphate from the two triosephosphates (Table 20.1).

Fructose 1,6-diphosphate   Dihydroxy-   D-Glyceraldehyde
                                         acetone   3-phosphate
                                         phosphate

Crystalline aldolase, obtained from rabbit muscle, is a trimer of three polypeptide chains; only the polymeric form exhibits enzymic activity. This enzyme appears capable of catalyzing an aldol condensation between dihydroxyacetone phosphate and a wide variety of aldehydes, including 3-phosphoglyceraldehyde. Among the other reactions demonstrated in vitro have been the following.

Dihydroxyacetone phosphate + D-glyceraldehyde $\rightleftharpoons$ D-fructose 1-phosphate
Dihydroxyacetone phosphate + L-glyceraldehyde $\rightleftharpoons$ L-sorbose 1-phosphate
Dihydroxyacetone phosphate + acetaldehyde $\rightleftharpoons$ methyltetrose 1-phosphate

In contrast, the enzyme exhibits absolute specificity for the dihydroxyacetone component. When the enzyme is incubated with the latter substrate, in the absence of an aldehyde, one of the two hydrogen atoms on the carbon atom which is not esterified to phosphate becomes labilized and can be shown to exchange with protons in the medium. If this mixture is treated with borohydride, a powerful reducing agent, the dihydroxyacetone phosphate becomes firmly bound to the amino group of a lysine residue on the enzyme, suggesting that the normal mode of attachment of the enzyme-substrate complex is a Schiff base. Presumably, formation of the Schiff base labilizes the specific hydrogen (shown in boldface) on the adjacent carbon, facilitating aldol condensation with an aldehydic carbonyl.

$$\text{Enzyme-NH}_2 + \underset{\substack{| \\ \text{HCOH} \\ | \\ \text{H}}}{\overset{\substack{\text{CH}_2\text{—OPO}_3\text{H}_2 \\ |}}{\text{O=C}}} \quad\rightleftharpoons\quad \text{Enzyme-N=}\underset{\substack{| \\ \text{HCOH} \\ | \\ \text{H}}}{\overset{\substack{\text{CH}_2\text{OPO}_3\text{H}_2 \\ |}}{\text{C}}}$$

It is noteworthy that, regardless of the nature of the aldehyde, the hydroxyl groups on the carbon atoms of the newly formed bond lie *trans* to each other.

Muscle aldolase exhibits no requirement for metal ions or other cofactors, whereas the yeast enzyme is activated by Fe^{++}, Co^{++}, or Zn^{++} and is inactivated by metal-binding reagents. This suggests that the manner of substrate binding and activation of the yeast enzyme may differ from that present in muscle.

Triose Isomerase. Dihydroxyacetone phosphate and D-glyceraldehyde 3-phosphate bear the same structural relationship to each other as do fructose and glucose 6-phosphates, and, as with the hexose phosphates, the triose phosphates are biologically interconvertible. The reaction is catalyzed by *triose phosphate isomerase*.

$$\underset{\substack{\text{Dihydroxyacetone} \\ \text{phosphate}}}{\underset{\substack{| \\ \text{CH}_2\text{OPO}_3\text{H}_2}}{\overset{\substack{\text{CH}_2\text{OH} \\ | }}{\text{C=O}}}} \quad\rightleftharpoons\quad \underset{\substack{\text{D-Glyceraldehyde} \\ \text{3-phosphate}}}{\underset{\substack{| \\ \text{CH}_2\text{OPO}_3\text{H}_2}}{\overset{\substack{\text{HC=O} \\ |}}{\text{HCOH}}}}$$

Oxidation of 3-Phosphoglyceraldehyde. The major fate of the triose phosphates stems from glyceraldehyde 3-phosphate, which is oxidized by DPN^+-requiring *phosphoglyceraldehyde dehydrogenase* to the level of a carboxylic acid. Inorganic orthophosphate is required, and the product of the reaction is the mixed acid anhydride, 1,3-diphosphoglyceric acid.

$$\underset{\substack{\text{D-Glyceraldehyde} \\ \text{3-phosphate}}}{\underset{\substack{| \\ \text{H}_2\text{COPO}_3\text{H}_2}}{\overset{\substack{\text{CHO} \\ |}}{\text{HCOH}}}} + DPN^+ + P_i \rightleftharpoons \underset{\substack{\text{1,3-Diphosphoglyceric} \\ \text{acid}}}{\underset{\substack{| \\ \text{H}_2\text{COPO}_3\text{H}_2}}{\overset{\substack{\text{O—PO}_3\text{H}_2 \\ | \\ \text{C=O} \\ |}}{\text{HCOH}}}} + DPNH + H^+$$

Phosphoglyceraldehyde dehydrogenase (triose phosphate dehydrogenase) has been obtained in crystalline form from rabbit muscle and yeast. It contains sulfhydryl groups which must be maintained in this state by cysteine or glutathione for maximal enzymic activity. Iodoacetate reacts with these sulfhydryl groups, thereby inactivating the enzyme; the inhibition of glycolysis by this poison is attributed to this effect. Two moles of DPN^+ are bound to each mole of crystalline enzyme. The DPN^+ may be removed by adsorption on charcoal; reactivation of the enzyme is achieved by addition of DPN^+.

Several lines of evidence suggest that an intermediate addition compound is formed by reaction of an enzyme-sulfhydryl group and the aldehyde group of the substrate. This is followed by reaction with DPN$^+$ to form a thioester which is phosphorolyzed to yield the enzyme and 1,3-diphosphoglyceric acid.

$$
\begin{array}{ccccc}
\text{Enz—SH} & & \text{Enz—S} & \text{H} & \text{Enz—SH} \\
+ & & | & + & | & + \\
\text{O=C—H} & & \text{O=C} & \text{O—PO}_3\text{H}_2 & \text{O=C—OPO}_3\text{H}_2 \\
| & & | & & | \\
\text{HCOH} & \longrightarrow & \text{HCOH} & \longrightarrow & \text{HCOH} \\
| & & | & & | \\
\text{H}_2\text{C—OPO}_3\text{H}_2 & & \text{H}_2\text{C—OPO}_3\text{H}_2 & & \text{H}_2\text{C—OPO}_3\text{H}_2 \\
+ & & + & & \\
\text{DPN}^+ & & \text{DPNH + H}^+ & &
\end{array}
$$

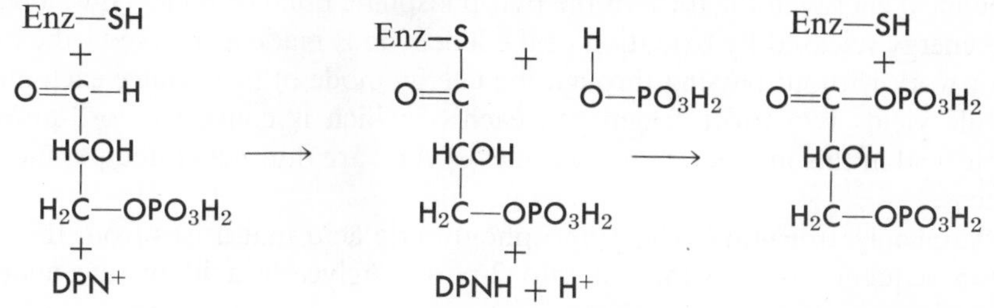

The details of the mechanism of the first step are uncertain, but formation of the 3-phosphoglyceryl-enzyme intermediate seems to be firmly established.

If arsenate rather than phosphate is present in the reaction medium, the enzyme effects the transfer of the 3-phosphoglyceryl residue to this ion. The resultant 1-arseno-3-phosphoglyceric acid is unstable and spontaneously rapidly hydrolyzes to 3-phosphoglyceric acid.

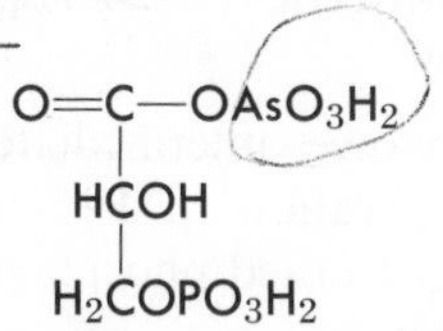

$$
\begin{array}{c}
\text{O=C—OAsO}_3\text{H}_2 \\
| \\
\text{HCOH} \\
| \\
\text{H}_2\text{COPO}_3\text{H}_2
\end{array}
$$

1-Arseno-3-phosphoglyceric acid

Phosphoglyceric Acid Kinase. 1,3-Diphosphoglyceric acid is an acid anhydride and is therefore an energy-rich compound of phosphoric acid. The energy is derived from the thioester, which, in turn, comes from the energy of oxidation of the aldehyde. A portion of the energy generally released when an aldehyde is oxidized to a carboxylic acid is, in this case, retained in the form of chemical bond energy. Indeed, $\Delta F°$ for the simple hydrolysis of 1,3-diphosphoglyceric acid is of the order of $-10,000$ cal. per mole, sufficient to permit transfer of phosphoric acid from the 1 position of 1,3-diphosphoglyceric acid to adenosine diphosphate, a reaction catalyzed by *3-phosphoglyceric acid kinase*.

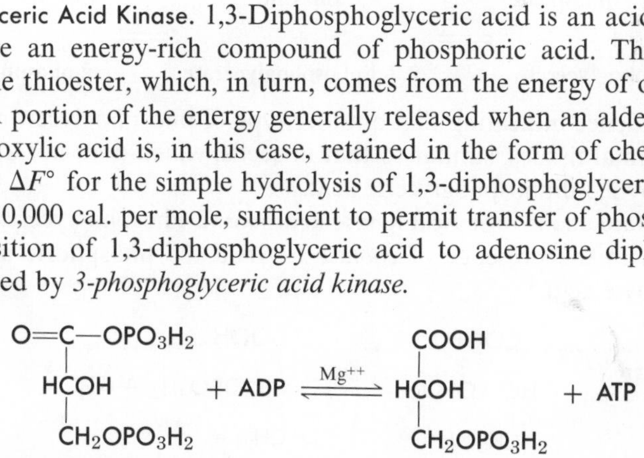

$$
\begin{array}{ccccc}
\text{O=C—OPO}_3\text{H}_2 & & & \text{COOH} & \\
| & & & | & \\
\text{HCOH} & + \text{ ADP} & \underset{\longleftarrow}{\overset{\text{Mg}^{++}}{\longrightarrow}} & \text{HCOH} & + \text{ ATP} \\
| & & & | & \\
\text{CH}_2\text{OPO}_3\text{H}_2 & & & \text{CH}_2\text{OPO}_3\text{H}_2 &
\end{array}
$$

1,3-Diphosphoglyceric acid   3-Phosphoglyceric acid

The sum of the two reactions, catalyzed by phosphoglyceraldehyde dehydrogenase and phosphoglyceric acid kinase, respectively, is the following.

Glyceraldehyde 3-phosphate $+ \text{ P}_i + \text{DPN}^+ + \text{ADP} \rightleftharpoons$

        3-phosphoglyceric acid $+ \text{DPNH} + \text{ATP} + \text{H}^+$

The equilibrium position of the above equation lies to the right, as written. From this equation it will be noted that, coincident with oxidation of triose phosphate to phosphoglyceric acid, an equivalent amount of ATP has been generated from ADP and inorganic phosphate. This is one of the best-known examples of the coupling of the exergonic oxidation of a metabolite with the generation of useful chemical energy in the form of the pyrophosphate bond of ATP. Thus, a portion of the energy released by oxidation of the aldehyde is made available to the organism for work without passing through the energy mode of heat. Since each glucose molecule yields two triose fragments, each of which is converted to 3-phosphoglyceric acid in this manner, two molecules of ATP are thus generated per molecule of glucose.

Phosphoglyceromutase. The 3-phosphoglyceric acid that arises from the above reaction sequence is transformed into 2-phosphoglyceric acid by the action of *phosphoglyceromutase*.

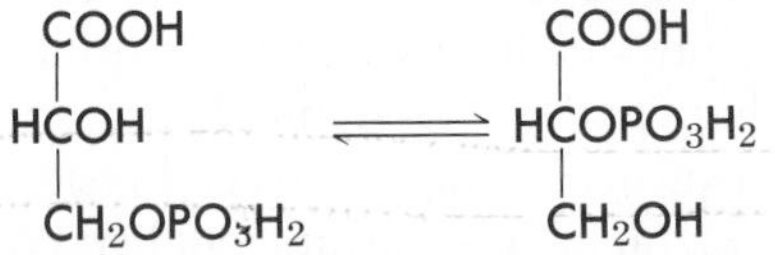

$$
\begin{array}{ccc}
\text{COOH} & & \text{COOH} \\
| & & | \\
\text{HCOH} & \rightleftharpoons & \text{HCOPO}_3\text{H}_2 \\
| & & | \\
\text{CH}_2\text{OPO}_3\text{H}_2 & & \text{CH}_2\text{OH} \\
\text{3-Phosphoglyceric} & & \text{2-Phosphoglyceric} \\
\text{acid} & & \text{acid}
\end{array}
$$

The reaction mechanism involves intermediate participation of 2,3-diphosphoglyceric acid. The rapid equilibration of P^{32} among all the participants and analogy to the more thoroughly studied phosphoglucomutase reaction (page 403) suggest the following mechanism.

$$
\begin{array}{ccccc}
\text{Enzyme—phosphate} & & \text{Enzyme} & & \text{Enzyme—phosphate} \\
+ & \rightleftharpoons & + & \rightleftharpoons & + \\
\text{3-phosphoglycerate} & & \text{2,3-diphosphoglycerate} & & \text{2-phosphoglycerate}
\end{array}
$$

There is evidence indicating that another type of phosphoglyceromutase may also occur in animal tissues, similar to that in seeds, which does not appear to require mediation by 2,3-diphosphoglyceric acid.

The Enolase and Pyruvic Acid Kinase Reactions. 2-Phosphoglyceric acid undergoes dehydration in the presence of *enolase* to yield the phosphoric acid ester of the enol of pyruvic acid.

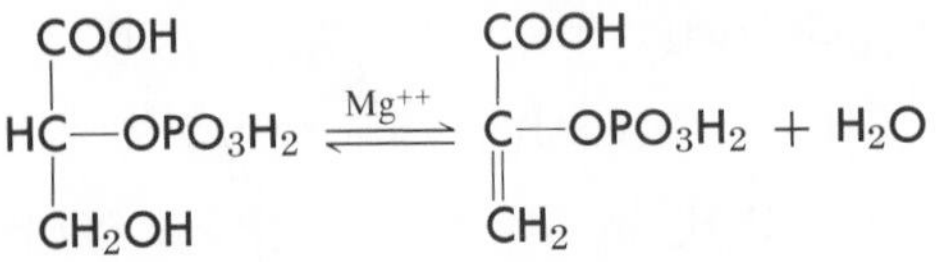

$$
\begin{array}{ccc}
\text{COOH} & & \text{COOH} \\
| & & | \\
\text{HC—OPO}_3\text{H}_2 & \xrightleftharpoons{\text{Mg}^{++}} & \text{C—OPO}_3\text{H}_2 + \text{H}_2\text{O} \\
| & & \| \\
\text{CH}_2\text{OH} & & \text{CH}_2 \\
\text{2-Phosphoglyceric} & & \text{Phosphoenolpyruvic} \\
\text{acid} & & \text{acid}
\end{array}
$$

The addition of fluoride to an actively glycolyzing system results in abolition of the enolase reaction and accumulation of phosphoglyceric acids, presumably because of formation of magnesium fluorophosphate which is bound to the enzyme.

The equilibrium position of the enolase reaction is close to 1. Hence there is almost no associated change in free energy. However, whereas the phosphate of 2-phosphoglyceric acid is esterified to a secondary alcohol, the product of the enolase reaction is the phosphate ester of the enol tautomer of pyruvic acid. At pH 7, the keto form is strongly favored and the free-energy change associated with hydrolysis of the phosphate ester of this enol is unusually high; $\Delta F°$ is approximately $-12,000$ cal. per mole, sufficient to permit transfer of the phosphoric acid residue to adenosine diphosphate.

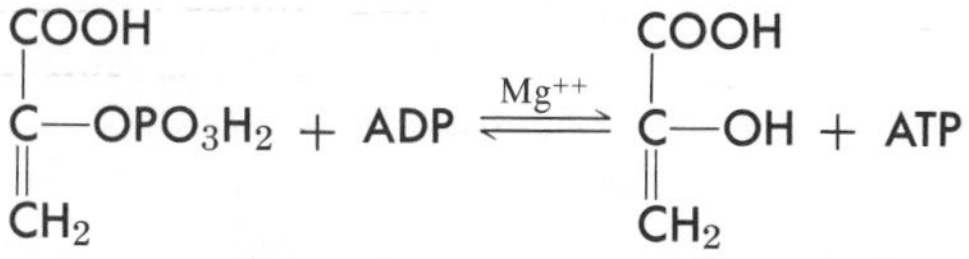

$$\begin{array}{c} COOH \\ | \\ C-OPO_3H_2 \\ || \\ CH_2 \end{array} + ADP \underset{Mg^{++}}{\rightleftharpoons} \begin{array}{c} COOH \\ | \\ C-OH \\ || \\ CH_2 \end{array} + ATP$$

The reaction is catalyzed by *pyruvic acid kinase,* which, like all kinases, exhibits an absolute requirement for Mg^{++}. Indeed, the substrates are more properly described as the tightly bound Mg^{++}-complexes of ADP and ATP, respectively. In addition, this enzyme functions only in the presence of a relatively high concentration of K^+, a requirement that is most evident for the back reaction, formation of phosphoenolpyruvic acid from ATP and pyruvic acid. The metabolic consequence of this phenomenon is considered later (page 382). Particularly noteworthy is the fact that the formation of two molecules of ATP, per molecule of glucose, by this reaction represents the net gain, to the cell, of ATP provided by the glycolytic sequence.

Formation of Lactic Acid. With the formation of pyruvic acid and ATP by pyruvic acid kinase, the function of anaerobic glycolysis has been accomplished; no further ATP can be formed. Under aerobic conditions, the further metabolism of pyruvic acid proceeds by oxidative decarboxylation with formation of acetyl coenzyme A, which then enters the citric acid cycle (page 318). Anaerobically, however, pyruvic acid does not accumulate. It will be recalled that the conversion of 3-phosphoglyceraldehyde to 3-phosphoglyceric acid was achieved by the reduction of DPN^+ to DPNH. Aerobically, this DPNH, like the pyruvic acid, would be oxidized by the mitochondrial electron transport system (page 325). As compared with the carbohydrate supply, DPN is present in only limited amount, and, were the DPN^+ reduced by oxidation of 3-phosphoglyceraldehyde not reoxidized, anaerobic glycolysis would cease when all the DPN^+ was reduced to DPNH. This is prevented by the action of *lactic acid dehydrogenase,* which catalyzes the following reaction.

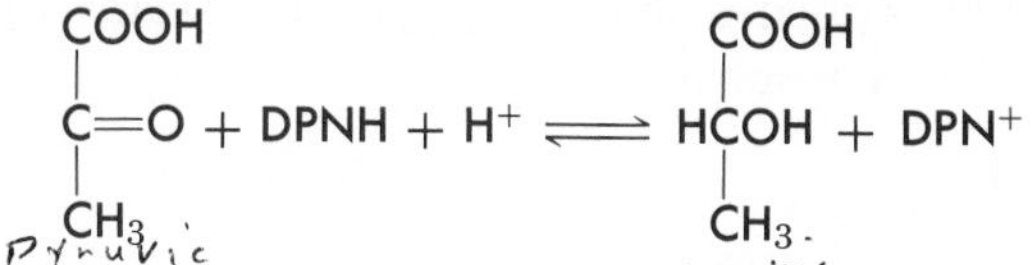

$$\begin{array}{c} COOH \\ | \\ C=O \\ | \\ CH_3 \\ {}_{Pyruvic} \end{array} + DPNH + H^+ \rightleftharpoons \begin{array}{c} COOH \\ | \\ HCOH \\ | \\ CH_3 \\ {}_{Lactic} \end{array} + DPN^+$$

This coupled relationship between these two reactions of the total glycolytic sequence may be summarized as follows.

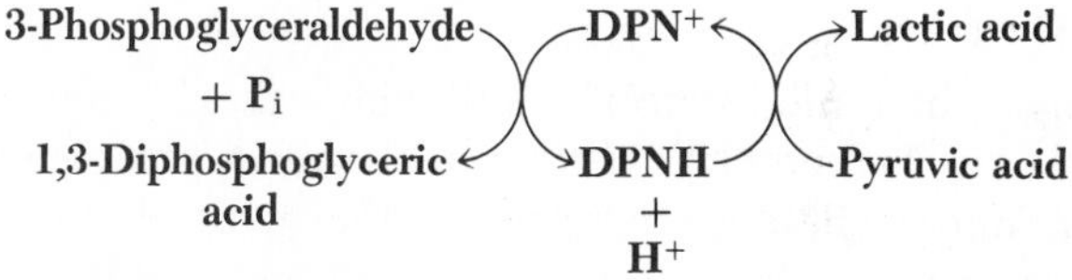

$$\begin{array}{ccc} \text{3-Phosphoglyceraldehyde} & DPN^+ & \text{Lactic acid} \\ + P_i & \times \times & \\ \text{1,3-Diphosphoglyceric} & DPNH & \text{Pyruvic acid} \\ \text{acid} & + & \\ & H^+ & \end{array}$$

The equilibrium position of the lactic acid dehydrogenase reaction, like that of all reactions involving an alcohol and DPN, strongly favors formation of lactic acid rather than its oxidation. Hence, glycolysis proceeds smoothly with net accumulation of two molecules of lactic acid per mole of glucose. It is noteworthy that lactic acid is a blind alley in metabolism. Once formed there is no means for its further utilization other than reversal of the lactic acid dehydrogenase reaction and re-formation of pyruvic acid, an event associated with reestablishment of aerobic conditions. In contrast to all the phosphorylated intermediates of glycolysis, lactic and pyruvic acids are not locked into the cells in which they are formed. Hence, in vivo, lactic acid diffuses from actively glycolyzing muscle cells and is removed by the circulation (page 420).

Alcoholic Fermentation. The sequence of reactions resulting in formation of pyruvic acid in the anaerobic metabolism of glucose by many microorganisms, notably yeast, is identical with that in animal tissues. In contrast to the reversible formation of lactic acid, described above, the further fate of pyruvic acid in yeast involves essentially irreversible decarboxylation to acetaldehyde by *pyruvic acid decarboxylase*, which is not found in animal tissues.

$$CH_3COCOOH \xrightarrow{Mg^{++}} CH_3CHO + CO_2$$

Thiamine pyrophosphate is an essential cofactor for this reaction. As in pyruvic acid oxidation (page 317), the initial step is formation of hydroxyethyl thiamine pyrophosphate. In this instance the acetaldehyde moiety is not transferred and the complex decomposes to free acetaldehyde with re-formation of the coenzyme. The acetaldehyde thus formed is reduced by DPNH in a reaction catalyzed by *alcohol dehydrogenase*.

$$CH_3CHO + DPNH + H^+ \rightleftharpoons CH_3CH_2OH + DPN^+$$

Thus, in yeast, acetaldehyde replaces pyruvic acid as the oxidant for the DPNH that arises in the oxidation of 3-phosphoglyceraldehyde.

An interesting variation in this mechanism was devised by Neuberg as a means for commercial production of glycerol. If yeast fermentation is conducted in the presence of sodium bisulfite, the latter combines with acetaldehyde to form an addition compound which is unavailable for reaction with DPNH. Under these conditions, the DPNH is then employed by *glycerol phosphate dehydrogenase* to reduce dihydroxyacetone phosphate.

$$
\begin{array}{ccc}
CH_2OH & & CH_2OH \\
| & & | \\
C{=}O & + DPNH + H^+ \rightleftharpoons & CHOH & + DPN^+ \\
| & & | \\
CH_2OPO_3H_2 & & CH_2OPO_3H_2 \\
\text{Dihydroxyacetone} & & \alpha\text{-Glycerophosphate} \\
\text{phosphate} & &
\end{array}
$$

This is the normal source of glycerol for lipid biosynthesis (page 453) and a means for oxidation of cytoplasmic DPNH by mitochondria aerobically (page 327). In anaerobic yeast, under these circumstances, the glycerol phosphate is rapidly hydrolyzed, by an appropriate phosphatase, to glycerol and P_i.

GLYCOLYSIS—GENERAL CONSIDERATIONS

Summarizing those of the foregoing reactions which are intermediate between glucose and lactic acid, the scheme of Fig. 20.2 (page 368) may be reconsidered. Table 20.1 (page 369) has presented the names and some of the characteristics of the enzymes participating in these steps. It is of interest that the relative amounts and activities of many of these enzymes remain constant, with respect to each other, when various tissues are compared. Moreover, in the living cell in a steady state, the relative quantities of each of the intermediate compounds is such that each reaction, $A \rightleftharpoons B$, is operating close to the equilibrium position it would attain if studied independently.

No oxygen is consumed in the over-all process, glucose to lactate. Although two of the individual steps are oxidoreductions—*viz.*, the oxidation of glyceraldehyde 3-phosphate to 1,3-diphosphoglyceric acid (reaction *8*) and the reduction of pyruvic acid to lactic acid (reaction *13*)—the participation of DPN in both these reactions results in no net oxidation or reduction.

The net yield of usable energy derived from glycolysis may be computed from a balance of the moles of ATP consumed and regenerated per mole of glucose degraded to lactate. One mole of ATP is consumed at each of the two kinase steps (reactions *1* and *4*) in the phosphorylation of glucose and of fructose 6-phosphate. Two moles of high-energy phosphate are delivered to ADP to regenerate ATP by reaction *9*, as 1,3-diphosphoglyceric acid goes to 3-phosphoglyceric acid, and two more moles of ATP are regenerated by reaction *12*, as phosphopyruvic acid surrenders its phosphate to ADP. Thus, per mole of glucose glycolyzed, two moles of ATP are invested initially, and four moles are ultimately regenerated, for a net gain of two moles of ATP.

From these relationships the over-all efficiency of glycolysis may be estimated. Whereas the standard free-energy yield, $\Delta F°$, for the total oxidation of glucose is $-686,000$ cal. per mole, only about 8 per cent of this, or some 56,000 cal. per mole, is produced when the degradation of glucose proceeds only as far as lactic acid. Available information does not permit calculation of the actual free-energy change, ΔF, under prevailing physiological conditions. The generation of 2 moles of ATP from ADP and inorganic orthophosphate consumes about 16,000 cal. under physiological conditions, from which it will be seen that $16,000/56,000 \times 100$ or about 30 per cent of the potentially available energy may be stored as chemical energy in ATP incident to the glycolysis of one mole of glucose.

It is useful, at this point, to reconsider the findings of Harden and Young (page 370). Clearly, the phosphate requirement for alcoholic fermentation in a yeast extract reflects the need for P_i in the operation of the 3-phosphoglycer-aldehyde dehydrogenase reaction, the only reaction in the sequence in which inorganic phosphate actually participates. In an intact cell, also, the presence of free orthophosphate must be essential for glycolysis to proceed. In such cells, as in these extracts, the amount of adenine nucleotide is small compared to the glucose available. When the ADP present is converted to ATP, the reaction sequence would halt at the stages of 1,3-diphosphoglyceric acid and phosphoenolpyruvic acid. In the living cell, the ATP is utilized in diverse endergonic processes, *e.g.*, protein synthesis or muscle contraction, thereby regenerating both ADP and P_i. In a yeast extract, however, these phenomena do not occur. The only means of utilizing ATP is the pair of kinases present in such extracts, which, together, make fructose 1,6-diphosphate from glucose. The over-all fermentation process in such extracts, therefore, may be represented as the sum of two partial systems.

(a) Glucose + 2P$_i$ + 2ADP $\longrightarrow$ 2 ethanol + 2CO$_2$ + 2ATP

(b) Glucose + 2ATP $\longrightarrow$ fructose 1,6-diphosphate + 2ADP

Sum: 2 Glucose + 2P$_i$ $\longrightarrow$ 2 ethanol + 2CO$_2$ + fructose 1,6-diphosphate

The accumulated fructose diphosphate is not metabolized further since the equilibrium of the aldolase reaction markedly favors formation of fructose diphosphate rather than the mixture of triose phosphates. The reasons for the requirement for DPN, Mg^{++}, and P$_i$, therefore, are apparent. It remains only to explain the arsenate effect. As already noted (page 373), 3-phosphoglyceraldehyde dehydrogenase can transfer the 3-phosphoglyceryl residue to arsenate, when phosphate is absent, forming a product that spontaneously decomposes. Under these circumstances, the need for phosphate is obviated, but no ATP can be formed at this stage. Hence, the only ATP formed is that from phosphoenolpyruvic acid. The two molecules of ATP thus formed exactly balance those required in the kinase steps. In this instance, therefore, fermentation or glycolysis can proceed, in the absence of phosphate, until the glucose supply is exhausted and without accumulation of fructose diphosphate. It will be evident that such glycolysis is entirely pointless in the living cell since, although it permits glucose conversion to lactic acid—or ethanol plus CO$_2$—it fails to provide ATP. Clear comprehension of this circumstance affords understanding of the entire glycolytic machinery.

AEROBIC FATE OF PYRUVIC ACID

Like glucose 6-phosphate, pyruvic acid occupies a central position in metabolism, since it occurs in several metabolic reaction pathways, as shown in Fig. 20.3. Pyruvic acid may undergo reversible reduction to lactic acid (page 375), it can be converted back to carbohydrate (page 382), used for formation of oxaloacetic or malic acids (page 380), or transaminated to form alanine, a process that is also reversible (page 493). However, the major fate of pyruvic acid in most mammalian cells is oxidation to CO$_2$ and acetyl coenzyme A as described on page 317 and briefly reconsidered below.

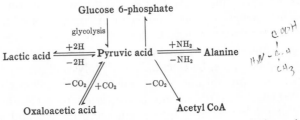

Fig. 20.3. Fates of pyruvic acid in mammals. Note that there are two independent mechanisms for formation of oxaloacetic acid from pyruvic acid (page 381).

Oxidative Decarboxylation of Pyruvic Acid. When the oxygen supply is not limiting, pyruvic acid is oxidatively decarboxylated to acetyl CoA (page 317) and CO_2.

$$CH_3COCOOH + CoA - SH + DPN^+ \longrightarrow CH_3CO - SCoA + CO_2 + DPNH + H^+$$

| Pyruvic acid | Coenzyme A | Acetyl CoA |

This process is essentially irreversible. The acetyl CoA may be used in a variety of reactions, such as acetylation of choline or aromatic amines, or the biogenesis of acetoacetate, long-chain fatty acids, or steroids. However, as noted previously, the major fate of this molecule is condensation with oxaloacetate to form citrate, the initial step in oxidation via the citric acid cycle (Chap. 18).

Like succinyl CoA, acetyl CoA is an energy-rich compound and might be employed for the generation of ATP, a reaction catalyzed by *acetate thiokinase*, the "acetate-activating enzyme" (page 316).

$$\text{Acetyl CoA} + \text{AMP} + \text{PP}_i \rightleftharpoons \text{acetate} + \text{CoA} + \text{ATP}$$

However, this potentiality is probably rarely realized physiologically, and the significance of the reaction shown derives from its reversal, which provides a means for synthesis of acetyl CoA from acetate.

Under aerobic circumstances, therefore, events in the cytoplasm may be summarized as follows.

$$\text{Glucose} + \text{ADP} + 2P_i + 2DPN^+ \longrightarrow 2 \text{ pyruvic acid} + 2ATP + 2DPNH + 2H^+$$

The pyruvic acid then enters the mitochondria. Oxidation of the DPNH that arises when pyruvic acid is transformed into acetyl CoA and CO_2 provides 6 moles of ATP per glucose equivalent. Complete oxidation of each mole of acetyl CoA yields 12 moles of ATP or 24 moles of ATP per glucose equivalent. Remaining for consideration is the DPNH that arose in the cytoplasm by oxidation of 3-phosphoglyceraldehyde. As described previously (page 327), such external DPNH is not readily oxidized by normal mitochondria. However, by using this DPNH to reduce dihydroxyacetone phosphate (page 327), the glycerol phosphate formed

Table 20.2: TOTAL ATP PRODUCTION FROM GLUCOSE IN A RESPIRING SYSTEM

Reaction sequence	ATP yield	Page
Glucose $\longrightarrow$ fructose 1,6-diphosphate	-2	370
2 Triose phosphate $\longrightarrow$ 2 3-phosphoglyceric acid	$+2$	373
$2DPN^+ \longrightarrow 2DPNH \longrightarrow 2DPN^+$	$+6$	328
2 Phosphoenolpyruvic acid $\longrightarrow$ 2 pyruvic acid	$+2$	375
2 Pyruvic acid $\longrightarrow$ 2 acetyl CoA $+ 2CO_2$		
$2DPN^+ \longrightarrow 2DPNH \longrightarrow 2DPN^+$	$+6$	328
2 Acetyl CoA $\longrightarrow$ $4CO_2$	$+24$	334
Net: $C_6H_{12}O_6 + 6O_2 \longrightarrow 6CO_2 + 6H_2O$	38	

may then enter mitochondria, yield electrons to the electron transport system, and thus provide the same ATP yield as if the external DPNH had directly entered the mitochondria, *viz.*, six ATP per two DPNH. As summarized in Table 20.2, this permits a total yield of 38 ATP per mole of glucose oxidized.

$$C_6H_{12}O_6 + 6O_2 + 38ADP + 38P_i \longrightarrow 6CO_2 + 6H_2O + 38ATP$$

Assuming that ΔF for formation of ATP *under physiological circumstances* is about $+8000$ cal. per mole, a total of about 304,000 cal. of the 686,000 cal. potentially available is actually conserved in this process. The "efficiency," therefore, is of the order of 45 per cent.

Metabolism of Oxaloacetic Acid. According to the scheme shown in Fig. 18.1 (page 315), for each turn of the citric acid cycle, an equivalent of oxaloacetic acid is regenerated to initiate the succeeding turn of the cycle. However, for several of the intermediates of the cycle, particularly oxaloacetic acid, α-ketoglutaric acid, and succinyl CoA, there are other metabolic fates, alternate to those of the citric acid cycle. Among such processes is the decarboxylation of oxaloacetic acid to pyruvic acid, which may occur both spontaneously and by enzymic catalysis.

$$HOOCCOCH_2COOH \longrightarrow CH_3COCOOH + CO_2$$
Oxaloacetic acid   Pyruvic acid

Loss of oxaloacetic acid in this manner would, inevitably, decrease the rate at which the cycle could operate unless the loss were offset by a renewal of the supply. A readily available source is the amino acid, aspartic acid, that gives rise to oxaloacetic acid by transamination (page 493). Similarly, glutamic acid (page 493) yields α-ketoglutaric acid, which may then enter the citric acid cycle. However, in many types of growing cells and in normal liver, the converse circumstances may be obtained with both oxaloacetic and α-ketoglutaric acids being removed by transamination to form their respective amino acids. It is essential, therefore, that other means be available to renew their supply.

Several processes are known by which the oxaloacetic acid supply may be replenished by CO_2 fixation with pyruvic acid. This phenomenon was first noted by Wood and Werkman in heterotrophic, nonphotosynthetic bacteria and has been well established for animal tissues. Ochoa and his collaborators demonstrated the presence of *malic enzyme*, which catalyzes the following reaction.

$$CH_3COCOOH + CO_2 + TPNH + H^+ \underset{}{\overset{Mn^{++}}{\rightleftharpoons}} HOOCCH_2CHOHCOOH + TPN^+$$
Pyruvic acid   l-Malic acid

The mechanism of this reaction is analogous to that of isocitric acid dehydrogenase, considered earlier (page 320). Malic acid is a normal intermediate of the citric acid cycle and is oxidized to oxaloacetic acid by DPN^+ in the presence of *malic acid dehydrogenase,* an enzyme entirely distinct from the malic enzyme considered above.

A second CO_2-fixing reaction, found by Utter, is catalyzed by *phosphoenolpyruvic acid carboxylase.*

2. Phosphoenolpyruvic acid + CO_2 + inosine diphosphate $\xrightarrow{Mg^{++}}$

oxaloacetic acid + inosine triphosphate

Nothing is known of the mechanism of this reaction; the enzyme has been only partially purified from liver and muscle. The reaction, to the left, is significant in the "reversal" of glycolysis (see below).

Utter has recently described a third enzyme, *pyruvic acid carboxylase,* which catalyzes oxaloacetate formation.

3.   Pyruvic acid + CO_2 + ATP $\xrightarrow{Mg^{++}}$ oxaloacetic acid + ADP + P_i

Several aspects of this system suggest that it may be the most significant single device for *de novo* formation of oxaloacetate. (1) Equilibrium strongly favors oxaloacetic acid synthesis. (2) K_m for CO_2 is much lower than that of the other CO_2-fixing enzymes cited above. (3) The enzyme exhibits an absolute requirement for acetyl CoA. The latter does not appear actually to participate in the reaction mechanism; rather, it seems to be required to maintain the protein in a conformation that is enzymically active. Hence, it is precisely when a supply of oxaloacetic acid is required, *viz.*, when acetyl CoA is being generated rapidly, that the activity of this enzyme is assured. Thus, the system has a "positive feedback" input and is automatically "turned on" when required. This may be contrasted with the "negative feedback" of several biosynthetic systems in which the final product of a synthetic sequence appears to bind and, by altering conformation, inhibit the enzyme responsible for the first reaction of the synthetic sequence (page 490). (4) The enzyme contains the vitamin biotin as its prosthetic group. The mechanism of action of biotin-enzymes is presented later (page 446). However, it is significant that many studies have indicated an impairment of CO_2 fixation into oxaloacetic acid in biotin-deficient animals, and this is the only enzyme of this group in which biotin serves as the functional group.

Reversal of Glycolysis. The reversibility of glycolysis was first suggested by the finding, by A. V. Hill, that isolated muscle, contracting anaerobically, converted glycogen to lactic acid and that if oxygen were introduced, the lactic acid disappeared, about one-fifth being oxidized to CO_2 while the remainder was reconverted to glycogen. It has already been noted that most of the steps of the glycolytic sequence are readily reversible reactions. The phosphofructokinase reaction, as such, is not; no ATP may be formed from fructose diphosphate and ADP. However, liver, muscle, and brain contain a *diphosphofructose phosphatase* that catalyzes the following reaction.

Fructose 1,6-diphosphate $\xrightarrow{H_2O}$ fructose 6-phosphate + P_i

If glucose were the final product of reversal of glycolysis, reversal of the hexokinase reaction could not be expected either. However, liver, kidney, and intestinal mucosa contain a microsomal glucose 6-phosphatase that catalyzes hydrolysis of glucose 6-phosphate to glucose and P_i.

Glucose 6-phosphate $\xrightarrow{H_2O}$ glucose + P_i

In all tissues, for glycogen resynthesis from lactic acid, glucose 6-phosphatase activity is unnecessary but an additional series of enzymes is required, as shown in Fig. 20.1 (page 367).

In any case, reversal of glycolysis to form glucose 6-phosphate should be theoretically possible if ATP, available from the aerobic oxidation of a fraction of the lactic acid (via pyruvic acid and the citric acid cycle), were provided to reverse the pyruvic kinase and phosphoglyceric kinase reactions (reactions *9* and *12* of Fig. 20.2, page 368). However, although this can indeed occur, it appears that the K^+-dependent pyruvic acid kinase reaction becomes seriously rate-limiting under these circumstances. This limitation is circumvented by a combination of enzymes already discussed. Instead of direct formation of phosphoenolpyruvate from pyruvate, either the consecutive action of malic enzyme and malic acid dehydrogenase or the direct action of pyruvic acid carboxylase, followed by phosphoenolpyruvic acid carboxylase in either case, catalyzes the following sequence.

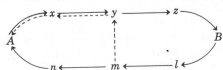

$$CO_2 + \text{pyruvate} \xrightarrow{\text{TPNH}} \text{malate}$$

$$\text{or} \quad \xrightarrow{\text{DPN}^+} \text{oxaloacetate} \xrightarrow{\text{ITP}} \text{phosphoenolpyruvate} + CO_2$$

$$CO_2 + \text{pyruvate} \xrightarrow{\text{ATP}}$$

Thus, "reversal" of glycolysis actually requires participation of several enzymes that are not operative in the forward sequence. This is but one illustration of a major principle governing metabolism. Whenever conversion of a precursor compound *A* to a product *B* proceeds by a series of intermediates, if *B* can also be reconverted, physiologically, to *A*, this is accomplished by a pathway that is either partly or completely independent of the enzymes and intermediates of the forward process.

As seen in the reversal of glycolysis, this rule is operative even though most or all of the reactions of one of the pathways are known to be reversible.

INHIBITION OF GLYCOLYSIS BY OXYGEN—THE PASTEUR EFFECT

It was recognized by Pasteur, and later by Meyerhof and Warburg, that glycolysis is linked to respiration, *i.e.*, oxygen consumption. The observation repeatedly made with a wide variety of tissue preparations and microorganisms is that the rate of glycolysis, as measured by the rate of disappearance of glucose or appearance of lactic acid, is lower under aerobic than under anaerobic conditions. The admission of oxygen to a glycolyzing system will often decrease the rate of glycolysis, or, in terms frequently employed, anaerobic glycolysis is more rapid than aerobic glycolysis. This inhibition of glycolysis by oxygen is called the *Pasteur effect*.

The benefits that accrue to the organism from the operation of the Pasteur effect are clear. The process of anaerobic glycolysis (glucose → 2 lactic acid) releases only about 8 per cent of the energy that would be obtained by complete oxidation of glucose. If oxygen is made available and the cells under consideration become capable of oxidizing lactic acid further, e.g., to CO_2 and H_2O, the energy yield per molecule of glucose is considerably increased; hence, the energy needs of the cell can be met by consumption of considerably less glucose. The Pasteur effect conserves nutrient glucose when the useful energy yield per molecule of glucose is rendered larger.

Although the benefits derived from operation of the Pasteur effect are readily understood, the mechanism by which it operates has proved elusive. Indeed, it appears that the Pasteur effect may actually be the resultant of a variety of chemical consequences of respiration and the availability of oxygen. Several of the factors that have been proposed as operating in the Pasteur effect will be discussed briefly.

1. The decrease in observed glycolysis may be in part apparent rather than real. In many cells, in the presence of oxygen, lactic acid formed by glycolysis is in part oxidized to CO_2 and H_2O, and a portion of the energy released by this oxidation is utilized to resynthesize glucose or glycogen from the remainder of the lactic acid. The net effect of this resynthesis is to decrease the total consumption of glucose as well as the accumulation of lactic acid, whereas the *rate* of glycolysis may not have diminished to quite the same extent.

2. Inorganic orthophosphate is required for both phosphorolysis of glycogen (page 417) and oxidation of 3-phosphoglyceraldehyde; the latter reaction and the pyruvic acid kinase reaction also require a supply of ADP. Orthophosphate and ADP are also consumed in the oxidation of lactate and pyruvate via the tricarboxylic acid cycle, while generating ATP. In this sense, glycolysis competes with respiration for available inorganic phosphate and ADP. When respiration is slow or absent, ample phosphate and ADP are provided for rapid glycolysis, but insofar as the oxidative reactions transform phosphate and ADP into ATP, they diminish the supply available for glycolysis. This mechanism is considered an attractive one to account for the Pasteur effect. It is supported by the observation that dinitrophenol, which "uncouples" the formation of ATP from oxidative reactions (page 330) and hence spares inorganic phosphate and ADP, enhances aerobic glycolysis in various systems.

3. Considerable evidence suggests that the phosphofructokinase reaction may become limiting under aerobic conditions. Since this enzyme is activated by P_i, AMP, and ADP, all of which are available under anaerobic conditions, but is inhibited by relatively low concentrations of ATP which would become abundant under aerobic conditions, its properties are compatible with this suggestion.

4. Certain of the enzymes involved in glycolysis contain sulfhydryl groups essential to their operation. Important among these are phosphoglyceraldehyde dehydrogenase and phosphofructokinase. It has been suggested that oxidation of sulfhydryl groups in these and possibly other enzymes may result in decreased enzymic activity and hence in diminished glycolysis.

5. Of the two possible fates of glucose 6-phosphate, viz., isomerization to

fructose 6-phosphate and oxidation to phosphogluconic acid (page 387), the latter reaction may be significantly favored at high oxygen tensions. This would tend to deflect glucose metabolism from the pathway of anaerobic glycolysis (Fig. 20.1) to the phosphogluconate pathway.

What might be described as the reciprocal of the Pasteur effect is the demonstration that high concentrations of glucose will inhibit cellular respiration, studied in isolated systems. This is known as the *Crabtree effect*.

SOME ALTERNATE PATHWAYS OF CARBOHYDRATE METABOLISM

The Glyoxylic Pathway. An additional pathway for generation of 4-carbon dicarboxylic acids functions in plants and microorganisms but is not known to be operative in animal tissues. This pathway is made possible by two specific enzymes. *Isocitritase* catalyzes a retrograde aldol condensation.

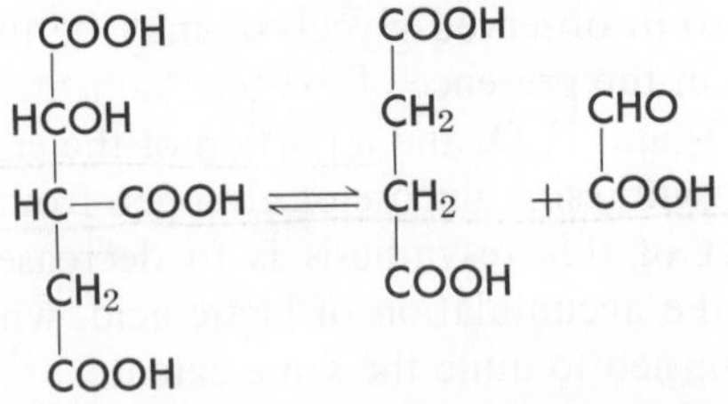

$$
\begin{array}{ccc}
\text{COOH} & \text{COOH} & \\
| & | & \\
\text{HCOH} & \text{CH}_2 & \text{CHO} \\
| & | & | \\
\text{HC—COOH} \rightleftharpoons & \text{CH}_2 & + \ \text{COOH} \\
| & | & \\
\text{CH}_2 & \text{COOH} & \\
| & & \\
\text{COOH} & &
\end{array}
$$

Isocitric acid   **Succinic**   **Glyoxylic**
                     acid   **acid**

Malic acid synthetase catalyzes the condensation of acetyl CoA with glyoxylic acid to form malic acid, a reaction analogous to the formation of citric acid from oxaloacetic acid (page 318).

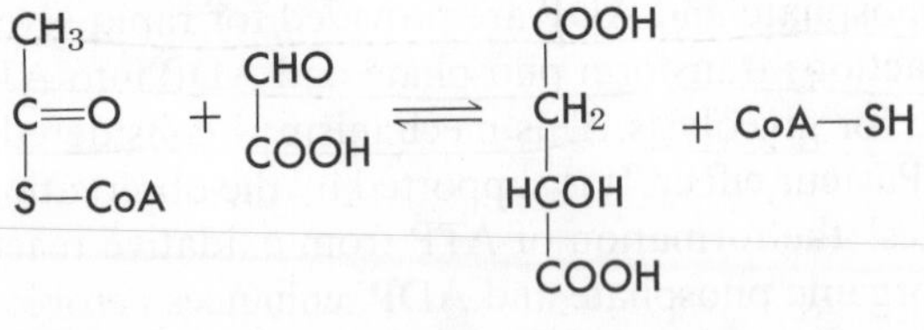

$$
\begin{array}{ccc}
\text{CH}_3 & & \text{COOH} \\
| & \text{CHO} & | \\
\text{C}{=}\text{O} \ + \ | & \rightleftharpoons & \text{CH}_2 \ + \ \text{CoA—SH} \\
| & \text{COOH} & | \\
\text{S—CoA} & & \text{HCOH} \\
& & | \\
& & \text{COOH}
\end{array}
$$

In conjunction with the previously described enzymes of the citric acid cycle, these enzymes permit the net formation of succinic acid from acetyl CoA, as shown in Fig. 20.4. The over-all reaction is as follows.

$$2 \text{ Acetyl CoA} + \text{DPN}^+ \longrightarrow \text{succinic acid} + 2\text{CoA} + \text{DPNH} + \text{H}^+$$

The succinic acid formed can be converted by reactions of the citric acid cycle to oxaloacetic acid, which can then react with acetyl CoA. Alternatively, the oxaloacetic acid may be converted to phosphoenolpyruvic acid and thence to glucose. In this manner the carbon of acetyl CoA, derived from the oxidation of fatty acids (Chap. 22), can be utilized for *net* formation of carbohydrate. This transformation, impossible in animals, is feasible in plants and various microorgan-

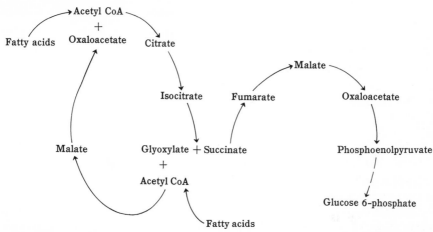

FIG. 20.4. The malate-isocitrate cycle. Oxidation of fatty acids can provide acetyl CoA, which enters the cycle at two points. Each turn of the cycle results in generation of one molecule of succinic acid. The latter can be oxidized to oxaloacetic acid by reactions of the citric acid cycle (Fig. 18.1); the oxaloacetic acid is decarboxylated and phosphorylated to phosphenolpyruvic acid (page 382), and the latter is converted to glucose 6-phosphate by reversal of the glycolytic sequence (Fig. 18.2). Thus, four molecules of acetyl CoA are required to make two molecules of succinic acid, which yields one molecule of hexose plus two molecules of CO_2.

isms by virtue of the operation of isocitritase and malate synthetase, which are lacking in animal tissues.

Acetyl Phosphate Metabolism in Microorganisms. Most microorganisms, like animal cells, oxidize pyruvate to acetyl CoA, which enters the citric acid cycle. An interesting alternate pathway is the _phosphoroclastic_ cleavage found in _E. coli_.

$$CH_3COCOOH + P_i \longrightarrow CH_3COOPO_3H_2 + HCOOH$$

      Pyruvic acid   **Acetyl phosphate   Formic acid**

The acetyl phosphate may then be converted to acetyl CoA under the influence of _phosphotransacetylase._

$$\text{Acetyl phosphate} + CoA \rightleftharpoons \text{acetyl CoA} + P_i$$

Propionic Acid Biosynthesis in Microorganisms. It has long been evident that animals can metabolize propionic acid (page 443). For example, propionic acid administered to the fasted animal soon appears, almost quantitatively, as an increment in liver glycogen. If given to a diabetic animal, propionic acid appears quantitatively in the urine as one-half mole equivalent of glucose. The pathway for this conversion remained obscure until Swick and Wood elucidated the reverse process, _viz._, formation of propionic acid from pyruvate, in propionibacteria.

In these bacteria, the initial event in propionic acid synthesis is an unusual transfer of CO_2 from methylmalonyl CoA to pyruvic acid, catalyzed by a biotin-containing enzyme, _methylmalonyl-oxaloacetic acid transcarboxylase._

$$\begin{array}{cccc}
\underset{|}{\overset{|}{\text{CH}_3}} & & \overset{|}{\text{COOH}} & \overset{|}{\text{COOH}} & \overset{|}{\text{CH}_3} \\
\text{C}=\text{O} & + \ \text{CH}_3-\text{C}-\text{H} & \rightleftharpoons & \text{CH}_2 & + & \text{CH}_2 \\
| & | & & | & & | \\
\text{COOH} & \text{CO}-\text{SCoA} & & \text{C}=\text{O} & & \text{CO}-\text{SCoA} \\
& & & | & & \\
& & & \text{COOH} & & \\
\end{array}$$

Pyruvic acid   Methylmalonyl   Oxaloacetic Propionyl CoA
                   CoA   acid

The oxaloacetate formed is reduced to succinic acid by reversal of the usual citric acid cycle reactions, via malic and fumaric acids. A *transthioesterase* catalyzes transfer of the CoA moiety from propionyl CoA to succinic acid, forming free propionic acid and succinyl CoA.

The final step in this process is the regeneration of methylmalonyl CoA from succinyl CoA. This is catalyzed by *methylmalonyl CoA mutase,* which utilizes, as coenzyme, dimethylbenzimidazole cobamide (Chap. 55), a derivative of vitamin B_{12}. The mechanism of this reaction is discussed elsewhere (page 444). This reaction sequence may be summarized as follows.

(a)   Pyruvic acid + methylmalonyl CoA $\rightleftharpoons$ oxaloacetic acid + propionyl CoA
(b)   Oxaloacetic acid + 4(H) $\rightleftharpoons$ succinic acid + H_2O
(c)   Succinic acid + propionyl CoA $\rightleftharpoons$ succinyl CoA + propionic acid
(d)   Succinyl CoA $\rightleftharpoons$ methylmalonyl CoA
_____
Sum: Pyruvic acid + 4(H) $\longrightarrow$ propionic acid + H_2O

The metabolism of propionic acid by animal tissues, essentially by a reversal of this pathway, is discussed on page 443.

Fates of Acetaldehyde. It was indicated earlier that acetaldehyde, formed by decarboxylation of pyruvate, is reduced to ethanol in the course of anaerobic fermentation. In certain aerobic fermentations, as in vinegar production, acetic acid is the terminal product. This may arise by hydrolysis of acetyl CoA or acetyl phosphate or by oxidation of acetaldehyde. Various enzymes are known that catalyze the latter reaction, including phosphoglyceraldehyde dehydrogenase (page 372). In mammals, this oxidation is catalyzed by *hepatic aldehyde oxidase,* by *xanthine oxidase,* and by a DPN-linked *aldehyde dehydrogenase.* Another reaction of acetaldehyde, of unknown significance, is that catalyzed by *carboligase.*

$$\underset{\text{O}}{\overset{\text{H}}{\text{CH}_3-\text{C}}} + \underset{\text{O}}{\overset{\text{H}}{\text{C}-\text{CH}_3}} \longrightarrow \underset{\text{OH O}}{\overset{\text{H}}{\text{CH}_3-\text{C}-\text{C}-\text{CH}_3}}$$

Acetoin

The source of acetaldehyde in animal metabolism, other than from exogenous ethanol, is unknown, but carboligase is widely distributed in animal tissues. Heterolactic acid bacteria catalyze analogous reactions between acetaldehyde and pyruvate and between two molecules of pyruvate.

THE PHOSPHOGLUCONATE OXIDATIVE PATHWAY

The glycolytic pathway is one of two major reaction sequences by which glucose is metabolized in animal tissues. The second prominent pathway has been called the phosphogluconate oxidative pathway, or the "hexose monophosphate shunt." The names of Warburg, Dickens, Lipmann, Horecker, and Racker have been associated with its elucidation.

The phosphogluconate oxidative pathway of glucose metabolism encompasses a series of reactions that include a number of novel transformations and compounds as well as several of the intermediates and enzymes encountered in glycolysis. The enzymes of both series of reactions are found in the cytoplasm of those cells in which they function. Interest attaches to the phosphogluconate pathway because it affords a means for the total combustion of glucose independent of the citric acid cycle, it is the important generator of TPNH necessary for synthesis of fatty acids and the functioning of various hydroxylases (page 356), and it serves as a source of D-ribose as well as of 4-carbon and 7-carbon sugars. Commencing with glucose 6-phosphate, there is no further requirement for ATP. In contrast to glycolysis and the citric acid cycle, the operation of this sequence cannot be visualized as a consecutive set of transformations leading in direct fashion from glucose 6-phosphate to 6 molecules of CO_2. To understand the phosphogluconate pathway it is desirable first to consider the participating enzymes, their substrates, and their reaction products.

Glucose 6-Phosphate Dehydrogenase. This enzyme catalyzes the oxidation of glucose 6-phosphate by TPN^+.

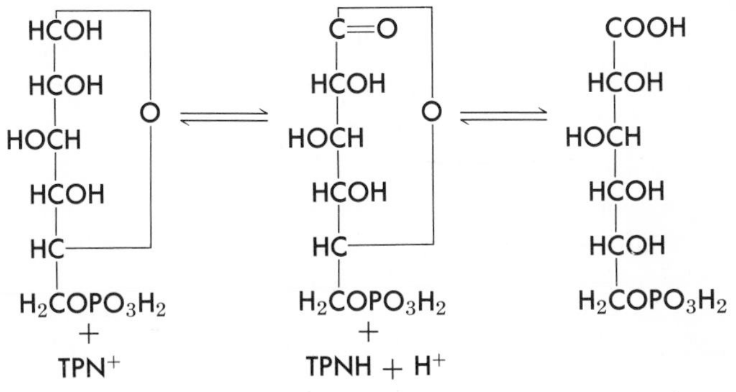

Glucose 6-phosphate	6-Phosphoglucono-δ-lactone	6-Phosphogluconic acid

The product is the δ-lactone of 6-phosphogluconic acid which is hydrolyzed to the corresponding acid by a specific *lactonase*. Equilibrium for this process lies far to the right, and it has frequently been used to generate TPNH in experiments with purified enzymic systems.

6-Phosphogluconic Acid Dehydrogenase. Further oxidation of 6-phosphogluconic acid is catalyzed by a TPN^+- and Mn^{++}-dependent enzyme which is a β-hydroxyacid oxidative decarboxylase and is similar, therefore, to malic enzyme and isocitric acid dehydrogenase.

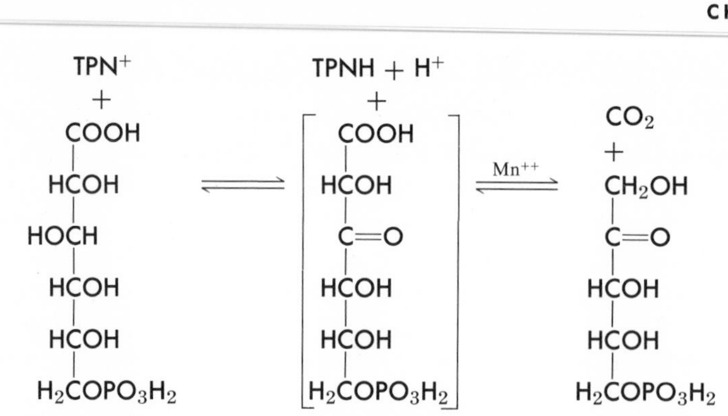

$$
\begin{array}{ccc}
\text{TPN}^+ & \text{TPNH + H}^+ & \\
+ & + & \text{CO}_2 \\
\text{COOH} & \text{COOH} & + \\
| & | & \text{CH}_2\text{OH} \\
\text{HCOH} & \text{HCOH} & | \\
| \quad\rightleftharpoons\quad & | \quad\xrightarrow{\text{Mn}^{++}}\rightleftharpoons & \text{C}=\text{O} \\
\text{HOCH} & \text{C}=\text{O} & | \\
| & | & \text{HCOH} \\
\text{HCOH} & \text{HCOH} & | \\
| & | & \text{HCOH} \\
\text{HCOH} & \text{HCOH} & | \\
| & | & \text{H}_2\text{COPO}_3\text{H}_2 \\
\text{H}_2\text{COPO}_3\text{H}_2 & \text{H}_2\text{COPO}_3\text{H}_2 & \\
\end{array}
$$

| 6-Phosphogluconic acid | 3-Keto-6-phospho-gluconic acid | D-Ribulose 5-phosphate |

The intermediary β-keto acid has not been isolated and is presumed to decarboxylate as it is formed on the enzymic surface.

Pentose Interconversions. Specific enzymes for transformation of ribulose 5-phosphate into isomeric pentoses are an integral aspect of the operation of the phosphogluconate oxidative pathway.

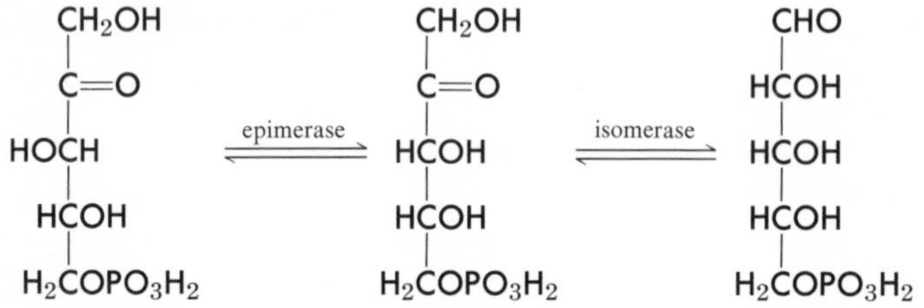

$$
\begin{array}{ccc}
\text{CH}_2\text{OH} & \text{CH}_2\text{OH} & \text{CHO} \\
| & | & | \\
\text{C}=\text{O} & \text{C}=\text{O} & \text{HCOH} \\
| \quad\xrightarrow{\text{epimerase}}\rightleftharpoons & | \quad\xrightarrow{\text{isomerase}}\rightleftharpoons & | \\
\text{HOCH} & \text{HCOH} & \text{HCOH} \\
| & | & | \\
\text{HCOH} & \text{HCOH} & \text{HCOH} \\
| & | & | \\
\text{H}_2\text{COPO}_3\text{H}_2 & \text{H}_2\text{COPO}_3\text{H}_2 & \text{H}_2\text{COPO}_3\text{H}_2 \\
\end{array}
$$

| D-Xylulose 5-phosphate | D-Ribulose 5-phosphate | D-Ribose 5-phosphate |

Phosphopentose epimerase catalyzes epimerization about carbon-3. *Phosphopentose isomerase* catalyzes interconversion of the ketopentose and aldopentose forms, a reaction which is formally similar to the action of hexose phosphate isomerase (page 370) and triose phosphate isomerase (page 372).

Transketolase. D-Xylulose 5-phosphate serves as a source of "active glycolaldehyde" in the *transketolase* reaction. This enzyme, which utilizes thiamine pyrophos-

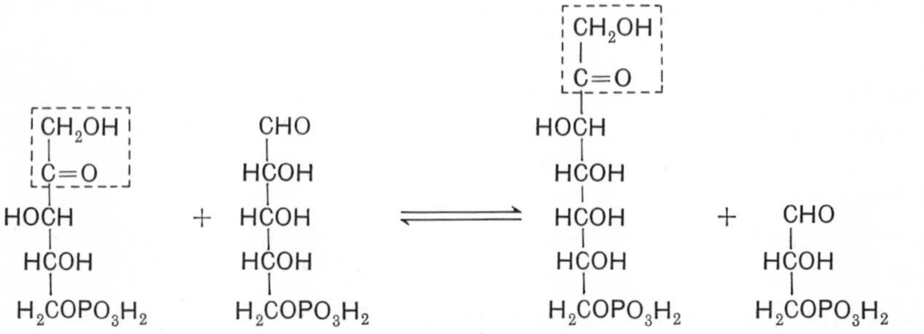

$$
\begin{array}{ccccc}
\overline{|\text{CH}_2\text{OH}|} & \text{CHO} & \text{HOCH} & & \\
|\text{C}=\text{O}| & \text{HCOH} & \text{HCOH} & & \\
\text{HOCH} \quad + & \text{HCOH} \quad\rightleftharpoons & \text{HCOH} \quad + & \text{CHO} \\
\text{HCOH} & \text{HCOH} & \text{HCOH} & \text{HCOH} \\
\text{H}_2\text{COPO}_3\text{H}_2 & \text{H}_2\text{COPO}_3\text{H}_2 & \text{H}_2\text{COPO}_3\text{H}_2 & \text{H}_2\text{COPO}_3\text{H}_2 \\
\end{array}
$$

| D-Xylulose 5-phosphate | D-Ribose 5-phosphate | D-Sedoheptulose 7-phosphate | D-Glyceraldehyde 3-phosphate |

phate as coenzyme and requires Mg^{++}, effects transfer of a 2-carbon unit from a 2-keto sugar to C-1 of various aldoses. Among the more important reactions catalyzed by transketolase is that in which the 7-carbon sugar sedoheptulose is formed. The "active glycolaldehyde" moiety is α,β-dihydroxyethyl thiamine pyrophosphate, a compound similar to the "active acetaldehyde" formed during oxidative decarboxylation of pyruvate (page 317). No free glycolaldehyde appears during the transketolase reaction, which is readily reversible.

Transaldolase. Another enzyme in this series is *transaldolase,* which can effect the transfer of carbon atoms 1, 2, and 3 of a ketose phosphate to C-1 of an aldose phosphate.

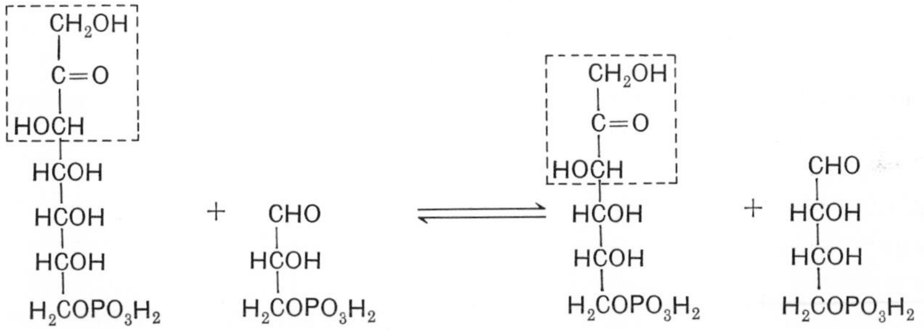

| D-Sedoheptulose 7-phosphate | D-Glyceraldehyde 3-phosphate | | D-Fructose 6-phosphate | D-Erythrose 4-phosphate |

Although the reaction appears similar to the aldolase reaction (page 371), free dihydroxyacetone or its phosphate ester cannot serve as substrates, nor do they appear in the course of the reaction; the enzyme catalyzes only transfers in the manner shown above. Horecker and his colleagues demonstrated that an intermediate Schiff base is formed between the carbonyl of the transferred dihydroxyacetone moiety and the ϵ-amino group of a lysine residue of the enzyme. A similar mode of substrate binding is involved in the action of aldolase (page 255).

The erythrose 4-phosphate formed by transaldolase has only one known metabolic fate, accepting a 2-carbon unit in a transketolase-catalyzed reaction to form fructose 6-phosphate.

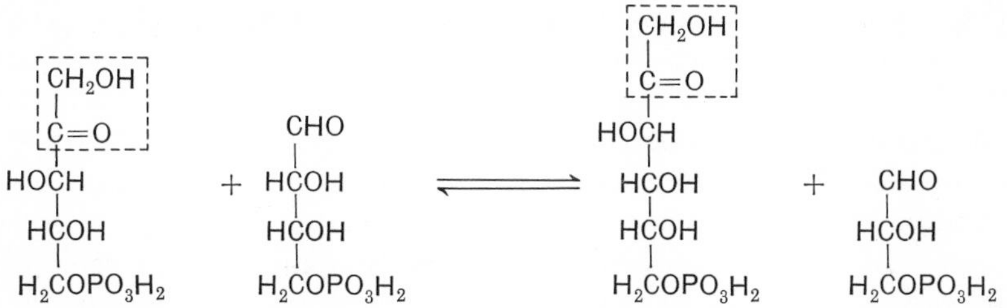

| D-Xylulose 5-phosphate | D-Erythrose 4-phosphate | | D-Fructose 6-phosphate | D-Glyceraldehyde 3-phosphate |

Cyclic Nature of the Phosphogluconate Oxidative Pathway. The discussion above has presented all the enzymes and intermediates unique to this pathway. For its operation, however, four of the enzymes concerned in glycolysis are also required.

These are triose phosphate isomerase (page 372) to catalyze interconversion of phosphoglyceraldehyde and dihydroxyacetone phosphate, aldolase to catalyze formation of fructose 1,6-diphosphate from the two triose phosphates, diphospho-fructose phosphatase to hydrolyze fructose 1,6-diphosphate to fructose 6-phosphate, and hexose phosphate isomerase to convert fructose 6-phosphate to glucose 6-phosphate. These will be recognized as the enzymes involved in the normal formation of hexose from triose or pyruvate by reversal of the glycolytic sequence (Table 20.1, page 369).

With the foregoing reactions in mind, it is possible to reconstruct a system into which hexose continually enters and from which CO_2 emerges as the sole carbon compound. This may be visualized by consideration of the set of balanced equations shown in Table 20.3, which, in sum, describe the conversion of 6 moles of hexose phosphate to 5 moles of hexose phosphate and 6 moles of CO_2. Note that the only reaction in which CO_2 is evolved is the oxidation of 6-phosphoglu-conic acid.

At first glance this description of the reaction sequence appears quite complex, but it may be more readily understood from the following considerations. The operation of this pathway as an *oxidizing* mechanism is accomplished entirely by reactions (a) and (b), in which TPN^+ is reduced and CO_2 is evolved. Oxidation of 6 moles of hexose by reactions (a) and (b) results in delivery of 12 pairs of electrons to TPN^+, the requisite amount for total oxidation of 1 mole of glucose to 6 moles of CO_2. As a consequence of reaction (b), there remain 6 moles of ribulose 5-phosphate. If these are employed for nucleotide formation, etc., they need only undergo isomerization to ribose 5-phosphate. However, if the carbon of the 6 moles of pentose were rearranged to form 5 moles of hexose, the net achievement would be the complete oxidation of one of the original 6 moles of hexose. This transformation of the carbon of the pentoses to hexose is initiated in reactions (c) and (d), with a balance of 2 moles of tetrose and 2 moles of pentose. Reactions (e) employ the latter to yield two additional moles of hexose and two of triose. Reactions (f) to (h) convert the two trioses to one hexose. In each series the hexose formed is fructose 6-phosphate. Finally, isomerization of the latter yields 5 moles of glucose 6-phosphate, which may now reenter the sequence at (a), etc.

Efforts have been made to estimate the relative amounts of glucose catabolized via the glycolytic and phosphogluconate pathways. Experimentally, these have sought to take advantage of the fact that in the operation of the phosphogluconate path, the CO_2 first formed must all be derived from C-1 of glucose, whereas in the concerted operation of glycolysis and the citric acid cycle, the rate of evolution of $C^{14}O_2$ from glucose 1-C^{14} and glucose 6-C^{14} should be indistinguishable. In mammalian striated muscle there appears to be no direct oxidation via phosphoglu-conate, and catabolism proceeds entirely via glycolysis and the citric acid cycle. In liver, an appreciable fraction, perhaps 30 per cent or more, of the CO_2 arising from glucose stems from operation of the phosphogluconate oxidative path. In mammary gland, testis, adipose tissue, leukocytes, and adrenal cortex an even larger proportion of glucose catabolism occurs via phosphogluconate oxidation. The special advantages that accrue to the organism by virtue of the operation of the direct pathway, other than pentose formation for nucleotide synthesis, appear to derive

Table 20.3: REACTIONS OF THE PHOSPHOGLUCONATE OXIDATIVE PATHWAY

Step	Enzyme	Reaction	Carbon balance
a	Glucose 6-phosphate dehydrogenase	6 Glucose 6-phosphate + 6TPN$^+$ $\longrightarrow$ 6 6-phosphogluconate + 6TPNH + 6H$^+$	6(6) $\longrightarrow$ 6(6)
b	Phosphogluconic acid dehydrogenase	6 6-Phosphogluconate + 6TPN$^+$ $\longrightarrow$ 6 ribulose 5-phosphate + 6TPNH + 6H$^+$ + 6CO$_2$	6(6) $\longrightarrow$ 6(5) + 6(1)
c	Pentose epimerase	2 Ribulose 5-phosphate $\longrightarrow$ 2 xylulose 5-phosphate	2(5) $\longrightarrow$ 2(5)
	Pentose isomerase	2 Ribulose 5-phosphate $\longrightarrow$ 2 ribose 5-phosphate	2(5) $\longrightarrow$ 2(5)
	Transketolase	2 Xylulose 5-phosphate + 2 ribose 5-phosphate $\longrightarrow$ 2 sedoheptulose 7-phosphate + 2 glyceraldehyde 3-phosphate	2(5) + 2(5) $\longrightarrow$ 2(7) + 2(3)
d	Transaldolase	2 Sedoheptulose 7-phosphate + 2 glyceraldehyde 3-phosphate $\longrightarrow$ 2 erythrose 4-phosphate + 2 fructose 6-phosphate	2(7) + 2(3) $\longrightarrow$ 2(4) + 2(6)
e	Pentose epimerase	2 Ribulose 5-phosphate $\longrightarrow$ 2 xylulose 5-phosphate	2(5) $\longrightarrow$ 2(5)
	Transketolase	2 Xylulose 5-phosphate + 2 erythrose 4-phosphate $\longrightarrow$ 2 glyceraldehyde 3-phosphate + 2 fructose 6-phosphate	2(5) + 2(4) $\longrightarrow$ 2(3) + 2(6)
f	Triose isomerase	Glyceraldehyde 3-phosphate $\longrightarrow$ dihydroxyacetone phosphate	(3) $\longrightarrow$ (3)
g	Aldolase	Dihydroxyacetone phosphate + glyceraldehyde 3-phosphate $\longrightarrow$ fructose 1,6-diphosphate	(3) + (3) $\longrightarrow$ (6)
h	Phosphatase	Fructose 1,6-diphosphate $\longrightarrow$ fructose 6-phosphate + P$_i$	(6) $\longrightarrow$ (6)
i	Hexose isomerase	5 Fructose 6-phosphate $\longrightarrow$ 5 glucose 6-phosphate	5(6) $\longrightarrow$ 5(6)
Net:		6 Glucose 6-phosphate + 12TPN$^+$ $\longrightarrow$ 5 glucose 6-phosphate + 6CO$_2$ + 12TPNH + 12H$^+$ + P$_i$	6(6) $\longrightarrow$ 5(6) + 6(1)

from the fact that no additional ATP is required, there is no dependence upon the availability of the 4-carbon dicarboxylic acids of the citric acid cycle, and, probably most significant, this pathway employs TPN$^+$ as the exclusive electron acceptor. As indicated elsewhere (page 328), it is not clear whether ATP can be efficiently generated by mitochondrial oxidation of TPNH, but operation of transhydrogenase (page 328) would permit generation of 3 moles of ATP per TPNH formed, or 36 moles for the total combustion of glucose. This value compares favorably with the yield of ATP from glycolysis and the citric acid cycle. However, it appears likely that most of the TPNH generated by the phosphogluconate pathway is employed as a reducing agent, particularly in the synthesis of fatty acids and steroids (pages 448 and 471). This is consonant with the distribution of the enzymes concerned with these processes. Liver, mammary gland, testis, and adrenal cortex are active sites of fatty acid and/or steroid synthesis, whereas these processes are not prominent in the metabolism of striated muscle, a tissue in which phosphogluconate oxidation is not known to occur. In those cells in which phosphogluconate oxidation is possible, it appears that the rate-limiting factor is the availability of TPN$^+$, thus indicating a coupling of glucose oxidation with the requirements of TPNH-utilizing reactions.

Anaerobic Origin of Ribose. As described above, the oxidation of glucose 6-phosphate affords a means for ribose formation. However, any cell equipped with transketolase, transaldolase, the enzymes for interconversion of pentoses, as well as the normal enzymes of glycolysis, can also generate ribose 5-phosphate by a nonoxidative pathway, as shown by the following equations.

(*a*) **Fructose 6-phosphate + glyceraldehyde 3-phosphate** $\xrightarrow[\text{ketolase}]{\text{trans-}}$

$\qquad\qquad\qquad\qquad\qquad$ **erythrose 4-phosphate + xylulose 5-phosphate**

(*b*) **Fructose 6-phosphate + erythrose 4-phosphate** $\xrightarrow[\text{aldolase}]{\text{trans-}}$

$\qquad\qquad\qquad\qquad\qquad$ **glyceraldehyde 3-phosphate + sedoheptulose 7-phosphate**

(*c*) **Sedoheptulose 7-phosphate + glyceraldehyde 3-phosphate** $\xrightarrow[\text{ketolase}]{\text{trans-}}$

$\qquad\qquad\qquad\qquad\qquad$ **ribose 5-phosphate + xylulose 5-phosphate**

(*d*) **2 Xylulose 5-phosphate $\longrightarrow$ 2 ribulose 5-phosphate $\longrightarrow$ 2 ribose 5-phosphate**

Sum: **2 Fructose 6-phosphate + glyceraldehyde 3-phosphate $\longrightarrow$ 3 ribose 5-phosphate**

The relative contributions of the oxidative and nonoxidative pathways for net pentose formation in animal tissues are uncertain.

PHOTOSYNTHESIS

The prime source of energy in the biosphere derives from the absorption of light by chlorophyll-containing cells. It has long been obvious that the energy so obtained is utilized to drive the fixation of CO_2 into carbohydrate.

$$6CO_2 + 6H_2O \xrightarrow{h\nu} C_6H_{12}O_6 + 6O_2$$

This process, is, in effect, the reverse of the oxidation of glucose as presented previously (page 293), and the energy required, as a minimum, is that which can be derived from glucose oxidation, viz., +686,000 cal. per mole. In plants this process occurs in organized subcellular bodies called *chloroplasts,* the structure of which will be considered below (page 394). If a suspension of chloroplasts is illuminated in the absence of CO_2 and placed in the dark, and if CO_2 is then admitted, fixation of CO_2 into carbohydrate proceeds for a brief but significant time. It is apparent, therefore, that the process of CO_2 fixation per se is not, strictly speaking, light-dependent. Understanding of the actual photosynthetic events will be facilitated if we first consider the phenomena, which, even in the dark, can accomplish CO_2 fixation.

CO₂ Fixation; the "Dark Reaction." The fate of the carbon atom of CO_2 during its incorporation into organic compounds has been studied by introduction of radioactive $C^{14}O_2$ for short periods of time into photosynthesizing systems. The radioactive products formed were identified by paper chromatography and radio-autography. After only 5 sec. of exposure to radioactive CO_2, appreciable fixation of C^{14} occurred; the earliest compound shown to be radioactive was 3-phospho-glyceric acid, labeled predominantly in the carboxyl carbon.

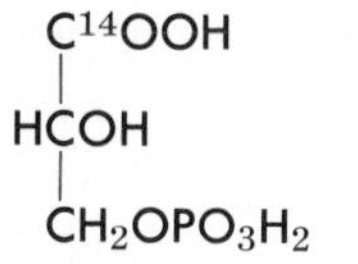

$$C^{14}OOH$$
$$|$$
$$HCOH$$
$$|$$
$$CH_2OPO_3H_2$$

3-Phosphoglyceric acid-1-C¹⁴

However, the primary acceptor of CO_2 is not a 2-carbon compound but, rather, ribulose 1,5-diphosphate. The reaction is catalyzed by *diphosphoribulose carboxylase.*

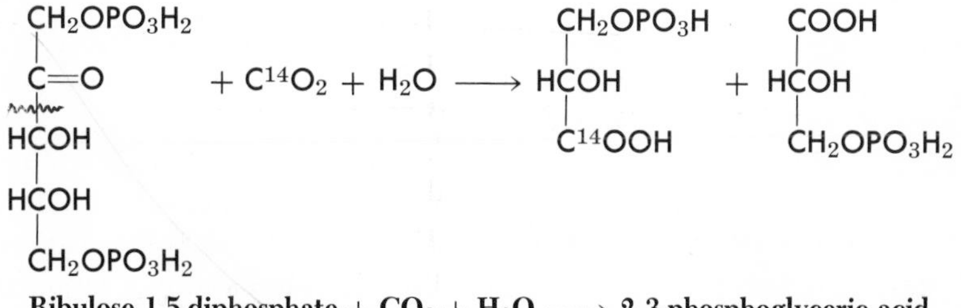

$$\begin{array}{l} CH_2OPO_3H_2 \\ | \\ C{=}O \\ | \\ HCOH \\ | \\ HCOH \\ | \\ CH_2OPO_3H_2 \end{array} + C^{14}O_2 + H_2O \longrightarrow \begin{array}{l} CH_2OPO_3H \\ | \\ HCOH \\ | \\ C^{14}OOH \end{array} + \begin{array}{l} COOH \\ | \\ HCOH \\ | \\ CH_2OPO_3H_2 \end{array}$$

Ribulose 1,5-diphosphate + CO₂ + H₂O ⟶ 2 3-phosphoglyceric acid

The carboxylation enzyme occurs in chloroplasts together with *phosphoribulokinase,* which catalyzes the following reaction.

Ribulose 5-phosphate + ATP ⟶ ribulose 1,5-diphosphate + ADP

All other enzymes required to complete the synthesis of hexose from 3-phospho-glyceric acid have been previously described in the discussion of glycolysis. However, were all the 3-phosphoglyceric acid converted to hexose by reversal of glycolysis, no ribulose diphosphate would be available to serve as acceptor for CO_2 in subsequent fixation reactions. The problem, therefore, is the converse of that considered in the operation of the phosphogluconate pathway, viz., to provide a regenerative system by means of which hexose may be accumulated and ribulose 1,5-diphosphate recovered for the carboxylation reaction. This is again achieved by concerted action of the enzymes of glycolysis and those of the phosphogluconate pathway. These reactions are summarized in the balanced equations of Table 20.4.

In reactions (b), the 3-phosphoglycerates formed by carboxylation of ribulose 1,5-diphosphate are reduced to 3-phosphoglyceraldehyde. Of the 12 moles of triose phosphate thus formed, 10 are employed in reactions (c) and (d) to make 5 moles of fructose 6-phosphate. One of these 5 moles will represent the net gain of photosynthesis. In reactions (e) to (g), 4 moles of fructose 6-phosphate and the 2 moles of 3-phosphoglyceraldehyde still remaining are arranged to yield 6 moles of xylulose 5-phosphate, which are then epimerized to ribulose 5-phosphate (h) and phosphorylated (i). These regenerated 6 moles of ribulose 1,5-diphosphate may then participate in the next cycle.

The summary equation in Table 20.4 reveals the manner in which energy must be provided to this system in order to effect fixation of CO_2 into carbohydrate. Synthesis of 1 mole of hexose phosphate requires 12 moles of DPNH and 18 moles of ATP. It is the synthesis of this DPNH and ATP which is accomplished by the photosynthetic system proper. Although DPNH is the reductant in CO_2 fixation in many species, the chloroplasts of green leaves frequently contain a TPNH-linked 3-phosphoglyceraldehyde dehydrogenase. In these instances it is TPNH which must be generated by the photosynthetic system.

The Chloroplast. The fundamental event in photosynthesis is the absorption of light. The energy of light quanta can be expressed in calories per mole (calories per einstein). Blue light has about 70,000 cal. per einstein, red light about 40,000 cal. per einstein. A given molecule, depending on its structure, can absorb light only of specific wavelengths. The absorbed energy is then part of the molecule, which is said to be "activated," i.e., one or more electrons have been dislocated and are in positions more remote from atomic nuclei than in the ground state. Chlorophyll (page 202) has a continuing system of alternating single and double bonds; in structures of this type the electrons involved are not distinguishable from one another, and when light is absorbed, it is this "π" electron system which is in a higher energetic state. When light is absorbed, the molecule can exist in a transient excited state called the "singlet." This can return to the ground state by loss of energy as heat, or by emission of a light quantum (fluorescence). Alternately, it can assume a somewhat more stable but still excited condition by transition to the "triplet" state in which not only is an electron dislocated and in a more energetic orbit, but its spin is reversed. Such a molecule can also accept yet another light quantum and arrive at a "second-triplet" excited-state level. A considerable body of evidence indicates that in photosynthesis, chlorophyll must be brought to the second-triplet state to be effective.

The chloroplast, a structure perhaps ten times the diameter of a mitochondrion, contains all the enzymes necessary for CO_2 fixation as described above. The chlorophyll is found in stacked layers, or lamellae, organized within the chloroplast, as grana, which contain hundreds of molecules of mixed phosphatides per molecule of chlorophyll. All plant chloroplasts contain chlorophyll a, and most of them contain lesser amounts of chlorophyll b (page 201) and an abundance of

Table 20.4: HEXOSE ACCUMULATION AND PENTOSE REGENERATION IN PHOTOSYNTHESIS

Step	Enzyme	Reaction	Carbon balance
a	Carboxylation enzyme	6 Ribulose 1,5-diphosphate + $6CO_2$ $\longrightarrow$ 12 3-phosphoglyceric acid	$6(5) + 6(1) \longrightarrow 12(3)$
b	Phosphoglyceric acid kinase	12 3-Phosphoglyceric acid + 12ATP $\longrightarrow$ 12 1,3-diphosphoglyceric acid + 12ADP	$12(3) \longrightarrow 12(3)$
	Phosphoglyceraldehyde dehydrogenase	12 1,3-Diphosphoglyceric acid + 12DPNH + $12H^+$ $\longrightarrow$ 12 3-phosphoglyceraldehyde + $12DPN^+ + 12P_i$	$12(3) \longrightarrow 12(3)$
c	Triose isomerase	5 3-Phosphoglyceraldehyde $\longrightarrow$ 5 dihydroxyacetone phosphate	$5(3) \longrightarrow 5(3)$
	Aldolase	5 3-Phosphoglyceraldehyde + 5 dihydroxyacetone phosphate $\longrightarrow$ 5 fructose 1,6-diphosphate	$5(3) + 5(3) \longrightarrow 5(6)$
d	Phosphatase	5 Fructose 1,6-diphosphate $\longrightarrow$ 5 fructose 6-phosphate + $5P_i$	$5(6) \longrightarrow 5(6)$
e	Transketolase	2 Fructose 6-phosphate + 2 3-phosphoglyceraldehyde $\longrightarrow$ 2 xylulose 5-phosphate + 2 erythrose 4-phosphate	$2(6) + 2(3) \longrightarrow 2(5) + 2(4)$
f	Transaldolase	2 Fructose 6-phosphate + 2 erythrose 4-phosphate $\longrightarrow$ 2 sedoheptulose 7-phosphate + 2 3-phosphoglyceraldehyde	$2(6) + 2(4) \longrightarrow 2(7) + 2(3)$
g	Transketolase	2 Sedoheptulose 7-phosphate + 2 3-phosphoglyceraldehyde $\longrightarrow$ 4 xylulose 5-phosphate	$2(7) + 2(3) \longrightarrow 4(5)$
h	Epimerase	6 Xylulose 5-phosphate $\longrightarrow$ 6 ribulose 5-phosphate	$6(5) \longrightarrow 6(5)$
i	Phosphoribulokinase	6 Ribulose 5-phosphate + 6ATP $\longrightarrow$ 6 ribulose 1,5-diphosphate + 6ADP	$6(5) \longrightarrow 6(5)$

Net: 6 Ribulose 1,5-diphosphate + $6CO_2$ + 18ATP + 12DPNH + $12H^+$ $\longrightarrow$ 6 ribulose 1,5-diphosphate + 1 fructose 6-phosphate + $17P_i$ + 18 ADP + $12DPN^+$ $6(5) + 6(1) \longrightarrow 6(5) + 1(6)$

carotenoids. Chloroplasts of the red and blue-green algae contain *phycobilins,* open chains of four pyrroles similar to the fundamental structure of bilirubin (Chap. 42). It is noteworthy that light absorption by these accessory pigments is particularly efficient at those wavelengths at which chlorophyll a absorbs poorly.

The grana, like the much smaller structures in photosynthetic bacteria (*chromatophores*), are effective light traps. Evidently, they are organized as photosynthetic "units," within which energy absorbed either by chlorophyll or by an accessory pigment can be transmitted to some particular single chlorophyll molecule which actually utilizes the absorbed energy. The unit may be regarded as being in the solid state, rather than in solution. Energy transfer from molecule to molecule within the unit can occur by either of two mechanisms. In "induced resonance energy transfer," energy is transferred as though, after absorbing a photon, each molecule fluoresces and thus passes its energy to its neighbor, although no light, as such, is actually emitted or reabsorbed. In a crystal or lattice arrangement, the excited electrons can leave their molecular "valence bands," enter the "conduction band" of the crystal, and migrate to an acceptor molecule. In any case, each photosynthetic unit serves as a light-gathering apparatus which, even in dim light, can collect light energy and deliver it to that chlorophyll molecule which will participate in the photochemical event.

Requirements for Photosynthesis. As developed previously, the actual enzymic process whereby CO_2 is fixed into carbohydrate requires a supply of DPNH and ATP. The electromagnetic energy absorbed by the photochemical system must, therefore, be transformed into a suitable mixture of reducing potential and high energy phosphate. In the green plant, as is evident from the overall equation descriptive of photosynthesis, oxygen is also evolved during this process. In effect, therefore, the energy of the absorbed light must be used to accomplish the photolysis of water into O_2 gas and H_2 or its equivalent as reduced pyridine nucleotide, while trapping some of the energy as ATP. These relationships may be summarized as in the following equation.

$$2H_2O + 2TPN^+ + xADP + xP_i \xrightarrow{h\nu} O_2 + 2TPNH + 2H^+ + xATP \qquad (1)$$

This equation accurately summarizes the events that occur during the "light reaction" in higher green plants. However, as will be seen, more primitive photosynthetic organisms are capable of accomplishing only portions of this over-all process.

The Photochemical Event. Much evidence suggests that the prime photochemical event is the ejection from a photoactivated chlorophyll molecule of an electron which is surrendered to the environment, leaving a chlorophyll free radical.

$$\text{Chlorophyll}° \xrightarrow{h\nu} \text{chlorophyll}^+ + e$$

The general parameters of this system in the green plant can also be stated. Some of the electrons must be at such potential as to make possible reduction of the pyridine nucleotides required for CO_2 fixation (E_0' for DPN $= -0.32$ volt), while some of the chlorophyll free radicals must be at a sufficiently high potential to oxidize water (or hydroxyl ions) with evolution of O_2 ($E_0' = +0.8$ volt). Partial separation of these two processes may be observed in the Hill reaction; illumination of chloroplasts in the absence of CO_2, but in the presence of an electron acceptor, such as Fe^{+++} or quinone, results in reduction of the latter accompanied by evolution of oxygen.

$$H_2O + \text{quinone} \xrightarrow{hv} \text{hydroquinone} + \tfrac{1}{2}O_2 \qquad (2)$$

Understanding the manner in which the photochemical event makes possible the fixation of CO_2 with evolution of O_2 will be facilitated by consideration of the simpler activities of some photosynthetic bacteria.

Electron Transport and Photophosphorylation in Photosynthetic Bacteria. Were the electron emitted by activated chlorophyll to return spontaneously to the chlorophyll free radical, no useful function could be served, since the energy absorbed as light would then simply appear as heat. This would be the wasteful equivalent of a direct reaction between DPNH and O_2 in a mitochondrion. Instead, as may be observed with the chromatophores of an obligate anaerobe, the purple sulfur bacterium *Chromatium*, the electron returns to the chlorophyll via a series of intermediates. Not all the components of the electron transfer chain have been identified nor is their order certain. As a minimum, they include a flavoprotein, one of a group of quinones resembling ubiquinone (page 314), and at least two cytochromes, one of which is cytochrome c–like, while the other, at higher potential, resembles the *Rhodospirillum* heme-protein (see below).

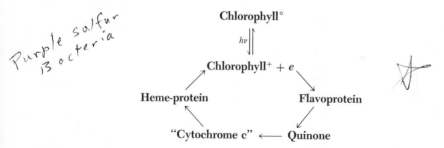

No substrate in the usual sense is involved in this system. The ejected electron moves through a series of catalytic carriers of increasing potential and returns to the chlorophyll$^+$ radical which serves as the terminal oxidant. Although the sites of energy conservation, the P/2 e ratio, and the detailed mechanisms are unknown, as the electron traverses this cyclic route, ATP is generated. This process, called *cyclic photosynthetic phosphorylation,* serves simply to transform light energy into chemical energy as ATP and can be observed in highly active, broken cell preparations. The mechanism is unlike those operative in mitochondrial oxidative phosphorylation in that dinitrophenol exerts no uncoupling effect. It has been suggested that this cyclic electron flow with associated phosphorylation may represent a primitive, early form of photosynthesis, since it provides a means for generation of ATP for an organism which lives in an anaerobic environment rich in organic nutrients. Since electron flow is completely cyclic, the organism must derive reducing power for its metabolic activities from exogeneous substrates.

A more complex situation is revealed by photosynthetic organisms, such as the nonpurple sulfur bacterium *Rhodospirillum rubrum,* which utilize light energy to effect carbon dioxide fixation but do not evolve O_2. The over-all accomplishment of photosynthesis in these organisms can be summarized by the following equation.

$$MH_2 + TPN^+ + xADP + xP_i \xrightarrow{h\nu} M + TPNH + H^+ + xATP \qquad (3)$$

Particularly noteworthy is the fact that succinic acid may serve as MH_2 in the above equation. In this instance, the oxidized form, M, is fumaric acid. Although succinic acid, thermodynamically, is of itself incapable of reducing TPN^+, the additional energy provided by the photoactivation of chlorophyll permits not only the reduction of the pyridine nucleotide but the generation of ATP as well. The pathway of electron flow may be summarized as follows.

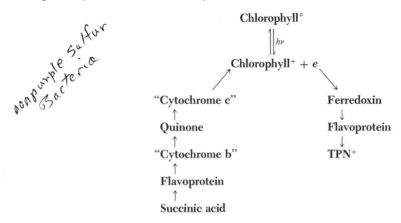

nonpurple Sulfur Bacteria

The electron liberated from the activated chlorophyll is accepted by *ferredoxin* and thence transmitted via a suitable flavoprotein to TPN^+, which accumulates as TPNH. Ferredoxin is a protein of molecular weight 12,000, containing two atoms of iron per molecule. The iron atoms are alternately reduced and reoxidized during the electron flow shown in the diagram above. E_0' for ferredoxin as isolated from the vigorous nitrogen-fixing organism *Clostridium pasteuranium* is about -0.5 volt. Hence, it is the member of lowest potential in this entire system and is the immediate acceptor of the electron liberated by activation of chlorophyll. Reduction to the ground state of the chlorophyll$^+$ thus generated is accomplished by electrons derived from succinic acid (or other metabolite) which are transmitted via a series of electron carriers. As will be seen, chlorophyll$^+$ serves in a manner analogous to O_2 in mitochondrial electron transport. It is in the course of this electron flow from succinic acid to chlorophyll$^+$ that ATP is generated. In sum, the oxidation of succinic acid plus the energy derived from the absorbed photons make possible accumulation of the TPNH and ATP required for CO_2 fixation.

Photosynthesis in Higher Plants. In yet more advanced forms of plant life, photochemical events alone meet all the requirements of photosynthesis, *i.e.*, generation of both ATP and reduced pyridine nucleotide in the absence of an exogenous organic chemical-reducing substrate; concomitantly, evolution of oxygen occurs. The over-all process is that described by equation (1) above. Note that it is similar in form to equation (3) but that, in the green plant, *water* (or hydroxyl ions) must serve as the external reductant in place of the succinic acid utilized by photosynthetic bacteria. The initial photochemical events, therefore, must provide an oxidant with an E_0' greater than that of O_2, $+0.8$ volt, and a reductant of sufficiently low potential to effect the reduction of pyridine nucleotide. Since a ferredoxin-like material again serves as more immediate reductant of TPN$^+$, the over-all difference in potential, $\Delta E_0'$, therefore, is greater than 1.3 volts, which represents an amount of energy considerably in excess of that available from a single quantum of blue light. The description to be presented has been developed only in the past few years, largely by the work of Arnon, San Pietro, Jagendorf, and Chance and their colleagues. Many details remain to be discovered and some of those described below may be incorrect. However, the general concept now appears to be relatively secure.

Much evidence indicates that photosynthesis in chloroplasts requires the absorption of light at two different wavelengths. In the summary of the over-all process presented in Fig. 20.5, light absorption is shown as occurring in chlorophyll a and chlorophyll b respectively, but it is not entirely certain whether the

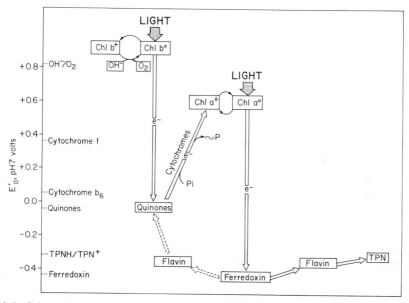

FIG. 20.5. Schematic representation of photosynthetic electron transport. Illumination of chlorophyll b with red light results in ejection of an electron which is accepted by one of the quinones (plastoquinone, coenzyme Q). The remaining (chlorophyll b)$^+$ is a free radical. The manner in which this free radical, or pairs thereof, react with hydroxyl ions of the medium is obscure, but the overall process results in formation of O_2 as the (chlorophyll b)$^+$ regains an electron. Some evidence suggests that ATP formation may also occur at this stage. Electron transport then occurs from the reduced quinone (probably now a semiquinone) via cytochrome b$_6$ to cytochrome f to chlorophyll a. High energy phosphate bonds are formed during this process. The chlorophyll a can only accept this electron if it has absorbed a photon of blue light and ejected an electron from itself to form (chlorophyll a)$^+$. The ejected electron is accepted by ferredoxin (photosynthetic pyridine nucleotide reductase). In this manner, two photons combine to accomplish electron transfer from OH$^-$ to ferredoxin, $\Delta E_0' = 1.25$ volts. Reduced ferredoxin then reduces the flavoprotein which, in turn, reduces TPN so that TPNH is available for reduction of 3-phosphoglyceric acid (page 394). A cyclic photophosphorylation can operate when only chlorophyll a is illuminated and electron transfer proceeds from chlorophyll a to ferredoxin to quinone and back to chlorophyll a. This system generates ATP, but neither reduces TPN nor oxidizes OH$^-$ to O_2.

two absorbing species are indeed chlorophylls a and b (page 201) or whether the same chemical species exhibits different absorption maxima in a hydrophobic *milieu* and at a water interface.

In freshly isolated chloroplasts, at low temperature, the cytochrome f is largely in the reduced state. Illumination at the temperature of liquid nitrogen, where ordinary thermal chemical reactions requiring molecular motion and collision are impossible, results in immediate oxidation of cytochrome f. This observation indicates that cytochrome f must be fixed in a rigid solid-state arrangement in immediate proximity to the affected chlorophyll and thus serves as the immediate reductant of "chlorophyll a$^+$." Similarly, there must exist an electron acceptor in position to receive an electron from the activated chlorophyll and prevent the electron from returning to the site from whence it came. This electron-acceptor role appears to be fulfilled by an iron-protein, termed *photosynthetic pyridine nucleotide reductase* (PPNR), with composition and properties resembling those of clostridial ferredoxin but in which the mode of iron binding, as indicated by its absorption spectrum, must differ from that in the clostridial protein. Accordingly, absorption of monochromatic light by "chlorophyll a$^\circ$" should make possible operation of a cyclic electron flow via ferredoxin (PPNR), a flavoprotein, a quinone such as ubiquinone, a series of cytochromes culminating in cytochrome f, and thence back to the "chlorophyll a$^+$" which arose by departure of the electron. High-energy phosphate is generated in the course of this electron flow, but again neither the mechanism nor the yield is known.

More important, however, is the operation of the total system when illuminated with white light, so that both types of chlorophyll are activated simultaneously. As will be seen in Fig. 20.5, under these circumstances the electron from activated chlorophyll a passes to TPN$^+$ so that TPNH accumulates. Instead of cyclic electron flow, chlorophyll a$^+$ captures from cytochrome f the electron emitted by activated chlorophyll b and which traversed the quinone-cytochrome chain with attendant phosphorylation. Meanwhile, "chlorophyll b$^+$" regains an electron by oxidation of OH$^-$ from the medium, thereby evolving O$_2$. This latter process, which must be quite complex and entails a series of intermediate complexes and radicals, remains the least understood aspect of the entire operation. Indeed, it has been suggested that, in some manner, ATP formation may also accompany this process. In sum, therefore, the concerted operation of the total system results in the effective photolysis of water, with accumulation of O$_2$, as well as the TPNH and ATP required for formation of carbohydrate from CO$_2$.

All three systems described above provide a means for the generation of ATP in the absence of oxygen. The first system of closed cyclic transport results only in the formation of ATP; the second system permits ATP formation and reduction of CO$_2$ if an external electron donor also is provided; the third system accomplishes both ATP formation and CO$_2$ fixation in the absence of any external electron donor and yields O$_2$ as a by-product. However, it is upon this by-product that all animal forms are dependent for respiration.

REFERENCES

See list following Chap. 21.

21. Carbohydrate Metabolism

Hexose Interconversions. Polysaccharides. Regulation of Blood Glucose

Living forms utilize a wide variety of polysaccharides for the storage of energy and as structural components of cell membranes and walls. The monosaccharide units present in these polysaccharides include a diversity of aldoses, ketoses, amino sugars, deoxy sugars, and uronic acids in various combinations. It is the purpose of this chapter to describe the synthesis of these monosaccharides, their utilization for polysaccharide synthesis, the formation and degradation of storage polysaccharides in mammals, and their role in the maintenance of the concentration of blood glucose.

INTERCONVERSIONS OF THE HEXOSES

In view of the great variety of hexoses, it is surprising that all are derived from glucose 6-phosphate by application of a limited group of general reactions. No attempt will be made to describe the detailed pathways of these syntheses; rather each of the general reactions will be presented, and the manner in which they are employed for synthesis of specific hexoses can be traced in Fig. 21.1.

Aldose-Ketose Transformations. Isomerases. The interconversion of glucose 6- and fructose 6-phosphates, catalyzed by *phosphoglucose isomerase,* was encountered in glycolysis (page 370). A series of these isomerases is known, including *phosphomannose isomerase;* they are thought to catalyze formation of an intermediate enediol. In this reaction, one of the two hydrogen atoms at C-1 of fructose exchanges with the protons of water. It is noteworthy that phosphoglucose isomerase and phosphomannose isomerase are both stereospecific, but only for the two different hydrogen atoms indicated, respectively, as H• and H* in the following structures.

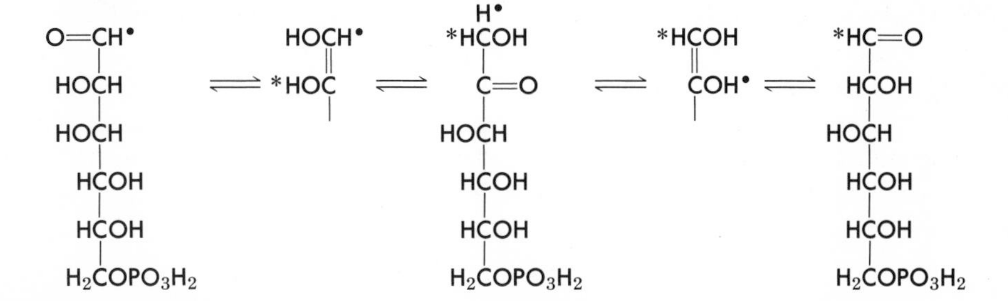

$$
\begin{array}{ccccc}
\mathrm{O{=}CH^\bullet} & \mathrm{HOCH^\bullet} & \overset{\mathrm{H}^\bullet}{*\mathrm{HCOH}} & *\mathrm{HCOH} & *\mathrm{HC{=}O} \\
| & \| & | & \| & | \\
\mathrm{HOCH} \rightleftharpoons & *\mathrm{HOC} \rightleftharpoons & \mathrm{C{=}O} \rightleftharpoons & \mathrm{COH}^\bullet \rightleftharpoons & \mathrm{HCOH} \\
| & & | & | & | \\
\mathrm{HOCH} & & \mathrm{HOCH} & & \mathrm{HOCH} \\
| & & | & & | \\
\mathrm{HCOH} & & \mathrm{HCOH} & & \mathrm{HCOH} \\
| & & | & & | \\
\mathrm{HCOH} & & \mathrm{HCOH} & & \mathrm{HCOH} \\
| & & | & & | \\
\mathrm{H_2COPO_3H_2} & & \mathrm{H_2COPO_3H_2} & & \mathrm{H_2COPO_3H_2}
\end{array}
$$

Mannose 6-phosphate   **Fructose 6-phosphate**   **Glucose 6-phosphate**

401

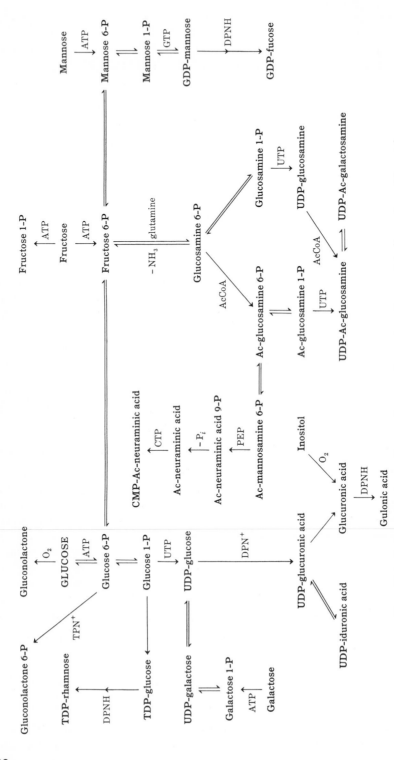

FIG. 21.1. Interconversions of some hexoses in mammalian metabolism. Ac = N-acetyl; PEP = phosphoenolpyruvate. See Table 21.1, page 405, for other abbreviations.

Mutases. Mutases catalyze the apparent migration of a phosphate group from one to another hydroxyl group of the same molecule. The conversion of 3- to 2-phosphoglyceric acid in glycolysis (page 374) is an example of such a reaction. The best-studied mutase is *phosphoglucomutase,* which has been obtained in pure form from rabbit muscle, yeast, and several bacterial species and catalyzes the following reversible reaction.

Glucose 6-phosphate $\rightleftharpoons$ glucose 1-phosphate

At equilibrium, the 6- and 1-phosphates are present in the ratio 94:6. This is in accord with the fact that $\Delta F°$ for hydrolysis of the 1-phosphate is somewhat greater than that for hydrolysis of the 6-phosphate. The 1-phosphate is also decidedly more labile in acid solution.

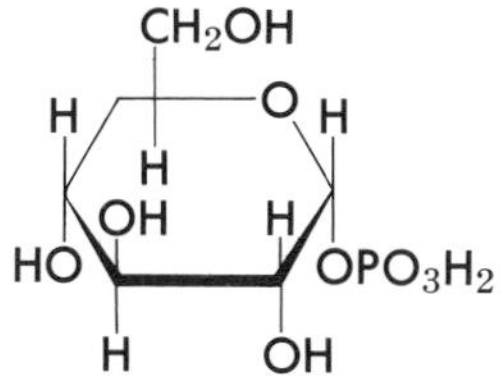

α-D-Glucose 1-phosphate

This reaction proceeds only in the presence of *glucose 1,6-diphosphate* and Mg^{++}. After addition of the P^{32}-labeled form of any one of the three esters, equilibration of isotope occurs rapidly among all three compounds. Incubation of the enzyme with P^{32}-labeled glucose 1,6-diphosphate resulted in labeled enzyme from which serine phosphate (page 249) was obtained by hydrolysis. These observations have suggested that the reaction may be represented as follows.

Enzyme-OH + glucose 1,6-diphosphate $\rightleftharpoons$ enzyme-O-PO$_3$H$_2$ + glucose 1- or 6-phosphate

By repeated operation of this reaction, either monoester may be converted to the other, *viz.,* a molecule of glucose 6-phosphate reacts with the enzyme-phosphate and is esterified at the 1 position. When the diphosphate reacts with the nonesterified form of the enzyme it surrenders the 6-phosphate group and glucose 1-phosphate remains.

A continuing source of glucose 1,6-diphosphate is supplied by the action of *phosphoglucokinase,* which catalyzes the following reaction.

Glucose 1-phosphate + ATP $\longrightarrow$ glucose 1,6-diphosphate + ADP

Phosphoglucomutase can catalyze mutase reactions, albeit more slowly, with several other hexose phosphates. The initial event, with mannose 1-phosphate, is represented as follows.

Glucose 1,6-diphosphate + mannose 1-phosphate $\rightleftharpoons$

mannose 1,6-diphosphate + glucose 6-phosphate

The distribution of other specific mutases has not been carefully studied.

Sugar Esters of Nucleoside Diphosphates. Pyrophosphorylases. As shown in Fig. 21.1, many of the important pathways of carbohydrate metabolism involve, as intermediates, esters formed between the C-1 of a sugar and the terminal phosphate of a nucleoside diphosphate. Formation of such compounds is catalyzed by specific *pyrophosphorylases,* as shown for the synthesis of uridine diphosphate glucose (UDP-glucose).

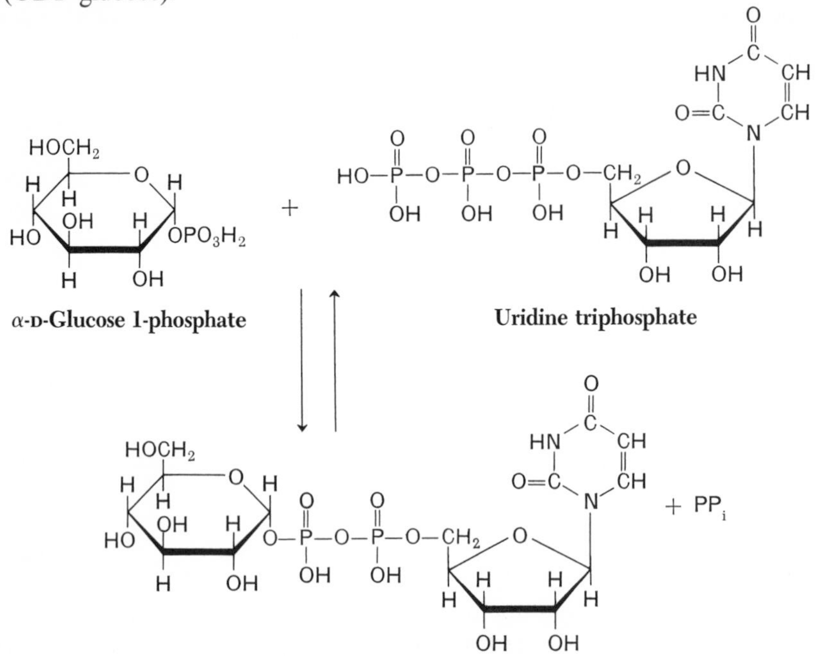

α-D-Glucose 1-phosphate   Uridine triphosphate

Uridine diphosphate glucose (UDP-glucose)

The inorganic pyrophosphate is derived entirely from the terminal pyrophosphate of the uridine triphosphate. Since a pyrophosphate bond is broken and replaced by a new pyrophosphate linkage, the reaction is freely reversible. Physiologically, however, hydrolysis of the inorganic pyrophosphate by *pyrophosphatase* (page 214) effectively results in irreversible synthesis of uridine diphosphate glucose.

A remarkable variety of nucleoside diphosphate sugar compounds has been isolated from cells and tissues at all phylogenetic levels. Only a fraction of these is listed in Table 21.1. It is apparent that five of the purine and pyrimidine bases commonly found in RNA and DNA are utilized in this manner. In all but one known instance (see below), synthesis of the nucleoside diphosphate sugar, from a simpler sugar derivative, occurs by a pyrophosphorylase-catalyzed reaction.

Nucleoside triphosphate + sugar 1-phosphate ⇌ nucleoside diphosphate sugar + PP_i

The one exception to the general pyrophosphorylase reaction shown above is the reaction between N-acetylneuraminic acid and cytidine triphosphate to form PP_i and N-acetylneuraminic acid-1-cytidine monophosphate (page 407). In this case a nucleoside *mono*phosphate ester of the 1-hydroxyl is formed. In the discussions to follow, the abbreviations for the nucleoside diphosphates shown in Table 21.1 will generally be employed. The pyrophosphorylase reaction is not limited to sugar phosphates; CDP-glycerol and CDP-ribitol are made similarly from glycerol

Table 21.1: Some Nucleoside Diphosphate Sugars

Uridine diphosphate esters (UDP-X*):

Glucose,† galactose,† glucosamine,† mannosamine, N-acetylglucosamine,† N-acetyl-galactosamine,† muramic acid, glucuronic acid,† iduronic acid,† galacturonic acid, xylose, arabinose, rhamnose

Adenosine diphosphate ester (ADP-X):

Glucose

Guanosine diphosphate esters (GDP-X):

Glucose,† galactose,† mannose,† fucose,† rhamnose

Cytidine diphosphate ester (CDP-X):

Glucose

Cytidine monophosphate ester (CMP-X)‡:

N-Acetylneuraminic acid†

Deoxythymidine diphosphate esters (dTDP-X):

Glucose, galactose, mannose, glucosamine, N-acetylglucosamine, N-acetylgalactosamine, rhamnose

* X in each instance can be any one of the sugars listed in the group below each specific heading.
† Known to occur in animal tissues.
‡ A nucleoside monophosphate sugar.
Source: Adapted from E. Cabib, *Ann. Rev. Biochem.,* **32,** 321, 1963.

and ribitol phosphates in those bacteria in which teichoic acid is a cell wall constituent (page 58). Many nucleoside diphosphate sugars are not formed directly from the sugar or sugar phosphate but can arise metabolically only by transformation of an existing nucleoside diphosphate sugar. Several examples will be found in Fig. 21.1.

Epimerases. Epimerization, *i.e.,* a Walden inversion about a single carbon atom, is a relatively common reaction in carbohydrate metabolism. Perhaps the best-known example is epimerization at C-4 of UDP-glucose to yield UDP-galactose, catalyzed in liver by *uridine diphosphate glucose epimerase.*

Uridine diphosphate glucose $\rightleftharpoons$ uridine diphosphate galactose

This enzyme and all other such epimerases exhibit an absolute requirement for DPN⁺. Neither DPNH nor TPN⁺ can substitute for DPN⁺, but the role of the DPN⁺ in this conversion is unknown.

A special case of epimerization is the mutarotation (page 16) of glucose, catalyzed by *mutarotase.* Although widely distributed in animal tissues, this enzyme was first encountered in extracts of *Penicillium notatum,* where it exists in association with glucose oxidase (page 366). The latter is specific for oxidation of β-D-glucose. The presence of mutarotase permits oxidation of the total α-glucose in solution more rapidly than the relatively slow process of spontaneous mutarotation would allow.

"Transferases." *Phosphogalactose uridyl transferase* of liver catalyzes the following reaction.

UDP-glucose + galactose 1-phosphate $\rightleftharpoons$ UDP-galactose + glucose 1-phosphate

In liver, ingested galactose is phosphorylated at C-1 by ATP in the presence of *galactokinase.* The product, galactose 1-phosphate, is used to make UDP-galactose from UDP-glucose by the above transferase reaction; the resultant UDP-galactose is epimerized to UDP-glucose, thus making galactose generally available for hepatic carbohydrate metabolism.

Hereditary lack of phosphogalactose uridyl transferase results in *galactosemia,* a disorder of infant life characterized by inability to metabolize the galactose derived from the lactose of milk. An alternate pathway to uridine diphosphate galactose is afforded by *uridine diphosphate galactose pyrophosphorylase,* which catalyzes synthesis of UDP-galactose from UTP and galactose 1-phosphate. This enzyme is present only at a low level in fetal and infant liver but increases in amount in later years. Hence, galactosemic individuals who survive develop the capacity to metabolize galactose during adolescence.

Formation of Deoxyhexoses. An increasing number of deoxyhexoses has been recognized in recent years. In each case the synthetic pathway proceeds by a common pair of reactions. In the first step the nucleoside diphosphate sugar undergoes a dehydration catalyzed by a DPN^+-requiring enzyme to yield the corresponding 4-keto, 6-deoxy sugar derivative. The role of DPN^+ is not clear. The 4-keto 6-deoxynucleoside diphosphate is then reduced by a TPNH-utilizing enzyme to form the nucleoside diphosphate 6-deoxy sugar. The synthesis of guanosine diphosphate fucose is shown as an example.

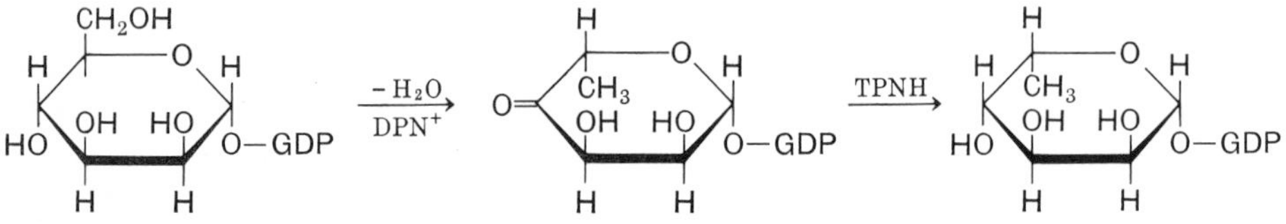

GDP-mannose   GDP-fucose

Formation of Uronic Acids. Uronic acids arise from the oxidation of the corresponding nucleoside diphosphate hexoses. For UDP-glucuronic acid formation:

Uridine diphosphate glucose + $2DPN^+$ $\longrightarrow$
                                                    uridine diphosphate glucuronic acid + 2DPNH + $2H^+$

One enzyme catalyzes the two consecutive oxidations required to obtain a carboxyl group from a primary alcohol; the presumed intermediate, in which C-6 should be at the aldehyde level of oxidation, has not been detected. An alternate mechanism for uronic acid formation is epimerization of an existing uronic acid, *e.g.*, epimerization of UDP-glucuronic acid to UDP-iduronic acid (Fig. 21.1).

Formation of Amino Sugars. Amino sugars are formed by transfer of the amide group of glutamine to 6-phosphate esters of ketoses. For glucosamine synthesis:

Fructose 6-phosphate + glutamine $\longrightarrow$ glucosamine 6-phosphate + glutamic acid

Presumably, it is the enediol form of fructose 6-phosphate which is the intermediate reactant, although no intermediates have been identified in this reaction. N-Acetylamino sugars are more common in polysaccharides than are simple amino sugars. Acetylation is catalyzed by specific enzymes, utilizing acetyl coenzyme A as the acylating agent for the corresponding 6-phosphate esters.

SIALIC ACIDS, GLUCURONIC ACID, AND POLYOLS

Formation of Sialic Acids. Sialic acids (page 36) are constituents of a variety of mammalian glycoproteins and bacterial cell wall structures. The biosynthesis of a widely distributed sialic acid, N-acetylneuraminic acid, in mammals begins with the formation of N-acetylmannosamine from N-acetylglucosamine by an epimerase which, uniquely, exhibits an absolute requirement for ATP although the latter does not participate in the reaction. Phosphorylation by ATP, catalyzed by a specific kinase, yields N-acetylmannosamine 6-phosphate. The latter then condenses in an aldol-type reaction with phosphoenolpyruvic acid to yield N-acetylneuraminic acid 9-phosphate. The 9-phosphate group must be removed by hydrolysis prior to the reaction with cytidine triphosphate, which leads to formation of CMP-N-acetylneuraminic acid, as described earlier (page 404).

N-Acetylglucosamine $\longrightarrow$ N-acetylmannosamine $\xrightarrow{\text{ATP}}$

N-acetylmannosamine 6-phosphate + phosphoenolpyruvic acid $\xrightarrow{-P_i}$

N-acetylneuraminic acid 9-phosphate $\xrightarrow{-P_i}$ N-acetylneuraminic acid + CTP $\longrightarrow$

CMP-N-acetylneuraminic acid + PP_i

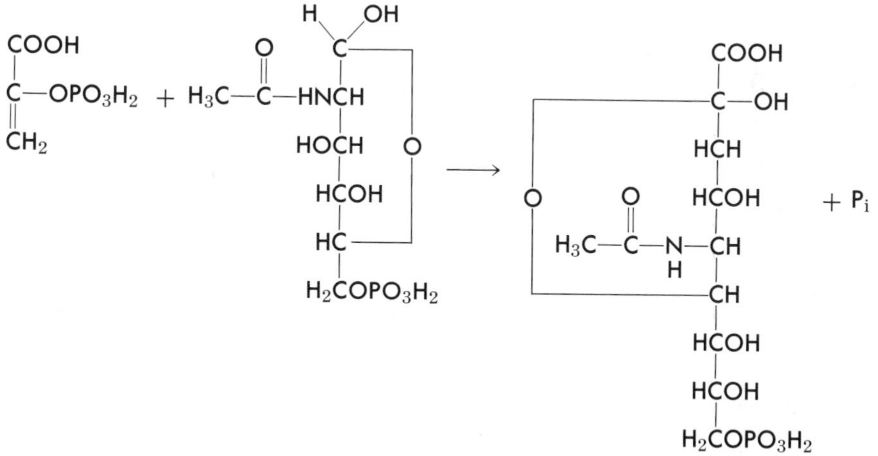

Phosphoenol- pyruvic acid	N-Acetylmannosamine 6-phosphate	N-Acetylneuraminic acid 9-phosphate

Metabolism of Glucuronic Acid. The formation of UDP-glucuronic acid was described previously. It is not certain how free glucuronic acid is made available in the cell. Whatever its origin, it can then be reduced to L-gulonic acid. In plants and in animals other than primates and guinea pigs, the L-gulonic acid thus formed is employed for synthesis of ascorbic acid (Chap. 55). In all mammals, gulonic acid may be oxidized to L-xylulose. However, it is D-xylulose 5-phosphate which participates in the reactions of the phosphogluconate oxidative pathway,

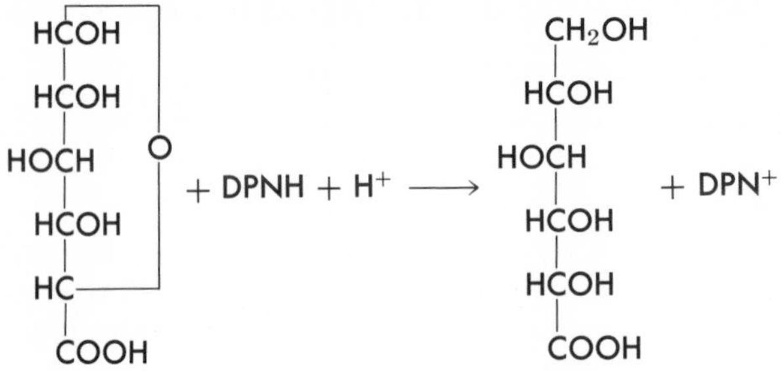

$$
\begin{array}{c}
\text{HCOH} \\
\text{HCOH} \\
\text{HOCH} \\
\text{HCOH} \\
\text{HC} \\
\text{COOH}
\end{array}
\quad + \text{ DPNH} + \text{H}^+ \longrightarrow
\begin{array}{c}
\text{CH}_2\text{OH} \\
\text{HCOH} \\
\text{HOCH} \\
\text{HCOH} \\
\text{HCOH} \\
\text{COOH}
\end{array}
\quad + \text{ DPN}^+
$$

D-Glucuronic acid   L-Gulonic acid

described earlier (Chap. 20). As shown below, L-xylulose may be converted to
D-xylulose by reduction to xylitol and reoxidation.

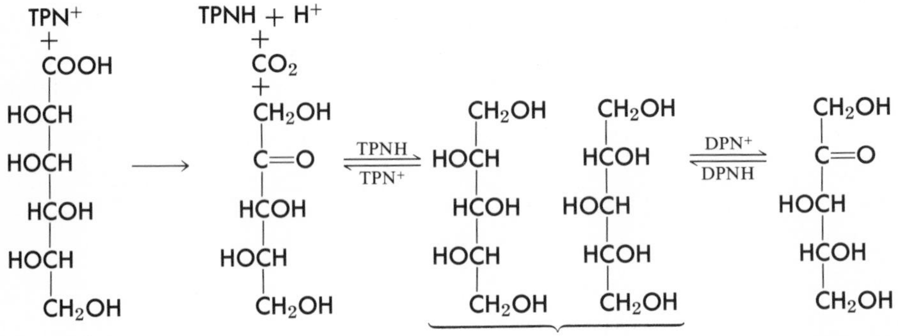

$$
\begin{array}{c}
\text{TPN}^+ \\
+ \\
\text{COOH} \\
\text{HOCH} \\
\text{HOCH} \\
\text{HCOH} \\
\text{HOCH} \\
\text{CH}_2\text{OH}
\end{array}
\longrightarrow
\begin{array}{c}
\text{TPNH} + \text{H}^+ \\
+ \\
\text{CO}_2 \\
+ \\
\text{CH}_2\text{OH} \\
\text{C}=\text{O} \\
\text{HCOH} \\
\text{HOCH} \\
\text{CH}_2\text{OH}
\end{array}
\underset{\text{TPN}^+}{\overset{\text{TPNH}}{\rightleftarrows}}
\begin{array}{c}
\text{CH}_2\text{OH} \\
\text{HOCH} \\
\text{HCOH} \\
\text{HOCH} \\
\text{CH}_2\text{OH}
\end{array}
\quad
\begin{array}{c}
\text{CH}_2\text{OH} \\
\text{HCOH} \\
\text{HOCH} \\
\text{HCOH} \\
\text{CH}_2\text{OH}
\end{array}
\underset{\text{DPNH}}{\overset{\text{DPN}^+}{\rightleftarrows}}
\begin{array}{c}
\text{CH}_2\text{OH} \\
\text{C}=\text{O} \\
\text{HOCH} \\
\text{HCOH} \\
\text{CH}_2\text{OH}
\end{array}
$$

L-Gulonic   L-Xylulose   Xylitol   D-Xylulose
acid

Presumably, D-xylulose may be phosphorylated by ATP and an appropriate kinase
to D-xylulose 5-phosphate and then enter reactions of the phosphogluconate oxidative pathway. In consequence, this represents yet another "shunt" pathway for
oxidation of glucose, bypassing the reactions of anaerobic glycolysis and the citric
acid cycle. Operation of this system yields an equal mixture of TPNH and DPNH.
The extent to which these reactions proceed has not been evaluated. It should be
noted that the CO_2 arising in this process represents carbon-6 of glucose in contrast
to the phosphogluconate oxidative pathway in which CO_2 arises from what had
been carbon-1 of glucose.

An abnormality known as *idiopathic pentosuria* is probably attributable to the
congenital absence of the enzyme that reduces L-xylulose. As a consequence, large
amounts of L-xylulose are found in the urine. In such individuals the feeding of
D-glucuronic acid results in massive excretion of L-xylulose.

Polyols. Although a wide variety of polyols is metabolized in bacteria, such
compounds have a restricted role in mammalian metabolism. In seminal vesicles,
reduction of glucose to sorbitol with reoxidation of the latter results in formation
of fructose (page 366), which appears in large concentration in seminal plasma.
Reduction of other sugars in similar manner must occur, although to a limited
degree, in many tissues. Thus dulcitol, the product expected from reduction of

galactose, has been found in significant quantity in the lens of galactose-fed rats. An *iditol dehydrogenase* has been obtained from sheep liver in crystalline form. The cyclic *myo*-inositol is found abundantly in plants as its hexaphosphate ester (page 35), and the presence of phosphatidyl inositol in brain (Chap. 39) indicates the importance of inositol in mammals. However, except for the demonstration that inositol can be made from glucose in germ-free animals, little is known about the origin of this compound in animals. Its degradative metabolism appears to begin by oxidation to glucuronic acid, catalyzed by *inositol oxygenase* (page 356).

BIOSYNTHESIS OF GLYCOSIDES

Glycoside synthesis occurs in all living cells since these compounds are universally utilized as a form of energy storage, as constituents of cell membranes, and, among plants, in the formation of cell walls. The hydrolysis of a simple glycoside, such as maltose, proceeds with a free-energy change, $\Delta F° = -4000$ cal. per mole. Hence, formation of the glycosidic bond can occur only when the requisite energy is provided. Three general mechanisms appear to account for all known instances of glycoside synthesis. These mechanisms may be illustrated by consideration of the synthesis of disaccharides.

Synthesis of Disaccharides. The enzyme *sucrose phosphorylase,* isolated from *Pseudomonas saccharophilia,* which had been grown in a sucrose-containing medium, was initially observed to catalyze the following reaction.

$$\text{Sucrose} + P_i \rightleftharpoons \alpha\text{-D-glucose 1-phosphate} + \text{D-fructose}$$

The glycosidic bond between the two anomeric carbon atoms in sucrose is unusual, and $\Delta F°$ for sucrose hydrolysis is -6600 cal. per mole, whereas that for glucose 1-phosphate is -4800 cal. per mole. Hence, equilibrium favors phosphorolysis of sucrose as shown above. If, however, the orthophosphate is removed from the solution, as by precipitation, sucrose formation from glucose 1-phosphate and fructose is readily demonstrated. Since glucose 1-phosphate arises in the phosphoglucomutase reaction (page 403) from glucose 6-phosphate and the latter is formed from glucose and ATP in the hexokinase reaction (page 365), the energy for formation of the glycosidic bond derives ultimately from the energy of ATP. The organism from which sucrose phosphorylase is obtained does not accumulate sucrose; rather, it degrades sucrose from the medium to glucose 1-phosphate and fructose, as shown above. Indeed this appears generally to be true; although phosphorylases catalyze the following reversible process,

$$\text{Sugar-phosphate} + \text{sugar} \rightleftharpoons \text{glycoside} + P_i$$

in cells in which phosphorylases are operative, it is the phosphorolytic cleavage of the preexisting glycoside which is metabolically significant.

The second mechanism for sucrose synthesis has been observed with extracts of various plants.

(a) $$\text{UDP-glucose} + \text{fructose 6-phosphate} \rightleftharpoons \text{sucrose 6'-phosphate} + \text{UDP}$$

(b) $$\text{Sucrose 6'-phosphate} \xrightarrow{H_2O} \text{sucrose} + P_i$$

Since $\Delta F°$ for hydrolysis of UDP-glucose is about -7500 cal. per mole, formation of the glycosidic bond of sucrose is favored.

In every instance known, nucleotide sugars have been found to be the immediate precursors for glycoside biosynthesis. For most glycosides, formation from a nucleotide sugar precursor would proceed with a favorable free-energy change of about -3500 cal. per mole. In the case of sucrose synthesis, the formation of sucrose phosphate by reaction (a) is favored by only -1000 cal. but hydrolysis of the 6'-phosphate is essentially irreversible and thus assures sucrose formation.

Many instances of glycoside formation from nucleotide sugar precursors have been demonstrated. Thus, lactose formation in mammary glands proceeds in the following manner.

$$\text{UDP-galactose} + \text{glucose} \longrightarrow \text{lactose} + \text{UDP}$$

The third mechanism for glycosidic bond formation is *transglycosylation,* a process that was also noted with sucrose phosphorylase. In addition to the reaction involving glucose 1-phosphate shown above, this enzyme also catalyzes reactions of the following type.

$$\text{Sucrose} + \text{L-sorbose} \rightleftharpoons \text{D-glucosido-L-sorboside} + \text{fructose}$$
$$\text{Sucrose} + \text{L-arabinose} \rightleftharpoons \text{D-glucosido-L-arabinoside} + \text{fructose}$$

Thus, the enzyme appears to cleave the glycosidic bond of sucrose, forming free fructose and an enzyme-glucose compound that can react with P_i to form glucose phosphate, with fructose to form sucrose, or with various other monosaccharides to form disaccharides. It will be evident that the energy of the glucosidic bond of sucrose is thus utilized for formation of each of the other glucosides. As will be seen subsequently, transglycosylation is rarely employed, physiologically, for oligosaccharide synthesis, but is widely utilized in polysaccharide formation.

Synthesis of Other Glycosides. As noted previously (page 46), there is a large variety of glycosides in which the glucosidic bond extends from a mono- or disaccharide to a phenol, alcohol, or amine. Current evidence indicates that most of these are formed enzymically in a reaction between a nucleoside diphosphate sugar and the aglycone.

In mammals, a variety of phenols and alicyclic alcohols are "conjugated" with glucuronic acid and the resultant *glucosiduronide* (glucosiduronic acid) is excreted in the urine. This conjugation is catalyzed by at least two microsomal enzymes of liver, with varying but broad specificity for the aglycone moiety.

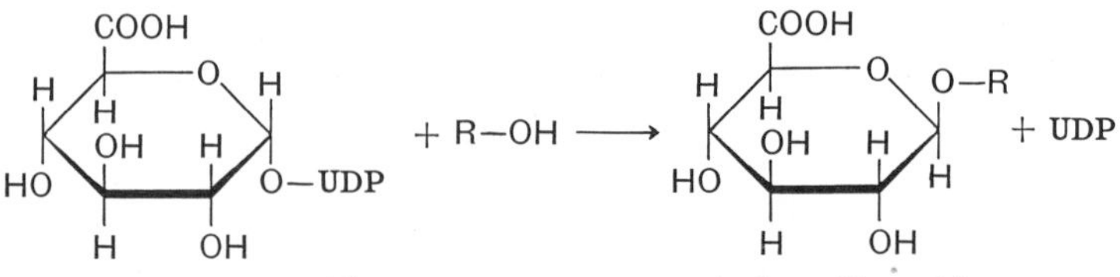

UDP-glucuronic acid   A glucosiduronide

Plants do not form glucosiduronides but contain many examples of phenolic glucosides. Thus, wheat germ utilizes uridine diphosphate glucose to form β-D-glucosyl hydroquinone (arbutin). Indeed the latter can serve as substrate for a second enzyme which couples a second glucose molecule, again as uridine diphosphate glucose, to the first, to form a gentiobioside [O-β-D-glucosyl ($1 \rightarrow 6$)-O-α-D-glucosyl]. In other instances it is rhamnose (page 36) which is coupled to the aglycone, using either uridine or thymidine diphosphate rhamnose. The latter has also been found to be the rhamnose donor in the formation of the rhamnosyl derivatives of hydroxy fatty acids in some bacteria. A similar reaction, using uridine diphosphate galactose, results in formation of galactose-containing cerebrosides in brain (Chap. 39).

POLYSACCHARIDE BIOSYNTHESIS

Polysaccharide formation is accomplished by the same types of reaction evident in the formation of disaccharides and glycosides, *i.e.*, from nucleoside diphosphate sugars or from preexisting glycosidic structures.

Transglycosylation. Many bacteria can effect the synthesis of a linear polysaccharide by utilizing a disaccharide present in the medium. Only the monosaccharide unit that contributes its anomeric carbon to the glycosidic bond of the disaccharide can be utilized for polysaccharide synthesis. Some *transglycosylases* and their bacterial origin are indicated in the reactions below.

$$n\text{Maltose} \underset{\textit{Escherichia coli}}{\overset{\text{amylomaltase}}{\rightleftharpoons}} \text{amylose} + n\text{glucose}$$

$$n\text{Sucrose} \underset{\textit{Neisseria perflava}}{\overset{\text{amylosucrase}}{\rightleftharpoons}} \text{amylose} + n\text{fructose}$$

$$n\text{Sucrose} \underset{\textit{Leuconostoc mesenteroides}}{\overset{\text{dextransucrase}}{\rightleftharpoons}} \text{dextran} + n\text{fructose}$$

$$n\text{Sucrose} \underset{\textit{Bacillus megatherium}}{\overset{\text{levansucrase}}{\rightleftharpoons}} \text{levan} + n\text{glucose}$$

Dextran is a linear polymer in which the anomeric carbon-1 of each glucose unit is in glycosidic linkage with the primary alcoholic hydroxyl at carbon-6 of the adjacent residue. Thus the repeating unit is isomaltose (page 49) rather than maltose. *Levan* is similarly built of fructose residues in 2,6-fructosidic linkage. Since the energy of the glycosidic bond of the disaccharides is conserved in the polysaccharides, these organisms need not furnish energy for polysaccharide synthesis if the appropriate disaccharide is available as precursor.

Synthesis of Homopolysaccharides from Nucleoside Diphosphate Sugars. In plants as well as animals, most polysaccharides are synthesized directly from hexose and pentose units rather than from disaccharides. In all instances presently known, the immediate precursor of the final polysaccharide is a nucleoside mono- or diphosphate sugar. Some of the better-known examples are listed in Table 21.2 The mechanisms involved in this process and the participating enzymes are little known. The enzymes that catalyze formation of cellulose, amylose, and chitin appear to require the presence of either a trace of the polysaccharide or of a low molecular weight dextrin derived from the polysaccharide synthesized. These dextrins serve as

Table 21.2: Polysaccharide Synthesis from Some Nucleoside Diphosphate Sugars

Precursor	Product	Biological source*
UDP-glucose.....................	β,1,3 Glucan (callose)	Bean extracts
GDP-glucose.....................	β,1,4 Glucan (cellulose)	Mung bean extracts
ADP-glucose.....................	α,1,4 Glucan (starch amylose)	Wheat germ
UDP-glucose.....................	α,1,4 Glucan (glycogen amylose)	Liver
UDP-xylose......................	β,1,4 Xylan	Plants
UDP-N-acetylglucosamine........	Chitin	*Neurospora crassa*
CMP-N-acetylneuraminic acid†.....	Colominic acid	*Escherichia coli*
UDP-glucuronic acid + UDP-N-acetylglucosamine..............	Hyaluronic acid	Rous sarcoma, streptococci
UDP-glucose + UDP-glucuronic acid	Capsular polysaccharide	Type III pneumococci

* The biological source is that which has been experimentally employed.

† A nucleoside monophosphate sugar.

"primers," in that additional hexose units are added to the priming dextrin, as acceptors, thus extending the polysaccharide chain. The synthesis of glycogen and of starch are considered in more detail below.

It will be seen that all of the monomer units listed in Table 21.2 are nucleoside diphosphate derivatives of either a pentose or a hexose, with the exception of CMP-N-acetylneuraminic acid. The mechanism by which this nucleoside monophosphate derivative of a 9-carbon atom sugar functions in the synthesis of colominic acid, or the nature of the primer or acceptor, if any, are unknown.

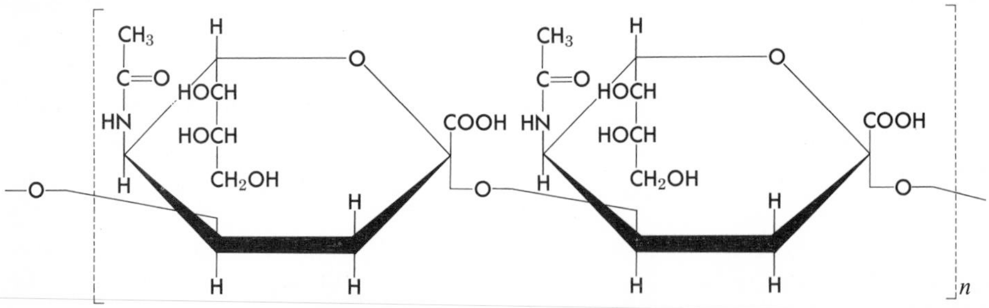

Repeating unit of colominic acid

Synthesis of Heteropolysaccharides. Virtually nothing is known of the mechanisms involved in formation of heteropolysaccharides except that they proceed from nucleoside diphosphate derivatives of appropriate monosaccharides. It is surmised that the repeating unit, *e.g.*, a disaccharide actually utilized by the final "synthetase," may be the nucleoside diphosphate derivative of that unit. This would account for the synthesis of hyaluronic acid and the antigenically specific polysaccharide of type III pneumococci (Table 21.2). These considerations must apply equally to more complex polysaccharides such as the blood group substances (Chap. 42). Alternatively, the enzyme catalyzing synthesis might have two different binding sites, or synthesis could involve two enzymes of selective specificity.

One of the initial clues to the structure of the cell walls of gram-positive bacteria (page 58) was the isolation by Park, from penicillin-inhibited *Staphylococcus aureus,* of the UDP derivative of muramic acid already linked to its characteristic pentapeptide (page 58). Presumably, this can be coupled with uridine diphosphate N-acetylglucosamine to form the complete repeating unit that is used by the enzyme responsible for cell wall synthesis. Similarly, the isolation and identification of CDP-ribitol and CDP-glycerol led, later, to the discovery of the teichoic acids (page 58), of which ribitol and glycerol are constituents. It is apparent that uridine diphosphate N-acetylglucosamine is utilized for placement of N-acetylglucosamine on the hydroxyl groups of ribitol or glycerol, after the long-chain polymer has been synthesized.

GLYCOGEN METABOLISM

Glycogen Synthesis. The synthesis of the amylose chain of glycogen is catalyzed by *uridine diphosphate glucose–glycogen glucosyl transferase* (glycogen synthetase), an enzyme discovered by Leloir that catalyzes the following reaction.

$$n\text{UDP-glucose} \rightleftharpoons (\text{glucose})n + n\text{UDP}$$

The free-energy change in this reaction is about -3200 cal. per mole of glucose equivalent; equilibrium, therefore, favors glycogen synthesis by a factor of about 250. Although uridine diphosphate glucose is undoubtedly the normal substrate, synthesis with ADP- and TDP-glucose proceeds at about 50 and 5 per cent, respectively, of the rate observed with UDP-glucose. The enzyme cannot form glycogen from UDP-glucose alone. Rather, the glucose moiety of the latter is transferred to an acceptor polyglucose chain. The preferred acceptor is glycogen itself; however, amylose, amylopectin, or a glucose oligosaccharide no smaller than the four-membered maltotetraose can also serve as acceptors.

Glycogen synthetase catalyzes formation only of $\alpha,1,4$ bonds; the product formed with maltotetraose as acceptor, therefore, is amylose, the linear $\alpha,1,4$ polymer of D-glucose. The enzyme has a marked affinity for glycogen and, in liver, is firmly bound to glycogen particles and is stabilized and activated by glucose 6-phosphate. Depending on the source and manner of preparation of the enzyme, it may exhibit an absolute requirement for glucose 6-phosphate, or stimulation of apparent V_{max} of from twofold to fiftyfold. In all cases, glucose 6-phosphate provides marked protection against denaturation during prolonged maintenance at 37°C. or at alkaline pH. If a similar situation exists in vivo, it will be apparent that precisely when it is physiologically desirable, *i.e.*, in the presence of an ample glucose supply which leads to a high concentration of glucose 6-phosphate, activation of glycogen synthetase would occur, and, thereby, facilitate storage of glucose as glycogen. Apparently, binding of glucose 6-phosphate to the enzyme stabilizes the catalytically active conformation. These relationships are reminiscent of the role of acetyl CoA in activating pyruvic acid carboxylase (page 381).

As noted, glycogen synthetase effects the synthesis only of $\alpha,1,4$ bonds. However, glycogen itself is a highly branched structure, the branches resulting from the presence of $\alpha,1,6$ bonds at a frequency of about every 8 to 12 glucose units. This structure is the result of the activity of a "glycogen branching enzyme," or *amylo-(1,4 → 1,6)-transglucosylase* (Fig. 21.2). This enzyme has been demonstrated in liver, muscle, and brain. It is a transglycosylase which cleaves fragments of the glycogen

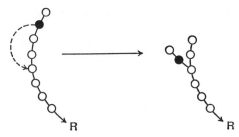

Fɪɢ. 21.2. The action of amylo-$(1,4 \rightarrow 1,6)$-transglucosylase. R represents the main body of the glycogen molecule; each circle represents a glucose unit. The darkened circle represents the glucose molecule whose aldehyde carbon is transferred from 1,4 to 1,6 linkage.

chain, at $\alpha,1,4$ linkages, and transfers them to the same, or another, glycogen molecule but in $\alpha,1,6$ linkage. It is the "specificity" of this "branching enzyme" which determines the interbranch distance along the polysaccharide chain.

Starch synthesis in plants appears to be analogous to that of glycogen in animal cells. The amylose synthetase is firmly bound to starch granules. Of a variety of nucleoside diphosphates, adenosine diphosphate glucose is preferentially utilized as substrate. Again, the action of the synthetase results in an amylose structure. The branched chains of amylopectin reflect the activity of a "branching enzyme" or transglycosylase.

Glycogen Phosphorylase. In contrast to the hydrolytic fragmentation of glycogen and starch in the gastrointestinal tract, within cells glycogen is degraded directly to α-glucose 1-phosphate by the action of *glycogen phosphorylase*, discovered by C. F. and G. T. Cori.

The equilibrium constant for this reaction is given by

$$K = \frac{[C_6H_{10}O_5)_{n+1}][HPO_4^=]}{[(C_6H_{10}O_5)_n][\text{glucose 1-phosphate}]}$$

However, since each molecule of polysaccharide is both a reactant and a product, K is determined by the ratio of orthophosphate to glucose 1-phosphate. Since glucose 1-phosphate is a stronger acid than $HPO_4^=$, the value of this ratio is pH-dependent, falling close to 3 at pH 7. The fact that the equilibrium constant is near unity is consonant with the ready reversibility of the reaction and reveals that the $\Delta F°$ for the reaction is quite small. This is in accord with the $\Delta F°$ for hydrolysis of glucose 1-phosphate (-4800 cal. per mole) and that of a maltosidic bond (-4200 cal. per mole).

Phosphorylase attacks the glycogen molecule from the terminus of each chain, releasing successive molecules of glucose residues, marked ⊙ (Fig. 21.3), as glucose 1-phosphate until the branch points are reached, when activity ceases. This results in a limit dextrin similar to that which remains after treatment of glycogen with β-amylase (page 52). Hydrolytic removal of the glucose present in 1,6 linkage at the branch point by *amylo-(1,6)-glucosidase* then permits phosphorolysis to continue until the next branch point is reached, etc.

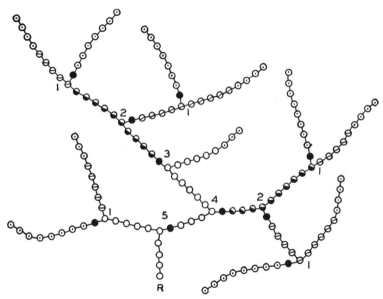

FIG. 21.3. Degradation of glycogen by combined action of glycogen phosphorylase and amylo-1,6-glucosidase. *R*, reducing end of molecule; ⊙,⊖,⊙, glucose units removed by first, second, and third digestions with phosphorylase, respectively; ●, glucose unit split off as free glucose from α,1,6 linkage by amylo-1,6-glucosidase. (*From data of J. D. Larner and G. T. Cori, according to B. Glass, in W. D. McElroy and B. Glass, "Phosphorus Metabolism," vol. I, p. 667, Johns Hopkins Press, Baltimore, 1951.*)

As indicated above, the equilibrium constant for the glycogen phosphorylase reaction is 3. Under suitable conditions, therefore, *i.e.*, a high concentration of glucose 1-phosphate or low concentration of inorganic phosphate, this enzyme should catalyze glycogen formation, and indeed, this is the case. In the presence of glycogen, dextrin, or a glucose oligosaccharide, amylose-like chains are formed by successive addition of glucose molecules in α,1,4 linkage. If glycogen "branching enzyme" (see above) is present, normal branched glycogen can be made.

For many years it was thought that glycogen phosphorylase is the enzyme responsible both for glycogen synthesis and degradation. That this is not the case was suggested by several observations. (1) Although K for the phosphorylase reaction is 3, glycogen synthesis occurs in muscle when the ratio P_i/glucose 1-phosphate is as high as 300. (2) When the activity of tissue phosphorylase is increased by hormones, *e.g.*, epinephrine (see below), increased glycogen breakdown results. (3) Certain hereditary disorders are characterized by a lack of liver or muscle phosphorylase. In each instance, the affected tissue is strikingly high in glycogen content. In sum, these observations suggested that, physiologically, glycogen phosphorylase is much more significant in glycogen breakdown than in glycogenesis. With the discovery of glycogen synthesis from uridine diphosphate glucose, catalyzed by glycogen synthetase, the unidirectional significance of glycogen phosphorylase became more readily comprehensible.

Control of Glycogen Phosphorolysis. The distinct pathways of glycogen synthesis and breakdown make possible independent control of these two processes. Thus, whereas glucose 6-phosphate activates glycogen synthetase, it is without influence on glycogen phosphorylase. The latter, however, is controlled in a rather involved manner.

Active glycogen phosphorylase of muscle is a tetramer with a molecular weight of 495,000. It consists of four apparently identical polypeptide chains, each of which contains one serine residue whose hydroxyl group is esterified to phosphate, and one lysine residue, the amino group of which is present as the Schiff base ($—N=CH—$) of pyridoxal phosphate (page 494). The function of these phosphate and pyridoxal phosphate groups is not understood, but if either is removed, the enzyme loses all catalytic activity. In this tetrameric form, the muscle enzyme is known as *phosphorylase a.*

Muscle also contains an enzyme called *phosphorylase phosphatase,* which hydrolytically removes those phosphate groups of phosphorylase which are esterified to the serine hydroxyl groups. This results in deaggregation of the enzyme to an inactive, dimeric form called *phosphorylase b.* The latter can function in the glycogen phosphorylase reaction in the presence, specifically, of AMP. The dimeric form of the enzyme is found in resting muscle, in which the concentration of AMP is much too low to activate the enzyme. Reactivation, *i.e.*, conversion of phosphorylase *b* to phosphorylase *a*, is accomplished by *phosphorylase kinase,* which promotes the following reaction.

$$\text{2 Phosphorylase } b + \text{4ATP} \longrightarrow \text{phosphorylase } a + \text{4ADP}$$

In turn, phosphorylase kinase exists in an active and an inactive form. The factors determining the transition from active to inactive forms of this enzyme are not known. Activation of the inactive enzyme occurs in the presence of Mg^{++}, an uncharacterized protein, and adenosine 3'5'-phosphate (cyclic adenylic acid). This cyclic nucleotide is formed from ATP by a specific enzyme, *adenyl cyclase,* which is stimulated by epinephrine (page 419).

The control of glycogen phosphorylase in liver appears to be essentially similar to that in muscle. However, the liver and muscle enzymes are under independent genetic control (see Chap. 31) and are immunochemically different. The dephosphorylated form of liver phosphorylase is also enzymically inactive, but both

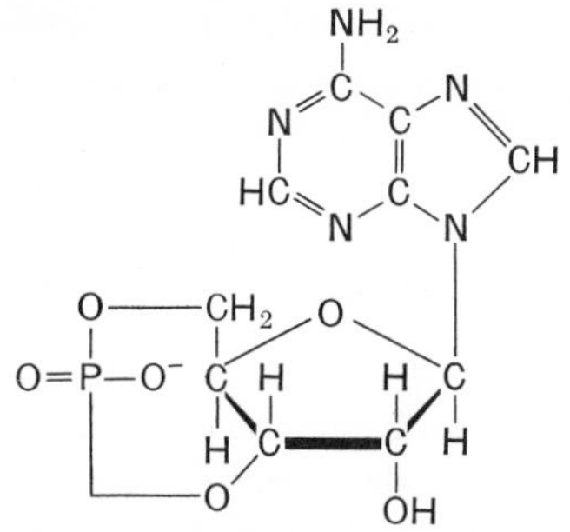

Adenosine 3′,5′-phosphate (cyclic adenylic acid)

active and inactive forms are identical in molecular weight, which is approximately that of muscle phosphorylase *b*. Inactive liver dephosphophosphorylase, which has lost two moles of phosphate per mole of enzyme, is not activated by AMP. Reactivation by a kinase and the role of adenosine 3′,5′-phosphate are identical with those for the enzyme in muscle. However, reactivation of liver phosphorylase is stimulated not only by epinephrine, as in the case for muscle, but also by glucagon (page 419), which is without effect on the muscle system.

PHYSIOLOGICAL ROLE OF GLYCOGEN

The large stores of chemical energy that the adequately nourished organism maintains in its tissues have little effect on osmotic pressure since they are either water-insoluble lipids or sparingly soluble polysaccharides of very high molecular weight. The storage of large amounts of polysaccharide is seen particularly in plants, where, with the exception of the seed parts, lipid storage is usually scanty. Among higher animals, lipids account for the bulk of energy storage, whereas polysaccharide storage occurs only in the form of relatively small amounts of glycogen.

Although glycogen occurs in most tissues, including certain areas of the depot lipid, the glycogen of liver and of skeletal muscle has attracted most attention.

Glycogenesis and Glycogenolysis. Formation of glycogen is termed *glycogenesis;* nutrients that enhance the glycogen content of tissues are called glycogenic substances. These include not only the several hexoses previously discussed but also a wide variety of other compounds. The glycogenic amino acids (Chap. 27), glycerol derived from lipids, intermediates in glycolysis such as lactic and pyruvic acids, products structurally related to the hexoses and enzymically convertible into them, *e.g.*, the sugar alcohol sorbitol—all these materials and many other substances, when administered to fasting animals, result in some degree of increase in the quantity of liver glycogen. In each instance, the substance in question must be converted via glucose 6- and glucose 1-phosphate to UDP-glucose before glycogen synthesis is possible.

The term *glycogenolysis* is used to connote glycogen breakdown. As we have seen, although this process is hydrolytic in the intestinal canal, only glycogen phosphorolysis is significant within cells. The resultant product is glucose 1-phosphate, which, by the phosphoglucomutase reaction, is converted to glucose 6-phosphate and thus enters the main pathways of carbohydrate metabolism.

Glucose formation from glucose 6-phosphate, with release to the surrounding interstitial fluid and thence to the circulating blood, is possible only in intestine, liver, and kidney. The cells of each of these tissues contain a specific microsomal *glucose 6-phosphatase.*

$$\text{Glucose 6-phosphate} \xrightarrow{\text{H}_2\text{O}} \text{glucose} + \text{P}_i$$

The glucose 6-phosphatase activity of liver is enhanced in diabetes, during starvation, and after administration of adrenal cortical steroids (Chap. 49). This appears to reflect a change in the physical structure of the microsomes rather than a direct effect on the enzyme. Figure 21.4 indicates the over-all pathways of glycogenesis and glycogenolysis.

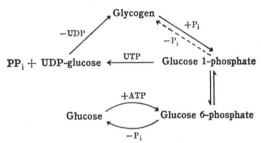

FIG. 21.4. Over-all pathways of glycogenesis and glycogenolysis. The reaction indicated by the dashed arrow, demonstrable in vitro, is not thought to be physiologically significant.

Tissue Glycogen. "Glycogen" of all tissues is polydisperse. As ordinarily obtained, glycogen has a range of molecular weight that may vary from 250,000 to 10^7. In addition, in various tissues the amount of glycogen that may be readily extracted, *e.g.*, with cold trichloroacetic acid solution, is always less than the total obtained by alkaline hydrolysis of the tissue. The residual glycogen, *viz.*, the non-readily extractable fraction, seems to be protein-bound and present as insoluble granules. However, the behavior of administered glucose-C^{14} indicates that even this glycogen fraction is metabolically active and undergoing constant turnover.

Glycogen of Liver. In various mammalian species, between 2 and 8 per cent of the wet weight of liver is glycogen. Liver glycogen is a relatively labile store of chemical energy and of carbohydrate. If an animal is fasted for 24 hr. or longer, the liver is virtually depleted of glycogen. Refeeding with some glycogenic material, *e.g.*, glucose, results in prompt reaccumulation of liver glycogen. However, even in the normal animal with constant access to food, although the quantity of glycogen in liver remains fairly constant, it is continuously being both formed and degraded.

In testing various compounds to determine their effectiveness as precursors of glucose, a widely employed procedure has been to fast animals until virtually no liver glycogen remains, then to administer the test substance and ascertain whether an increase in quantity of liver glycogen has occurred. Any material capable of yielding glycogen under these conditions is presumed also to yield glucose 6-phosphate; hence the terms glycogenic and glucogenic have been construed as being synonymous.

Factors Affecting Liver Glycogen. The amount of glycogen in the liver depends not only on the quantity of food consumed but also on the composition of the diet. Thus, animals maintained on carbohydrate-poor diets have less liver glycogen than those on high-carbohydrate diets. Exercise reduces the quantity of glycogen in the liver. Experimentally, poisoning with phlorhizin, a procedure that lowers the renal threshold for glucose, thereby causing glucosuria, imposes a drain upon body reserves of carbohydrate and leads to diminution of liver glycogen. Hypoxia and acidosis also lower liver glycogen; the basis of this is unknown.

In addition to these factors, liver glycogen is under endocrine regulation. The administration of epinephrine (Chap. 49) to a well-nourished animal results in prompt disappearance of much of the liver glycogen. A considerable portion is converted to glucose and added to the blood; this is reflected in a rise in blood glucose, a *hyperglycemia.* Cannon regarded this hyperglycemia in response to epinephrine as a protective mechanism in time of stress, which makes available to the musculature an abundance of nutrient at the precise time when it may be required. The glycogenolytic function of epinephrine is shared by *glucagon,* the hyperglycemic-glycogenolytic principle of the α cells of the pancreas (Chap. 50), which, like epinephrine, promotes conversion of inactive liver phosphorylase into active phosphorylase (page 416).

Several other hormones may alter the abundance of glycogen in the liver. Deficiency in insulin supply results in a decrease in liver glycogen, presumably as a consequence of a diminution in synthesis of glycogen from blood glucose. Administration of excessive insulin might be expected to increase the quantity of liver glycogen, but this does not necessarily occur. Muscle appears to have a higher priority than liver, since it is muscle, not liver, glycogen that increases following insulin injection. The adenohypophysis (Chap. 51) produces one or more substances that tend to increase liver glycogen. The 11-oxysteroids of the adrenal cortex (Chap. 49), by augmenting the supply of glucose from noncarbohydrate precursors, favor accumulation of liver glycogen. Excessive administration of thyroid hormone (Chap. 46) results in a mobilization and disappearance of liver glycogen.

Muscle Glycogen. Although the normal concentration of glycogen in mammalian skeletal muscle, 0.5 to 1 per cent, is lower than that in liver, because of the large mass of muscle most of the total glycogen of the body normally resides in this tissue. In contrast to liver glycogen, muscle glycogen is not readily depleted by fasting, even over prolonged periods. Convulsions, however, result in a dramatic decrease in muscle glycogen; insulin administration generally enhances muscle glycogen concentration, but if the dosage is adequate to provoke hypoglycemic convulsions, the muscle glycogen content may fall to very low levels.

An important contrast is apparent between muscle and liver in regard to the response to epinephrine. The decline in liver glycogen and rise in blood glucose level following epinephrine administration to well-nourished animals have been described. If the animal is previously fasted, liver glycogen all but disappears, and if epinephrine is then injected, the effect observed is primarily upon muscle, presumably initiated by an activation of phosphorylase. However, glucose 6-phosphate cannot be hydrolyzed to glucose in muscle, since the requisite phosphatase is lacking. Further metabolism of glucose phosphate, *viz.*, glycolysis, ensues, and the first readily diffusible products are pyruvic and lactic acids. When pyruvic and lactic acids appear in the circulation of an animal that has previously fasted, rapid glycogenesis from these substances occurs in the liver. Thus, the sequence of events that follows epinephrine administration to the fasting animal is (1) a fall in muscle glycogen, (2) a rise in blood lactate, and (3) a rise in liver glycogen.

Enhanced glycogenesis in muscle in response to insulin is readily demonstrable in vitro with the rat diaphragm. The rat diaphragm is sufficiently thin to serve as a naturally occurring "tissue slice" and consequently has been used in a variety of metabolic studies. Employing this preparation, Stadie showed that rather firm binding of insulin by diaphragm precedes the enhancement of glycogenesis due to insulin.

It is noteworthy that cardiac muscle, in contrast to voluntary muscle, is insensitive to the concentration of insulin in the blood and that the quantity of glycogen in the heart may vary in the opposite direction from that in other muscles.

Hereditary Disorders of Glycogen Metabolism. The accumulation of large amounts of glycogen in the liver was recognized as a manifestation of a specific disorder by von Gierke in 1929. Perhaps surprisingly, independent hereditary disorders of glycogen metabolism involving at least five separate enzymes have been detected.

Table 21.3: HEREDITARY DISORDERS OF GLYCOGEN METABOLISM

Clinical type	Organ affected	Glycogen structure	Missing enzyme
Type I (von Gierke's)	Liver, kidney	Normal	Glucose 6-phosphatase
Type II (Pompe's)	All	Normal	?
Type III	Liver, muscle, heart	Short outer branches	Amylo-1,6-glucosidase
Type IV.................	Liver	Few branches	Amylo-(1,4→1,6)-transglycosylase
Type V (McArdle's)	Muscle	Normal	Muscle phosphorylase
Type VI (Hers')	Liver	Normal	Liver phosphorylase

These are summarized in Table 21.3. Absence of liver glucose 6-phosphatase in von Gierke's disease prevents response to the demand for addition of glucose to the blood. Lack of debranching or branching enzymes results in accumulation of an abnormal glycogen with different branch length. The independent failure to make liver and muscle phosphorylases indicates that these enzymes are under separate genetic control. It is noteworthy that there is, as yet, no known disorder in which glycogen synthetase is lacking.

BLOOD GLUCOSE AND ITS REGULATION

The continual utilization of glucose by all body tissues requires the delivery of glucose to these tissues by the circulating blood. The concentration of glucose in the blood of normal man 8 to 12 hr. after a meal is usually 70 to 90 mg. per 100 ml., depending somewhat on the analytical method employed. Slightly higher values are obtained immediately postprandially; more prolonged fasting results in little or no decline in blood glucose concentration.

The dependence of various tissues on circulating blood glucose varies widely. The central nervous system is perhaps most critically dependent, since glucose is the major energy source that crosses the blood-brain barrier (Chap. 39) at a rate sufficient to sustain normal function. If the blood glucose concentration falls abruptly, the earliest symptoms observed are referable to the central nervous system. Many tissues, such as muscle, can derive a considerable portion of their chemical energy from other nutrients, such as ketone bodies (page 458), and hence are not so critically dependent on a sustained blood glucose concentration. The myocardium effectively removes fatty acids and lactic acid from the blood and utilizes them as sources of energy. This capacity of heart muscle renders it relatively insensitive to fluctuations in the level of blood glucose and confers upon the heart a great degree of adaptability to variations in composition of the nutrient medium.

From the study of the normal fluctuations and of the mechanisms operating to offset these fluctuations has grown some understanding of the diseases that result in abnormal variations in the level of blood glucose. The relative constancy of the normal blood glucose concentration, despite various disturbing factors, is an example of "homeostatic" regulation. The term *homeostasis* was coined by Cannon to describe the reaction of the body to stimuli which, by altering the concentration of some constituent in the body, initiate a series of events that tend to restore this concentration to normal. Homeostatic mechanisms are the physiological counterparts of the "inverse feedback" mechanisms of engineering.

Sources of Blood Glucose. The portal absorption of the products of carbohydrate digestion represents a very large though variable contribution of glucose to the blood. In addition to being variable from day to day and from individual to individual, it is discontinuous, since a few hours after ingestion of a high-carbohydrate meal, most of the digestible carbohydrate will have left the intestinal lumen.

The second source of blood glucose results from hydrolysis of glucose 6-phosphate in liver, kidney, and intestine, which contain the requisite phosphatase, but not in striated muscle. This glucose derives less immediately either from glycogen or from all other potential precursors. Glucose derived from glycogen is a result of *glycogenolysis;* the formation of glucose from all other precursors is described as *glucogenesis.* The latter also encompasses *gluconeogenesis,* a term occasionally used to designate new glucose formation from noncarbohydrate precursors.

The reactions involved in glycogenolysis have already been discussed. Glucogenesis includes formation of glucose from any of the intermediates arising during glycolysis. Any compound that can be converted into one of these intermediates will also be glucogenic. Glucogenic materials include many of the amino acids (Chap. 27), glycerol, and a variety of quantitatively less important substances. The pathways by which glycerol and alanine may serve as sources of glucose are described elsewhere (pages 376 and 378).

It has been clearly established that *carbon atoms* initially present in fatty acids may ultimately appear in glucose. However, in animals, introduction into glucose of carbon atoms derived from fatty acids involves simultaneous loss, from other glucogenic materials, of at least as many carbon atoms as CO_2 as are introduced into glucose from the fatty acid. No *net* gain in glucose content can result from this process. There is no evidence of glucogenesis, in the sense of net gain of glucose, at the expense of fatty acid in human beings or other nonruminants. The major products of the fermentation of cellulose in the rumen and reticulum of ruminants (cow, sheep, camel, goat) are acetic acid and other short-chain fatty acids. Although these animals normally maintain lower blood glucose concentrations than other species, there is no evidence that their tissues can effect net synthesis of glucose from acetate.

Fates of Blood Glucose. After diffusion into cells, the only important fate of blood glucose is phosphorylation to yield glucose 6-phosphate, which may then be transformed into the variety of products indicated previously (Fig. 20.1, page 367). The hexokinase reaction has been construed as a capturing mechanism, by means of which the cells of the body abstract from the extracellular fluids the glucose they need. As intracellular glucose is irreversibly phosphorylated, equilibrium across the cell membrane is disturbed in favor of further migration of glucose into the intracellular compartment. By this means, even cells with large requirements for glucose can derive adequate nutrition from a fluid environment containing less than 0.1 per cent of glucose.

In the normal animal, no more than a trace of glucose is lost in the urine, regardless of diet. Under various abnormal circumstances, however, urinary loss of glucose may approximate the sum of all the glucose ingested plus such additional glucose as may arise from glucogenic materials of the diet. The abnormal appearance of glucose in the urine, *glucosuria,* can be readily understood in the light of the normal treatment of glucose by the kidney (Chap. 37).

Summary of Factors Influencing Blood Glucose Concentration. Figure 21.5 relates certain of the major sources and fates of blood glucose. In an individual exhibiting no glucosuria, the sum of the fates of glucose must equal the sum of the sources. The concentration of glucose in the blood is the resultant of the relative rates of glucose production from glycogen, amino acids, and other sources, glucose absorption from the intestinal tract, glucose utilization, and glucose loss in the urine. The rate of glucose utilization, both in the intact animal and in an isolated tissue, is governed in part by the concentration of glucose in the extracellular compartment; the higher the concentration of glucose, the more rapid is its assimilation by tissues such as muscle and liver. Sustaining blood glucose at hyperglycemic levels favors formation in the body of products derived from glucose, particularly liver glycogen and fatty acids.

Administration of insulin is promptly followed by a decline in blood glucose concentration and an increase in formation of products derived from glucose. The bulk of current evidence favors the view that it is the translocation of glucose from the extra- to the intracellular compartment, rather than the transformation of intracellular glucose to its 6-phosphate, which is responsive to insulin. Synthesis of glycogen by muscle and of fatty acids by liver and adipose tissue is enhanced,

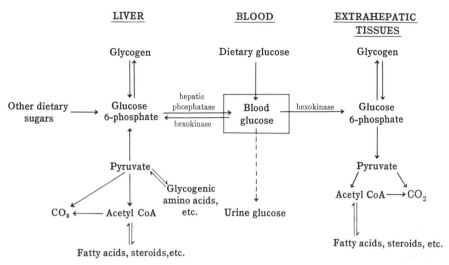

FIG. 21.5. Sources and fates of blood glucose.

lactic and pyruvic acids are formed abundantly, and a rise in the fasting respiratory quotient (page 284) toward unity indicates that more of the expired CO_2 is derived from glucose. Conversely, in spontaneous *diabetes mellitus,* in the pancreatectomized animal, or in the animal poisoned with alloxan (page 164), which preferentially damages pancreatic β cells, evidences of underutilization of glucose are manifest. Blood glucose tends to rise to glucosuric levels; glycogen production decreases in the intact diabetic animal as well as in the isolated diaphragm of this animal. Fatty acids are synthesized at subnormal rates both in liver and in adipose tissue. Administration of glucose fails to evoke the rise in blood lactic acid seen in the nondiabetic animal, and little or no rise in respiratory quotient follows glucose injection. Even in the diabetic animal, however, glucose utilization continues to occur, especially in brain and myocardium, and, furthermore, the rate of utilization is dependent on the blood glucose level. In this sense the hyperglycemia of diabetes may be regarded as serving a useful function, favoring glucose assimilation in an organism in which, because of lack of insulin, glucose entry into cells would otherwise be seriously restricted. The muscles and liver of the diabetic subject are incapable of deriving normal nutrition from their hyperglycemic environment; this situation has been aptly described as "starvation in the midst of plenty."

Many of the consequences of diabetes resemble the effects of starvation, or more specifically of carbohydrate deprivation. The most striking difference is that the blood of the diabetic individual is excessively rich in glucose, whereas blood of the fasted subject may contain slightly subnormal concentrations of glucose.

The presence of excessive insulin in the circulation is termed *hyperinsulinism.* This may arise spontaneously because of hyperplasia or neoplasia of the β cells of the islets of Langerhans, or may result from injection of insulin. The responsiveness of various organs to insulin differs widely. Whereas assimilation of blood glucose by muscle cells is stimulated in hyperinsulinism, this is not the case in brain.

The central nervous system is thus placed in an unfavorable position in its competition with other tissues for available glucose, and as the blood glucose level falls, central nervous system symptoms, including convulsions, may ensue.

The adenohypophysis secretes a substance, or more than one, that is, at least superficially, antagonistic to the action of insulin. Extirpation of the hypophysis of the pancreatectomized animal largely corrects its defective carbohydrate metabolism (see discussion of the Houssay preparation, Chap. 51). The hypophysectomized animal is extremely sensitive to injected insulin, and this sensitivity can be abolished by repeated injection of certain adenohypophyseal hormones (Chap. 51). Prolonged administration of these hormonal fractions may produce a continued hyperglycemia and glucosuria and, ultimately, histologically demonstrable injury to pancreatic β cells. This damage, which may lead to permanent diabetes, is, however, directly attributable not to the hypophyseal substances but to the hyperglycemia. If severe hyperglycemia is maintained in some animals simply by excessive injection of glucose solutions, a similar injury can be produced.

Glucose 6-phosphatase activity is abnormally high in the livers of diabetic animals, and decreases following injection of insulin into the intact animal. This implies that the release of glucose by the liver is abnormally high in the diabetic patient and is subnormal in the individual with excessive insulin. However, there is no evidence of a *direct* effect of insulin on the activity of this microsomal enzyme.

Epinephrine and glucagon (Chap. 50) appear to operate at the same level. Both favor the breakdown of liver glycogen to yield blood glucose, presumably by virtue of their influence on the activation of glycogen phosphorylase (page 416). Epinephrine administration to the well-nourished animal elicits a prompt hyperglycemia, sometimes even in excess of the renal threshold, with consequent glucosuria. This simulates extreme emotional states when discharge of epinephrine initiates a series of phenomena, including hyperglycemia.

The role of certain of the steroids derived from the adrenal cortex (Chap. 49) in the regulation of blood glucose may be twofold. These hormones inhibit amino acid incorporation into protein, reflected in excessive protein catabolism, thus augmenting the supply of glucogenic materials. The adrenal cortical steroids may also retard peripheral utilization of glucose. The net result of administration of certain adrenal cortical steroids, *e.g.*, cortisol, is to induce hyperglycemia. Conversely, in the adrenalectomized animal or in the patient with Addison's disease, hypoglycemia occurs if food is withheld (Chap. 49).

One additional hormone, thyroxine, has a marked effect on carbohydrate metabolism. In severe thyrotoxic states there may be a mild diabetes, which disappears when the thyrotoxicosis is corrected. Particularly striking is the almost complete absence of glycogen in the liver of the thyrotoxic animal. Thyroxine appears to enhance many different catabolic pathways and to increase oxidative phenomena in the body. How these effects contribute to the diabetic manifestations is not clear (Chap. 46).

In summary, the level of blood glucose may become elevated as a result of overproduction of glucose or as a result of its underutilization. Excessive secretion of certain hypophyseal substances or insulin deficiency can cause a hyperglycemia that is chiefly attributable to underutilization. The hyperglycemia that may result from excessive secretion of adrenal cortical steroids is probably chiefly the result of abnormally rapid glucogenesis from amino acids, together with a component of underutilization. The hyperglycemia due to excessive epinephrine secretion is the result of the excessively rapid breakdown of liver glycogen. Conversely, hypoglycemia due to hyperinsulinism is held to be the result of overutilization of glucose, but in adrenal cortical insufficiency is largely a consequence of impaired glucogenesis.

Glucose Tolerance. The capacity of the animal to dispose of administered glucose is referred to as the *glucose tolerance*. When glucose is administered, either by mouth or by vein, the concentration of glucose in blood rises rapidly. In the oral glucose tolerance test, with the usual dose of 1 g. of glucose per kilogram of body weight, the blood glucose concentration will rise from a fasting level of about 90 mg. to a maximum of perhaps 140 mg. per 100 ml. in about 1 hr. At this time, in normal man, the rate of entry of glucose into the blood will have decreased while the rate of removal by the several tissues will have increased so that the concentration in the blood now begins to fall.

There are apparently two reasons for the increase in glucose utilization: (1) the rate of glucose assimilation by cells is dependent on the concentration of glucose in extracellular fluid, without regard to changing hormonal influences; (2) as the level of blood glucose rises, the normal pancreas discharges insulin into the blood at an increased rate (Chap. 50). Glycogenesis, especially in muscle, is enhanced, glycolysis increases, as is evidenced by a rise in the level of blood lactic acid, the respiratory quotient rises toward unity, indicating a greater carbohydrate oxidation, and the blood glucose concentration falls rapidly. Generally by the end

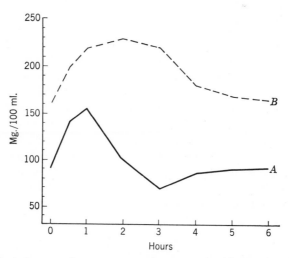

FIG. 21.6. Typical glucose tolerance curves. *A* = normal subject; *B* = diabetic subject.

of the second hour, the blood glucose concentration will have returned to approximately normal and often continues to fall below the initial level, probably as a result of continued increased insulin secretion (Fig. 21.6). As the stimulus of hyperglycemia upon the islands of Langerhans declines, insulin secretion returns to lower values.

In the course of this type of oral glucose tolerance determination in the normal subject, the concentration of glucose in the blood at no time exceeds the renal threshold, no glucosuria occurs, and the subject may be said to tolerate the dose of glucose that has been administered.

In the diabetic individual, deficient in insulin, the fasting blood glucose concentration will be elevated. After oral administration of glucose, the blood level will rise even higher, often exceeding the renal threshold and provoking glucosuria. The insulin response will be deficient or lacking, and as a result the decline in blood glucose concentration will be slow, while the expected rise in blood lactate will be minimal or undetectable. An individual showing this type of response is said to have a decreased glucose tolerance or an elevated glucose tolerance curve (Fig. 21.6).

In individuals suffering from hyperinsulinism, the initial concentration of glucose in the blood is often lower than normal. Very shortly after the blood glucose commences to rise, following glucose ingestion, insulin will be secreted. Blood glucose concentration will then start to fall and, because of the excessive insulin response, will often continue to fall. In such patients, following administration of a test dose of glucose, the blood glucose concentration may fall to 40 mg. per 100 ml. or below and result in central nervous system symptoms such as hypoglycemic convulsions. Thus, these individuals exhibit an abnormally high glucose tolerance. Various deviations from the normal glucose tolerance pattern have been noted. One extreme situation is that observed in sprue, in which, because of a defect in absorption of glucose from the intestinal lumen, a flat curve may be obtained after ingestion of glucose although a normal pattern is seen after parenteral glucose administration.

Tolerance for Other Sugars. For various reasons the tolerance of the organism for sugars other than glucose is sometimes determined. Fructose tolerance is occasionally studied; the rationale is that tolerance for fructose is not dependent on the integrity of the islands of Langerhans. This is taken to mean that whatever the effect of insulin upon glucose utilization, it is without effect upon fructose utilization. The utilization of fructose, independent of the action of insulin, has led to occasional use of this sugar as an energy source for diabetic individuals.

The shape of the fructose tolerance curve is largely conditioned by the capacity of the liver to use fructose in the synthesis of glycogen. In some types of hepatic disease the glycogenic function is disturbed, and the tolerance for fructose is diminished. The tolerance for galactose has been utilized in similar fashion to assess the glycogenic function of the liver.

REFERENCES

Books

Clark, F., and Grant, J. K., eds., "The Biochemistry of Mucopolysaccharides of Connective Tissue," Cambridge University Press, Cambridge, 1961.

Horecker, B. L., "Pentose Metabolism in Bacteria," John Wiley & Sons, Inc., New York, 1962.

Review Articles

Arnon, D. I., Cell-free Photosynthesis and the Energy Conversion Process, in W. D. McElroy and B. Glass, eds., "Light and Life," pp. 489–569, The Johns Hopkins Press, Baltimore, 1961.

Axelrod, B., Other Pathways of Carbohydrate Metabolism, in D. M. Greenberg, ed., "Metabolic Pathways," vol. I, pp. 205–250, Academic Press, Inc., New York, 1960.

Bassham, J. A., Photosynthesis: Energetics and Related Topics, *Advances in Enzymol.,* **25,** 39–118, 1963.

Bernfeld, P., Enzymes of Starch Degradation and Synthesis, *Advances in Enzymol.,* **12,** 379–428, 1951.

Cabib, E., Carbohydrate Metabolism, *Ann. Rev. Biochem.,* **32,** 321–354, 1963.

Cohn, M., Phosphorylases, in P. D. Boyer, H. A. Lardy, and K. Myrbäck, eds., "The Enzymes," vol. 5, pp. 179–206, Academic Press, Inc., New York, 1961.

Cori, C. F., Enzymatic Reactions in Carbohydrate Metabolism, *Harvey Lectures,* **41,** 253–272, 1945–1946.

Cori, G. T., Glycogen Structure and Enzyme Deficiencies in Glycogen Storage Disease, *Harvey Lectures,* **48,** 145–171, 1952–1953.

Glaser, L., Biosynthesis of Deoxysugars, *Physiol. Revs.,* **43,** 215–242, 1963.

Gunsalus, I. C., Horecker, B. L., and Wood, W. A., Pathways of Carbohydrate Metabolism in Microorganisms, *Bacteriol. Revs.,* **19,** 79–128, 1955.

Hassid, W. Z., Biosynthesis of Complex Saccharides, in D. M. Greenberg, ed., "Metabolic Pathways," vol. I, pp. 251–300, Academic Press, Inc., New York, 1960.

Hassid, W. Z., Biosynthesis of Polysaccharides from Nucleoside Diphosphate Sugars, in D. J. Bell and J. K. Grant, eds., "The Structure and Biosynthesis of Macromolecules," pp. 63–79, Cambridge University Press, Cambridge, 1962.

Hehre, E. J., Enzymic Synthesis of Polysaccharides: A Biological Type of Polymerization, *Advances in Enzymol.,* **11,** 297–337, 1951.

Horecker, B. L., Interdependent Pathways of Carbohydrate Metabolism, *Harvey Lectures,* **57,** 35–61, 1961–1962.

Imsande, J., and Handler, P., Pyrophosphorylases, in P. D. Boyer, H. A. Lardy, and K. Myrbäck, eds., "The Enzymes," vol. 5, pp. 281–304, Academic Press, Inc., New York, 1961.

Jagendorf, A., Photosynthesis, *Survey of Biol. Progress,* **4,** 183–344, 1962.

Jonsen, J., and Laland, S., Bacterial Nucleosides and Nucleotides, *Advances in Carbohydrate Chem.,* **17,** 201–234, 1962.

Kalckar, H. M., Uridinediphosphategalactose: Metabolism, Enzymology and Biology, *Advances in Enzymol.,* **20,** 111–134, 1958.

Krebs, E. G., and Fischer, E. H., Molecular Properties and Transformations of Glycogen Phosphorylase in Animal Tissues, *Advances in Enzymol.,* **24,** 263–290, 1962.

Krebs, H. A., and Lowenstein, J. M., The Tricarboxylic Acid Cycle, in D. M. Greenberg, ed., "Metabolic Pathways," vol. 1, pp. 129–204, Academic Press, Inc., New York, 1960.

Manners, D. J., Enzymic Synthesis and Degradation of Starch and Glycogen, *Advances in Carbohydrate Chem.,* **17,** 371–430, 1962.

Neufeld, E. F., and Hassid, W. Z., Biosynthesis of Saccharides from Sugar Nucleotides, *Advances in Carbohydrate Chem.,* **18,** 309–356, 1963.

Racker, E., Alternate Pathways of Glucose and Fructose Metabolism, *Advances in Enzymol.,* **15,** 141–182, 1954.

Sols, A., Carbohydrate Metabolism, *Ann. Rev. Biochem.,* **30,** 213, 1961.

Stetten, D., and Stetten, M. R., Glycogen Metabolism, *Physiol. Revs.,* **40,** 505–537, 1960.

Sutherland, E. W., Jr., The Biological Role of Adenosine-3',5'-Phosphate, *Harvey Lectures*, **57**, 17–33, 1961–1962.

Vishniac, W., Horecker, B. L., and Ochoa, S., Enzymic Aspects of Photosynthesis, *Advances in Enzymol.*, **19**, 1–77, 1957.

Wassink, E. C., Photosynthesis, in M. Florkin and H. S. Mason, eds., "Comparative Biochemistry," vol. V, part C, pp. 347–462, Academic Press, Inc., New York, 1963.

Wood, H. G., Significance of Alternate Pathways in the Metabolism of Glucose, *Physiol. Revs.*, **35**, 841–859, 1955.

22. Lipid Metabolism

Digestion and Absorption. Degradation and Synthesis of Neutral Fats. Mobilization and Deposition. Ketone Bodies and Ketosis

In this and the following chapter will be presented the metabolism of the neutral fats, or triglycerides, the phosphatides, sphingomyelin, and the sterols. The metabolism of the "lipid-soluble" vitamins, A, D, E, and K, is presented in Chap. 56. A relative paucity of information exists regarding metabolic features in mammals of the other classes of lipids (page 61).

The mammal requires, for optimal growth and maintenance, small amounts of the lipid-soluble vitamins and certain unsaturated fatty acids. With these exceptions, lipid is apparently not essential in the diet; this implies that all other lipids can be synthesized from other nutrients at a rate adequate for normal growth and health. The importance of lipid in the diet should, however, not be underestimated. Lipids are the most concentrated source of energy to the organism, yielding, per gram, over twice as many calories as do carbohydrates or proteins (page 282).

DIGESTION OF DIETARY LIPID

The bulk of dietary lipid is triglyceride of animal or vegetable origin. In the gastrointestinal tract a portion undergoes hydrolysis to constituent fatty acids and glycerol.

$$
\begin{array}{ll}
H_2COOCR & H_2COH \\
| & | \\
HCOOCR + 3H_2O \rightleftharpoons 3RCOOH + HCOH \\
| & | \\
H_2COOCR & H_2COH
\end{array}
$$

Incomplete hydrolysis yields a mixture of the mono- and diglycerides in addition to the final products of the process. A group of esterases, called *lipases,* are of primary importance in the hydrolysis of triglycerides.

Gastric Digestion of Lipids. It has long been known that a lipase is present in gastric juice. The optimal action of this enzyme is near neutrality, and at the low pH levels encountered in the stomach it is essentially inactive; its significance is therefore uncertain, although some fatty acids appear to be liberated in the stomach. However, it has been suggested that gastric lipase may be more important in the infant since the gastric acidity is far lower in infancy and since the normal lipid of the infant diet occurs in a highly emulsified state in milk, a condition favorable to rapid attack by a water-soluble enzyme.

Intestinal Digestion of Lipid. The major site of lipid digestion is the small intestine. In the duodenum the bolus of food encounters the *bile* and the *pancreatic juice,* and in the lower small intestine the secretion of the intestinal mucosa, the *succus entericus,* also participates in lipid digestion.

The Role of Bile. Bile apparently contains no lipolytic enzymes. Its function in lipid digestion and absorption is to promote emulsification and solubilization of lipids, and this function is associated with the salts of bile acids (page 86). Bile secretion is considered in Chap. 36.

The bile and the pancreatic juice are somewhat alkaline and serve in part to neutralize the acidic gastric chyme. In the approximately neutral environment of the duodenal lumen the bile acids, largely taurocholic and glycocholic acids, exist as anions, and serve as detergents or emulsifying agents (page 66). In the presence of these detergents the churning effect of peristalsis results in a progressively finer and finer state of distribution of the dietary lipid in the continuous aqueous phase, facilitating lipolysis.

Since lipolysis involves participation of water and water-soluble lipases, and since dietary lipids are essentially insoluble in water, hydrolysis occurs only at the interface between the lipid droplet and the aqueous phase. The rate of reaction is in part determined by the area of this interface, and the higher the degree of emulsification, the smaller the individual lipid droplet and the larger this area will be. As a first approximation, per unit volume of lipid, the area of the interface will vary inversely as the radius of the average droplet and directly as the cube root of the number of droplets.

The function of bile in lipid digestion is to promote contact between water-soluble and water-insoluble components of the lipolytic reaction. However, this function is apparently not essential for digestion, in that the lipid residue appearing in the feces when bile is totally excluded from the gastrointestinal tract is mostly hydrolyzed and consists largely of soaps of fatty acids. The well-known intolerance for dietary lipid in patients with biliary obstruction suggests that lipid digestion is retarded in such individuals. However, the soaps as well as the monoglycerides which result from the partial digestion of fats also act as detergents and thus supplement the function of the bile salts.

Pancreatic Lipase. The flow of pancreatic juice, like the flow of bile, is regulated hormonally after the introduction of gastric chyme into the duodenum. A precursor of lipase in the pancreatic juice becomes active in the intestinal lumen. The mechanism of activation of pancreatic lipase is not clear, but it has been suggested that a cofactor is needed for its activity.

Pancreatic lipase acts best on fatty acid esters in the emulsified state. The degree of unsaturation (0 to 2 double bonds) and chain length (C_{12} to C_{18}) have no significant effect on the rate of hydrolysis. Ca^{++} has an accelerating effect on the enzyme, mainly because it forms insoluble soaps with liberated fatty acids. This prevents their inhibitory action on the enzyme and also retards resynthesis of glyceride, effectively shifting the reaction in the direction of hydrolysis.

Hydrolysis occurs predominantly at the α or α' positions, producing an α,β-diglyceride. This is then hydrolyzed to a monoglyceride, predominantly the β form (80 per cent). Indeed, since acyl migration occurs, it is not certain that pancreatic lipase can hydrolyze the β-monoglyceride. The main course of the reactions is pictured as follows, where R, R', and R'' are different fatty acid chains.

$$
\begin{array}{llll}
\alpha & \text{H}_2\text{COOCR} & \text{H}_2\text{COH} & \text{H}_2\text{COOCR} \\
\beta & 2\,\text{HCOOCR}' \longrightarrow & \text{HCOOCR}' + & \text{HCOOCR}' \quad + \text{ RCOOH} \\
\alpha' & \text{H}_2\text{COOCR}'' & \text{H}_2\text{COOCR}'' & \text{H}_2\text{COH} \quad + \text{ R}''\text{COOH}
\end{array}
$$

$$
\begin{array}{c}
\text{H}_2\text{COH} \\
2\,\text{HCOOCR}' + \text{RCOOH} + \text{R}''\text{COOH} \\
\text{H}_2\text{COH}
\end{array}
$$

Complete hydrolysis is not a prerequisite to absorption. Fatty acid esters which are resistant to hydrolysis, *e.g.*, methyl elaidate, are absorbed and deposited in the body lipids. Apparently, such fat as is not absorbed is rather completely hydrolyzed, since in feces the fatty acids are present almost entirely as soaps.

A pancreatic *lecithinase* liberates lysolecithin (page 74) from lecithin. Lysolecithin is a good detergent and aids in emulsification of the dietary lipid. Since some lecithin is present in bile, this fluid contributes a precursor of lysolecithin in addition to supplying other detergents. The presence of a lecithinase in the intestinal mucosa has also been indicated.

In the completely pancreatectomized human being, if dietary lipid is restricted in quantity it is fairly well tolerated; this tolerance is attributed to the presence of accessory lipolytic activity in the succus entericus.

INTESTINAL ABSORPTION OF LIPIDS

After ingestion of a fatty meal, the small intestine contains free fatty acids, as their soaps, together with a mixture of mono-, di-, and triglycerides well emulsified by the bile salts and the soaps themselves. A major portion of this mixture is absorbed across the wall of the small intestine. Such glycerol as is liberated is water-soluble, and together with other water-soluble nutrients is absorbed by the portal route. The fatty acids, on the other hand, are delivered to the organism predominantly via the intestinal lymph, where they appear in the form of triglycerides.

The classical demonstration of the chylous absorption of lipids was due to Munk, who in 1891 studied a patient with a lymph fistula draining at the thigh. Munk fed a variety of fats to his patient and noted that over 60 per cent of the ingested fat could generally be recovered from the discharge of the fistulous tract. Shortly after feeding of a fatty meal, the lymph, clear during fasting, became milky owing to the appearance of minute fat droplets, which subsequently were termed *chylomicra*. The preponderant lipid of the lymph was always triglyceride, and even when the fatty acids were fed as esters of other alcohols, it was mainly as esters of glycerol that they were recovered from the chyle.

These observations and others led to the idea that esters were completely hydrolyzed in the small intestine and that fatty acids crossed the mucosal barrier and entered the terminal lymphatics of the intestinal villi, reesterified to glycerol.

It will be noted that there are two independent concepts in this picture of lipid absorption: (1) total hydrolysis is a prerequisite for absorption; (2) products of lipid digestion enter the circulation exclusively by the lymphatic route. Neither of these concepts has proved to be entirely correct.

Quantitative studies with isotopically labeled triglycerides have permitted a more precise evaluation of these two problems. Present estimates indicate that approximately 40 per cent of fed triglycerides are hydrolyzed to glycerol and fatty acids, 3 to 10 per cent are absorbed as triglyceride, and the remainder is partially hydrolyzed, mainly to the β-monoglycerides.

Long-chain fatty acids (those with more than 14 carbon atoms), whether fed in the form of triglycerides or as free fatty acids, appear in the chyle almost quantitatively as regenerated triglycerides. The mechanism of this synthesis is considered later (page 453). These products enter the blood via the thoracic duct and accessory channels, chiefly at the angle of the left jugular and subclavian veins. Certain exceptions should, however, be noted. In general those lipids which are liquid at body temperature are efficiently absorbed. Lipids which melt significantly above body temperature are poorly digested and absorbed, and fatty acids which are solids above body temperature will not be well absorbed unless mixed with lower-melting lipids.

Present evidence indicates that fatty acids of chain length less than 10 carbon atoms are absorbed predominantly in nonesterified form by the portal rather than the lymphatic route and consequently are presented directly to the liver. Since of all the common dietary lipids only those of milk are rich in fatty acids of shorter chain length, this fact is of interest in infant nutrition.

Factors Affecting Absorption of Lipids. The mechanisms responsible for the partition of fatty acids of different chain length to the lymph and the blood are unknown. It has been suggested that such factors as differences in water solubility, protein interaction, micelle formation, and enzymic specificity with respect to triglyceride resynthesis (see below), in combination with permeability influences, affect the different routes of absorption. Certain factors, however, affect the passage through the intestinal mucosa, and perhaps the most important relates to the presence of detergents, chiefly bile salts and to a lesser extent monoglycerides and soaps, in the intestinal lumen.

When bile is totally excluded from the intestinal tract as a result of severe liver dysfunction, extrahepatic biliary obstruction, or biliary fistula, lipid absorption is markedly impeded. As a result, the total lipid content of acholic feces is elevated owing to an abundance of salts of fatty acids. The presence of these soaps, chiefly insoluble calcium salts, together with the absence of bile pigment, results in the characteristic "clay-colored" stools seen in biliary obstruction. Not only is absorption of fatty acids impeded, but other lipid-soluble substances are also poorly absorbed. Most striking are the signs of vitamin K deficiency which are observed in biliary obstruction; these may be promptly relieved by oral administration of bile salts or by parenteral administration of vitamin K (Chap. 56). This is an important consideration in relation to surgery performed on patients with biliary disease, since vitamin K is required to ensure the normal rate of clotting of blood (Chap. 33).

The role of bile salts in fat absorption is most probably associated with their detergent properties. It is noteworthy that, although associated with lipid during passage across the mucosal barrier, the bile acids do not enter the lymphatic circulation. Rather, they are confined to an *enterohepatic circulation,* entering the portal blood, from which they are removed by the liver and reinjected with the bile into the duodenum. From this circuit relatively little bile acid is lost, little appears in the peripheral blood, and about 200 mg. appears per day in the feces.

A second factor which influences the absorption of lipids from the intestinal lumen is the metabolic activity of the intestinal mucosa per se. Enzymic systems are present in the cells of the intestinal mucosa which can convert free fatty acids and mono- and diglycerides to the triglycerides. One of these systems is similar to that found first in liver and is described later (page 453).

A degree of selectivity is exhibited by the intestinal mucosa in regard to the absorption of sterols. Of the abundant dietary sterols, only cholesterol crosses the intestinal wall with ease and is readily absorbed via the chylous route. Neither the products of cholesterol reduction, coprosterol and cholestanol (see page 476), nor its homologues in plants, the phytosterols, are absorbed to an appreciable extent. However, some absorption of the plant sterol β-sitosterol is indicated. Indeed, this sterol appears to compete with cholesterol for "absorption sites" in the intestinal mucosa; consequently, when administered for prolonged periods of time, β-sitosterol may effect a reduction in plasma cholesterol values. It should be noted that many physiologically active steroids, including the digitalis glycosides (page 88), cortisol (page 87), and vitamin D (page 85), do cross the intestinal barrier at rates sufficient to permit their use by oral administration for therapeutic purposes.

The Lipids of the Feces—Steatorrhea. Lipids are present in the feces in part because of failure of quantitative absorption of dietary lipids, in part by virtue of excretion of lipids into the intestinal lumen. Lipids, notably steroids, also are present in the bile, in which they enter the intestine. In addition, direct excretion takes place across the intestinal barrier. Lipids excreted either via the bile or by the intestinal mucosa may appear in the feces, as will products formed from these lipids by intestinal bacteria. This last factor is of significance in sterol metabolism and will be considered later (page 475).

Excessive lipid in the stools is referred to as *steatorrhea.* Three important types of disturbance are recognized as resulting in steatorrhea: exclusion of bile, exclusion of pancreatic juice, and defect of the intestinal mucosa. Steatorrhea due to biliary insufficiency is, as indicated above, usually recognizable by the presence in the stools of excessive amounts of digested but unabsorbed lipid, chiefly in the form of soaps. The characteristic lack of bile pigment in the feces facilitates classification. Such steatorrhea may result from obstruction to the biliary passages caused by stone or neoplasm, biliary fistula, or severe diffuse liver disease.

The steatorrhea which results from deficiency of pancreatic juice is characterized by the presence in the stools of excessive amounts of undigested triglyceride. The pathological lesion may be *pancreatic fibrosis;* the same picture may be seen after total pancreatectomy. If, in such subjects, the quantity of dietary fat is kept low, steatorrhea may not be observed.

Chronic disease of the pancreas must on occasion be differentiated from certain diseases of the intestinal tract proper, such as celiac disease in children or sprue in the adult. In these conditions, emulsification and digestion of fat are apparently normal, since the flow of bile and of pancreatic juice is not impaired. The steatorrhea, often of impressive proportions, is therefore attributed to failure of the active absorptive processes in the intestinal mucosa. The lipid of the feces is predominantly in the form of soaps. It is noteworthy that in these conditions not only lipids but a variety of other nutrients fail to cross the intestinal barrier at a normal rate.

BLOOD LIPIDS AND LIPEMIA

Normal blood plasma in the postabsorptive state in man contains some 500 mg. of total lipid per 100 ml., of which about one-quarter is triglyceride. There are 180 mg. or more of cholesterol, of which some two-thirds is esterified with fatty acids and one-third is present as free sterol. Phosphatides comprise about 160 mg. per 100 ml., lecithins predominating over cephalins. (See also Table 32.1, page 628.)

In the postabsorptive state, the mesenteric and thoracic duct lymph is a clear, watery fluid. A short time after introduction of a fatty meal into the duodenum, the chyle changes dramatically in quality and quantity. The lymphatic channels, previously visualized with great difficulty, now become distended with a milky fluid rich in triglycerides. Most of the fat of the chyle is present in droplets approximately 1 μ in average diameter—the chylomicra, which contain chiefly lipid and a small amount of protein. The discharge of this chyle into the venous blood results in a rapid rise in the lipid content of the plasma, occasionally sufficient to result in a milky opalescence. The increase in blood lipid is called *lipemia,* and specifically that which transiently follows ingestion of fat is called *absorptive lipemia.*

A number of lipoprotein fractions can be separated by repeatedly centrifuging plasma at high speeds after appropriately increasing the plasma density by addition of salts or D_2O. These lipoproteins may be characterized by their flotation constants, S_f, which are analogous to the sedimentation constants of ordinary proteins (page 134), and by the densities at which they separate. Some of the properties of the lipoprotein fractions are given in Table 22.1 (also see Table 32.5, page 633). It is seen that the fractions of lowest density (high S_f) are richest in triglycerides and poorest in protein. The high water solubility of these macromolecules suggests that they may be large spheres containing lipid which is partially covered by a thin film of hydrophilic protein. Thus the water-soluble plasma proteins play a major role in the transport of lipids. Even in the chylomicra, the small amount of protein apparently aids in stabilizing the droplets. There is probably no *free* lipid in blood plasma, *i.e.,* no lipid which is not associated with protein.

Lipoprotein Lipase. In 1943 Hahn observed that intravenous injection of heparin markedly accelerated the elimination of turbidity of lipemic plasma in vivo.

Table 22.1: LIPOPROTEINS OF HUMAN PLASMA

Fraction	Density	S_f	Diameter, Å.	Electrophoretic fraction	Amount, mg/ 100 ml. plasma	Approximate percentage composition					
						Protein	Phospha- tide	Cholesterol		Trigly- ceride	Fatty acids
								Free	Ester		
Chylomicra........	.....	>400	5,000–10,000	α_2	100–250	2	7	2	6	83	.....
Very low-density.......	0.98	10–400	300–700	β_1	130–200	9	18	7	15	50	1
Low-density.........	1.035	3–9	200–250	β_1	210–400	21	22	8	38	10	1
High-density........	1.09	......	100–150	α_1	50–130	33	29	7	23	8	.....
Very high-density........	1.14	......	<100	α_1	290–400	57	21	3	14	5	.....

SOURCE: Adapted from J. L. Oncley, in F. Homburger and P. Bernfeld, eds., "The Lipoproteins: Methods and Clinical Significance," S. Karger, New York, 1958.

435

Clearing factors (*lipoprotein lipases*) have since been found in various tissues, notably heart, lung, and adipose tissue. The lipase which appears in blood is distinct from those which function in the cells of adipose tissue. It appears in plasma during lipemia, and its activity is enhanced by heparin, other acidic polysaccharides, or various inorganic macromolecules. Incubation of clearing factor with a bacterial *heparinase* inactivates the lipase, which suggests that heparin or a similar mucopolysaccharide is an integral part of the enzyme. The latter is active only in the presence of an added cation such as Ca^{++}, Mn^{++}, Mg^{++}.

Plasma lipoprotein lipase catalyzes the hydrolysis of triglycerides present in chylomicra and in lipoproteins and only when they are bound to protein. Moreover, the presence of an acceptor of liberated fatty acids, such as serum albumin, is essential. Thus albumin plays a major role in the transport of unesterified fatty acids, present in a concentration of 8 to 30 mg. per 100 ml. of plasma (Table 32.1, page 629). These fatty acids have a high metabolic turnover rate.

The lipoprotein lipases of the tissues are important in the mobilization of fatty acids from the lipid depots (page 455).

Lipemia. Unexplained "idiopathic" lipemia is occasionally observed. Of greater interest are the lipemias frequently seen in diabetic acidosis and glycogen storage disease. In some patients with the nephrotic syndrome, the normal utilization of lipoproteins with S_f 0 to 20 appears to be impaired. Individuals surviving a myocardial infarction have elevated levels of lower-density lipoproteins, particularly of the S_f 12 to 20 class. Such patients also may have hypercholesterolemia. However, marked alterations may occur in the normal relative concentrations of lipoproteins, *e.g.*, the ratio of α- and β-lipoproteins, without significant changes in the plasma total cholesterol values. Therefore, determinations of the distribution or relative concentrations of the lipoprotein fractions or of the lipids in these fractions are more informative than estimations of the total concentration of a specific lipid in plasma.

Males between the ages of twenty and forty show a higher plasma content of low-density lipoproteins and a lower content of high-density lipoproteins than do women in the same age group. Older males and females have higher concentrations of low-density lipoproteins than young males and females. Aspects of the postulated significance of this information to atherosclerosis will be referred to in Chap. 53.

THE LIPIDS OF THE BODY

In the normal mammal 10 per cent or more of the body weight may be lipid, the bulk of which is *triglyceride*. This lipid is distributed in varying amounts in all organs as well as in certain *depots* of highly specialized connective tissue, the adipose tissue, in which a large fraction of the cytoplasm of the cells appears to be replaced by droplets of lipid. The large amount of lipid found in most animal tissues is in contrast to the situation in plants, where lipid is found in abundance only in seeds.

Functions of Body Lipid. Body lipid is a reservoir of potential chemical energy. There is, in the normal mammal, a far greater quantity of mobilizable lipid than of mobilizable carbohydrate. This lipid yields over twice as many calories per gram as does carbohydrate (page 282) and, in addition, is stored in a relatively water-free state in the tissues, in contrast to carbohydrate, which is heavily hydrated. In most normally nourished animals the lipid depots represent by far the largest reservoir of energy, available in times of restricted nutrition for the operation of the numerous endergonic processes necessary for maintenance of life.

A second function relates to the fact that much of the lipid of mammals is located subcutaneously. This results in protection of the more thermosensitive tissues against excessive heat loss to the environment. This function, of particular importance in homoiotherms, is perhaps best exemplified in marine mammals, whose environment is both colder than body temperature and a far better thermal conductor than air. Among the whales an impressively thick and continuous layer of subcutaneous adipose tissue, blubber, serves to reduce heat losses to the environment.

A third function, again most obvious in the subcutaneous lipid depots, is that of insulation against mechanical trauma. A dramatic example is seen in marine mammals. The destructive capacity of the sperm whale is largely related to the depot of highly specialized lipid, spermaceti (page 79), at its cephalic extremity, which permits it to deliver blows of great force with its head.

The absence of any considerable amount of depot lipid during the intrauterine life of the mammalian fetus is of interest in relation to the functions of depot lipid during adult life. The fetus derives its nutrition across the placenta from the maternal circulation and does so continuously, in contrast to the adult, who eats intermittently. The fetus therefore can sustain itself without long-term energy reservoirs. It resides in a thermoregulated environment and needs little additional insulation. Furthermore, the fetus is well protected by amniotic fluid and maternal tissues against mechanical blows and thus requires none of the cushioning which the adult derives from its depot lipid. It is only shortly prior to term, as though in anticipation of the abandonment of its parasitic state, that the fetus acquires its investiture of depot lipid.

Characteristics of Depot Lipid. The lipid of the depots consists chiefly of triglyceride. From analyses of samples of fatty acid of depot lipid in various species (page 71), considerable variation is evident. Within any species, however, the composition of depot lipid is fairly uniform. Silicic acid chromatography of the lipids of human adipose tissue, obtained by needle biopsy, reveals that more than 99 per cent of the lipid is triglyceride. It is noteworthy that the composition of the various adipose depots of man is similar, regardless of anatomical source, but differs markedly from the composition of serum lipids (page 629). Also, in general, depot lipid is richer in saturated fatty acids than is liver lipid (page 71). Lipid as it exists in the depots of living animals is in the liquid state, and it would appear that the lipid which is deposited subcutaneously is as saturated as is compatible with the liquid state. The more nearly saturated a sample of lipid, the larger the energy yield from oxidation. Thus, it would seem that mammals deposit under their skins that type of lipid richest in chemical potential energy and still liquid at the ambient temperature.

Although the composition of depot lipid within a species is reasonably uniform, variations may be induced by extremes of temperature or of diet. The effect of diet on the composition of depot lipid reflects the origins of depot fatty acids, *viz.*, from dietary fatty acids as well as from carbohydrate (see below). Prolonged feeding to human subjects of high corn oil–containing diets (40 per cent of calories as corn oil) resulted, beginning at 20 weeks on the diet, in significant increases in the unsaturated fatty acid content of the adipose tissue. At 160 weeks the adipose composition resembled corn oil more than it did normal adipose tissue. Earlier influences of dietary lipid on the composition of depot lipid are seen if an animal is fasted to deplete the major portion of the depots and then refed a diet rich in lipid of different physical properties from its native lipid. Thus, if hogs or rats are fed a diet rich in a highly unsaturated oil like peanut oil, the depots will contain a lipid resembling peanut oil in its high degree of unsaturation. Repletion of depot lipid by the feeding of an essentially lipid-free, high-carbohydrate diet leads to a depot lipid notably poor in unsaturated fatty acids.

The depot lipid of some mammals contains certain areas of tissue in which the lipid is somewhat differentiated. In the adipose tissue of these areas high concentrations of glycogen are found, and also a brown pigment. Such an area occurs in the interscapular region of the rat.

Metabolic Aspects of Body Lipid. When an animal is excessively nourished, the quantity of body lipid increases and, conversely, during periods of prolonged fasting the amount of body lipid decreases. It is possible, however, to adjust food intake so that the quantity of body lipid is constant over a long period of time, and indeed in most adult animals there seems to be some degree of regulation of appetite such that the lipid content of the body does not change rapidly.

It will be recalled that application of the technique of isotopic tracers to studies of metabolism (Chap. 15) has established the concept of continuous turnover (synthesis, degradation, and replacement of most body constituents), even at constant body composition (page 278). The lipids of the depots are continuously being mobilized, new lipid is continuously being deposited, and the constancy of the quantity of depot lipid is the result of a relatively precise adjustment of the rates of these two processes. This continuing turnover has been indicated above in the influence of dietary lipid on body lipid composition, even in a normal individual in caloric balance.

Application of isotopic methods to the determination of the half-life (page 275) of lipids has revealed that in the steady state the half-life of depot lipid in the mouse is about 5 days, in the rat about 8 days. This means that in the rat almost 10 per cent of the fatty acids in the depot lipid is replaced daily by new fatty acid. In the liver of the rat, the fatty acids have a half-life of about 2 days; in the brain, 10 to 15 days.

Adipose tissue exhibits two major metabolic features: (1) the assimilation of carbohydrate and lipids and their intermediates for fat synthesis and storage, and (2) the mobilization of lipid as free fatty acids, and to a more limited extent, as glycerol. Both these aspects are profoundly influenced by hormones. The fatty acids of adipose tissue, present as triglyceride, derive from both dietary fatty acids and carbohydrate. The pathway of fatty acid synthesis from intermediates of carbohydrate metabolism is considered below (page 445), as are triglyceride formation (page 452) and the mobilization of lipids from depots (page 455). Discussion here will be directed to the assimilation of lipid by adipose tissue.

The assimilative and storage activities of adipose tissue are reflected in its apparent capacity to take up both triglycerides and free fatty acids. In vivo, Bragdon and Gordon showed that glucose feeding enhances the incorporation of intravenously injected chylomicra labeled with C^{14}-palmitic acid into rat adipose tissue. The triglycerides may be taken up without prior hydrolysis, although maximal uptake by adipose tissue apparently involves triglyceride hydrolysis and reesterification. Metabolism of carbohydrate promotes esterification. Both the glycolytic and the phosphogluconate oxidative pathways operate in adipose tissue, with the latter being relatively more active than the former. The glycerol portion of the stored triglyceride is derived from glucose at the triose phosphate step in glycolysis (page 376), presumably from dihydroxyacetone phosphate via α-glycerophosphate. Adipose tissue in vitro is unable to assimilate glycerol itself.

Many of the hormones influence the above-described processes in adipose tissue. Thus, insulin augments glucose uptake and lactate and glycerol production, as well as the assimilation of triglyceride by adipose tissue (Chap. 50). There is increased lipogenesis from carbohydrate. Epinephrine acts in a manner opposite to that of insulin (Chap. 49). Other hormonal effects on adipose tissue will be described in Part Six.

Insulin or prolactin (Chap. 51) added to adipose tissue in vitro has been shown by Barrnett and Ball to initiate pynocytosis. Although a functional interpretation of these observations can be suggested, e.g., stimulation of a mechanism for metabolite assimilation by adipose tissue, their significance is not established.

DEGRADATION OF FATTY ACIDS

The action of the lipases results in the hydrolysis of neutral fats to glycerol and fatty acids. Glycerol, derived from fats or phosphatides, is glycogenic, entering the glycolytic pathway via formation of α-glycerophosphate by the action of ATP and glycerokinase (page 469).

β-Oxidation. Degradation of fatty acids proceeds in stages by a series of reactions in which, beginning at the carboxyl end of the chain, successive 2-carbon fragments are removed. This idea is due to Knoop and was based upon experiments reported in 1904. A series of ω-phenylaliphatic acids was fed to dogs, and the nature of the excretory products examined. It was found that the aromatic nucleus resisted disruption, whereas the side chain either was not attacked or was shortened by an *even number of carbon atoms:* thus β-phenylpropionic acid $\longrightarrow$ benzoic acid, and γ-phenylbutyric acid $\longrightarrow$ phenylacetic acid.

What was postulated on the basis of Knoop's studies has become one of the securely established pathways of metabolism. The characteristics of fatty acid degradation are that by a repetitive sequence of reactions, the fatty acyl chain is shortened in stages by two carbon atoms at a time, that it is the coenzyme A derivatives, not the free fatty acids, that are involved in these reactions, and that the liberated 2-carbon fragment is acetyl CoA. The responsible enzymes have all been isolated from mitochondria. Many of the successive steps were discovered independently in several laboratories, and the enzymes involved were, in some cases, given different names. The present nomenclature is based on that collectively suggested by several investigators in this field.

If we begin with a fatty acid derivative of coenzyme A, the shortening of the fatty acid chain by two carbon atoms is due to four successive reactions: (1) dehydrogenation catalyzed by a flavoprotein to yield the α,β-unsaturated derivative, (2) hydration of the double bond to form the β-hydroxy compound, (3) dehydrogenation involving DPN to yield the β-keto derivative, and (4) reaction of the β-keto acyl CoA with CoA to yield acetyl CoA and a fatty acid derivative of CoA which is shorter by two carbon atoms. Successive repetitions of this sequence of four reactions result in the complete degradation of an even-numbered carbon atom fatty acid to acetyl CoA and, starting with a fatty acid containing an odd number of carbon atoms, to successive molecules of acetyl CoA and one of propionyl CoA.

The four reactions are written to show that the acyl derivatives are linked to the thiol group of CoA.

$$\overset{\beta}{R}CH_2\overset{\alpha}{C}H_2CH_2COSCoA + FAD \xrightarrow[\text{dehydrogenase}]{\text{acyl}} RCH_2CH{=}CHCOSCoA + FADH_2 \quad (1)$$

$$RCH_2CH{=}CHCOSCoA + H_2O \underset{\text{hydrase}}{\overset{\text{enoyl}}{\rightleftharpoons}} RCH_2\overset{\beta}{C}HOH\overset{\alpha}{C}H_2COSCoA \quad (2)$$

$$RCH_2CHOHCH_2COSCoA + DPN^+ \underset{\text{dehydrogenase}}{\overset{\beta\text{-hydroxyacyl}}{\rightleftharpoons}}$$

$$RCH_2COCH_2COSCoA + DPNH + H^+ \quad (3)$$

$$\overset{\beta}{R}CH_2\overset{\alpha}{C}OCH_2COSCoA + HSCoA \underset{}{\overset{\text{thiolase}}{\rightleftharpoons}} RCH_2COSCoA + CH_3COSCoA \quad (4)$$

Each of the major types of reaction can now be considered further.

Activation Reactions. Degradation of free fatty acids requires an initial transformation to the corresponding acyl CoA derivatives. This may be accomplished in two ways.

The *thiokinases* catalyze directly the formation of the CoA derivatives according to the following reaction.

$$RCOOH + CoA + ATP \overset{Mg^{++}}{\rightleftharpoons} RCOCoA + AMP + PP_i$$

Several such enzymes are known, and they are named according to the length of the carbon chain of the compound which reacts most rapidly, *e.g.*, *acetic thiokinase* (acts on C_2 and C_3 fatty acids), *octanoic thiokinase* (C_4 to C_{12} fatty acids), and *dodecanoic thiokinase* (C_{10} to C_{18} fatty acids). Present knowledge of the mechanism of such reactions has already been discussed (page 316).

A second mechanism for synthesis of acyl CoA derivatives of fatty acids is by transfer reactions catalyzed by *thiophorases*.

$$\text{Succinyl CoA} + R{-}COOH \overset{\text{thiophorase}}{\rightleftharpoons} \text{succinic acid} + R{-}COSCoA$$

Activation of fatty acids occurs mainly by thiokinase reactions in animal tissues, such as liver, heart, and kidney, whereas in some microorganisms, reactions catalyzed by thiophorases predominate.

Acyl CoA Dehydrogenases. These enzymes, which catalyze the formation of the α,β-unsaturated fatty acyl CoA derivatives [reaction (1) above], all contain FAD. Three such enzymes have been isolated from pig liver and are named for the most sensitive substrates, *e.g., butyryl CoA dehydrogenase*, a green protein, and two yellow flavoproteins, *octanoyl CoA dehydrogenase* and *hexadecanoyl CoA dehydrogenase*. The type of reaction catalyzed by each of these enzymes is the following.

Saturated fatty acyl CoA + FAD ⟶ α,β-unsaturated fatty acyl CoA + FADH$_2$

The known relative specificity of the three acyl CoA dehydrogenases is shown in Fig. 22.1

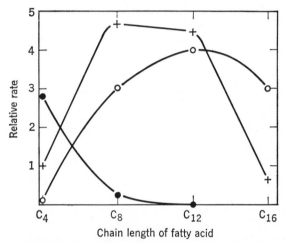

FIG. 22.1. Relative specificity of acyl dehydrogenases of swine liver. The three enzymes are designated butyryl dehydrogenase (•), octanoyl dehydrogenase (+), and hexadecanoyl dehydrogenase (○). (*Data from F. L. Crane, J. G. Hauge, and H. Beinert, Biochim. Biophys. Acta,* **17**, 292, 1955.)

Enoyl CoA Hydrase (Crotonase). Only one enzyme is presently known which catalyzes reversibly the hydration of the unsaturated fatty acyl CoA [reaction (2) above], according to the following general reaction.

α,β-Unsaturated fatty acyl CoA + H$_2$O ⇌ β-hydroxyacyl CoA

Although of broad specificity, the enzyme is most active with crotonyl CoA as substrate, hence the name *crotonase*, given in analogy with fumarase (page 322). Crystalline crotonase, a sulfhydryl enzyme, does not appear to contain a prosthetic group or to require a cofactor. The β-hydroxy acid formed is of the L configuration.

β-Hydroxyacyl CoA Dehydrogenase. The reaction catalyzed, (3) above, requires DPN.

L-β-Hydroxyacyl CoA + DPN$^+$ ⇌ β-ketoacyl CoA + DPNH + H$^+$

It is not yet clear whether substrates of different chain length require a single or different enzymes.

Thiolases. The reaction catalyzed by thiolases [reaction (4) above] involves a thiolytic cleavage by CoA with formation of acetyl CoA.

$$C_n\text{-}\beta\text{-Ketoacyl CoA} + \text{CoA} \rightleftharpoons C_{(n-2)}\text{-fatty acyl CoA} + \text{acetyl CoA}$$

Several thiolases exist which possess different chain length specificity. They appear to be thiol enzymes, and an acyl-S-enzyme may be an intermediate in a two-step reaction of the type shown below.

$$C_n\text{-}\beta\text{-Ketoacyl CoA} + \text{HS-enzyme} \rightleftharpoons C_{(n-2)}\text{-fatty acyl-S-enzyme} + \text{acetyl CoA}$$
$$C_{(n-2)}\text{-Fatty acyl-S-enzyme} + \text{CoA} \rightleftharpoons C_{(n-2)}\text{-fatty acyl CoA} + \text{HS-enzyme}$$

Although the over-all reaction is reversible, the equilibrium position is greatly in the direction of cleavage. The equilibrium constant is 6×10^4 for formation of 2 moles of acetyl CoA from acetoacetyl CoA.

In summary, the shortening of a fatty acyl CoA derivative by two carbon atoms is shown by the following equation.

$$RCH_2CH_2CH_2COSCoA + FAD + DPN^+ + CoA \longrightarrow$$
$$RCH_2COCoA + CH_3COSCoA + FADH_2 + DPNH + H^+$$

The acetyl CoA generated by fatty acid degradation mixes with acetyl CoA arising from other biochemical reactions, including the oxidative decarboxylation of pyruvate (page 317), as well as from the degradative reactions of many amino acids (Chap. 27). The numerous fates of acetyl CoA, including its entry into the tricarboxylic acid cycle, into fatty acid and sterol synthesis, etc., are described elsewhere in this text.

In addition to the CoA derivatives, the other major products of fatty acid catabolism are the reduced coenzymes DPNH and $FADH_2$. These are ultimately oxidized by the steps outlined in Chap. 18. Energy for useful work accrues to the organism in two ways as a result of fatty acid breakdown. The oxidation of $FADH_2$ and DPNH results in formation of ATP, estimated as 5 moles of energy-rich phosphate per mole of O_2 used for each acetyl CoA produced by the described degradation cycle. Oxidation of the acetyl CoA produced, via the tricarboxylic acid cycle, yields an additional 12 moles of ATP per mole of acetyl CoA oxidized (Table 18.2, page 334). Net energy yield from the oxidation of a mole of palmityl CoA is calculated in Table 22.2. Assuming ΔF of $+10,000$ cal. per mole of ATP

Table 22.2: Energy-rich Phosphate Derived from Fatty Acid Oxidation

Reaction	Moles $\sim$ P formed
Palmityl CoA + $7O_2 \longrightarrow$ 8 acetyl	35
8 Acetyl + $16O_2 \longrightarrow 16H_2O + 16CO_2$ (8 revolutions of tricarboxylic acid cycle yielding 12 $\sim$ P per revolution)	96
Total	131

under physiological circumstances, this represents a conservation of about 1,310,000 cal. of chemical energy in the form of energy-rich phosphate resulting from the complete oxidation of one mole of palmityl CoA. This energy yield is more than half of the 2,400,000 cal. released when one mole (256 g.) of palmitic acid is oxidized to CO_2 and H_2O in a bomb calorimeter.

The relationship of the cyclic reactions involving fatty acid oxidation to the tricarboxylic acid cycle is shown in Fig. 22.2.

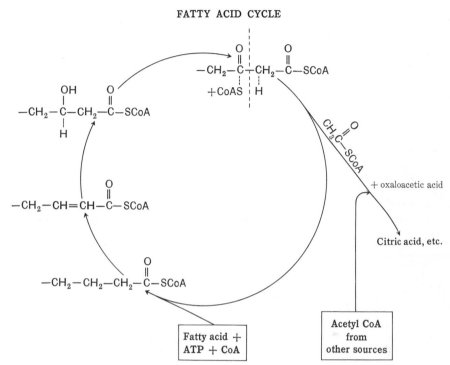

FIG. 22.2. Relationship of fatty acid degradation to the citric acid cycle.

Propionate Metabolism. As already noted, oxidation of a fatty acid with an even number of carbon atoms results in complete degradation to acetyl CoA. Oxidation of an odd-numbered carbon atom fatty acid also yields acetyl CoA and, in addition, one equivalent of propionyl CoA. Furthermore, propionic acid or propionyl CoA is produced by the oxidation of branched aliphatic amino acids (page 547). Formation of propionyl CoA from propionic acid derived from any source is catalyzed by *acetic thiokinase* (page 440). In animal tissues the major pathway of propionyl CoA metabolism is as follows.

$$\text{Propionyl CoA} + \text{ATP} + CO_2 \underset{\text{carboxylase, } Mg^{++}}{\overset{\text{propionyl CoA}}{\rightleftharpoons}} \text{ADP} + P_i + \underset{\underset{\text{COSCoA}}{|}}{\overset{\overset{\text{COOH}}{|}}{\text{CHCH}_3}} \qquad (1)$$

Methylmalonyl CoA

$$\text{Methylmalonyl CoA } (a) \underset{\text{racemase}}{\overset{\text{methylmalonyl CoA}}{\rightleftharpoons}} \text{methylmalonyl CoA } (b) \qquad (2)$$

$$\text{Methylmalonyl CoA } (b) \underset{\text{mutase}}{\overset{\text{methylmalonyl CoA}}{\rightleftharpoons}} \text{succinyl CoA} \qquad (3)$$

Each of these reactions will be considered in turn.

It will be seen that this series of reactions is, in part, the reverse of the mechanism whereby certain bacteria produce propionic acid (page 385).

Propionyl CoA carboxylase, crystallized from pig heart by Ochoa and coworkers, contains one mole of bound biotin per 175,000 gm. of protein or four moles per mole of protein of 700,000 molecular weight. Biotin, a member of the vitamin B complex (Chap. 55), has been found to be the coenzyme in a number of reactions concerned with the fixation of CO_2, notably the acetyl CoA carboxylase-catalyzed reaction (page 446). The essential role of biotin has been demonstrated by the complete inhibition of propionyl CoA carboxylase produced by *avidin,* a protein of egg white which combines strongly with biotin (Chap. 55). The inhibition is reversed by addition of biotin. Biotin is covalently bound to the apoenzyme, probably through an amide linkage to ϵ-amino groups of lysine residues, as in biocytin (Chap. 55). The carboxylase reaction involves formation of an enzyme-biotin-CO_2 complex similar to that described for the acetyl CoA carboxylase (page 446).

Conversion of methylmalonyl CoA to succinyl CoA appears to proceed in two steps: in reaction (2) by isomerization of the product of the carboxylase reaction by a specific racemase, and in reaction (3) by conversion of one of the optical isomers to succinyl CoA. The configuration of the two isomers, noted as *a* and *b* in the equations above, is unknown.

In step (3), there is an absolute requirement for vitamin B_{12} (cyanocobalamine, Chap. 55) as coenzyme. When $2\text{-}C^{14}$-methylmalonyl CoA was converted by the specific mutase, the label (marked * below) was found in the 3 position of succinyl CoA, indicating an intramolecular transfer of the entire thioester group, $-CO\text{-}S\text{-}CoA$, rather than migration of the carboxyl carbon.

$$
\begin{array}{ccc}
\text{COOH} & & \text{COOH} \\
| & & | \\
_2\text{C}^*\text{HCH}_3 & \rightleftharpoons & _3\text{C}^*\text{H}_2 \\
| & & | \\
_1\text{COSCoA} & & _2\text{CH}_2 \\
& & | \\
& & _1\text{COSCoA}
\end{array}
$$

Methylmalonyl CoA   Succinyl CoA

The mechanism by which the cobamide coenzyme effects this transfer is not yet understood. It may be noted that the B_{12}-coenzyme is also involved in the analogous isomerization of methylaspartate to glutamate (Chap. 55).

The net result of the above series of reactions is formation from propionyl CoA of succinyl CoA, an intermediate of the tricarboxylic acid cycle (page 320). The equilibrium position of step (3) above greatly favors formation of succinyl CoA.

ω-**Oxidation.** In some instances the CH_3 group most remote from the carboxyl end of the fatty acid molecule, the ω-carbon atom, undergoes oxidation to a carboxyl group. Dicarboxylic acids of the type $HOOC-(CH_2)_n-COOH$ are formed in the dog to a very limited extent after administration of fatty acids of 8 to 10 carbon atoms in length.

Extracts of hog liver catalyze ω-oxidation of monocarboxylic acids having 9 to 11 carbon atoms. The reactions appear to proceed via formation of ω-hydroxy and ω-carbonyl intermediates.

$$CH_3(CH_2)_nCOOH \xrightarrow{\text{TPNH} + O_2} HO-CH_2(CH_2)_nCOOH$$

$$\downarrow \text{DPN}^+$$

$$HOOC(CH_2)_nCOOH \xleftarrow{\text{DPN}^+} O=CH(CH_2)_nCOOH$$

BIOSYNTHESIS OF FATTY ACIDS

The chief source of fatty acids that has been considered thus far is the lipid of the diet. In addition, the mammal can synthesize, from nonlipid precursors, the major portion of the fatty acids required for growth and maintenance. Saturated fatty acids as well as the common singly unsaturated fatty acids are readily and abundantly formed from acetyl CoA. Thus any substance capable of yielding acetyl CoA is a potential source of carbon atoms in the process of fatty acid synthesis, or *lipogenesis.*

Long before the mechanism of lipogenesis was studied, it was recognized that dietary carbohydrate could serve as a source of fatty acids. This was conclusively demonstrated by Lawes and Gilbert as early as 1860 in balance studies on fattening pigs, and these findings agree with countless observations in clinical medicine and in animal husbandry that a high-carbohydrate intake can result in obesity. The corn-fed hog deposits more lipid subcutaneously than is contained in the diet. The demonstration that dietary protein can serve as a source of precursor for lipogenesis proved far more difficult, in that it was not easy to develop obese animals on diets consisting chiefly of protein.

The occurrence of lipogenesis during the process of fattening could be studied by balance experiments, in which the quantities of each class of nutrient ingested were compared with the increase in body lipid. With the isotopic technique, estimates could be made of the rate of lipogenesis. In the animal maintained in the steady state on a high-carbohydrate, lipid-free diet, a portion of the ingested carbohydrate is used to regenerate depot lipid, which is simultaneously mobilized and catabolized. It has been estimated that in the normal rat as much as 30 per cent of the dietary carbohydrate is utilized in lipogenic processes.

The rate of lipogenesis is not rapid under all circumstances. Synthesis of fatty acids is disturbed by a variety of conditions. If, for example, the total calories of the diet are restricted and become insufficient to maintain body weight, the rate of lipogenesis may fall to 5 per cent of its normal value. Similar decreases in rate of lipogenesis have been observed in the thiamine-deficient animal, compatible with the role of thiamine pyrophosphate in the transformation of pyruvate into acetyl CoA (page 317).

When the pathway of fatty acid degradation was first elucidated, it was assumed that all the major steps were reversible and that fatty acid synthesis could proceed catalytically with the same enzymes. It soon became apparent, however, that there were several major difficulties with this notion. First was the finding that for isolated mitochondria or mitochondrial extracts to effect fatty acid synthesis, TPNH is required, a coenzyme unnecessary for the reactions of fatty acid oxidation. Second, fatty acid synthesis proceeds far more efficiently in nonmitochondrial (high-speed supernatant) fractions than in mitochondria. Actually, evidence has accumulated that there are at least two different systems for synthesis of fatty acids, both of which involve acetyl CoA. These are (1) a nonmitochondrial system that converts acetyl CoA to long-chain fatty acids when supplemented with ATP, CO_2, Mn^{++}, and TPNH; and (2) a mitochondrial system that utilizes DPNH, TPNH, and ATP; this system appears to be mainly involved in elongation of fatty acids by addition of acetyl CoA to fatty acyl CoA compounds. The nonmitochondrial system will be considered first.

THE NONMITOCHONDRIAL SYSTEM

Gurin and coworkers first noted the synthesis of long-chain fatty acids from acetate by soluble extracts of pigeon liver; this was later observed by Popják and Tietz with extracts of mammary gland. Major advances were made by Wakil and coworkers, who established the requirements of the system for acetyl CoA, TPNH, ATP, and Mn^{++}. In addition, CO_2 is essential for the process, yet when $C^{14}O_2$ is employed, the isotope is not incorporated in the newly synthesized product, mainly palmitic acid. The reactions will now be described.

Malonyl CoA Formation. The first intermediate in the synthesis of long-chain fatty acids has been shown by Wakil and others to be malonyl CoA, formed in the following reaction catalyzed by *acetyl CoA carboxylase.*

$$CH_3COSCoA + CO_2 + ATP \xrightarrow{Mn^{++}} ADP + P_i + \begin{matrix} COOH \\ | \\ CH_2 \\ | \\ O{=}C{-}SCoA \end{matrix}$$

Malonyl CoA

The enzyme, purified from chicken liver, contains covalently bound biotin (Chap. 55), which is essential for the reaction, as demonstrated by the inhibition produced by avidin (Chap. 55), and is specific for Mn^{++}. ATP can be replaced by UTP, but higher concentrations of the latter are required. Propionyl CoA can be carboxylated to methylmalonyl CoA (page 443) but at about one-fourth the rate of the acetyl CoA carboxylation. The activity of the carboxylase is strongly stimulated by various di- and tricarboxylic acids, notably citric and isocitric acids, as well as by α-ketoglutaric acid. This stimulatory effect appears to indicate that these acids maintain the enzyme in an active conformation, an effect analogous, for example, to that of glucose 6-phosphate on glycogen synthetase (page 413).

Malonyl CoA can be formed by reactions other than carboxylation of acetyl CoA, *viz.,* (1) by activation of malonate by a specific thiokinase in the presence of ATP and CoA, (2) by CoA transferase reactions between succinyl CoA or aceto-acetyl CoA and malonate, and (3) by microbial oxidation of malonyl semialdehyde CoA to malonyl CoA. These reactions are of little significance in mammalian metabolism.

Mechanism of CO_2 Fixation. The mechanism of action of this type of CO_2-fixation enzyme can be represented as occurring in two steps:

(a) $HCO_3^- + ATP + \text{biotin-enzyme} \rightleftharpoons CO_2\text{-biotin-enzyme} + ADP + P_i$
(b) $CO_2\text{-biotin-enzyme} + \text{acetyl CoA} \rightleftharpoons \text{biotin-enzyme} + \text{malonyl CoA}$

Lynen and coworkers have provided evidence that the CO_2-biotin-enzyme complex is an N-carboxybiotin as shown.

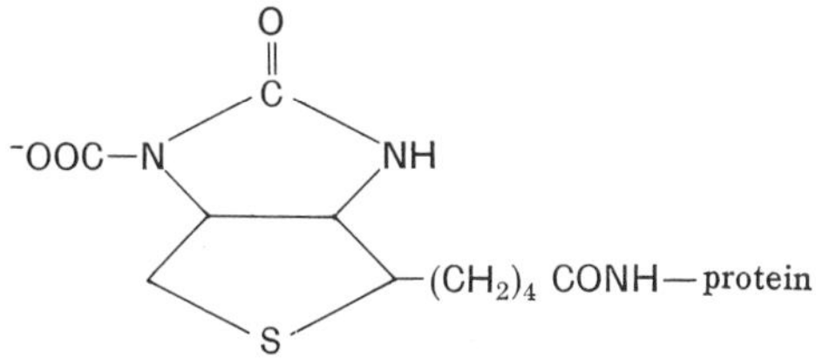

N-Carboxybiotin complex

This conclusion was reached by using free biotin as a CO_2 acceptor, followed by the isolation of a free CO_2-biotin complex with the structure shown. Furthermore, the same CO_2-biotin complex has been demonstrated with other CO_2-fixation reactions in which biotin participates, *e.g.*, propionyl CoA carboxylase (page 444) and β-methylcrotonyl CoA carboxylase (page 548).

Conversion of Malonyl CoA to Palmitic Acid. Malonyl CoA is readily converted to fatty acids in the presence of acetyl CoA and TPNH. The stoichiometry of the over-all process is as follows.

1 Acetyl CoA + 7 malonyl CoA + 14TPNH + 14H$^+$ $\longrightarrow$

1 palmitic acid + 7CO$_2$ + 8CoA + 14TPN$^+$ + 6H$_2$O

It is noteworthy that all the CO_2 fixed in the carboxylation of acetyl CoA to form malonyl CoA reappears as free CO_2 during the condensation process. Acetyl CoA provides carbon atoms 15 and 16 of the palmitic acid, whereas malonyl CoA provides the C_2 units for the remaining carbons.

The mechanism of the above reactions for palmitic acid synthesis is not clear. However, there is evidence that essential thiol groups are involved and that acetyl CoA and malonyl CoA react with these, forming acetyl-S-enzyme and malonyl-S-enzyme, and that decarboxylation accompanies condensation.

(*a*)   Acetyl CoA + HS-enzyme $\rightleftharpoons$ acetyl-S-enzyme + CoA
(*b*)   Acetyl-S-enzyme + malonyl CoA $\longrightarrow$ keto acyl enzyme + CO$_2$

Lynen and coworkers, studying the enzyme complex of yeast, have provided evidence that the ketoacyl enzyme is reduced by TPNH to the D-β-hydroxybutyryl-enzyme, followed by dehydration to crotonyl-enzyme and another reduction involving TPNH and flavin mononucleotide to form the saturated butyryl-enzyme. All the reactions occur as acyl residues bound to a sulfhydryl group. The butyryl-enzyme can now accept another malonyl residue, lengthening the chain by a repetition of the cycle. The process terminates at the level of palmityl CoA or stearyl CoA with the purified yeast enzymic preparation, whereas in animal tissues mainly free palmitic acid is obtained, as a result of the hydrolytic action of a deacylase.

Points of difference between the mitochondrial fatty acid degradation system and the nonmitochondrial synthetic system are noted in Table 22.3.

Table 22.3: COMPARISON OF COMPOUNDS INVOLVED IN FATTY ACID METABOLISM

Step or component	Degradation	Synthesis*
SH-component..............	CoA	Cysteine residues of enzymes
CoA derivative..............	Acetyl CoA	Malonyl CoA + acetyl CoA
Keto-hydroxy..............	DPN, L-β-hydroxybutyryl CoA	TPN, D-β-hydroxybutyryl-enzyme
Hydroxy-crotonyl	L-β-hydroxybutyryl CoA	D-β-Hydroxybutyryl-enzyme
Crotonyl-butyryl	FAD	FMN, TPNH

*Identification of the β-hydroxybutyryl derivative and of FMN pertains, thus far, only to the yeast system.

SOURCE: Adapted from F. Lynen, *Federation Proc.,* **20**, 941, 1961.

THE MITOCHONDRIAL SYSTEM

In contrast to the malonyl CoA–utilizing system, the mitochondrial system is not sensitive to avidin, indicating that CO_2 fixation is not involved. Mitochondrial extracts contain activating enzymes for synthesis of fatty acyl CoA derivatives and can utilize such preformed derivatives. The mitochondrial process involves successive addition of acetyl CoA units, thus producing longer-chain fatty acids. This is essentially, then, an *elongation* system for fatty acids rather than a method of *de novo* synthesis, the products of which are C_{18}, C_{20}, C_{22}, and C_{24} fatty acids.

The exact steps and the responsible enzymes involved in elongation of fatty acids are unknown. However, the requirements for an acyl CoA, DPNH, and TPNH have suggested that three of the enzymes involved in the fatty acid β-oxidation cycle (page 440) also participate in this process, *viz., thiolase, β-hydroxylacyl CoA dehydrogenase,* and *enoyl CoA hydrase.* Since the action of the fatty acyl dehydrogenase is irreversible (page 441), final reduction is probably accomplished by a TPNH-dependent enoyl CoA reductase. This postulated sequence of chain elongation by four steps is as follows.

$$CH_3COSCoA + RCH_2COSCoA \underset{\longleftarrow}{\overset{\text{thiolase}}{\rightleftharpoons}} RCH_2COCH_2COSCoA + CoA \qquad (1)$$

$$RCH_2COCH_2COSCoA + DPNH + H^+ \underset{\text{dehydrogenase}}{\overset{\beta\text{-hydroxyacyl}}{\rightleftharpoons}}$$
$$RCH_2CHOHCH_2COSCoA + DPN^+ \quad (2)$$

$$RCH_2CHOHCH_2COSCoA \underset{\text{hydrase}}{\overset{\text{enoyl}}{\rightleftharpoons}} RCH_2CH{=}CHCOSCoA + H_2O \qquad (3)$$

$$RCH_2CH{=}CHCOSCoA + TPNH + H^+ \underset{\text{reductase}}{\overset{\text{enoyl}}{\rightleftharpoons}}$$
$$RCH_2CH_2CHCOSCoA + TPN^+ \quad (4)$$

This system is active not only on intermediate chain length saturated fatty acids, C_{12}, C_{14}, C_{16}, but also on unsaturated compounds, lengthening these by two carbon atoms at each step. The metabolism of the unsaturated compounds is considered below (pages 449*ff.*).

Sources of Reduced Nucleotides. For the processes of lipogenesis to operate, it is apparent that sources of TPNH are required for the malonyl CoA route and of TPNH and DPNH for the chain elongation pathway. DPNH is produced by many dehydrogenations, but the major nonmitochondrial source of TPNH involves the dehydrogenations of the phosphogluconic acid oxidative pathway (page 387), although TPNH may also be formed by the transhydrogenase-catalyzed reaction (page 328). This suggests that fatty acid synthesis is linked to the oxidative pathway of glucose metabolism, particularly since mitochondria may not readily oxidize external TPNH. Thus, lipogenesis and glucose 6-phosphate oxidation may be associated through the requirement of the former process for TPNH, which is in turn supplied in part by the latter. Since oxidation of acetyl CoA via the citric acid cycle depends on a source of oxaloacetate and this may arise by carboxylation of pyruvate, derived from glycolysis, it is evident that fatty acid oxidation also depends on carbohydrate metabolism. Therefore, fatty acid metabolism is closely linked to carbohydrate metabolism, lipogenesis being coupled with glucose 6-phosphate oxidation, and fatty acid oxidation being influenced by glycolysis.

FATTY ACID TRANSFORMATIONS

The organism obtains fatty acids from the lipid of the diet and by lipogenesis from the acetyl CoA derived from carbohydrates and certain amino acids. The composition of the mixture of fatty acids from the diet will vary considerably in the degree of unsaturation and chain length. The process of lipogenesis favors formation of saturated over unsaturated fatty acids. This is indicated both from the "hardening" effect (page 438) of a high-carbohydrate diet upon depot lipid and the observation, based upon isotopic data, of the more rapid synthesis of saturated than of singly unsaturated fatty acids.

From the mixture of fatty acids available to it, the mammalian liver produces a composite of fatty acids that is characteristic of the species. The operations involve shortening and elongation of the carbon skeleton as well as the introduction of double bonds and their elimination by reduction.

Shortening and Elongation of the Carbon Skeleton. If isotopic palmitic acid (C_{16}) is fed to rats, isotope is recovered in highest concentration in the palmitic acid of the body lipid. However, appreciable concentrations of isotope are also found in the stearic (C_{18}) and myristic (C_{14}) acids of the body. Similarly, the feeding of labeled stearic acid leads to labeling of the palmitic acid of the body lipid. These findings clearly indicate that lengthening or shortening of the carbon skeleton of saturated fatty acids occurs in the animal body and that it takes place by the gain or loss of two carbon atoms at a time. These processes find ready explanation in the series of reactions of degradation and elongation previously described.

Formation of Monoenoic Acids. When isotopic palmitic or stearic acid, both saturated, is fed, isotope can be recovered both in the saturated and in the unsaturated fatty acids of body lipid. The feeding of the C_{18}-saturated fatty acid leads to accumulation of isotope in oleic acid (C_{18}, one double bond), and feeding of the C_{16}-saturated acid yields palmitoleic acid (C_{16}, one double bond). Thus, the mammal is capable of dehydrogenating these saturated fatty acids to give the corresponding 9,10-unsaturated derivatives. It should be noted that the dehydrogenation involved in forming oleic or palmitoleic acid bears no relation to the α,β dehydrogenation that occurs in the shortening of saturated fatty acids.

Bloch and coworkers have shown that many *aerobic* microorganisms, including yeast, can form oleic and palmitoleic acids by desaturation of the corresponding saturated acids. In extracts of these organisms, the fatty acyl CoA derivatives, rather than free fatty acids, serve as substrates and TPNH and O_2 are essential for the conversion, suggesting that the initial reaction is a hydroxylation of the mixed oxygenase type (page 356). Recent evidence indicates that the same mechanism obtains in animal tissues. The process must occur readily and continuously in animals since, it will be recalled, oleic is generally the most abundant fatty acid of depot fat (Table 5.4, page 71).

In higher plants, however, Stumpf and other investigators have presented evidence indicating that conversion of long-chain saturated to unsaturated fatty acids does not occur and that oleic acid is formed by a different pathway.

Although desaturation of fatty acids to form the 9,10-unsaturated acids occurs in animal tissues, feeding experiments with labeled oleic or palmitoleic acids showed that only small amounts of the saturated acids were formed therefrom. Since this could have taken place, at least in part, by breakdown to C_2 units and resynthesis, it is apparent that hydrogenation of monounsaturated acids is not a major process in animal tissues.

Formation and Transformation of Polyenoic Acids. Animal tissues contain a great variety of polyunsaturated fatty acids. Of these, one series can be fabricated by the animal, *de novo*. These are the fatty acids of which all the double bonds lie between the seventh carbon from the terminal methyl group and the carboxyl group. As seen from Fig. 22.3, such fatty acids may be made by alternate desaturation and chain elongation, commencing with oleic acid. However, other polyunsaturated acids cannot be made by *de novo* synthesis; these are the fatty acids in which one or more double bonds are situated within the terminal seven carbon atoms. This is evident from the fact that such polyunsaturated acids are essential in the diet and the observation that no label is found in tissue linoleic or linolenic acid (C_{18}, two and three double bonds, respectively) after administration of labeled stearic acid.

There are apparently four families of polyunsaturated acids in the mammal; two are derived from the dietary compounds, linoleic and linolenic acids, and two are synthesized from the monounsaturated acids, oleic and palmitoleic acids, these in turn being formed from the corresponding saturated acids (page 449). The four families can be recognized by the distance between the terminal methyl group and the nearest double bond.

Linoleic family:	$CH_3-(CH_2)_4-CH=CH-$
Linolenic family:	$CH_3-CH_2-CH=CH-$
Palmitoleic family:	$CH_3-(CH_2)_5-CH=CH-$
Oleic family:	$CH_3-(CH_2)_7-CH=CH-$

All other multiply unsaturated acids can be made from these four precursors by reaction series in which the chain is alternately elongated and desaturated. Elongation occurs by operation of the mitochondrial chain elongation system con-

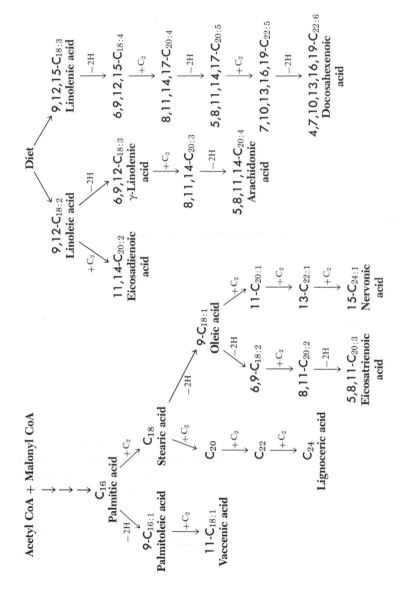

FIG. 22.3. Biosynthesis of some fatty acids in mammals. The numbers in boldface indicate the position of the double bonds; the subscripts indicate the number of carbon atoms, with the number of double bonds to the right of the colon.

sidered previously, while desaturation is presumed to be accomplished in a manner analogous to the *de novo* formation of oleic and palmitoleic acids; the specificity of the system is such that conjugated double bonds, *i.e.*, alternating double and single bonds, are never formed. Nutritional evidence, considered in Chap. 55, suggests that pyridoxal phosphate may be essential for formation of longer chain, polyunsaturated acids, but its role in this process is obscure. The formation of arachidonic acid is presented in more detail (Fig. 22.4), while Fig. 22.3 summarizes the operation of the various pathways which account for the diverse polyunsaturated fatty acids of animal tissues. It should be noted that the convention with regard to numbering the carbon atoms of a fatty acid chain is unfortunate since it renders difficult the visualization of these various transformations, obscuring the fact that the double bonds, indicated as 9,12, of linoleic acid are those in the 11,14 positions of arachidonic acid (5,8,11,14). This difficulty could be obviated if the convention designated the terminal methyl carbon as C-1.

$$CH_3—(CH_2)_4—CH{=}CH—CH_2—CH{=}CH—(CH_2)_7—COOH$$

Linoleic acid

$$\downarrow {-2H}$$

$$CH_3—(CH_2)_4—CH{=}CH—CH_2—CH{=}CH—CH_2—CH{=}CH—(CH_2)_4—COOH$$

γ-Linolenic acid

$$\downarrow {+C_2}$$

$$CH_3—(CH_2)_4—(CH{=}CH—CH_2)_3—(CH_2)_5—COOH$$

Homo-γ-linolenic acid

$$\downarrow {-2H}$$

$$CH_3—(CH_2)_4—(CH{=}CH—CH_2)_4—(CH_2)_2—COOH$$

Arachidonic acid

FIG. 22.4. Formation of arachidonic acid from linoleic acid.

Although oxidation of polyunsaturated fatty acids to CO_2 does occur, this is not an important source of energy in the animal economy; the major role of these compounds relates to their unique localization in specialized structures such as cell membranes.

BIOSYNTHESIS OF NEUTRAL TRIGLYCERIDES

In the normal animal, free fatty acids are not found in significant quantity in the tissues or body fluids. Palmitic acid, the product of cytoplasmic lipogenesis, can be converted to palmityl CoA by the activation reaction. It is as the CoA derivatives that the various fatty acids are incorporated in phosphatidic acid, a precursor of both the neutral triglycerides and the various phosphatides (Chap. 23).

The primary reaction was discovered by Kornberg and Pricer.

$$
\begin{array}{cccc}
& H_2COH & & H_2COOCR \\
& | & & | \\
2RCOCoA \; + & HCOH & \longrightarrow & RCOOCH \quad + \quad 2CoA \\
& | & & | \\
& H_2COPO_3H_2 & & H_2COPO_3H_2
\end{array}
$$

Acyl CoA α-Glycerophosphoric acid   L-α-Phosphatidic acid

This reaction shows an absolute specificity for α-glycerophosphate and proceeds preferentially with the 16- and 18-carbon acid derivatives, palmityl CoA and stearyl CoA.

Hydrolysis of α-phosphatidic acid by a *phosphatase* yields a 1,2-diglyceride, which in turn reacts with another mole of acyl CoA to form a neutral triglyceride.

$$
\text{L-}\alpha\text{-Phosphatidic acid} \xrightarrow[+H_2O]{\text{phosphatase}} \text{D-1,2-diglyceride} + P_i
$$

$$\downarrow + \text{acyl CoA}$$

triglyceride

It should be noted that no change in configuration is involved in conversion of L-phosphatidic acid to the D-1,2-diglyceride. As indicated previously (page 73), phosphatidic acid is designated as L because of its relationship to L-glyceryl phosphate, whereas the 1,2-diglyceride is designated as D because of its stereochemical relationship to D-glyceraldehyde.

Although it is generally agreed that the liver is the major organ concerned with lipogenesis, other tissues contribute to the process, including adipose tissue itself (page 439).

Intestinal mucosa synthesizes triglycerides from free fatty acids and mono- and diglycerides (page 432). The path of synthesis of triglycerides from free fatty acids, and of 1,2-diglycerides, is undoubtedly the same as that given above. However, the evidence that monoglycerides can be incorporated into the triglycerides that appear in the chyle led to the discovery of a reaction that appears to be unique to intestinal mucosa. A microsomal system from rat and rabbit intestine catalyzes the following reaction.

Monoglyceride + fatty acyl CoA $\longrightarrow$ **diglyceride + CoA**

Liver microsomes fail to catalyze this reaction under the same conditions.

Mechanism of Lipogenesis from Carbohydrate. Inasmuch as carbohydrate is a major source of acetyl CoA for lipogenesis, it is of interest to examine the over-all picture of fatty acid synthesis from glucose. The process of glycolysis and pyruvate decarboxylation, already described (Chap. 20), results in formation of 2 moles of CO_2 and 2 moles of acetyl CoA from each mole of glucose. Thus four of every six atoms of glucose are available for fatty acid synthesis. Fatty acids arising from the malonyl CoA pathway yield primarily palmitic acid. The process may be represented as follows.

$$4C_6H_{12}O_6 + O_2 \longrightarrow C_{16}H_{32}O_2 + 8CO_2 + 8H_2O$$

Glucose　　　　　　　Palmitic acid

The theoretical energetic efficiency of this process is high. Although the metabolic efficiency cannot be stated precisely, it may be noted that 4 moles of glucose approximate 2,744,000 cal., whereas 1 mole of palmitate approximates 2,400,000 cal. when these are completely oxidized.

It is evident that lipogenesis from carbohydrate not only is an efficient process but occurs abundantly (page 438). In contrast to this, the mammal is apparently unable to effect a net conversion of fatty acids into carbohydrate. This is because formation of acetyl CoA and CO_2 from pyruvate is irreversible, thus preventing direct entrance of acetyl CoA into carbohydrate precursors. Since fatty acids are degraded to acetyl CoA, the only possible route whereby the carbon atoms of fatty acids can later be located in carbohydrate is by condensation of acetyl CoA with oxaloacetate to enter the citric acid cycle. One turn of this cycle yields oxaloacetate, which contains carbon atoms initially present in the fatty acid. However, one mole of oxaloacetate is required for condensation with acetyl CoA, and only 1 mole of oxaloacetate is formed; hence there is no *net* gain of oxaloacetate. Since oxalo-acetate is the potentially glucogenic product, by decarboxylation to pyruvate and reversal of glycolysis, it follows that there can be no net increase in available glucose as a result of fatty acid oxidation. In accord with this picture is the failure of numerous attempts to demonstrate gluconeogenesis at the expense of fatty acids by balance techniques in diabetic or phlorhizinized animals. It should be emphasized, however, that plants can achieve a net synthesis of carbohydrate from stored fatty acids (page 384), a process that occurs in germinating seeds.

Energy Storage. There may appear to be no striking gains derived from the storage of lipid rather than of polysaccharide as the preponderant long-term caloric reservoir. It is not known what determines, in a particular species, which habit of storage will dominate. Whether it is lipid or polysaccharide that is mobilized, the yield in energy-rich phosphate per calorie of compound oxidized is about the same. One point of difference, however, relates to the weights of isocaloric stores of lipid and of polysaccharide. Even in the dry state, 1 cal. of lipid weighs less than half as much as 1 cal. of carbohydrate, and, as stored, this discrepancy is actually greater since the polysaccharide, but not the lipid, is heavily hydrated. From the point of view of survival of the species or of the individual, some advantage may accrue from the deposition of lipid rather than of carbohydrate provided the organism depends upon motility for capture of food or evasion of enemies. It is noteworthy that preponderant lipid storage is characteristic of most animals, which are motile, whereas in plants, which are sessile, polysaccharides are the chief stores of nutrient. Certain molluscs, notably scallops and clams, are among the poorest of all animals in lipid and among the richest in glycogen, but these molluscs are not notably dependent on motility for survival. The seeds of plants may be quite rich in lipid, and it is peculiarly in the seeds that motility may be of importance, to permit adequate dissemination. It has been suggested that lipid rather than polysaccharide storage, with consequent reduction in body mass, may be a form of adaptation to motility as an important mechanism for survival.

MOBILIZATION OF DEPOT LIPID AND TRANSPORT OF FATTY ACIDS

The major site of synthesis and of degradation of fatty acids is the liver, which is remote from the adipose tissue, the major site of storage. The transport of lipid from the depots to the liver, and vice versa, is a subject of great interest and importance, and has been studied by various methods.

Mobilization of Depot Lipid. Even in the animal in caloric balance, a considerable fraction of the depot lipid is mobilized daily (page 438), enters the blood stream, and is delivered to the various organs. Rapid mobilization to the liver is particularly striking; here the lipid may be stored temporarily or degraded by the reactions discussed previously (page 439). Lipid leaving adipose cells is largely transported as unesterified fatty acids bound to plasma albumin (page 436). The release of fatty acids is accompanied by the appearance in plasma of glycerol as well, although in amounts significantly less than the equivalent of fatty acids.

Little can be said about the mechanism of fatty acid release from adipose cells except that it is catalyzed by a lipase and the fatty acids derive from stored triglyceride. As previously noted (page 436), although the quantity of fatty acids in plasma is normally very small, the turnover of this material is extremely rapid.

The precise mechanism of mobilization of depot lipid is unknown, but numerous experimental data have clarified the factors which regulate or modify its rate. These factors are largely of two types: (1) substances which are toxic for hepatic cells and (2) hormonal influences.

Hepatic Poisons and Lipid Mobilization. The mechanism by which a substance inducing hepatic injury can elicit mobilization of depot lipid is not clear, although the phenomenon has long been known in relation to studies of experimental production of fatty liver. By labeling the depot lipid in dogs with highly unsaturated oils, Lebedev in 1882 demonstrated that lipid depots were the source of the bulk of the lipid which accumulated in the liver after poisoning with white phosphorus. He suggested that the sequence of events was, first, an accelerated mobilization of depot lipid, then a lipemia, and finally an accumulation of lipid in the liver. These observations have been amply confirmed. Numerous poisons produce fatty liver; among the worst offenders are the chlorinated aliphatic and aromatic hydrocarbons. Carbon tetrachloride, because of its volatility and wide industrial application, is the one most often encountered in clinical medicine.

Fatty liver, however, is frequently seen clinically following conditions other than overt poisoning. Thus in chronic infectious diseases, such as tuberculosis, and in metabolic disturbances, including starvation, the lipid content of the liver may increase markedly. The most striking cases of fatty infiltration were observed in severe, untreated diabetes in the preinsulin era. As will be indicated subsequently, the liver of the diabetic person is less than normally competent to synthesize fatty acids but is believed to be normally able to degrade fatty acids. The fatty liver in this disease is therefore, by exclusion, attributed to excessive migration of depot lipid to the liver, and the lipemia observed in diabetes is taken to represent in part lipid in transit from the depots. Indeed, the augmenting effect of a number of hormones on lipid mobilization from depots (see below) suggests that most clinical cases of fatty liver arise from excessively rapid mobilization of depot lipid. On the other hand, liver lipid accumulation in circumstances of liver poisoning may reflect, in addition to accelerated depot lipid mobilization, a diminished capacity of injured hepatic cells to degrade fatty acids.

Hormonal Influences on Lipid Mobilization. Both in vivo and in vitro studies have revealed that certain hormones induce lipid mobilization from the depots. In general, the sequence of events initiated by these hormones in vitro is (1) conversion of triglycerides to free fatty acids within the adipose tissue; (2) release of these fatty acids into the blood, a process which is favorably influenced by the presence of serum albumin; and (3) oxidation and, in the presence of adequate glucose, reesterification to triglyceride of a portion of the liberated fatty acids. In vivo, there occur, in addition, (4) transport of fatty acids by the circulation to diverse organs and tissues, with uptake and reesterification into triglyceride and cholesterol esters, chiefly in the liver and kidney, of the major portion of the mobilized free fatty acids; and (5) discharge of triglyceride and cholesterol esters from the liver, as lipoproteins, with resultant lipemia. The list of hormones known to be active in lipid mobilization from adipose tissue, as judged by either in vitro or in vivo criteria, and occasionally by both, includes the following: epinephrine and norepinephrine (Chap. 49); adrenocorticotropin (Chap. 51); somatotropin (Chap. 51); luteotropin (Chap. 51); glucagon (Chap. 50); thyrotropin (Chap. 51); and the lipid-mobilizing principle of the adenohypophysis (Chap. 51). In addition, serotonin (page 536), not generally classed as a hormone, also effects fatty acid release from adipose tissue in vitro.

The evidence available indicates that these hormones effect fatty acid release from adipose tissue by stimulating a lipolytic process with, perhaps, a simultaneous inhibition of the reesterification mechanism. The hormones that augment lipolysis in adipose tissue will, in general, inhibit in vitro the effects of insulin on this tissue, described on page 439. Description of the degree of similarity of the in vitro and in vivo effects of these hormones would require too lengthy a discussion here. However, there are several noteworthy aspects of hormonal influence on lipid mobilization from adipose tissue. The in vitro effects of epinephrine are mimicked in vivo in the striking increase in plasma unesterified fatty acids resulting from augmented blood levels of this hormone. Indeed, exaggerated epinephrine secretion in man, as seen in adrenal medullary tumors (pheochromocytoma, Chap. 49), may be accompanied by a several hundredfold increase in plasma unesterified fatty acid levels. Also of interest is the fact that the effects of adrenocorticotropin on adipose tissue are exerted directly on the tissue, independent of the normal trophic influence of this hormone on the adrenal cortex (Chap. 51). This direct action on adipose tissue is seen also with the other hormonal substances listed above. Finally, the wide diversity of humoral agents stimulating lipid release from adipose tissue affords a basis for explanation of the hyperlipemia and liver lipid deposition seen in a variety of experimental and clinical circumstances (page 455).

Mobilization of Liver Lipid. With the discovery of insulin, it became possible to maintain totally pancreatectomized dogs in reasonably good health. However, even when adequate insulin was supplied to control the diabetes the animals developed severe fatty livers. Furthermore, these fatty livers could be corrected or prevented by addition to the diet of lecithin or choline. It was noted subsequently that fatty livers could be produced in rats by administration of a diet poor in choline and low in protein and that this fatty liver could be cured or prevented by administration of choline.

It appears that the fatty liver observed in these experimental animals arises by a different mechanism from that previously considered. Choline is a constituent of lecithin, and the capacity of the liver to generate lecithin is dependent on a supply of choline or a supply of methyl groups from S-adenosylmethionine (page 504). It is noteworthy that certain analogues of choline, such as arsenocholine,

$$(CH_3)_3\overset{+}{N}CH_2CH_2OH \qquad (CH_3)_3\overset{+}{As}CH_2CH_2OH$$

$$\text{Choline} \qquad\qquad\qquad \text{Arsenocholine}$$

although foreign to nature, are incorporated into lecithin and prevent the fatty liver of choline deficiency. The term *lipotropic* substance has been assigned to compounds capable of preventing or correcting the fatty liver of choline deficiency.

These findings have suggested that, although fatty acids may be delivered to the liver in a variety of forms, *e.g.,* unesterified or esterified to glycerol or to cholesterol, and may in addition, be synthesized in the liver from carbohydrate or amino acid precursors, they leave the liver not only in these forms, as lipoproteins (page 434), but also in the form of choline-containing phosphatides of lipoproteins. Indeed, the liver is the major site of synthesis of the plasma phosphatides. According to this view, when the availability of choline or methyl groups for its synthesis is restricted, the rate of lecithin synthesis decreases and consequently the rate at which fatty acids are discharged from the liver falls below normal. If other processes continue at normal rate, an accumulation of lipid in the liver results.

One finding in discord with this picture is the observation that in the hepatectomized dog, the phosphatides of the plasma are not utilized, indicating that the liver, in addition to being the main source of plasma lecithin, is also the main site of its destruction. If this is so, it is difficult to understand how, by forming lecithin, the liver effectively gets rid of fatty acids. It has been suggested that choline in the diet in some way enhances degradation of fatty acids, but not all the experimental evidence conforms to this contention. An alternative view is that release of triglyceride and cholesterol esters to the circulation as lipoproteins requires the synthesis of sufficient lecithin to form the stable, soluble lipoprotein complex. Clarification of this question must await further experiments.

Any material capable of contributing methyl groups for choline synthesis has the property of being lipotropic. Conversely, materials that deflect methyl groups from choline synthesis will, under appropriate conditions, enhance dietary fatty liver. Guanidoacetic acid (page 530) and nicotinamide (page 531) are examples of antilipotropic substances that are irreversibly methylated in the body.

Other Lipotropic Effects. Besides choline and methyl donors which permit choline synthesis, certain other materials have been shown or claimed to reduce the quantity of liver lipid in experimental animals. Exclusion of inositol from the diet may lead to a slight increase in liver lipids even in the presence of adequate choline; under these circumstances inositol becomes lipotropic. The mode of action of inositol in this regard is not known, but some phosphatides contain inositol. The formation of such phosphatides may depend on a supply of exogenous inositol much as the synthesis of lecithin depends on a dietary supply of methyl groups or choline.

THE KETONE BODIES AND KETOSIS

In the normal animal fatty acid degradation and synthesis proceed without significant accumulation of intermediates. Under some circumstances certain products accumulate in the blood which are traditionally but inaccurately termed *ketone bodies*. These are acetoacetic acid, β-hydroxybutyric acid, and acetone. All these products stem from acetoacetyl CoA, a normal intermediate in the oxidation of fatty acids (page 442). Moreover, it is readily formed by the reversal of the *thiolase* reaction.

$$\text{2 Acetyl CoA} \rightleftharpoons \text{acetoacetyl CoA} + \text{CoA}$$

The major fate of acetoacetyl CoA in liver is conversion to β-hydroxy-β-methylglutaryl CoA, an important intermediate in the biogenesis of cholesterol and steroids (page 471) and in the degradation of leucine (page 548).

$$\underset{\text{Acetoacetyl CoA}}{CH_3COCH_2COCoA} + \underset{\text{Acetyl CoA}}{CH_3COCoA} + H_2O \longrightarrow \underset{\substack{\beta\text{-Hydroxy-}\beta\text{-methyl-}\\ \text{glutaryl CoA}}}{HOOCCH_2\overset{\overset{\displaystyle OH}{|}}{\underset{\underset{\displaystyle CH_3}{|}}{C}}-CH_2COCoA} + CoA$$

Cleavage of β-hydroxy-β-methylglutaryl CoA by an enzyme different from that catalyzing the above synthesis appears to be the major route of formation of free acetoacetate in liver.

$$\beta\text{-Hydroxy-}\beta\text{-methylglutaryl CoA} \longrightarrow \text{acetoacetic acid} + \text{acetyl CoA}$$

A thiophorase reaction may also be effective to a limited degree; however, it is probably mainly concerned in resynthesis of acetoacetyl CoA in peripheral tissues.

$$\text{Acetoacetyl CoA} + \text{succinic acid} \underset{\substack{\text{acetoacetyl-succinic}\\ \text{thiophorase}}}{\rightleftharpoons} \text{succinyl CoA} + \text{acetoacetic acid}$$

An acetoacetyl CoA deacylase may also contribute to formation of the free acid.

The reduction of acetoacetate is effected by DPNH in the presence of a specific β-*hydroxybutyric acid dehydrogenase* and yields D-β-hydroxybutyric acid. In contrast, reduction of acetoacetyl CoA catalyzed by β-hydroxyacyl dehydrogenase (page 441) yields L-β-hydroxybutyryl CoA.

$$\underset{\text{Acetoacetic acid}}{CH_3COCH_2COOH} + DPNH + H^+ \underset{\text{dehydrogenase}}{\rightleftharpoons} \underset{\text{D-}\beta\text{-Hydroxybutyric acid}}{CH_3CHOHCH_2COOH} + DPN^+$$

Although this reaction is reversible, wide variations in the amount and in the ratio of the two acids in the circulation are encountered: in situations where there is an abundance of liver glycogen, the formation of β-hydroxybutyrate is favored; when liver glycogen is relatively low, acetoacetate predominates.

A second product, arising from acetoacetic acid by decarboxylation and found in the circulation, is acetone. This decarboxylation occurs spontaneously in vitro when acetoacetic acid is dissolved in water, and is catalyzed by diverse nonenzymic, basic catalysts, *e.g.*, aniline citrate. In the body it is not known to be enzyme-catalyzed and is of minor significance as a pathway of acetoacetate metabolism. Two metabolic fates of acetone are recognized. It may undergo further cleavage to yield a 2-carbon acetyl and a 1-carbon formyl fragment.

$$CH_3COCH_3 \longrightarrow CH_3{-}\overset{|}{C}{=}O + H\overset{|}{C}{=}O$$

| Acetone | | Acetyl | Formyl |

On the other hand, acetone can undergo transformation to propanediol, which is then oxidized to pyruvic acid,

$$CH_3COCH_3 \longrightarrow CH_3CHOHCH_2OH \longrightarrow CH_3COCOOH$$

| Acetone | Propane-1,2-diol | Pyruvic acid |

and thus contributes to all products that may arise from pyruvic acid (pages 378*ff.*).

Although the parent compound of the ketone bodies, acetoacetyl CoA, is a normal intermediate in both fatty acid degradation and cholesterol synthesis, certain facets of its metabolism merit special mention, particularly because of its importance in ketosis.

In Fig. 22.5, some of the primary interrelationships of lipid metabolism are shown. The key factors would appear to be the central role of acetyl CoA and β-hydroxy-β-methylglutaryl CoA. In the case of acetyl CoA, the three major fates are oxidation via the citric acid cycle, formation of acetoacetyl CoA, and synthesis of fatty acids, primarily via the malonyl CoA pathway.

The central role of β-hydroxy-β-methylglutaryl CoA is evident. It is unknown what factors regulate the relative degree to which this compound channels into its two major pathways of utilization, acetoacetate formation or cholesterol synthesis. Under normal conditions, the pathway leading to cholesterol synthesis is highly favored. It is not clear whether exaggerated production of ketone bodies, as in diabetes (see below), is a result of a shift in emphasis between the above two pathways, or reflects overproduction of acetyl CoA, leading to excessive production of β-hydroxy-β-methylglutarate and of both products derived therefrom. The latter case seems indicated (see below).

The release of acetoacetate by liver is a continuing, normal process. The total ketone body concentration in blood, expressed as β-hydroxybutyrate, is normally below 1 mg. per 100 ml., and the average total daily excretion in the urine is approximately 20 mg. This is because of efficient mechanisms for removal of acetoacetic acid by peripheral tissues, especially muscle, which can derive a sizable fraction of its total energy requirement from this nutrient. In order to be utilized acetoacetic acid must first be reconverted into its CoA derivative by transfer of a CoA residue from succinyl CoA by the action of a specific thiophorase (page 458).

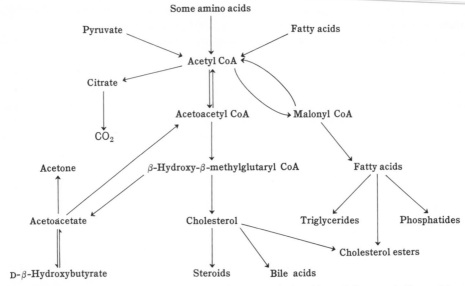

Fig. 22.5. A schematic representation of major interrelationships of the metabolism of fatty acids, cholesterol, and ketone bodies.

The acetoacetyl CoA thus formed may then be cleaved by thiolase (page 442), yielding two molecules of acetyl CoA, which then enter the citric acid cycle.

An elevation of the concentration of ketone bodies in the blood above normal levels is called *ketonemia;* if the blood level exceeds the renal threshold and appreciable amounts of ketone bodies appear in the urine, *ketonuria* is said to exist. Of the ketone bodies, acetone alone has a significant vapor pressure, and whenever a marked degree of ketonemia and ketonuria exists, the odor of acetone is likely to be detected in the exhaled air. This triad of ketonemia, ketonuria, and acetone odor of the breath is commonly termed *ketosis.*

Causes of Ketosis. A diminution in the quantity of carbohydrate catabolized may cause ketosis. Perhaps the most readily understood condition is *starvation.* When no food is allowed, the animal rapidly consumes its own stores of glycogen in the liver, and thereafter it survives largely upon energy derived from its depot lipid. Starvation results in a lipemia which reflects migration of excessive quantities of lipid from the depots to the liver, and this in turn produces a fatty liver. The degradation of fatty acids in the liver proceeds at greater than usual rate. As a consequence, there is a plethora of acetoacetyl CoA, which results in an excess of acetoacetate and its products, acetone and β-hydroxybutyrate. Ketosis incident to starvation is most frequently encountered clinically in gastrointestinal disturbances in infancy or pregnancy.

Etiologically related to the ketosis of starvation is that seen when the normal diet is abruptly replaced by one very poor in carbohydrate and very rich in lipid. Within wide limits isocaloric replacement of carbohydrate by lipid in the diet is well tolerated. If carried to extremes, however, ketosis may supervene. With excessive amounts of lipid presented to it, the liver generates an excess of ketone bodies, and when the rate of ketogenesis exceeds the capacity of other tissues to assimilate ketone bodies, ketonemia and ketonuria develop.

Again etiologically related is the ketosis that may develop in phlorhizin poisoning or renal glucosuria from other causes (Chap. 37). Under these circumstances, owing to a decline in the renal threshold for glucose, although carbohydrate is ingested, much is lost as glucose in the urine so that the tissues of the body are in effect starved with respect to carbohydrate.

Clinically, by far the most important cause of ketosis is diabetes. In the diabetic individual, in contrast to the preceding situations, glucose is present in excessive amounts in the fluids of the body. The metabolic defect, *viz.*, insulin deficiency, in diabetes, however, prevents glucose utilization from operating at normal rate. From the point of view of the effect upon lipid metabolism, diabetes and starvation are similar in several regards. Despite the hyperglycemia in diabetes, glucose is not being catabolized at normal rate in muscle or in liver. Excessive mobilization of depot lipid leads to lipemia and fatty liver. Generation of acetoacetyl CoA from fatty acids proceeds at an excessive rate in the liver while resynthesis of fatty acids is inhibited. If acetoacetate is formed at a rate in excess of the capacity of the extrahepatic tissues to utilize it, ketosis will develop. In diabetic individuals with severe ketosis, urinary excretion of ketone bodies may be as high as 5,000 mg. per hr. and the blood concentration may reach 90 mg. per 100 ml.

Not only have great species differences been encountered with regard to the ease with which ketosis is produced, but marked individual differences within one species are also found. Thus if insulin is withheld from a series of diabetic patients of comparable severity of disease, some will lapse into severe ketosis within a few days and others will fail to develop ketosis over a period of weeks. Furthermore, it appears that animals can be conditioned to tolerate high lipid diets, if the lipid content is gradually increased, without development of ketosis. Clinical ketosis with significant ketonuria depends upon the resultant of at least two processes: the generation of ketone bodies, chiefly in the liver, and the oxidation of ketone bodies, largely in the muscle. Adaptation to tolerate high lipid diets, without development of ketosis, is probably a consequence of increased peripheral utilization of ketone bodies. The capacity of the muscles of different individuals and of different species to subsist largely on ketone bodies is varied. Thus it is reported that the Eskimos, living normally on a high-lipid, carbohydrate-poor diet, do not exhibit ketosis under conditions which will result in ketosis in other individuals.

In all the above conditions, there is diminution of lipogenesis as well as abundant production of acetoacetate. Inasmuch as fatty acid oxidation to the level of acetyl CoA appears to be unimpaired, as well as operation of the citric acid cycle, the difficulty must be attributed to other factors. Increased carbohydrate utilization has a sparing action on lipid mobilization and, presumably, diminishes ketogenesis in this manner. The effect of carbohydrate in increasing lipogenesis is not understood. Citric acid and other intermediates of the tricarboxylic acid cycle activate acetyl CoA carboxylation (page 446). Vagelos has suggested that this effect may be a regulatory one, *i.e.*, increased operation of the cycle being favored by carbohydrate, lipogenesis will be stimulated. On the other hand, acetyl CoA carboxylase is inhibited by fatty acids; this provides an explanation for the inhibition of lipogenesis in starvation or in diabetes.

It has also been suggested that lipogenesis is diminished in conditions of limited carbohydrate utilization because of a lack of α-glycerophosphate, which apparently must be generated from carbohydrate, and which is a precursor of α-phosphatidic acid and hence of both triglycerides and phosphatides (page 464). In addition, TPNH is required for lipogenesis (page 448), and the major source is the phosphogluconic acid oxidative pathway (page 387).

Consequences of Ketosis. The ketone bodies do not appear to be exceptionally toxic materials when injected intravenously into experimental animals. The complications encountered in the man or animal that persists in generating more ketone bodies than can be utilized relate predominantly to the mode of renal excretion of acetoacetic and β-hydroxybutyric acids. These two substances are moderately strong acids and, even in the most acidic urine that the kidney can excrete, exist in large part as anions (Chap. 37). In the maintenance of the requisite electroneutrality of the urine, cations are necessarily lost as these anions are excreted, and this means in general a loss of Na^+. As the plasma and other body fluids become depleted of cations, incident to the persistent loss of the sodium salts of acetoacetic and β-hydroxybutyric acids, acidosis develops (Chap. 35).

Coincident with renal excretion of salts of acetoacetic and β-hydroxybutyric acids (as well as of glucose, in the diabetic patient), large quantities of fluid are lost in the urine. A tendency to nausea and consequent emesis cause additional fluid loss, while depression of the central nervous system, leading ultimately to profound coma with areflexia, interferes with normal drinking of water. All these factors, if not corrected, complicate the acidosis by producing a state of severe dehydration.

The complications of persistent ketosis may be in large part explained by the acidosis due to loss of Na^+ and the dehydration due to uncompensated fluid loss. Clinically, the patient may present severe central nervous system depression, including profound coma, hyperpnea, dryness of mucous surfaces, and loss of tissue turgor. The dehydration and acidosis due to ketosis are distinguishable from those due to other causes by the odor of acetone on the breath and the presence of ketone bodies in the urine. If due to diabetes, the additional findings of glucosuria and hyperglycemia will almost invariably be present.

REFERENCES

See list following Chap. 23.

23. Lipid Metabolism

Phosphatides and Sterols

THE PHOSPHATIDES

The phosphatides are of ubiquitous occurrence in living organisms and this has led to suggestions of a number of important functions for these compounds. As the most polar representatives of the lipids, with a marked solubility both in nonpolar solvents and in water, they have unique physical properties. Indeed, some of them, *e.g.*, lecithin, are dipolar ions possessing cationic and anionic groups. As such, they appear to participate uniquely in cellular structures such as mitochondria and various membranes. Together with the related galactolipids, phosphatides are found in abundance in the myelin sheath of nerve (Chap. 39). The phosphatides are also found in various functional organelles of the cell and have been implicated as playing a major role in the cytochrome complex of respiratory enzymes (page 351).

The character of the phosphatides appears to be ideally suited for functioning as structural bridges between water-soluble proteins and nonpolar lipids. The phosphatides possessing both hydrophobic and hydrophilic ionic groups can interact strongly with both types of structures.

Some evidence has been presented that phosphatides play special roles in secretory processes, in ion transport, and in selective permeability. The stability of chylomicra in body fluids has been attributed in part to the electrical charges in these droplets, resulting from their content of ionic phosphatides and proteins. The possible role of the cephalin fraction in blood clotting is discussed elsewhere (Chap. 33).

Distribution and Turnover of Phosphatides. The phosphatides are not uniformly distributed in the body lipids and are, in fact, almost totally absent from depot lipid. They do occur in the lipid of the various glandular organs, notably the liver, as well as in blood plasma, where they may comprise as much as half the total lipid. The phosphatides are found abundantly in certain specialized tissues, such as the myelinated portions of the nervous system, the yolks of bird eggs, and the seed parts of legumes.

The turnover of various phosphatides in diverse sites in the animal has been studied with different isotopes, most frequently with P^{32}. The biological half-lives range from less than 1 day for liver lecithin to more than 200 days for brain cephalin. Plasma lecithin arises chiefly or exclusively in the liver and is believed to be also degraded in the liver.

FORMATION OF PHOSPHATIDES

The formation of the phosphatide bases—serine, ethanolamine, and choline—can occur in animals. The other nitrogenous constituents of phosphatides—sphingosine and dihydrosphingosine—are also synthesized in vivo since they are not essential in the diet. Clarification of the biogenesis of the phosphatides stems largely from the discovery by Kennedy and Weiss in 1955 that cytidine derivatives play a major role in the formation of these compounds. There are two major pathways for the synthesis of lecithin, the most abundant phosphatide: (1) a *de novo* synthesis, in which phosphatidyl serine serves as a precursor for other phosphatides; (2) a utilization of exogenous choline, available from dietary sources or as a salvage pathway.

Phosphatidic Acid. The key substance in the formation of phosphatides is *phosphatidic acid*. Its formation from α-glycerophosphoric acid and 2 moles of acyl CoA has already been described (page 453). In addition, there are alternate routes for formation of phosphatidic acid from triglycerides. Over-all, these pathways may be outlined as follows.

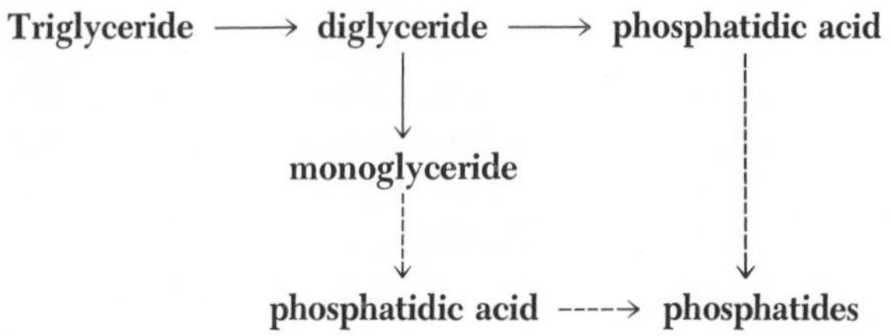

Triglyceride ⟶ **diglyceride** ⟶ **phosphatidic acid**
                         ↓   ⋮
                monoglyceride   ⋮
                         ⋮   ↓
            phosphatidic acid ----→ **phosphatides**

The 1,2-diglyceride is converted to phosphatidic acid by a kinase reaction.

ᴅ-1,2-Diglyceride + ATP ⟶ ʟ-α-phosphatidic acid + ADP

The monoglyceride is converted by an enzyme of brain tissue to ʟ-α-lysophosphatidic acid, which is then transformed to phosphatidic acid.

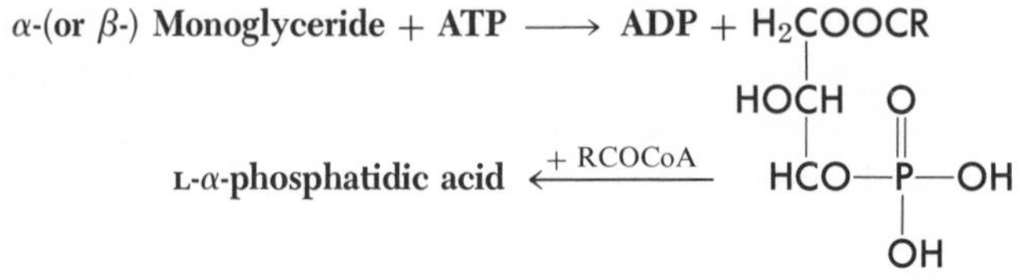

α-(or β-) Monoglyceride + ATP ⟶ ADP + H_2COOCR
                                                                    |
                                                          $HOCH$ O
                                                            | ‖
ʟ-α-phosphatidic acid $\xleftarrow{+ RCOCoA}$ HCO—P—OH
                                                                    |
                                                                  OH

ʟ-α-Lysophosphatidic acid

Formation of Phosphatidyl Serine. Phosphatidyl serine is formed via a cytidine intermediate, cytidine diphosphate diglyceride (CDP-diglyceride), which in turn is derived from ʟ-α-phosphatidic acid. Formation of CDP-diglyceride has been found to occur in mammalian liver and in bacterial sources. The reactions are the following.

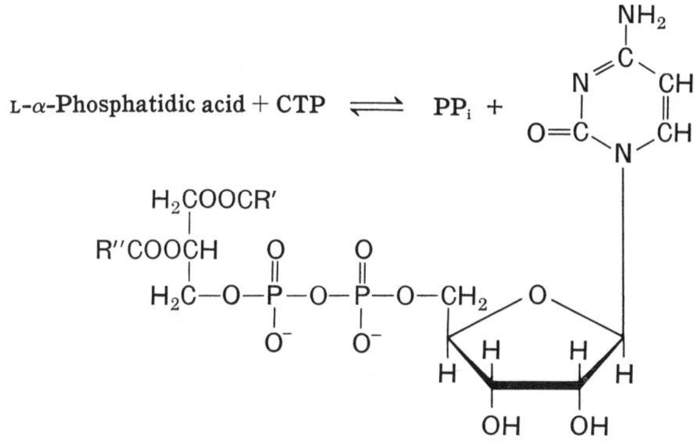

$$\text{L-}\alpha\text{-Phosphatidic acid} + \text{CTP} \rightleftharpoons \text{PP}_i +$$

Cytidine diphosphate diglyceride

The next step results in formation of phosphatidyl serine.

$$\text{CDP-diglyceride} + \text{L-serine} \longrightarrow \text{phosphatidyl serine} + \text{CMP}$$

Synthesis of phosphatidyl serine by the above reaction has been reported thus far only in extracts of *Escherichia coli* but undoubtedly also occurs in mammalian tissues.

Formation of Phosphatidyl Ethanolamine. The major route of formation of phosphatidyl ethanolamine in mammalian tissues involves the decarboxylation of phosphatidyl serine; the enzyme requires pyridoxal phosphate.

$$\text{Phosphatidyl serine} \longrightarrow \text{phosphatidyl ethanolamine} + \text{CO}_2$$

This decarboxylation is in accord with many earlier studies with labeled serine which showed that the ethanolamine of phosphatides is derived by decarboxylation of serine and that this occurs in the phosphatide rather than with free serine.

De Novo Formation of Lecithin. This occurs in stages by successive transfer of three methyl groups from S-adenosylmethionine (page 504) to phosphatidyl ethanolamine. Although the responsible enzymes have not been isolated, all the available evidence indicates that the methylation occurs only in the liver and only with the phosphatides as substrates. This is the mechanism for endogenous formation of choline. In studies with C^{14}-methyl–labeled S-adenosylmethionine, the label was incorporated in stages by successive methylation of phosphatidyl ethanolamine to form, successively, the corresponding monomethylaminoethanol-, dimethyl-aminoethanol-, and choline-containing phosphatides. With a mutant of *Neurospora* which cannot form choline, the mono- and dimethylaminoethanol phosphatides accumulate in this organism. The formation of S-adenosylmethionine and its role in transmethylation are presented later (Chap. 24).

Phosphatidyl Inositol. Formation of the inositol-containing phosphatide occurs from CDP-diglyceride by a reaction analogous to synthesis of phosphatidyl serine.

$$\text{CDP-diglyceride} + \text{inositol} \xrightarrow{\text{Mn}^{++}} \text{phosphatidyl inositol} + \text{CMP}$$

Isotopic evidence indicates that formation of the di- and triphosphoinositides (page 77) occurs by successive phosphorylations of the monoinositide.

Other Routes of Phosphatide Formation. An alternate route of lecithin formation may be regarded as a salvage pathway for utilization of free choline. The key intermediate in this process is *cytidine diphosphate choline.*

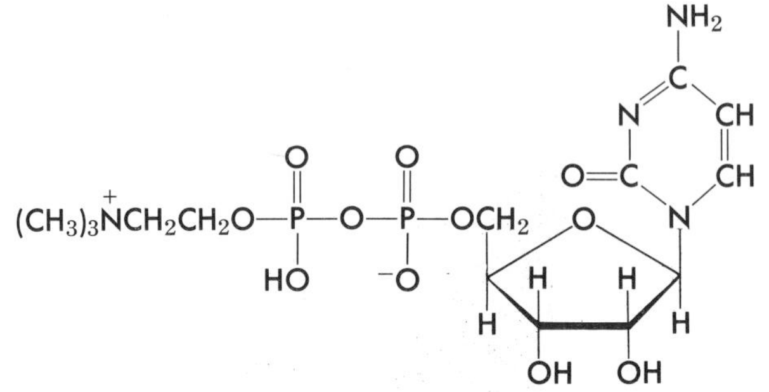

Cytidine diphosphate choline

The phosphorylcholine portion of the above molecule is formed by the following reaction.

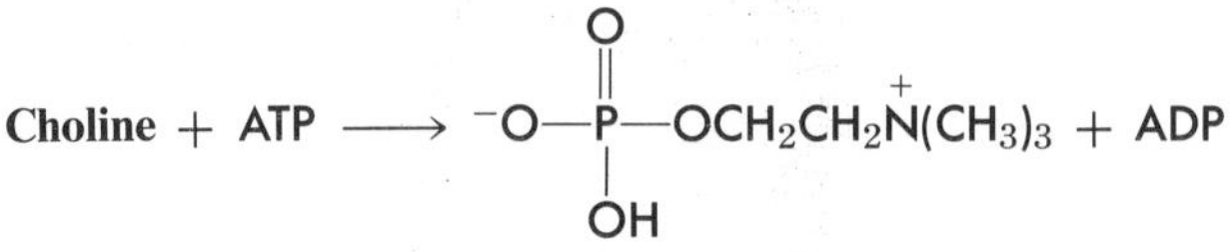

Choline + ATP $\longrightarrow$

Phosphorylcholine

Formation of cytidine diphosphate choline from cytidine triphosphate and phosphorylcholine involves elimination of pyrophosphate and is thus analogous to the generation of uridine diphosphate glucose from uridine triphosphate and glucose 1-phosphate (page 404).

Cytidine triphosphate + phosphorylcholine $\rightleftharpoons$ cytidine diphosphate choline + PP_i

Interaction of cytidine diphosphate choline (CDP-choline) with 1,2-diglyceride yields lecithin and cytidine monophosphate.

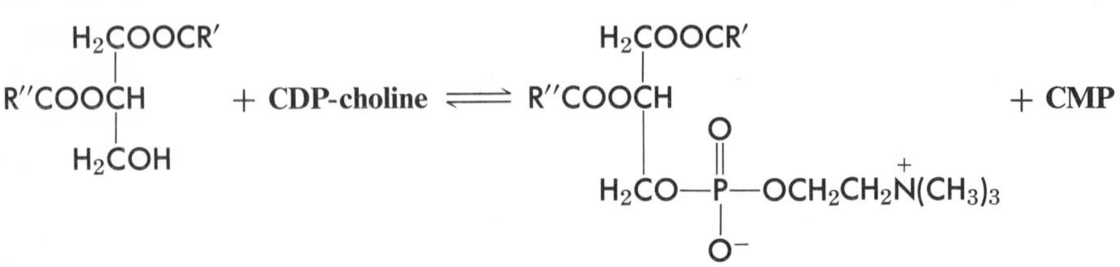

D-1,2-Diglyceride α-Lecithin

At the expense of ATP, cytidine triphosphate is regenerated from cytidine monophosphate.

By an analogous series of reactions, phosphorylethanolamine

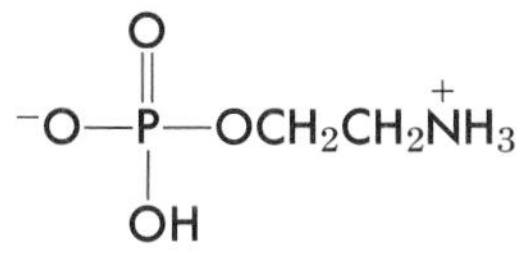

$$-O-\overset{\overset{\displaystyle O}{\|}}{\underset{\underset{\displaystyle OH}{|}}{P}}-OCH_2CH_2\overset{+}{N}H_3$$

can be converted into cytidine diphosphate ethanolamine, which reacts with the diglyceride to give the cephalin, phosphatidyl ethanolamine.

Although phosphatidyl serine is primarily formed by the *de novo* route previously described, it can also be made in mammalian tissues by an exchange of free serine with the ethanolamine moiety of phosphatidyl ethanolamine.

Phosphatidyl ethanolamine + L-serine $\rightleftharpoons$ phosphatidyl serine + ethanolamine

Plasmalogens. Some evidence is available that an acyl CoA derivative is the source of the α,β-unsaturated ether moiety of plasmalogens (page 75).

An enzymic preparation from rat liver catalyzes formation of plasmalogens from CDP-choline or CDP-ethanolamine.

CDP-choline + plasmalogenic diglyceride $\rightleftharpoons$ phosphatidal choline + CDP
CDP-ethanolamine + plasmalogenic diglyceride $\rightleftharpoons$ phosphatidal ethanolamine + CDP

Sphingomyelin. Studies with isotopically labeled compounds have shown that carbon atoms 1 and 2 of sphingosine and dihydrosphingosine are derived from the β- and α-carbon atoms, respectively, of serine. Moreover, the amino group is also derived from serine and remains attached to the α-carbon of serine during the transfer; however, the carboxyl group of serine is lost, presumably by decarboxylation.

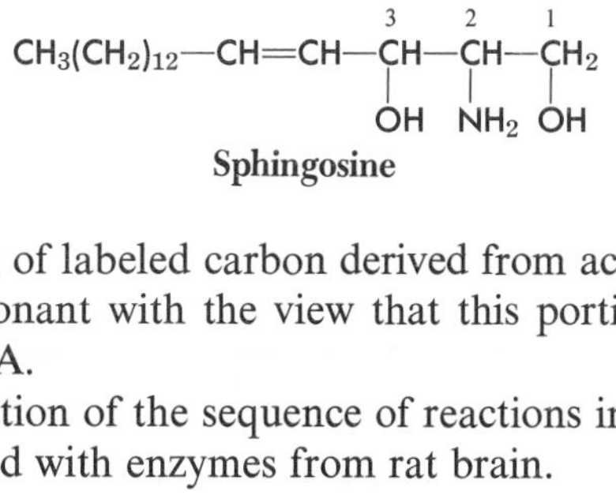

$$CH_3(CH_2)_{12}-CH=CH-\overset{3}{\underset{\underset{\displaystyle OH}{|}}{CH}}-\overset{2}{\underset{\underset{\displaystyle NH_2}{|}}{CH}}-\overset{1}{\underset{\underset{\displaystyle OH}{|}}{CH_2}} \qquad HOOC-\overset{\alpha}{\underset{\underset{\displaystyle NH_2}{|}}{CH}}-\overset{\beta}{\underset{\underset{\displaystyle OH}{|}}{CH_2}}$$
Sphingosine 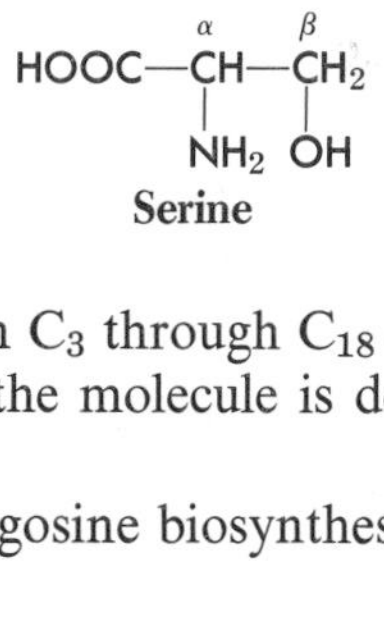   Serine

Distribution of labeled carbon derived from acetate in C_3 through C_{18} of sphingosine is consonant with the view that this portion of the molecule is derived from palmityl CoA.

Elucidation of the sequence of reactions in sphingosine biosynthesis has been accomplished with enzymes from rat brain.

Palmityl CoA + TPNH + H$^+$ $\rightleftharpoons$ palmitic aldehyde + TPN$^+$ + CoA

Palmitic aldehyde + serine $\xrightarrow{\text{pyridoxal phosphate}\atop\text{Mn}^{++}}$ dihydrosphingosine + CO$_2$

Dehydrogenation is accomplished by a flavin enzyme.

Dihydrosphingosine + flavin $\longrightarrow$ sphingosine + flavin $\cdot$ H$_2$

It is assumed that sphingosine is N-acylated by a fatty acyl CoA to form a ceramide (page 78), which then reacts with cytidine diphosphate choline.

Cytidine diphosphate choline + ceramide $\rightleftharpoons$ sphingomyelin + CMP

Cleland and Kennedy have found an enzyme in microsomes of brains of guinea pigs and young rats which catalyzes the formation of *psychosine* (galactosyl-sphingosine) from sphingosine and UDP-galactose (page 405).

$$\text{Sphingosine} + \text{UDP-galactose} \longrightarrow \text{psychosine} + \text{UDP}$$

The presence of this enzyme (*galactosyl-sphingosine transferase*) indicates that psychosine is an intermediate in the biosynthesis of the cerebrosides (galactolipids). Brady has reported that the amino group of psychosine is acylated by stearyl CoA to form a cerebroside.

$$\text{Stearyl CoA} + \text{psychosine} \longrightarrow \text{cerebroside} + \text{CoA}$$

The interrelationships of phosphatide and triglyceride synthesis are shown in Fig. 23.1.

HYDROLYSIS OF PHOSPHATIDES

The action of several hydrolytic enzymes on phosphatides has been useful in studying the structure of these compounds as well as in indicating routes of their degradation. The several susceptible bonds in lecithin may be considered as an example.

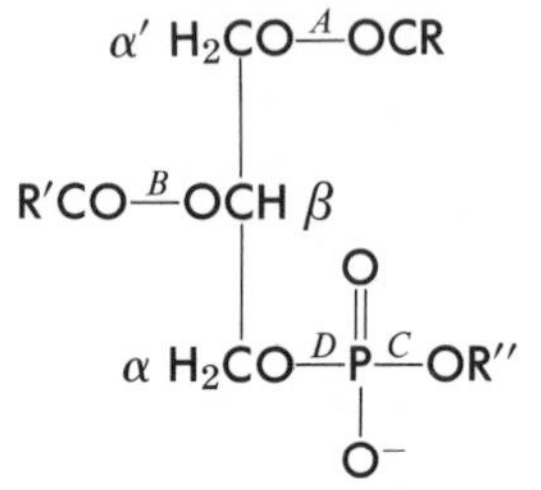

$$\alpha' \ H_2\overset{|}{C}O\overset{A}{-}OCR$$
$$R'CO\overset{B}{-}O\overset{|}{C}H \ \beta$$
$$\alpha \ H_2\overset{|}{C}O\overset{D}{-}\overset{\overset{O}{\|}}{P}\overset{C}{-}OR''$$
$$\underset{O^-}{|}$$

A Ca^{++}-requiring enzyme, *phosphatidase A* (*lecithinase A*), found in certain snake venoms and in pancreas, hydrolyzes at B. The product, lecithin minus one fatty acid residue, is a lysolecithin (page 74), and is a strong detergent and a potent hemolytic agent. With the aid of this enzyme, it has been shown that in some lecithins, *e.g.*, those of liver and egg, an unsaturated fatty acid is present at the β position and a saturated fatty acid at the α' position. However, lecithins from other sources possess different structures; *e.g.*, lecithin from yeast had unsaturated residues at both α' and β positions, whereas one from lung had saturated residues at both positions. Clearly, there is considerable specificity in lecithin synthesis.

Phosphatidase A also cleaves the susceptible bond, B, in cephalin, phosphatidyl ethanolamine, and in the plasmalogens containing choline and ethanolamine.

Lysophosphatidase of pancreas and other animal tissues catalyzes hydrolysis of the single fatty acid ester bond, at A, in lysophosphatidyl choline (lysolecithin) or lysophosphatidyl ethanolamine.

$$\text{Lysolecithin} + H_2O \longrightarrow \text{glycerylphosphorylcholine} + \text{fatty acid}$$

It is evident that the two enzymes, phosphatidase A and lysophosphatidase, may play an important role in the turnover of fatty acids in the above phosphatides.

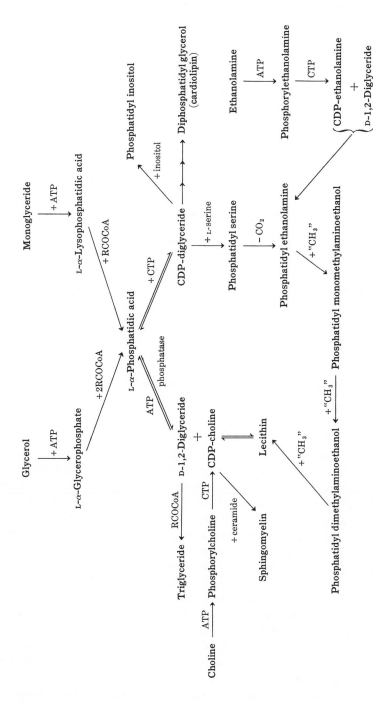

Fig. 23.1. Schematic representation of some of the interrelationships of phosphatide and triglyceride synthesis. "CH₃" designates the methyl group which is transferred from S-adenosylmethionine. It is evident from the above scheme that pathways exist by which glycerol, monoglycerides, or diglycerides can be utilized for formation of lipids or phosphatides. The key intermediate is phosphatidic acid.

An enzyme, *phosphatidase C*, has been found in many plant tissues, *e.g.*, carrot, cabbage, etc. This enzyme removes the base by hydrolysis at *C*.

$$\text{Phosphatide} + H_2O \xrightarrow{Ca^{++}} \text{phosphatidic acid} + \text{nitrogenous base}$$

Phosphatidase D catalyzes hydrolysis at position *D* (above) in a glycerylphosphatide and of the ceramide-phosphate linkage in sphingomyelin.

$$\text{Glycerylphosphatide} + H_2O \xrightarrow{Ca^{++}} \alpha,\beta\text{-diglyceride} + \text{phosphorylated nitrogenous base}$$

$$\text{Sphingomyelin} \xrightarrow{Ca^{++}} \text{N-acylsphingosine (ceramide)} + \text{phosphorylcholine}$$

This enzyme was discovered in the α toxin of *Clostridium welchii;* it has since been found in culture filtrates of other strains of clostridia and bacilli. Some evidence has been obtained for the presence of a similar enzyme in animal tissues.

ASPECTS OF STEROL METABOLISM

The present discussion will center about the metabolism of cholesterol, the most abundant sterol of animal tissues. Other related compounds will be mentioned only incidentally. More detailed discussion of the steroid hormones will be found in Chaps. 48 and 49.

With the exception of the sterol-like vitamins D, steroids are not essential in the diet. Even in the case of the vitamin D group, the mammal can synthesize an entirely satisfactory steroid precursor, 7-dehydrocholesterol (page 84), and it is only the requirement for radiant energy for the reaction sequence

$$\text{7-Dehydrocholesterol} \xrightarrow{\text{photons}} \text{vitamin D}_3$$

that makes vitamin D a dietary essential.

SOURCES OF BODY CHOLESTEROL

Diet. Cholesterol is contained in all animal tissues, hence all carnivores ingest this sterol. Its absorption from the intestinal lumen is exclusively into the intestinal lacteals, thence to the thoracic duct. The absorption of cholesterol shows a virtually absolute dependence upon the presence of bile salts in the intestinal lumen, but the mechanism of their participation is not clear. In the process of absorption, the major portion of the cholesterol is esterified with fatty acids and appears in lymphatic chylomicra as cholesterol esters. The absorption of sterols from the intestine has been considered previously (page 433). Two products formed from cholesterol by bacterial action in the intestine, *viz.*, β-cholestanol (page 82) and coprosterol (page 476), are poorly absorbed from the gastrointestinal tract and are found abundantly in the feces. Certain steroids, *e.g.*, β-sitosterol, have been shown to interfere with cholesterol absorption (page 433), as have a variety of other substances. Thus ferric chloride, presumably by formation of an insoluble iron salt of bile acids, as well as ion exchange resins which bind bile acids, markedly reduce absorption of intestinal cholesterol. All such agents have come into consideration in relation to prevention of hypercholesterolemia and its postulated role in vascular disease (page 436).

Biosynthesis of Cholesterol. All the carbon atoms of endogenous cholesterol are derived from acetyl CoA. Almost all tissues known to synthesize cholesterol which have been tested, including liver, adrenal cortex, arterial wall, etc., can generate cholesterol in vitro from acetate. The enzymes involved are associated with cytoplasmic particles (microsomes) and have been obtained in water-soluble form; however, cholesterol synthesis as catalyzed by these enzymes has an absolute dependency on cofactor(s) present in the supernatant fluid obtained by sedimentation of microsomes.

The sequence of events intervening between acetate and cholesterol can be reconstructed, on the basis of experiments in the laboratories of Bloch, Gurin, Lynen, Popják, Rudney, Tavormina, and others. The initial series of reactions involves formation of β-hydroxy-β-methylglutaryl CoA; this compound derives principally from 3 moles of acetyl CoA as described previously (page 458). β-Hydroxy-β-methylglutaryl CoA may also be produced as an intermediate in the metabolic degradation of leucine (page 548).

β-Hydroxy-β-methylglutaryl CoA is the immediate precursor of *mevalonic acid,* formed under the catalytic influence of a sulfhydryl-containing, TPNH-requiring enzyme, *β-hydroxy-β-methylglutaryl CoA reductase.* The reaction involves reduction of one of the carboxyl groups of hydroxymethylglutaryl CoA (Fig. 23.2). Previous consideration has been given (page 458) to the cleavage of β-hydroxy-β-methylglutaryl CoA to acetoacetyl CoA. It is of interest that the livers of fasting animals, which show decreased cholesterol formation, exhibit decreased β-hydroxy-β-methylglutaryl CoA reductase activity. This could increase relatively the significance of the cleavage reaction and afford an explanation for the augmented formation of ketone bodies accompanying the fasting state (page 460).

Sterol biosynthesis occurs from six 5-carbon units, each of which is derived from mevalonate. The sequence of reactions between mevalonate and squalene (the precursor of sterols) is shown in Fig. 23.2. Mevalonic acid is phosphorylated with ATP in three successive reactions catalyzed by three distinct enzymes, with sequential formation of 5-phospho-, 5-pyrophospho-, and 5-pyrophospho-3-phospho-mevalonate. The last compound is a transient intermediate which simultaneously loses the tertiary phosphate and decarboxylates to isopentenyl pyrophosphate. The latter is rapidly isomerized to dimethylallyl pyrophosphate by addition of a proton to the terminal doubly bound methylene carbon, followed by elimination of a proton from C-2. These two isomers are key substances in polyisoprenoid synthesis and are the basis for subsequent reactions involving carbon to carbon bond biosynthetic reactions in sterol formation. Dimethylallyl pyrophosphate, by virtue of its double bond and esterification with a strong acid, is an electrophilic reagent, whereas isopentenyl pyrophosphate, by virtue of its terminal doubly bound methylene carbon, is a nucleophilic reagent. The two compounds are therefore ideally suited for condensation with one another to form geranyl pyrophosphate. Repetition of this reaction between the latter and another mole of isopentenyl pyrophosphate leads to formation of farnesyl pyrophosphate. Under anaerobic conditions, with TPNH as coenzyme, reductive coupling of 2 moles of farnesyl pyrophosphate, an acyclic terpene, leads to formation of squalene, a symmetrical 30-carbon triterpene.

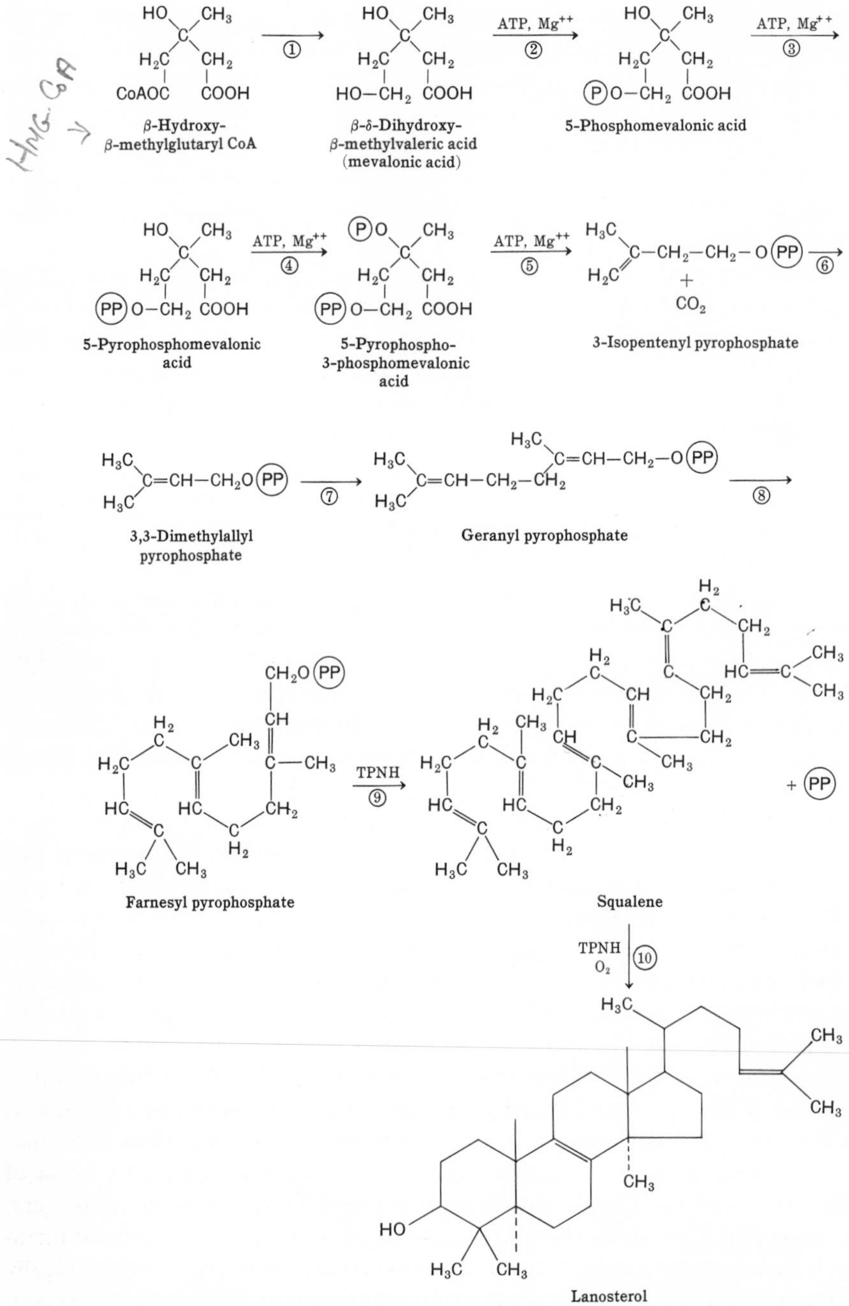

FIG. 23.2. Sequence of reactions between β-hydroxy-β-methylglutaryl CoA and lanosterol. P = phosphate; PP = pyrophosphate. Enzymes catalyzing the above reactions have been designated as follows: 1. β-hydroxy β-methylglutaryl CoA reductase; 2. mevalonic kinase; 3. phosphomevalonic kinase; 4. pyrophosphophoryl mevalonic kinase; 5. pyrophospho-3-phosphomevalonic anhydrodecarboxylase; 6. isopentenyl pyrophosphate isomerase; 7. geranyl-condensing enzyme; 8. farnesyl-condensing enzyme; 9. squalene synthetase; 10. squalene oxydocyclase I.

The hydrocarbon squalene, originally detected in shark oil but now known to be present in mammalian tissues, is transformed into the tetracyclic steroidal configuration under the influence of an enzyme termed *squalene oxidocyclase I* in a reaction requiring molecular oxygen and TPNH (Fig. 23.2). This enzymic system in liver cyclizes squalene to lanosterol exclusively. Other squalene-cyclizing enzymic systems must occur in other forms, including plants, to account for the formation of other triterpenes and sterols; hence the designation of the liver system as I. The mechanism of squalene cyclization is postulated as involving an initial electrophilic attack by an oxidant, "activated molecular oxygen," whose identity is still unknown. Concerted electron shifts following electrophilic attack lead to ring closure and the formation of a transient, intermediary carbonium ion. Lanosterol can be derived from the latter by a series of concerted hydride and methyl shifts. The conversion of lanosterol to cholesterol (Fig. 23.3) requires the removal of three angular methyl groups, the saturation of the double bonds in the side chain and at the C,D ring juncture, and the introduction of the double bond in the 5,6 position. Removal of the methyl groups is an oxidative process. The carbon atoms eliminated appear as carbon dioxide; the mechanism of this demethylation is still unknown. Formaldehyde is not an intermediate, suggesting that detachment of carbon may occur by decarboxylation, although intermediate carboxylic acids have not been isolated. It is known that the methyl group at C-14 is the first to be eliminated. Desmosterol, a postulated intermediate in cholesterol formation, has been isolated from tissues and accumulates in excessive quantities subsequent to prolonged administration of certain substances known to interfere with cholesterol biosynthesis (see below).

Alternative pathways from lanosterol to cholesterol may be postulated on the basis of the isolation of other possible intermediates (Fig. 23.3). Thus, labeled 4α-methyl-Δ^7-cholesten-3β-ol was isolated from the skin, liver, and small intestine of rats injected with C^{14}-labeled acetate. Moreover, feeding of this sterol to rats led to its rapid conversion to cholesterol. Also, 4α-methyl-Δ^8-cholesten-3β-ol has been isolated from preputial gland tumors of mice. Finally, 24,25-dihydrolanosterol, 4α-methyl-Δ^8-cholesten-3β-ol, Δ^7-cholesten-3β-ol, and 7-dehydrocholesterol are rapidly converted to cholesterol by cell-free homogenates of liver. The order in which the individual steps occur in conversion of lanosterol to cholesterol is still uncertain.

Although all the carbon atoms of cholesterol may derive from acetate, in the biosynthesis of ergosterol (page 85) the additional carbon atom, a methyl group at C-24, has its origin in a methylation reaction with S-adenosylmethionine (page 504). Mevalonate has also been established as the source of the isoprenoid side chain in the biosynthesis of carotenoids (page 80) and coenzyme Q (page 314) and serves as the precursor of the rubber hydrocarbons.

Factors Affecting Rate of Cholesterol Synthesis. The liver is the major site of cholesterol synthesis, although other tissues, *e.g.*, intestine, adrenals, skin, nervous tissue, aorta, and the reproductive organs, also can synthesize this sterol. The intestine is particularly active, and cholesterol synthesis here is not influenced by feeding of cholesterol (see below). Except for nervous tissue, cholesterol in tissues exhibits a continuous turnover. However, relatively small, rapidly turning over pools and rather large, inert, reserve pools may exist in the same tissue, for example, the adrenal.

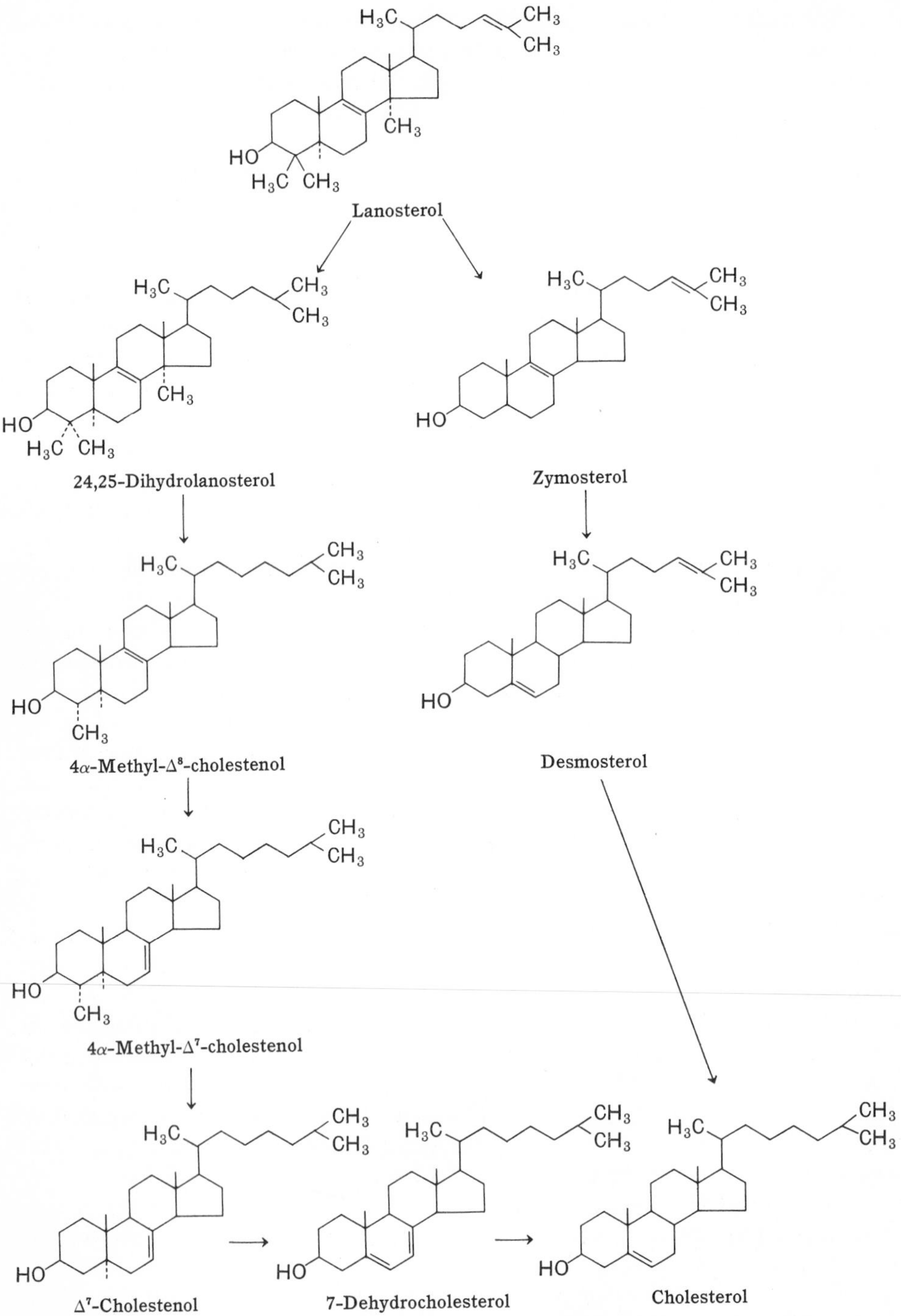

FIG. 23.3. Two theoretical pathways from lanosterol to cholesterol, based on available data. The pathway via zymosterol and desmosterol has slightly more supportive evidence, although both pathways, and others, may exist.

The rate of cholesterol synthesis in the body is markedly influenced by the available supply of this sterol, suggesting a feedback control of the biosynthetic pathway (see below). This control is exerted chiefly in the liver. Thus, cholesterol synthesis is depressed by cholesterol feeding or injection, or by administration of squalene or other sterols which can be converted to cholesterol, or which may arise from cholesterol, *e.g.*, bile acids. Conversely, when the available cholesterol is reduced by fasting, by increased carbohydrate in the diet, or by drainage of endogenous sterol via a bile or lymphatic fistula, cholesterol biogenesis is greatly stimulated. Bucher and Lynen and their associates have demonstrated that the rate-limiting step in cholesterol biogenesis which is influenced under the above-described circumstances is the reduction of β-hydroxy-β-methylglutaryl CoA to mevalonate.

Alterations in the level of blood cholesterol have been noted in response to changes in the degree of saturation of dietary fatty acids (Chap. 53). The more saturated the fatty acids of the diet, the higher the level of serum cholesterol concentration.

In diabetes, when lipogenesis is markedly depressed, the corresponding rate for cholesterol synthesis is normal or greater than normal. The elevations in blood cholesterol level seen in nephrosis and noted to follow the injection of various detergents appear to be due not to a direct effect on cholesterol synthesis but rather to an inhibition of removal of cholesterol from the blood.

Cholesterol of Body Fluids. A large portion of the cholesterol in lymph and in blood plasma is found in chylomicra. Since the dispersed state of these fat droplets is due chiefly to their content in phosphatide, it is not surprising that the ratio of phosphatide to cholesterol in the blood remains fairly constant.

Of the cholesterol in plasma, roughly two-thirds exists esterified with fatty acids. The maintenance of this ratio is a function of the liver, and decreases in this value due to lowering of cholesterol ester concentration are seen in liver disease. The liver serves both as the chief synthetic source and the chief agent for disposal of plasma cholesterol, a portion of that removed from the blood appearing in the bile.

The normally high concentration of cholesterol in human bile is of consequence clinically. Though sparingly soluble in water, cholesterol readily dissolves in aqueous bile salt solutions, probably because of the formation of choleic acids, specific coordination compounds of bile acids and sterols. In the gallbladder, both water and bile salts are reabsorbed by the action of the cholecystic mucosa, and if this process continues excessively, cholesterol crystals separate from the bile. Either biliary stasis or inflammatory disease of the gallbladder can lead to this situation. Concretions made up chiefly of cholesterol crystals are among the common *calculi* of the biliary tract, the disease being termed *cholelithiasis*. Such calculi in the gallbladder may be undetected ("silent"), but if they descend the biliary tract, and particularly if they occlude the common bile duct, a variety of clinically important events ensue.

Cholesterol enters the intestinal tract by direct excretion across the intestinal mucosa as well as via the bile. In the lumen of the gut a portion is reduced microbially to coprosterol via the following steps and thereby excluded from reabsorption.

R represents:

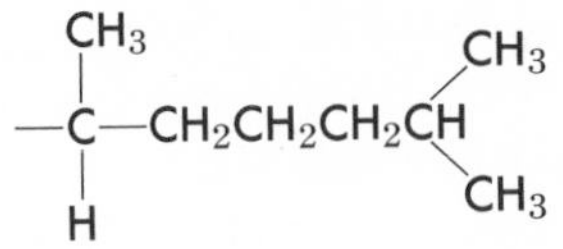

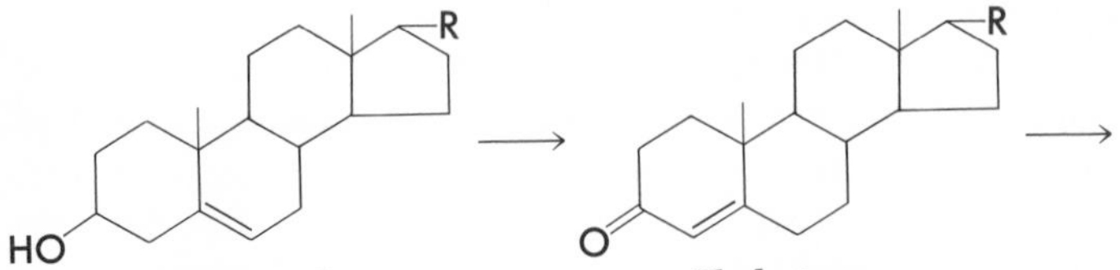

Cholesterol → Cholestenone →

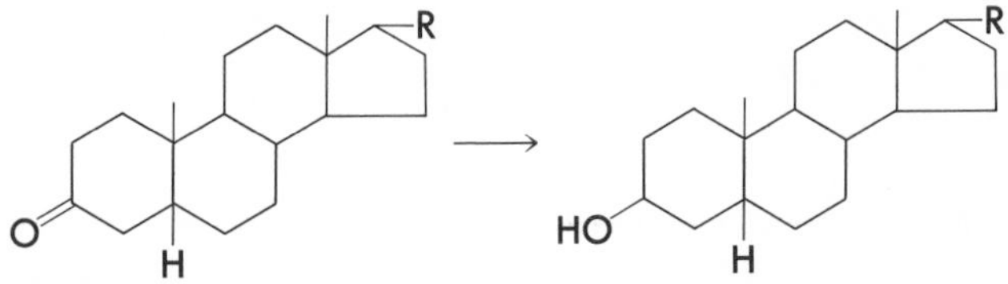

Coprostanone → Coprosterol

Abnormal elevations of cholesterol in the plasma are considered below.

Catabolism of Cholesterol—Conversion to Bile Acids. Only a fraction of the cholesterol metabolized daily is excreted as sterols in the feces. Virtually none appears in the urine. The fate of cholesterol in animal tissues is therefore of interest. It appears that cholesterol serves as precursor for a variety of biologically important, structurally related steroids.

Approximately 80 per cent of the cholesterol metabolized is transformed by liver tissue into various bile acids. Experimental evidence indicates that hydroxylation of cholesterol is more or less completed before the degradation of the side chain is finished, although some data support the suggestion that shortening of the side chain of cholesterol may precede hydroxylation of the ring structure. A sequence of events in the formation of cholic acid from cholesterol which has experimental support visualizes successive formation of 7α-hydroxycholesterol, 3α,7α-dihydroxycoprostane, and 3α,7α,12α-trihydroxycoprostane. The last-named compound is then transformed into the CoA derivative of 3α,7α,12α-trihydroxycoprostanic acid; oxidation of the side chain yields cholyl CoA (Fig. 23.4). The shortening of the side chain involves initial removal of the terminal three carbon atoms. This is an oxidative sequence wherein a terminal methyl group appears as CO_2. A β-ketoacyl CoA derivative is pictured as forming, which in a typical β-ketothiolase reaction (page 442) would yield cholyl CoA (Fig. 23.4). Conjugation to glycine or taurine is believed to occur with the CoA derivatives of the bile acids (Chap. 36).

It should be noted that the bile acids, excreted in high concentration in the bile, are reabsorbed via cholecystic and intestinal mucosa, enter the portal blood, and thus return to the liver. Little bile acid escapes normally in the feces or passes the normal liver to enter the caval blood. This minor circuit of bile acids is termed the *enterohepatic circulation* and is shared by a number of metabolites, *e.g.*, urobilinogen (Chap. 42).

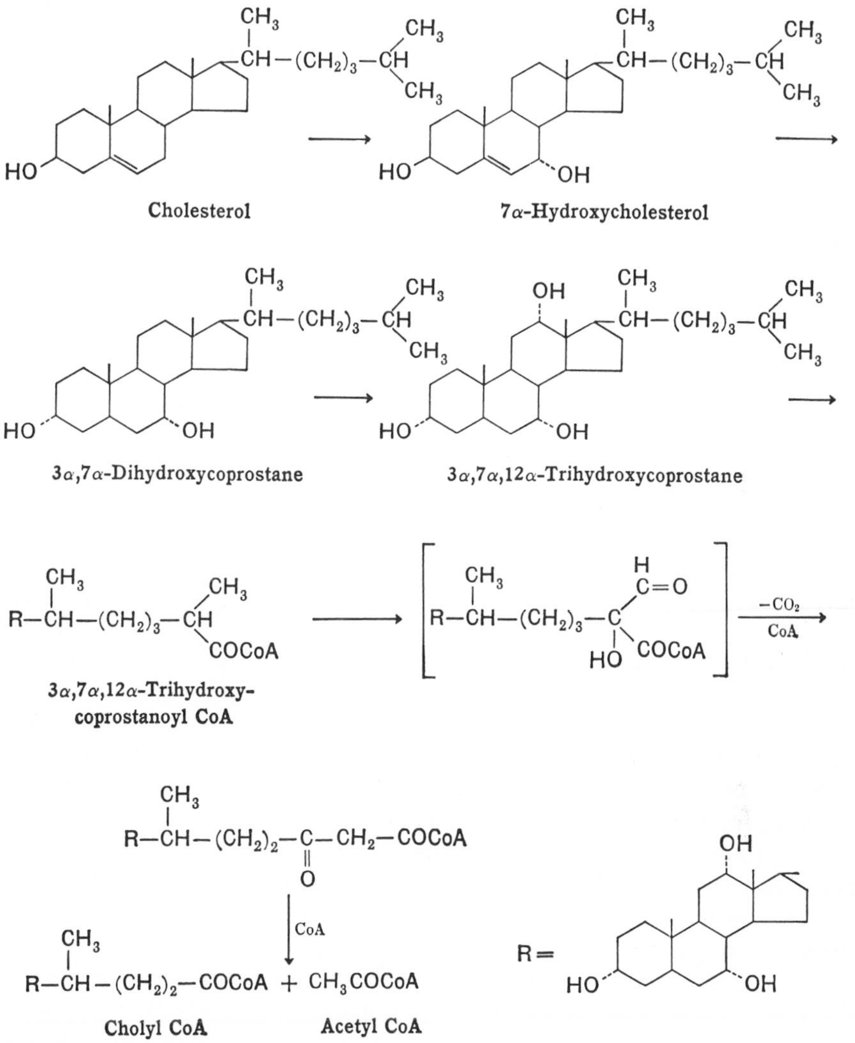

Fig. 23.4. Sequence of postulated reactions leading from cholesterol to cholyl CoA.

Other Products of Cholesterol Catabolism. Another significant catabolic fate of cholesterol relates to the origin of the 19- and 21-carbon steroid hormones. Soluble enzymes from adrenal gland, testis, and ovary can catalyze scission of the side chain of cholesterol between C-20 and C-22, yielding pregnenolone and the anticipated isocaproaldehyde. The reaction requires TPNH and molecular oxygen. In the adrenal, a 20,22-dihydroxycholesterol has been identified as an intermediate. The sequence is depicted in Fig. 23.5. The data suggest that degradation of the cholesterol side chain in organs producing steroid hormones differs from the mode of cleavage of this portion of cholesterol in bile acid formation in the liver (see above). Pregnenolone formed from cholesterol may serve as a precursor of a num-

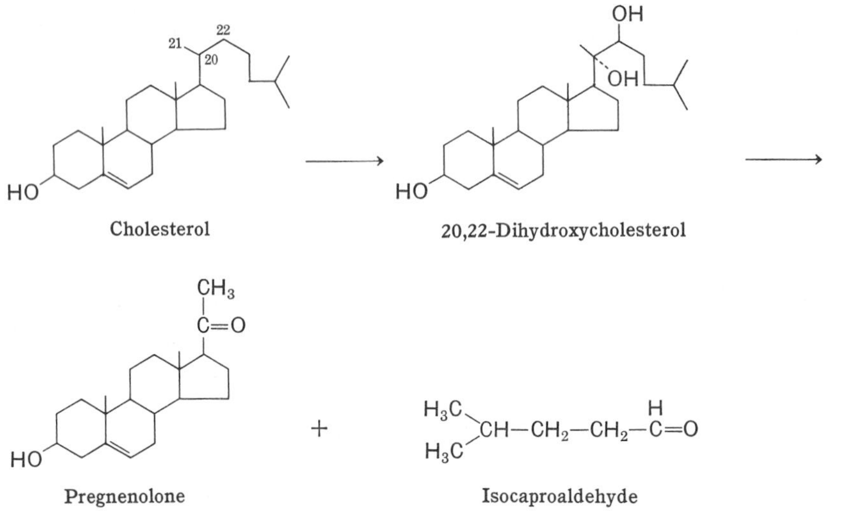

FIG. 23.5. Postulated steps in scission of the cholesterol side chain in the sequence of reactions leading from cholesterol to steroid hormones.

ber of steroid hormones; these transformations will be discussed in Chaps. 48 and 49.

During intestinal absorption of cholesterol, a portion is dehydrogenated to 7-dehydrocholesterol by the intestinal mucosa. This transformation is also effected by skin and other tissues. Skin contains stored quantities of 7-dehydrocholesterol and, it may be noted, more squalene than cholesterol.

Pathological Accumulations of Cholesterol. The formation of cholesterol calculi in the biliary tract has been described (page 475). The pathological deposition of cholesterol-containing plaques in the intima of the aorta is the characteristic lesion of *atheromatosis,* and is seen in *arteriosclerosis* and *arteriolar sclerosis.* The mechanism of this deposition in man is uncertain, but concomitant changes in the composition of the blood have been noted. Although the concentration of cholesterol in plasma may not be strikingly elevated, the ratio of cholesterol to phosphatides generally is, with an increase in the lipoprotein fraction S_f 12 to 20 (page 436), which is rich in cholesterol.

Because the excessive deposition of cholesterol in vascular tissue may have undesirable consequences, efforts have been directed toward reduction of levels of blood cholesterol in the hope that this would lessen the degree of vascular cholesterol deposition. These attempts have utilized a variety of dietary and therapeutic procedures. Previous mention was made of the apparently favorable influence of unsaturated, compared with saturated, dietary lipids on blood cholesterol levels (page 475). The relation of dietary lipid to atherosclerosis is considered more fully in Chap. 53. Drug therapy designed to interfere with endogenous cholesterol biosynthesis has not had practical success. Certain drugs which diminish cholesterol formation lead to an accumulation of intermediates of cholesterol synthesis, including desmosterol, in the liver and in the intima of the larger blood vessels.

The basis of the hypocholesterolemia of hyperthyroidism (Chap. 46) is not understood, but its occurrence has led to the search for thyroid hormone-like substances which may lower blood cholesterol without exerting the other effects of thyroidal hormones (Chap. 46). The lower incidence of atherosclerosis in the human female, as compared to that in the male, and the blood cholesterol–lowering effects of female sex hormones (Chap. 48) have similarly stimulated a search for compounds which mimic the female sex hormones in reducing blood cholesterol levels, but have minimal feminizing effects (Chap. 48).

Familial hypercholesterolemia is a genetically transmitted disorder. In the light of modern understanding of genetic control of metabolic phenomena (Chap. 31), it seems possible that the genetic defect in this condition is the failure of the repressor mechanism (page 490) that functions at the point of the cholesterol feed-back control of cholesterol biosynthesis (page 475).

A less frequent disease in which lipid deposits often rich in cholesterol are found is *xanthomatosis*. Multiple benign fatty tumors of skin, tendon sheaths, and bone are found in this condition, associated with a lipemia and a striking hypercholesterolemia. Patients suffering from this disease have been reported to benefit by the exclusion of all animal lipid, hence of all cholesterol, from their diets.

An even rarer condition is *Schüller-Christian syndrome,* characterized by xanthomatous deposits in the flat bones of the skull, the liver, and the spleen, associated with diabetes.

Changes in the level of blood cholesterol without overt deposition are seen in certain clinical conditions. Lipemia and especially hypercholesterolemia occur in hypothyroidism (Chap. 46) as well as in the nephrotic syndrome. In neither case is the significance of the chemical change understood. Hypercholesterolemia may also be produced by increased blood levels of certain adrenal cortical steroids (Chap. 49) as well as by some hypophyseal preparations (Chap. 51).

CERTAIN DISTURBANCES OF LIPID METABOLISM

The normal operation of the processes outlined in the preceding pages results in the simultaneous synthesis and deposition, mobilization, and degradation of body lipid, *i.e.,* a dynamic biological steady state. In the normal adult the quantity of body lipid may remain essentially constant for long periods of time. The most obvious disturbances of lipid metabolism result from an imbalance between the processes leading to deposition and those leading to mobilization of lipid in the depots. If deposition exceeds mobilization for a prolonged period, accrual of depot lipid, or *obesity,* ensues. If mobilization exceeds deposition, depot lipid diminishes in quantity, leading ultimately to *cachexia* and virtually complete loss of lipid from the depots.

Obesity. The sum of all the caloric requirements in the mammal, including the basal requirement plus increments for muscle work, other forms of work, and specific dynamic action, is met by the caloric yield of the diet. If the diet provides more calories than are required, the difference will appear in the form of stored chemical potential energy. Since in mammals the elastic compartment for such storage is the depot lipid, it is this compartment which expands under these conditions.

Other things being equal, a surplus of 9 Cal. may be expected to result in the deposition of 1 g. of additional fat.

Although the commonest cause of obesity is overeating, other operative factors must be considered. A pathological decline in the basal metabolic rate or a change from an active to a sedentary life, if not compensated for by a decreased food intake, will result in an increase in quantity of adipose tissue. Experimental damage to specific areas of the hypothalamus results in an extreme polyphagia, which, if not restricted, leads to extraordinary obesity. Poisoning with certain gold salts and with sulfanilamide has also been reported to result in obesity, and in the mouse a hereditary obesity has been discovered which is transmitted as a mendelian dominant characteristic. In the obesity which results from hypothalamic injury, as well as in the hereditary disease of mice, it appears that the defect is predominantly one of impaired mobilization of depot lipid rather than an excessive deposition of lipid in the depots. Whether this is true of the other forms of obesity remains to be determined. Obesity is a common finding in the history of diabetic individuals and is supposed to predispose to this and other diseases. There is no doubt that it materially decreases life expectancy in the older age groups.

The therapeutic restriction of caloric intake below the total caloric requirement necessarily leads to loss of body lipid, although, owing to transient water retention, this may not be immediately reflected in changes in body weight.

Cachexia. Imbalance in the sense opposite to that of obesity may lead to the complete disappearance of gross adipose tissue from the subcutaneous and omental depots. This may occur in the course of a neoplastic or chronic infectious disease, in malnutrition, or in untreated disturbances of metabolism such as diabetes or hyperthyroidism. Specific damage to areas of the hypothalamus has been shown experimentally to produce anorexia, even in previously starved animals. *Anorexia nervosa* may often have a psychogenic component in its etiology.

Whereas the loss of body lipid incident to hyperthyroid disease is apparently attributable to excessively rapid mobilization of depot lipid, an important contribution to the cachexia of starvation, thiamine deficiency, or diabetes is a decreased capacity of the organism to synthesize fatty acids from carbohydrate precursors.

Niemann-Pick Disease and Tay-Sachs Disease. These two conditions, possibly adult and juvenile manifestations of similar disturbances, are characterized by accumulation of phosphatides, chiefly lecithin and sphingomyelin, in the liver, spleen, and various cells of the central nervous system, including the macula retina in Tay-Sachs disease. In the latter, the brain and spleen contain abnormally high amounts of gangliosides, one of which apparently does not occur in normal individuals (Chap. 39). In Niemann-Pick disease, ganglioside concentration in brain also is higher than normal. The fundamental nature of the disturbance in these conditions is not understood.

Gaucher's Disease. This disturbance of lipid metabolism is distinguished chemically from the foregoing by the fact that the lipids which accumulate in liver, spleen, and bone marrow are cerebrosides (page 77) and ceramide mono- and disaccharides (page 78). Again the mechanism of the disturbance remains to be elucidated.

All three disorders mentioned in the above two paragraphs appear to be genetically transmitted (Chap. 31).

REFERENCES

Books

Bloch, K., ed., "Lipide Metabolism," John Wiley & Sons, Inc., New York, 1960.

Cook, R. P., ed., "Cholesterol: Its Chemistry, Biochemistry and Pathology," Academic Press, Inc., New York, 1958.

Deuel, H. J., Jr., "The Lipids: Their Chemistry and Biochemistry," vol. II, 1955; vol. III, 1957, Interscience Publishers, Inc., New York.

Kinsell, L. W., ed., "Adipose Tissue as an Organ," Charles C Thomas, Publisher, Springfield, Ill., 1962.

Kritchevsky, D., "Cholesterol," John Wiley & Sons, Inc., New York, 1958.

Mead, J. F., and Howton, D. R., "Radioisotope Studies of Fatty Acid Metabolism," Pergamon Press, New York, 1960.

Page, I. H., ed., "Chemistry of Lipides as Related to Atherosclerosis," Charles C Thomas, Publisher, Springfield, Ill., 1958.

Pincus, G., ed., "Hormones and Atherosclerosis," Academic Press, Inc., New York, 1959.

Popják, G., and Le Breton, E., eds., "Biochemical Problems of Lipids," Butterworth and Co. (Publishers), Ltd., London, 1956.

Schoenheimer, R., "The Dynamic State of Body Constituents," Harvard University Press, Cambridge, Mass., 1942.

Searcy, R. L., and Bergquist, L. M., "Lipoprotein Chemistry in Health and Disease," Charles C Thomas, Publisher, Springfield, Ill., 1962.

Review Articles

Best, C. H., and Lucas, C. C., Choline-Chemistry and Significance as a Dietary Factor, *Vitamins and Hormones,* **1,** 1–59, 1943.

Conn, J. W., Obesity: 2. Etiological Aspects, *Physiol. Revs.* **24,** 31–45, 1944.

Dawson, R. M. C., The Metabolism of Phospholipids, in M. Florkin and H. S. Mason, eds., "Comparative Biochemistry," vol. IIIA, pp. 265–285, Academic Press, Inc., New York, 1962.

Dole, V. P., and Hamlin, J. T., III, Particulate Fat in Lymph and Blood, *Physiol. Revs.,* **42,** 674–701, 1962.

Eder, H., The Lipoproteins of Human Serum, *Am. J. Med.,* **23,** 269–282, 1957.

Frazer, A. C., Fat Absorption and Its Disorders, *Brit. Med. Bull.,* **14,** 212–220, 1958.

Frederickson, D. S., and Gordon, R. S., Jr., Transport of Fatty Acids, *Physiol. Revs.* **38,** 585–630, 1958.

French, J. B., Morris, B., and Robinson, D. S., Removal of Lipids from the Blood Stream, *Brit. Med. Bull.,* **14,** 234–238, 1958.

Grant, J. K., Lipids: Steroid Metabolism, in M. Florkin and H. S. Mason, eds., "Comparative Biochemistry," vol. IIIA, pp. 163–203, Academic Press, Inc., New York, 1962.

Green, D. E., and Gibson, D. M., Fatty Acid Oxidation and Synthesis, in D. M. Greenberg, ed., "Metabolic Pathways," vol. I, pp. 301–340, Academic Press, Inc., New York, 1960.

Jeanrenaud, B., Dynamic Aspects of Adipose Tissue Metabolism: A Review, *Metabolism,* **10,** 535–581, 1961.

Kennedy, E. P., Biosynthesis of Phospholipides, *Federation Proc.,* **16,** 847–853, 1957.

Kennedy, E. P., The Metabolism and Function of Complex Lipids, *Harvey Lectures,* **57,** 143–171, 1961–1962.

Lindgren, F. T., and Nichols, A. V., Structure and Function of Human Serum Lipoproteins, in F. W. Putnam, ed., "The Plasma Proteins," vol. II, pp. 2–58, Academic Press, Inc., New York, 1960.

McHenry, E. W., and Patterson, J. M., Lipotropic Factors, *Physiol. Revs.,* **24,** 128–167, 1944.

Mead, J. F., Lipid Metabolism, *Ann. Rev. Biochem.,* **32,** 241–268, 1963.

Newburgh, L. H., Obesity: 1. Energy Metabolism, *Physiol. Revs.,* **24,** 18–30, 1944.

Olson, R. E., and Vester, J. W., Nutrition-endocrine Interrelationships in the Control of Fat Transport in Man, *Physiol. Revs.,* **40,** 677–733, 1960.

Popják, G., Some Aspects of Lipid Biochemistry, *Proc. Roy. Soc., London,* **B, 156,** 376–387, 1962.

Popják, G., and Cornforth, J. W., The Biosynthesis of Cholesterol, *Advances in Enzymol.,* **22,** 281–335, 1960.

Portman, O. W., and Stare, F. J., Dietary Regulation of Serum Cholesterol Levels, *Physiol. Revs.,* **39,** 407–442, 1959.

Rossiter, R. J., Metabolism of Phosphatides, in D. M. Greenberg, "Metabolic Pathways," vol. I, pp. 357–388, Academic Press, Inc., New York, 1960.

Rudman, D., Hirsch, R. L., Kendall, F. E., Seidman, F., and Brown, S. J., An Adipokinetic Component of the Pituitary Gland: Purification, Physical, Chemical, and Biologic Properties, *Recent Progr. Hormone Research,* **18,** 89–123, 1962.

Stumpf, P. K., and Barber, G. A., Comparative Mechanisms for Fatty Acid Oxidation, in M. Florkin and H. S. Mason, eds., "Comparative Biochemistry," vol. I, pp. 75–105, Academic Press, Inc., New York, 1960.

Tchen, T. T., Metabolism of Sterols, in D. M. Greenberg, ed., "Metabolic Pathways," vol. I, pp. 389–429, Academic Press, Inc., New York, 1960.

Vandenheuvel, F. A., The Origin, Metabolism, and Structure of Normal Human Serum Lipoproteins, *Can. J. Biochem. Physiol.,* **40,** 1299–1326, 1962.

Vaughn, M., The Metabolism of Adipose Tissue in Vitro, *J. Lipid Research,* **2,** 293–316, 1961.

Wertheimer, E., and Shafrir, E., Influence of Hormones on Adipose Tissue as a Center of Fat Metabolism, *Recent Progr. Hormone Research,* **16,** 467–495, 1960.

24. Amino Acid Metabolism

Digestion of Protein and Absorption of Amino Acids. Utilization of Inorganic Nitrogen. General Aspects of Amino Acid Biosynthesis. Essential Amino Acids. Biosynthesis of Nonessential Amino Acids. Dynamic Aspects of Mammalian Nitrogen Metabolism

This and the succeeding three chapters are, as the titles indicate, concerned with the metabolism of amino acids that are present in mammals. Historically, the metabolism of amino acids has been generally viewed as a segment of protein metabolism because protein is the major source of *dietary* amino acids. However, except for information relating to the nutritive aspects of protein, *i.e.*, its role in the diet (Chap. 53), and the hydrolysis in the gastrointestinal tract of ingested protein, the prime processes of protein nitrogen metabolism, particularly in mammals, are those involving amino acids or products of their metabolism. The metabolic relation of amino acids to proteins stems from the facts that (1) amino acids are derived from protein degradation in the gut as well as in the continuing metabolism of cells, and (2) the major metabolic role of amino acids is to serve as precursors of proteins. This latter role is discussed in Chap. 30.

The present chapter considers (1) the digestion of protein and the absorption of the liberated amino acids; (2) the mechanisms available to cells for utilization of inorganic nitrogen; (3) the pathways by which mammalian cells synthesize adequate quantities of approximately half of their diverse amino acids, the so-called nonessential amino acids (page 492), and (4) the continuing nature of nitrogen metabolism in mammals. The following chapter presents the biosynthesis of those amino acids, termed essential amino acids, which cannot be produced by mammals and must be provided by dietary protein, but can be fabricated by plants and microorganisms. The third chapter of this group describes the contributions of the nitrogen and carbon of various amino acids to the synthesis of some important nitrogenous compounds; the fourth chapter indicates known degradative, or catabolic, pathways of mammalian amino acid metabolism.

DIGESTION OF PROTEIN

The digestion of protein in the gastrointestinal tract produces at least two significant results. The primary one is the degradation of high molecular weight, nondiffusible protein molecules to small diffusible compounds which may be absorbed readily from the intestine. In addition, digestion of protein in mammals causes destruction of the biological specificity, including the species differences, which makes intact proteins antigenic.

Hydrolysis of proteins in the gastrointestinal tract is accomplished by specific enzymes secreted in gastric juice and in pancreatic juice, and by enzymes of the mucosa of the small intestine.

With the exception of certain of the peptidases of the intestine, the proteolytic enzymes of the gastrointestinal tract are elaborated and secreted as inactive zymogens (page 247) which are converted to active enzymes in the gut. The alterations in protein structure accompanying zymogen transformation to enzyme have been described previously for the reaction chymotrypsinogen → chymotrypsin (page 247). In a broad sense, similar changes may be visualized for other zymogen conversions to active enzymes.

Gastric Digestion. Factors affecting the quantity and composition of gastric and pancreatic secretions are discussed in a later chapter (Chap. 36). At this point attention will be directed to a brief consideration of protein digestion in relation to the enzymes involved, aspects of their specificity, and their effects upon dietary proteins. Previous consideration has been given to the specificity of proteolytic enzymes in relation to their use as tools in studies of protein structure (Chap. 9).

The proteinase of the gastric juice is *pepsin;* it is derived from its zymogen precursor *pepsinogen,* which is elaborated and secreted by the chief cells of the gastric mucosa (Chap. 36). The inactive zymogen is converted to the active enzyme, pepsin, both by the acidity of the gastric juice and by pepsin itself; the process is therefore autocatalytic. During this conversion, a polypeptide of molecular weight 3,100, which can act as a pepsin inhibitor, is liberated from pepsinogen.

$$\text{Pepsinogen} \xrightarrow{\text{H}^+,\ \text{pepsin}} \text{pepsin} + \text{inhibitor}$$

The prime materials serving as substrates for peptic activity in the stomach are either the native proteins of the diet or denatured proteins resulting from cooking of food. Pepsin rapidly initiates hydrolysis of proteins. Studies with synthetic substrates revealed that the linkages most susceptible to this enzyme are peptide bonds involving an aromatic amino acid (phenylalanine, tryptophan, or tyrosine). In addition, pepsin has a significant action on peptide bonds involving other amino acids, *e.g.*, leucine and acidic residues.

Although pepsin liberates free amino acids from proteins in vitro, this is a slow process. Since food remains in the stomach for a limited time, pepsin in vivo hydrolyzes dietary protein chiefly to a mixture of polypeptides. If gastric hydrochloric acid production fails to maintain gastric contents at the pH optimum of 2 to 3, necessary for peptic action, protein digestion in the stomach may be very limited. This is seen, for example, in *pernicious anemia* (Chap. 36). In *achylia gas-*

trica, the absence of pepsin as well as acid from gastric contents precludes protein digestion in the stomach.

Pepsin has a strong clotting action on milk. A number of plant and animal enzymes exhibit this activity, which is the initial reaction in the digestion of milk. In ruminants, clotting of milk may result from the action of a *specific* enzyme, *rennin,* which is obtained from the abomasum, or fourth stomach, of the suckling calf. The reactions involved in milk clotting are presented later (Chap. 36).

Proteolysis in the Intestine. The material which enters the intestine comes in contact with a mixture of proteases. The pancreas secretes a slightly alkaline fluid (Chap. 36) containing several inactive zymogen precursors of proteases, *e.g., trypsinogen,* two *chymotrypsinogens,* two *procarboxypeptidases,* and *proelastase.* An intestinal enzyme, termed *enterokinase,* converts trypsinogen to *trypsin,* as does trypsin itself, autocatalytically.

Trypsinogen consists of a single peptide chain, and the activation process involves scission of a single bond, liberating the hexapeptide, Val-(Asp)$_4$-Lys, from the amino-terminal end of the zymogen. Release of the peptide is accompanied by the appearance of enzymic activity and a decrease in levorotation of the protein, indicating an alteration in the conformation of the molecule. Chymotrypsinogen is converted to several active chymotrypsins; the nature of these transformations has been described (page 247). Procarboxypeptidases and proelastase are converted by trypsin to active carboxypeptidases and elastase, respectively.

The alkaline pancreatic juice neutralizes the acidic chyle from the stomach and provides the slightly alkaline pH optimal for the hydrolytic action of the pancreatic enzymes, each of which has characteristic specificity (page 150). It will be recalled that *trypsin* acts upon peptide linkages involving the carboxyl group of arginine and lysine. The *chymotrypsins* are most active toward peptide bonds involving phenylalanine, tyrosine, and tryptophan. Thus the action of these enzymes is additive, resulting in more complete degradation to small peptides. *Carboxypeptidase A,* a zinc-containing enzyme, rapidly liberates carboxyl-terminal amino acid residues. Its most rapid action is on residues that possess aromatic or aliphatic side chains. *Carboxypeptidase B,* a distinct enzyme, acts only on peptides possessing terminal arginine or lysine residues.

The mucosa of the intestine also contains enzymes that hydrolyze peptide bonds. It is not clear whether these enzymes are actually secreted into the intestinal juice or whether they remain within the cells and participate in proteolysis as the smaller products of digestion traverse the villi. Extracts of intestinal mucosa contain a group of *aminopeptidases,* enzymes that act on polypeptides or peptide chains containing a free amino group, liberating an amino acid by scission of the peptide bond adjacent to the free amino group. Thus, *leucine aminopeptidase* rapidly hydrolyzes L-leucylglycine, but not the unnatural antipode. The enzyme has a broad specificity with respect to the N-terminal residue of the polypeptide. By successive hydrolysis of N-terminal peptide bonds, it can degrade peptides to free amino acids. This enzyme requires Mn^{++} or Mg^{++} for its action, and it has been postulated that the metal ion functions in a coordination complex with the enzyme and its substrate. Mucosal extracts also contain *dipeptidases,* enzymes that act specifically on certain dipeptides. An example is *glycylglycine dipeptidase,* which requires Co^{++} or Mn^{++} for its action. This enzyme does not attack the tripeptide, glycylglycylglycine. Thus the enzymic action is dependent on the presence of both amino and carboxyl groups adjacent to the sensitive peptide bond.

The successive action of the proteolytic enzymes present in the stomach and in the small intestine results in ultimate hydrolysis of dietary protein to free amino acids. It may be pointed out that, although trypsin and chymotrypsin appear to act more rapidly and more completely if preceded by the action of pepsin, these two pancreatic enzymes together can liberate amino acids from native proteins. This is of some significance in individuals in whom gastric resection has been performed. Indeed, while absence of gastric secretion does not have serious consequences with respect to the utilization of dietary protein, exclusion of pancreatic juice from the intestine results in marked impairment in protein digestion. Extensive destruction of pancreatic tissue or obstruction of the pancreatic ducts limits the quantity of pancreatic juice reaching the duodenum, and under these conditions significant amounts of dietary protein are not digested and appear in the feces.

ABSORPTION OF AMINO ACIDS FROM THE INTESTINE

The major products of intestinal digestion of protein are the amino acids, and these are rapidly absorbed. For example, within 15 min. after ingestion of N^{15}-labeled yeast protein by man, significant absorption of amino acids could be demonstrated, with maximum amino acid concentration in the blood attained between 30 and 50 min. after eating. These values may be considered excessively short since they were obtained with a very small amount of fed protein and without simultaneous feeding of carbohydrate or lipid, which may delay gastric emptying. Nonetheless, they reflect the speed with which ingested protein may be digested and the amino acids absorbed. Absorption of amino acids is confined chiefly to the small intestine and is an active, energy-requiring process which reflects a high degree of structural specificity. Impairment of absorption occurs with anoxia or in the presence of metabolic inhibitors or poisons. Experimental studies with everted sacs of rat or hamster intestine and isolated segments of rat intestine have demonstrated that the L isomers of amino acids are more rapidly absorbed than the D isomers, and that, in general, the neutral and the more hydrophilic amino acids are more rapidly absorbed than are the basic and the more hydrophobic amino acids. A role for the participation of pyridoxal (vitamin B_6, Chap. 55) and Mn^{++} in amino acid concentration by cells in general has been suggested (Chap. 35). Indeed, studies in the rat reveal that variations in the endogenous vitamin B_6 economy greatly influence intestinal transport and tissue uptake of amino acids. The diminished rate of amino acid absorption from the intestine of B_6-deficient rats can be stimulated by administration of pyridoxal phosphate. It may be noted that vitamin B_6, or its derivatives, may participate as cofactors in a number of enzymic systems concerned with the metabolism of amino acids (see below and the following three chapters).

Amino acids absorbed from the intestine enter the circulation almost wholly by way of the portal blood; very small quantities leave the intestine via the lymphatic vessels. In addition to amino acids, low molecular weight peptides may also be absorbed from the small intestine, as evidenced by a rise in blood peptide nitrogen during active protein digestion and absorption. Under special circumstances, native protein may also penetrate the intestinal mucosa and appear in the blood. In the young mammal the permeability of the mucosa appears to be somewhat greater than in the adult. Also, the colostral milk, or colostrum (Chap. 36), obtained from the mother during the first few days after parturition, contains a protein which is a potent trypsin inhibitor. These factors, together with a low concentration of proteolytic enzymes in the digestive fluids, may lead to a sufficient degree of absorption of native proteins to cause immunological sensitization. This may be the basis for idiosyncrasies sometimes encountered toward food proteins, e.g., milk proteins and egg white.

UTILIZATION OF INORGANIC NITROGEN

The prime form of inorganic nitrogen utilizable by all living cells is ammonia, which can be fixed at all phylogenetic levels, including mammals, by the operation of three major synthetic reactions resulting in formation of glutamic acid, glutamine, and carbamyl phosphate, respectively. Ammonia nitrogen derives in plants from reduction of the nitrogen of the atmosphere or of the nitrate present in the soil. Plants and many microorganisms can synthesize all the amino acids found in proteins by virtue of their capacity to utilize ammonia and to fabricate the carbon structures corresponding to each of the amino acids. In contrast, mammals lack the ability to make approximately half of these carbon structures and hence of the corresponding amino acids as well. This relative synthetic capacity for amino acids, therefore, represents a major contrast, with regard to amino acid metabolism, between plants and microorganisms on the one hand and mammals on the other.

One additional contrasting aspect of nitrogen metabolism between plants and microorganisms on the one hand and mammals on the other may be noted here and will be discussed later in this chapter under the continuing nature of nitrogen metabolism in mammals. Plants and microorganisms manifest self-regulatory mechanisms which permit utilization from the environment of needed amino acids only to the degree required for synthesis of cellular nitrogenous constituents to provide normal cellular needs and concentrations of these substances. In contrast, similar mechanisms for regulation of amino acid intake are not prevalent in mammals. The latter are generally confronted with a supply of amino acids in excess of needs, arising from the digestion of dietary protein. Consequently, mammals, in contrast to plants and microorganisms, must have a disposal mechanism for removal of surplus amino acids. This mechanism is dual in nature: (1) amino nitrogen disposal via synthesis and excretion of urea, and (2) carbon chain disposal by channeling into oxidative or storage pathways of carbohydrate or lipid metabolism.

Utilization of N_2 and Nitrate for Ammonia Formation. Nitrogen exists as N_2 in the atmosphere and, frequently, as NO_3^- in soil. The details of the major processes for reduction of N_2 and NO_3^- to the level of NH_3 remain obscure. *Nitrate reductase* obtained from *Neurospora crassa* or *Escherichia coli* is a molybdoflavoprotein (page 347) which catalyzes the following reaction.

$$H^+ + TPNH + NO_3^- \longrightarrow TPN^+ + NO_2^- + H_2O$$

Nitrite and *hydroxylamine reductases* have been described, but the intermediate stages from NO_2^- to NH_3 are uncertain. Cytochromes appear to serve as nitrate and nitrite reductases in chemosynthetic anaerobes. Among the intermediates which have been considered are NO, N_2O, and NH_2OH. Similarly, although cell-free preparations of *Clostridium pasteurianum* reduce N_2 and fix it into glutamic acid, the details remain unknown.

As mentioned previously, at all phylogenetic levels, including mammals, ammonia is fixed by three major reactions, the syntheses of *glutamic acid, glutamine,* and *carbamyl phosphate,* respectively. In some microorganisms alanine or aspartic acid formation may substitute for that of glutamic acid. With nitrogen fixed into these three compounds, they serve in plant and microbial cells as precursors of all the other amino acids, and participate in formation of purines, pyrimidines, and diverse other nitrogenous compounds.

Synthesis of Glutamic Acid. Glutamic acid formation occurs in a reaction catalyzed by *glutamic acid dehydrogenase,* an almost universally distributed enzyme.

$$DPNH \text{ (or } TPNH) + \alpha\text{-ketoglutarate} + H^+ + NH_3 \rightleftharpoons$$
$$\text{L-glutamate} + DPN^+ \text{ (or } TPN^+) + H_2O$$

The thermodynamic equilibrium for this reaction strongly favors the reductive synthesis of glutamate. The α-amino group of glutamic acid can be transferred to other α-keto acids, corresponding to the other normally occurring amino acids, thereby providing a mechanism for synthesis of most of the other amino acids by a process termed *transamination.* This will be considered later (page 493).

Glutamine Synthesis. Glutamine formation is catalyzed by *glutamine synthetase.*

$$HOOC-CH_2-CH_2-CHNH_2-COOH + ATP + NH_3 \xrightarrow{Mg^{++}}$$

Glutamic acid

$$H_2N-CO-CH_2-CH_2-CHNH_2-COOH + ADP + P_i$$

Glutamine

According to Meister, glutamine synthetase catalyzes a two-step process. Initially there is formed an enzyme-bound, γ-carboxyl-activated form of glutamic acid with cleavage of ATP to ADP + P_i. In the second step, this intermediate reacts with NH_3 to form glutamine. The extent and rate of glutamine synthesis exceed those of all other forms of NH_3 fixation in mammals. The amide N of glutamine can be transferred to other carbon chains in diverse synthetic pathways, *e.g.*, hexosamines (page 406), purines (page 562), histidine (page 526), and DPN (page 580). In several instances, the mammalian enzyme in these biosynthetic pathways has been found to be glutamine-specific, whereas the comparable reaction in bacteria is accomplished with ammonia. In at least two instances, the mammalian enzyme can use either glutamine or NH_3, and K_m for each is approximately the same. However, only 1 per cent of total ammonia exists as NH_3 at pH 7.4 and the remainder as NH_4^+. Thus a physiologically intolerable concentration of ammonia would be required. Glutamine, therefore, provides a means of presenting to an enzyme an unprotonated nitrogen atom at the reduction level of NH_3 and in physiologically acceptable concentration.

In addition, glutamine which has been synthesized from NH_3, as described above, may serve as an ammonia store. The ammonia can be released through the intervention of *glutaminase*, a widely distributed enzyme which catalyzes the following reaction.

$$\text{Glutamine} + H_2O \longrightarrow \text{glutamic acid} + NH_3$$

The enzyme of kidney is of particular interest because of its special physiological role in providing ammonium ion for base conservation (Chaps. 35 and 37).

Synthesis of Carbamyl Phosphate. As obtained from bacterial sources, *carbamyl phosphate synthetase* catalyzes the following reaction.

$$CO_2 + NH_3 + ATP \rightleftharpoons H_2N\text{---}CO\text{---}OPO_3H_2 + ADP$$
$$\text{Carbamyl phosphate}$$

The process is reversible and in some microorganisms can represent a useful source of ATP. However, carbamyl phosphate synthesis in mammalian liver is somewhat more complex and is essentially irreversible; an additional equivalent of ATP is required.

$$H_2O + CO_2 + NH_3 + 2ATP \longrightarrow H_2N\text{---}CO\text{---}OPO_3H_2 + 2ADP + P_i + H^+$$

The enzyme shows an absolute requirement for N-acetylglutamic acid; the precise role of this compound has not been elucidated.

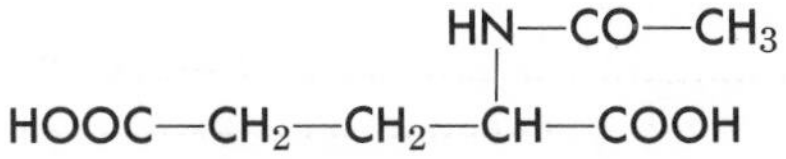

$$\begin{array}{c} HN\text{---}CO\text{---}CH_3 \\ | \\ HOOC\text{---}CH_2\text{---}CH_2\text{---}CH\text{---}COOH \end{array}$$
$$\text{N-Acetylglutamic acid}$$

Carbamyl phosphate, made by either of the above two reactions, is then available to cells for carbamylation of amino groups.

$$H_2N\text{---}CO\text{---}OPO_3H_2 + RNH_2 \longrightarrow H_2N\text{---}CO\text{---}NHR + P_i$$

GENERAL ASPECTS OF AMINO ACID BIOSYNTHESIS

Before presentation of the pathways by which certain of the amino acids are synthesized, some characteristic aspects of these biosyntheses may be noted. These comments also pertain in part to the biosynthesis of other substances as well, *viz.*, purines, pyrimidines, porphyrins, etc.

1. Having fixed NH_3 into organic linkage by the three reactions described previously, amino acids are then fabricated from carbon compounds which are available as products of carbohydrate metabolism, *e.g.*, pyruvate and oxaloacetate.

2. Each reaction in these biosynthetic pathways is catalyzed by a specific enzyme.

3. In order for these synthetic pathways to provide a continuing supply of amino acids, each pathway must be essentially irreversible, *viz.*, it must proceed

with a relatively large loss of free energy. This is accomplished by those reactions in which ATP is utilized and, effectively, split to ADP + P_i. Even more effective, in this regard, are those instances in which, over-all, ATP → AMP + PP_i, since the subsequent hydrolysis of PP_i, catalyzed by pyrophosphatase, is irreversible. In other instances, synthesis is assured by a reductive reaction, employing DPNH or TPNH, in which the equilibrium strongly favors oxidation of the reduced pyridine nucleotide.

4. Frequently, in metabolic systems, experiments with isotopically labeled compounds suggest that a series of reactions may be reversible. In reality, this is rarely the case. Indeed, if A is convertible to B, and B reconvertible to A, this generally reflects the existence of two completely or partially independent pathways (reaction series) via distinct and separate intermediates:

$$X \longrightarrow Y \longrightarrow Z$$
$$A \nearrow \qquad \qquad \searrow B$$
$$N \longleftarrow M \longleftarrow L$$

Examples of this generalization have already been encountered, *i.e.*, the independent pathways for oxidation and formation of fatty acids, for formation and degradation of glycogen, for formation of pyruvic acid from glucose and its effective reversal.

5. Many synthetic pathways may be formulated as shown below:

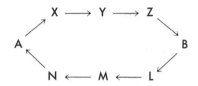

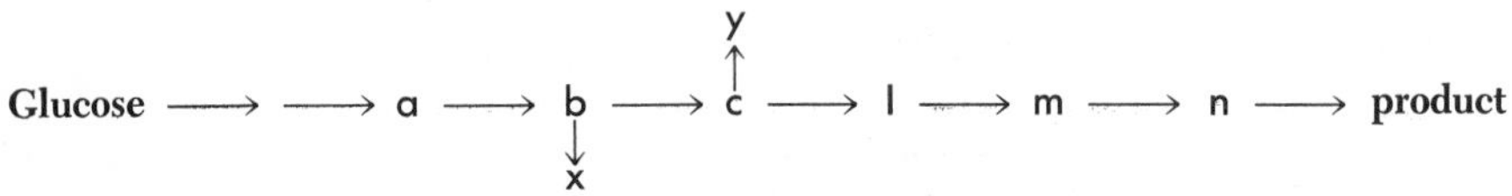

In this scheme, a, b, and c may be intermediates in carbohydrate metabolism, *e.g.*, pyruvic acid or acetyl CoA, common to many metabolic pathways. The reaction $c \rightarrow l$ is termed the "committed step" since l, m, and n are intermediates with no metabolic role other than to serve as precursor of the final product of the pathway. It will be apparent that if the rate of biosynthesis of the final product is to be regulated, this would best be accomplished by regulation of the rate of reaction $c \rightarrow l$. Modification of earlier reactions would interfere with other metabolic events; halting reaction $m \rightarrow n$ would result in useless, and perhaps toxic, accumulation of l and m. Regulation at the level of the committed step has been amply demonstrated for biosynthetic pathways operative in bacteria. Similar situations probably exist in mammalian metabolism, but as yet this has not been unequivocally demonstrated.

The above-described control, in bacteria, is by two distinct types of mechanisms. In one, a product of the reaction sequence serves, in low concentration compatible with the life of the cell, as a noncompetitive inhibitor of the enzyme which catalyzes the committed step. Some examples of such inhibitions are summarized in Table 24.1. A second mechanism of control obtains when the product of the reaction sequence serves as a *repressor* (page 620) and inhibits the biosynthesis of the enzyme which catalyzes the reaction at the committed step. Indeed,

Table 24.1: END-PRODUCT INHIBITION IN BIOSYNTHESIS OF AMINO ACIDS

Amino acid	Sensitive reaction	Organism or tissue	Page
Arginine...	N-Acetylglutamic acid $\longrightarrow$ N-acetylglutamic-γ-semialdehyde	*Micrococcus glutamicus*	497
Histidine...	ATP + 5-phosphoribosylpyrophosphate $\longrightarrow$ phosphoribosyl ATP	*Salmonella typhimurium*	526
Isoleucine..	Threonine $\longrightarrow$ α-ketobutyric acid	*Escherichia coli*	520
Leucine....	α-Ketoisovaleric acid + acetyl CoA $\longrightarrow$ β-carboxy-β-hydroxyisovaleric acid	*S. typhimurium*	520
Lysine.....	Aspartic acid $\longrightarrow$ β-aspartyl phosphate	*E. coli*	518
Threonine..	Aspartic acid $\longrightarrow$ β-aspartyl phosphate	*E. coli*	518
	Homoserine $\longrightarrow$ 4-phosphohomoserine	*E. coli*	
Serine.....	Phosphoserine $\longrightarrow$ serine	Rat liver	501
Tryptophan.	5-Phosphoshikimic acid $\longrightarrow$ anthranilic acid	*E. coli*	523
Valine.....	Pyruvic acid $\longrightarrow$ acetolactic acid	*Aerobacter aerogenes*	520

SOURCE: Modified from H. S. Moyed and H. E. Umbarger, *Physiol. Revs.,* **42,** 444, 1962.

the presence of the product may result in repression of formation of the enzymes responsible for all the reactions at and beyond the committed step. Examples of both types of control mechanisms will be found in the material to follow. Their operation may be appreciated from the dramatic differences in the behavior of bacteria growing in media of varying composition. An organism that grows in a medium containing inorganic salts and carbohydrate does so by synthesizing all its amino acids, purines, pyrimidines, etc. If it is placed in a medium containing all 20 amino acids, these are accepted from the medium and used for protein synthesis and the cell makes little or no amino acids for itself. Its amino acid biosynthetic activities virtually cease. Similar observations may be made with addition of purines, pyrimidines, vitamins, etc., to the medium.

6. Living cells vary widely in their genetic capacity for biosynthesis. As already noted, higher plants and many microorganisms are entirely self-sufficient in that they can synthesize all the amino acids. In contrast, for example, are the *lactobacilli,* organisms found in milk. These bacteria flourish in milk, the proteins of which provide all the amino acids. But these cells are practically incapable of synthesizing amino acids *de novo* and remain entirely dependent upon their environment to provide amino acids for continuing metabolism and growth. Man and most other vertebrates are in an intermediary position, capable of the synthesis of a limited group of amino acids and dependent upon the environment for all others.

AMINO ACIDS NUTRITIONALLY ESSENTIAL FOR MAN

In the course of evolution, the animal organism lost the ability to synthesize the carbon chain of certain of the α-keto acids. Accordingly, the corresponding α-amino acids cannot be formed via transamination reactions. These amino acids, which must therefore be provided preformed in the diet either as free amino acids or as constituents of dietary proteins, have been termed *essential amino acids*. This term is at present used to designate those amino acids which cannot be synthesized by the organism at a rate adequate to meet metabolic requirements and must be supplied in the diet. The essential amino acids are listed in Table 24.2, as are those amino acids which need not be present in the diet. It should be emphasized that this classification is based upon growth studies in the rat (page 266). The proportion of essential amino acids provided by various dietary proteins is one factor influencing the biological value of proteins (Chap. 53).

Table 24.2: CLASSIFICATION OF THE AMINO ACIDS WITH RESPECT TO THEIR GROWTH EFFECT IN THE WHITE RAT

Essential	*Nonessential*
Arginine*	Alanine
Histidine	Aspartic acid
Isoleucine	Cystine
Leucine	Glutamic acid
Lysine	Glycine
Methionine	Hydroxyproline
Phenylalanine	Proline
Threonine	Serine
Tryptophan	Tyrosine
Valine	

* Arginine can be synthesized by the rat but not at a sufficiently rapid rate to meet the demands of *normal* growth.

SOURCE: After W. C. Rose, *Physiol. Revs.,* **18,** 109, 1938.

The failure of young animals to grow on a diet deficient in one or more of the essential amino acids is a reflection of the inability to synthesize adequate quantities of protein under these experimental conditions. In response to an amino acid deficiency in the diet, the tissues do not make proteins lacking that particular amino acid; they simply make less protein.

It should be emphasized that the terms *essential* and *nonessential* relate only to dietary requirements and have no meaning with respect to the relative importance which the amino acids may have in metabolism. The amino acids which are essential in the diet are compounds with carbon skeletons which cannot readily be synthesized by the body. In a real sense, the so-called nonessential amino acids are of equal or greater significance for the economy of the organism in that they participate in diverse cellular reactions and functions and provide precursors for the synthesis of many important cellular constituents. Indeed, certain of the nonessential amino acids, *e.g.,* glutamic acid, have so many important metabolic roles that, were a mammal to lose suddenly its capacity to synthesize glutamic acid, serious disorganization of key reactions of metabolism might result since the animal could not wait until the next meal to replenish its supply, as would be possible in the case of the so-called "essential" amino acids.

BIOSYNTHESIS OF NONESSENTIAL AMINO ACIDS IN MAMMALS

The nonessential amino acids are by definition those amino acids which need not be provided in the mammalian diet since they can be synthesized in adequate amounts. It may be noted that although arginine is listed in Table 24.2 as an essential amino acid, its biosynthesis will be discussed in this chapter inasmuch as mammals have some capacity to fabricate arginine.

In discussion of the synthesis of glutamic acid (page 488), it was indicated that amino group transfer from glutamic acid provides a mechanism for synthesis of most of the other amino acids by transamination. Indeed, this is the prime mechanism for synthesis of the nonessential amino acids, as well as for achieving intramolecular exchange of amino groups among amino acids. The nature and mechanism of transamination will be presented first as a background for consideration of synthesis of individual amino acids.

TRANSAMINATION

General Nature of Transamination. In 1937 Braunstein and Kritzmann demonstrated that there are widely distributed enzymes, *transaminases,* which catalyze the following general reaction.

$$R\text{—}\underset{\underset{\displaystyle NH_2}{|}}{CH}\text{—}COOH + R'\text{—}\underset{\underset{\displaystyle O}{\|}}{C}\text{—}COOH \rightleftharpoons R\text{—}\underset{\underset{\displaystyle O}{\|}}{C}\text{—}COOH + R'\text{—}\underset{\underset{\displaystyle NH_2}{|}}{CH}\text{—}COOH$$

In animal tissues, one couple of the reactants is almost invariably the pair, glutamic/α-ketoglutaric acids. The most abundant of the transaminases catalyze transamination from glutamic to oxaloacetic and pyruvic acids, respectively.

L-Glutamic acid + oxaloacetic acid $\rightleftharpoons$ α-ketoglutaric acid + L-aspartic acid

L-Glutamic acid + pyruvic acid $\rightleftharpoons$ α-ketoglutaric acid + L-alanine

Liver contains transaminases specific for transamination from glutamic acid to the α-keto acids corresponding to each of the naturally occurring α-amino acids, except possibly glycine, threonine, and lysine, and similar enzymes are found in plant and microbial cells. It is evident that, having fixed NH_3 into glutamic acid (page 488), transamination provides a mechanism for synthesis of those α-amino acids in a cell which can synthesize the corresponding α-keto acids. Moreover, transamination provides a means for redistributing nitrogen. For example, in any given meal, an animal may ingest a mixture of amino acids quite different from that which is optimal to its metabolism. Thus, were the meal rich in phenylalanine and poor in aspartic acid, the following pair of reactions would provide the necessary nitrogen for aspartic acid formation.

(a)   L-Phenylalanine + α-ketoglutaric acid $\rightleftharpoons$ phenylpyruvic acid + L-glutamic acid
(b)   L-Glutamic acid + oxaloacetic acid $\rightleftharpoons$ α-ketoglutaric acid + L-aspartic acid

---

Sum: L-Phenylalanine + oxaloacetic acid $\rightleftharpoons$ phenylpyruvic acid + L-aspartic acid

Simultaneous and continuous operation of all the transaminase reactions accounts for the observation that shortly after administration to rats of any amino acid labeled with N^{15} in the α-amino group, N^{15} appears in all the amino acids except lysine, with maximal abundance of N^{15} in glutamic and aspartic acids and in the amide group of glutamine. It should be noted that transamination is not limited to α-amino/α-keto acids. A number of transaminases catalyze reversible transfer of an amino group from glutamic acid to specific aldehydes, with formation of the corresponding primary amines. Also, transaminases utilizing amino acid amides in place of an amino acid are also present in tissues (see below).

Mechanism of Transamination. Pyridoxal phosphate, derived from vitamin B_6 (Chap. 55), is a component of each of the transaminases studied.

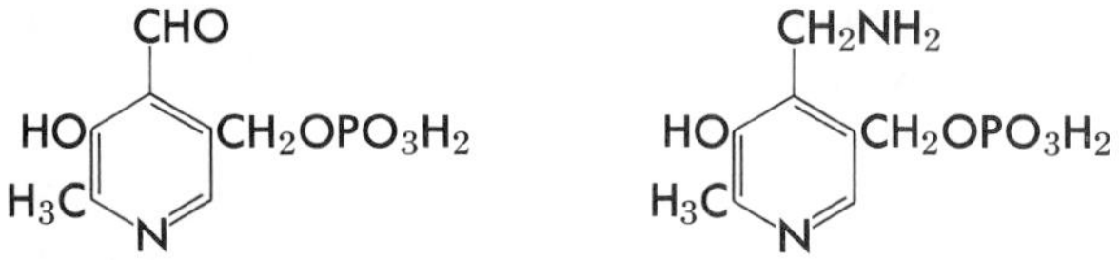

Pyridoxal phosphate   Pyridoxamine phosphate

Complete details of the mechanism of transamination are not known. Model systems have been studied in which trivalent cations, *e.g.*, Al^{+++}, plus pyridoxal phosphate catalyze transamination in vitro in the absence of enzyme, but the normal cellular mechanism is uncertain. In a general way, the following events are indicated for a single cycle of enzymic activity. P represents the remainder of the pyridoxal phosphate nucleus bound to enzyme.

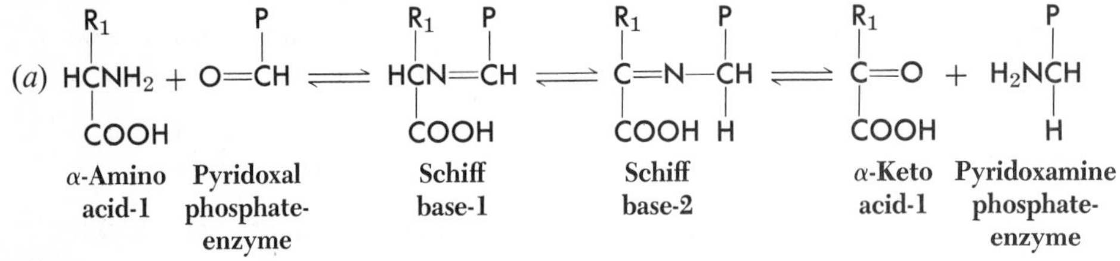

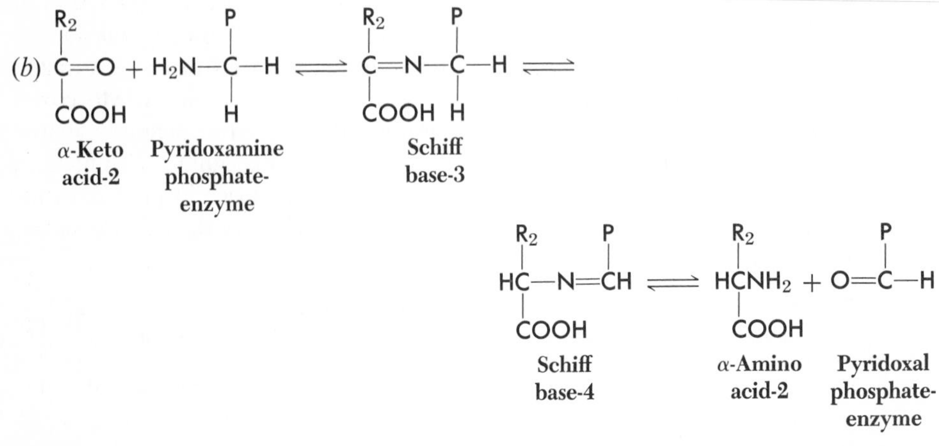

(a) α-Amino acid-1 + Pyridoxal phosphate-enzyme $\rightleftharpoons$ Schiff base-1 $\rightleftharpoons$ Schiff base-2 $\rightleftharpoons$ α-Keto acid-1 + Pyridoxamine phosphate-enzyme

(b) α-Keto acid-2 + Pyridoxamine phosphate-enzyme $\rightleftharpoons$ Schiff base-3 $\rightleftharpoons$

Schiff base-4 $\rightleftharpoons$ α-Amino acid-2 + Pyridoxal phosphate-enzyme

Glutamine and Asparagine in Transamination. It was indicated above that amino acid amides may also participate in transamination. This is the case for glutamine and asparagine, the two widely distributed amino acid amides of tissues. The reaction for glutamine may be represented as a transamination, with subsequent hydrolysis of the α-keto acid-ω-amide catalyzed by a specific *transaminase-amidase*.

(*a*) $H_2N-\underset{\underset{O}{\|}}{C}-CH_2-CH_2-\underset{\underset{NH_2}{|}}{CH}-COOH + R-\underset{\underset{O}{\|}}{C}-COOH \longrightarrow$

   Glutamine   **α-Keto acid**

$H_2N-\underset{\underset{O}{\|}}{C}-CH_2-CH_2-\underset{\underset{O}{\|}}{C}-COOH + R-\underset{\underset{NH_2}{|}}{CH}-COOH$

   α-Ketoglutaramic acid   **α-Amino acid**

(*b*) $H_2N-\underset{\underset{O}{\|}}{C}-CH_2-CH_2-\underset{\underset{O}{\|}}{C}-COOH \longrightarrow HOOC-CH_2-CH_2-\underset{\underset{O}{\|}}{C}-COOH + NH_3$

   α-Ketoglutaramic acid   **α-Ketoglutaric acid**

The glutamine and asparagine transaminase systems have a broad specificity; more than 30 α-keto acids are active, including the α-keto acids corresponding to many amino acids. The amide transaminase reactions, in contrast to amino acid transaminase systems, are irreversible because of rapid deamidation of the α-keto acid amides.

AMINO ACID BIOSYNTHESIS

Glutamic Acid, Aspartic Acid, and Alanine. Each of these amino acids is derived from an α-keto acid (α-ketoglutaric acid, oxaloacetic acid, and pyruvic acid, respectively); these α-keto acids also participate in the tricarboxylic acid cycle. The synthesis of glutamic acid has been described earlier (page 488). Aspartic acid and alanine are formed by transamination from glutamic acid. These three amino acids and glutamine are generally the most abundant of the nonprotein amino acids in cells. Thus the concentration of free glutamic acid in brain is approximately 100 to 150 mg. per g. of tissue. In various microorganisms, alanine and/or aspartic acid may play the central role reserved for glutamic acid in mammalian metabolism.

Glutamine and Asparagine. The synthesis of glutamine described earlier (page 488) provides glutamine for transamination reactions (see above) as well as a reserve pool of both ammonia and glutamic acid. Asparagine is present in most proteins and occurs in abundance as the free amino acid in higher plants. The mode of asparagine synthesis in mammals has not been established, but in plants and microorganisms appears to occur by a mechanism similar to that of glutamine, *i.e.*, from aspartic acid, NH_3, and ATP. However, a possible alternative route may obtain in which the amide-N of glutamine is transferred to aspartic acid. In plants, asparagine serves as a reservoir of NH_3 and of aspartic acid, formed by the hydrolytic activity of *asparaginase*.

Proline, Hydroxyproline, and Ornithine. Glutamic acid serves directly as the precursor for biosynthesis of proline, hydroxyproline, and ornithine. The last is not present in proteins but is the precursor for synthesis of arginine and, accordingly, participates in the urea cycle (page 512). The initial step in the conversion of glutamate to proline and ornithine is formation of glutamic semialdehyde; the details of this step are uncertain. Transamination of glutamic semialdehyde results in formation of ornithine (Fig. 24.1). Ring closure yields Δ^1-pyrroline 5-carboxylic acid, which, upon reduction by DPNH, gives proline.

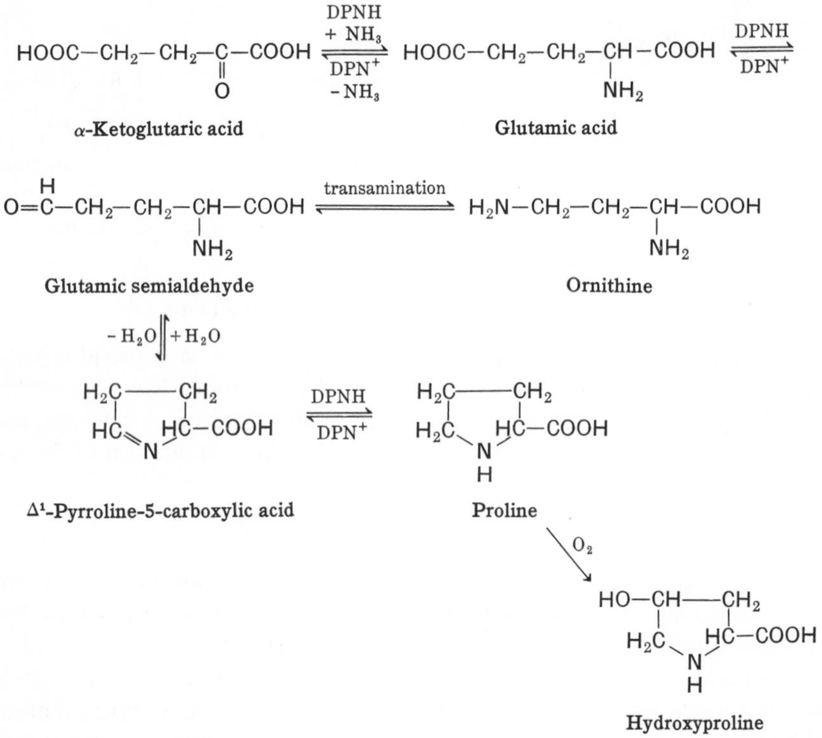

Fig. 24.1. Interrelationships in the biosynthesis of glutamic acid, ornithine, proline, and hydroxyproline.

The pathway for ornithine biosynthesis depicted in Fig. 24.1 appears to be a minor one in certain microorganisms. Vogel has discovered in *Escherichia coli* and in *Neurospora* an alternate pathway of ornithine biosynthesis from glutamic acid involving N-acetylglutamic acid (Fig. 24.2). The significance of this mode of ornithine biosynthesis for mammals is unknown. Three relevant enzymes have been found in *E. coli* extracts: an *acetylase* that catalyzes formation of N-acetylglutamate from glutamic acid and acetyl CoA, a *transaminase* that results in formation of N-α-acetylornithine, and *acetylornithinase* that catalyzes hydrolysis of N-α-acetylornithine to ornithine.

The distribution of hydroxyproline is extremely limited as this amino acid is known to occur only in collagen (page 144). It is formed from proline by an ascorbic acid-dependent, oxygen-utilizing hydroxylation of proline, apparently

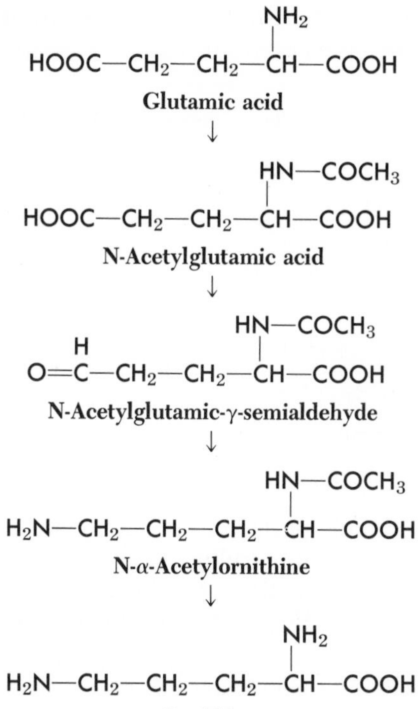

$$NH_2$$
$$HOOC—CH_2—CH_2—CH—COOH$$
Glutamic acid

↓

$$HN—COCH_3$$
$$HOOC—CH_2—CH_2—CH—COOH$$
N-Acetylglutamic acid

↓

$$HN—COCH_3$$
$$O{=}C—CH_2—CH_2—CH—COOH$$
(H above O=C)
N-Acetylglutamic-γ-semialdehyde

↓

$$HN—COCH_3$$
$$H_2N—CH_2—CH_2—CH_2—CH—COOH$$
N-α-Acetylornithine

↓

$$NH_2$$
$$H_2N—CH_2—CH_2—CH_2—CH—COOH$$
Ornithine

FIG. 24.2. N-Acetylglutamic acid pathway for biosynthesis of ornithine in microorganisms.

after the latter has been activated and bound in polypeptide linkage to a microsomal RNA in the course of protein biosynthesis (page 601).

These relationships among glutamic acid, proline, hydroxyproline, and ornithine have been established by studies in vitro and in vivo. Administration of glutamic-C^{14} leads to a high degree of labeling of proline, hydroxyproline, and arginine in the tissue proteins. As will be seen later (page 540) the relationships are, in part, reversible.

Arginine. Arginine synthesis commences with the ornithine derived from glutamic acid as described above. The first step is citrulline synthesis in a reaction catalyzed by *ornithine transcarbamylase*.

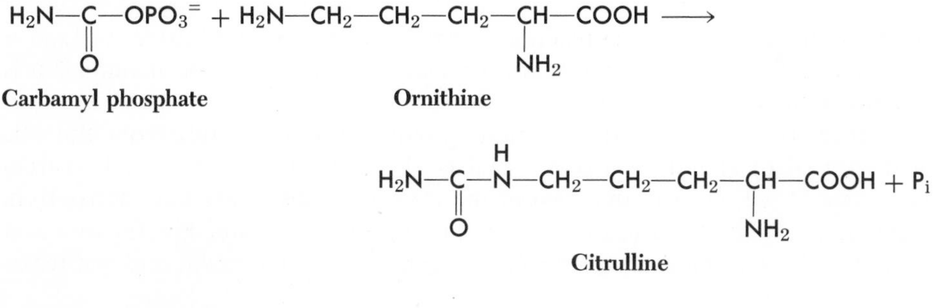

$$H_2N—C—OPO_3^{=} + H_2N—CH_2—CH_2—CH_2—CH—COOH \longrightarrow$$
(O below C; NH_2 below CH)
Carbamyl phosphate   Ornithine

$$H_2N—C—N—CH_2—CH_2—CH_2—CH—COOH + P_i$$
(H above N; O below C; NH_2 below CH)
Citrulline

The next reaction, catalyzed by *argininosuccinic acid synthetase,* requires ATP and Mg^{++} and involves a condensation of citrulline and aspartic acid.

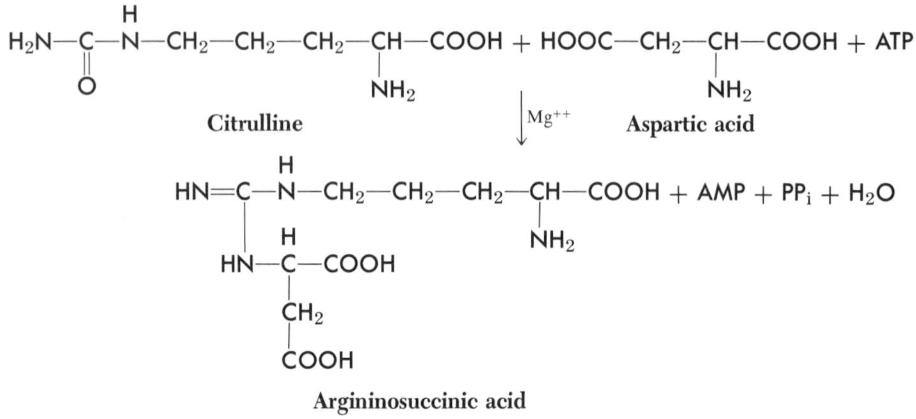

$$H_2N-\underset{\underset{O}{\|}}{\overset{\overset{H}{|}}{C}}-N-CH_2-CH_2-CH_2-\underset{\underset{NH_2}{|}}{CH}-COOH + HOOC-CH_2-\underset{\underset{NH_2}{|}}{CH}-COOH + ATP$$

Citrulline $\qquad \downarrow Mg^{++} \qquad$ Aspartic acid

$$HN=\overset{\overset{H}{|}}{\underset{\underset{HN-\overset{|}{C}-COOH}{|}}{C}}-N-CH_2-CH_2-CH_2-\underset{\underset{NH_2}{|}}{CH}-COOH + AMP + PP_i + H_2O$$

$$\overset{\overset{H}{|}}{\underset{\underset{COOH}{|}}{\underset{CH_2}{|}}}$$

Argininosuccinic acid

This enzyme has been partially purified from mammalian liver by Ratner and her associates. Exchange studies with citrulline labeled in the ureido group with O^{18} showed a transfer of isotope to AMP, suggesting an initial interaction between the ureido group and ATP with activation of citrulline. The detailed mechanism of this step remains to be elucidated.

Argininosuccinic acid is cleaved by an enzyme called *argininosuccinase* to yield arginine and fumaric acid.

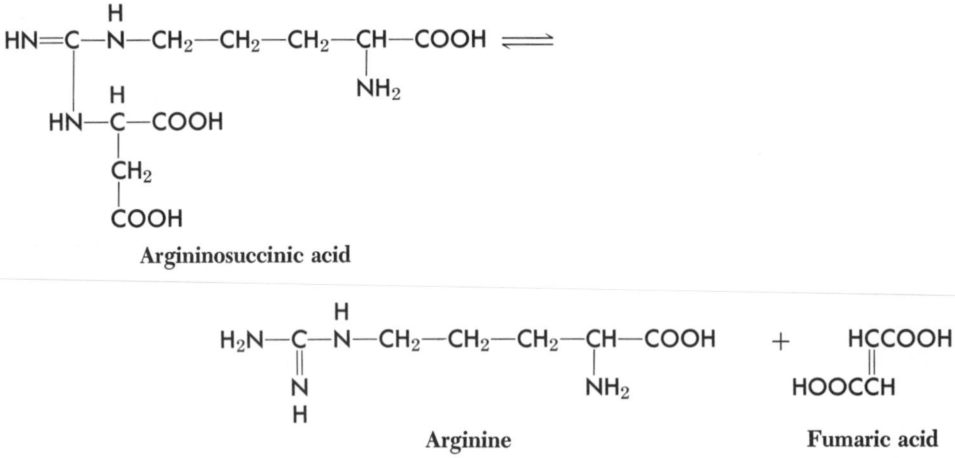

$$HN=\overset{\overset{H}{|}}{C}-N-CH_2-CH_2-CH_2-\underset{\underset{NH_2}{|}}{CH}-COOH \rightleftharpoons$$

$$\overset{\overset{H}{|}}{\underset{\underset{\underset{COOH}{|}}{\underset{CH_2}{|}}}{HN-\overset{|}{C}-COOH}}$$

Argininosuccinic acid

$$H_2N-\overset{\overset{H}{|}}{\underset{\underset{H}{|}}{\underset{N}{\|}}}{C}-N-CH_2-CH_2-CH_2-\underset{\underset{NH_2}{|}}{CH}-COOH \quad + \quad \underset{HOOCCH}{\overset{HCCOOH}{\|}}$$

Arginine $\qquad\qquad\qquad\qquad\qquad\qquad\qquad$ Fumaric acid

It should be noted that this reaction is neither hydrolytic nor oxidative, and is readily reversible. The enzyme is widely distributed in nature; in mammals it is present in kidney, liver, and brain.

Since ornithine received its γ-amino group by transamination from glutamic acid (page 496) and since aspartic acid is also formed by transamination from glutamate, it will be seen that two of the three N atoms of arginine derive from glutamic acid. The third has its origin in carbamyl phosphate. The fumaric acid formed in the argininosuccinase reaction can be hydrated to malic acid and reoxidized to oxaloacetic acid in the citric acid cycle. The oxalacetate can then acquire a new amino group, by transamination, with aspartate formation and repetition of the sequence.

Cysteine. Formation of cysteine, a nonessential amino acid, occurs in mammals from methionine, an essential amino acid for mammals. If sufficient methionine is fed, the dietary requirement for cysteine (and cystine) disappears. The reactions involved in cysteine biosynthesis are the following.

1. Demethylation of methionine to homocysteine.

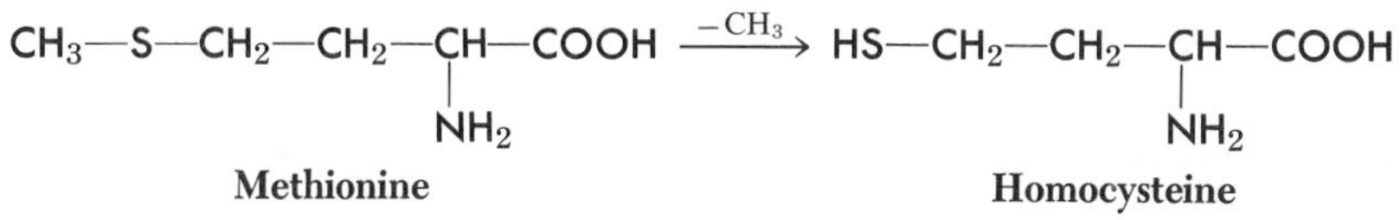

$$CH_3—S—CH_2—CH_2—CH—COOH \xrightarrow{-CH_3} HS—CH_2—CH_2—CH—COOH$$

$$\underset{\underset{\text{Methionine}}{NH_2}}{|} \qquad\qquad\qquad\qquad \underset{\underset{\text{Homocysteine}}{NH_2}}{|}$$

Homocysteine (homologue of cysteine) was first described as a product of chemical demethylation of methionine in the laboratory. Demethylation of methionine will be considered again later in relation to transmethylation (page 530).

2. Condensation of homocysteine with serine yields cystathionine; this reaction is catalyzed by an enzymic system termed *transsulfurase* and requires pyridoxal phosphate.

$$HOOC—CH—CH_2—CH_2—SH + CH_2—CH—COOH \longrightarrow$$

$$\underset{\underset{\text{Homocysteine}}{NH_2}}{|} \qquad\qquad \underset{OH}{|}\; \underset{\underset{\text{Serine}}{NH_2}}{|}$$

$$HOOC—CH—CH_2—S—CH_2—CH_2—CH—COOH + H_2O$$

$$\underset{NH_2}{|} \qquad\qquad\qquad \underset{NH_2}{|}$$

$$\text{Cystathionine}$$

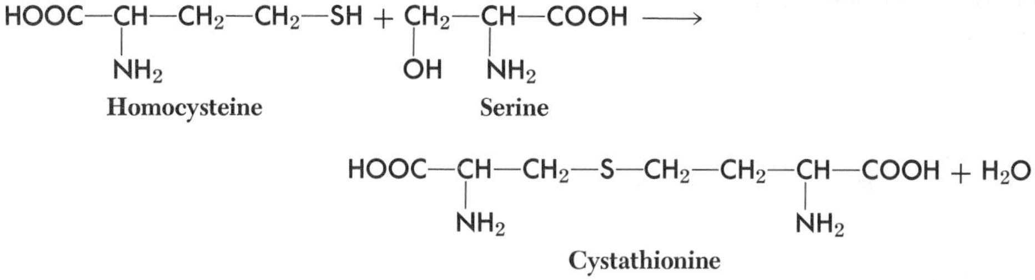

Cystathionine is found in high concentrations in the brain of primates (Chap. 39); this is of unknown significance.

3. Cleavage of cystathionine is a reaction catalyzed by a liver enzyme, *cystathionase,* which has been obtained in crystalline form and which utilizes pyridoxal phosphate. The products are cysteine and homoserine; the latter is rapidly converted to α-ketobutyric acid.

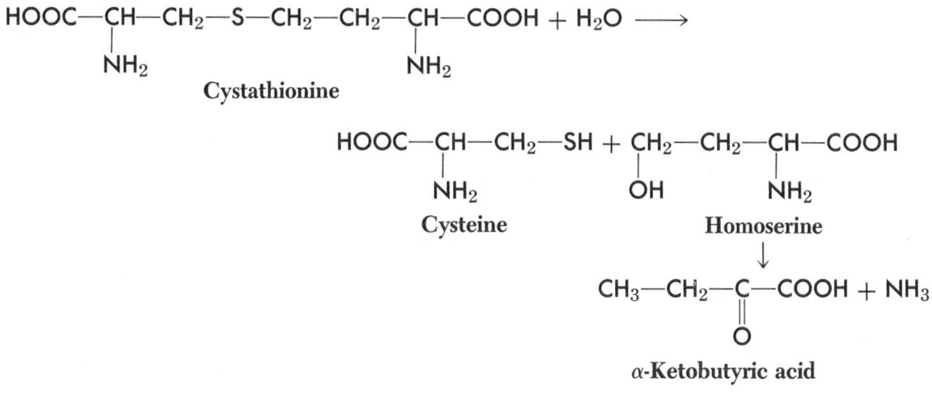

$$HOOC—CH—CH_2—S—CH_2—CH_2—CH—COOH + H_2O \longrightarrow$$

$$\underset{NH_2}{|} \qquad\qquad\qquad \underset{NH_2}{|}$$

$$\text{Cystathionine}$$

$$HOOC—CH—CH_2—SH + CH_2—CH_2—CH—COOH$$

$$\underset{\underset{\text{Cysteine}}{NH_2}}{|} \qquad\qquad \underset{OH}{|}\qquad \underset{\underset{\text{Homoserine}}{NH_2}}{|}$$

$$\downarrow$$

$$CH_3—CH_2—\underset{\underset{O}{\|}}{C}—COOH + NH_3$$

$$\text{α-Ketobutyric acid}$$

The net effect of the above reactions is an exchange of the sulfhydryl group of homocysteine with the hydroxyl group of serine in a process termed *transsulfuration*. Thus in the biosynthesis of cysteine, the carbon chain, including the amino group, arises from serine, whereas the sulfur is derived from methionine.

Although the dietary and metabolic equivalence of cysteine and cystine have been established, an enzymic system catalyzing their interconversion has not been described in mammalian tissue. A DPN^+-linked *cystine reductase* occurs in pea seedlings and yeast, but is different from oxidized glutathione reductase (see below). As described below, oxidized glutathione can function in a nonenzymic oxidation of cysteine to cystine.

Little or no free cystine is present in cells. The cystine of proteins appears to be formed by oxidation of cysteine residues after their incorporation into polypeptide chains (page 594). However, in the presence of O_2 and cations such as Fe^{++} or Cu^{++}, cystine may be formed from cysteine nonenzymically. If this occurs, ready reversal can be catalyzed by *glutathione reductase*. Glutathione is γ-glutamylcysteinylglycine. Its synthesis is described on page 527. Glutathione (G—SH, below) reacts nonenzymically with any disulfide to form a mixed disulfide.

$$G—SH + R'—S—S—R'' \rightleftharpoons G—S—S—R'' + R'—SH$$

A second molecule of glutathione, reacting with the mixed disulfide, yields oxidized glutathione.

$$G—SH + G—S—S—R'' \longrightarrow G—S—S—G + R''—SH$$

Glutathione reductase is a flavoprotein which catalyzes the following reaction.

$$TPNH + H^+ + G—S—S—G \rightleftharpoons TPN^+ + 2G—SH$$

In this manner, cystine (R'—S—S—R'' in the above reactions), which may form, is reduced back to cysteine for use by the cell.

Tyrosine. Tyrosine biosynthesis in mammals occurs by hydroxylation of phenylalanine, an essential amino acid. Much of the dietary requirement for phenylalanine is, in fact, due to the need for tyrosine. If the latter is fed, the dietary requirement for phenylalanine is reduced substantially. In this sense, tyrosine bears the same relationship to phenylalanine as cysteine does to methionine. In normal metabolism, the only known fate of phenylalanine, other than that of its utilization for protein synthesis, is its conversion to tyrosine. *Phenylalanine hydroxylase* has been studied by Kaufman. Like other hydroxylases, this is a microsomal enzyme, and over-all, hydroxylating radicals are formed from O_2 in the presence of TPNH (page 356). The system differs from other hydroxylases in that the role of TPNH appears to be to ensure a supply of the reduced form (5,6-dihydro) of a pteridine which has been tentatively identified as having the following structure.

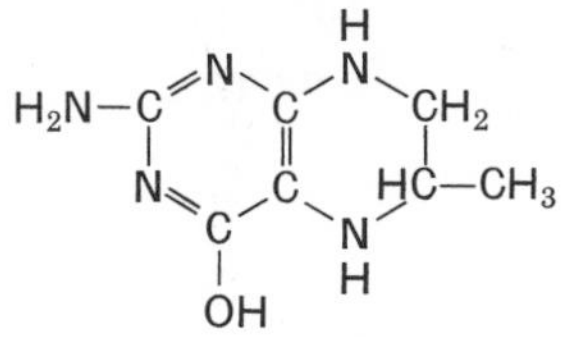

2-Amino–4-hydroxy–6-methyl–
5,6,7,8-tetrahydropteridine

In the microsomal oxidation of this reduced pteridine, the necessary hydroxylating radicals are formed.

Hereditary lack of phenylalanine hydroxylase results in phenylketonuria, an "inborn error of metabolism." The recessive gene is carried by about one in every two hundred individuals. In the absence of this enzyme, a group of minor pathways of phenylalanine metabolism, little used in normal individuals, becomes prominent. Transamination from phenylalanine yields phenylpyruvic acid, which may be excreted in as much as 1 to 2 g. per day. Presence of this compound in excessive amounts in early childhood is accompanied by severe mental retardation. Restriction of the dietary intake of phenylalanine by phenylketonuric children reduces the blood level of phenylalanine, abolishes excretion of phenylpyruvic acid, and prevents, in considerable degree, the mental retardation. The accumulation of phenylpyruvic acid leads also to formation and excretion of phenyllactic acid, o-hydroxyphenylacetic acid, benzoic acid, and phenylacetic acid. All appear in the urine, the last as phenylacetylglutamine (page 528).

Serine. The carbon chain of serine derives from 3-phosphoglyceric acid formed during glycolysis. The latter may be utilized by one of several pathways which lead either to serine or its 3-phosphate ester. Hydrolysis of the phosphate ester bond yields glyceric acid. The latter, with a DPN$^+$-requiring enzyme, provides hydroxypyruvic acid, which may be transaminated in a reaction catalyzed by *alanine transaminase* to form serine. Alternatively, 3-phosphoglyceric acid may be oxidized to 3-phosphohydroxypyruvic acid in a DPN$^+$-requiring reaction catalyzed by 3-phosphoglyceric acid dehydrogenase. Transamination with glutamic acid yields 3-phosphoserine. The latter may be used for phosphatide synthesis, etc., or hydrolyzed by *serine phosphatase*. Available evidence suggests that the last described pathway is the major route of serine synthesis. The fact that serine phosphatase is inhibited by serine may provide a means of regulating the rate of serine formation. Serine biogenesis is depicted in Fig. 24.3.

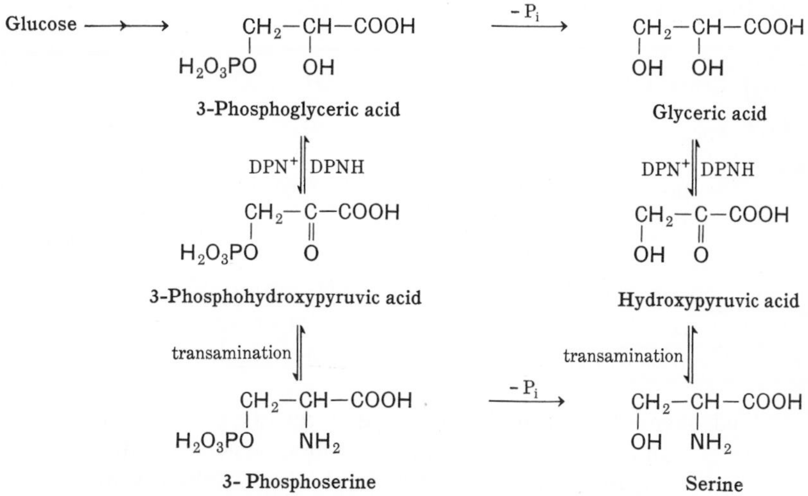

Fig. 24.3. Pathways of serine biosynthesis.

Glycine. The initial demonstration of glycine formation from serine was provided by Shemin, who administered serine, labeled with N^{15} in the amino position and C^{13} in the carboxyl position, together with benzoic acid, to rats and guinea pigs. Examination of the glycine excreted in the urine as benzoylglycine (hippuric acid, page 528) revealed an N^{15}/C^{13} ratio identical with that of the administered serine, thereby indicating formation of glycine by loss of the β-carbon of serine.

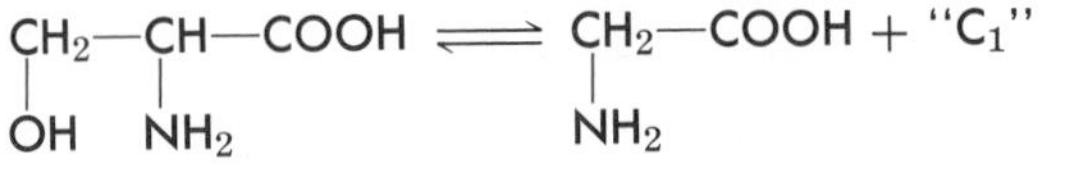

$$\begin{array}{cc} CH_2-CH-COOH \rightleftharpoons & CH_2-COOH + \text{``}C_1\text{''} \\ & \\ OH \quad NH_2 & NH_2 \end{array}$$

Serine   Glycine

It has been shown subsequently that this reaction is significant not only for the biosynthesis of glycine but as the prime metabolic source of a group of active C_1 compounds which exist at the oxidation level of CH_3OH, $HCHO$, or $HCOOH$, respectively. Their transformations make possible the addition to diverse compounds of the groups $-CH_3$, $-CH_2OH$, and $-CHO$, respectively.

C_1 Compounds. The transformation of serine to glycine is accomplished by *serine transhydroxymethylase* in the presence of pyridoxal phosphate and Mn^{++}. The acceptor for the hydroxymethyl group is tetrahydrofolic acid, a reduced form of the vitamin, folic acid (page 239). Although folic acid is designated as the vitamin, its tetrahydroderivative serves as the biological carrier for C_1 groups.

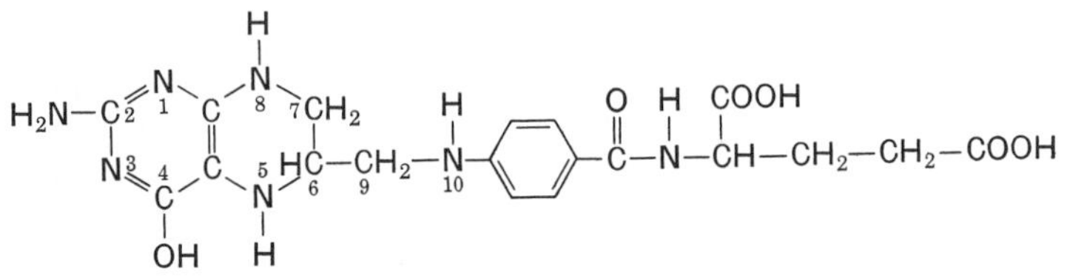

Tetrahydrofolic acid

The nitrogen atoms at the 5 and 10 positions function as the reactive sites of the molecule. In glycine formation the reaction, schematically, is the following.

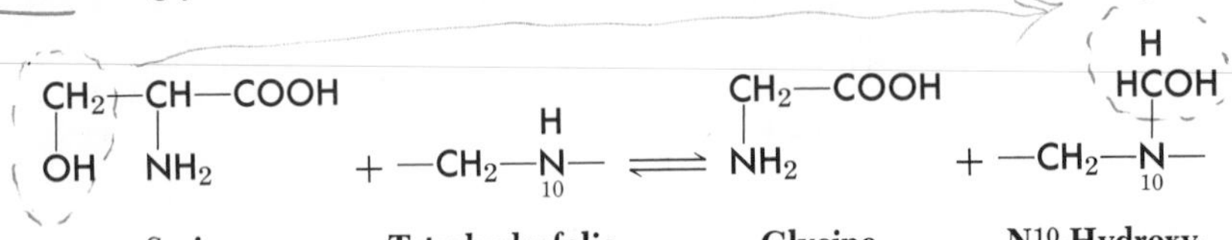

| Serine | Tetrahydrofolic acid | Glycine | N^{10}-Hydroxy-methyltetra-hydrofolic acid |

Presumably, on the enzymic surface the $-NH_2$ group of serine is bound as a Schiff's base to pyridoxal phosphate before transfer of the β-carbon to tetrahydrofolic acid; after the transfer, the Schiff's base must hydrolyze, thereby releasing glycine.

N^{10}-Hydroxymethyltetrahydrofolic acid is readily cyclized by loss of water between the N-5 and N-10 positions to N^5,N^{10}-methylenetetrahydrofolic acid. The latter in turn may be oxidized by TPN^+ to yield N^5,N^{10}-anhydroformyltetrahydrofolic acid.

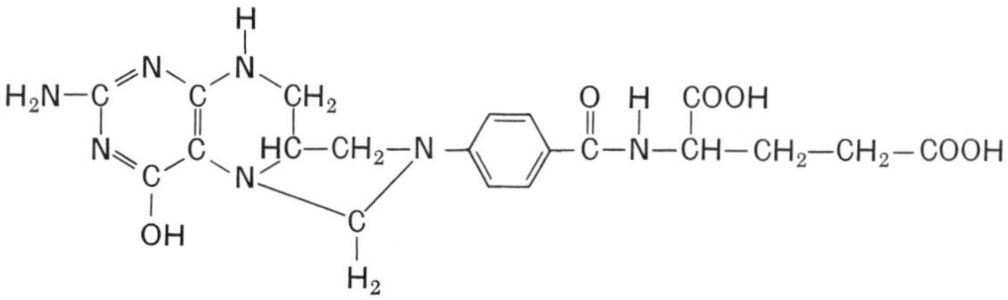

N^5,N^{10}-Methylenetetrahydrofolic acid

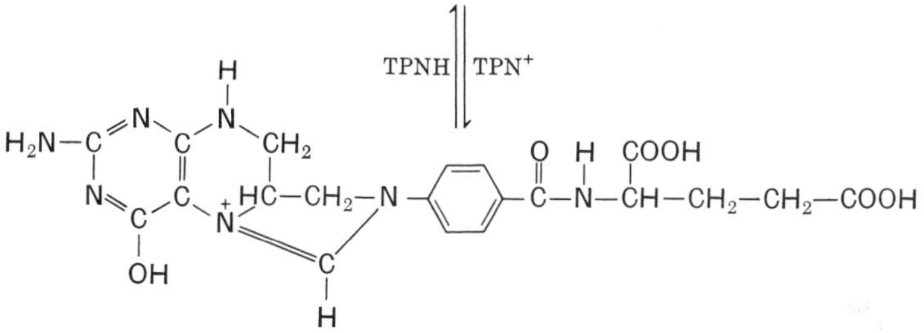

N^5,N^{10}-Anhydroformyltetrahydrofolic acid

Hydrolysis of N^5,N^{10}-anhydroformyltetrahydrofolic acid yields N^{10}-formyltetrahydrofolic acid, the form which is utilized for formyl transfer in many biosynthetic pathways. N^{10}-Formyltetrahydrofolic acid may also be formed directly from formic acid in a reaction requiring ATP and catalyzed by *tetrahydrofolic acid formylase.*

The latter reaction is of limited significance in mammalian metabolism since free formic acid is not a major metabolite; the reaction depicted does explain the appearance of the carbon of administered HC^{14}OOH in those compounds normally formed from N^{10}-formyltetrahydrofolic acid.

In some reactions, a formyl group is transferred directly from a metabolite to the N-5 position of tetrahydrofolic acid. In these instances, a second reaction, requiring utilization of an ATP, must occur to form the N^5,N^{10}-anhydroformyltetrahydrofolic acid, which then is converted to the N^{10} derivative or may be reduced to the N^{10}-hydroxymethyl compound. Finally, in a limited number of cases, tetrahydrofolic acid may accept a formimino group, —CH=NH, at the N^5 position. This is hydrolyzed to the N^5,N^{10}-anhydroformyl compound which is utilized in the usual manner. These relationships are summarized in Fig. 24.4.

Genesis of Methyl Groups. The C$_1$ group on tetrahydrofolic acid is the source of the methyl group for synthesis of both methionine (page 517) and thymine (page 577). For methionine synthesis, the methyl group is formed, in *Escherichia coli,* by reduction of N^5,N^{10}-methylenetetrahydrofolic acid. The responsible enzyme is a flavoprotein which catalyzes the following reaction.

N^5,N^{10}-Methylenetetrahydrofolic acid + DPNH + H$^+$

$$\Big\Vert \text{FAD}$$

N^5-Methyltetrahydrofolic acid + DPN$^+$

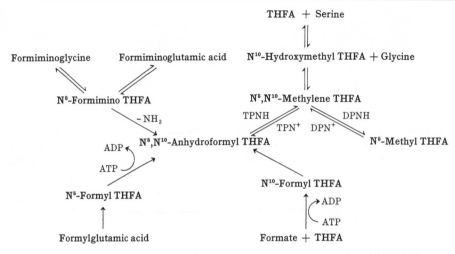

FIG. 24.4. Relationships among C_1 derivatives of tetrahydrofolic acid (THFA).

Since N^5-methyltetrahydrofolic acid is found in liver, it is likely that it is generated and utilized in mammalian tissues in a manner similar to that above in *E. coli*. The formation of N^5-methyltetrahydrofolic acid by the above reactions affords a pathway for *de novo* genesis of methyl groups from the diverse substances which contribute to the C_1 pool.

The transfer of the methyl group to homocysteine to form methionine is discussed in Chap. 55 (see Vitamin B_{12}). The enzyme catalyzing the transfer requires a cobamide derivative as coenzyme, and ATP. Labeling experiments indicate that the CH_3 group of N^5-methyltetrahydrofolic acid is transferred intact.

Transmethylation. The transfer of the methyl group of methionine to appropriate acceptors, *transmethylation,* and the general metabolic significance of this reaction were first demonstrated by du Vigneaud and his colleagues. Loss of the methyl group from methionine results in formation of homocysteine (page 499).

The active form of methionine which functions in methylation reactions was identified by Cantoni and his associates as S-adenosylmethionine.

S-Adenosylmethionine

This compound is a sulfonium form of methionine, with a free energy of scission comparable to that of the pyrophosphate linkage of ATP. Its synthesis is catalyzed by an enzyme which has been purified from liver but is widely distributed in nature.

$$\text{L-Methionine} + \text{ATP} \longrightarrow \text{S-adenosylmethionine} + PP_i + P_i$$

This process is unique in biological systems, being the only known instance in which, in a single reaction, the phosphates of ATP appear as a molecule of P_i plus a molecule of PP_i. The detailed enzymic mechanism is not understood. In the presence of the appropriate specific enzymes, the methyl group of S-adenosylmethionine may be transferred, for example, to guanidoacetic acid to form creatine (page 530), to phosphatidyl ethanolamine to form lecithin (page 465), or to nicotinamide to form N^1-methylnicotinamide (Chap. 55). In each case the other product formed from S-adenosylmethionine appears to be S-adenosyl-L-homocysteine which is cleaved to adenosine and homocysteine. The homocysteine formed may be utilized in several ways. In plants, which can also form homocysteine *de novo* (page 517), the homocysteine may be remethylated, using methyl groups formed *de novo*. In animals, another mode of re-forming methionine derives from the fact that choline, liberated from lecithin, may be oxidized in two stages to betaine; the latter then transmethylates to homocysteine, with formation of methionine.

(a) $(CH_3)_3\overset{+}{N}-CH_2-CH_2OH \xrightarrow{FAD} (CH_3)_3\overset{+}{N}-CH_2-CHO \xrightarrow{DPN^+}$

   Choline   Betaine aldehyde

$(CH_3)_3\overset{+}{N}-CH_2-COO^-$

   Betaine

(b) $(CH_3)_3\overset{+}{N}-CH_2COO^- + HS-CH_2-CH_2-\overset{\overset{\displaystyle NH_2}{|}}{CH}-COOH \longrightarrow$

   Betaine   Homocysteine

$(CH_3)_2N-CH_2-COOH + H_3C-S-CH_2-CH_2-\underset{\underset{\displaystyle NH_2}{|}}{CH}-COOH$

   Dimethylglycine   Methionine

If homocysteine (homocystine) is fed to rats on a methionine-deficient diet, these processes of methylation of homocysteine provide sufficient methionine for normal growth. However, homocystine is not present in the normal diet, and, under ordinary circumstances, homocysteine formed by transmethylation is not remethylated but is used for cysteine synthesis (page 499); the total pathway, therefore, is irreversible. Accordingly, dietary methionine is by far the major source of methyl groups in the animal economy. *De novo* methyl group synthesis remains important for thymine synthesis (page 577), but dietary methionine supplies most of the methyl groups in mammals.

DYNAMIC ASPECTS OF MAMMALIAN NITROGEN METABOLISM

The metabolism of protein and amino acids by bacteria growing logarithmically in a rich nutrient broth is in marked contrast to that of the mammal. Bacteria accept from the medium those amino acids, and in the correct quantity, needed for maximal protein synthesis. Available evidence suggests that no protein degradation occurs and that the removal of amino acids from the medium is balanced by the sum of amino acids incorporated into protein plus those utilized for synthesis of the diverse nitrogenous compounds found in such organisms. Little or no nitrogen, in any form, is returned to the medium, and amino acids not needed are not accepted into the cell.

No comparable situation occurs in mammalian life. At all stages in the existence of a human being, there is a continuing entry and loss of nitrogen compounds. Amino acids and lesser amounts of other nitrogenous compounds enter the body and are processed, and the metabolic products are excreted in urine and feces. During infancy and childhood, and during convalescence from a debilitating disease, the intake of nitrogen exceeds the output (*positive nitrogen balance*); the opposite situation may prevail in senescence or, relatively briefly, during starvation or certain wasting diseases (*negative nitrogen balance*). But in infancy or senescence the daily departure from *nitrogen equilibrium* is usually only a small fraction of the total amount of nitrogen metabolized.

Ingested amino acids or those derived from protein degradation in the gastrointestinal tract or in tissues may be channeled into one of the following pathways: (1) incorporation into protein; (2) incorporation into a small peptide; (3) utilization of the nitrogen and/or carbon for synthesis of a different amino acid; (4) utilization for synthesis of a nitrogenous compound which is not an amino acid; (5) removal of the α-amino group by transamination or oxidation, with subsequent formation of urea and oxidation of the resultant α-keto acid. The latter process, (5), as well as (4), may be regarded as a disposal device for surplus amino acids. These last two pathways are essential to the animal for two general reasons: (1) Daily food consumption is related to caloric need. In satisfying that need, the animal may ingest and digest an amount of protein which provides amino acids in excess of physiological requirements. In contrast to glycogen and triglycerides, there is no equivalent storage form of protein or amino acids. Accordingly, surplus amino acids must be excreted per se or, more economically, their nitrogen must be removed and excreted and the corresponding α-keto acids oxidized for their caloric value or converted to glycogen or fatty acids for storage. (2) There is a continuing need for the biosynthesis of an array of nitrogenous compounds, *e.g.*, purines, pyrimidines, porphyrins, epinephrine, thyroxine, nicotinic acid, etc.

In some instances the nitrogen and carbon skeleton derive from a nutritionally essential amino acid; in others only the nitrogen atoms need have their origin in the dietary amino acid since the remainder of the molecule can be provided from carbohydrate precursors. The capacity of the mammal to perform these conversions is apparent from the fact that a synthetic diet which provides nitrogen only in the form of the nutritionally essential amino acids, plus the small amount in the vitamins, supports maximal growth. However, in circumstances of inadequate intake of protein nitrogen, *e.g.*, starvation, ingestion of an inadequate amount of protein, or ingestion of a diet which provides adequate quantities of all but one of the essential amino acids, synthesis of nitrogenous compounds continues. For example, nicotinic acid synthesis from tryptophan would continue, albeit at a reduced level, even on a tryptophan-free diet. The tryptophan utilized would be derived from the pool of amino acids generated by the continuing hydrolysis of tissue proteins (see below). Since incomplete or imperfect proteins are not made, the amino acids remaining in the pool could not be used for resynthesis of proteins. Hence, they now are not useful, they are catabolically degraded, and their nitrogen appears in the urine as urea. It is of interest that the extent of negative nitrogen balance is of the same magnitude, *i.e.*, about 4 to 5 g. of nitrogen per day, in human adults on a diet which provides no amino acids as it is in individuals provided a diet which lacks only one essential amino acid but is otherwise complete.

Removal of Amino Acids from the Circulation. The plasma concentration of amino acids is normally about 4 to 8 mg. of α-amino nitrogen (35 to 65 mg. of mixed amino acids) per 100 ml. (see Table 32.1, page 628). Amino acids which enter the circulation by absorption from the intestine or by intravenous administration are quickly removed and appear in all tissues and organs of the body. Thus, within 5 min., 85 to 100 per cent of a large intravenously administered quantity (5 to 10 g.) of a single amino acid may be removed by the tissues.

The liver exhibits the greatest capacity to take up circulating amino acids, with kidney also participating significantly; other tissues take up lesser quantities. Some tissues, notably brain, exhibit a selective capacity. Thus, while intravenously administered methionine, histidine, glycine, arginine, glutamine, and tyrosine rapidly appear in the brain, glutamic acid cannot readily enter this structure from the blood, and lysine, proline, and leucine do so very slowly. Rates of entry of the last three amino acids into brain are greater in young individuals than in adults.

Amino acids enter into cells by an active, energy-requiring process. It occurs against a concentration gradient; entry of amino acids is accompanied by accumulation of water and some Na^+. K^+ may leave the cell simultaneously, particularly when lysine or arginine enters, thus preserving electrical neutrality of the cell contents. Studies of amino acid absorption across the intestine and amino acid uptake by bacterial cells and by mammalian cells in tissue culture have demonstrated the energy-utilizing "active" nature of amino acid transport. Christensen and his colleagues have shown that pyridoxal phosphate stimulates this process, perhaps as a "carrier" (Chap. 35). It appears likely that several independent transport mechanisms exist, each of which may be responsible for a group of structurally related amino acids, *e.g.*, lysine and arginine; leucine, isoleucine, and valine; etc.

The metabolic fate of an amino acid molecule is presumably the same whether it enters the blood from the intestine or is derived from endogenous sources, *i.e.*, by intracellular synthesis or from the degradation of cellular proteins. However, mixing of amino acids entering a tissue from the blood and those arising from metabolism of the tissue may not be quite complete. Indeed, evidence indicates that discrete, nonmixing "pools" of amino acids may exist within a given cell, with differing turnover rates. While this phenomenon is still of unknown physiological significance for the total organism, it is a serious variable in the interpretation of experimental data obtained with isotopically labeled amino acids, particularly in studies of protein turnover and product-precursor relationships.

Many factors influence the extent to which amino acids are distributed among the various metabolic reactions in which they may participate. For example, the growing organism or the individual convalescing from a debilitating disease uses a significant proportion of available amino acids for construction of new tissue proteins. The availability of carbohydrate and lipid must influence the proportion of the total caloric requirement which must be supplied by amino acids. In addition, the pattern of the amino acid mixture supplied to the tissues, *i.e.*, the relative amounts of the various amino acids, will determine the suitability of these substances for the synthesis of a specific type of cellular protein. Finally, the influence of hormones in modifying the direction and rate of certain metabolic reactions is an important factor in amino acid and protein metabolism.

Utilization of Amino Acids for Protein Synthesis. It is abundantly clear from the increment in total body protein during growth and in the convalescing adult in positive nitrogen balance that dietary amino acids can be utilized for net protein synthesis. Even in the adult in nitrogen equilibrium it is evident that continual protein synthesis is required for the elaboration of digestive enzymes which may be lost in the feces, protein hormones which are made in endocrine glands and degraded elsewhere in the body, formation of plasma proteins, including antibodies, and replacement of the entire protein complement of those cell populations of relatively short existence, *e.g.*, erythrocytes and leukocytes.

Demonstration that there is a continuing incorporation of dietary nitrogen into constitutive tissue proteins even in an adult animal in nitrogen equilibrium was possible only through application of isotopic methods. In a series of investigations by Schoenheimer and his colleagues in which amino acids labeled with N^{15} and/or D were given to adult rats in nitrogen balance, the labeled amino acids were invariably found in the mixed, precipitable tissue proteins. These data led to the present-day concept of protein metabolism as a dynamic process in which body proteins are continually turning over, *i.e.*, undergoing synthesis and degradation. Since the proteins remain constant in amount, the two processes must occur at equal rates.

Although it is clear that new protein synthesis is always associated with formation of new cells, *e.g.*, regeneration of tissues, the rates of turnover of proteins within existing structures vary widely, depending only in part upon the degree to which new cells are being elaborated. Thus, isotopically labeled amino acids are rapidly incorporated into liver protein when liver regeneration is taking place with formation of new liver cells. But the constitutive enzymes of the normal, nondividing cells of adult liver, *e.g.*, aldolase, also contain isotopically labeled amino acids, after these have been administered. For such proteins, the data indicate half-life times of many weeks. Less labile is the metabolism of "structural" proteins such as the myosin of muscle (Chap. 38), which exhibits a half-life of more than 6 months. This does not reflect a difference between liver and muscle with respect to all constituent proteins. Thirty minutes after injection of eight labeled amino acids into rabbits, the ratio of the specific activities of all eight was found to be the same in three different crystalline enzymes isolated from skeletal muscle. This experiment indicates that (1) muscle cells constantly synthesize new protein, (2) the synthetic process is rapid, (3) in a given cell, all proteins are fabricated from a common pool of free amino acids, and (4) this process involves *de novo* synthesis of entire protein molecules, and resynthesis of proteins from partial degradation products does not occur.

Proteins which are normally found extracellularly also turn over at varying rates. In general, proteins which leave the cellular sites of their syntheses undergo replacement by new molecules relatively more rapidly than do proteins which remain as intracellular components. Thus, in man in nitrogen balance, the half-life of serum proteins is approximately 10 days. In contrast, however, is the extracellular protein of connective tissue, collagen, which exhibits almost no significant incorporation of labeled amino acids in adult animals and from which labeled amino acids, incorporated when the animal was young and growing, do not disappear.

Similar studies, in which labeled amino acids were administered, have permitted estimation of the total rate of protein synthesis. In man, dog, and rat, the rates of protein synthesis, expressed as grams of nitrogen per kilogram per day, were found to be 0.6 to 1.0, 0.6, and 2.0, respectively. Thus, a 70-kg. adult man synthesizes and degrades about 400 g. of protein per day, whereas an average American diet provides about 160 g. of amino acids during this time and, at any instant, the total amount of free amino acids in the body fluids is of the order of 30 g.

The fact that although protein synthesis proceeds at this great rate it is exactly balanced by protein degradation is indeed remarkable. Much has been learned recently concerning the mechanisms of protein synthesis, and these are described in detail in Chap. 30. However, the factors which regulate the *rate* of protein synthesis and degradation are not understood. Apparently it is not the supply of amino acids which is primarily rate-limiting; net protein synthesis cannot be increased by augmenting the amino acid supply when the latter is adequate. The influence of various endocrine factors on protein synthesis will be discussed in Part Six of this book, but in no case is the actual mechanism clear. In contrast to the energy- and information-requiring apparatus for protein synthesis, protein degradation occurs by simple hydrolysis catalyzed by intracellular proteinases present in the lysosomes (page 270).

REMOVAL OF AMINO GROUPS OF AMINO ACIDS

A major metabolic pathway for amino acids involves an initial removal of the α-amino group.

Site of Amino Group Removal. The liver is quantitatively a major site of removal of amino groups from amino acids, although the process is a general one in all tissues studied. The importance of the liver in this metabolic process probably stems from its size and its receipt of amino acids absorbed from the intestine via the portal circulation. The capacity of the liver to take up absorbed amino acids, and their rapid metabolism in this organ, has been referred to previously (page 507). The loss of amino acid nitrogen from liver is accompanied by an increase in blood urea, implicating the liver and amino acid nitrogen in urea synthesis (see below).

In classical studies, Mann and his associates demonstrated that hepatectomy in the dog prevents the rapid removal of intravenously administered amino acids and the concomitant rise in blood urea. Moreover, the usual increase in blood urea, following injection of amino acids into dogs with both kidneys removed, did not occur if the liver was also removed. Blood amino acids may be elevated in patients either with severe acute liver atrophy or following surgical portocaval anastomoses with evidence of liver dysfunction.

Mode of Amino Group Removal. Amino groups are removed by one of two mechanisms: (1) transamination, which has been previously described (pages 493*ff.*), and (2) other deamination reactions. These latter include (*a*) oxidative deamination catalyzed by L-amino acid oxidase and (*b*) a "dehydrase" reaction.

Transamination Followed by Deamination. The presence in liver of transaminases specific for the reaction between α-ketoglutaric acid and most of the individual amino acids, together with a high order of glutamic acid dehydrogenase activity in hepatic mitochondria, has led to general acceptance of the concept that the α-amino groups of most amino acids are converted to ammonia by consecutive transamination to α-ketoglutaric acid and oxidation of the glutamic acid thus formed.

(*a*) α-Ketoglutaric acid + amino acid $\longrightarrow$ glutamic acid + α-keto acid

(*b*)   Glutamic acid + DPN$^+$ + H$_2$O $\longrightarrow$ α-ketoglutaric acid + DPNH + H$^+$ + NH$_3$

Sum: Amino acid + DPN$^+$ + H$_2$O $\longrightarrow$ α-keto acid + DPNH + H$^+$ + NH$_3$

Presumably, the DPNH which arises in this manner may be reoxidized by the mitochondrial electron transport system, thereby opposing the otherwise very unfavorable equilibrium of the glutamic acid dehydrogenase reaction which, of itself, markedly favors formation of glutamic acid from α-ketoglutaric acid, DPNH, and ammonia (page 488). Although several other experimental observations suggest that this concept of the general mechanism for deamination of amino acids should be regarded with some reservation, it remains the most plausible mechanism suggested to date.

Oxidative Deamination of Amino Acids. Liver and kidney of the rat exhibit a low order of general L-amino acid oxidase activity. This enzyme is a flavoprotein with flavin adenine dinucleotide (FAD) as the prosthetic group. The general reaction may be indicated as follows.

(*a*)   R—CHNH$_2$—COOH + FAD $\rightleftharpoons$ R—CO—COOH + NH$_3$ + FADH$_2$

(*b*)   FADH$_2$ + O$_2$ $\longrightarrow$ FAD + H$_2$O$_2$

The peroxide formed is decomposed by *catalase* (page 357).

The L-amino acid oxidase catalyzes oxidation of all naturally occurring L-amino acids except serine, threonine, and the dicarboxylic and dibasic amino acids. At this time it seems unlikely that this enzyme is a very significant factor in normal amino acid oxidation because of its low order of activity.

Also unclear is the role of the highly potent D-amino acid oxidase of liver and kidney. This enzyme (page 345) also utilizes FAD as its prosthetic group and is present in the cytoplasm. It catalyzes oxidation of the unnatural D antipode of a large number of amino acids; however, D-amino acids are not known to occur in mammalian metabolism. This enzyme does provide a means of oxidizing the D-amino acids of bacterial cell walls should any of them be absorbed from the intestine. Perhaps more significant is the fact that this enzyme is identical with *glycine oxidase,* catalyzing the following reaction.

$$H_2N—CH_2—COOH \longrightarrow \underset{\text{Glyoxylic acid}}{O{=}\overset{H}{C}—COOH} + NH_3$$

Glycine

There are also present in liver *monoamine* and *diamine oxidases* (page 346). These flavoproteins catalyze the aerobic oxidation of a wide variety of physiological amines to the corresponding aldehydes and NH_3. Although the amounts of each individual amine are small, the total of such activity may contribute significantly to the pool of ammonia. Similarly, the several transaminases which can transfer from amino acids such as γ-aminobutyric acid contribute to the formation of glutamic acid; deamination of the latter was considered above.

Amino Group Removal by a "Dehydrase" Reaction. A significant contribution to total NH_3 production is provided by the group of pyridoxal phosphate-dependent "dehydrases." These are encountered (Chap. 27) in the metabolism of serine, cysteine, homoserine, threonine, and, perhaps, homocysteine; in each instance NH_3 and the corresponding α-keto acid is formed.

Amino group removal may also occur by other specific mechanisms in the case of individual amino acids, *e.g.,* histidine (page 550).

UREA SYNTHESIS

Reference has been made previously to the role of urea formation in the disposal of surplus amino acids (page 506). Most of the nitrogen of these amino acids appears in the urine as urea.

The nitrogen compounds of the urine of an adult in nitrogen equilibrium may be regarded as comprising three classes: (1) a large number of diverse compounds excreted daily in small but relatively constant amount, *e.g.,* creatinine, uric acid, N^1-methylnicotinamide, etc.; (2) NH_3 excretion, which is a function of the acid-base economy of the body and is generated in the kidney as a means of excreting excess protons (Chap. 37); and (3) urea, the amount of which represents the difference between the dietary intake of nitrogen and the sum of (1) + (2). Circumstances which result in positive nitrogen balance lead to a diminution in urea excretion; in those conditions in which there is excessive excretion of nitrogen, at the expense of body protein, the increment in urinary nitrogen occurs as urea. Thus, it is the formation and excretion of urea which is the "leveling device" by which nitrogen balance is maintained.

Cyclic Mechanism of Urea Formation. Urea is synthesized in *ureotelic* organisms (those which utilize urea as the major vehicle for excretion of surplus nitrogen) by adaptation of a reaction sequence which is thought to have evolved in much more primitive creatures. The enzyme that, uniquely, makes urea synthesis possible is *arginase,* which catalyzes the irreversible hydrolysis of arginine to ornithine and urea.

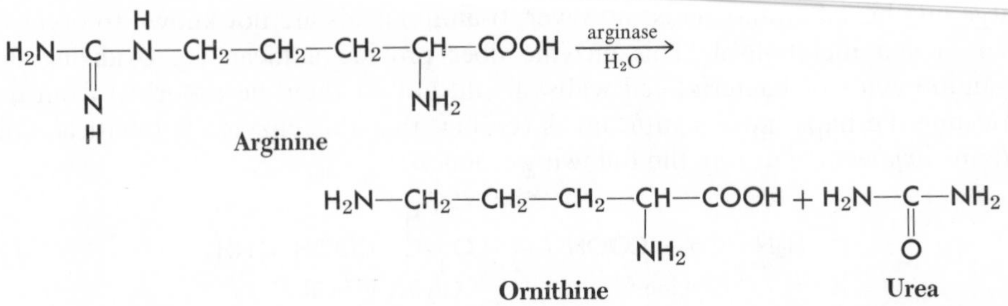

$$H_2N-\underset{\underset{H}{\overset{\|}{N}}}{\overset{H}{\underset{}{C}}}-N-CH_2-CH_2-CH_2-\underset{\underset{NH_2}{|}}{CH}-COOH \xrightarrow[H_2O]{arginase}$$

Arginine

$$H_2N-CH_2-CH_2-CH_2-\underset{\underset{NH_2}{|}}{CH}-COOH + H_2N-\underset{\overset{\|}{O}}{C}-NH_2$$

Ornithine   Urea

Since arginine is ubiquitous in animal cells (it is required for protein synthesis), it follows that urea could be made by any cell which possesses arginase. In mammals, the liver, which contains not only arginase but also all the other enzymes required for arginine synthesis, is the major site of urea formation. Classic experiments by Bollman and Mann demonstrated failure of urea synthesis and accumulation of amino acids in hepatectomized dogs. Impaired urea synthesis is also evident in clinical and experimental liver damage. A low level of urea synthesis occurs in kidney and brain, but this seems of minor significance in the total nitrogen economy.

The catalytic role of ornithine in urea synthesis was first demonstrated by Krebs and Henseleit, who also established the position of citrulline in this process. They formulated the following cycle.

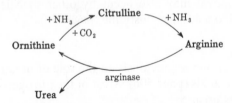

The reaction sequence: ornithine → citrulline → arginine will be recognized as the normal pathway for arginine synthesis, not only in mammals but also in bacteria and plants (page 497). It is the presence of arginase in mammalian liver which converts this reaction sequence from a one-way synthetic system to a cyclic process in which the carbon chain of ornithine may be used repeatedly, with one urea molecule fabricated for each turn of the cycle.

Although the abbreviated mechanism depicted above indicates the entry of nitrogen as NH_3, it will be recalled (page 497) that citrulline formation actually utilizes carbamyl phosphate as N donor and that the second nitrogen enters as the α-amino nitrogen of aspartic acid. The energy for urea synthesis, therefore, is provided by the two molecules of ATP needed for carbamyl phosphate synthesis and the single ATP needed to make argininosuccinic acid. Since during the latter step, ATP → AMP + PP_i, and the pyrophosphate is then hydrolyzed by pyrophosphatase action, $PP_i + H_2O \rightarrow 2P_i$, a total of four high-energy phosphate equivalents is required per urea molecule.

The details of the operation of the mammalian urea-forming system have been largely revealed in the laboratories of P. P. Cohen, Ratner, Grisolia, and

Lipmann. Of interest is the rare disorder, *argininosuccinic acidemia,* characterized by a high blood concentration and renal excretion of argininosuccinic acid. Individuals with this condition are mentally deficient. Although brain can make small amounts of urea, the large amounts of argininosuccinate present in the circulation and urine appear to arise outside the brain, probably in the kidney because of deficiency in that organ of the enzyme catalyzing scission of argininosuccinic acid (page 498). Urea synthesis in the liver of such individuals is thought to proceed normally.

For the liver to serve effectively as the locus of urea formation, using the α-amino nitrogen of all 20 amino acids, it must possess not only the enzymic capacity to operate the urea-forming cycle, but also the capacity to direct into the synthesis of carbamyl phosphate and aspartic acid, nitrogen from all those 20 amino acids. The role of aspartic acid in transamination and in providing one of the two nitrogen atoms for urea synthesis has been referred to above (page 512). It will be recalled that aspartic acid contributes this nitrogen atom via the synthesis of argininosuccinic acid, an intermediate in arginine formation (page 498). Aspartate formation from glutamate via transamination with oxaloacetate thus provides a mechanism for channeling amino groups from amino acids into urea. Although the second nitrogen atom of urea is depicted as arising from carbamyl phosphate via citrulline formation (page 497), the source of the ammonia for carbamyl phosphate synthesis (page 489), and therefore of the second nitrogen atom of urea, remains somewhat uncertain. Inasmuch as nitrogen from almost all other amino acids can be transferred to glutamic acid by transamination, ammonia formation by the glutamic acid dehydrogenase reaction appears attractive. However, as indicated previously, it is not certain that the latter reaction does, in fact, proceed in this direction.

Since urea formation is irreversible, the α-keto acids remaining after amino group removal cannot be utilized for reamination and must be degraded. Thus, in the starving animal, α-keto acids formed by amino acid group removal are immediately oxidized for energy production (Chap. 27).

Uricotelic and Ammonotelic Organisms. Whereas mammals utilize urea for excretion of surplus nitrogen, this is not universally true among the vertebrates. Two other compounds also serve in this regard. Many species which live in the sea or in fresh water and can dispose of excreta readily and constantly simply excrete ammonia as such. Indeed this is the dominant mode of excretion among the teleost fishes; the latter also excrete urea in lesser amount, but in this case urea derives from the ultimate metabolism of purines via uric acid (page 570). In this regard, the metabolism of the frog is of interest. The tadpole, like teleosts, excretes ammonia. As shown by Cohen, during metamorphosis the various enzymes of the urea cycle appear in the liver and the adult organism synthesizes and excretes urea. Thus, amphibia occupy a position between the teleosts and the mammals. Those species for which the water supply may be precarious and which commonly have a semisolid excreta, *viz.,* birds and land-dwelling reptiles, channel nitrogen metabolism into formation of uric acid. The details of this process are given in Chap. 28.

It is noteworthy that only in ureotelic organisms is carbamyl phosphate synthesized by the irreversible synthetase reaction that requires expenditure of two molecules of ATP (page 489). Other organisms, for which it is not equally imperative that ammonia be channeled into urea via carbamyl phosphate, utilize the reversible carbamate kinase reaction (page 489) which permits the nitrogen of carbamyl phosphate to return to the pool of NH_3.

REFERENCES

See list following Chap. 27.

25. Amino Acid Metabolism

Biosynthesis of Essential Amino Acids

The biosynthesis of those amino acids which can be made by mammals as well as other species was discussed in the previous chapter. In contrast is the group of essential amino acids which cannot be made by mammals but can be fabricated by plants and microorganisms. The biosynthetic pathways for these amino acids are presented in this chapter.

Methionine. The relationships of cysteine and methionine to each other are reversed in plants and animals. In plants and heterotrophic microorganisms, inorganic sulfur is fixed into organic linkage as cysteine and transferred to a different carbon chain for the synthesis of methionine. Animals, which are unable to fabricate the 4-carbon chain of methionine, are dependent on their food for supply of this amino acid.

Fixation of Inorganic Sulfur. The metabolism of sulfur must begin with the reduction of inorganic sulfate, the form in which it is most abundant. The reduction occurs in plants and many microorganisms, but not in most animals. The initial step appears to be the formation from inorganic sulfate of the same compound which, in mammals, serves as a general agent for esterification of sulfate with alcoholic and phenolic compounds, *viz., 3'-phosphoadenosine 5'-phosphosulfate.*

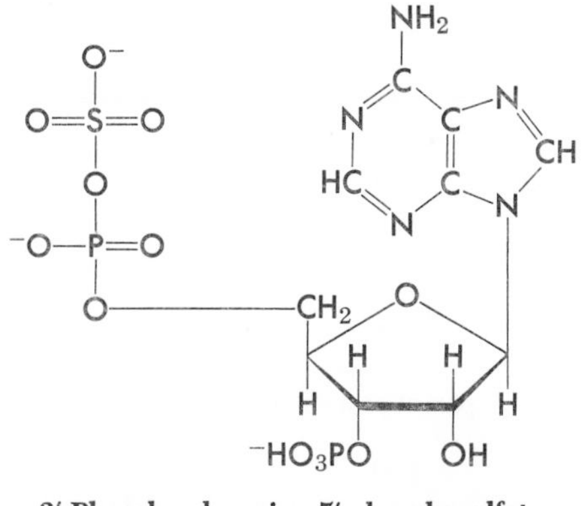

3'-Phosphoadenosine 5'-phosphosulfate

This compound is formed by a two-step reaction catalyzed by two distinct enzymes, present in liver as well as yeast. Each requires Mg^{++} for activity.

$$\text{Inorganic sulfate} + \text{ATP} \xrightarrow{\text{Mg}^{++}} \text{adenosine 5}'\text{-phosphosulfate} + \text{PP}_i$$

$$\text{Adenosine 5}'\text{-phosphosulfate} + \text{ATP} \xrightarrow{\text{Mg}^{++}} 3'\text{-phosphoadenosine 5}'\text{-phosphosulfate} + \text{ADP}$$

Little is known of the reductive process other than that a lipoic acid–containing enzyme is required for reduction of 3′-phosphoadenosine 5′-phosphosulfate to the level of free $SO_3^=$. The pathway thereafter is not known. Indeed the major reaction by which sulfur is fixed into organic linkage is uncertain. Certainly many organisms can effect the reduction of sulfite to the level of $S_2O_3^=$ (thiosulfate) and H_2S as well as elemental sulfur. The reverse processes have also been observed. Various of the "sulfur bacteria" can accomplish the aerobic oxidation of H_2S, S, $S_2O_3^=$, and $SO_3^=$ to sulfate as a major source of energy.

The most likely initial step in sulfur fixation is the reversal of the *cysteine desulfhydrase* reaction (page 543). The responsible enzyme is known to be present in plants and microorganisms, and the reaction is reversible. The enzyme requires pyridoxal phosphate and catalyzes the following reaction.

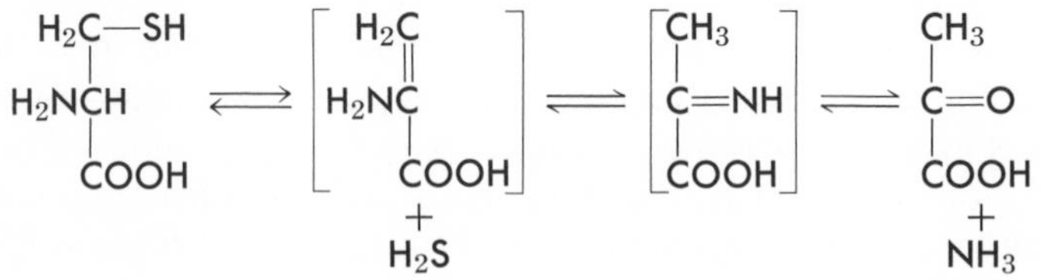

$$
\begin{array}{ccccccc}
\text{H}_2\text{C--SH} & & \left[\begin{array}{c}\text{H}_2\text{C} \\ \| \\ \text{H}_2\text{NC} \\ | \\ \text{COOH}\end{array}\right] & & \left[\begin{array}{c}\text{CH}_3 \\ | \\ \text{C}{=}\text{NH} \\ | \\ \text{COOH}\end{array}\right] & & \begin{array}{c}\text{CH}_3 \\ | \\ \text{C}{=}\text{O} \\ | \\ \text{COOH}\end{array} \\
\text{H}_2\text{NCH} & \rightleftharpoons & & \rightleftharpoons & & \rightleftharpoons & \\
| & & & & & & + \\
\text{COOH} & & + & & & & \text{NH}_3 \\
& & \text{H}_2\text{S} & & & &
\end{array}
$$

The reaction sequence to the right, as shown, is markedly favored. Although the enzyme in rat liver will catalyze the reverse reaction, it would seem that reversal would proceed more favorably were a means provided to supply the necessary energy. This has not yet been observed, and the initial step in sulfur fixation remains somewhat uncertain.

Methionine synthesis is accomplished by first transferring the sulfur of cysteine to a 4-carbon precursor, *homoserine,* which serves in a number of synthetic pathways and is formed as follows.

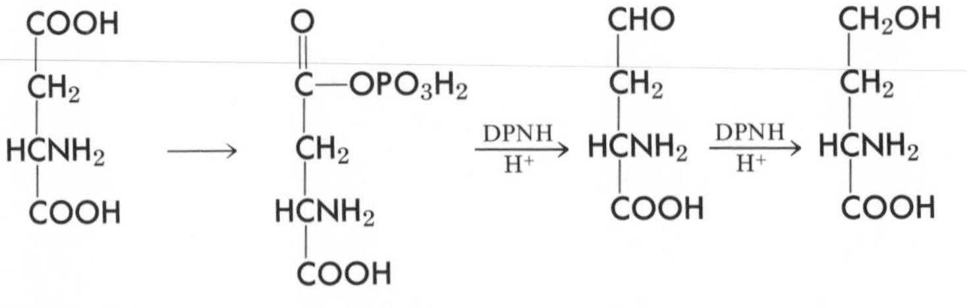

$$
\begin{array}{cccc}
\text{COOH} & \text{O} & \text{CHO} & \text{CH}_2\text{OH} \\
| & \| & | & | \\
\text{CH}_2 & \text{C--OPO}_3\text{H}_2 & \text{CH}_2 & \text{CH}_2 \\
| & | & | & | \\
\text{HCNH}_2 & \text{CH}_2 & \text{HCNH}_2 & \text{HCNH}_2 \\
| & | & | & | \\
\text{COOH} & \text{HCNH}_2 & \text{COOH} & \text{COOH} \\
 & | & & \\
 & \text{COOH} & &
\end{array}
$$

Aspartic acid → β-Aspartyl phosphate $\xrightarrow[\text{H}^+]{\text{DPNH}}$ Aspartic semialdehyde $\xrightarrow[\text{H}^+]{\text{DPNH}}$ Homoserine

Aspartic acid + ATP   **β-Aspartyl phosphate** + ADP   **Aspartic semialdehyde** + P_i **Homoserine**

The mode of formation of aspartic semialdehyde resembles the reversal of the triose phosphate dehydrogenase reaction (page 372). Homoserine then reacts with cysteine in a reaction catalyzed by *cystathionase* (page 499) to form cystathionine, a mixed thioether. The latter is then cleaved at the bond to the right of the thio-ether bond by *transsulfurase,* yielding serine and homocysteine.

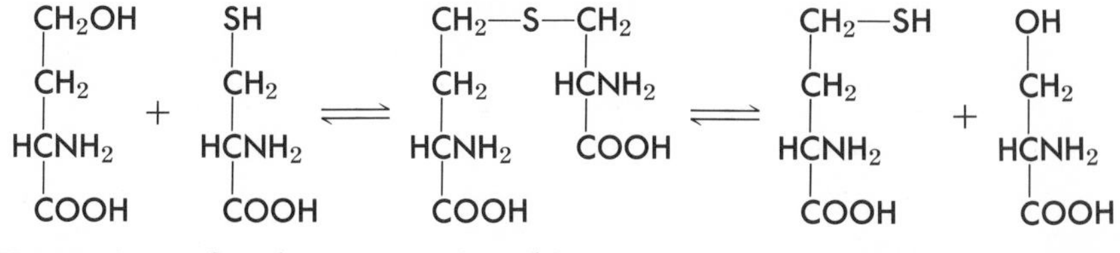

$$
\begin{array}{cccccc}
\underset{|}{CH_2OH} & \underset{|}{SH} & \underset{|}{CH_2-S-CH_2} & & \underset{|}{CH_2-SH} & \underset{|}{OH} \\
\underset{|}{CH_2} + \underset{|}{CH_2} & \rightleftharpoons & \underset{|}{CH_2} \quad \underset{|}{HCNH_2} & \rightleftharpoons & \underset{|}{CH_2} + \underset{|}{CH_2} \\
\underset{|}{HCNH_2} & \underset{|}{HCNH_2} & \underset{|}{HCNH_2} \quad \underset{|}{COOH} & & \underset{|}{HCNH_2} & \underset{|}{HCNH_2} \\
COOH & COOH & COOH & & COOH & COOH
\end{array}
$$

Homoserine   Cysteine   Cystathionine   Homocysteine   Serine

Homocysteine then acts as acceptor of a methyl group from the CH_3-cobamide compound, formed by *de novo* methyl group synthesis (page 504), to complete the biosynthesis of methionine. Both transsulfurase and cystathionase require the presence of pyridoxal phosphate.

Animals, characteristically, lack the ability to synthesize homoserine from aspartic acid and, hence, are dependent on dietary provision of methionine. On the other hand, animals can form homocysteine from such ingested methionine and, by a reversal of the transsulfurase and cystathionase reactions, accomplish the synthesis of cysteine (page 499). This is reflected in the growth of rats on synthetic rations; if sufficient cysteine (cystine) is included, the dietary requirement for methionine is less than half that required in the absence of cystine.

An unusual mechanism for methionine synthesis has been observed in cultures of mutants of *Aerobacter aerogenes.*

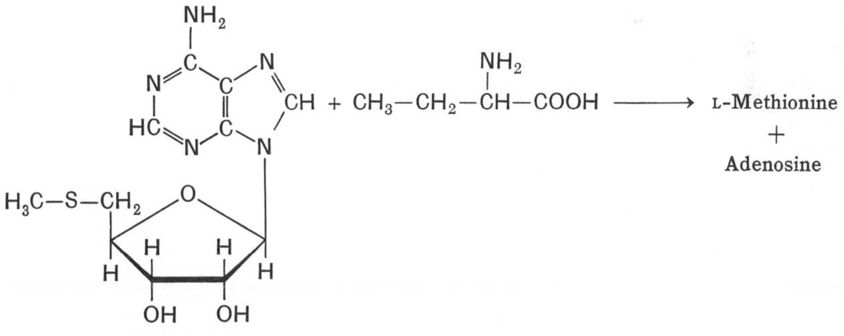

Thiomethyladenosine   α-Aminobutyric acid

This direct transfer of a thiomethyl group from thiomethyladenosine to α-amino-butyric acid has been termed *transmethiolation.* A reaction which may be in part the reverse of this occurs in yeast and in rat liver with formation of α-aminobutyric acid and methyl mercaptan. Evidence is lacking for the presence of thiomethyl-adenosine in mammalian tissues, although α-aminobutyric acid may be formed in metabolism from methionine via α-ketobutyric acid (page 546). S-Adenosylmethio-nine may also be cleaved at the adenosyl linkage, since its administration to rats resulted in significant formation of methionine.

Threonine. Threonine synthesis, like that of methionine (page 516), requires prior formation of homoserine from aspartic acid (page 516). Homoserine is then phosphorylated to phosphohomoserine by *homoserine kinase,* and, in a reaction catalyzed by *threonine synthetase* and requiring pyridoxal phosphate, the phosphate is split out and the hydroxyl migrates to the β position.

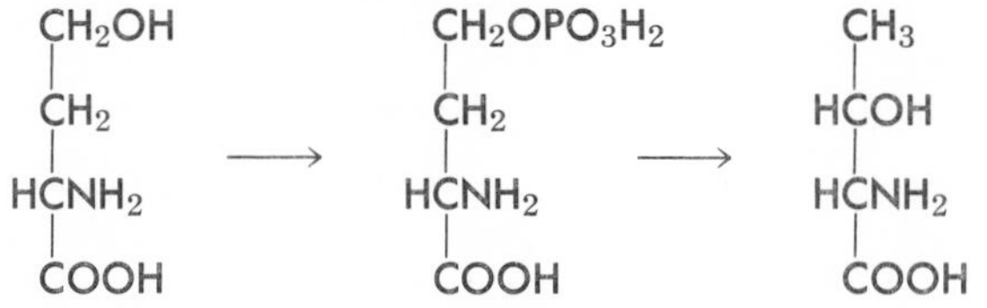

$$
\begin{array}{ccccc}
CH_2OH & & CH_2OPO_3H_2 & & CH_3 \\
| & & | & & | \\
CH_2 & \longrightarrow & CH_2 & \longrightarrow & HCOH \\
| & & | & & | \\
HCNH_2 & & HCNH_2 & & HCNH_2 \\
| & & | & & | \\
COOH & & COOH & & COOH \\
\text{Homoserine} & & \text{O-Phosphohomoserine} & & \text{Threonine} \\
+ & & + & & + \\
\text{ATP} & & \text{ADP} & & P_i
\end{array}
$$

The presence of threonine in the medium of certain microorganisms results in feedback repression of the synthesis of *aspartyl kinase,* the enzyme necessary for aspartyl phosphate formation in the first step in threonine synthesis from aspartic acid (page 516).

Escherichia coli, liver, and kidney are known to contain *threonine aldolase,* which utilizes pyridoxal phosphate to catalyze the following reversible reaction.

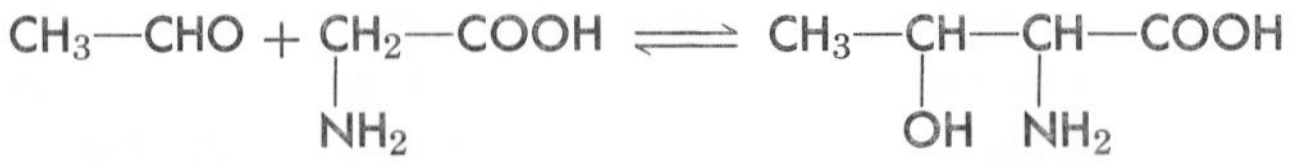

$$
\begin{array}{c}
CH_3-CHO + CH_2-COOH \rightleftharpoons CH_3-CH-CH-COOH \\
\qquad\qquad | \qquad\qquad\qquad\qquad | \ \ \ | \\
\qquad\qquad NH_2 \qquad\qquad\qquad\qquad OH \ \ NH_2
\end{array}
$$

$\qquad$ Acetaldehyde $\qquad$ Glycine $\qquad\qquad$ Threonine

Since in animals acetaldehyde formation occurs only from ethanol, it is likely that, in animals, and possibly in *E. coli,* the above reaction represents a degradative process rather than a synthetic mechanism.

Lysine. Lysine biosynthesis occurs by two different pathways. That characteristic of yeast, *Neurospora crassa,* and higher plants commences with conversion of α-ketoglutaric acid to α-ketoadipic acid; the mechanism of this reaction is not understood. Transamination to α-aminoadipic acid is followed by reduction of the ϵ-carboxyl to the corresponding aldehyde, which transaminates to form lysine.

In *E. coli,* a complex pathway has been demonstrated beginning with aspartic acid, which is converted to aspartyl β-semialdehyde, as described previously. The latter condenses with pyruvic acid in an aldol condensation. The enzyme responsible for this condensation has been purified. Presumably the resultant hydroxy compound is then dehydrated and reduced. At some stage in this series succinyl CoA reacts with the α-amino group so that the next identified compound in the sequence is N-succinyl-α-amino-ϵ-ketopimelic acid. This is transaminated and then desuccinylated to form L,L-α,ϵ-diaminopimelic acid. However, the enzyme which decarboxylates this compound to lysine is specific for the *meso* form, and a *racemase* isomerizes one end of the L,L-α-ϵ-diaminopimelic acid to the meso acid, which is decarboxylated to L-lysine. These pathways are summarized in Fig. 25.1. It is of interest that *E. coli* contains two genetically independent aspartyl kinases. If lysine is present in the medium, formation of one of these is repressed, while threonine represses formation of the other.

Valine. The biosynthesis of valine includes a reaction rare in biological systems, a pinacol rearrangement. The sequence commences with condensation of the

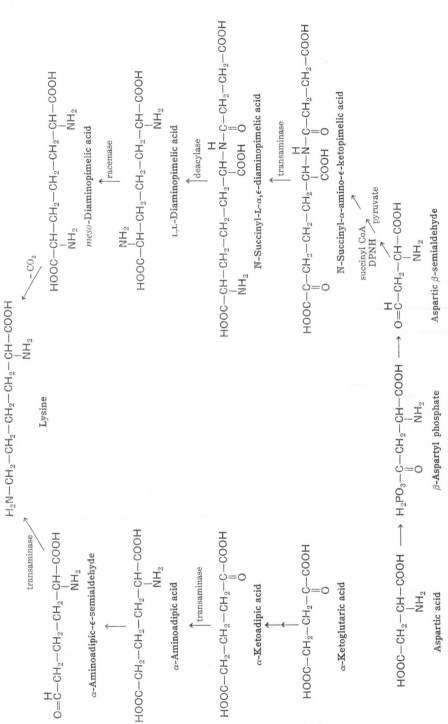

FIG. 25.1. Suggested pathways for biosynthesis of lysine in yeast and in *Neurospora* (reactions on left of chart) and in bacteria, *e.g.*, *Escherichia coli* (reactions on right of chart).

acetaldehyde moiety of a pyruvic acid molecule with a second molecule of pyruvic acid. Since thiamine pyrophosphate (ThPP) and Mg^{++} are required, it may be presumed that α-hydroxyethyl thiamine pyrophosphate (page 317) serves as "active acetaldehyde" in this instance. The condensation product is α-acetolactic acid. A single enzyme, *acetohydroxy acid isomeroreductase,* requiring Mg^{++} and utilizing DPNH, then catalyzes transformation to α,β-dihydroxyvaleric acid. A dehydration reaction follows, with formation of α-ketoisovaleric acid, which transaminates with glutamic acid to yield valine (Fig. 25.2). Of interest is the fact that in *A. aerogenes,* which normally converts pyruvic acid to acetoin, there are two independent en-

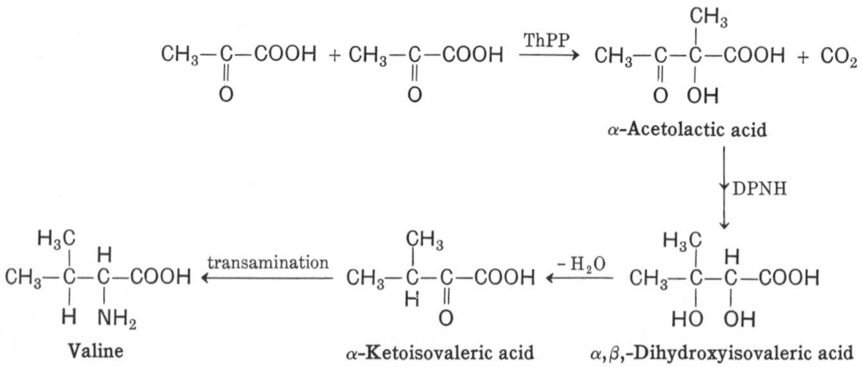

FIG. 25.2. Biosynthesis of valine. ThPP = thiamine pyrophosphate.

zymes which catalyze the condensation to α-acetolactic acid. When grown in the presence of valine, formation of one of these is repressed, leaving enough activity to produce sufficient acetolactic acid to meet the demands for growth without wasteful formation of valine.

Isoleucine. Synthesis of isoleucine occurs in a manner analogous to that of valine. The initial step is condensation of "active acetaldehyde" with α-ketobutyric acid; the latter is only known to be derived from threonine. The *threonine deaminase* reaction, which requires pyridoxal phosphate, is completely analogous to the serine deaminase (page 541) and cysteine desulfhydrase (page 543) reactions and produces α-ketobutyric acid in a single step. The reaction sequence is depicted in Fig. 25.3.

Leucine. The details of leucine biosynthesis are known only in a few microorganisms. Synthesis begins by utilizing α-ketoisovaleric acid, which is also the immediate precursor of valine. Condensation occurs with acetyl CoA, in a manner reminiscent of the formation of citric acid. Subsequent steps, leading to formation of α-ketoisocaproic acid, are analogous to the formation of α-ketoglutaric acid from citric acid. Transamination in the usual manner completes the reaction sequence (Fig. 25.4).

Phenylalanine. The biosynthesis of phenylalanine, which cannot be accomplished by vertebrates, has been elucidated in microorganisms by Davis and by Sprinson; available evidence indicates that the same general pathway is operative

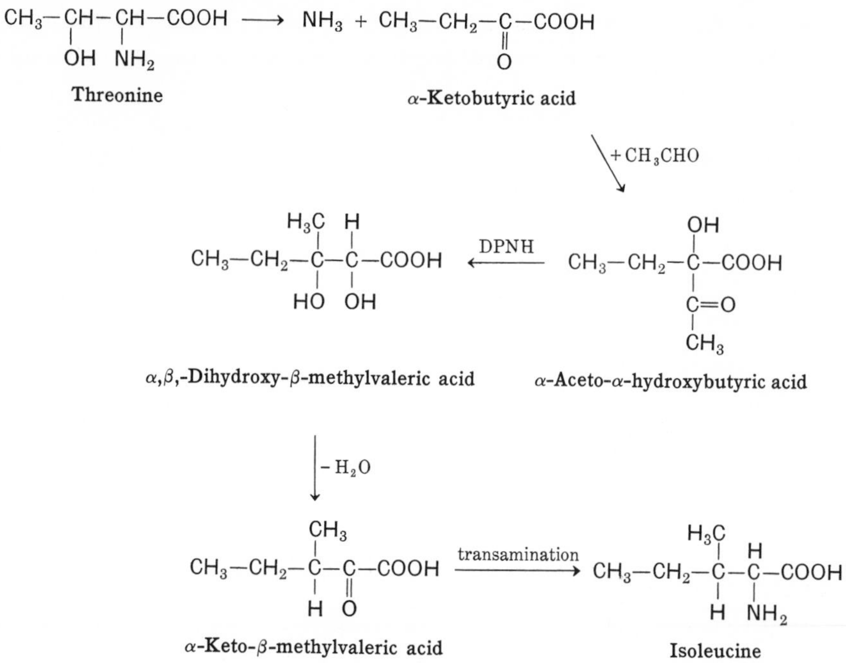

$$CH_3-CH-CH-COOH \longrightarrow NH_3 + CH_3-CH_2-C-COOH$$
$$\underset{OH}{|} \quad \underset{NH_2}{|} \qquad\qquad\qquad\qquad \underset{O}{||}$$

Threonine $\qquad\qquad\qquad\qquad$ α-Ketobutyric acid

$+CH_3CHO$

α,β,-Dihydroxy-β-methylvaleric acid $\qquad$ α-Aceto-α-hydroxybutyric acid

$-H_2O$

α-Keto-β-methylvaleric acid $\qquad\qquad$ Isoleucine

FIG. 25.3. Biosynthesis of isoleucine.

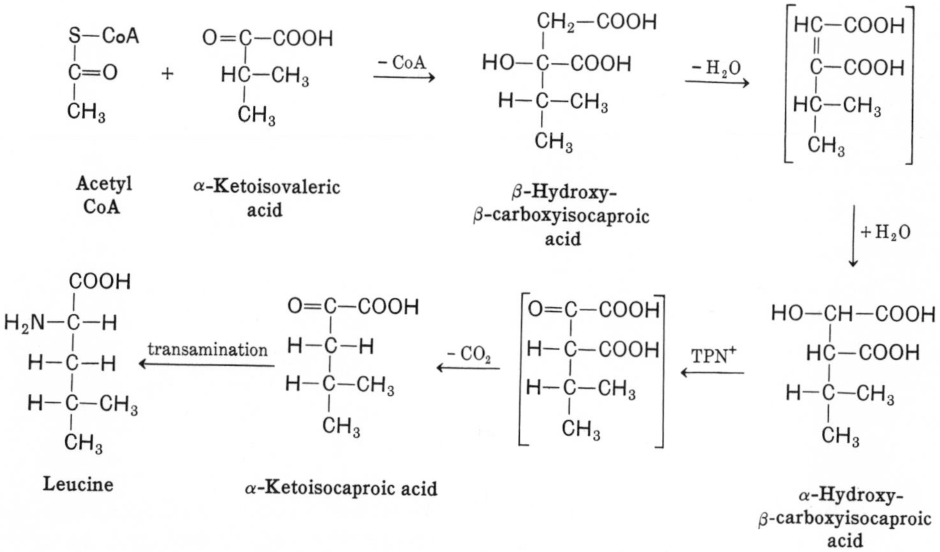

Acetyl CoA $\qquad$ α-Ketoisovaleric acid $\qquad$ β-Hydroxy-β-carboxyisocaproic acid

$-CoA$ $\qquad$ $-H_2O$

$+H_2O$

Leucine $\qquad$ α-Ketoisocaproic acid $\qquad$ α-Hydroxy-β-carboxyisocaproic acid

transamination $\qquad$ $-CO_2$ $\qquad$ TPN^+

FIG. 25.4. Pathway of leucine biosynthesis.

in higher plants. All nine carbons are derived from erythrose 4-phosphate, a normal intermediate both in photosynthetic hexose formation and in the direct oxidative pathway of glucose metabolism, and from two molecules of phosphoenolpyruvic acid, which arises in glycolysis. Few of the enzymes have been purified, and much remains to be learned of the mechanisms of the interesting reactions summarized in Fig. 25.5. The reaction sequence has been elucidated by combining

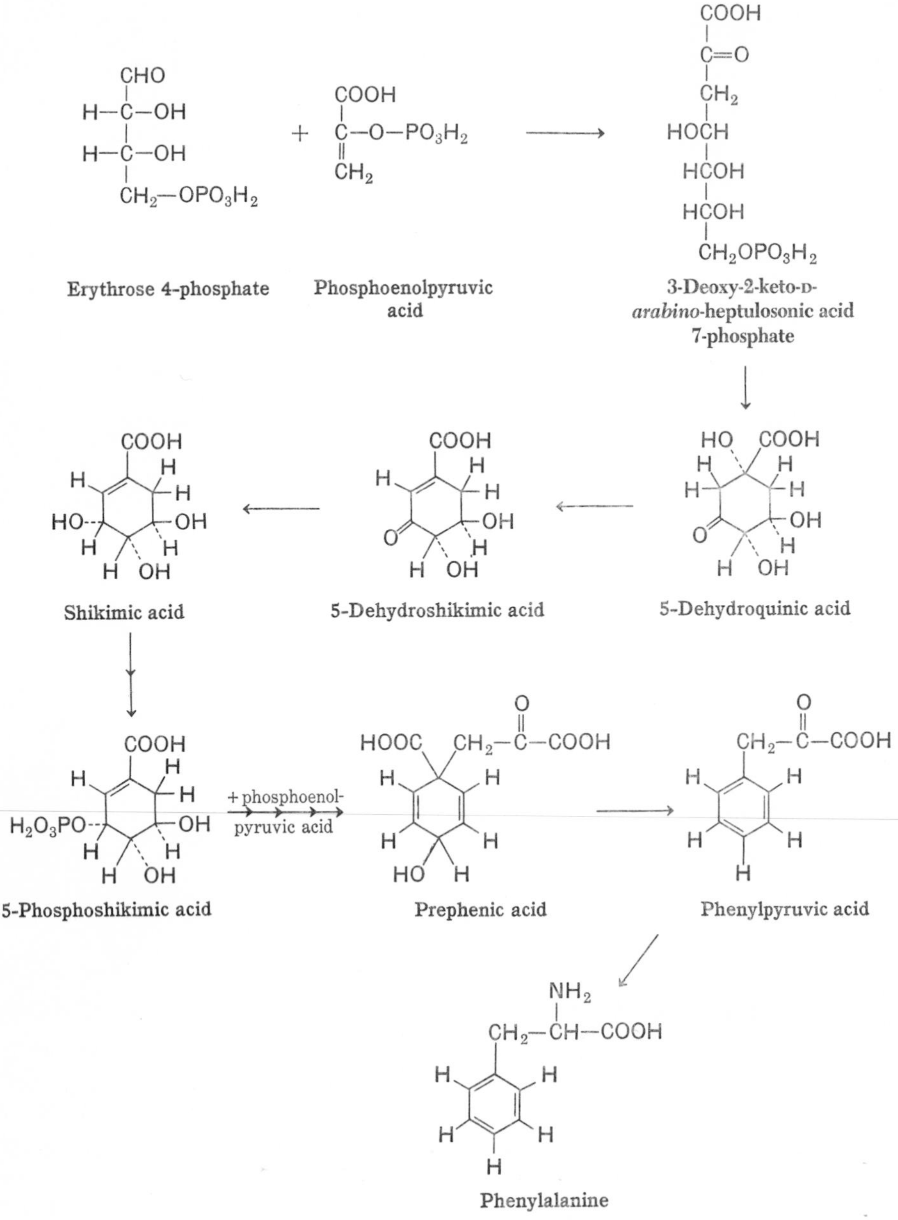

FIG. 25.5. Biosynthesis of phenylalanine.

studies with C^{14}-labeled precursors with examination of the materials which accumulate in the growth media of mutants blocked at various stages of the synthetic pathway.

Tryptophan. The pathway of tryptophan biosynthesis in higher plants is unknown. Quite distinct pathways have been found operative in *E. coli* and species of *Saccharomyces*. Both commence with anthranilic acid. The latter is formed, at least in *E. coli,* in a system which, utilizing ATP and DPN, transfers the N atom from the amide position of glutamine to the carbon skeleton of 5-phosphoshikimic acid, which is also an intermediate in phenylalanine synthesis (Fig. 25.5). The synthetic pathway for tryptophan in yeast is shown in Fig. 25.6, and that in *E. coli* is summarized in Fig. 25.7.

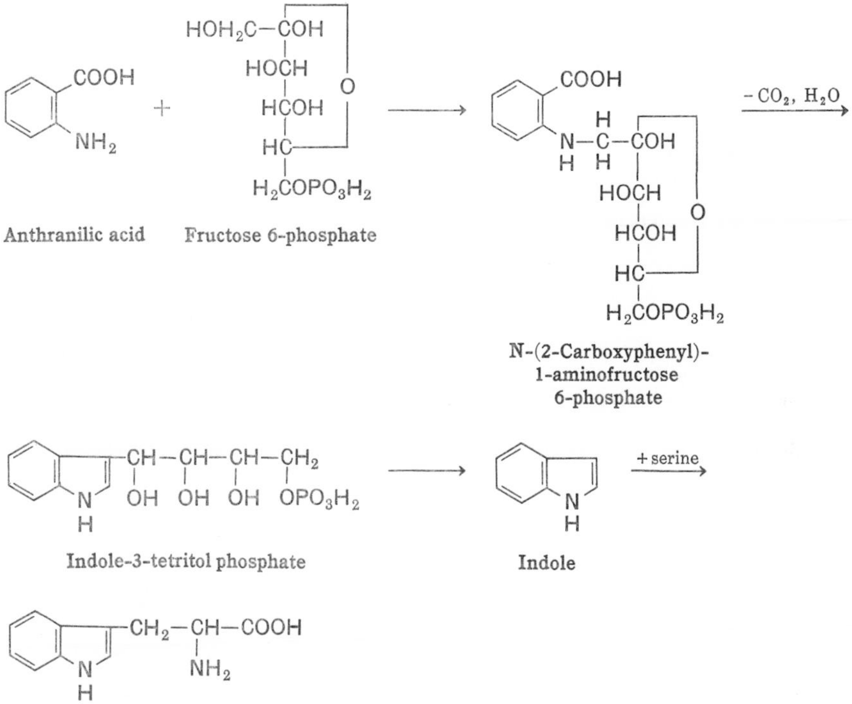

FIG. 25.6. A pathway of tryptophan biosynthesis in yeast.

The initial reaction in *E. coli* utilizes 5-phosphoribosyl 1-pyrophosphate (page 524), which is also employed in the synthesis of nucleotides (page 561).

The final reaction in each sequence of tryptophan synthesis is catalyzed by the same enzyme, *tryptophan synthetase*. As will be seen, it can, reversibly, effect condensation of indole with serine and also promote displacement of the glycerol phosphate moiety of indoleglycerol phosphate by serine. The genetic aspects of synthesis of this enzyme have been intensively studied by Bonner and Yanofsky and their colleagues. The tryptophan synthetase system of *E. coli* consists of two proteins, termed components A and B (sometimes referred to as tryptophan synthetase A and B). Component A is concerned primarily with the reaction, indoleglycerol phosphate → indole, and component B with the reaction, indole → tryptophan. Furthermore, it was established that free indole does not appear to be involved in

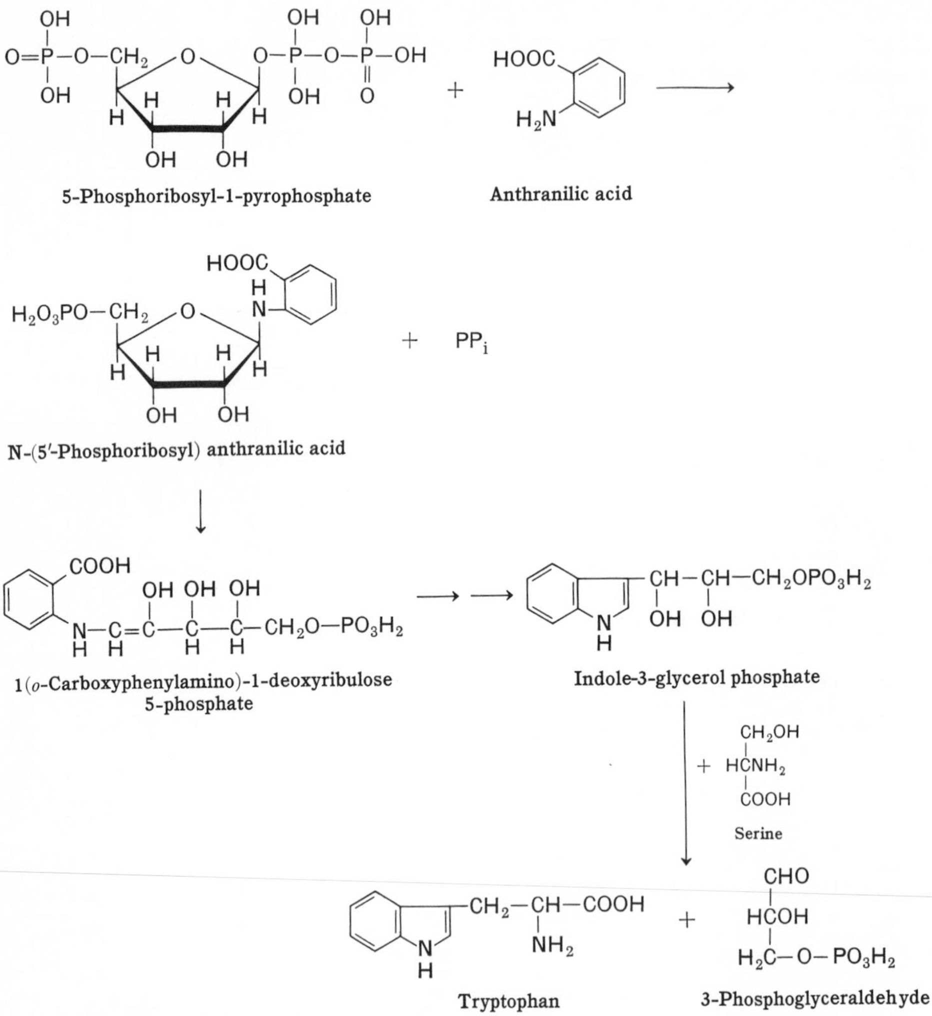

5-Phosphoribosyl-1-pyrophosphate

Anthranilic acid

N-(5'-Phosphoribosyl) anthranilic acid

1(*o*-Carboxyphenylamino)-1-deoxyribulose
5-phosphate

Indole-3-glycerol phosphate

Serine

Tryptophan

3-Phosphoglyceraldehyde

FIG. 25.7. A pathway of tryptophan biosynthesis in *Escherichia coli.*

tryptophan biosynthesis in *E. coli,* and that the terminal reaction should be represented as follows, with indole formation and utilization considered as an alternative route.

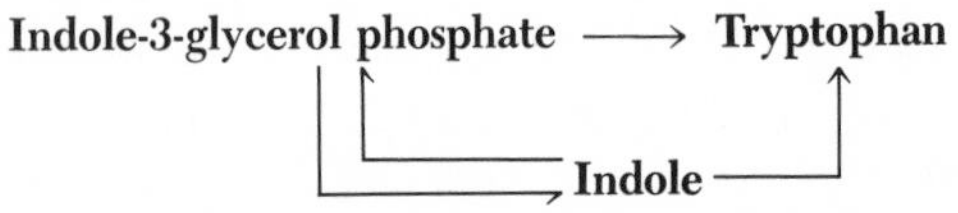

Indole-3-glycerol phosphate ⟶ Tryptophan

Indole

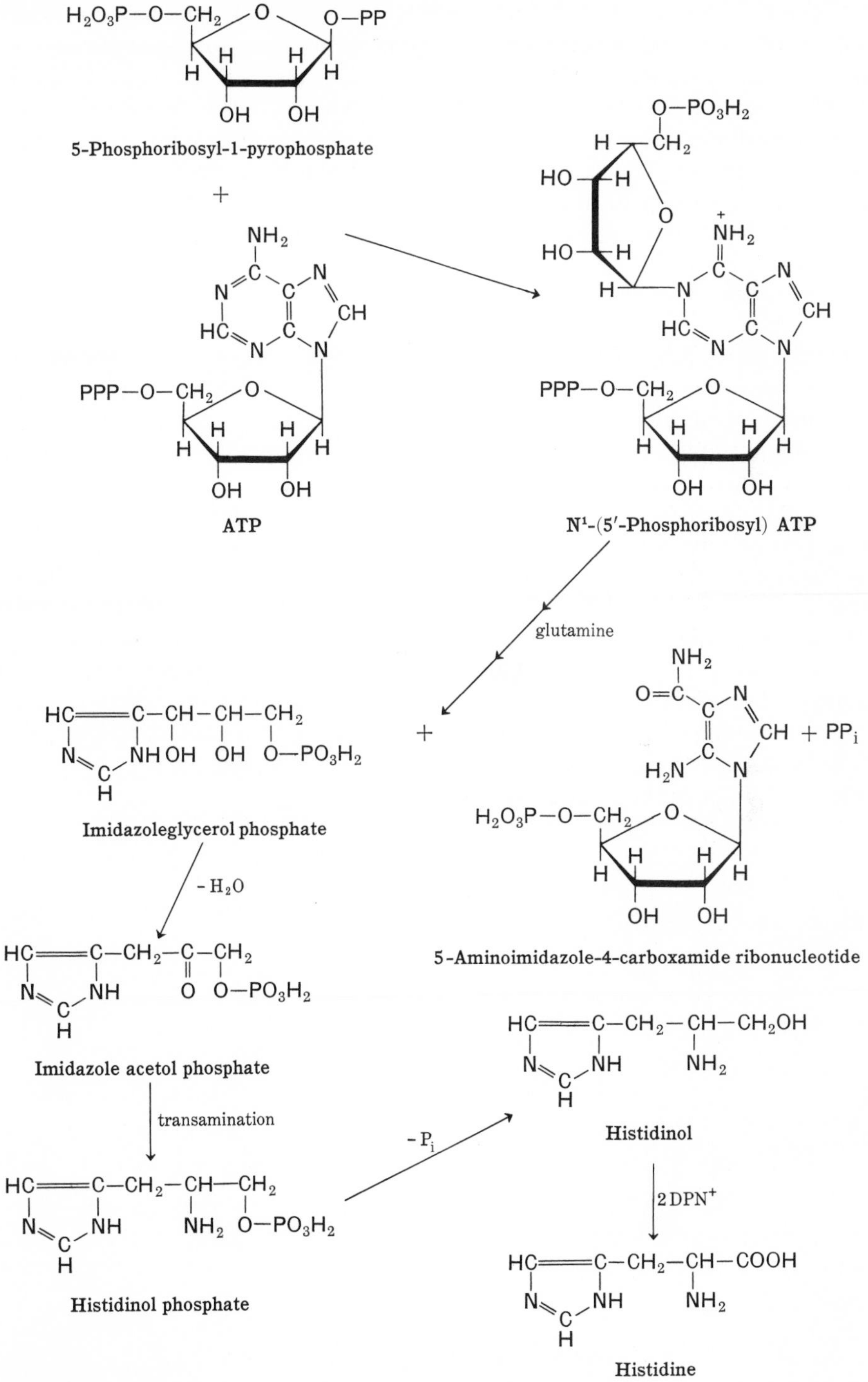

FIG. 25.8. Histidine biosynthesis in microorganisms. PP = pyrophosphate; PPP = triphosphate.

Histidine. The mechanism for histidine biosynthesis, largely established by study of mutants of *E. coli* and of *Salmonella,* is among the most complex and remarkable in intermediary metabolism (Fig. 25.8). In essence, the carbon chain of ribose 5-phosphate is affixed to the amino group of adenylic acid. The purine ring of the latter is opened and, after provision of a nitrogen atom from glutamine, the structure breaks apart to yield imidazoleglycerol phosphate, in which the imidazole ring of histidine is fully formed and attached to a 3-carbon chain, and 5-amino-imidazole-4-carboxamide ribonucleotide, a normal intermediate in purine synthesis (page 563).

In the synthesis of imidazoleglycerol phosphate, the side chain and connecting two carbons of the ring derive from the five carbons of the ribose of 5-phosphoribosyl 1-pyrophosphate. The —N=C— adjoining stems from the pyrimidine portion of the fused purine nucleus. Since the carbon atom of this fragment originates, during purine synthesis, from the formyl of N^{10}-tetrahydrofolic acid (page 503), it must ultimately derive from the β-carbon of serine or from administered formate. The final N atom is provided by the amide nitrogen of glutamine. The details of this reaction are obscure, but the over-all sequence has been strongly indicated by Magasanik. Thus, the histidine-synthesizing system utilizes a portion of an existing purine nucleus but leaves behind a fragment (5-aminoimidazole-4-carboxamide ribonucleotide), which is readily reconverted to purines (page 564). Finally, the last step in the reaction sequence may be noted, in which a primary hydroxyl group of histidinol is oxidized by two equivalents of DPN+ to the corresponding carboxyl group. Consecutive oxidations occur on the surface of a single enzyme without appearance in the free state of the presumed aldehydic intermediate. The reaction, therefore, is reminiscent of the DPN+-linked oxidation of UDP-glucose to UDP-glucuronic acid (page 406).

REFERENCES

See list following Chap. 27.

26. Amino Acid Metabolism

Amino Acids as Precursors of Some Nitrogenous Compounds

As indicated previously (page 483), the prime physiological role of amino acids is in protein synthesis. But, perhaps because of the continual presence of this group of amino acids throughout all of evolution, they have also been utilized by cells as starting materials for synthesis of diverse chemical compounds which are necessary or useful in metabolism. Several such roles have already been encountered, e.g., glutamic acid as a contributor of an amino group by transamination, glutamine as an ammonia donor, methionine as a source of methyl groups, and serine as a source of biologically active —CH_2OH and —CHO groups. Aspartic acid also donates its amino group, as in the synthesis of the guanidine moiety of arginine, and contributes to purine synthesis (page 564). The special roles of glycine in purine synthesis and of aspartic acid in pyrimidine synthesis will be found in Chap. 28. The present chapter will present a résumé of other instances in which amino acids are employed for the synthesis of biologically useful compounds.

PEPTIDE AND AMIDE SYNTHESIS

Glutathione. Relatively few small peptides are found in living cells. One of the most abundant is glutathione, γ-glutamylcysteinylglycine. Studies by Bloch and Snoke showed that synthesis of glutathione occurs in two independent enzymic steps.

(a) L-Glutamic acid + L-cysteine + ATP $\xrightarrow{Mg^{++}, K^+}$ L-γ-glutamylcysteine + ADP + P_i

(b) L-γ-Glutamylcysteine + glycine + ATP $\longrightarrow$ L-γ-glutamylcysteinylglycine + ADP + P_i

The mechanism of these two reactions is like that catalyzed by glutamine synthetase (page 488). Meister has found that L-γ-glutamylcysteinyl phosphate is formed as a stable enzyme-bound intermediate in the second reaction.

Carnosine (β-Alanylhistidine). This peptide is found in muscle and is synthesized in situ. Although the responsible enzyme, named carnosine synthetase, has not been extensively purified, the reported exchange of PP_i^{32} with ATP in the presence of β-alanine suggests, as an intermediate, enzyme-bound β-alanyl adenylate, which then reacts with histidine. Anserine (page 115), a methyl derivative of carnosine, is formed from the latter by a transmethylation reaction (page 504).

It may be noted that carnosine synthetase appears to be a relatively nonspecific enzyme in that it can utilize a variety of amino acids in place of histidine and

β-alanine. γ-Aminobutyric acid is one of the more active amino acids in substituting for β-alanine; the resulting peptide, γ-aminobutyrylhistidine, has been named homocarnosine. In view of the formation of γ-aminobutyric acid from glutamate in brain, it is of interest that this tissue contains approximately ten times as much homocarnosine as carnosine (Chap. 39).

N-Acyl Amino Acids. The formation and excretion of N-acyl derivatives of amino acids have long been known. Originally obtained from horse urine, hippuric acid (N-benzoylglycine) is present in small amount in normal human urine, and its formation can be increased greatly by administration of benzoic acid. Since hippuric acid synthesis occurs in the liver, the efficiency of hippuric acid formation was used, for some time, as a liver function test. Biosynthesis of hippuric acid and related compounds has been shown to resemble that of esters in that the carboxylic acid is activated as the corresponding acyl CoA, which serves as the immediate acylating agent. Acyl CoA formation is via an intermediate, enzyme-bound acyl-adenylate.

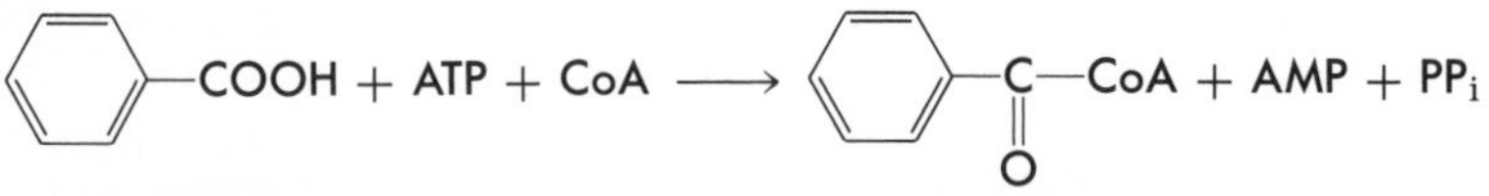

Benzoic acid   Benzoyl CoA

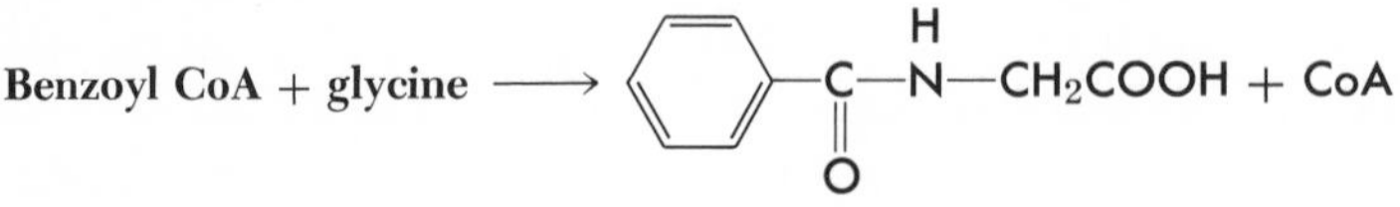

Hippuric acid

Phenylacetic acid arising in metabolism, or administered, gives rise to phenaceturic acid,

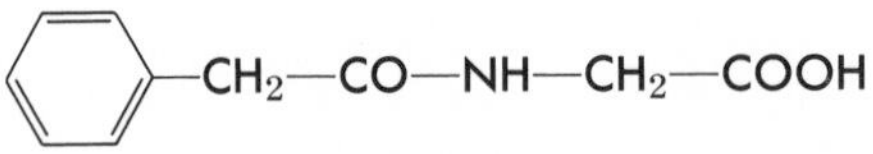

in the same manner.

In some birds, both benzoic and phenylacetic acids are activated similarly, but then react with both the α- and δ-amino groups of ornithine to form N,N-dibenzoyl- or N,N-diphenylacetylornithine. In man, although benzoic acid is conjugated with glycine, phenylacetyl CoA reacts with the α-amino group of glutamine, yielding phenylacetylglutamine.

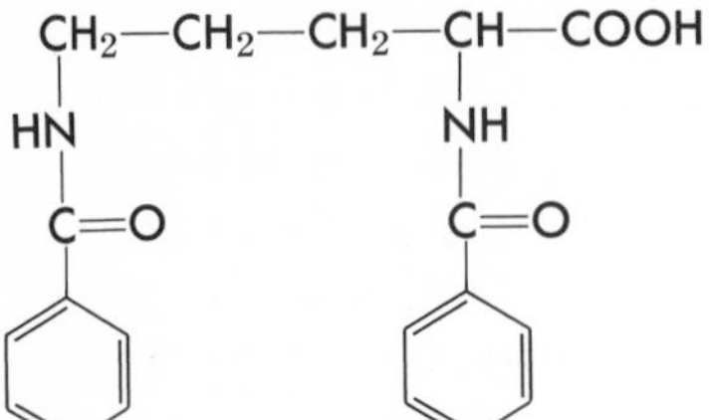

Ornithuric acid   Phenylacetylglutamine
(N,N-dibenzoylornithine)

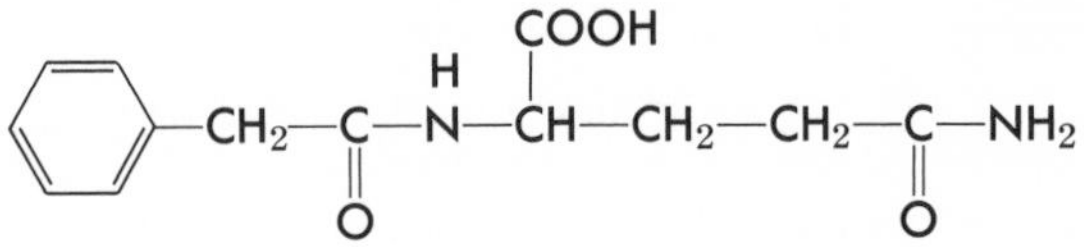

Numerous other low molecular weight aromatic acids, given to animals, form similar compounds.

Administration of excessive quantities of many α-amino acids results in excretion of the corresponding N-acetyl derivatives. These are thought to be formed by reaction with acetyl CoA. This fact has been utilized by Rittenberg and his colleagues to estimate the daily production of acetyl in the body. The normal physiological role of the enzymes responsible for these various syntheses is not known.

It may be noted that a number of proteins appear to lack an N-terminal residue because the N-terminal amino acid is acetylated. Also, several hormones of the neurohypophysis have, in peptide linkage at the C-terminal end, glycinamide,

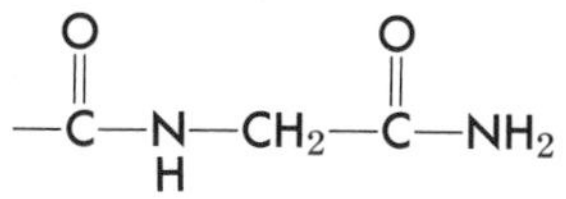

$$-\overset{\displaystyle O}{\overset{\|}{C}}-\underset{H}{N}-CH_2-\overset{\displaystyle O}{\overset{\|}{C}}-NH_2$$

It is not presently clear whether acetylation and/or amide formation occur after synthesis of the polypeptide chain or whether the N-acetyl and carboxamide derivatives are preformed and then incorporated into the polypeptide.

Mercapturic Acids. Administration of halogen-substituted aliphatic or aromatic hydrocarbons, *e.g.*, bromobenzene, to animals leads to urinary excretion of mercapturic acids. In the case of bromobenzene, the product is the following.

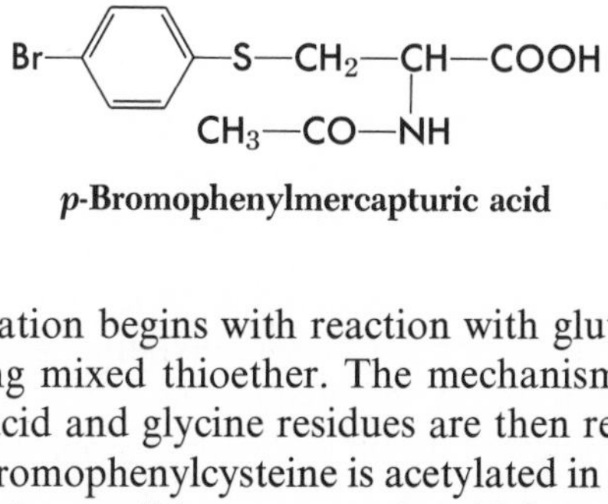

$$Br-\!\!\left\langle\!\!\!\bigcirc\!\!\!\right\rangle\!\!-S-CH_2-\underset{\underset{\displaystyle CH_3-CO-NH}{|}}{CH}-COOH$$

p-Bromophenylmercapturic acid

Mercapturic acid formation begins with reaction with glutathione, in the liver, to make the corresponding mixed thioether. The mechanism of this reaction is unknown. The glutamic acid and glycine residues are then removed by hydrolysis in the kidney, and the S-bromophenylcysteine is acetylated in the liver, utilizing acetyl CoA. Similar events make possible mercapturic acid formation from certain other halohydrocarbons.

TRANSAMIDINATION

Early in the history of biochemistry it was recognized that man excretes daily in the urine a quantity of creatinine, an anhydride of creatine (page 530), considerably in excess of the total creatine and creatinine ingested. Hence it followed that these compounds may be synthesized in the animal organism. This process commences with the readily reversible transfer of the guanidine moiety of arginine to glycine, a process called transamidination and catalyzed by *transamidinase*.

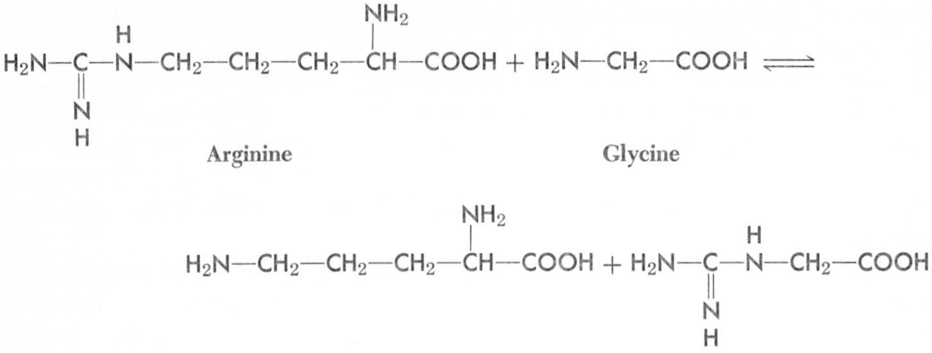

$$H_2N-\underset{\underset{H}{\overset{\parallel}{N}}}{\overset{H}{\underset{}{C}}}-N-CH_2-CH_2-CH_2-\underset{\overset{|}{NH_2}}{CH}-COOH + H_2N-CH_2-COOH \rightleftharpoons$$

Arginine   Glycine

$$H_2N-CH_2-CH_2-CH_2-\underset{\overset{|}{NH_2}}{CH}-COOH + H_2N-\underset{\underset{H}{\overset{\parallel}{N}}}{\overset{H}{\underset{}{C}}}-N-CH_2-COOH$$

Ornithine   Guanidoacetic acid

Guanidoacetic acid, formed in this manner in the kidney, is then methylated in the liver to form creatine (see below). This system is one of the few known instances of negative feedback regulation in mammals. Walker has shown that feeding of creatine results in marked suppression of the level of renal transamidinase activity. The kidney enzyme can also effect transamidination from arginine to canaline with formation of canavanine. Both of the last two compounds are found in the jack bean but are not known to participate in mammalian metabolism.

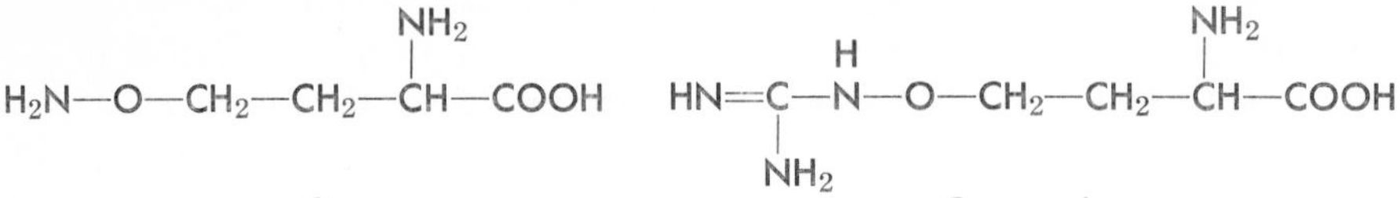

$$H_2N-O-CH_2-CH_2-\underset{\overset{|}{NH_2}}{CH}-COOH \qquad HN=\underset{\underset{NH_2}{|}}{C}-N-O-CH_2-CH_2-\underset{\overset{|}{NH_2}}{CH}-COOH$$

Canaline   Canavanine

TRANSMETHYLATION

As indicated previously (page 505), methionine, formed *de novo* in plants or microorganisms, or ingested by animals, is the source of methyl groups for diverse biosyntheses. In each instance, the initial step is formation of S-adenosylmethionine (page 504), which serves as the immediate methylating agent. Some of the known instances of methyl transfer are the following.

Creatine synthesis, initiated in the kidney by formation of guanidoacetic acid (see above), is completed in the liver.

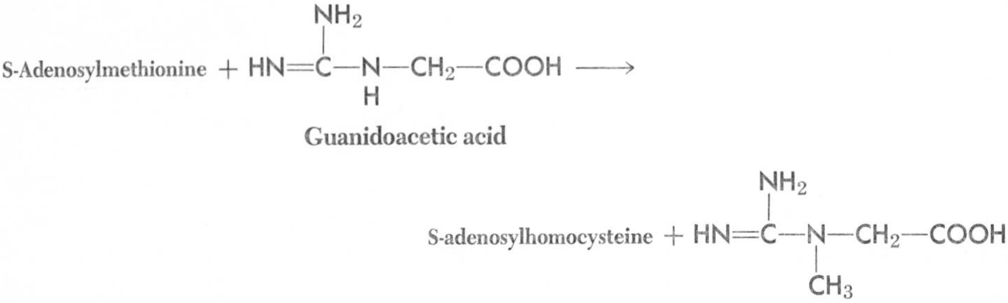

$$\text{S-Adenosylmethionine} + HN=\underset{\overset{|}{H}}{C}-N-CH_2-COOH \longrightarrow$$

Guanidoacetic acid

$$\text{S-adenosylhomocysteine} + HN=\underset{\underset{CH_3}{|}}{C}-N-CH_2-COOH$$

Creatine

Similar methylations utilizing S-adenosylmethionine are involved in the synthesis of choline (page 465), carnitine (Chap. 38), N^1-methylnicotinamide (Chap. 55), epinephrine (Chap. 49), and ergosterol (page 473), as well as in the formation of O-methyl–substituted metabolites (Chap. 49). None of the methylation reactions described is reversible.

Fate of Methyl Groups. It will be recalled that S-adenosylmethionine is a sulfonium compound with a high energy level. Transmethylation from this compound to most acceptors proceeds with a favorable change in free energy. Most, if not all, compounds which serve as methyl donors in living systems also appear to be "onium" compounds. Thus, the remethylation of homocysteine from betaine, with methyl group migration from a quaternary nitrogen, is catalyzed by a specific enzyme, and no additional energy source, such as ATP, is required. In contrast, dimethylglycine and sarcosine cannot serve as methylating agents, and their methyl groups must be removed by oxidation and transfer to tetrahydrofolic acid (page 502). Similarly the thetins, which are abundant in marine algae, are effective methyl donors in such cells and in liver preparations, whereas S-methylcysteine, found in plants such as cabbage, is not capable of thus functioning.

$$
\begin{array}{cc}
\underset{\text{Dimethylpropiothetin}}{\overset{\displaystyle H_3C}{\underset{\displaystyle H_3C}{>}} \overset{+}{S}\!-\!CH_2\!-\!CH_2\!-\!COO^-} & \underset{\text{S-Methylcysteine}}{\overset{\displaystyle NH_2}{H_3C\!-\!S\!-\!CH_2\!-\!\overset{|}{C}H\!-\!COOH}}
\end{array}
$$

As noted earlier, choline may be oxidized to betaine (page 505) and one methyl group can then be transferred to homocysteine, when homocysteine is available. Otherwise, betaine may lose all its methyl groups, sequentially, by oxidation. Each is oxidized to the level of HCHO, transferred to tetrahydrofolic acid, and thus returned to the C_1 pool. This is the basis of the sequence choline → betaine aldehyde → betaine → dimethylglycine → monomethylglycine (sarcosine) → glycine.

The earliest such conversion noted was the oxidative demethylation of sarcosine, observed by Handler and his colleagues and shown by Mackenzie to yield formaldehyde or its equivalent. The previous steps are not equally well characterized, but it is clear that all three of the methyl groups of choline return to the C_1 pool at the level of N^{10}-hydroxymethyltetrahydrofolic acid.

The ultimate fate of the C_1 unit in animals is not well understood. When methionine or sarcosine, labeled with C^{14} in their methyl groups, is administered, the C^{14} may be found in the expected positions in the various compounds already cited. However, a significant fraction of administered isotope also appears as $C^{14}O_2$, and this is the ultimate fate of this carbon, except for that lost in the urine in small amounts as creatinine, N^1-methylnicotinamide, etc. No reaction is known in animal metabolism in which direct conversion occurs of the carbon present as the N^{10}-hydroxymethyl group of tetrahydrofolic acid to carbon dioxide. The most likely pathway by which C_1 compounds can be oxidized to CO_2 is their utilization by recombination with glycine to form serine (page 502), which is converted to pyruvic acid under the influence of *serine dehydrase* (page 541). Oxidation of the pyruvic acid via the citric acid cycle would result in formation of CO_2 from the carbon which had once been in the C_1 pool. Some of the relationships considered above are shown in Fig. 26.1.

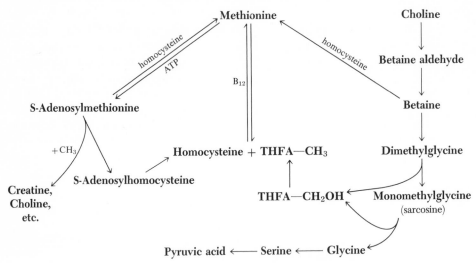

FIG. 26.1. Aspects of methyl group metabolism.

GLYCINE AND PORPHYRIN BIOSYNTHESIS

The contribution of glycine to purine biosynthesis is described in Chap. 28. The roles of this amino acid in serine and in hippuric formation were considered previously. An additional important metabolic contribution is made by glycine to heme biosynthesis. This role of glycine was demonstrated by Shemin and his associates, and by Neuberger, Rimington, Granick, and their colleagues. Synthesis of isotopically labeled protoporphyrin of hemoglobin was achieved either by administration of labeled glycine to experimental animals, including man, or by incubating in vitro nucleated red cells (from chicken or duck), or hemolysates of these cells, with isotopically labeled glycine.

The first step in porphyrin biosynthesis is the reaction of succinyl CoA (page 320) with glycine to form α-amino-β-ketoadipic acid, which is readily decarboxylated to δ-aminolevulinic acid (Fig. 26.2). This reaction proceeds in mitochondria which supply succinyl CoA by way of the tricarboxylic acid cycle, and is catalyzed by δ-*aminolevulinic acid synthetase,* which appears to be bound to mitochondria. Pyridoxal phosphate is required for δ-aminolevulinic acid formation. Two moles of the latter condense, under the influence of a specific enzyme, δ-*aminolevulinic acid dehydrase,* to yield porphobilinogen (Fig. 26.2). The enzyme catalyzing this condensation has also been designated as δ-*aminolevulinic acid hydro-lyase.* The reaction apparently involves an addition of one molecule of δ-aminolevulinic acid to a second molecule, followed by a dehydration and cyclization.

Four molecules of porphobilinogen are utilized in porphyrin synthesis (Chap. 42). Thus, all the porphyrin nitrogens are contributed by the nitrogen of glycine.

In addition, isotopic studies have established that 8 of the methylene carbon atoms of glycine are used in the synthesis of each porphyrin nucleus. Of these 8 carbon atoms, 4 become atom 2 in each pyrrole ring, *i.e.*, are in the ring adjacent to the nitrogen atom of the pyrrole nucleus, and an additional 4 are utilized for the methene bridge carbon atoms between the rings. The remaining 26 carbon atoms, not derived from glycine, have their origin in succinyl CoA (Chap. 42).

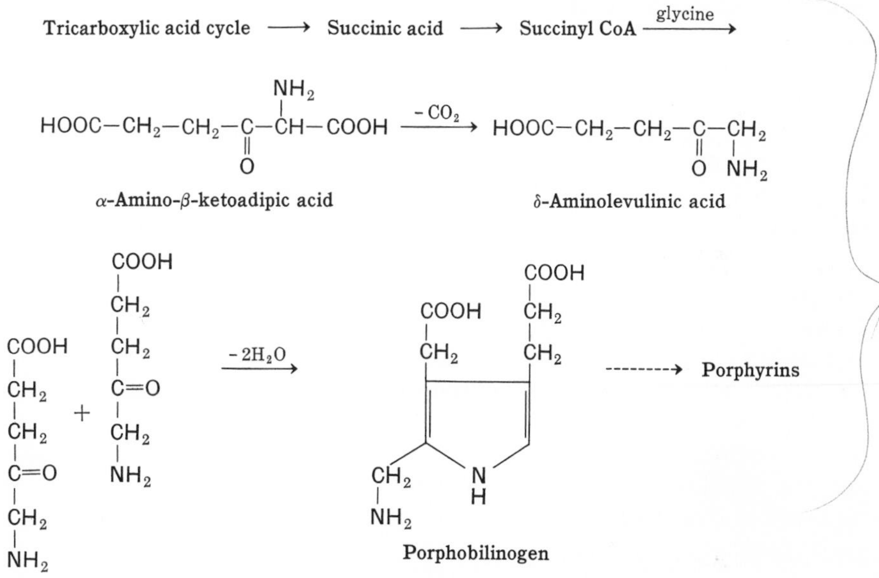

Tricarboxylic acid cycle $\longrightarrow$ Succinic acid $\longrightarrow$ Succinyl CoA $\xrightarrow{\text{glycine}}$

$$\underset{\alpha\text{-Amino-}\beta\text{-ketoadipic acid}}{HOOC-CH_2-CH_2-\underset{\underset{O}{\|}}{\overset{\overset{NH_2}{|}}{C}}-CH-COOH} \xrightarrow{-CO_2} \underset{\delta\text{-Aminolevulinic acid}}{HOOC-CH_2-CH_2-\underset{\underset{O}{\|}}{C}-\underset{\underset{NH_2}{|}}{CH_2}}$$

FIG. 26.2. Pathway of porphobilinogen synthesis.

METABOLITES FORMED BY AMINO ACID DECARBOXYLATION

Amino acid decarboxylases are widely distributed in nature; each of these enzymes requires pyridoxal phosphate as coenzyme and catalyzes removal of CO_2 from the α-carbon of a specific L-α-amino acid. This reaction is relatively rare in pathways of amino acid metabolism in animals but is more common in microorganisms. The reaction mechanism involves Schiff base formation on the enzymic surface between pyridoxal phosphate and the amino acid, followed by decarboxylation as a proton, from the medium, replaces the carboxyl carbon in its attachment to the α-carbon atom. Equilibrium lies far to the right, as written.

$$R-CH_2-CHNH_2-COO^- + H^+ \longrightarrow R-CH_2-CH_2NH_2 + CO_2$$

However, it has been possible to show reversibility in at least one instance, *viz.*, *glutamic acid decarboxylase* (see below), with the demonstration that during reversal it is the proton which entered in the decarboxylation reaction which returns to the medium in the back reaction. Some metabolically significant α-amino acid decarboxylases are presented below.

γ-Aminobutyric Acid. An α-decarboxylase for L-glutamic acid is present in many bacteria, but the significance of this compound in bacterial metabolism is obscure. A highly active enzyme is present in brain; its role in that tissue is considered elsewhere (Chap. 39).

$$HOOC—CH_2—CH_2—CHNH_2—COOH \longrightarrow HOOC—CH_2—CH_2—CH_2NH_2 + CO_2$$

Glutamic acid   γ-Aminobutyric
acid

γ-Aminobutyric acid transaminates to α-ketoglutarate with formation of succinic semialdehyde. The latter is oxidized to succinic acid, which enters the tricarboxylic acid cycle.

Histamine. Histidine decarboxylation to histamine is catalyzed by *histidine decarboxylase,* an enzyme present in microorganisms of the large intestine and in many tissues, *e.g.*, lung, liver, muscle, and gastric mucosa, as well as in mast cells, which have a high histamine content. Histamine is a powerful vasodilator and in excessive concentrations may cause vascular collapse. The base is liberated in traumatic shock and in localized areas of inflammation. Histamine stimulates secretion of both pepsin and acid by the stomach and is useful in studies of gastric activity. *Diamine oxidase,* a widely distributed flavoprotein (page 346), converts histamine to the corresponding aldehyde and NH_3. Some undegraded histamine is excreted in the urine as the N-acetyl and as the 1-methyl derivatives; the latter is the major metabolite of histamine in man.

Tyramine and Related Compounds. A specific tyrosine decarboxylase is present in low activity in liver and is abundant in some microorganisms. No specific physiological function is known for tyramine. A specific hydroxylase, termed *tyrosinase,* catalyzes hydroxylation of tyrosine in the liver and in melanin-forming cells, to yield 3,4-dihydroxyphenylalanine (dopa). The latter is then decarboxylated by *dopa decarboxylase* to dihydroxyphenylethylamine (*o*-hydroxytyramine), an intermediate in melanin formation. Dopa decarboxylase is also present in kidney and adrenal tissue as well as in sympathetic ganglia and nerves. In man and the rat, administration of hydroxytyramine led to excretion in the urine of homoprotocatechuic acid (3,4-dihydroxyphenylacetic acid) and 3,4-dihydroxyphenylethanol, as well as their methylated derivatives, homovanillic acid and 3-methoxy-4-hydroxyphenylethanol, respectively. The structures of these compounds are shown in Fig. 26.3. Dopa also serves as precursor for norepinephrine in epinephrine biosynthesis (Chap. 49), as well as for melanin formation (Chap. 44).

β-Alanine. The only β-amino acid of physiological significance is *β-alanine* which, in addition to being present in many tissues and in plasma as the free amino acid, occurs in muscle as a component of carnosine and of anserine (page 115) and in all tissues as part of the pantothenic acid moiety of coenzyme A. Pantothenic acid, a vitamin, cannot be made by most animals. In bacteria, and perhaps plants, there is present a low level of *aspartic acid decarboxylase* activity which accounts for β-alanine synthesis.

$$HOOC—CH_2—CHNH_2—COOH \longrightarrow HOOC—CH_2—CH_2—NH_2 + CO_2$$

Aspartic acid   β-Alanine

In animals, β-alanine arises in the degradative metabolism of the pyrimidines (page 578). Transamination from β-alanine leads to malonic semialdehyde. Oxida-

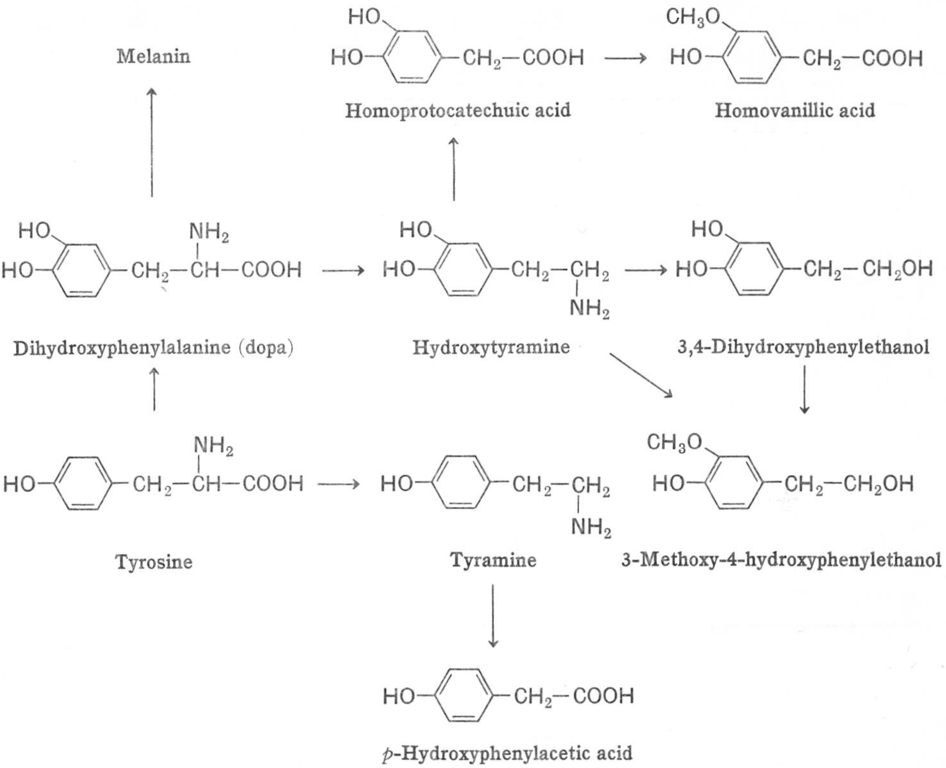

Melanin

$$HO-\overset{HO}{\underset{}{\bigcirc}}-CH_2-COOH \longrightarrow HO-\overset{CH_3O}{\underset{}{\bigcirc}}-CH_2-COOH$$

Homoprotocatechuic acid   Homovanillic acid

$$HO-\overset{HO}{\underset{}{\bigcirc}}-CH_2-\overset{NH_2}{\underset{}{CH}}-COOH \longrightarrow HO-\overset{HO}{\underset{}{\bigcirc}}-CH_2-\overset{}{\underset{NH_2}{CH_2}} \longrightarrow HO-\overset{HO}{\underset{}{\bigcirc}}-CH_2-CH_2OH$$

Dihydroxyphenylalanine (dopa)   Hydroxytyramine   3,4-Dihydroxyphenylethanol

$$HO-\bigcirc-CH_2-\overset{NH_2}{\underset{}{CH}}-COOH \longrightarrow HO-\bigcirc-CH_2-\overset{}{\underset{NH_2}{CH_2}} \qquad HO-\overset{CH_3O}{\underset{}{\bigcirc}}-CH_2-CH_2OH$$

Tyrosine   Tyramine   3-Methoxy-4-hydroxyphenylethanol

$$HO-\bigcirc-CH_2-COOH$$

p-Hydroxyphenylacetic acid

FIG. 26.3. Formation and fate of tyramine and related compounds.

tion of the latter to malonic acid followed by decarboxylation with formation of acetate would result in disposal via the citric acid cycle (page 315). An alternate synthetic and disposal pathway is represented by the following reaction series.

$$CH_3-CH_2-CO-SCoA \rightleftharpoons CH_2=CH-CO-SCoA \rightleftharpoons HO-CH_2-CH_2-CO-SCoA$$
Propionyl CoA   Acrylyl CoA   β-Hydroxypropionyl CoA

$$\Updownarrow$$

$$H_2N-CH_2-CH_2-COOH \rightleftharpoons OHC-CH_2-COOH \rightleftharpoons HO-CH_2-CH_2-COOH$$
β-Alanine   Malonic semialdehyde   β-Hydroxypropionic
                                                          acid

Tryptophan Derivatives. Weak *tryptophan decarboxylase* activity has been detected in liver and is probably present in plants. The resulting product, *tryptamine*, has no specific role, but when oxidized by *amine oxidase* yields an aldehyde which is readily oxidized by *aldehyde oxidase* to indoleacetic acid. This compound is present in small quantities in normal urine and in increased amount in the urine of pellagrins. However a major route of indoleacetic acid formation, both in plants, where it serves as an *auxin* (plant growth hormone), and in animals, is by oxidative decarboxylation of indolepyruvic acid, formed from tryptophan transamination.

Tryptophan may also be hydroxylated, apparently by the phenylalanine hydroxylase (page 500), to 5-hydroxytryptophan. Decarboxylation is effected by the enzyme *5-hydroxytryptophan decarboxylase* to yield 5-hydroxytryptamine, or *serotonin*, a potent vasoconstrictor found particularly in brain, intestinal tissue, blood platelets, and mast cells. Serotonin was first isolated from blood by Rapport and his associates, who had been studying a vasoconstrictor substance present in serum. The compound is also a constituent of many venoms, *e.g.*, wasp venom and

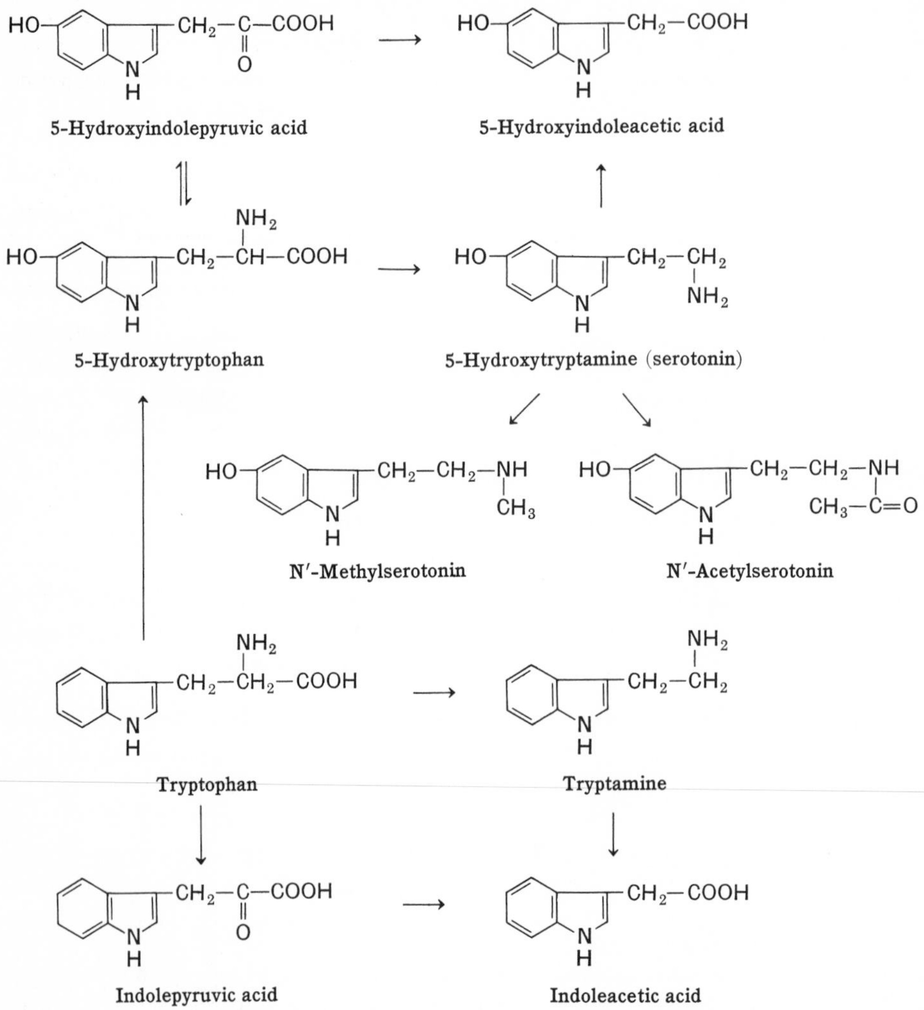

FIG. 26.4. Pathways among tryptophan and related compounds.

toad venom. N-Methylated derivatives of serotonin, *e.g.*, bufotenin, are fairly widely distributed among amphibia and cause central nervous system damage in mammals. A possible role for serotonin as a neurohumoral agent in man has been indicated (Chap. 39). Serotonin and its major metabolic product, 5-hydroxyindole-acetic acid, are present in urine. The latter is formed by a DPN-catalyzed oxidation of 5-hydroxyindolealdehyde, which arises in turn from serotonin by action of *monoamine oxidase.* Inhibition of serotonin metabolism by administration of monoamine oxidase inhibitors leads to increased formation of the N-acetyl and N-methyl derivatives of serotonin.

Approximately 7 mg. of 5-hydroxyindoleacetic acid is excreted in normal urine per day. It has been estimated that 3 per cent of the dietary tryptophan is metabolized via this pathway. In patients with *malignant carcinoid,* as much as 400 mg. of this compound is excreted daily; its excretion also rises in alkaptonuria (page 549) and in a metabolic abnormality of tryptophan metabolism, *Hartnup's disease.* It may be noted that liver microsomes also catalyze hydroxylation of indole-containing compounds to the corresponding 6-hydroxy derivatives; the possible metabolic significance of this is not known. Certain of these relationships are shown in Fig. 26.4.

Numerous other instances of amino acid decarboxylation will be cited elsewhere in this book. However, it may be noted here that not all decarboxylations of amino acids occur while the amino acids are in the free state. Decarboxylation of serine occurs while serine is in ester linkage as part of phosphatidyl serine (page 465), with formation of phosphatidyl ethanolamine. No similar decarboxylation of free serine appears to occur in biological systems. Somewhat analogous is the formation of coenzyme A (Chap. 55), in which pantoic acid first forms the pantoyl amide of cysteine, which is then decarboxylated to form pantotheine (page 581) and CO_2. Again, no analogous decarboxylation of free cysteine to cysteamine (aminoethylmercaptan, H_2N—CH_2—CH_2—SH) is known to occur biologically.

BIOSYNTHESIS OF POLYAMINES

Widely distributed among living forms are small quantities of a group of polyamines, including the following.

H_2N—$(CH_2)_4$—NH_2	H_2N—$(CH_2)_5$—NH_2	H_2N—$(CH_2)_4$—NH—$(CH_2)_3$—NH_2
1,4-Diaminobutane	**1,5-Diaminopentane**	**Spermidine**
(putrescine)	(cadaverine)	

$$H_2N—(CH_2)_3—NH—(CH_2)_4—NH—(CH_2)_3—NH_2$$
Spermine

As implied by their names, putrescine and cadaverine have long been known, from their unpleasant odor, as a result of bacterial fermentation of protein. Cadaverine arises by decarboxylation of lysine; putrescine is formed by decarboxylation of ornithine. Putrescine is found not only in diverse bacteria but in mammalian tissues such as pancreas, lung, liver, and semen. Spermidine and spermine are much more abundant and almost universally distributed. Although synthesized by many organisms, at various phylogenetic levels, these substances are essential growth factors for a number of microorganisms, *e.g., Hemophilus parainfluenzae, Aspergillus nidulans.* In general, these polyamines serve as agents which stabilize membranous structures. Thus, in their absence, the microorganisms listed above show increased permeability in hypotonic media, with loss of cell constituents. Protoplasts (bacteria without cell walls) from several species cannot withstand hypotonic media in the absence of members of this group of compounds. The swelling of mitochondria in various media is similarly prevented, and bacteriophages inactivated by chelating agents are protected by prior addition of spermine. Spermine and spermidine are present in significant amounts in ribosomes and appear to be essential to their structure and function (Chap. 30).

The synthesis of spermidine by *Escherichia coli* is accomplished in an unusual reaction in which the carbon chain of methionine, including the amino group, rather than the methyl group as in transmethylations, is transferred to putrescine. The reactions are shown in Fig. 26.5. Both the decarboxylation and the transfer reaction are presently known only for this reaction sequence. Presumably, spermine is synthesized by a repetition of the decarboxylation of S-adenosylmethionine and transfer to the spermidine formed in the first transfer.

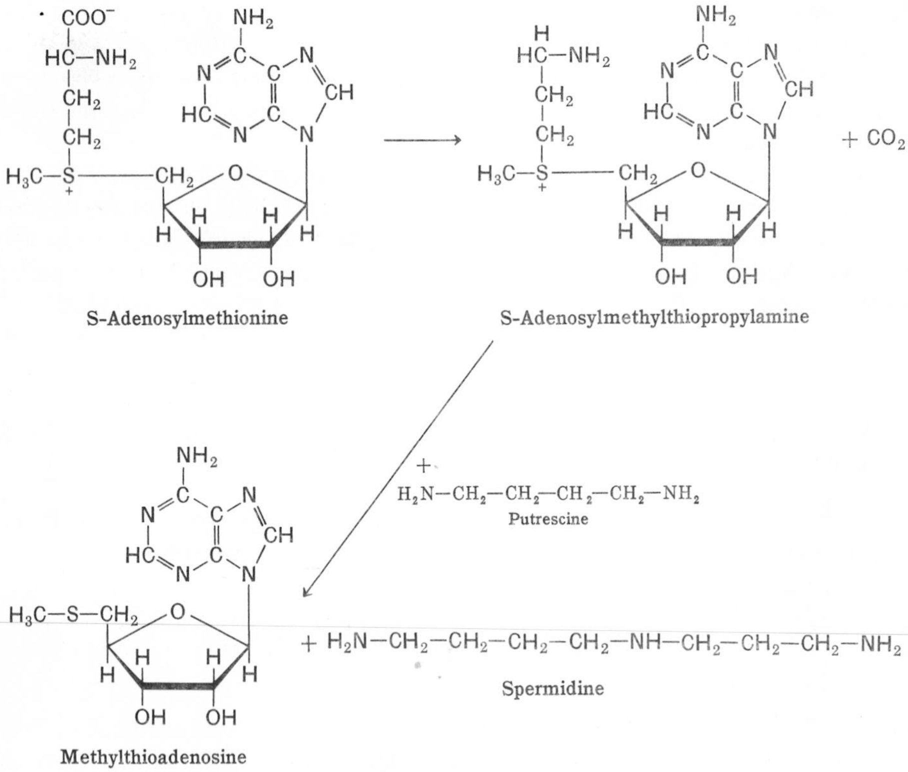

FIG. 26.5. Biosynthesis of spermidine.

All the polyamines in this group may be oxidized by the diamine oxidase present in human blood plasma. However, the products of these oxidations have not been well characterized.

REFERENCES

See list following Chap. 27.

27. Amino Acid Metabolism

Metabolic Fates of Amino Acids

The metabolic fates of amino acids have been studied by a variety of in vivo and in vitro techniques. One of the early interests in amino acid metabolism involved studies of their conversion to carbohydrate and to ketone bodies.

GLYCOGENIC AND KETOGENIC AMINO ACIDS

Initial studies of the metabolic fates of amino acids were based on their administration to animals made diabetic either by pancreatectomy or by administration of phlorhizin, with subsequent observation of whether the amino acid in question would increase urinary excretion of either glucose or acetone bodies. These studies were significant, since they provided definite evidence of *net* formation of additional glucose from one group of amino acids and of additional ketone bodies from a smaller group. Somewhat later, with the development of accurate methods for the determination of liver glycogen, amino acids were administered to normal, fasted rats with observation of an increment, if any, in liver glycogen.

In the years since, detailed studies of the fate of individual amino acids, by using isotopically labeled amino acids in vivo and in vitro and by the isolation of specific enzymes, have confirmed these early observations and have provided a description of the reaction pathways. In general, transformations which lead to pyruvic acid make possible net glucose formation whereas pathways which lead to acetyl CoA or to acetoacetate result in ketone body formation (page 458). On this basis, amino acids may, in general, be classified with respect to those which are glycogenic and those which are ketogenic (Table 27.1).

Table 27.1: GLYCOGENIC AND KETOGENIC AMINO ACIDS

Glycogenic		Ketogenic	Glycogenic and/or ketogenic
Alanine	Hydroxyproline	Leucine	Isoleucine
Arginine	Methionine		Lysine
Aspartic acid	Proline		Phenylalanine
Cystine	Serine		Tyrosine
Glutamic acid	Threonine		
Glycine	Tryptophan		
Histidine	Valine		

With few exceptions, the initial step in amino acid metabolism is removal of the α-amino group by transamination (page 492) or oxidation (page 510). Hence, it is largely the fate of the corresponding α-keto acid which is described in the discussions to follow.

METABOLIC FATES OF INDIVIDUAL AMINO ACIDS

Alanine; Glutamic and Aspartic Acids. Removal of the amino group of each of these three amino acids results in formation of α-keto acids which are normal intermediates of the tricarboxylic acid cycle. Glutamic acid may transaminate to one of a variety of keto acids or be oxidized in mitochondria by glutamic acid dehydrogenase; aspartic acid and alanine transaminate to α-ketoglutaric acid. The metabolism of the α-keto acids formed from these amino acids follow pathways previously discussed for these compounds in carbohydrate metabolism.

Ornithine, Proline, Hydroxyproline. Ornithine and proline, formed originally from glutamic acid (page 495), are reconvertible to glutamic acid. *Proline dehydrogenase* of mitochondria effects oxidation to Δ¹-pyrroline-5-carboxylic acid; this enzyme is distinct from the DPNH-linked reductase, which is responsible for proline formation (page 496). Hydrolysis then yields glutamic semialdehyde, which can also be formed from ornithine by transamination. Oxidation to glutamic acid completes these sequences.

Experiments with isotopically labeled hydroxyproline indicate that it is readily metabolized. Dehydrogenation by a DPN-linked enzyme yields Δ¹-pyrroline-3-hydroxy-5-carboxylic acid, which, by reactions analogous to those described for proline metabolism, leads to L-γ-hydroxyglutamic acid. Transamination forms α-keto-γ-hydroxyglutaric acid, which appears to be cleaved in an aldolase type of reaction to one molecule each of glyoxylic acid and pyruvic acid. The fate of glyoxylic acid will be described below (page 541).

Glutamine. Two pathways of glutamine metabolism have been indicated in earlier discussion. One of these is catalyzed by the widely distributed glutaminase, with conversion of glutamine to glutamic acid and ammonia (page 489). Glutamic acid metabolism is considered above. A second pathway for glutamine metabolism, with conversion of the amino acid to α-ketoglutaric acid and ammonia, derives from the previously discussed role of glutamine in transamination (page 495). It will be recalled that glutamine transaminates actively with a variety of keto acids, forming the corresponding amino acids and α-ketoglutaramic acid. Hydrolysis of the latter produces α-ketoglutaric acid and ammonia. Thus the operation of this latter enzymic system serves to reverse the total pathway of glutamine synthesis from α-ketoglutaric acid (page 495). The possible special role of this mode of glutamine degradation in metabolism is unclear.

Interest in glutamine metabolism is heightened by several considerations. (1) The equilibrium position of the glutamic acid dehydrogenase reaction strongly favors glutamic acid synthesis, and there is uncertainty whether, as indicated earlier (page 510), glutamate can serve as a source of ammonia. (2) α-Methylaspartic acid, a potent inhibitor of the argininosuccinate synthetase reaction, has been reported not to interfere with urea synthesis in the intact rat, suggesting that sources other than aspartate, perhaps glutamine, may play a role in ammonia contribution to urea synthesis. (3) A major metabolic role of glutamine relates to its contributions to the supply of ammonia in the kidney. Here the operation of the active glutaminase makes possible the key functioning of the kidney in the conservation of cations by the organism, and in the maintainance of the normal hydrogen ion concentration of body fluids. This role of glutamine in metabolism is considered in detail in Chap. 35. (4) Several lines of evidence have indicated that glutamine may play some special role in urea synthesis, other than mere hydrolysis to ammonia. However, the manner of this participation, if such a process does exist, is unclear.

Serine and Glycine. The major ultimate pathway of serine metabolism occurs by an α-β dehydration analogous to that of cysteine (page 543). The reaction is catalyzed by a pyridoxal phosphate-requiring enzyme, *serine dehydrase;* the products are ammonia and pyruvic acid.

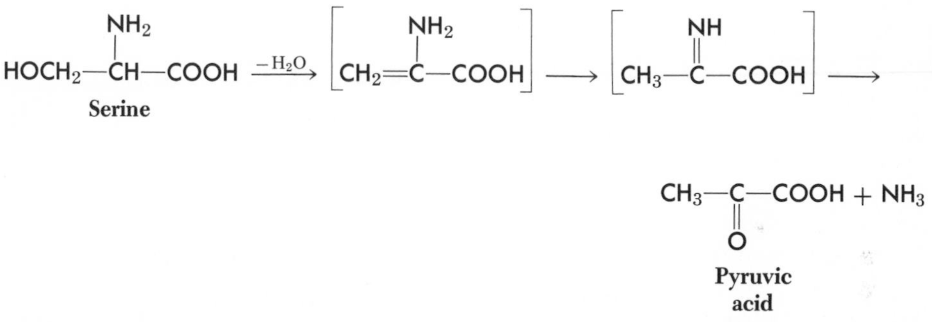

$$HOCH_2-\underset{\underset{NH_2}{|}}{CH}-COOH \xrightarrow{-H_2O} \left[CH_2=\underset{\underset{NH_2}{|}}{C}-COOH\right] \longrightarrow \left[CH_3-\underset{\underset{NH}{||}}{C}-COOH\right] \longrightarrow$$

Serine

$$CH_3-\underset{\underset{O}{||}}{C}-COOH + NH_3$$

Pyruvic
acid

Glycine catabolism can be accomplished by several paths. Thus, by the action of *glycine transhydroxymethylase,* glycine may accept a hydroxymethyl group from N^{10}-hydroxymethyltetrahydrofolic acid to form serine, which is directed into pyruvic acid metabolism as shown above. Alternately, *glycine oxidase* (D-amino acid

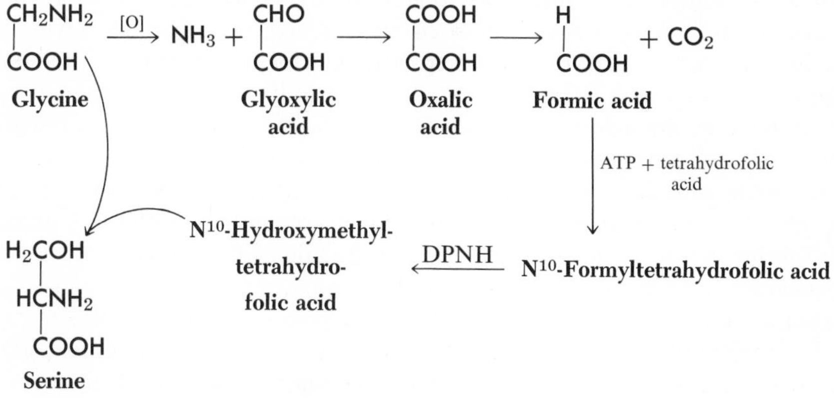

$$\underset{\text{Glycine}}{\overset{CH_2NH_2}{\underset{COOH}{|}}} \xrightarrow{[O]} NH_3 + \underset{\text{Glyoxylic}\atop\text{acid}}{\overset{CHO}{\underset{COOH}{|}}} \longrightarrow \underset{\text{Oxalic}\atop\text{acid}}{\overset{COOH}{\underset{COOH}{|}}} \longrightarrow \underset{\text{Formic acid}}{\overset{H}{\underset{COOH}{|}}} + CO_2$$

ATP + tetrahydrofolic
acid

$$\underset{\text{Serine}}{\overset{H_2COH}{\underset{COOH}{\overset{|}{\underset{|}{HCNH_2}}}}} \qquad \underset{\text{folic acid}}{\overset{N^{10}\text{-Hydroxymethyl-}}{\text{tetrahydro-}}} \xleftarrow{\text{DPNH}} N^{10}\text{-Formyltetrahydrofolic acid}$$

oxidase) catalyzes oxidation of glycine to glyoxylic acid and NH_3. Glyoxylic acid, normally, may be oxidized to formic acid and CO_2; the formic acid is then reutilized by conversion to N^{10}-formyltetrahydrofolic acid, which, among other fates, may be reduced to the N^{10}-hydroxymethyl compound and added to a second molecule of glycine to form serine. Glyoxylic acid may also be oxidized to oxalic acid and the latter excreted in the urine; when this occurs excessively, the insolubility of oxalates may lead to formation of renal stones.

The metabolism of glyoxylic acid may assume greater significance in photosynthetic plants than in animals, since such plants have a vigorous *glyoxylic acid reductase* system for handling the glyoxylate which arises in the isocitritase reaction (page 384). No comparable enzyme is present in animals.

Cysteine. The ultimate fate of cysteine in metabolism is formation of inorganic sulfate and pyruvate. The initial step involves oxidation of the sulfur atom of cysteine. The first intermediate which has been definitely established is cysteine sulfinic acid; the nature of the intermediates between the sulfinic acid and cysteine is not known.

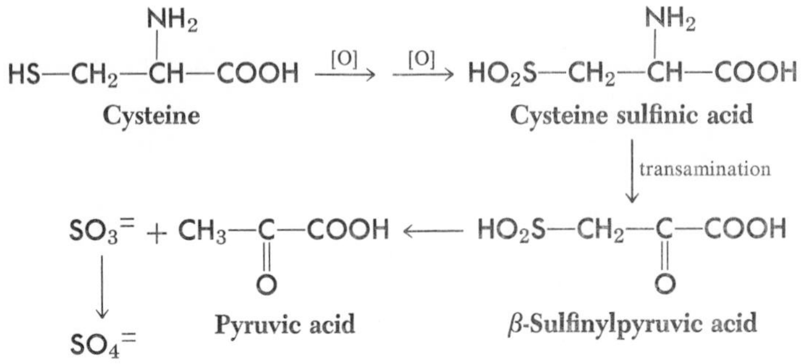

Cysteine sulfinic acid loses its amino group to α-ketoglutaric acid; the resultant β-sulfinylpyruvic acid is an analogue of oxaloacetic acid. Desulfination is catalyzed by a specific *desulfinase,* yielding pyruvic acid and sulfite. It may be presumed, in analogy with decarboxylation reactions, that it is SO_2 which is removed by the enzyme and that $SO_3^=$ is formed by hydration and ionization. The sulfite is then oxidized to sulfate by a microsomal enzyme, which, containing a flavin and a heme-like component, can reduce either O_2 or a cytochrome. Sulfate, the ultimate form in which ingested sulfur is excreted, is also utilized for synthesis of 3′-phosphoadenosine 5′-phosphosulfate (page 515), the compound involved in biosynthesis of diverse sulfate esters.

Cysteine sulfinic acid is also the starting point for the synthesis of several sulfur-containing compounds of biological interest, including taurine and isethionic acid. Taurine is utilized for the formation of the bile acid, taurocholic acid (Chap. 36). Isethionic acid accumulates in rather large quantity in the brain, but its physiological significance is not known.

Taurine synthesis occurs in the liver, starting with cysteine sulfinic acid. Two pathways of taurine formation are possible; that via hypotaurine, elucidated in the rat, appears responsible for the major fraction of taurine synthesis.

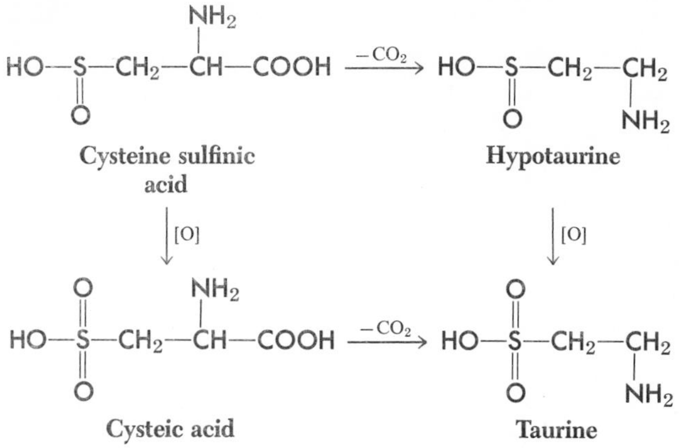

$$\text{HO—S—CH}_2\text{—}\overset{\overset{\displaystyle NH_2}{|}}{\text{CH}}\text{—COOH} \xrightarrow{-CO_2} \text{HO—S—CH}_2\text{—}\overset{\underset{\displaystyle NH_2}{|}}{\text{CH}_2}$$

**Cysteine sulfinic
acid**

Hypotaurine

$\downarrow [O] \qquad\qquad\qquad\qquad\qquad \downarrow [O]$

$$\text{HO—S—CH}_2\text{—}\overset{\overset{\displaystyle NH_2}{|}}{\text{CH}}\text{—COOH} \xrightarrow{-CO_2} \text{HO—S—CH}_2\text{—}\overset{\underset{\displaystyle NH_2}{|}}{\text{CH}_2}$$

Cysteic acid

Taurine

Isotopic tracer experiments reveal that isethionic acid,

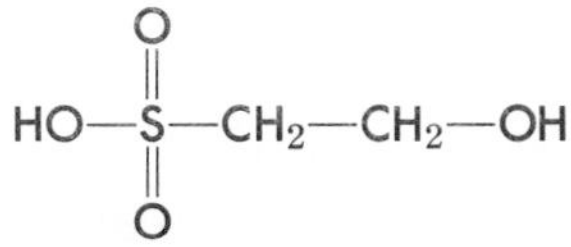

$$\text{HO—}\overset{\overset{\displaystyle O}{||}}{\underset{\underset{\displaystyle O}{||}}{S}}\text{—CH}_2\text{—CH}_2\text{—OH}$$

is made from taurine, but the site and nature of the reaction are not established.

Transamination from cysteine yields β-mercaptopyruvic acid, which is known to participate in three different reactions, each of which results in formation of pyruvic acid. The other products shown in Fig. 27.1 are, respectively, thiosulfate, thiocyanate, and, in bacteria, elemental sulfur which can be oxidized to thiosulfate or reduced to H_2S. Liver contains *rhodanese,* a sulfhydryl-containing enzyme, which promotes formation of thiocyanate from CN^- and $S_2O_3^=$.

The thioethanolamine (cysteamine) derived from cysteine and present in coenzyme A is liberated upon hydrolysis of this coenzyme. Its subsequent fate appears to be oxidation to hypotaurine and thence to taurine. A small amount of cystine undergoes cleavage by *cystathionase,* with formation of S-thiocysteine. Decarboxylation and oxidation of the latter result in formation of a minor quantity of thiotaurine. These pathways are summarized in Fig. 27.1.

Other pathways of cysteine catabolism are also operative in the liver but are of lesser significance. Of interest because of its mechanism is the "cysteine desulfhydrase" reaction catalyzed by the pyridoxal phosphate–requiring *cystathionase.* The major function of this enzyme, conversion of cystathionine to homoserine plus cysteine in animal metabolism, has already been considered (page 499). In the presence of cystine, this enzyme catalyzes the reaction series shown below.

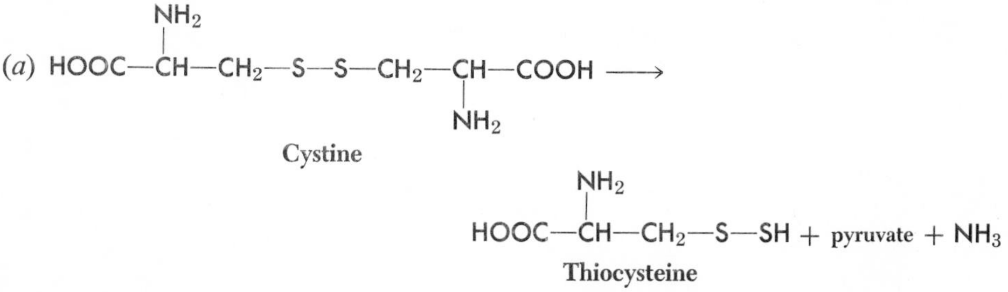

(*a*) $\text{HOOC—}\overset{\overset{\displaystyle NH_2}{|}}{\text{CH}}\text{—CH}_2\text{—S—S—CH}_2\text{—}\overset{\underset{\displaystyle NH_2}{|}}{\text{CH}}\text{—COOH} \longrightarrow$

Cystine

$$\text{HOOC—}\overset{\overset{\displaystyle NH_2}{|}}{\text{CH}}\text{—CH}_2\text{—S—SH} + \text{pyruvate} + NH_3$$

Thiocysteine

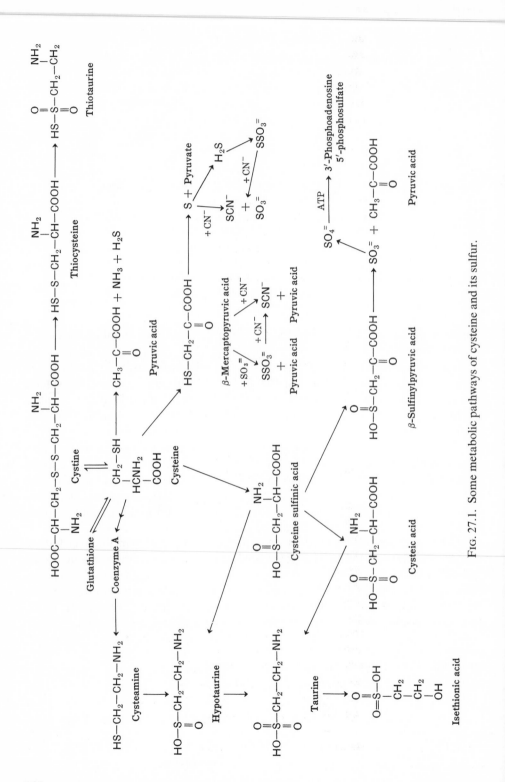

Fig. 27.1. Some metabolic pathways of cysteine and its sulfur.

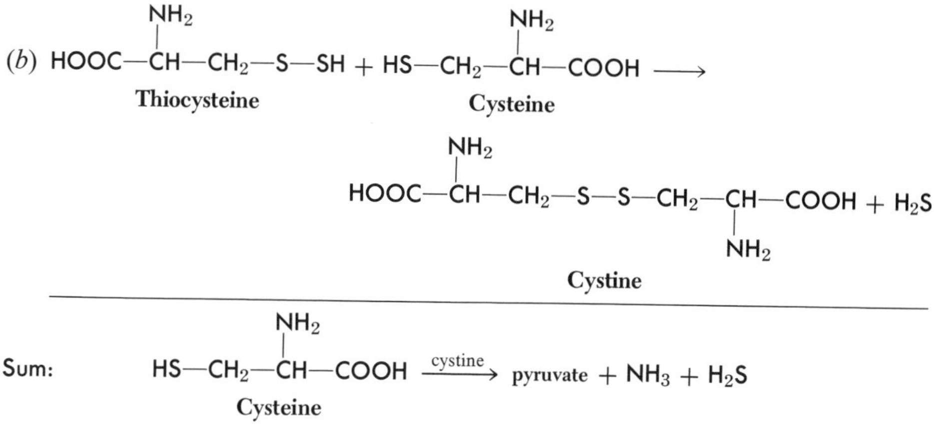

(b)

$$\underset{\text{Thiocysteine}}{\text{HOOC}-\overset{\displaystyle \overset{\text{NH}_2}{|}}{\text{CH}}-\text{CH}_2-\text{S}-\text{SH}} + \underset{\text{Cysteine}}{\text{HS}-\text{CH}_2-\overset{\displaystyle \overset{\text{NH}_2}{|}}{\text{CH}}-\text{COOH}} \longrightarrow$$

$$\underset{\text{Cystine}}{\text{HOOC}-\overset{\displaystyle \overset{\text{NH}_2}{|}}{\text{CH}}-\text{CH}_2-\text{S}-\text{S}-\text{CH}_2-\underset{\displaystyle \underset{\text{NH}_2}{|}}{\text{CH}}-\text{COOH}} + \text{H}_2\text{S}$$

Sum:

$$\underset{\text{Cysteine}}{\text{HS}-\text{CH}_2-\overset{\displaystyle \overset{\text{NH}_2}{|}}{\text{CH}}-\text{COOH}} \xrightarrow{\text{cystine}} \text{pyruvate} + \text{NH}_3 + \text{H}_2\text{S}$$

Even lesser amounts of other sulfur compounds, some of unknown origin, can be found in the urine. Among these are isobuteine, isovalthine, and felinine.

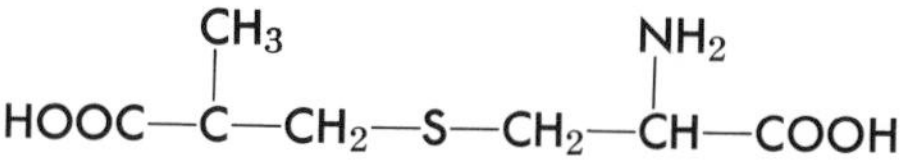

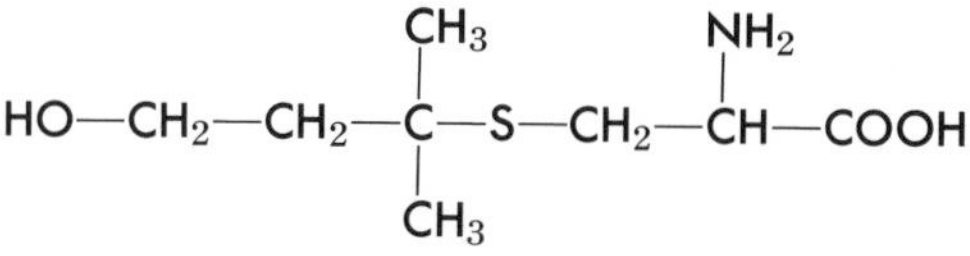

$$\underset{\text{Isobuteine}}{\text{HOOC}-\overset{\displaystyle \overset{\text{CH}_3}{|}}{\text{C}}-\text{CH}_2-\text{S}-\text{CH}_2-\overset{\displaystyle \overset{\text{NH}_2}{|}}{\text{CH}}-\text{COOH}}$$

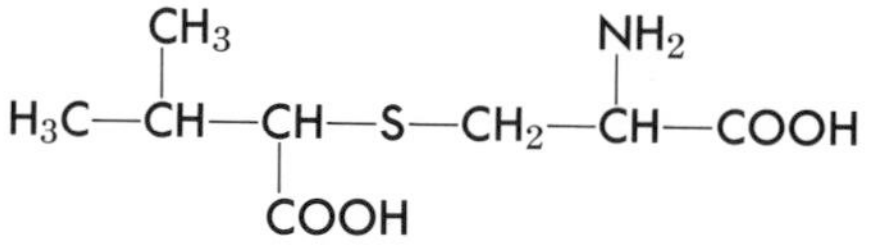

$$\underset{\text{Isovalthine}}{\text{H}_3\text{C}-\overset{\displaystyle \overset{\text{CH}_3}{|}}{\underset{\displaystyle \underset{\text{COOH}}{|}}{\text{CH}}}-\text{CH}-\text{S}-\text{CH}_2-\overset{\displaystyle \overset{\text{NH}_2}{|}}{\text{CH}}-\text{COOH}}$$

$$\underset{\text{Felinine}}{\text{HO}-\text{CH}_2-\text{CH}_2-\overset{\displaystyle \overset{\text{CH}_3}{|}}{\underset{\displaystyle \underset{\text{CH}_3}{|}}{\text{C}}}-\text{S}-\text{CH}_2-\overset{\displaystyle \overset{\text{NH}_2}{|}}{\text{CH}}-\text{COOH}}$$

It may be noted that isovalthine was first obtained from the urine of hypercholesterolemic individuals and its excretion in the urine of normal animals is augmented by administration of cholesterol.

Of the diverse sulfur-containing compounds described above, it is as sulfate that most of the ingested protein sulfur is excreted. Daily excretion of sulfur in the urine totals about 700 mg., of which about 75 per cent is as sulfate, 5 per cent as sulfate esters (esters of phenols and oligosaccharides), and somewhat less than 20 per cent as organic sulfur in the many forms cited above.

Methionine. The major aspects of methionine metabolism have already been presented. Its final metabolic disposal requires transfer of the methyl group to an appropriate acceptor. Ultimately, this group is either excreted, e.g., as creatinine or N^1-methylnicotinamide, or oxidized and transferred to tetrahydrofolic acid and thence to glycine, becoming the β-carbon of serine, which becomes the methyl carbon of pyruvic acid. The sulfur atom is utilized for cysteine metabolism and, hence, leaves the body as sulfate. The cystathionase reaction, in which the sulfur atom becomes part of a cysteine molecule, results in the original carbon chain of methionine remaining as homoserine. A pyridoxal phosphate enzyme–catalyzed reaction, the mechanism of which is somewhat uncertain, converts this compound to α-ketobutyrate plus NH_3. Oxidative decarboxylation of α-ketobutyrate, analogous to that of pyruvic acid, results in formation of propionyl CoA, the subsequent metabolism of which has already been considered (page 443). These reactions are indicated in Fig. 27.2.

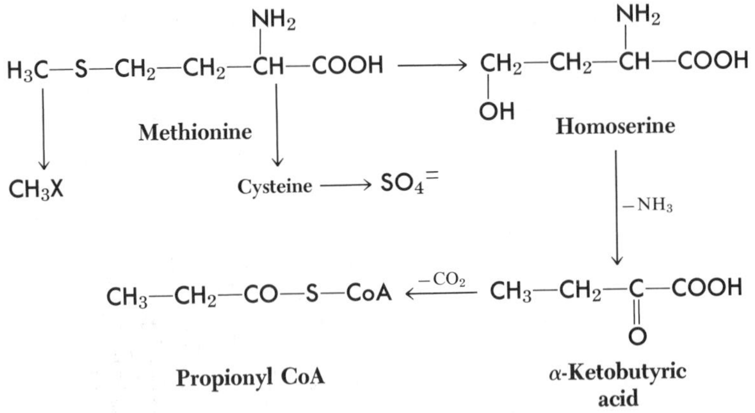

FIG. 27.2. Metabolic fate of methionine. X = acceptor of methyl group.

Threonine. Studies in which N^{15} has been administered in several forms, *e.g.*, glutamic acid, have failed to reveal any incorporation of isotope into threonine, and no threonine transaminase has been described. Hence, threonine degradation does not commence by loss of its nitrogen via transamination. However, liver and kidney both contain *threonine aldolase,* a pyridoxal phosphate–requiring enzyme which catalyzes the following reaction.

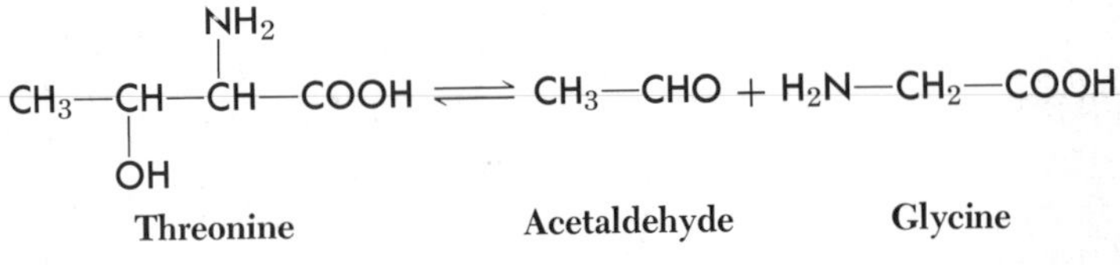

To the extent that this reaction occurs, the glycine formed can follow its various normal pathways; acetaldehyde is oxidized to acetic acid and the resulting acetyl CoA is oxidized or otherwise utilized in the diverse manners described.

The alternate fate of threonine is its initial deamination catalyzed by a separate pyridoxal phosphate–utilizing enzyme, *threonine deaminase.* The products are NH_3 plus α-ketobutyrate, as in the case of the corresponding reaction with homoserine. This pathway, leading to propionyl CoA, makes possible the ultimate appearance of three of the four carbon atoms of threonine as glucose in the diabetic animal, whereas the threonine aldolase reaction should provide two carbons to glucose, via glycine, and two carbons to ketone bodies, via acetaldehyde. Since threonine is glucogenic, not ketogenic, the threonine deaminase reaction is probably dominant in threonine degradation.

Fates of Valine, Leucine, and Isoleucine. Although valine may be used in plants for synthesis of the pantoic acid moiety of pantothenic acid, valine, leucine, and isoleucine are not known to play any special roles in mammalian metabolism. Their only known functions are to serve in protein structure, in which they contribute hydrophobic residues prominent in determining protein conformation (page 155).

The catabolic fates of this group of branched chain aliphatic amino acids exhibit several features in common. Initial transamination yields the corresponding α-keto acids, which are then subjected to oxidative decarboxylation, with formation of the acyl CoA derivatives of one less carbon atom. Subsequent reactions, in each instance, resemble those encountered in the pathways for fatty acid oxidation.

Valine oxidation (Fig. 27.3) leads to methylmalonyl CoA (page 444), which is converted to succinyl CoA and completely oxidized, or provides three of five carbons for gluconeogenesis, in accord with observations in vivo.

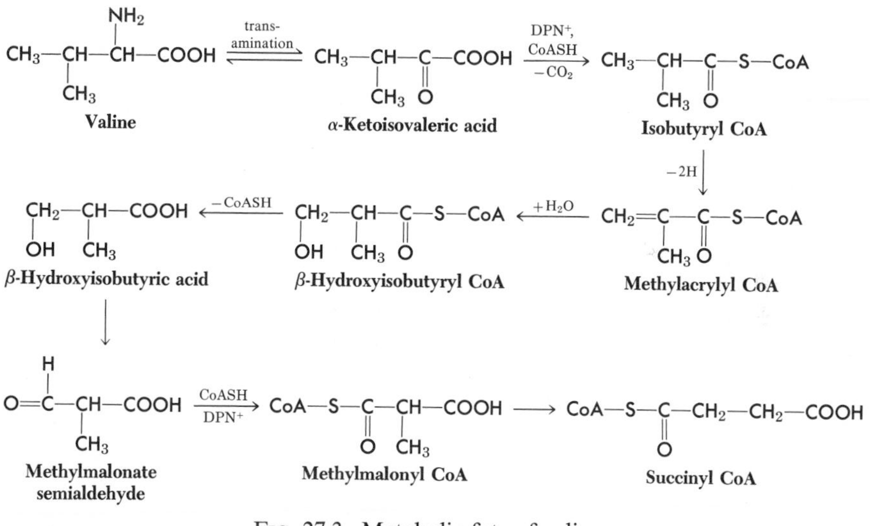

FIG. 27.3. Metabolic fate of valine.

Leucine oxidation (Fig. 27.4) terminates with formation of one molecule of acetoacetic acid and one molecule of acetyl CoA, in keeping with the finding that in the diabetic animal, each mole of leucine yields 1.5 moles of acetoacetic acid. Noteworthy also is the production of β-hydroxy-β-methylglutaryl CoA in this pathway; this is also a key intermediate in steroid synthesis from acetyl CoA.

Isoleucine metabolism (Fig. 27.5) is concluded with formation of one molecule each of acetyl CoA and propionyl CoA, in accord with experimental evidence that this amino acid is both weakly glucogenic and weakly ketogenic.

In 1954 a rare hereditary anomaly of the metabolism of valine, leucine, and isoleucine was described as *maple syrup urine disease,* because of the characteristic odor of the urine. Clinically, rapid deterioration is observed in the first few months of life. Some children may survive for several years but show severe mental deteri-

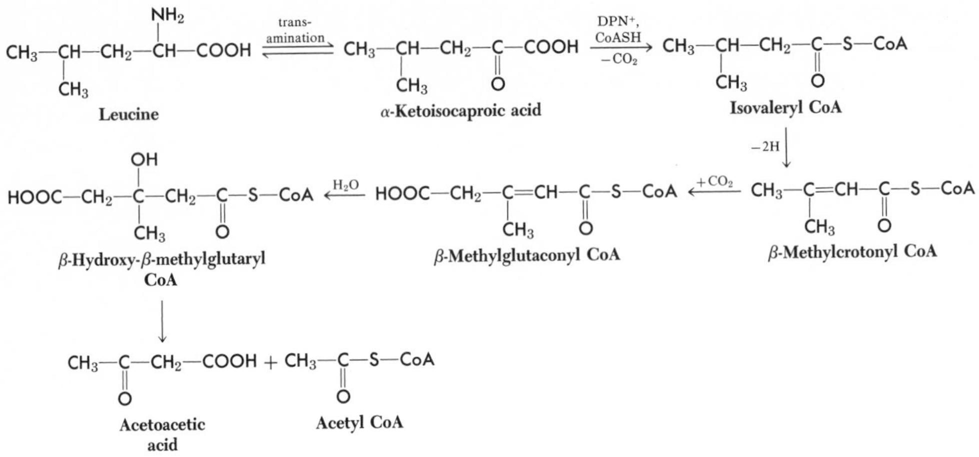

FIG. 27.4. Metabolic fate of leucine.

oration; extensive failure of myelination is evident at autopsy. The urinary odor is that of the α-keto acids corresponding to these three amino acids. Transamination is unaffected, but normal oxidative decarboxylation with acyl CoA formation does not occur. The fact that all three α-keto acids accumulate indicates (1) that a single enzyme catalyzes all three oxidations, and (2) that no major alternate pathway of metabolism is available.

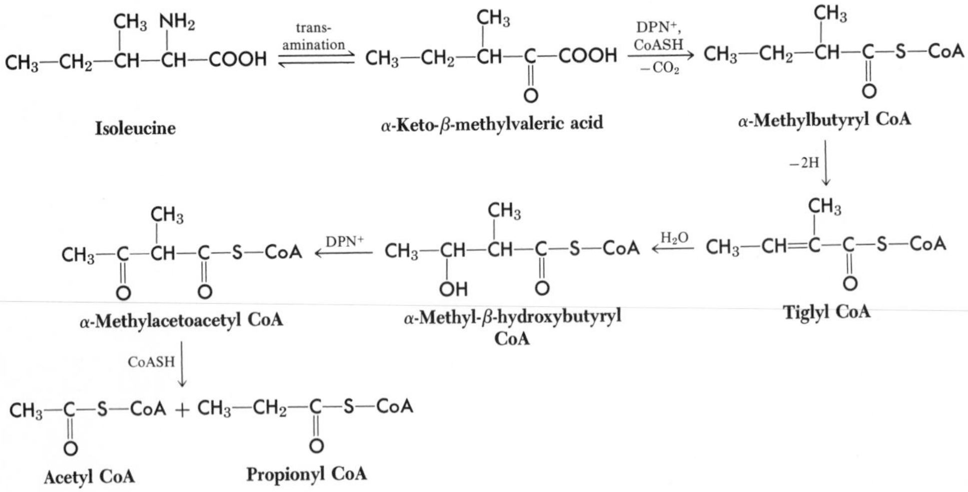

FIG. 27.5. Metabolic fate of isoleucine.

Phenylalanine and Tyrosine. In normal individuals, almost all of phenylalanine metabolism is channeled through tyrosine by virtue of the action of phenylalanine hydroxylase (page 500). Only in phenylketonuria (page 501) is metabolism diverted to formation of phenylpyruvic acid, which accumulates or is reduced to phenyllactic acid; a small fraction of the latter is oxidized to phenylacetic acid, which is excreted as phenylacetylglutamine. The initial event in tyrosine metabolism is transamination, catalyzed by a specific, copper-containing enzyme. This is an inducible enzyme in that hepatic tyrosine-α-ketoglutarate transaminase activity increases significantly after tyrosine administration.

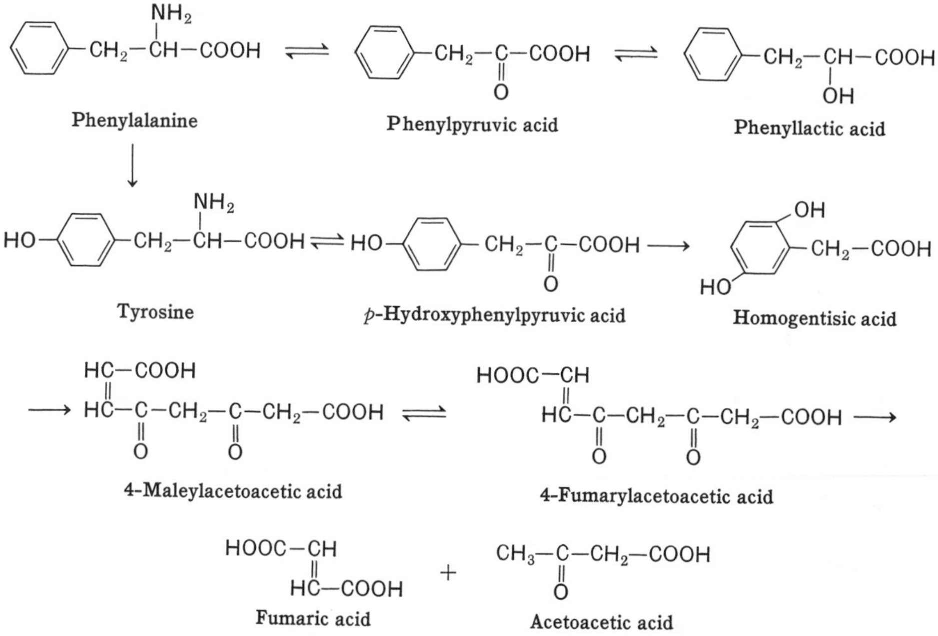

FIG. 27.6. The principal pathways of phenylalanine and tyrosine metabolism.

p-Hydroxyphenylpyruvic acid oxidase, a copper-containing protein, catalyzes formation of homogentisic acid. Comparison of the structures of *p*-hydroxyphenyl-pyruvic acid and its oxidation product, homogentisic acid, indicates that this conversion involves hydroxylation of the ring, oxidation, decarboxylation, and migration of the side chain. It has not yet been possible to separate these reactions, which appear, at present, to be catalyzed by a single enzyme. The activity of this enzyme is low in fetal liver and increases slowly following birth; this may account in part for the urinary excretion of *p*-hydroxyphenylpyruvic acid in premature infants or in normal infants who are fed tyrosine. Ascorbic acid is apparently essential for the normal activity of this enzyme since ascorbic acid–deficient guinea pigs and infants excrete substantial amounts of phenylpyruvic acid in response to an administered dose of tyrosine.

The further metabolism of homogentisic acid is accomplished in the liver by an oxygenase, *homogentisic acid oxidase,* requiring Fe^{++} and a high concentration of —SH groups for activity. The oxygen effects a scission of the aromatic ring between the side chain and the adjacent hydroxyl groups; an entire oxygen molecule is thereby introduced into the product, 4-maleylacetoacetic acid. Ascorbic acid is also required for homogentisic acid oxidase activity, but its actual function in this system is obscure. Its significance is revealed by the fact that scorbutic guinea pigs and human beings excrete substantial quantities of homogentisic acid when fed tyrosine.

4-Maleylacetoacetic acid, a *cis* compound, is converted by *maleylacetoacetic acid isomerase,* which requires glutathione as cofactor, to the *trans* form, fumaryl-acetoacetic acid. Hydrolysis then yields a molecule each of fumaric and acetoacetic acids, which enter their normal metabolic channels. This is consonant with the demonstration that phenylalanine and tyrosine are both glucogenic and ketogenic in the diabetic animal. Pathways of phenylalanine and tyrosine metabolism are depicted in Fig. 27.6.

Failure to oxidize homogentisic acid and its consequent accumulation are seen in *alkaptonuria,* one of the "inborn errors of metabolism" originally recognized by Garrod. La Du demonstrated that the livers of alkaptonuric individuals lack homogentisic acid oxidase but are normal with respect to all the prior and subsequent enzymes of the tyrosine catabolic pathway. The excretion of homogentisic acid is apparent from the fact that the urine, when made slightly alkaline, rapidly darkens on exposure to air because of ready oxidation of homogentisic acid to a quinone, which polymerizes to a melanin-like material. The urine is strongly reducing and gives a transitory blue color with each drop of dilute ferric chloride added. A single drop of alkalinized urine causes immediate blackening of exposed photographic paper and reduction of oxidizing agents frequently used for detection, in the urine, of glucose. In early life there is no other abnormality; in later years abnormal pigmentation of cartilage and other connective tissue (*ochronosis*) may become apparent.

Lysine. As in the case of threonine (page 546), there is no evidence for participation of lysine in transamination. Oxidative deamination can be catalyzed, however, by the L-amino acid oxidase of liver, and this appears to be the initial step in lysine degradation. Figure 27.7 summarizes the subsequent steps in the metabolism of the resultant α-keto-ϵ-aminocaproic acid. Ring closure yields Δ^1-dehydropipecolic acid, which is reduced by a liver enzyme that employs DPNH or TPNH. The L-pipecolic acid thus formed is reoxidized to the Δ^6-dehydropipecolic acid. Opening of the ring leads to α-aminoadipic δ-semialdehyde. Thus this series of reactions has the total effect of having oxidized the ϵ-amino group rather than the α-amino group of lysine. Oxidation of the aldehyde group and removal of the amino group, by oxidative deamination or transamination, give rise to α-ketoadipic acid. The succeeding reactions resemble those familiar in other areas of metabolism.

Histidine. Histidine can transaminate to form the corresponding imidazolepyruvic acid, but this does not represent the major route of histidine metabolism. Rather, histidine is deaminated by *histidase,* which catalyzes the α-β removal of a molecule of NH_3 with formation of urocanic acid, in an essentially irreversible process. This enzyme is lacking in individuals with the hereditary disorder *histidinemia,* leading to elevated blood and urine levels of histidine. A pyridoxal phosphate–requiring enzyme, *urocanase,* then catalyzes transformation of urocanic acid to imidazolonepropionic acid. This reaction involves the elements of water and an internal oxidation and reduction; its mechanism remains to be elucidated. *Imidazolonepropionic acid hydrolase* effects hydrolysis of this compound to α-formiminoglutamic acid. The formimino group can then be transferred, by a specific *transferase,* to the N^5 position of tetrahydrofolic acid. The N^5-formiminotetrahydrofolic acid hydrolyzes, cyclizes to the $N^{5,10}$-formyl derivative, and then yields

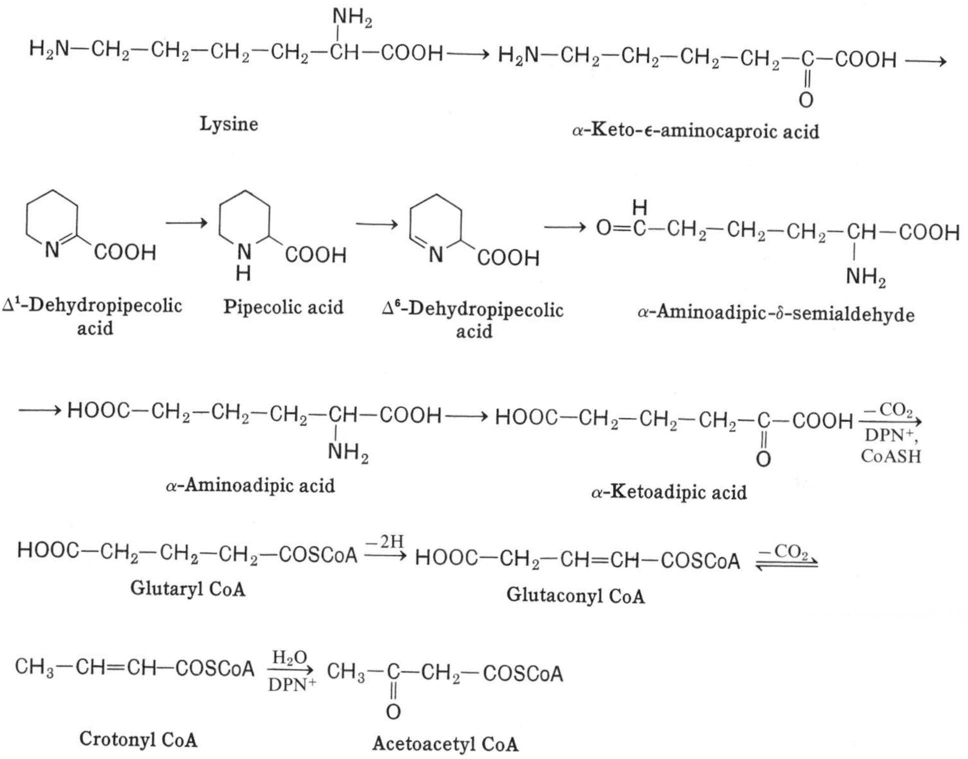

$$NH_2$$
$$H_2N-CH_2-CH_2-CH_2-CH_2-\overset{|}{CH}-COOH \longrightarrow H_2N-CH_2-CH_2-CH_2-CH_2-\underset{\overset{\|}{O}}{C}-COOH \longrightarrow$$

Lysine α-Keto-ϵ-aminocaproic acid

Δ^1-Dehydropipecolic acid $\longrightarrow$ Pipecolic acid $\longrightarrow$ Δ^6-Dehydropipecolic acid $\longrightarrow$ $O=\overset{H}{\underset{}{C}}-CH_2-CH_2-CH_2-\underset{\overset{|}{NH_2}}{CH}-COOH$

α-Aminoadipic-δ-semialdehyde

$$\longrightarrow HOOC-CH_2-CH_2-CH_2-\underset{\overset{|}{NH_2}}{CH}-COOH \longrightarrow HOOC-CH_2-CH_2-CH_2-\underset{\overset{\|}{O}}{C}-COOH \xrightarrow[\substack{DPN^+, \\ CoASH}]{-CO_2}$$

α-Aminoadipic acid α-Ketoadipic acid

$$HOOC-CH_2-CH_2-CH_2-COSCoA \xrightarrow{-2H} HOOC-CH_2-CH=CH-COSCoA \underset{}{\overset{-CO_2}{\rightleftharpoons}}$$

Glutaryl CoA Glutaconyl CoA

$$CH_3-CH=CH-COSCoA \xrightarrow[DPN^+]{H_2O} CH_3-\underset{\overset{\|}{O}}{C}-CH_2-COSCoA$$

Crotonyl CoA Acetoacetyl CoA

FIG. 27.7. Suggested pathways for the metabolic degradation of lysine.

the N^{10}-formyl compound (page 503). In this manner C-2 of the histidine imidazole ring returns to the C_1 pool. This last reaction is reflected in the fact that animals or human beings deficient in folic acid have an excessive excretion of formiminoglutamic acid; this may serve as an indicator of the adequacy of the folic acid content of the diet.

A small amount of imidazolone 3-propionic acid may also be oxidized to hydantoin 5-propionic acid, which is not metabolized further but is excreted in the urine.

Pathways of histidine metabolism are depicted in Fig. 27.8.

Ergothioneine, the betaine of 2-mercaptohistidine, is present in high concentration in human erythrocytes (20 to 30 mg. per 100 ml. whole blood). It is also found in liver and brain and in large concentration in boar semen. It is not known to serve a metabolic role in mammals, but is concentrated in the tissues after ingestion in foodstuffs of plant origin. Nothing is known of its final disposition.

Tryptophan. The utilization of tryptophan for formation of serotonin and indoleacetic acid was presented previously (page 536). These products account for a significant fraction of the tryptophan degraded. A second and major pathway, initiated by the action of *tryptophan pyrrolase*, results in formation of a series of intermediates and by-products (Fig. 27.9), all but one of which (glutaryl CoA) appear in the urine in varying amounts, and the sum of which accounts approxi-

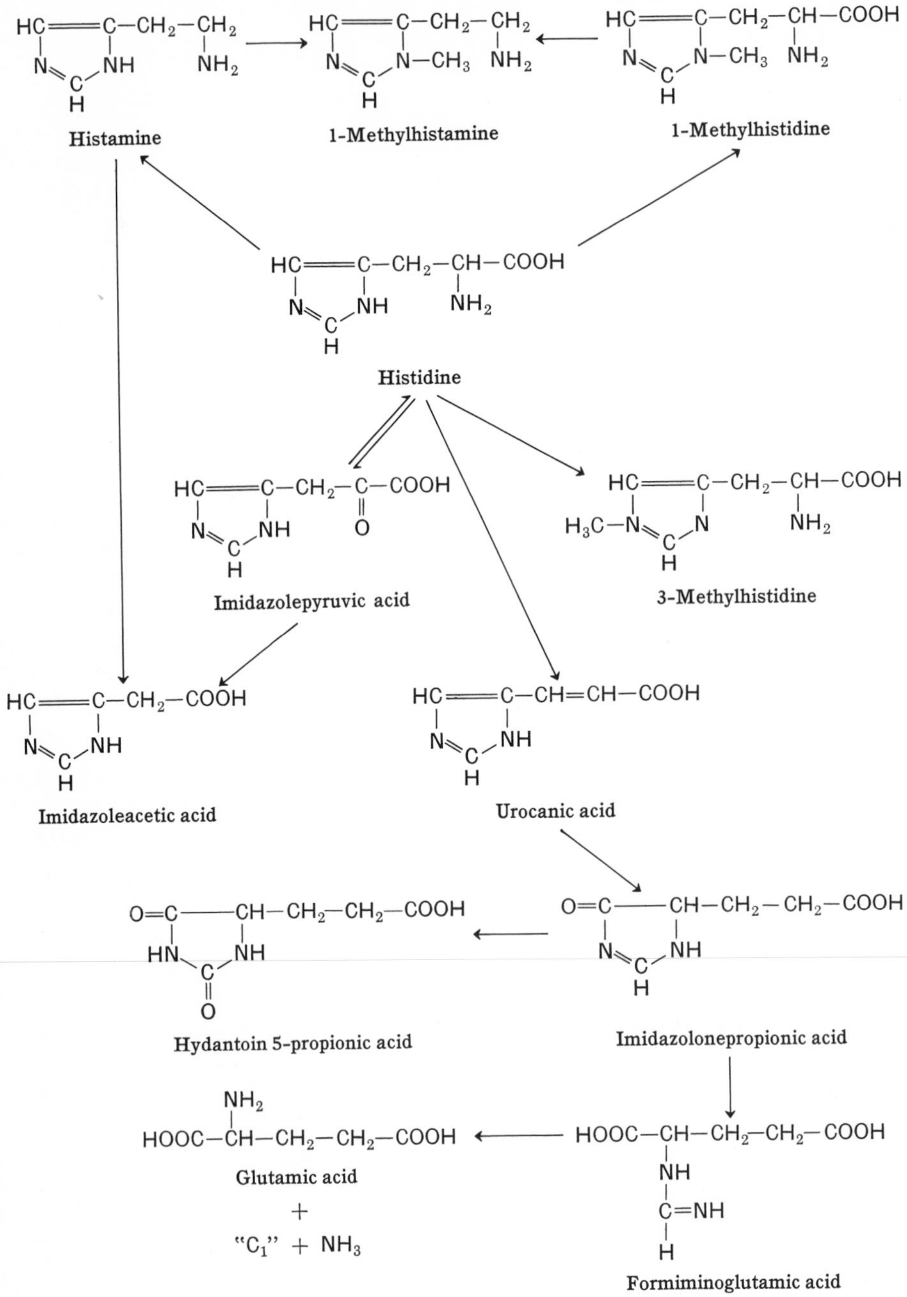

FIG. 27.8. Pathways of histidine metabolism.

mately for the total metabolism of tryptophan. Of the entire group, only the serotonin, considered previously; the glutaryl CoA, which is metabolized to acetyl CoA (page 551); the vitamin nicotinic acid, which is used for DPN biosynthesis (page 580); and a minor amount of alanine, made in bypaths of this set of reactions, are physiologically useful. The further metabolism of glutaryl CoA accounts for partial conversion of the benzene ring of tryptophan to acetate and CO_2.

Tryptophan pyrrolase, whose prosthetic group is protoheme IX, uses molecular oxygen to oxidize tryptophan to N-formylkynurenine (Fig. 27.9). Tryptophan pyrrolase is an adaptive enzyme, and its activity in the liver can be increased by administration of tryptophan or elevation of the blood level of adrenal cortical steroids. The enzyme dissociates readily into an apoenzyme and its prosthetic group. Other proteins which bind the porphyrin inhibit the enzyme. Feigelson and Greengard have suggested that the increase in enzymic activity in rat liver after tryptophan administration is due to the influence of the raised levels of tryptophan in diminishing dissociation of the enzyme to porphyrin and inactive apoenzyme, thus favoring tryptophan pyrrolase in its competition with other proteins for its prosthetic group. An abnormally low fraction of ingested tryptophan is oxidized to formylkynurenine in *Hartnup's disease*, a disorder associated with mental retardation.

L-N-Formylkynurenine is converted to kynurenine by a liver enzyme, *kynurenine formylase*. Kynurenine is present in normal urine in trace amounts, which may be increased after tryptophan administration or in circumstances of accentuated protein catabolism.

Hydroxylation of kynurenine is catalyzed by *kynurenine 3-hydroxylase*, which requires TPNH and molecular oxygen (page 356). The enzyme is specific for kynurenine, and hydroxylation occurs only at position 3. 3-Hydroxykynurenine, which in insects is also a precursor of eye pigments (ommochromes), is found in mammalian urine as the glucosiduronate, the O-sulfate, or the N-α-acetyl derivative. A pyridoxal phosphate-requiring enzyme, *kynureninase*, can catalyze cleavage of both kynurenine and 3-hydroxykynurenine to anthranilic and 3-hydroxyanthranilic acids, respectively. Alanine is the other reaction product in both instances. 3-Hydroxykynurenine is split approximately twice as rapidly as kynurenine. The latter also transaminates; the corresponding keto acid undergoes ring closure to yield kynurenic acid. This compound is dehydroxylated to quinaldic acid. Quinaldic acid accounted for approximately 30 per cent of ingested kynurenic acid in human subjects.

3-Hydroxyanthranilic acid oxidation is catalyzed by *3-hydroxyanthranilic acid oxidase*, present in liver and kidney. The enzyme is an oxygenase, requiring Fe^{++} and a sulfhydryl compound; molecular oxygen is incorporated into the product. The latter is an unstable intermediate which may yield nicotinic acid, picolinic acid, and quinolinic acid, important products of tryptophan metabolism. The formation of the vitamin nicotinic acid (Chap. 55) in tryptophan metabolism has been demonstrated both in the rat and in man; if administered in sufficient amount, the amino acid can meet the growth requirements in nicotinic acid deficiency. Picolinic acid appears in the urine as its glycine conjugate, picolinuric acid.

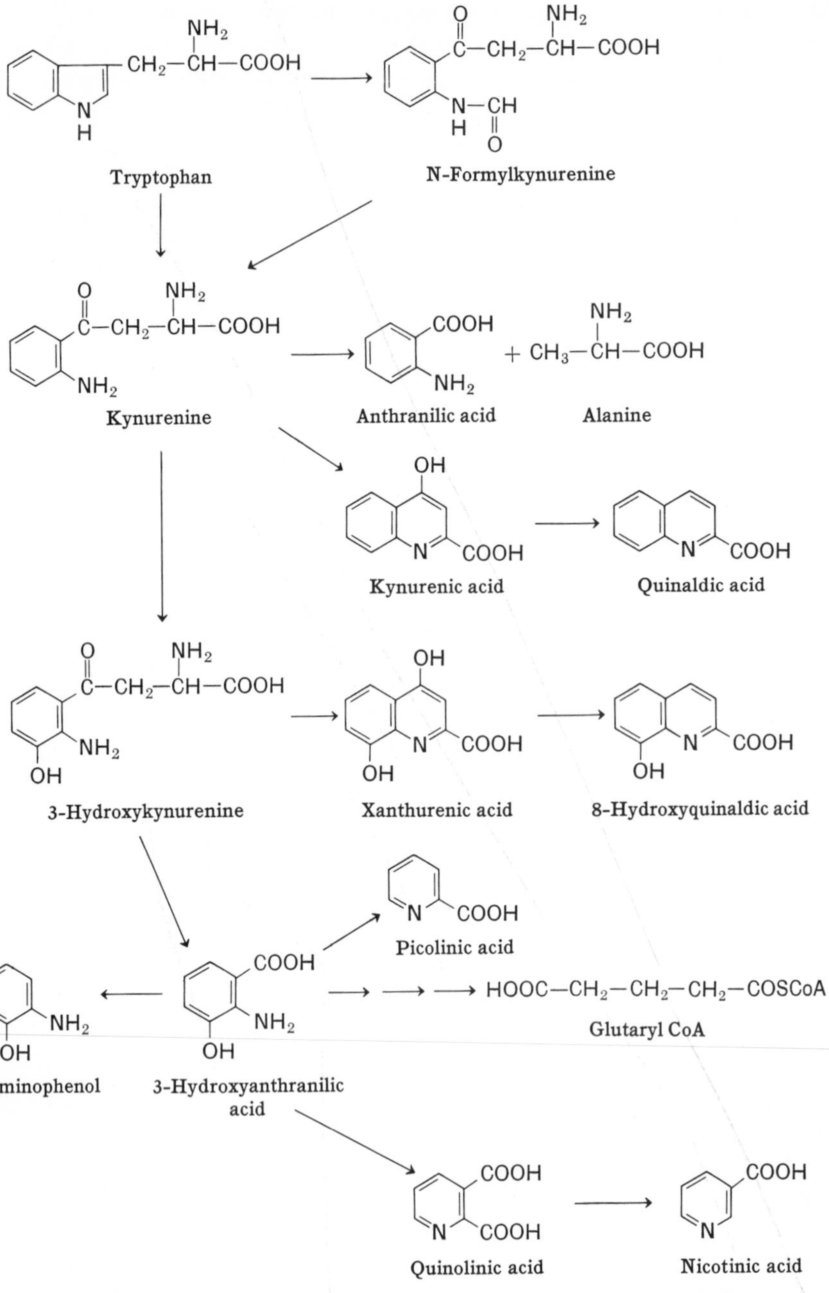

Fig. 27.9. Metabolic relationships among tryptophan and its metabolites.

A pathway of tryptophan metabolism, recently disclosed by Hayaishi and his associates, affords explanation of in vivo evidence that the benzene ring of tryptophan is rapidly degraded to CO_2 via 3-hydroxyanthranilic acid, with glutaric acid an intermediate in this conversion. An enzymic system from cat liver converted 3-hydroxyanthranilic acid to glutaric acid and CO_2, with evidence that several intermediate compounds, including α-ketoadipic acid, are formed. Tryptophan metabolism is thus convergent with the pathway of lysine degradation at the level of α-ketoadipic acid (Fig. 27.7).

Pyridoxine-deficient rats excrete abnormally large amounts of kynurenine and xanthurenic acid. Formation of the latter and of anthranilic, kynurenic, and quinaldic acids can be considered side reactions not on the main pathways of tryptophan metabolism. Xanthurenic acid may suffer loss of a hydroxyl group with formation of 8-hydroxyquinaldic acid.

Indoleacetic acid (page 535) is present in the urine of mammals as indoleaceturic acid formed by conjugation with glycine. A possible precursor is tryptamine, known to arise in the large intestine by bacterial decarboxylation of tryptophan. Indoleacetic acid and indolelactic acid are excreted in increased amounts in the urine of phenylketonuric patients (page 501). The microorganisms of the large intestine can further degrade indoleacetic acid to yield skatole, skatoxyl, indole, and indoxyl.

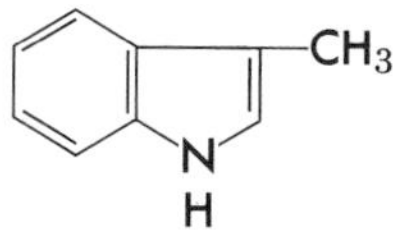

Skatole

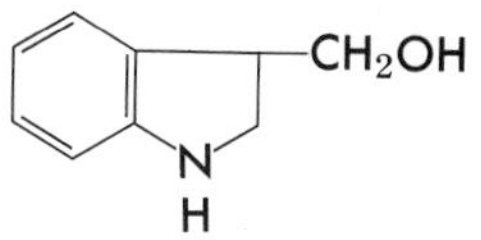

Skatoxyl

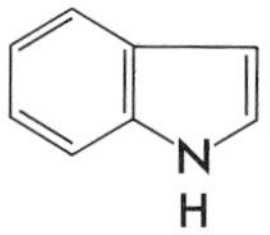

Indole

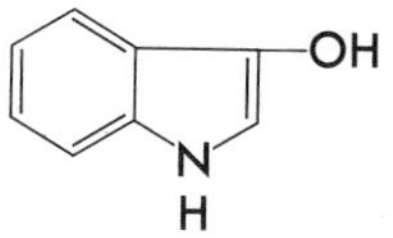

Indoxyl

Indole may also arise directly from tryptophan as a result of bacterial action. Various bacteria contain the enzyme *tryptophanase* which catalyzes cleavage of the side chain of tryptophan, with formation of indole, ammonia, and pyruvic acid. Pyridoxal phosphate is a coenzyme for the reaction.

Skatole and indole contribute to the unpleasant odor of feces. Small amounts of indoxyl and skatoxyl enter the circulation from the gut, are conjugated either with sulfate or glucuronic acid in the liver, and excreted in the urine as ester sulfates or as glucosiduronates. The potassium salt of indoxylsulfate is known as indican; the urinary concentration of indoxylsulfate has been used as a qualitative indication of the extent of bacterial activity in the large intestine.

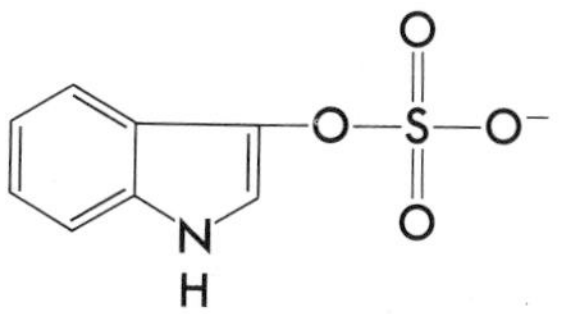

Indoxylsulfate

REFERENCES

Books

Baldwin, E., "Dynamic Aspects of Biochemistry," 3d ed., Cambridge University Press, New York, 1957.

Du Vigneaud, V., "A Trail of Research in Sulfur Chemistry and Metabolism and Related Fields," Cornell University Press, Ithaca, N.Y., 1952.

Garrod, A. E., "Inborn Errors of Metabolism," 2d ed., H. Frowde and Hodder & Stoughton, Ltd., London, 1923.

Greenberg, D. M., ed., "Metabolic Pathways," vol. II, Academic Press, Inc., New York, 1961.

Gross, F., ed., "Protein Metabolism," Springer Verlag OHG, Berlin, 1962.

Harris, H., "Human Biochemical Genetics," Cambridge University Press, New York, 1959.

McElroy, W. D., and Glass, B., eds., "Amino Acid Metabolism," Johns Hopkins Press, Baltimore, 1955.

Meister, A., "Biochemistry of the Amino Acids," Academic Press, Inc., New York, 1957.

Schoenheimer, R., "The Dynamic State of Body Constituents," Harvard University Press, Cambridge, Mass., 1942.

Stanbury, J. B., Wyngaarden, J. B., and Fredrickson, D. S., eds., "The Metabolic Basis of Inherited Disease," McGraw-Hill Book Company, Inc., Blakiston Division, New York, 1960.

Young, L., and Maw, A., "The Metabolism of Sulphur Compounds," John Wiley & Sons, Inc., New York, 1958.

Review Articles

Adams, E., Amino Acid Metabolism, *Ann. Rev. Biochem.,* **31**, 173–212, 1962.

Black, S., Biochemistry of Sulfur-containing Compounds, *Ann. Rev. Biochem.,* **32**, 399–418, 1963.

Christensen, H. N., and Oxender, D. L., Transport of Amino Acids into and across Cells, *Am. J. Clin. Nutrition,* **8**, 131–136, 1960.

Cohen, P. P., and Brown, G. W., Jr., Ammonia Metabolism and Urea Biosynthesis, in M. Florkin and H. S. Mason, eds., "Comparative Biochemistry," vol. II, pp. 161–244, Academic Press, Inc., New York, 1961.

Cohen, P. P., and Sallach, H. J., Nitrogen Metabolism of Amino Acids, in D. M. Greenberg, ed., "Metabolic Pathways," vol. II, 1–78, Academic Press, Inc., New York, 1961.

Dalgliesh, C. E., Metabolism of the Aromatic Amino Acids, *Advances in Protein Chem.,* **10**, 31–150, 1955.

Davis, B. D., Intermediates in Amino Acid Biosynthesis, *Advances in Enzymol.,* **16**, 247–312, 1955.

Davis, B. D., The Teleonomic Significance of Biosynthetic Control Mechanisms, *Cold Spring Harbor Symp. Quant. Biol.,* **26**, 1–10, 1961.

Davison, H., Physiological Role of Monamine Oxidase, *Physiol. Revs.,* **38**, 729–747, 1958.

Ennor, H., and Morrison, J. F., Biochemistry of the Phosphagens and Related Guanidines, *Physiol. Revs.,* **38**, 631–674, 1958.

Friedkin, M., Enzymatic Aspects of Folic Acid, *Ann. Rev. Biochem.,* **32**, 185–214, 1963.

Greenberg, D. M., Biological Methylation, *Advances in Enzymol.,* **25**, 395–432, 1963.

Knox, W. E., Sir Archibald Garrod's "Inborn Errors of Metabolism." I. Cystinuria, *Am. J. Human Genet.,* **10**, 3–32, 1958.

Knox, W. E., Sir Archibald Garrod's "Inborn Errors of Metabolism." II. Alkaptonuria, *Am. J. Human Genet.,* **10**, 95–124, 1958.

La Du, B. N., and Zannoni, V., The Role of Ascorbic Acid in Tyrosine Metabolism, *Ann. N.Y. Acad. Sci.*, **92**, 175–191, 1961.

Larner, J., Inborn Errors of Metabolism, *Ann. Rev. Biochem.*, **31**, 569–587, 1962.

Mann, F. C., The Effects of Complete and of Partial Removal of the Liver, *Medicine*, **6**, 419–511, 1927.

Moyed, H. S., and Umbarger, H. E., Regulation of Biosynthetic Pathways, *Physiol. Revs.*, **42**, 444–466, 1962.

Quastel, J. H., Intestinal Absorption of Sugars and Amino Acids, *Am. J. Clin. Nutrition*, **8**, 137–146, 1960.

Raacke, I. D., The Synthesis of Proteins, in D. M. Greenberg, ed., "Metabolic Pathways," vol. II., pp. 263–388, Academic Press, Inc., New York, 1961.

Ratner, S., Urea Synthesis and Metabolism of Arginine and Citrulline, *Advances in Enzymol.*, **15**, 319–387, 1954.

Sakami, W., and Harrington, H., Amino Acid Metabolism, *Ann. Rev. Biochem.*, **32**, 355–398, 1963.

Schayer, R. W., Catabolism of Physiological Quantities of Histamine in Vivo, *Physiol. Revs.*, **39**, 116–126, 1959.

Sprinson, D. B., The Biosynthesis of Aromatic Compounds from D-Glucose, *Advances in Carbohydrate Chem.*, **15**, 235–270, 1960.

Wilson, L. G., Metabolism of Sulfate, *Ann. Rev. Plant Physiol.*, **13**, 201–224, 1962.

28. Metabolism of Purines, Pyrimidines, and Nucleotides

The chemistry of the nucleic acids has been presented earlier (Chap. 10), and the important biological roles of various nucleotides have been discussed in several of the preceding chapters. This chapter will be concerned with the origin and metabolic fate of the nucleotides and their constituents. The biosynthesis of the nucleic acids and their role in protein synthesis are considered in the following chapters.

The purines and pyrimidines in nucleic acids are not required in the animal diet and can be synthesized in vivo. It is known from the work of Miescher in 1874 that although salmon fast during their long migration to headwaters of rivers for spawning, there is during this time a growth of the gonads at the expense of muscle proteins. This gonadal hypertrophy includes synthesis of large amounts of nucleoproteins. It has also been realized since the studies of Osborne and Mendel in 1912 that man excretes a considerably greater quantity of purines than is ingested. On the other hand, many microorganisms require the presence of specific purines or pyrimidines in the culture media, and, indeed, some even appear to require, either absolutely or for optimal growth, certain nucleosides, such as thymidine. In addition, mutant strains of various bacteria and fungi (*Neurospora*) have been studied which are unable to synthesize purines or pyrimidines.

DIGESTION AND ABSORPTION OF NUCLEIC ACIDS

The acidity of the gastric juice results in cleavage of the nucleoproteins found in natural dietary constituents, and digestion of the resulting proteins (histones, protamines, etc.) begins in the stomach. The nucleic acids are unaffected by gastric enzymes, and their digestion occurs mainly in the duodenum. The pancreas forms *nucleases,* and these are secreted in the pancreatic juice. Pancreatic *ribonuclease* hydrolyzes only ribonucleic acids, liberating pyrimidine mononucleotides and oligonucleotides terminating in pyrimidine nucleoside 3′-phosphate residues (page 181). *Deoxyribonuclease* acts in the presence of Mg^{++} or Mn^{++} and specifically hydrolyzes deoxyribonucleic acids to small oligonucleotides (page 171). The intestinal mucosa is also believed to form *nucleases* and *diesterases* which aid in the digestion of low molecular weight nucleic acids and oligonucleotides.

Liberated nucleotides are hydrolyzed by intestinal *phosphatases* or *nucleotidases,* yielding nucleosides and orthophosphate. Little is known concerning the individuality or specificity of such enzymes, although it is probable that many separate enzymes exist. A specific intestinal *phosphatase* cleaves adenosine 5'-phosphate but does not attack the isomeric adenosine 3'-phosphate or adenosine 2'-phosphate.

It is doubtful that nucleosides are hydrolyzed in the intestine; they are probably absorbed as such. Extracts of various tissues, *e.g.*, spleen, liver, kidney, bone marrow, etc., cleave the N-glycosidic linkage of nucleosides. The metabolism of these compounds probably occurs mainly in these tissues. The so-called *nucleosidases* have not been extensively investigated or purified, and knowledge of these enzymes is fragmentary. Present evidence indicates that there are probably specific *purine* and *pyrimidine nucleosidases.* The enzymes are of two types and may be classed as hydrolytic and phosphorolytic; these actions are illustrated by the following examples.

$$\text{Uridine} + \text{H}_2\text{O} \xrightarrow[\text{nucleosidase}]{\text{pyrimidine}} \text{uracil} + \text{ribose}$$

and

$$\text{Guanosine} + \text{phosphate} \underset{\text{phosphorylase}}{\overset{\text{nucleoside}}{\rightleftharpoons}} \text{guanine} + \text{ribose 1-phosphate}$$

The latter enzyme, *purine nucleoside phosphorylase,* is found in liver and other tissues and acts upon several purine nucleosides. The equilibrium point of the reaction suggests that this enzyme may have a synthetic as well as a degradative role (see below).

ORIGIN OF PURINES AND PYRIMIDINES

As mentioned previously, purines and pyrimidines can be formed in vivo. Young animals exhibit normal growth on synthetic diets which do not contain purines or pyrimidines. This is perhaps the most definitive proof that these substances are formed from simpler dietary constituents. Knowledge of the biosynthesis of these compounds has advanced very rapidly since the development of isotopic tracer techniques. Schoenheimer and his colleagues showed that when ammonium citrate containing N^{15} was administered to rats and pigeons, the isotopic nitrogen was incorporated into purines and pyrimidines. When N^{15}-labeled uracil or thymine was fed to rats, the N^{15} was not found in nucleic acids but the excreted urea contained N^{15}. Similarly, labeled guanine did not appear to be incorporated into nucleic acids but was excreted by pigeons as uric acid and by rats as allantoin, an oxidation product of uric acid.

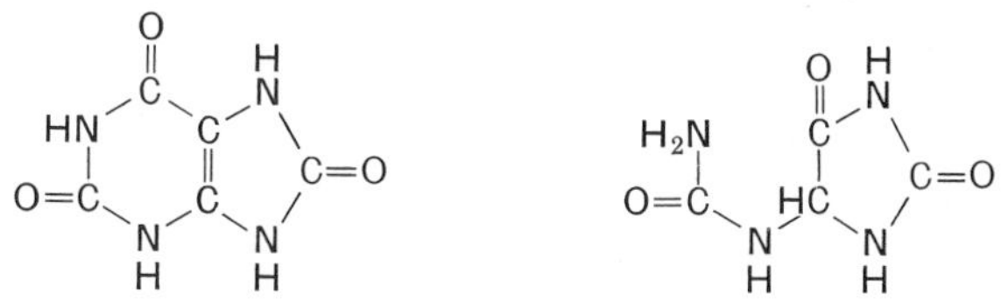

Uric acid (lactam form)   **Allantoin**

In later work, Brown and his coworkers showed that adenine containing N^{15} in positions 1 and 3 of the molecule was utilized by rats and N^{15} was found both in the adenine and in the guanine of tissue nucleic acids, indicating that adenine can be converted to guanine.

The incorporation of adenine by the tissues of adult rats appears to be largely into ribonucleic acids (RNA). Incorporation of adenine into deoxyribonucleic acids (DNA) is slow or negligible under ordinary circumstances, but in partially hepatectomized animals undergoing rapid regeneration of liver tissue, there is extensive incorporation of adenine into the DNA. This difference between DNA and RNA has also been repeatedly observed in studies of the rate of incorporation of orthophosphate containing P^{32} into nucleic acids. The P^{32} is taken up rapidly by RNA and very slowly by DNA. On the basis of these observations, it has been suggested that DNA is formed to an appreciable extent only as a cell initiates active mitosis.

PATHWAYS OF PURINE BIOSYNTHESIS

The origin of the atoms of the purine ring was first established in the intact animal by administering suitable precursors containing labeled atoms. These studies, mainly by Buchanan and coworkers, yielded the following general picture of the origin of the purine nucleus.

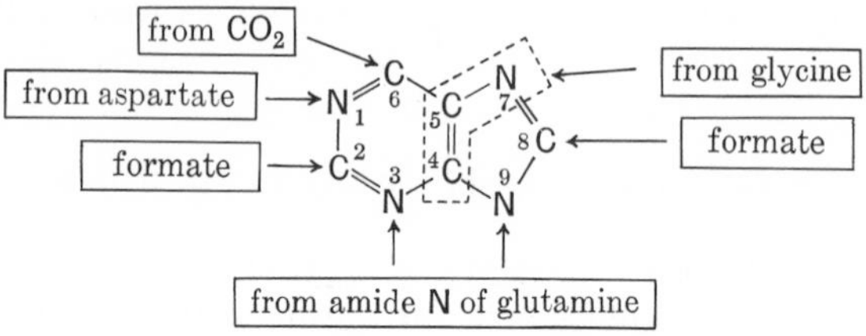

Carbon atoms 2 and 8 are derived from formate or the 1-carbon unit arising from various compounds, *e.g.*, serine and glycine (page 502). Carbon atom 6 originates from carbon dioxide. Glycine contributes carbon atoms at positions 4 and 5 and the nitrogen at 7; the nitrogen atom at position 1 derives from aspartic acid, and glutamine amide nitrogen contributes the nitrogen atoms at positions 3 and 9.

The pathway leading to purine biosynthesis has been studied in many species (mammals, birds, yeast, bacteria), and the general route is essentially the same in all organisms. In essence, this *de novo* process consists of a stepwise synthesis of the purine ring system on carbon 1 of ribose 5-phosphate, leading directly to the formation of purine ribonucleotides. Neither free purines nor nucleosides appear as intermediates in this sequence. Formation of deoxyribonucleotides is considered later. The successive reactions described below were independently studied by a number of investigators, particularly Buchanan, G. R. Greenberg, Kornberg, and their associates.

5-Phosphoribosyl-1-pyrophosphate. This compound is a key substance in the biosynthesis of both purine and pyrimidine nucleotides. Synthesis of 5-phosphoribosyl-1-pyrophosphate occurs from ribose 5-phosphate and ATP in a reaction which is unusual in that it is catalyzed by a kinase which transfers pyrophosphate rather than phosphate.

(a)

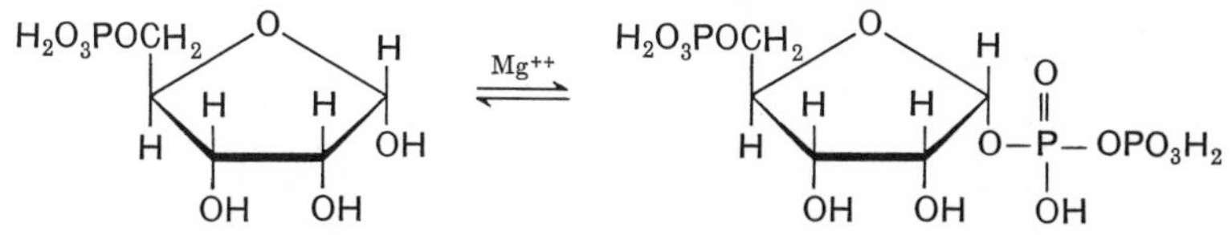

Ribose 5-phosphate ⇌ (Mg⁺⁺) 5-Phosphoribosyl-1-pyrophosphate

ATP + ... AMP + ...

5-Phosphoribosyl-1-amine. The 5-phosphoribosyl-1-pyrophosphate reacts enzymically with glutamine to yield an acid-labile amino sugar, 5-phosphoribosyl-1-amine.

(b)   5-Phosphoribosyl-1-pyrophosphate + glutamine $\xrightarrow{\text{Mg}^{++}}$

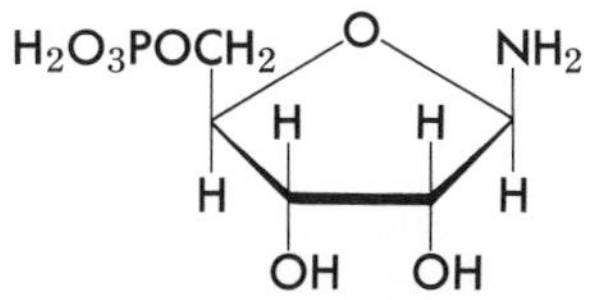

+ glutamic acid + PP$_i$

5-Phosphoribosyl-1-amine

It may be noted that the pyrophosphate bond in phosphoribosyl pyrophosphate is in α linkage, whereas the glycosidic bond in the purine nucleotides, as well as the configuration at C-1′ in 5-phosphoribosyl-1-amine, are of the β configuration. Thus in reaction (b) the displacement of pyrophosphate by the amino group of glutamine is accompanied by an inversion of spatial configuration at C-1′. This reaction is the "committed" metabolic step in purine biosynthesis. Since, as will be developed later, the rate of purine biosynthesis is subject to feedback inhibition by one or more of the purine nucleotides, it seems likely that this inhibitory influence affects the enzyme that catalyzes this reaction.

It is of interest that azaserine, an antibiotic isolated from a species of *Streptomyces*, inhibits utilizaton of glutamine in the formation of 5-phosphoribosyl-1-amine.

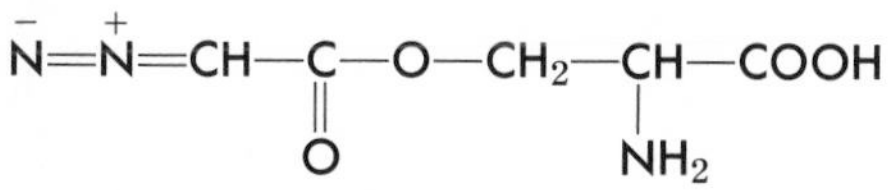

Azaserine

Azaserine inhibits the growth of certain neoplasms, presumably because of its ability to interfere with the synthesis of purine nucleotides. Another reaction shown below (e), the formation of formylglycinamidine ribonucleotide from formylglycinamide, ATP, and glutamine, is also inhibited by azaserine. Indeed, azaserine appears to inhibit each of the known enzymic reactions in which the amide N of glutamine is transferred to another carbon chain.

Glycinamide Ribonucleotide. In this next reaction, the entire structure of glycine is conjugated with 5-phosphoribosyl-1-amine. The details of the reaction remain to be elucidated; it may be noted that the linkage, —C—N—, resembles a peptide bond.

(c)   Phosphoribosylamine + ATP + glycine $\xrightarrow{\text{Mg}^{++}}$

ADP + P$_i$ +

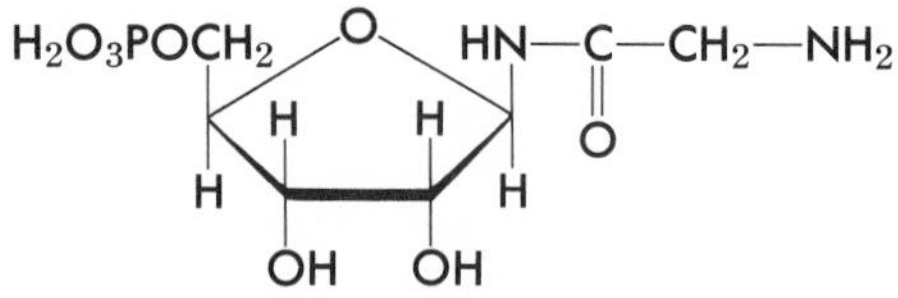

Glycinamide ribonucleotide

Formylglycinamide Ribonucleotide. Formylation of glycinamide ribonucleotide is accomplished by a transfer from the formyl folic acid derivative (page 503) in a reaction catalyzed by *glycinamide ribonucleotide transformylase.* Ribose-P in the formula below and in subsequent reactions represents the ribose 5'-phosphate portion of the compound.

(d) Glycinamide ribonucleotide $\longrightarrow$

+

N^5,N^{10}-anhydroformyltetrahydrofolate

+

H$_2$O

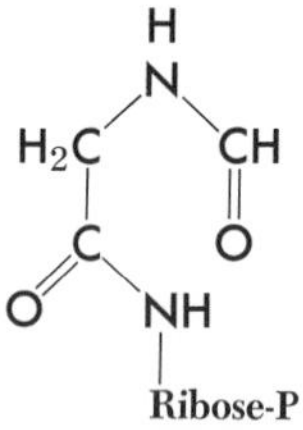

α-N-Formylglycinamide ribonucleotide
+ tetrahydrofolate + H$^+$

Formylglycinamidine Ribonucleotide. The next step involves transfer of an NH$_2$ group from glutamine to α-N-formylglycinamide ribonucleotide.

(e)

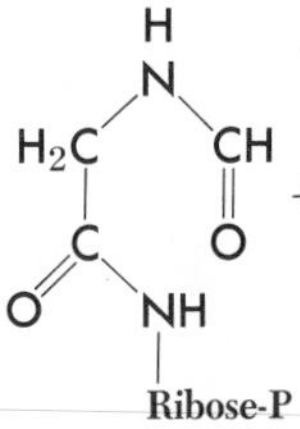

+ glutamine + ATP + H$_2$O $\xrightarrow{\text{Mg}^{++}}$ 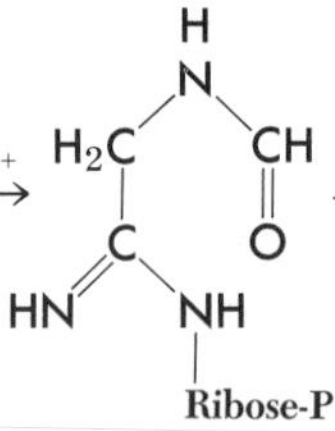 + glutamic acid + ADP + P$_i$

α-N-Formylglycinamide
ribonucleotide

α-N-Formylglycinamidine
ribonucleotide

This step resembles reaction (b), which also involves glutamine, in being strongly inhibited by azaserine and in being irreversible.

5-Aminoimidazole Ribonucleotide. The first ring closure yields an imidazole derivative.

(f) α-N-Formylglycinamidine ribonucleotide + ATP $\xrightarrow{\text{Mg}^{++}}$ + ADP + P$_i$

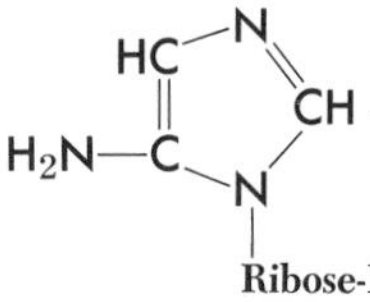

5-Aminoimidazole
ribonucleotide

The enzyme catalyzing this essentially irreversible reaction also requires K^+ ions.

5-Aminoimidazole-4-carboxylic Acid Ribonucleotide. High concentrations of bicarbonate are required for the following reaction.

(g)   5-Aminoimidazole ribonucleotide + CO_2 $\rightleftharpoons$

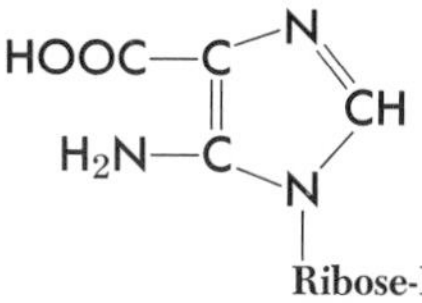

5-Aminoimidazole-4-carboxylic acid
ribonucleotide

In a bacterial system, biotin appears to be involved in this carboxylation reaction. However, there seems to be no biotin participation in the pigeon liver enzyme.

5-Aminoimidazole-4-N-succinocarboxamide Ribonucleotide. Formation of this compound is readily reversible.

(h)   5-Aminoimidazole-4-carboxylic acid ribonucleotide + ATP + aspartic acid $\overset{Mg^{++}}{\rightleftharpoons}$

$ADP + P_i +$

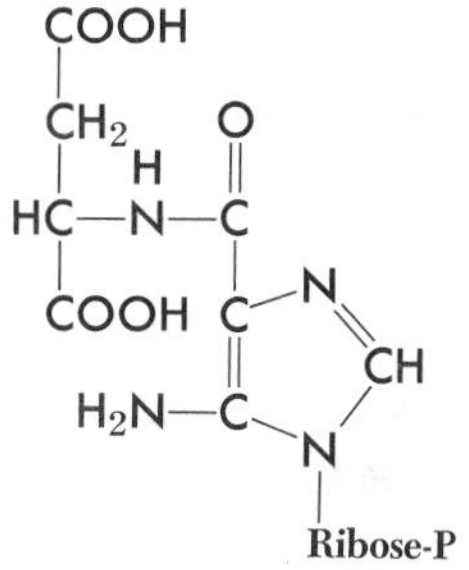

5-Aminoimidazole-4-N-succinocarboxamide
ribonucleotide

5-Aminoimidazole-4-carboxamide Ribonucleotide. The enzyme catalyzing this nonhydrolytic cleavage reaction is believed to be identical with *adenylosuccinase* (see below).

(i)   5-Aminoimidazole-4-N-succinocarboxamide ribonucleotide $\rightleftharpoons$

fumarate +

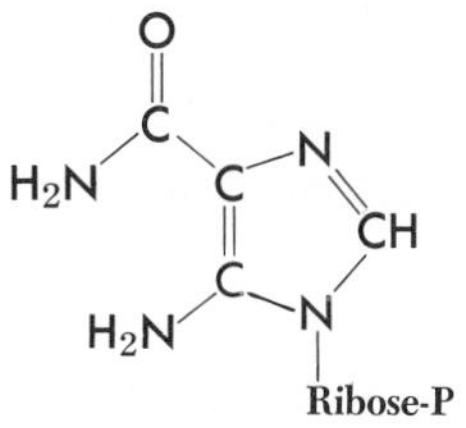

5-Aminoimidazole-4-carboxamide
ribonucleotide

Aminoimidazolecarboxamide was first isolated from cultures of *Escherichia coli* which had been inhibited with sulfonamides, and later from cultures of mutant strains of other microorganisms unable to form purines. Subsequently, the ribonucleoside and ribonucleotide of this substance were isolated from sulfonamide-inhibited cultures of *E. coli*. The action of sulfonamides in preventing bacterial growth has been ascribed to an inhibition of folic acid synthesis (page 239). Inasmuch as a derivative of formyl folic acid (page 503) is required for the formylation of 5-aminoimidazole-4-carboxamide ribonucleotide, as shown below, it is possible to explain the accumulation of aminoimidazolecarboxamide ribonucleotide in the presence of sulfonamides. The formation of the nucleoside and the carboxamide undoubtedly result from hydrolysis of the ribonucleotide.

5-Formamidoimidazole-4-carboxamide Ribonucleotide. The *transformylase* catalyzing this reaction requires K^+ ions.

(j) 5-Aminoimidazole-4-carboxamide ribonucleotide + N^{10}-formyltetrahydrofolic acid $\xrightarrow{K^+}$

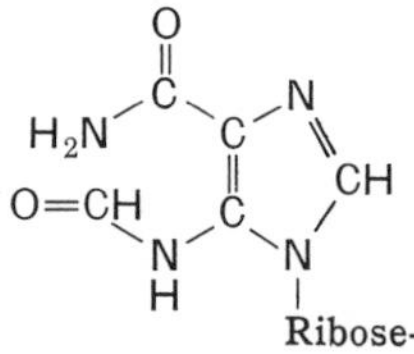

5-Formamidoimidazole-4-carboxamide
ribonucleotide

Many metabolic antagonists of folic acid (page 239) which inhibit growth do so by inhibition of purine nucleotide biosynthesis at reaction (j).

Inosinic Acid. Closure of the ring by *inosinicase* yields inosinic acid (hypoxanthine ribonucleotide), the first product in the synthetic pathway with the completed purine ring structure.

Formamidoimidazolecarboxamide ribonucleotide $\rightleftharpoons$

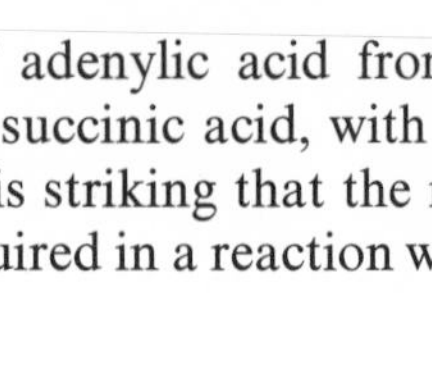

Inosinic acid

Purine Nucleotide Interconversions. Formation of adenylic acid from inosinic acid occurs through the initial formation of adenylosuccinic acid, with participation of aspartic acid and guanosine triphosphate. It is striking that the nucleoside triphosphate derivative of one purine (guanine) is required in a reaction which leads to formation of another purine nucleotide.

Inosinic acid + GTP + L-aspartic acid $\xrightarrow{Mg^{++}}$ GDP + P_i +

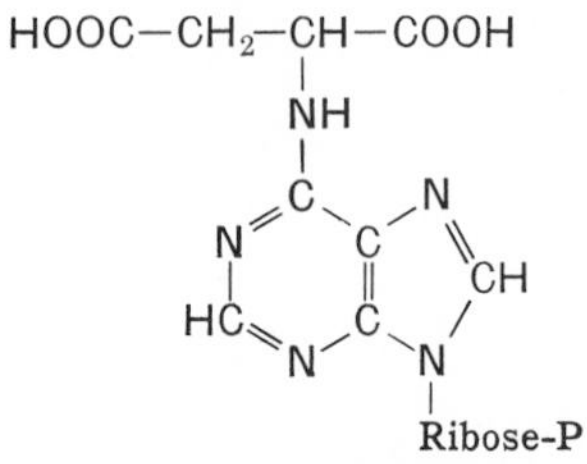

Adenylosuccinic acid

Nonhydrolytic cleavage of adenylosuccinic acid yields adenylic acid and fumaric acid.

$$\text{Adenylosuccinic acid} \rightleftharpoons \text{adenylic acid} + \text{fumaric acid}$$

This reaction is analogous to the cleavage of 5-amino-4-imidazole-N-succino-carboxamide ribonucleotide (reaction *i*) and is probably catalyzed by the same enzyme, *adenylosuccinase*. On extensive purification of the enzyme, the ratio of the two activities is unchanged. Moreover, mutant strains of several microorganisms which lack the ability to catalyze one reaction cannot catalyze the other.

The synthesis of guanylic acid from inosinic acid proceeds first by oxidation to xanthylic acid; this reaction requires K^+ ions. The next step requires glutamine and ATP.

Inosinic acid $\underset{\text{DPNH}+\text{H}}{\overset{\text{DPN}^+}{\rightleftharpoons}}$

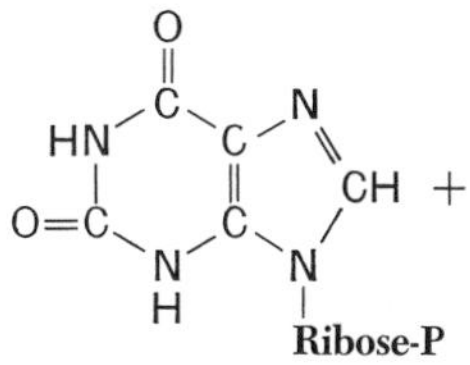

Xanthylic acid

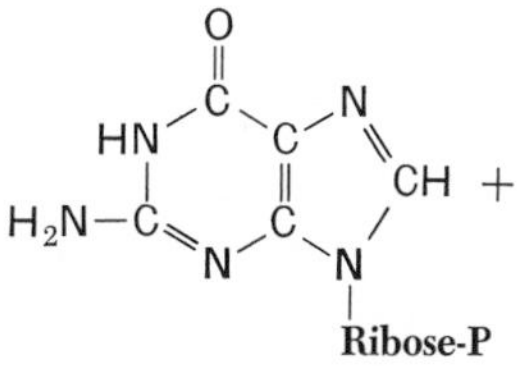

Guanylic acid

As in other reactions requiring glutamine (page 561), the formation of guanylic acid is irreversible and is inhibited by azaserine.

In summary, Buchanan has noted that the synthesis of inosinic acid from elementary precursors can be regarded as the result of the sum of the following equations (*a*) and (*b*).

(*a*) $2NH_4^+ + 2HCOO^- + HCO_3^- + \text{glycine} + \text{aspartate} + \text{ribose 5-phosphate} \longrightarrow$
   $\text{inosinic acid} + \text{fumarate} + 9H_2O$

(*b*) $9ATP + 9H_2O \longrightarrow 8ADP + 8P_i + AMP + PP_i + 9H^+$

The driving force involved utilizes the energy provided from nine equivalents of ATP, including two equivalents required for glutamine formation and two equivalents for formate activation.

Other Pathways of Purine Nucleotide Formation. As described above, adenylic acid and guanylic acid are formed through the intermediate, inosinic acid. In most species, including mammals, these pathways are undoubtedly the primary ones for purine nucleotide formation. However, purine nucleotides can also be formed from free purines and from purine nucleosides. These routes may be regarded as salvage pathways in the tissues, permitting reutilization of purines or purine derivatives derived by breakdown of nucleic acid or nucleotides.

Free purines can react directly with 5-phosphoribosyl-1-pyrophosphate to yield 5'-nucleotides. The three reversible reactions shown below are catalyzed by specific *pyrophosphorylases* which have been found in liver.

$$\text{Adenine} + \text{phosphoribosylpyrophosphate} \rightleftharpoons \text{adenylic acid} + \text{PP}_i$$
$$\text{Guanine} + \text{phosphoribosylpyrophosphate} \rightleftharpoons \text{guanylic acid} + \text{PP}_i$$
$$\text{Hypoxanthine} + \text{phosphoribosylpyrophosphate} \rightleftharpoons \text{inosinic acid} + \text{PP}_i$$

Inasmuch as nucleotides can be utilized for nucleic acid synthesis (Chaps. 29 and 30), these reactions explain how purines can be incorporated into nucleic acids.

Other salvage pathways involve conversion of free purines to nucleosides and nucleosides to nucleotides. Such routes may also be involved in explaining incorporation of purines and their respective nucleosides into nucleic acids.

Known reactions for purine nucleoside formation, catalyzed by *nucleoside phosphorylase,* are the following.

$$\text{Hypoxanthine} + \text{ribose 1-phosphate} \rightleftharpoons \text{inosine} + \text{P}_i$$
$$\text{Guanine} + \text{ribose 1-phosphate} \rightleftharpoons \text{guanosine} + \text{P}_i$$

Conversion of a nucleoside to a nucleotide occurs by the following reaction.

$$\text{Adenosine} + \text{ATP} \xrightarrow[\text{kinase}]{\text{adenosine}} \text{adenylic acid} + \text{ADP}$$

In summary, the primary pathway of formation of purine nucleotides in mammalian tissues is a *de novo* route which involves synthesis from acyclic precursors and simple compounds. There is no evidence that synthesis of free purines ever occurs. Secondary pathways may be regarded as salvage routes in which purines or nucleosides, originating from the intestinal tract or from intracellular degradative processes, are recaptured by conversion to nucleotides.

CATABOLISM OF PURINES

In mammals, most of the nitrogen in the rings of administered adenine, guanine, xanthine, or hypoxanthine eventually appears in the urine in the form of uric acid or allantoin. The purine ring is therefore not completely degraded; only small amounts of urea or ammonia are derived from this source.

Adenase and *guanase* are highly specific deaminases which act hydrolytically according to the following reactions.

$$\text{Adenine} + \text{H}_2\text{O} \xrightarrow{\text{adenase}} \text{hypoxanthine} + \text{NH}_3$$

$$\text{Guanine} + \text{H}_2\text{O} \xrightarrow{\text{guanase}} \text{xanthine} + \text{NH}_3$$

Guanase is widely distributed in liver, kidney, spleen, etc. However, adenase appears to be of more limited distribution, and deamination of adenine may occur mainly in combination in the nucleotide, adenylic acid, through the irreversible action of the enzyme, *adenylic acid deaminase,* which is present in large amounts in muscle (Chap. 38).

$$\text{Adenylic acid} + \text{H}_2\text{O} \xrightarrow{\text{adenylic acid deaminase}} \text{inosinic acid} + \text{NH}_3$$

Inosinic acid is frequently found in muscle as a result of the high activity of adenylic acid deaminase. *Guanosine* and *adenosine deaminases* have also been found in animal tissues.

Xanthine oxidase (page 216), a flavin enzyme, catalyzes the oxidation of both hypoxanthine and xanthine.

$$\text{Hypoxanthine} + O_2 \xrightarrow[\text{oxidase}]{\text{xanthine}} \text{xanthine} + H_2O_2$$

$$\text{Xanthine} + O_2 \xrightarrow[\text{oxidase}]{\text{xanthine}} \text{uric acid} + H_2O_2$$

This enzyme also has the unusual dual specificity of being able to catalyze the oxidation of a variety of aldehydes.

It should be emphasized that uric acid formation in mammals occurs in the liver; hepatectomy results in cessation of uric acid production.

In some species, uric acid is aerobically oxidized by a liver enzyme called *uricase,* a copper protein. The over-all reaction catalyzed by this enzyme is the following.

$$\text{Uric acid} + 2H_2O + O_2 \longrightarrow \text{allantoin} + CO_2 + H_2O_2$$

The stages of purine degradation from adenine and guanine to uric acid and allantoin are summarized in Fig. 28.1.

Man and other primates do not possess an active uricase; hence, uric acid is the main end product of purine metabolism in these species. Other mammals which have uricase excrete allantoin as the terminal compound of purine metabolism. The Dalmatian dog, like other dogs, possesses uricase in the liver, yet excretes uric acid. This is believed to be because of a very low renal threshold for uric acid. The pig, which is deficient in guanase, excretes guanine as well as allantoin. Indeed, guanine gout has been reported in this species; it is due to the deposition of guanine crystals in the joints and is analogous to human gout, in which monosodium urate may accumulate in the cartilages (see below). It may be noted that guanine is the terminal product of purine metabolism in spiders.

The utilization of free guanine or adenine for nucleotide or nucleic acid synthesis in various species undoubtedly depends on the relative activities of the corresponding deaminases and the oxidases versus the activities of the enzymes which can convert these purines to the nucleotides. Thus, some species can utilize adenine or guanine for nucleic acid synthesis, by employing salvage pathways (see above), whereas others cannot do so.

Uric Acid Production in Man. Uric acid production and excretion proceed at a rather constant rate in man when the diet is free of purines. This uric acid is derived from the endogenous purine metabolism and, as with many body constituents, reflects a steady state in which the rates of purine synthesis and purine catabolism, measured by the excretion of uric acid, are approximately equal. Some protein foods, such as milk, cheese, and eggs, are low in purines, whereas foods rich in nucleoproteins, *e.g.,* liver and pancreas, are high in purines.

The concentration of uric acid in normal plasma is about 2 to 6 mg. per 100 ml., with an average for adults of approximately 3.5 mg. per 100 ml. for females and about 4.5 mg. per 100 ml. for males. These levels are elevated in gout, a dis-

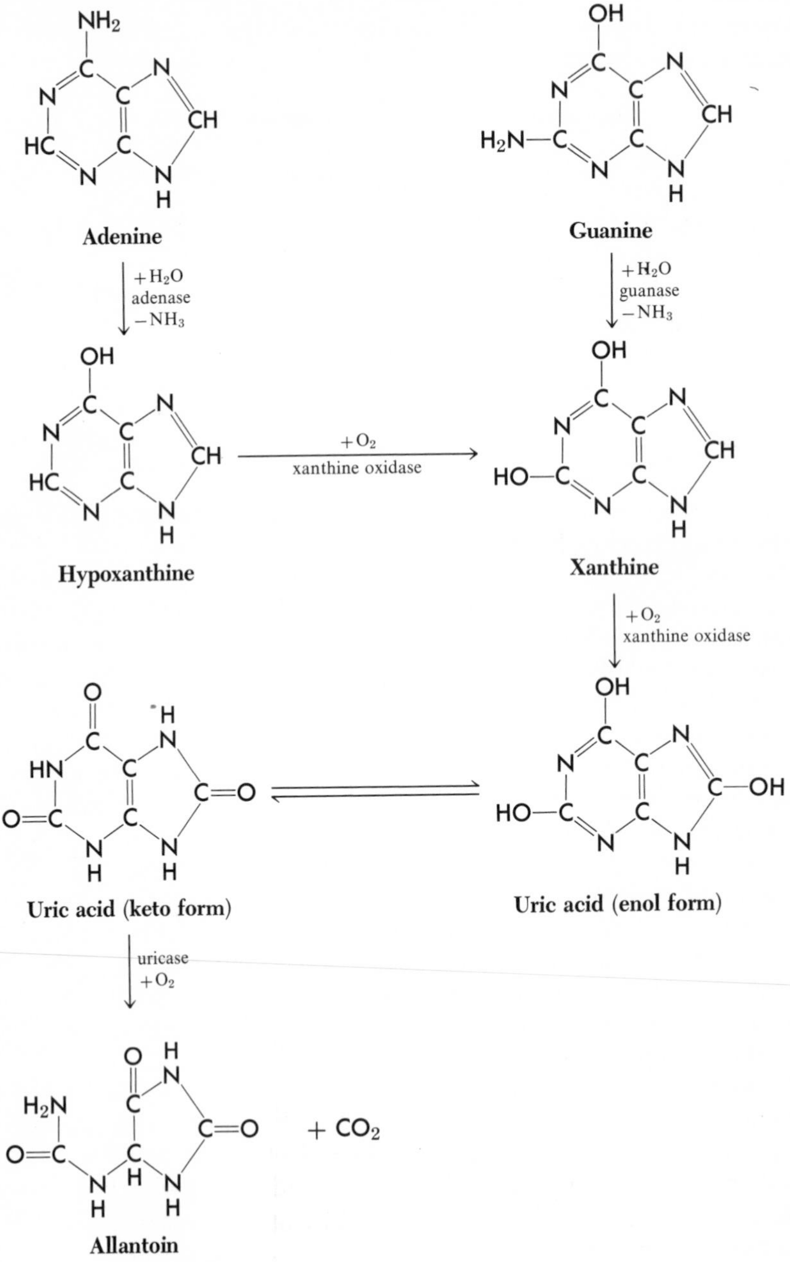

FIG. 28.1. The metabolic degradation of adenine and guanine.

ease in which large amounts of the sparingly soluble monosodium urate are deposited as so-called *tophi* in cartilage. Uric acid deposits may also be found as calculi in the kidney, with resultant renal damage. A large fraction of all renal calculi consists of the sparingly soluble uric acid and its salts.

There is a large sex difference in the occurrence of gout; only about 5 per cent of the cases occur in females. In many of the cases there appears to be a familial incidence. Hyperuricemia (elevated blood uric acid) is frequently observed in the asymptomatic male relatives of gouty individuals. It should be mentioned, however, that many cases of hyperuricemia may be due to such diverse factors as impaired renal function, toxemia of pregnancy, essential hypertension, and leukemia.

Because of the clinical importance of gout, studies have been made of rates of uric acid production and excretion in man. Injection of uric acid isotopically labeled with N^{15} permits estimation of total stores of miscible uric acid from isotope dilution measurements. Stetten and coworkers have shown that normal individuals contain about 1.1 g. of uric acid, with about one-sixth of this in the plasma and about five-sixths in the extravascular water. From the rate of decline of the abundance of N^{15} in the urinary uric acid, it was calculated that 50 to 75 per cent of the uric acid was replaced each day by newly formed uric acid. This represents a daily production of about 0.5 to 0.86 g. of uric acid, presumably arising from degradation of nucleic acids and nucleotides of the body. The production of uric acid exceeded the urinary output by 100 to 250 mg. per day. Some of the isotopic nitrogen was found in urinary urea and ammonia, indicating a partial catabolic breakdown of the purine nucleus.

In gouty individuals, the miscible pool of uric acid is uniformly elevated. It appears to include a portion of the solid phase urate of tophi as well as urate in solution in body fluids.

The metabolic disorder of gout could represent either an increased endogenous production of uric acid or a decreased rate of elimination. Since glycine is a specific precursor of atoms 4, 5, and 7 of the purine nucleus, Stetten and his colleagues administered glycine containing N^{15} to normal and gouty individuals and determined the abundance of N^{15} in urinary uric acid. It was found that most of the N^{15} appeared in urea, as would be expected from the variety of metabolic roles of glycine. In normal individuals, after 10 days, only about 0.15 per cent had been excreted as uric acid, whereas about three times as much, 0.5 per cent, was excreted in this form by several gouty subjects. These and other experiments favor the view that in so-called primary gout the metabolic defect is an overproduction of uric acid, presumably the consequence of overproduction of purine nucleotides.

It will have been noted that in purine biosynthesis, the committed step (page 561) is the formation of phosphoribosylamine. Some evidence indicates that, in analogy with other biosynthetic pathways, control of the rate of purine biosynthesis occurs as a consequence of a feedback device operative at this locus. Although the details are uncertain, it appears that gout may reflect an alteration of this feedback system.

Further Degradation of Purines. In animals other than mammals, purine metabolism may proceed through further degradation reactions as a result of the mediation of the enzymes, *allantoinase* and *allantoicase*. The action of these enzymes may be illustrated as follows.

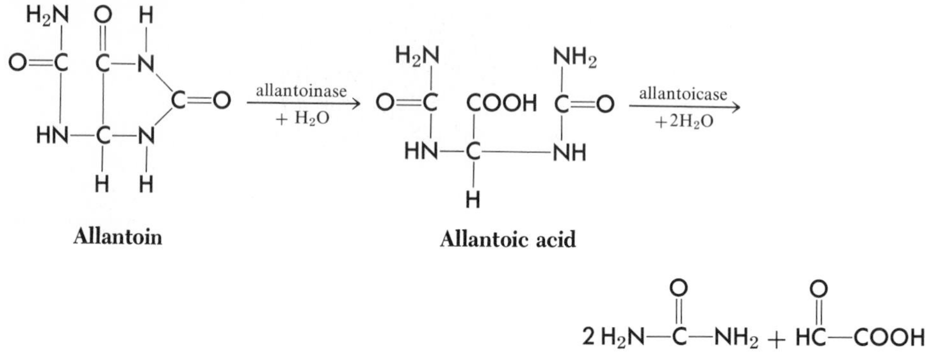

Allantoin   **Allantoic acid**

$$2 H_2N-\overset{\overset{O}{\|}}{C}-NH_2 + H\overset{\overset{O}{\|}}{C}-COOH$$

Urea   Glyoxylic acid

Urea may be hydrolyzed to ammonia and CO_2 in some species, because of the presence of intestinal microorganisms which contain *urease*.

A summary of the interesting biological distribution of the end products of purine metabolism is given in Table 28.1. Birds and some reptiles, which do not synthesize urea, direct almost all amino acid nitrogen into glycine, aspartic acid, and glutamine synthesis. Total purine formation far exceeds actual requirements for purine nucleotides, and uric acid is the major end product of all nitrogen metabolism in these species. Those species which excrete nitrogen mainly as uric acid are called *uricotelic*, in contrast to *ureotelic* animals, which excrete nitrogen primarily as urea.

Table 28.1: Final Excretory Products of Purine Metabolism

Product excreted	*Animal group*
Uric acid.........	Man and other primates, Dalmatian dog, birds, some reptiles (snakes and lizards)
Allantoin.........	Mammals other than primates, some reptiles (turtles), gastropod mollusks
Allantoic acid......	Some teleost fishes
Urea.............	Most fishes, amphibia, fresh-water lamellibranch mollusks
Ammonia........	Some marine invertebrates, crustaceans, etc.

As noted by Clementi in 1924, *arginase* is present in the livers of vertebrates that have a ureotelic metabolism but not in the livers of animals that have a uricotelic metabolism. Thus, the end products of purine and amino acid metabolism depend on the survival of a small group of enzymes. Loss of arginase diverts amino acid nitrogen into purines in uricoteles. It should be recalled that nitrogen from glycine, glutamine, and aspartic acid is directly utilized in formation of purine nucleotides. By the reactions of transamination and glutamine formation (Chap. 24), additional amino nitrogen and ammonia can be furnished for purine formation and hence for disposal in the form of uric acid.

Because the degradation of purines is much less complete in higher animals, it is apparent that certain enzymes have been lost during animal evolution, *e.g.*, uricase, allantoinase, allantoicase, and urease.

A summary of the interconversions of purine derivatives (Fig. 28.2) shows that reactions may occur at the nucleotide or nucleoside level as well as with the free purines. Not all these reactions necessarily occur in every tissue or in every species, but there is evidence for each pathway shown. Of the pathways given, only two are known to be reversible by the same enzymic system. The reaction pathways include oxidative, hydrolytic, pyrophosphorolytic, and phosphorolytic reactions. The first three types of reaction may be considered to be essentially irreversible. In most instances, the biosynthetic pathways and the enzymes involved differ from the degradative reactions; this is indicated in the diagram by separate pathways of the arrows.

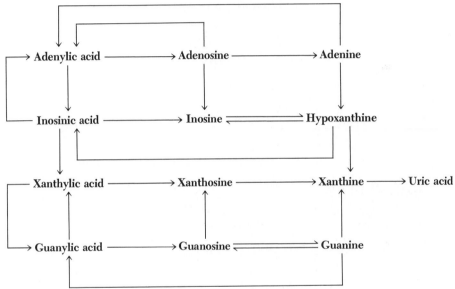

Fig. 28.2. Summary of interconversions of purine derivatives.

BIOSYNTHESIS OF PYRIMIDINE NUCLEOTIDES

As already mentioned, administered uracil and cytosine containing N^{15} are rapidly metabolized, and the N^{15} is found in the excreted urea and ammonia. This is not the case for pyrimidine nucleotides. When N^{15}-labeled nucleic acid was fed to rats, or when the mixture of mononucleotides obtained by partial hydrolysis was injected intraperitoneally, appreciable amounts of the pyrimidines of the tissue nucleic acids contained isotopic nitrogen. These results suggest that extensive breakdown to free pyrimidines did not occur, either by the oral or the intraperitoneal route, and that larger molecules, nucleosides or nucleotides, are utilized for the formation of nucleic acids. This also indicates that the intestinal digestion of nucleic acids does not proceed to the stage of free pyrimidines.

Evidence concerning the nature of pyrimidine precursors was first derived from studies with microorganisms. Orotic acid (6-carboxyuracil), first found in cow's milk, was shown to satisfy the growth requirements of "pyrimidineless" mutants of *Neurospora*. Mitchell and coworkers have isolated orotic acid from other mutant strains of *Neurospora* which are incapable of forming pyrimidines. This compound, isotopically labeled, was found by Hammarsten and collaborators to serve as a precursor of nucleic acid pyrimidines. This provided the first indication of the route by which pyrimidines are synthesized in vivo. The structures of orotic acid and uracil are shown for comparison.

Orotic acid (6-carboxyuracil)   Uracil

Orotic acid is a growth factor for certain microorganisms, notably *Lactobacillus bulgaricus*. For this organism, ureidosuccinic acid (N-carbamylaspartic acid) has about 10 to 20 per cent of the activity of orotic acid in stimulating growth. Ureidosuccinic acid containing C^{14} in the ureido carbon has been shown to be incorporated into the pyrimidines isolated from the nucleic acids of *L. bulgaricus;* thus the acyclic compound serves as a precursor of the pyrimidine ring.

The main enzymic pathways leading to the formation of orotic acid and of pyrimidine nucleotides have been elucidated. A key substance is carbamyl phosphate (page 489).

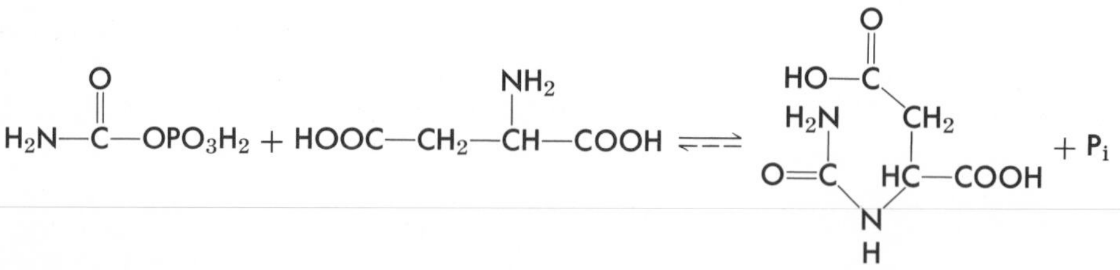

Carbamyl phosphate   L-Aspartic acid   L-Ureidosuccinic acid
                                                      (N-carbamylaspartic acid)

The formation of ureidosuccinate, an effective precursor of pyrimidines in animals, is catalyzed by *aspartate carbamyl transferase*. The equilibrium for this reaction is strongly in favor of synthesis. As obtained from *Escherichia coli* this enzyme is a tetramer. The monomeric form is enzymically active but, as shown in Fig. 28.3, the kinetics of the reaction catalyzed by the monomeric and tetrameric forms differ markedly. This enzyme, which catalyzes the committed step in pyrimidine biosynthesis, is subject to end-product feedback inhibition by cytidine triphosphate, an ultimate product of pyrimidine biosynthesis.

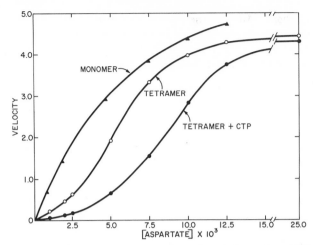

FIG. 28.3. Feedback inhibition of aspartate carbamyl transferase by cytidine triphosphate. The enzyme can be prepared as a monomer but the normal state is tetrameric. In the monomeric form, the velocity of the reaction increases with increasing concentration of substrate in the conventional manner, and in this form, the enzyme is insensitive to CTP. In the tetrameric form, the plot shown is sigmoid, indicating that binding of substrate to one or two of the units of the tetramer enhances the enzymic activity of the other units. This situation is analogous to the influence of oxygen concentration on the affinity of hemoglobin for oxygen (Fig. 34.2). The tetrameric enzyme exhibits marked sensitivity to CTP; the concentration of CTP used in this experiment was $2.0 \times 10^{-4}M$. (*Courtesy, Dr. A. B. Pardee.*)

Recognition of the feedback inhibition influence, which a product of a biosynthetic pathway may exert on a specific enzymic step in the pathway, led to the introduction by Monod and Jacob of the term "allosteric site." This designates an enzymic site, different from the active site, which noncompetitively binds molecules other than the substrate and may influence the activity of the enzyme. The influence of cytidine triphosphate on the activity of aspartate carbamyl transferase is an example of the concept of an allosteric site on an allosteric protein.

Formation of Orotic Acid. Ring closure of L-ureidosuccinic acid, catalyzed by *dihydroorotase,* yields L-dihydroorotic acid. The equilibrium favors the ureido compound in the ratio 2:1.

L-Ureidosuccinic acid $\underset{+H_2O}{\overset{-H_2O}{\rightleftharpoons}}$ L-Dihydroorotic acid

The dihydroorotic acid is oxidized to orotic acid by *dihydroorotic acid dehydrogenase,* an unusual enzyme found by Friedmann and Vennesland to contain equal amounts of flavin mononucleotide and flavin adenine dinucleotide as well as two atoms of iron per molecule (page 348); the electrons are transferred to DPN$^+$.

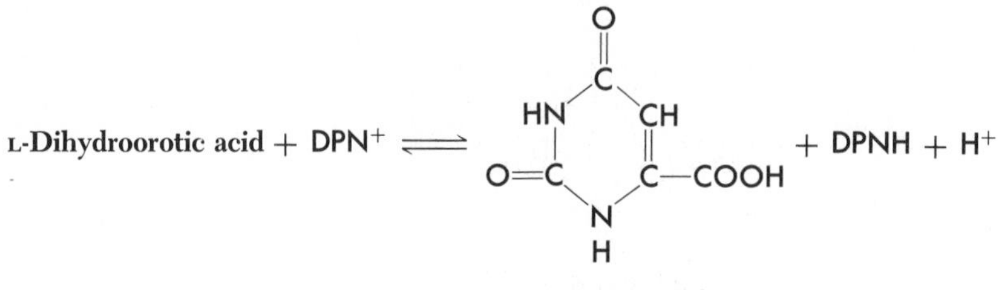

$$\text{L-Dihydroorotic acid} + \text{DPN}^+ \rightleftharpoons \quad\quad\quad\quad + \text{DPNH} + \text{H}^+$$

Orotic acid

Pyrimidine Nucleotide Formation. Nucleotide synthesis involves the coupling of orotic acid with 5-phosphoribosyl-1-pyrophosphate in the same manner as described previously for the formation of purine nucleotides (page 561). The reaction is catalyzed by *orotidine 5′-phosphate pyrophosphorylase.*

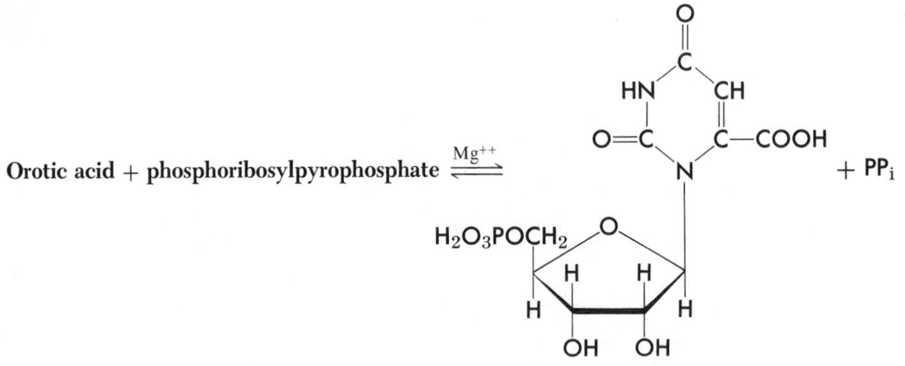

$$\text{Orotic acid} + \text{phosphoribosylpyrophosphate} \xrightarrow{\text{Mg}^{++}} \quad\quad\quad\quad + \text{PP}_i$$

Orotidine 5′-phosphate (orotidylic acid)

Orotidine 5′-phosphate is decarboxylated to yield the corresponding uracil-containing nucleotide. Ribose-P in structure below represents ribose 5-phosphate.

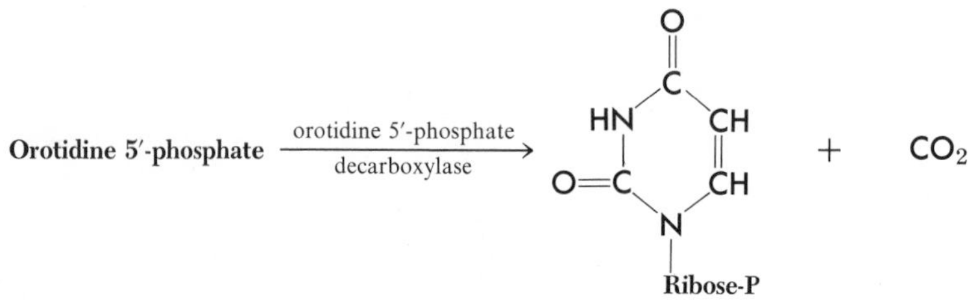

$$\text{Orotidine 5′-phosphate} \xrightarrow[\text{decarboxylase}]{\text{orotidine 5′-phosphate}} \quad\quad\quad\quad + \quad \text{CO}_2$$

Uridine 5′-phosphate (uridylic acid)

The pathway which results in the formation of uridine triphosphate involves consecutive transfers of phosphate from ATP to uridine 5'-phosphate, with intermediate formation of uridine diphosphate.

$$\text{Uridine 5'-phosphate} + \text{ATP} \rightleftharpoons \text{uridine diphosphate} + \text{ADP}$$
$$\text{Uridine diphosphate} + \text{ATP} \rightleftharpoons \text{uridine triphosphate} + \text{ADP}$$

The only known pathway for formation of a cytidine nucleotide involves amination of uridine triphosphate to yield the corresponding cytidine triphosphate. Addition of uridine diphosphate to the partially purified enzyme also yields cytidine polyphosphate, but it is likely that the diphosphate must first be converted to the triphosphate. Ribose-PPP in structures below represents ribose triphosphate.

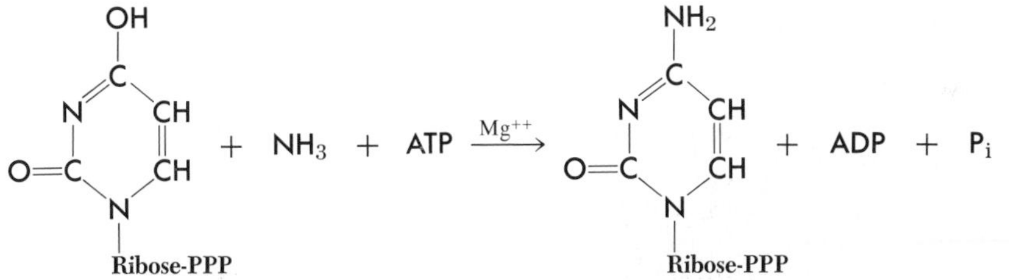

Uridine triphosphate $\qquad$ Cytidine triphosphate

The stoichiometric release of one mole of inorganic phosphate from ATP suggests that a phosphorylated intermediate may be involved in the reaction. It is noteworthy that ammonia itself is utilized in this reaction with an enzymic preparation from *E. coli*. However, in mammalian systems, indirect evidence indicates that the amino group of CTP is derived from the amide nitrogen of glutamine.

Although the above reaction is irreversible, it has been demonstrated that labeled cytidine is an effective precursor of both cytosine and uracil of rat nucleic acids. It is evident that other pathways must exist for interconversion of such compounds.

A hereditary disorder of pyrimidine metabolism in man, known as *orotic aciduria*, is characterized by accumulation and urinary excretion of orotic acid. The latter apparently cannot be metabolized further at a normal rate in individuals with this disorder. Administration of uracil or cytosine abolishes the excretion of orotic acid, thus providing evidence of the operation of a feedback inhibition mechanism at an early stage of pyrimidine biosynthesis in man.

It may be noted that the pathways of formation of purine and pyrimidine nucleotides differ. In the former, all intermediates are derivatives of ribose 5-phosphate, whereas in pyrimidine nucleotide biosynthesis the pyrimidine ring is formed prior to coupling with ribose phosphate. Furthermore, the initial nucleotides formed in both cases, inosinic acid and orotidylic acid, are not constituents of nucleic acids. Although purines contain a pyrimidine ring fused to an imidazole, the precursors of the two ring systems are different. It is of interest that 5-phosphoribosyl-1-pyrophosphate plays a key role in formation of both types of nucleotides.

FORMATION OF DEOXYRIBONUCLEOTIDES

Tissue extracts contain the 5'-mono-, di-, and triphosphates of the deoxyribo-nucleotides of adenine, guanine, thymine, cytosine, and methylcytosine. Evidence has also been obtained that the polyphosphates are rapidly formed from the corre-sponding 5'-deoxynucleotides. The questions to be considered regarding formation of the deoxynucleotides then are (1) the origin of the deoxysugar, (2) the bio-synthesis of the methylated pyrimidines, thymine and methylcytosine, and (3) the formation of the 5'-polyphosphates. These problems will be considered in turn.

Although deoxyribonucleotides might be formed by reactions involving com-pounds analogous to those concerned in ribonucleotide synthesis, no evidence has been obtained to support this view. The demonstration by Hammarsten and co-workers that ribonucleotides are very effective precursors of the deoxyribonucleo-tides of DNA led them to suggest the existence of pathways involving a direct conversion of ribonucleotides to deoxyribonucleotides. It was subsequently estab-lished in several laboratories that cytidine, randomly labeled with C^{14}, is incorpo-rated into the nucleotides of DNA, with the same relative distribution of C^{14} in the deoxyribose and the base in thymidine as well as deoxycytidine. In the same man-ner evidence has been obtained that purine deoxyribonucleotides of DNA are derived from corresponding ribonucleotides, *i.e.*, AMP and GMP are converted to dAMP, and dGMP, respectively. Thus, deoxygenation of the sugar appears to occur at the nucleotide level.

The general pathway of interconversion of pyrimidine nucleotides may be summarized as follows:

$$\text{UTP} \longrightarrow \text{CTP} \longrightarrow \text{CMP} \longrightarrow \text{CDP} \longrightarrow \text{dCDP} \longrightarrow \text{dCMP} \longrightarrow \text{dUMP} \longrightarrow \text{TMP}$$

Two enzymic fractions from extracts of *E. coli* are required for the conversion of CMP to dCDP. One of these contains a CMP kinase.

$$\text{CMP} + \text{ATP} \underset{}{\overset{\text{Mg}^{++}}{\rightleftarrows}} \text{CDP} + \text{ADP}$$

The second fraction is a system which shows an absolute requirement for ATP, Mg^{++}, and TPNH and, in addition, a heat-stable protein factor. This system catalyzes the conversion of CDP to dCDP. Reichard has suggested that the reac-tion proceeds in several distinct enzymic steps, involving (1) a pyrophosphorylation at the 2'-hydroxyl group, (2) removal of pyrophosphate with dehydrogenation between either 1' and 2' or 2' and 3', followed by (3) a hydrogenation to yield the deoxy derivative. It is hypothesized that the reduction is a result of an action of —SH groups which appear in the heat-stable protein of this system following its reduction by TPNH. This sequence of reactions is indicated in Fig. 28.4.

It is noteworthy that such enzymic preparations from *E. coli* also catalyze the formation of the deoxyribosyl derivatives of uridine, adenosine, and guanosine phosphates from the ribosyl compounds. It is as yet unknown whether the reduc-tion of all these compounds is catalyzed by the same enzymic systems or whether different enzymes are involved.

Deamination of dCMP to yield dUMP is catalyzed by an enzyme, *deoxy-cytidylic acid aminohydrolase*. In the formulas below, d-ribose-P represents deoxy-ribose 5'-phosphate.

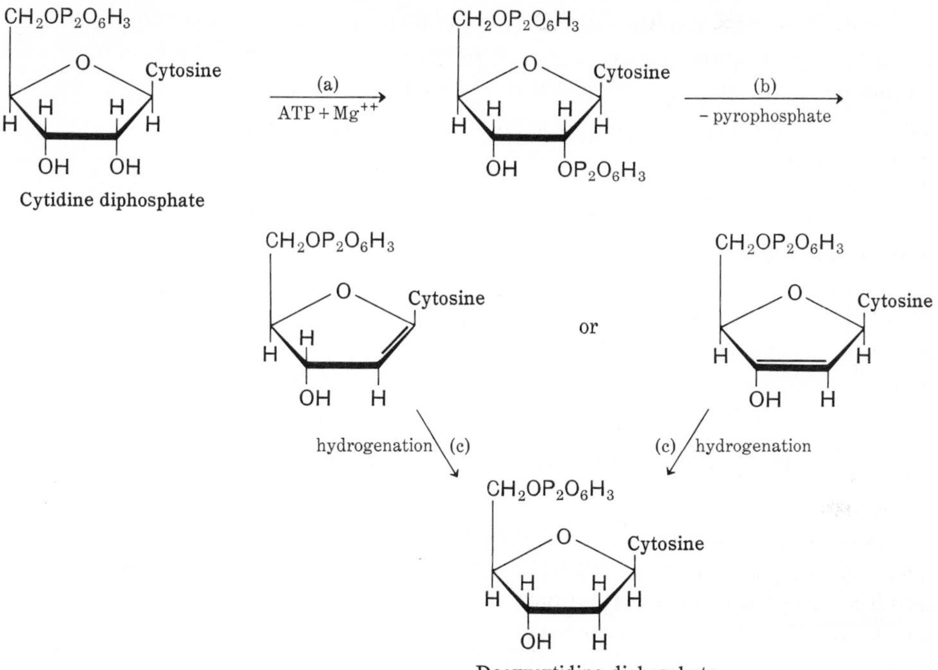

FIG. 28.4. Postulated reactions in the sequence for conversion of cytidine diphosphate to deoxycytidine diphosphate.

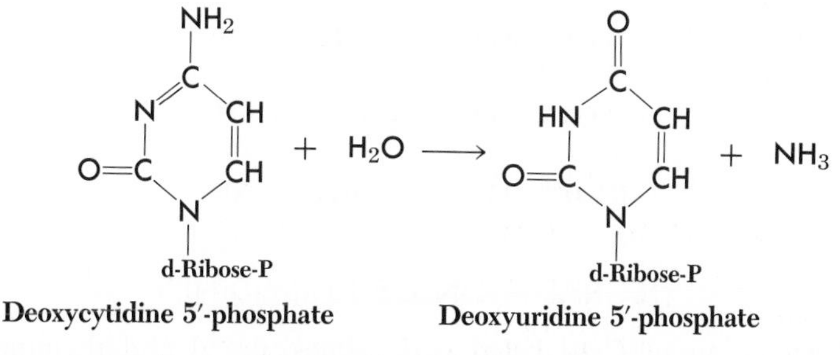

This enzyme, present in monkey and rabbit liver, also catalyzes the deamination of the methyl- and hydroxymethyldeoxycytidylic acids.

$$\text{5-Methyldeoxycytidylic acid} + H_2O \longrightarrow \text{thymidylic acid} + NH_3$$
$$\text{5-Hydroxymethyldeoxycytidylic acid} + H_2O \longrightarrow \text{5-hydroxymethyldeoxyuridylic acid} + NH_3$$

Thymidylate synthetase from *E. coli* and other sources catalyzes the following reaction.

$$\text{Deoxyuridine 5'-phosphate} + N^5,N^{10}\text{-methylenetetrahydrofolate} \xrightarrow{Mg^{++}}$$

$$\text{thymidine 5'-phosphate} + \text{dihydrofolate}$$

It is of interest that tetrahydrofolate serves both as a carbon carrier and as a direct hydrogen donor in this complex reaction. Vitamin B_{12} has been implicated in this reaction, but its exact role is unknown.

An analogous reaction occurs in the formation of 5-hydroxymethyldeoxy-cytidine 5'-phosphate in cells of *E. coli* infected with T2, T4, or T6 bacteriophages (Table 10.5), although no reduction is involved.

N^5,N^{10}-Methylenetetrahydrofolic acid   tetrahydrofolic acid

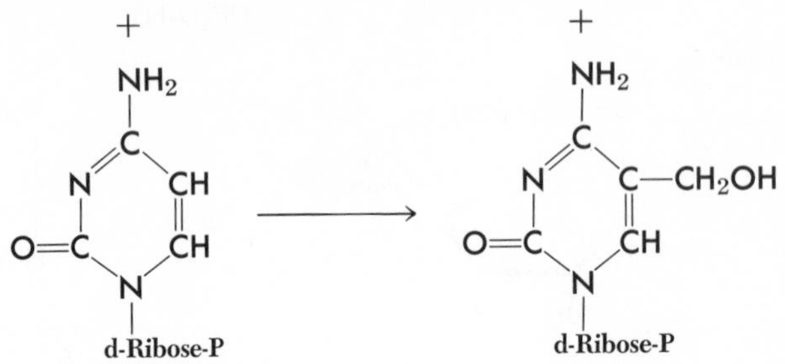

Deoxycytidine 5'-phosphate   5-Hydroxymethyldeoxycytidine 5'-phosphate

Deoxyribonucleotide Polyphosphates. Formation of the deoxyribonucleotide di- and triphosphates occurs in separate steps. Enzymes from *E. coli* and liver catalyze the following transphosphorylations.

$$\text{dAMP} + \text{ATP} \xrightleftharpoons{\text{Mg}^{++}} \text{dADP} + \text{ADP}$$

$$\text{TMP} + \text{ATP} \xrightleftharpoons{\text{Mg}^{++}} \text{TDP} + \text{ADP}$$

Nucleoside diphosphokinase of liver catalyzes the following reactions.

$$\text{TDP} + \text{ATP} \xrightleftharpoons{\text{Mg}^{++}} \text{TTP} + \text{ADP}$$

$$\text{dADP} + \text{ATP} \xrightleftharpoons{\text{Mg}^{++}} \text{dATP} + \text{ADP}$$

$$\text{dGDP} + \text{ATP} \xrightleftharpoons{\text{Mg}^{++}} \text{dGTP} + \text{ADP}$$

DEGRADATION OF PYRIMIDINES

The degradation of C^{14}-labeled pyrimidines, uracil and thymine, has been elucidated mainly by injection of large quantities of these substances and of possible intermediates, followed by examination of urinary excretion products. Some studies have also been performed by incubation of these substances with liver slices and with individual enzymes. Figure 28.5 shows the presently known pathways for the degradation of uracil and thymine. It is believed that cytosine and methylcytosine are deaminated first to yield, respectively, uracil and thymine.

It is noteworthy that the metabolism of uracil and thymine is initiated by *reduction* reactions to give the dihydro compounds, dihydrouracil and dihydrothymine. These are then hydrolyzed by *hydropyrimidine hydrase* to the β-ureido compounds. Further hydrolysis yields the β-amino acids. The utilization and fate of β-alanine have been discussed (page 535). β-Aminoisobutyrate may yield methylmalonate, an intermediate as the CoA derivative in the metabolism of propionate

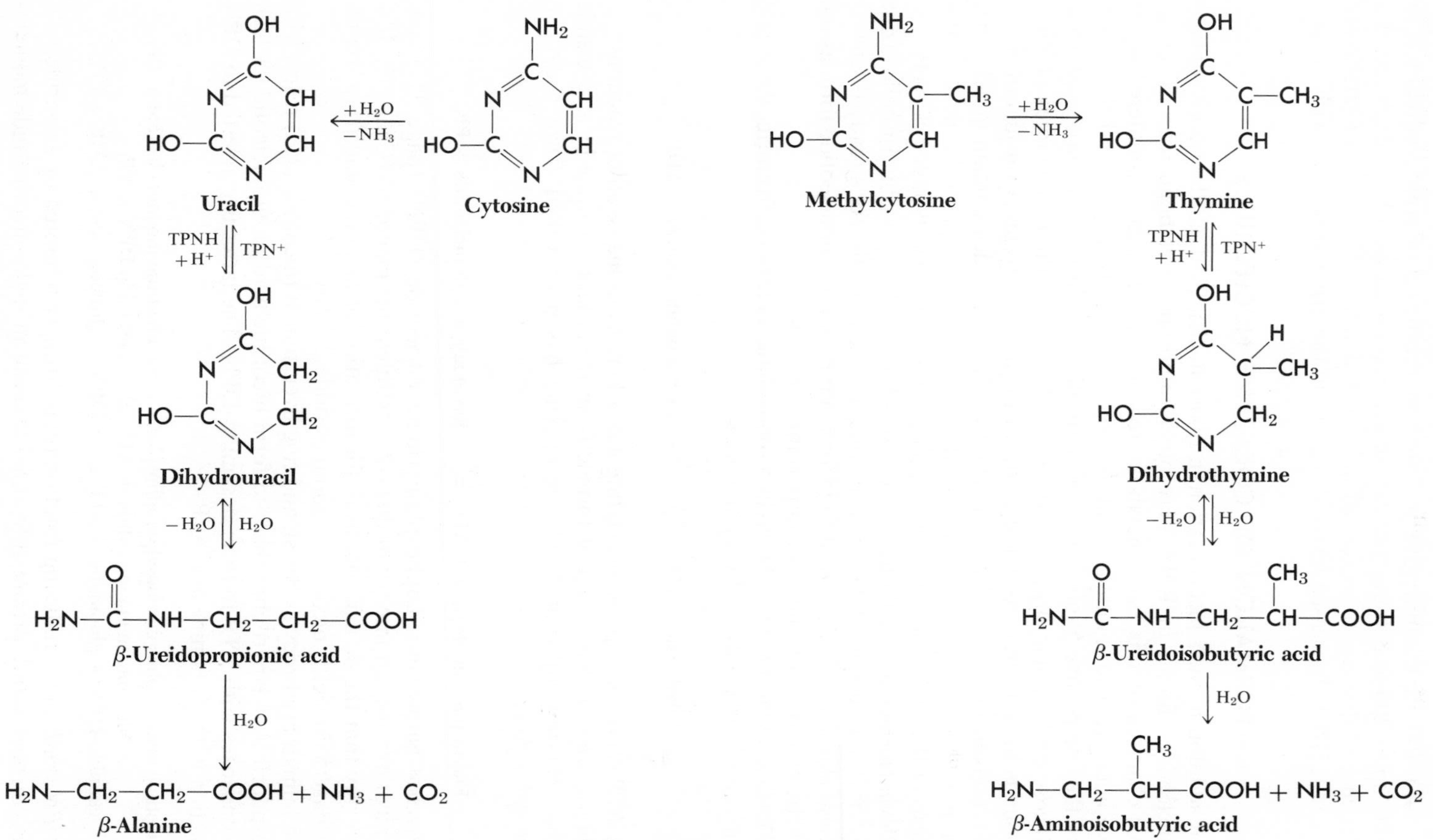

FIG. 28.5. Metabolic fate of the free pyrimidines.

(page 443). β-Aminoisobutyrate is found in the urine of some individuals in amounts up to 200 to 300 mg. per day, either because of an inherited trait or as a consequence of disease. It is excreted in increased amounts after administration of diets rich in DNA. Increased levels also occur in the urine of patients with tumors.

FORMATION OF COENZYME NUCLEOTIDES

In addition to their incorporation in ribose nucleic acid, all the ribose-containing nucleotides found in RNA play other important metabolic roles. Thus, in various chapters of this part, metabolic reactions have been encountered which involve adenylic acid, guanylic acid, uridylic acid, cytidylic acid, and thymidylic acid or their respective 5'-polyphosphates, or other derivatives, *e.g.*, uridine diphosphoglucose and similar uridine derivatives. The biosynthesis and roles of these compounds have been considered in detail in previous pages. Consideration has also been given to certain other important nucleotides which contain moieties not found in nucleic acids, *e.g.*, nicotinic acid amide, flavin, and pantothenic acid. Biosynthesis of the nucleotides containing these substances mainly involves ATP.

Flavin Nucleotides. Riboflavin, or 6,7-dimethyl-9-(1'-D-ribityl)isoalloxazine (Chap. 55), is an essential dietary constituent for mammals. As already discussed in several chapters of this part, it functions in a mono- or dinucleotide form as the prosthetic group of a number of important enzymes.

Flavin mononucleotide, riboflavin 5'-phosphate, is formed from riboflavin and ATP in a reaction catalyzed by a *flavokinase.*

$$\textbf{Riboflavin + ATP} \xrightarrow[\text{Mg}^{++}]{\text{flavokinase}} \textbf{flavin mononucleotide + ADP}$$

Thus, ATP serves as a phosphorylating agent here as in many other reactions.

Flavin adenine dinucleotide is formed from the mononucleotide by a reversible enzymic reaction utilizing ATP. The enzyme has been called *flavin nucleotide pyrophosphorylase.*

$$\textbf{Flavin mononucleotide + ATP} \xrightleftharpoons{\text{Mg}^{++}} \textbf{flavin adenine dinucleotide + PP}_i$$

Pyridine Nucleotides. Diphosphopyridine nucleotide (DPN) (page 312) contains nicotinamide, an important dietary constituent for mammals (Chap. 55). It is noteworthy that the *de novo* pathway for formation of nicotinic acid from tryptophan (page 553) yields nicotinic mononucleotide directly.

In human erythrocytes, yeast, and hog liver, niacin (nicotinic acid) reacts with 5-phosphoribosyl-1-pyrophosphate to form nicotinic acid mononucleotide, which then condenses with ATP to form desamido-DPN. The latter is converted to DPN by reaction with glutamine and ATP.

(*a*) **Nicotinic acid + phosphoribosylpyrophosphate $\rightleftharpoons$ nicotinic mononucleotide + PP$_i$**
(*b*)   **Nicotinic mononucleotide + ATP $\rightleftharpoons$ desamido-DPN + PP$_i$**
(*c*)   **Desamido-DPN + glutamine + ATP $\rightleftharpoons$ DPN + glutamic acid + AMP + PP$_i$**

The *DPN synthetase* catalyzing reaction (*c*) is strongly inhibited by azaserine.

Erythrocytes and, presumably, other tissues can make nicotinamide mononucleotide by the following reaction.

(*d*) Nicotinamide + phosphoribosylpyrophosphate $\rightleftharpoons$ nicotinamide mononucleotide + PP$_i$

Reaction (*b*) is catalyzed by *diphosphopyridine nucleotide pyrophosphorylase,* which can also catalyze the reaction:

(*e*)   Nicotinamide mononucleotide + ATP $\rightleftharpoons$ DPN + PP$_i$

The responsible enzyme is in the nucleus of mammalian cells and may play a significant regulatory role in the life of the cell while also being important as a contributor to the net synthesis of the pyridine nucleotides. The enucleated mature erthrocyte contains only a trace of this enzyme.

No enzyme capable of catalyzing direct synthesis of nicotinamide from nicotinic acid has been found in plant or animal systems. However, nicotinamide can arise from nicotinic acid by consecutive operation of reactions (*a*), (*b*), and (*c*) followed by the action of *diphosphopyridine nucleotidase* (*DPNase*), which catalyzes the hydrolysis of DPN at the N-glycosidic (nucleoside) linkage between ribose and nicotinamide.

$$\text{DPN} + \text{H}_2\text{O} \longrightarrow \text{nicotinamide} + \text{adenosine 5'-pyrophosphoryl-5-ribose}$$

Adenosine diphosphate ribose is hydrolyzed to adenylic acid and ribose 5-phosphate, which then follow the usual metabolic routes of these compounds.

Another enzyme catalyzing hydrolysis of dinucleotides is a *nucleotide pyrophosphatase* which cleaves various pyrophosphate linkages as follows:

$$\text{DPN} \longrightarrow \text{nicotinamide mononucleotide} + \text{adenylic acid (AMP)}$$
$$\text{TPN} \longrightarrow \text{nicotinamide mononucleotide} + \text{adenosine 2',5'-diphosphate}$$
$$\text{FAD} \longrightarrow \text{flavin mononucleotide} + \text{adenylic acid}$$
$$\text{ATP} \longrightarrow \text{ADP} + \text{P}_i \longrightarrow \text{adenylic acid} + \text{P}_i$$
$$\text{Thiamine pyrophosphate} \longrightarrow \text{thiamine monophosphate} + \text{P}_i$$

The physiological role of this enzyme is unknown, but it has been useful in the elucidation of the structures of a number of coenzymes containing the pyrophosphoryl group, *e.g.,* TPN and CoA.

Triphosphopyridine nucleotide (TPN) is formed from DPN by the following enzyme-catalyzed reaction.

$$\text{Diphosphopyridine nucleotide} + \text{ATP} \xrightarrow{\text{Mg}^{++}} \text{triphosphopyridine nucleotide} + \text{ADP}$$

Coenzyme A. The complete structure of coenzyme A is given on page 316. The pantothenic acid (pantoyl-β-alanine) portion of the molecule is required in the mammalian diet; its synthesis in microorganisms is described in Chap. 55.

Pantothenic acid also occurs in nature in combination with β-mercaptoethylamine (cysteamine) as pantetheine or *Lactobacillus bulgaricus* factor (LBF), so called because it is an essential nutrient for this and certain other microorganisms.

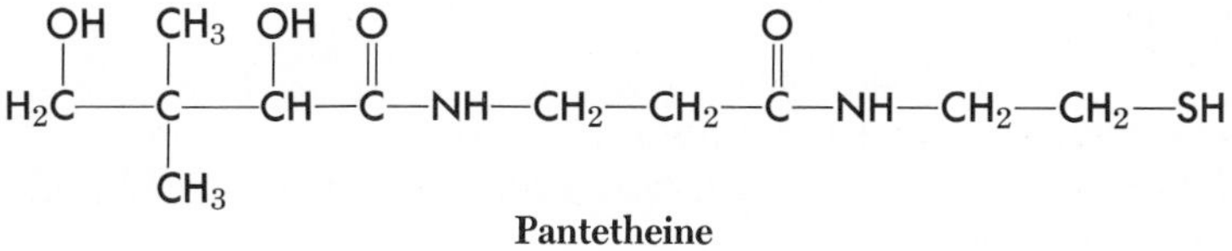

Pantetheine

Pantetheine is an intermediate in the pathway of CoA formation in mammalian liver and some microorganisms, as shown in the following reactions.

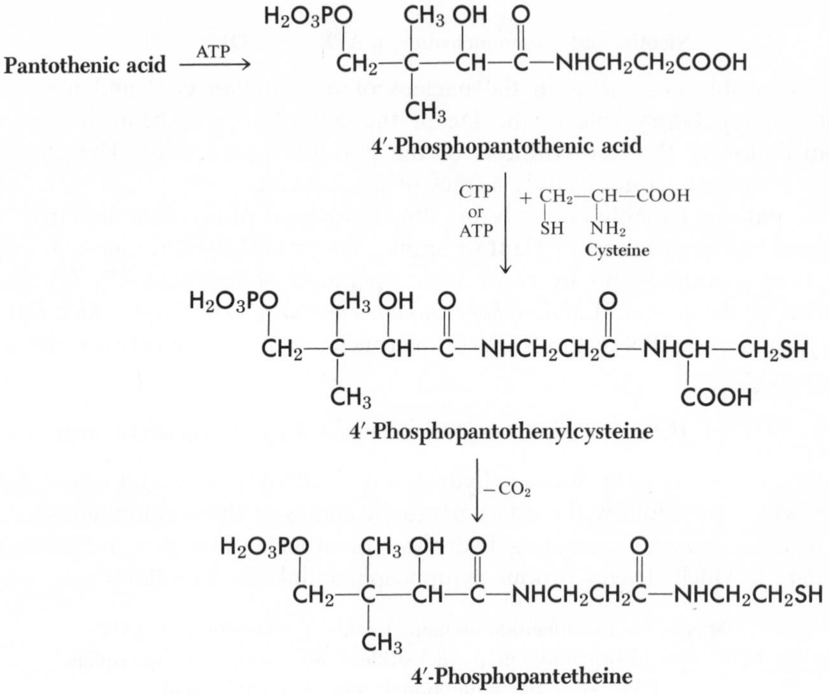

$$
\text{Pantothenic acid} \xrightarrow{\text{ATP}}
\begin{array}{c}
\text{H}_2\text{O}_3\text{PO} \quad\quad \text{CH}_3\ \text{OH}\ \ \text{O} \\
\quad\quad\ |\quad\quad\quad\quad |\quad\ \ |\quad\ \ \| \\
\text{CH}_2\text{—C—CH—C—NHCH}_2\text{CH}_2\text{COOH} \\
\quad\quad\ |\\
\quad\quad \text{CH}_3
\end{array}
$$

4′-Phosphopantothenic acid

$$
\text{CTP or ATP} \quad + \quad
\begin{array}{c}
\text{CH}_2\text{—CH—COOH}\\
\ |\quad\quad\ |\\
\text{SH}\quad \text{NH}_2
\end{array}
$$
Cysteine

$$
\begin{array}{c}
\text{H}_2\text{O}_3\text{PO} \quad\quad \text{CH}_3\ \text{OH}\ \ \text{O} \quad\quad\quad\quad\quad\quad \text{O} \\
\quad\quad\ |\quad\quad\quad\quad |\quad\ \ |\quad\ \ \|\quad\quad\quad\quad\quad\quad\quad \| \\
\text{CH}_2\text{—C—CH—C—NHCH}_2\text{CH}_2\text{C—NHCH—CH}_2\text{SH} \\
\quad\quad\ |\quad\quad\quad\quad\quad\quad\quad\quad\quad\quad\quad\quad\quad\quad\ |\\
\quad\quad \text{CH}_3 \quad\quad\quad\quad\quad\quad\quad\quad\quad\quad\quad\quad \text{COOH}
\end{array}
$$

4′-Phosphopantothenylcysteine

$$-\text{CO}_2$$

$$
\begin{array}{c}
\text{H}_2\text{O}_3\text{PO} \quad\quad \text{CH}_3\ \text{OH}\ \ \text{O} \quad\quad\quad\quad\quad\quad \text{O} \\
\quad\quad\ |\quad\quad\quad\quad |\quad\ \ |\quad\ \ \|\quad\quad\quad\quad\quad\quad\quad \| \\
\text{CH}_2\text{—C—CH—C—NHCH}_2\text{CH}_2\text{C—NHCH}_2\text{CH}_2\text{SH} \\
\quad\quad\ |\\
\quad\quad \text{CH}_3
\end{array}
$$

4′-Phosphopantetheine

$$\text{4′-Phosphopantetheine} + \text{ATP} \xrightarrow{\text{Mg}^{++}} \text{dephospho-CoA} + \text{PP}_i$$

The 3′-phosphate of the adenosine moiety of CoA is lacking in dephospho-CoA; the latter is converted to CoA by a specific *dephospho-CoA kinase*.

$$\text{Dephospho-CoA} + \text{ATP} \xrightarrow{\text{Mg}^{++}} \text{CoA} + \text{ADP}$$

REFERENCES

Books

Boyer, P. D., Lardy, H., and Myrbäck, K., eds., "The Enzymes," selected articles in vols. 2, 3, and 5, Academic Press, Inc., New York, 1960.

Chargaff, E., and Davidson, J. N., eds., "The Nucleic Acids," vol. III, Academic Press, Inc., New York, 1960.

Review Articles

Buchanan, J. M., and Hartman, S. C., Enzymic Reactions in the Synthesis of Purines, *Advances in Enzymol.,* **21,** 199–261, 1959.

Glaser, L., Biosynthesis of Deoxysugars, *Physiol. Revs.,* **43,** 215–242, 1963.

Kornberg, A., Pyrophosphorylases and Phosphorylases in Biosynthetic Reactions, *Advances in Enzymol.,* **18,** 191–240, 1957.

Reichard, P., The Enzymic Synthesis of Pyrimidines, *Advances in Enzymol.,* **21,** 263–294, 1959.

Stetten, D., Jr., On the Metabolic Defect in Gout, *Bull. N.Y. Acad. Med.,* **28,** 664–672, 1952.

29. Genetic Aspects of Metabolism

Nature of the Gene and Its Replication. The Coding Problem and Protein Structure

The classical problems of genetics can be posed as a series of questions. What is the nature of the genetic material? How is this material replicated so that at each cell division, each daughter cell possesses the same complement of genetic material as the parent cell? What are the mechanisms by which this material determines the chemical, metabolic, and morphological characteristics of the individual cell or organism? In brief, it is now recognized that all genes of higher organisms consist of DNA and that its role as genetic material is to determine the nature of each of the cellular proteins synthesized, most of these being the enzymes that catalyze individual metabolic reactions.

THE GENE AND METABOLISM

Inheritance is achieved through the genes, factors which are carried in the chromosomes. The mode of inheritance of characteristics attributable to genes is now well known and has been studied experimentally in a large number of species which show sexual differentiation, a prerequisite for demonstrating behavior and existence of single genes. Mendelian inheritance operates in man as in other more thoroughly studied species, and many characteristics caused by single gene differences have been described. Such traits as color blindness, the various blood groups, and hemophilia (Chap. 33) are familiar examples.

The general concept, proposed many years ago, is that a single gene can influence only a single step in metabolism. This hypothesis arose largely from studies of anomalies in man and other species in which a metabolic reaction is blocked. An excellent example is the metabolic defect called alkaptonuria (page 549), which is inherited in man as a simple mendelian recessive trait. As long ago as 1908, in the book "Inborn Errors of Metabolism," Garrod marshaled the data existing at the time and concluded that homogentisic acid, excreted in the urine of alkaptonuric persons, is a normal intermediate in the oxidation of phenylalanine and tyrosine and that alkaptonuria is due to an inability to oxidize homogentisic acid. Garrod's conclusion was verified almost 50 years later by La Du, who showed an absolute lack of homogentisic acid oxidase in alkaptonuria (page 549). The pathways of oxidation of the aromatic amino acids have already been described (pages 548*ff.*), and much has been learned about the intermediate compounds in the oxidation of these amino acids by studies of the metabolic anomalies found in man, such as alkaptonuria, phenylketonuria, tyrosinosis, and albinism. Since certain of these anomalies are inherited as single genic factors, it is indicated that a change in a single gene has blocked an individual reaction in the metabolism of these compounds.

One of the first broad studies showing the effect of single genes in influencing chemical structures was that of R. Scott-Moncrieff and other workers on the nature of the plant pigments in primroses, dahlias, and other plants. The anthocyanins are blue, purple, and red water-soluble pigments which are glycosidic derivatives of pelargonidin and occur as oxonium salts.

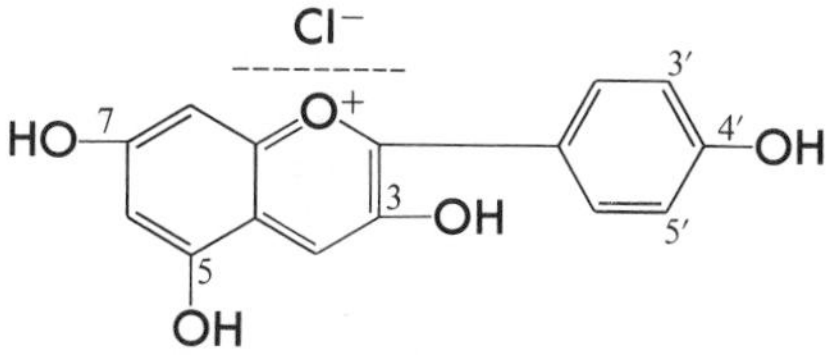

Pelargonidin

Individual genes are known which produce the following effects: (1) oxidation to OH at 3′ (formation of cyanidin); (2) oxidation to OH at both 3′ and 5′ (formation of delphinidin); (3) methylation of the OH group at 3′; (4) methylation of the OH groups at 3′ and 5′; (5) methylation of the OH group at 7; (6) glycoside formation as 3-monosides, 3-biosides, or 3,5-diglycosides with one hexose or pentose residue, or more, being involved. Thus, *single* genes control each biochemical step, state of oxidation, methylation, or change of glycosidal type. In no case has a single genic difference been found which modifies two characteristics of the molecule simultaneously.

Genetic investigations of the bread mold, *Neurospora crassa,* initiated in 1941 by Beadle and Tatum, greatly extended the limited information available from other species. Since the nucleus of the sexual spore of *Neurospora* is haploid, it contains only one of each of the seven chromosomes and, correspondingly, of each gene. Each *ascus* contains eight spores which are identical in the wild type. These can be isolated and tested individually. If a mutant is crossed with the wild type, four spores will show the wild-type character and four the mutant character. The wild-type strain can be cultured on a medium containing only glucose, an inorganic source of nitrogen, salts, and biotin (Chap. 55). Various mutant strains, produced by irradiation with ultraviolet light or x-rays, are unable to grow unless certain compounds are added to the medium, indicating loss of the ability to synthesize one or more substances.

In testing for mutants, the *Neurospora* spores can be cultured in a complete medium, *i.e.,* one containing all known growth factors, amino acids, vitamins, etc. If the strain can grow normally on the minimal medium containing inorganic salts, sugar, and biotin, no mutation has occurred. If it cannot grow on this medium, it is tested further to determine whether the missing factor is a vitamin, an amino acid, etc. Tests are made first with large groups of substances, then with smaller groups, and finally with individual compounds. In this way many mutants have been found which lack the ability to synthesize one or another of the amino acids, the B group of vitamins, purines, or pyrimidines.

Let us suppose that for a certain mutant strain, substance D is required for growth. Since the synthesis of such a substance proceeds in a series of steps, the metabolic block may occur at any point along the chain of synthesis from A to D.

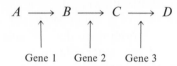

If gene 3 is altered and the block occurs between C and D, supplying D is the only way in which the strain can be grown. However, if gene 1 is altered, then addition of B or C, as well as D, will permit the growth of the mutant. In other words, alteration of several different genes will result in the requirement for D although the metabolic block may occur at any one of the different steps. Many such cases have been encountered. Although the wild type of *Neurospora* can synthesize arginine from ammonia, Srb and Horowitz have found several mutants which cannot grow unless arginine is supplied in the medium. Some "arginineless" strains can use only arginine, others can use citrulline or arginine, and still others can use ornithine, citrulline, or arginine. It is evident that the sequence of steps must be in the order $X \rightarrow$ ornithine $\rightarrow$ citrulline $\rightarrow$ arginine, exactly as it occurs in mammals (pages 497*ff.*). Similar studies greatly expedited elucidation of the pathways of biosynthesis of such amino acids as lysine, tryptophan, histidine, etc.

In every instance, it was demonstrated that a single gene controls the formation of a single enzyme. Thus, genes determine the detailed reactions of metabolism by control of the biosynthesis of enzymes. This has frequently been stated as the one gene–one enzyme hypothesis. Studies similar to those in *Neurospora* have been made with mutant strains of various bacteria, higher plants, and animals.

THE GENE AS DNA

The above evidence led to the view that the gene controls the synthesis of enzymes but offered no information as to the chemical nature of the gene. This has been provided by a variety of studies which may be summarized as follows.

1. The experimental biologists of the late nineteenth century demonstrated, largely by excision methods, that the hereditary factors of cells are located in the nuclei. In 1902 Sutton showed that the segregation and independent assortment of the mendelian factors of inheritance can be explained on the basis that these factors are located in the chromosomes.

2. The isolation in pure form of various viruses led to the recognition that plant viruses are ribonucleoproteins and that most bacterial viruses (bacteriophages) and animal viruses are deoxyribonucleoproteins (Chap. 10). Later, it was demonstrated that replication is due entirely to the nucleic acid of such viruses.

3. Mutation of genes is produced by ultraviolet light. The action spectrum (those wavelengths of light which cause this effect) which is effective in producing mutations is in close agreement with the absorption spectra of the nucleic acids. Similarly, other physical and chemical agents which are mutagenic have been shown to alter nucleic acids.

4. The transforming substances of bacteria (page 186) which carry hereditary information consist of DNA.

5. Data have slowly accumulated which indicate that the DNA content of a set of chromosomes is an absolute constant for each species, consonant with the role of DNA as the carrier of genetic information.

All the above information led to the view that the genetic material is DNA in all cases except for certain plant and animal viruses in which RNA serves this function. This being so, DNA must possess certain of the fundamental properties of the gene: the ability to direct the formation of an exact replica of itself; mutability, the ability to be altered without loss of reproductive ability; and, finally, the ability to direct the formation of enzymes or other proteins. The mechanism of DNA replication will be considered first.

REPLICATION OF DNA

As already noted (pages 175ff.), the Watson-Crick formulation of the structure of native DNA has indicated that each DNA molecule consists of a double-stranded helix in which the two strands are bound by hydrogen bonds between amino and keto groups: adenine (A) to thymine (T), and guanine (G) to cytosine (C); hence, A = T and G = C. On the basis of this structure, it was suggested that replication might proceed by separation of the two strands and that a new chain of nucleotides is formed complementary to each of the strands. It should be noted that each single strand serves as a "template" to form a new DNA strand, which must be not identical with, but complementary, to the template. When the process is complete, two new double-stranded molecules of DNA have been formed, one strand of each molecule having served as template, or primer, and the other strand being newly fabricated. A large body of evidence has since accumulated in support of this hypothesis.

Consistent with this concept is an experiment by Meselson and Stahl in which bacteria (*Escherichia coli*) were grown in a medium which would label their DNA completely with N^{15}. The bacteria were then washed carefully and, by appropriate means, permitted to undergo one cell division in a medium in which all the nitrogen was in the form of N^{14}. During this cell division the total DNA of the culture doubled. By accurate density determinations in a concentrated solution of cesium chloride (page 178), it was shown that the DNA of this culture did not consist of two types, *i.e.*, DNA with N^{15} and DNA with N^{14}, but rather that all the DNA behaved as if it were composed of $N^{14.5}$. This is the result to be expected from the mechanism of replication described above. During replication each double-stranded N[15]-labeled DNA separated to yield two single strands. Each of the latter served as a template on which N[14]-labeled DNA was fabricated, yielding a new double-stranded molecule with one strand containing N[15], the other containing N[14]. Such molecules behave physically as if they were built of N[14.5]. The process is shown schematically in Fig. 29.1.

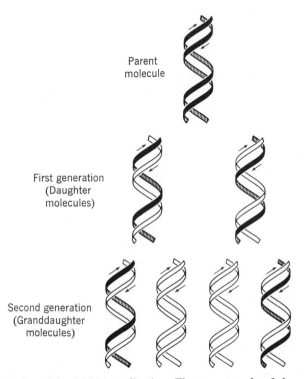

Parent molecule

First generation (Daughter molecules)

Second generation (Granddaughter molecules)

FIG. 29.1. Proposed model of DNA replication. The two strands of the parent molecule, shown in black, contain N[15]. In the daughter molecules, each DNA contains N[15] in one strand and N[14] in the other. In the second generation, two molecules contain N[14] exclusively and two molecules contain equal amounts of N[14] and N[15]. The arrows indicate the direction of the strands in the sense that phosphate diester bonds connect C-3' of one sugar with C-5' of the next. (*From M. Meselson and F. Stahl, Cold Spring Harbor Symp. Quant. Biol.,* **23**, 10, 1958.)

Although the Watson-Crick model provides a concept of how replication of DNA occurs, it does not illuminate the actual chemical processes involved. Knowledge of this mechanism has been provided largely by Kornberg and his collaborators.

Net synthesis of DNA can be obtained with a highly purified enzyme, *DNA polymerase*, obtained initially from *E. coli.* In the presence of the four deoxyribonucleoside triphosphates and of primer DNA, as well as Mg^{++}, the enzyme catalyzes an over-all process which may be represented as follows.

$$
\begin{array}{l}
\text{m TTP} \\
+ \\
\text{n dGTP} \quad + \quad \text{DNA} \; \rightleftharpoons \; \text{DNA} \\
+ \\
\text{m dATP} \\
+ \\
\text{n dCTP}
\end{array}
\left[
\begin{array}{l}
\text{TMP} \\
\\
\text{dGMP} \\
\\
\text{dAMP} \\
\\
\text{dCMP}
\end{array}
\right]_{2m + 2n}
+ \quad 2(m + n)\text{PP}_i
$$

Pyrophosphate is released in quantities equivalent to the deoxyribonucleotides utilized. The nucleoside diphosphates cannot substitute for the triphosphates. If one of the four substrates is omitted, the yield of polymer is reduced by a factor of more than 10^4. If the DNA primer is omitted, no immediate reaction takes place.

All present lines of evidence indicate that the reaction described involves a net synthesis of a polydeoxyribonucleotide directed by the added DNA which serves as a template, the purine or pyrimidine nucleotide being added at specific loci in the growing chains by virtue of hydrogen bonding and steric fit with the complementary base on the template. At this time it is not possible to assess the full role of DNA polymerase. As a minimum it must possess a general specificity for deoxyribonucleotide triphosphates, a binding site for a portion of a DNA strand, and an active site that catalyzes the reaction in which internucleotide linkages are formed. The physical properties of the newly synthesized DNA molecules are closely similar to those of double-stranded DNA isolated from natural sources. Sedimentation studies in the ultracentrifuge and viscosimetric measurements indicate molecular weights similar to that of the primer DNA. The molecules are degraded by pancreatic deoxyribonuclease to form acid-soluble fragments. When the DNA is heated, it undergoes the characteristic changes in viscosity and in optical properties of native DNA (Chap. 10).

It is noteworthy that heated DNA, which is single-stranded, serves as an excellent primer for formation of double-stranded DNA. Native DNA is inert unless it is pretreated in some manner to produce unfolding of the molecule. It should be emphasized that it is unknown at present how native intracellular DNA may be uncoiled at the time that replication occurs intracellularly.

The most important evidence indicating that the added DNA serves as a primer derives from results obtained with DNA preparations which possess a different base composition (Table 29.1). The data indicate that the added primer determines the composition of the enzymically synthesized DNA. It is particularly striking that the use of the A-T copolymer results in synthesis of new A-T copolymer. Although all four nucleoside triphosphates are present in the medium, there is no significant incorporation of nucleotides containing G or C. Such results supply strong evidence for the view that base composition is replicated during the enzymic synthesis by a guiding mechanism involving hydrogen bonding of A to T and G to C (Fig. 29.2).

This conclusion would be fortified if base sequences of DNA were known. In

Table 29.1: Base Composition of Enzymically Synthesized DNA

DNA	A	T	G	C	(A + G)/(T + C)	(A + T)/(G + C)
Mycobacterium phlei:						
Primer.................	0.65	0.66	1.35	1.34	1.01	0.49
Product...............	0.66	0.65	1.34	1.37	0.99	0.48
Escherichia coli:						
Primer.................	1.00	0.97	0.98	1.05	0.98	0.97
Product...............	1.04	1.00	0.97	0.98	1.01	1.02
Calf thymus:						
Primer.................	1.14	1.05	0.90	0.85	1.05	1.25
Product...............	1.12	1.08	0.85	0.85	1.02	1.29
Bacteriophage T2:						
Primer.................	1.31	1.32	0.67	0.70*	0.98	1.92
Product...............	1.33	1.29	0.69	0.70	1.02	1.90
A-T copolymer	1.99	1.93	0.05	0.05	1.03	40.00

Note: For each experiment, a different primer was used. The A-T copolymer used as primer contained equal amounts of the two bases. A, adenine; T, thymine; G, guanine; C, cytosine. The results are given as the molar ratios for each of the four bases.

* Hydroxymethylcytosine.

Source: A. Kornberg, in J. M. Allen, ed., "The Molecular Control of Cellular Activity," p. 245, McGraw-Hill Book Company, Inc., New York, 1962.

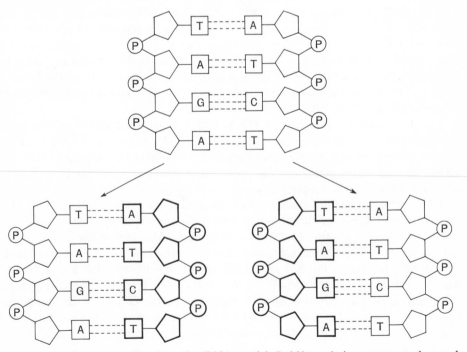

Fig. 29.2. Scheme of replication of a DNA model. Boldface chains represent the newly synthesized strands of the two daughter molecules. (*From J. Josse, A. D. Kaiser, and A. Kornberg, J. Biol. Chem.,* **236**, 864, 1961.)

the absence of procedures for such analyses, Kornberg and his colleagues resorted to an approximation called "nearest-neighbor analysis." The internucleotide bonds of enzymically produced DNA are 3'-5', as in natural DNA. This is readily demonstrated by using P^{32}-labeled nucleoside triphosphates in which the radioactive P is 5'. This P becomes the bridge between the substrate nucleotide and the nucleotide at the next position. Hydrolysis of the synthesized DNA is accomplished with a mixture of a micrococcal deoxyribonuclease and splenic diesterase (page 172), yielding from the DNA the nucleoside 3'-phosphates quantitatively. When only one of the four added nucleoside triphosphates is labeled, e.g., dATP, the P^{32} content of each of the isolated 3'-deoxyribonucleotides is a measure of the relative frequency with which the dATP reacted with each of the four available substrates during the synthesis of the DNA chains to yield the nucleotide sequences AA, AT, AG, AC. This method, when performed four times with a differently labeled substrate in each case, i.e., with dATP, dGTP, dCTP, and TTP, yields the relative frequencies of all the 16 possible varieties of dinucleotide (nearest-neighbor) sequences.

Such studies have led to the following conclusions. All 16 possible dinucleotide (nearest-neighbor) sequences are found, and the pattern of relative frequencies is unique for each type of primer DNA used. The replication involves base pairing of A to T and of G to C. Finally, and most important, the replication produces two strands which are synthesized in opposite direction, exactly as predicted by the Watson-Crick model. The data given in Fig. 29.3 show the results obtained and those expected on the basis of this model.

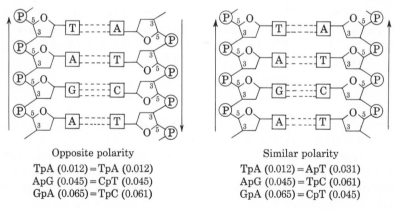

Opposite polarity

TpA (0.012) = TpA (0.012)
ApG (0.045) = CpT (0.045)
GpA (0.065) = TpC (0.061)

Similar polarity

TpA (0.012) = ApT (0.031)
ApG (0.045) = TpC (0.061)
GpA (0.065) = CpT (0.045)

Fig. 29.3.   Contrast of a Watson-Crick DNA model with strands synthesized of opposite polarity with a model with strands of similar polarity. The predicted nearest-neighbor frequencies are different. Values in parentheses are sequence frequencies determined with DNA of *Mycobacterium phlei*. The strands shown are the newly synthesized ones of Fig. 29.2; for comparison, they are aligned as though they were complementary strands of the same helix. (*From J. Josse, A. D. Kaiser, and A. Kornberg, J. Biol. Chem.,* **236,** 864, 1961.)

Nothing is presently understood of the phenomena that initiate DNA synthesis. The latter can begin only after the strands of the existing DNA helix begin to separate. The magnitude of this task may be evident from the structure of the

DNA of *E. coli*. In this organism, as in other bacteria, the "chromosome" appears to be a single molecule of DNA in a closed circular structure. The total length of such a molecule is about 0.5 mm. or approximately 200,000 complete helical turns. Whatever mechanism accomplishes the enormous task of strand separation, once separation has occurred the formation of new, complementary strands can be accomplished by a single enzyme. The specificity of this synthesis is provided by the preexisting DNA template, base pairing being dictated by hydrogen bonding, extremely close stereospecific geometric requirements for fit into the new helical structure, and the hydrophobic and van der Waals forces which result in "stacking" of bases so that they may fit in a single, specific manner. This is further indicated by the use of nucleoside triphosphates containing analogues of the naturally occurring bases. Deoxyuridine triphosphate or 5-bromodeoxyuridine triphosphate could replace TTP but not dATP, dGTP, or dCTP. Similarly, 5-methyl- and 5-bromocytidine triphosphates could specifically replace deoxycytidine triphosphate, and hypoxanthine could substitute for guanine in the nucleoside triphosphates. These findings are readily interpreted only on the basis of hydrogen bonding between polynucleotide strands involving A-T and G-C pairs. Furthermore, certain bases, *e.g.*, 2-aminopurine and 5-bromouracil, supplied to growing bacterial cultures not only are incorporated into DNA but prove to be mutagenic. In effect, these compounds lead to copying errors in the replication of DNA. Further evidence that mutation involves base replacement in the nucleic acid will become apparent later.

The above discussion has been concerned with DNA synthesis involving the four bases: A, T, G, and C. The *E. coli* T even bacteriophages represent a special case insofar as they contain 5-hydroxymethylcytosine (HMC) in place of cytosine (Table 10.5). When T2 DNA is used as primer in the presence of dCTP and the other triphosphates, the polymerase synthesizes a product containing C instead of HMC (Table 29.1). In T2-infected cells of *E. coli* this is prevented by an enzyme, absent in normal cells, which hydrolyzes dCTP or dCDP to dCMP.

$$\text{dCTP} + \text{H}_2\text{O} \longrightarrow \text{dCMP} + \text{PP}_i$$
$$\text{dCDP} + \text{H}_2\text{O} \longrightarrow \text{dCMP} + \text{P}_i$$

In effect, this makes more dCMP available for formation of 5-hydroxymethyl dCMP which is then converted to the triphosphate.

Kornberg and coworkers have also demonstrated that glucosylation of HMC residues occurs at the level of DNA and not with the nucleotides. These reactions are catalyzed by specific α- or *β-glucosyl transferases* present only in phage-infected cells.

$$\text{UDP-glucose} + \text{HMC-DNA} \rightleftharpoons \text{UDP} + \text{glucosyl-HMC-DNA}$$

AMINO ACID SEQUENCES IN PROTEINS AND THE CODING PROBLEM

The heredity information is contained in the chemical structure of DNA. Inasmuch as DNA consists of a linear array of bases held together in polynucleotide form, the information must be specifically conveyed by the sequences of the bases, the sugar phosphate backbones of the chains being identical in every instance. The immense possibilities of variation of sequences of purines and pyrimidines have already been noted (page 175). Earlier in this chapter some evidence was presented that individual genes are responsible for directing the synthesis of enzymes.

Inasmuch as all known enzymes are proteins, this hypothesis has been extended to include other proteins as well. Indeed, genetic variants are known in man in which certain proteins are lacking, e.g., agammaglobulinemia, afibrinoginemia, etc. (Chap. 31).

The present view is that genes determine not only their own replication but also the synthesis of specific proteins. In plant viruses and bacteriophages, nucleic acid may be infective without protein, yet newly formed virus contains specific proteins, e.g., in the case of the T2 phage, cited above, the information for the synthesis of the enzymes for glucosylation of HMC and for dCTP hydrolysis is conveyed by the phage DNA. Thus the information for such specific protein synthesis is contained in the nucleic acid. In man, some individuals have a peculiar hemoglobin (Hb S) which, in the reduced state, is much less soluble than normal hemoglobin. Corpuscles containing Hb S undergo a change in shape known as "sickling," caused by crystallization of reduced hemoglobin (Chap. 42). The ability to form Hb S is inherited as a single genic factor. It was demonstrated by Ingram in 1957 that Hb S differs from Hb A (normal Hb) by a single amino acid residue in the β chain (Chap. 11). Subsequently, many other abnormal hemoglobins have also been shown to differ from the normal in single amino acid replacements (Chap. 31), and similar substitutions have been found in other proteins. Furthermore, species differences among homologous proteins, e.g., insulin (Chap. 31), involve replacement of a few residues at specific loci in the peptide chains. From the above it has been concluded that the gene must determine the amino acid sequence of a protein; a mutation, i.e., an alteration in the DNA, produces a change in the amino acid sequence.

Human hemoglobin contains α and β chains (pages 194ff.), each of which is under separate genetic control. Thus, the "one gene–one enzyme" hypothesis may be restated as one gene–one polypeptide chain, since individual enzymes and other proteins consist of only one chain or a few chains. Furthermore, it is assumed that the *genetic* determination of protein structure is primarily or exclusively concerned with the specific kind and linear arrangement of amino acids in the polypeptide chain or chains. The "sequence hypothesis" can now be stated, as follows: the amino acid sequence of a protein is determined by the sequence of nucleotides in a definite portion of a particular molecule of DNA. Some of the evidence for and implications of this hypothesis may now be examined.

Specific Protein Conformation. Inasmuch as globular proteins manifest their important properties only in their native state, we may inquire how the complex specific folding is achieved, if this is not under direct genetic control. Available evidence suggests that the primary amino acid sequence determines how the polypeptide chain folds into the proper native conformation. In effect, this implies that there is only one conformation of maximal stability, a view supported by observations that many highly purified proteins can be denatured, i.e., assume a random form, and then under suitable experimental conditions, spontaneously regain their native properties. It should be emphasized that this is seldom achieved with crude extracts of tissues in which many denatured proteins can react with one another or with the metabolites of the cell. Moreover, such extracts frequently contain proteinases which cannot readily hydrolyze native proteins but rapidly attack denatured proteins.

The reversible denaturation of hemoglobin has already been cited (pages 160*ff*.). Hemoglobin does not contain disulfide bonds, and the folding presumably involves only secondary forces, *i.e.*, hydrophobic forces, hydrogen bonds, ionic interactions, etc. (pages 153*ff*.). A similar situation obtains with many other proteins which lack disulfide bonds, *e.g.*, myoglobin, enolase, various amylases, cytochrome c, etc.

For proteins such as ribonuclease, which contains four disulfide bridges (page 160), this situation is not entirely dissimilar. Anfinsen and White showed that the disulfide bonds may be reduced to yield a linear polypeptide chain and that, under favorable conditions, reoxidation will produce the native, active enzyme. These results suggest that in this case, also, folding is determined by the specific amino acid sequence which brings the correct pairs of cysteine residues into juxtaposition prior to oxidation.

Thus, the *genetic* influence on folding appears to be exerted by determining the positions of the amino acid residues which are critical for the conformation and, therefore, for the functional properties of the protein. Conformation is, however, markedly dependent on a number of extrinsic factors: temperature, pH, ionic environment, presence of prosthetic groups, etc.

Although many proteins contain only a single peptide chain, others consist of two or more chains. In some proteins individual chains are linked by disulfide bridges, as in insulin (Fig. 9.1); in others, the chains are held together by noncovalent forces, as in hemoglobin (page 160), aldolase (page 371), glutamic acid dehydrogenase (page 488), etc. In these last instances, dissociation and association are readily reversible by specific environmental factors in the same way that chain conformation is controlled. Thus there appear to be no special genetic factors for the formation of multichain proteins, although the synthesis of each chain is, as already noted, under separate genetic control. A rare genetic defect occurs in man in which the synthesis of the α chain of hemoglobin is partially suppressed (Chap. 42). Such individuals possess Hb H which is β_4. Clearly, not only is the β chain formed independently of the α chain, but the association of four β chains can also occur.

Prosthetic Groups. Inasmuch as many enzymes and other proteins contain non-amino acid prosthetic groups, the question of genetic control over synthesis of such conjugated proteins must be considered. Once again, in the case of hemoglobin, the spontaneous recombination of heme with globin (page 160) indicates that it is unnecessary to assume any special genetic control. Similarly, many enzymes which possess dissociable prosthetic groups, *e.g.*, flavins, heme, pyridoxal phosphate, DPN, TPN, metal ions, etc., are spontaneously regenerated by adding the prosthetic group to the apoenzyme (protein) under suitable conditions. A further striking example may be cited. A porphyrinless mutant of *E. coli* lacks catalase activity. If, however, hemin (ferriprotoporphyrin) is added, active catalase is formed, indicating that biosynthesis of the apoenzyme has occurred without concurrent synthesis of the prosthetic group.

The above examples have been of conjugated proteins in which the prosthetic group is not held by covalent bonds to the protein. When covalent bonds are present, these may be expected to be formed by enzyme-catalyzed reactions since in many of these compounds the bonds involved require energy for synthesis. The following examples may be cited to illustrate the problems involved: the thioether bonds linking the heme in cytochrome c (page 199), the amide bond linking biotin to the ϵ-amino group of lysine in certain enzymes (page 444), the carboxamide bond linking the polysaccharide moiety to the protein in γ-globulins (page 636), ovalbumin, and other glycoproteins, the N-acetyl of cytochrome c, ovalbumin, and other proteins, etc. In these and other cases, the biosynthetic processes are unknown but may be controlled by genetic determination of the responsible synthetic enzymes.

Amino Acid Modification in Peptide Chains. Only 20 amino acids are generally present in proteins (page 143). Other amino acid residues are formed by subsequent modification of some residues during or after formation of the polypeptide chains. Nonphosphorylated ovalbumin is synthesized in the hen's oviduct prior to phosphorylation. Phosphorylserine (page 720), phosphorylthreonine (page 720), tyrosine-O-sulfate (page 648), hydroxyprolines (page 95), hydroxylysine (page 97), and iodinated amino acids (page 99) are formed by enzymic, energy-requiring processes. However, little is known of the mechanisms involved, particularly as to whether the choice of residues so affected is under specific genetic influence or is a consequence of the conformation of the proteins concerned.

Direction of Synthesis of Peptide Chains. The studies of Dintzis and coworkers indicate that protein synthesis occurs by sequential addition of amino acids to the growing end of a peptide chain. Isolated rabbit reticulocytes continue to form hemoglobin in the presence of free amino acids. When such cells were given a 4-min. exposure to a mixture of H^3-leucine and all other amino acids were unlabeled, the greatest labeling occurred at the unfinished carboxyl ends of the α and β chains (Fig. 29.4). With longer exposures, progressively greater incorporation occurred at all positions, the radioactivity incorporated increasing with the distance of the particular leucine residue from the amino-terminal end. After 1 hr., the labeling approached equality at all positions. These results clearly demonstrate that protein synthesis is initiated at the amino-terminal end of the peptide chain and proceeds sequentially.

The Coding Problem. The above considerations lead to a picture of protein synthesis in which a genetic control determines only the sequence of amino acids. Since both the DNA and the peptide chain are linear polymers, they are presumed to be colinear in some manner—the base sequence determining the amino acid sequence.

However, there are only four primary bases in DNA, viz., A, G, C, and T, whereas there are 20 amino acids in proteins. Although small amounts of other bases may be present in DNA, these appear to function as occasional substitutes for one of the usual bases. For example, methylcytosine pairs with guanine in the

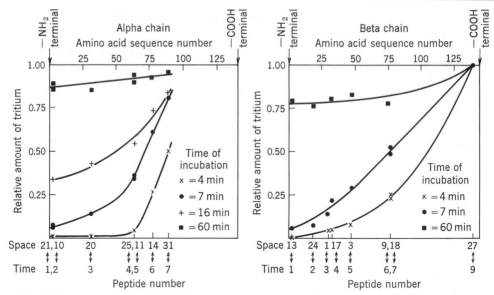

FIG. 29.4. Incorporation of labeled leucine into the α and β chains of rabbit hemoglobin. The position of each leucine residue is given at the top with the tryptic peptide numbers at the bottom of each graph. (*From M. A. Naughton and H. M. Dintzis, Proc. Nat. Acad. Sci., U.S., 48, 1822, 1962.*)

same manner as does cytosine. For the present there is no evidence for any special function of the unusual bases in DNA, except in certain bacteriophages (page 185), and the problem can be considered in terms of the common four bases.

The 20 amino acids usually present in proteins are, in abbreviated form, Ala, Arg, Asp, AspNH$_2$, CySH, Glu, GluNH$_2$, Gly, His, Ileu, Leu, Lys, Met, Phe, Pro, Ser, Thr, Try, Tyr, and Val (page 114). Cystine is omitted since cysteine is probably incorporated as such and cystine, when present, is formed by subsequent oxidation of two cysteine residues. Glutamine and asparagine are included with their corresponding dicarboxylic acids; the specific incorporation into a protein of each of these four amino acids is apparently under separate genetic control, as indicated by mutation data (page 611).

With only four bases in DNA, and 20 amino acids in proteins, the coding ratio, *i.e.*, the specific combination of bases controlling the incorporation of an amino acid, must be larger than one. If the coding ratio were two bases (doublet) per amino acid, this would permit only 4^2, or 16, codes. For a coding ratio of three bases (triplet), there are 4^3, or 64, possible combinations, more than enough to code for 20 amino acids. Present evidence, largely indirect, suggests that the coding ratio is probably three, although other types of codes cannot be completely excluded, *e.g.*, a code consisting of some doublets and some triplets.

If the code involves triplets, another problem becomes apparent, *viz.*, how many functional triplets actually exist. If only 20 triplets are functional, then there must be 44 nonfunctional or "nonsense" triplets. In a fully *degenerate* code all the triplets would be meaningful and there would be an average of three functional code designations for each amino acid. The possible existence of a partially degenerate code must also be considered.

In order to discuss additional problems related to the code, some of the concepts, findings, and definitions, derived mainly from genetic studies, should be introduced. The concept of the gene as the unit of inheritance has had to be refined in order to describe more clearly current knowledge. A *cistron* is that portion of the genetic material (DNA) which codes a protein or a protein subunit (one polypeptide chain). The *muton* (mutation unit) is the smallest element of the cistron which can be altered by mutation. Present evidence indicates that this unit probably represents a single base in one strand of DNA.

Studies with various enzymes and proteins have shown that genetic variations involving point mutations, which are inherited in mendelian fashion, affect only a single amino acid in the polypeptide chain. This has been shown most strikingly for mutations which have altered the structure of human hemoglobin and for the modified sequence of the protein formed after appropriate treatment of the RNA of tobacco mosaic virus (pages 613*ff*.). Furthermore, mutants near one another on the genetic map (determined by crossing-over studies) produce amino acid replacements close to one another in the amino acid sequence. This has been found with the A protein of tryptophan synthetase of *E. coli* (page 612) by Yanofsky and coworkers and with the alkaline phosphatase of *E. coli* by Levinthal et al. Such studies also provide important evidence for the colinearity of the peptide chain and the DNA of the gene (Chap. 31).

Another aspect of the coding problem should be mentioned. In an overlapping type of code, a given base forms part of the sequence of several coding units whether these be doublets, triplets, or larger units. If a triplet code unit is assumed and a portion of the base sequence is $\cdots$ AGCTAG, the base C will be part of the coding units AGC, GCT, and CTA; in a nonoverlapping code, the units would be AGC and TAG. In an overlapping code, an alteration of C would alter three amino acids. Since known point mutations involve only a single amino acid replacement, the code appears to be of the nonoverlapping type.

REFERENCES

See list following Chap. 31.

30. Genetic Aspects of Metabolism

Biosynthesis of Protein and RNA

THE GENE AND PROTEIN SYNTHESIS

Although DNA provides information necessary for protein synthesis, this process must be indirect, since it seems unlikely that free amino acids could react directly and specifically with DNA to produce an ordered polypeptide sequence. Moreover, the energy required for formation of peptide bonds must be supplied by some chemical driving force involving special intermediate compounds. That DNA has no direct role in protein synthesis was evident initially from the fact that enucleated single cells, lacking DNA, continue to synthesize enzymes. Moreover, mammalian reticulocytes which lack a nucleus synthesize hemoglobin.

Before considering protein synthesis in detail, the main features may be briefly outlined. The sites of protein synthesis are the ribosomes (page 270). The genetic message is brought to the ribosomes by a unique type of RNA known as "messenger" RNA, "template" RNA, or "informational" RNA; for simplicity it will be called mRNA. This mRNA is made in the nucleus by copying the base sequence of DNA, and the base composition of mRNA is related to that of the specific DNA. Thus, mRNA contains the information for protein synthesis. Amino acids attached to RNA molecules known as soluble RNA (sRNA), transfer RNA, or acceptor RNA are conveyed to the ribosomes. The sRNA molecules are specific, and there is at least one for each of the 20 amino acids. The over-all process is presented in schematic form in Fig. 30.1. Thus, at least three distinct kinds of RNA are involved in protein biosynthesis: the low molecular weight sRNA molecules, which contain a number of unusual nucleotides (page 183); the structural RNA of the ribosomes (rRNA); and mRNA.

Much of our present information concerning protein synthesis has come from the use of a crude cell-free system, developed mainly by Zamecnik, Hoagland, and their associates; this system permitted the study of incorporation of labeled amino acids into peptide linkage. Such cell-free preparations were obtained initially from rat liver but have since been derived from other mammalian tissues and from microorganisms and plants. The general features of preparations from all these sources have proved to be essentially similar. The system consists of the following components: ribosomes, proteins precipitable at pH 5 from supernatant solution

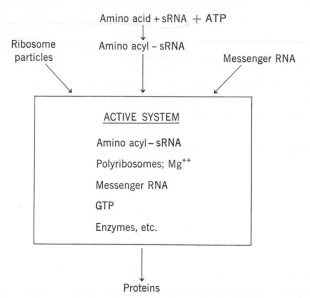

Amino acid + sRNA + ATP

Ribosome particles   Amino acyl – sRNA

                                                          Messenger RNA

ACTIVE SYSTEM

Amino acyl – sRNA

Polyribosomes; Mg^{++}

Messenger RNA

GTP

Enzymes, etc.

Proteins

Fig. 30.1.   A schematic representation of the main features of protein biosynthesis. Each sRNA, specific for a single amino acid, presumably bears a sequence of three nucleotide bases complementary to a similar triplet in mRNA. Amino acids are transferred from their attachment to the sRNA to form the polypeptide sequence through the intervention of mRNA, which is attached to a polyribosome unit.

of a broken cell suspension, sRNA, ATP, GTP, amino acids, Mg^{++}, and soluble enzymes.

Formation of Amino Acyl–sRNA Compounds. This first step of protein synthesis, discovered by Hoagland, involves formation of an enzyme-bound amino acyl–adenylate complex [reaction (1)]. This is followed by transfer of the amino acyl moiety to a specific sRNA [reaction (2)]. Both steps are catalyzed by a single enzyme, an *amino acyl synthetase*, which is essentially specific for the amino acid involved as well as for the sRNA acceptor.

$$\text{Amino acid} + \text{ATP} + \text{enzyme} \rightleftharpoons \text{amino acyl-AMP-enzyme} + \text{PP}_i \qquad (1)$$
$$\text{Amino acyl-AMP-enzyme} + \text{sRNA} \rightleftharpoons \text{amino acyl-sRNA} + \text{AMP} + \text{enzyme} \quad (2)$$

Sum: $$\text{Amino acid} + \text{ATP} + \text{sRNA} \rightleftharpoons \text{amino acyl-sRNA} + \text{AMP} + \text{PP}_i$$

The net result of the two reactions is that the carboxyl group of the amino acid is linked by an ester bond to a hydroxyl group of the ribose of a terminal adenylic acid residue of the sRNA. It is unknown as yet whether it is the 2'- or 3'-hydroxyl group of the ribosyl group which is linked to the amino acid.

Thus, the mechanism of activation of the carboxyl groups in reaction (1) resembles that of acetic acid (page 316) and of fatty acids (page 440). Specific enzymes for individual amino acids have been separated, and several have been highly purified. Separation of reactions (1) and (2) has not been achieved, indicating that a single synthetase catalyzes both steps for each amino acid. If, however, sRNA is omitted from the reaction mixture, amino acyl adenylate can be detected in amounts equivalent to that of the enzyme.

Specificity for Amino Acids. There are two aspects to the enzymic specificity involved in formation of the amino acyl–sRNA compounds: formation of amino acyl–AMP–enzyme and transfer to sRNA. A variety of synthetic amino acyl adenylates can be utilized by *tryptophanyl-sRNA synthetase* for the reverse of reaction (1), *i.e.*, for ATP formation as induced by addition of PP_i and the synthetase. However, only L-tryptophanyl adenylate is a substrate for amino acyl–sRNA formation. Similarly, *isoleucyl-sRNA synthetase* catalyzes $ATP-PP_i$ exchange with either L-isoleucine or L-valine, but the purified enzyme catalyzes formation of the sRNA compound only with L-isoleucine. The formation of the sRNA compound appears in each case to be specific for a *single* natural amino acid and is of great importance inasmuch as these compounds are directly involved in transfer of the amino acid residues to their proper sites in the protein. However, the amino acyl synthetases do not have absolute specificity for their amino acid substrates, as indicated by the reported incorporation into certain proteins of such analogues as *p*-fluorophenylalanine, ethionine, selenomethionine, norleucine, and others.

Evidence has been provided that the template on which the protein is to be synthesized interacts only with the specific sRNA and not with the attached amino acyl portion of the compound. This was shown in an experiment suggested by Benzer to Lipmann and coworkers who utilized C^{14}-labeled cysteinyl-sRNA. This substance was oxidized to the corresponding cysteic acid derivative.

$$HS-CH_2-\overset{\overset{\displaystyle NH_3^+}{|}}{CH}-\overset{\overset{\displaystyle }{\underset{\underset{\displaystyle O}{\|}}{C}}}-sRNA \xrightarrow[\text{acid}]{\text{performic}} {}^-O-\overset{\overset{\displaystyle O}{\|}}{\underset{\underset{\displaystyle O}{\|}}{S}}-CH_2-\overset{\overset{\displaystyle NH_3^+}{|}}{CH}-\overset{\overset{\displaystyle }{\underset{\underset{\displaystyle O}{\|}}{C}}}-sRNA$$

Addition of this compound to a preparation of rabbit reticulocytes capable of forming hemoglobin in vitro showed that the characteristic peptides, obtained by tryptic digestion, which ordinarily contain cysteine now contain cysteic acid. Thus, "recognition" of the amino acyl–sRNA by the protein-synthesizing system depends only on the sRNA bearing the residue, not on the attached amino acyl group. Further evidence for this conclusion is presented later (page 609).

Specificity of sRNA. At least one specific sRNA molecule must exist for each of the 20 amino acids to account for the specificity of protein synthesis. Different types of sRNA have been separated by countercurrent distribution and by column chromatography. Furthermore, it has been demonstrated that for some amino acids, *e.g.*, leucine, methionine, and others, there is more than one specific sRNA. Since there must be at least one "code word" for each amino acid–specific sRNA, this evidence indicates the existence of alternate codes and of some degeneracy in the code (page 596).

In view of the specificity of the different types of sRNA, it is noteworthy that at the acceptor end of sRNA preparations studied thus far, there is an identical trinucleotide sequence, which can be written as: RNApCpCpA. (For this method of describing polyribonucleotides, see page 171.)

It has also been shown that the nonacceptor end of each RNA chain is generally guanosine 5′-monophosphate. It is evident that the specificity must then reside in the interior of the chain of each sRNA. Berg and his coworkers have shown with several types of sRNA from *Escherichia coli* that there are differences in sequence in the first six nucleotide residues of isoleucyl-sRNA and two types of leucyl-sRNA. Whether these particular sequences are involved in the specificity of the synthetases or in amino acid transfer is as yet unknown.

The simplest explanation of the specificity of amino acid transfer into the correct position in a polypeptide chain is binding of a portion of the sRNA, such as a triplet sequence of nucleotides, with a complementary triplet on the completely assembled system of the ribosomes. Such complementarity would be dependent on pairing as a result of hydrogen bonding and other forces, similar to that in DNA, except that uracil (U) in both sRNA and mRNA replaces the thymine of DNA. The triplet binding between the chains would involve the base pairs G-C and A-U.

The sRNA molecules possess considerable intramolecular organization as judged by a large hyperchromic effect (page 177) on heating. X-ray diffraction, as well as other studies, indicates that each sRNA molecule of approximately 70 nucleotides is partly helical and partly nonhelical in structure and that in a non-helical portion there are at least three unpaired bases. It has been suggested that these could serve as a coding area and a "recognition site" if sRNA acceptors for different amino acids differ in base sequence at this site.

In summary, studies of the formation of amino acyl–sRNA indicate that reaction specificity depends on the amino acyl synthetases and their capacity to distinguish among specific amino acids as well as among sRNA molecules with unique sequences. For subsequent transfer of the amino acid, it is only a specific part of the structure of the sRNA that is "recognized" by the protein-synthesizing system, since for each specific sRNA, the amino acid is linked to an identical unit, a terminal adenylic acid residue linked to a cytidylyl-cytidylyl sequence.

Ribosomes and rRNA. The first in vitro studies of amino acid incorporation into proteins by Zamecnik and coworkers clearly showed that certain cytoplasmic particles were essential for this process, and, indeed, that the labeled amino acids became attached to these particles. In preparations from animal tissues, particularly liver, amino acid–incorporating activity is associated with *microsomes* (page 270). However, such microsomal preparations not only are functionally heterogeneous, *i.e.*, capable of performing many kinds of metabolic reactions, but can be subfractionated. Protein biosynthesis was found to be associated with nucleoprotein particles, called *ribosomes*. In animal cells most of the ribosomes are attached to membranes representing the endoplasmic reticulum (page 269). When the microsomal fraction is treated with a detergent such as deoxycholate, lipoproteins are dissolved, and the ribosomes may be isolated by sedimentation in the ultracentrifuge. Small numbers of ribosomes have been reported to occur in the nucleus.

Ribosomes of bacterial cells are readily isolated, free of detectable amounts of other cellular components, by repetitive differential ultracentrifugation. Ribosomes of *E. coli* consist almost entirely of ribonucleoprotein in which the rRNA content is approximately 60 to 65 per cent; ribosomes from mammalian and plant sources contain 40 to 50 per cent rRNA. Ribosomes show very characteristic components in the analytical ultracentrifuge, the kinds and amounts being strongly dependent on the Mg^{++} concentration. Ribosomes from *E. coli* show four components. In 0.01 M Mg^{++} the material consists for the most part of two boundaries with sedimentation constants of 70 S and 100 S (S = Svedberg units, page 135). In $0.001M$ Mg^{++} chiefly 70 S particles are present, with some 30 S and 50 S. In the presence of low concentration of Mg^{++}, $0.0001M$ or less, principally 30 S and 50 S particles are present. Electron micrographs as well as sedimentation studies indicate that one 30 S and one 50 S particle can combine to give a 70 S particle. Two 70 S particles yield one 100 S ribosome.

These nucleoprotein particles may be dissociated by extraction with phenol or detergents to yield rRNA and protein in separate fractions. The rRNA from the 30 S particles is a molecule with 16.3 S ($M = 5.6 \times 10^5$), and from the 50 S particles the rRNA consists of 23.5 S material ($M = 1.1 \times 10^6$). Both types of RNA exhibit identical absorption spectra, hyperchromicity, and nucleotide composition. The composition of rRNA from *E. coli* is given in Table 30.1. Essentially similar values for rRNA from other sources have also been obtained. Ribosomal proteins from different species resemble one another, although there is marked heterogeneity of the material as judged by determination of amino end groups and other criteria.

Rich and his coworkers have obtained evidence by sedimentation studies and electron micrographs with extracts of rabbit reticulocytes that protein is synthesized on an aggregate of ribosomes (170 S), five or more in number. This *polyribosome*, or *polysome*, is held together by a thread of RNA, probably mRNA (see below). Treatment with ribonuclease destroys the thread of RNA, but not rRNA, liberating the individual ribosomes and terminating protein synthesis.

Messenger RNA (mRNA). The abundance of RNA in cytoplasm and recognition of its important role in protein synthesis suggested that the genetic information of nuclear DNA is somehow transmitted to an RNA which functions at the sites of protein synthesis. sRNA is excluded from the role of carrier from DNA of genetic information for protein synthesis by virtue of its small size, 70 nucleotides, which could not transmit the information required for the synthesis of proteins containing as many as several hundred amino acid residues. Furthermore, the specificity of sRNA for reaction with single amino acids also excludes it from a role as genetic carrier. rRNA cannot so serve inasmuch as the gross DNA composition of a variety of microorganisms varies considerably (the observed A + T to G + C ratio being from approximately 0.35 to 2.70, Table 10.2, page 185), whereas the nucleotide composition of rRNA from similar sources is remarkably constant and does not reflect the DNA composition of the source of rRNA.

In 1961, Jacob and Monod postulated that control of protein formation, at least in certain microorganisms, is determined by the rate of synthesis of templates. This requires that the templates be somewhat unstable and that they do not accumulate, in contrast to the relatively constant presence of DNA, sRNA, and rRNA. They suggested, therefore, the transient existence of a new material, probably an RNA, which they called "the messenger," or mRNA. Such an RNA could represent no more than a small percentage of the total RNA of the cell, most of which can be accounted for as rRNA and sRNA. This prediction has been amply verified.

As early as 1948, S. S. Cohen observed that in cells of *E. coli* infected with bacteriophage T2, there was no significant *net* synthesis of RNA; nevertheless, about 1 to 3 per cent of the total RNA showed rapid incorporation of labeled nucleotides. Volkin and Astrachan in 1956 then demonstrated not only that this newly formed RNA is different from the bulk *E. coli* RNA but also that the nucleotide composition of the newly formed RNA is very similar to that of bacteriophage DNA, with uracil taking the place of thymine of DNA (see also below). Later, others found that the newly formed RNA is present in ribosomes when the Mg^{++} concentration is high but that if it is lowered, the new RNA could be separated readily from the ribosomes. Study of this process has indicated that the newly formed mRNA carries the genetic information for protein synthesized during phage infection. It has also been shown that in uninfected bacteria exposed for a short time to P^{32}, RNA with base ratios similar to those of DNA is formed, although U is present in place of T. These rapidly formed mRNA molecules appear to be genetic messengers, as suggested by Jacob and Monod.

Table 30.1 presents the base compositions of the nucleic acids of normal and phage-infected cells of *E. coli*. Only the mRNA molecules resemble in composition the appropriate DNA. This is particularly striking for phage-infected cells, in which the virus inhibits production of normal mRNA and utilizes host ribosomes for production of its own protein.

Table 30.1: NUCLEOTIDE COMPOSITION OF DNA AND RNA IN NORMAL AND BACTERIOPHAGE-INFECTED *Escherichia coli*

	Moles per 100 moles					Purine	A + T (or U)
	A	C	G	U or T	Minor bases	Pyrimidine	G + C
Normal cells:							
DNA	24–25	25–26	25–26	24–25	....	0.96–1.04	0.92–1.00
rRNA	25.2	21.6	31.5	21.7	....	1.30	0.88
mRNA	25.1	24.1	27.1	23.7	....	1.09	0.95
sRNA	20.3	28.9	32.1	15.0	3.7	1.12	0.64
Phage-infected cells:							
T2 DNA	32	17*	18	32	....	0.98	1.83
mRNA	31	17	20	31	....	1.06	1.68

* Hydroxymethylcytosine (see Table 10.5, page 185).

SOURCE: The data are from the work of several investigators and were compiled by F. Gros, W. Gilbert, H. H. Hiatt, G. Attardi, P. F. Spahr, and J. D. Watson in *Cold Spring Harbor Symp. Quant. Biol.,* **26,** 111, 1961.

The most direct evidence that mRNA is a complementary copy of DNA was obtained by Hall and Spiegelman. When DNA of T2 bacteriophage was heated, the helices separated and single strands were formed (page 177). When slowly cooled in the presence of mRNA made by *E. coli* infected with T2 bacteriophage, hybrid DNA-RNA double-stranded helices were detected by density gradient centrifugation in CsCl. When a sample of the same mRNA was heated with genetically unrelated DNA, no evidence was obtained for hybrid formation. This suggests that base pairing occurs between complementary strands of DNA and the related mRNA to form a double-stranded molecule, analogous in structure to double-stranded DNA.

The mRNA molecules of *E. coli* are heterogeneous in size and have molecular weights in the range of 200,000 to 500,000 or higher. Such sizes would appear to be adequate for containing the information necessary for protein synthesis.

5-Fluorouracil, added to *E. coli* cells, is rapidly incorporated into mRNA in place of uracil residues. This pyrimidine analogue is, of course, not incorporated into DNA, sRNA, or rRNA when the experiments are limited to short periods, *e.g.*, 1 min. at 37°C. However, the average amino acid composition of newly synthesized proteins is modified, and this leads to the production of altered enzymes. These experiments cannot be explained by postulating alterations of preexisting RNA components and are consonant with an effect on rapidly renewable molecules, such as those of mRNA.

Enzymic Synthesis of mRNA. Independently, Hurwitz, Weiss, Stevens, and their associates described an enzyme, *RNA polymerase,* which catalyzes formation of an RNA whose base composition reflects that of the DNA present in the system. Thus, this synthetic system for RNA formation fulfills the criteria for mRNA formation.

$$
\begin{array}{c}
mATP \\
+ \\
nGTP \\
+ \\
nCTP \\
+ \\
mUTP
\end{array}
\xrightarrow[\text{Mg}^{++}]{\text{DNA}}
\begin{array}{c}
mAMP \\
| \\
nGMP \\
| \\
nCMP \\
| \\
mUMP
\end{array}
+ \quad 2(m + n)PP_i
$$

The reaction is completely dependent on the presence of DNA; if DNA is omitted or treated first with deoxyribonuclease, no reaction occurs. All RNA preparations are inactive as primers in the system. Synthesis of RNA occurs only when all four ribonucleoside triphosphates are present. The synthesized RNA has normal 3'-5' phosphodiester linkages. Most strikingly, the composition of the synthesized RNA reflects that of added DNA. This suggests that nucleotide incorporation is dependent on ability of the bases of the ribonucleotides to pair with the bases in the primer DNA, by a mechanism similar to that for DNA replication and found for the action of DNA polymerase (page 588).

Table 30.2 shows the ribonucleotide incorporation obtained when different DNA preparations are used as primers. The ratio (A + U)/(C + G) in the RNA

Table 30.2: COMPOSITION OF RNA SYNTHESIZED IN PRESENCE OF DIFFERENT DNA PREPARATIONS

DNA added	$\dfrac{A + T}{C + G}$ in DNA	Nucleotide incorporation in mμmoles				$\dfrac{A + U}{C + G}$ observed	$\dfrac{A + G}{U + C}$
		AMP	UMP	GMP	CMP		
T2 phage	1.86*	0.54	0.59	0.31	0.30	1.85	0.96
Thymus	1.35	3.10	3.30	2.0	2.2	1.52	0.93
Escherichia coli . .	1.0	2.70	2.74	2.90	2.94	0.93	0.98
Micrococcus	0.40	0.55	0.52	1.10	1.12	0.48	1.01

* Contains hydroxymethylcytosine instead of cytosine (Table 10.5, page 185).

SOURCE: J. Hurwitz, J. J. Furth, M. Anders, P. J. Ortiz, and J. T. August, in *Cold Spring Harbor Symp. Quant. Biol.,* **26,** 91, 1961.

formed is identical with the ratio $(A + T)/(C + G)$ of the DNA added, despite the wide range of compositions of the DNA primers. Furthermore, the synthesized RNA resembles DNA in possessing a ratio of purines to pyrimidines $[(A + G)/(U + C)]$ equal to one. Thus, these compositions correspond to those expected for messenger RNA and do not resemble the compositions of sRNA or rRNA.

Of particular interest are experiments performed with the single-stranded DNA of the bacterial virus φX-174. The viral DNA has the relative base composition: $A = 1$, $T = 1.33$, $G = 0.98$, and $C = 0.75$. On the basis of complementarity, the synthesized RNA would have the expected composition $U = 1$, $A = 1.33$, $C = 0.98$, and $G = 0.75$, where the base pairing would be $A \rightarrow U$, $T \rightarrow A$, $G \rightarrow C$, and $C \rightarrow G$. This prediction was fulfilled as found by Hurwitz and coworkers. Chamberlin and Berg reported similar results, but, in addition, they also used the double-stranded DNA of φX-174, which had been synthesized with the DNA polymerase, using the single-stranded DNA as a primer. With this double-stranded DNA which has the composition of the *average* of the two complementary strands and where $A = T$ and $G = C$, the synthesized RNA had a base composition identical with that of the DNA primer, except that U replaces T. These experiments furnish further evidence to support the view that the RNA polymerase synthesizes RNA which is complementary to that of the DNA present and that under these conditions both strands of the viral DNA serve as templates for RNA synthesis with the isolated enzymic system. However, evidence has been obtained by hybridization studies that mRNA formed in vivo is complementary to only one strand of DNA. This is in accord with present information concerning the code (page 610).

A particularly striking instance of the copying ability of the RNA polymerase has been demonstrated by Hurwitz and coworkers with a pneumococcal DNA with transforming activity (page 186). With the four nucleoside triphosphates and the enzyme, an RNA was formed which proved to be phenotypically active as a *transforming factor*. Clearly, the biologically active RNA synthesized in vitro acts as a messenger for formation of the essential enzyme.

The above investigations indicate a mechanism for copying genetic DNA and for forming a messenger RNA which is active in protein synthesis. The RNA polymerase is of exceedingly wide distribution; it has been found in a variety of microorganisms and in various animal and plant tissues.

The Transfer Enzyme. Although certain of the factors involved in protein synthesis are known, many facets of the process are still obscure. Reconstructed systems are being used to investigate the role of other components in the over-all process. A crude *minimal* in vitro system which yields some incorporation of labeled amino acids into peptide bonds can be reconstructed as follows: (1) a mixture of the various amino acyl–sRNA compounds; (2) washed ribosomes; (3) GTP; (4) factors from the supernatant solution. The amino acyl–sRNA compounds also may be formed in the system from sRNA, amino acids, ATP, and proteins precipitated at pH 5 from supernatant solutions of broken cells (page 269). Active minimal amino acid–incorporating systems have been obtained from mammalian liver, from growing plants such as pea seedlings, from bacterial cells, from reticulocytes, and from other sources. The reticulocyte system is a particularly favorable one since the major protein formed is globin or hemoglobin, which can be isolated and studied separately.

Transfer of amino acids from their sRNA linkages to the ribosome requires an enzyme from the supernatant fraction. This *transfer enzyme* has been partially purified from *E. coli*, reticulocytes, and liver. The enzyme from most sources appears to require a sulfhydryl compound, such as glutathione, for stabilization. Whether one or more specific enzymes is involved in this process is still uncertain. The precise role of GTP is unknown; it is utilized in the transfer process since a mixture of GMP and GDP is formed experimentally. Available evidence suggests that one equivalent of GTP is consumed for each equivalent of amino acid transferred to the ribosome from amino acyl–sRNA.

The transfer enzyme appears to show species specificity with respect to the source of the ribosomes. For example, with amino acyl–sRNA from *E. coli*, *E. coli* transfer enzyme was not effective with rat liver ribosomes, nor was rat liver transfer enzyme effective with *E. coli* ribosomes. However, with *E. coli* amino acyl–sRNA, transfer occurred with rat liver enzyme to rat liver ribosomes.

OTHER ASPECTS OF RIBONUCLEIC ACID SYNTHESIS

The previous discussion has indicated that there are at least three known types of RNA involved in protein biosynthesis, *viz.*, sRNA, rRNA, and mRNA. Only in the case of mRNA is there definite information concerning the specificity of its formation and the responsible enzyme. This has been discussed above.

Spiegelman and his coworkers have used the hybridization technique (page 603) to study the relationship of DNA of *E. coli* to both sRNA and rRNA. With uniformly labeled RNA containing P^{32} or tritiated uridine, rRNA and the total sRNA were isolated. Each of these types of RNA was then heated with DNA under conditions which could break hydrogen bonds and permit mixed nucleic acid hybrid formation. Hybrid formation, detected by density gradient sedimentation in CsCl, was found to occur between rRNA and DNA and the total sRNA and DNA of homologous origin. When hybridization was attempted between an RNA and a DNA of genetically unrelated species, no hybrids could be detected.

These findings indicate the existence of complementary sequences in DNA and the three types of RNA, *viz.*, sRNA, rRNA, and, as previously indicated, mRNA, (page 604), suggesting that all types of RNA originate on DNA templates. In essence, the role of DNA as genetic material can then be stated as providing templates not only for self-replication but for the synthesis of all types of RNA. Only mRNA provides coding information for specific sequences of amino acids (see section below on synthetic mRNA). The portion of DNA concerned with synthesis of rRNA and the specific sRNA molecules represents only a small part of the total DNA in *E. coli*. For sRNA this is estimated to be approximately 0.02 per cent of the DNA. From the size of each sRNA, this is calculated to be the equivalent of at least 40 types of sRNA, indicating considerable degeneracy in the code. For rRNA, this is approximately 0.15 per cent of the DNA.

It is assumed that all RNA must be synthesized by polymerases in the nucleus since DNA is present only in the nucleus. RNA-forming polymerases have been obtained from various microorganisms, but the mode of action and the specificity of these various enzymic preparations are still unknown.

sRNA. Although sRNA is presumably formed on DNA templates, the synthesis of these molecules poses several problems since they contain unusual nucleotides (page 183). Borek and Hurwitz and their coworkers have obtained evidence that methylation of various bases occurs after polynucleotide formation. Methionine is the source of the methyl groups. It is of interest that the thymine ribonucleotides of sRNA are formed by methylation of bound uridine nucleotides whereas the thymine of DNA is formed by methylation of free dUMP (page 577).

Formation of pseudouridine may also occur at the polynucleotide level, but the mode of synthesis is unknown.

Polynucleotide Phosphorylase. The first enzyme discovered which catalyzes formation of polyribonucleotides was described in 1955 by Grunberg-Manago and Ochoa. This *polynucleotide phosphorylase* was obtained initially from *Azotobacter vinelandii* and subsequently from other microorganisms; however, it is absent or present at negligible levels in tissues of higher plants and animals. The over-all reaction catalyzed is

$$n(\text{XRPP}) \underset{}{\overset{\text{Mg}^{++}}{\rightleftharpoons}} (\text{XRP})_n + n\text{P}_i$$

where R is ribose, P is phosphate, and X is a purine or pyrimidine base. The internucleotide linkages are 3'–5', as in RNA. The polymerization will occur with a single nucleoside diphosphate, *e.g.*, ADP, UDP, or with a mixture of diphosphates. The action of the enzyme is in some respects analogous to that of glycogen phosphorylase (page 414).

The availability of the polynucleotide phosphorylase has permitted synthesis of high molecular weight polymers which have been useful as model compounds for study of nucleic acids in general. Studies of the interaction of poly A and poly U and of poly I (inosinic acid) and poly C showed complementary base pairing in the manner predicted by Watson and Crick for the two-stranded structure of DNA (page 175). Such polymers have also been used for study of the optical properties and hyperchromicity of polynucleotides and their behavior toward various enzymes. Interestingly, when mixed polynucleotides are formed, they appear to be essentially random in composition with respect to the distribution of the various nucleotides, in contrast to the directed synthesis catalyzed by the RNA polymerase (pages 604*ff.*) which is dependent on the presence of DNA. Polymers prepared with the aid of polynucleotide phosphorylase have proved to be of great utility as synthetic "messengers" (see below).

The limited biological distribution of polynucleotide phosphorylase, as well as the fact that its action is reversible, suggests that it may play a role in degradation or regulation rather than in synthesis of RNA.

EFFECT OF SYNTHETIC POLYNUCLEOTIDES AS mRNA ON AMINO ACID INCORPORATION

The role of mRNA in protein biosynthesis and its formation under the influence of DNA have been considered (pages 602*ff.*). More direct evidence for the participation of such messengers has been obtained by use of cell-free systems. Nirenberg and Matthaei utilized crude extracts of *E. coli* freed of DNA by treatment with DNase and containing sRNA, amino acyl synthetases, transfer enzymes, and ribosomes with added GTP and amino acids. Amino acid incorporation was strongly stimulated by addition of ribosomal RNA from the same species as well as by heterologous RNA from yeast or tobacco mosaic virus (TMV). Presumably, minimal amino acid incorporation always occurs because even washed ribosomes contain some bound mRNA. When a mixture of unlabeled amino acids with C^{14}-valine was used, incorporation of valine into protein was increased seventy-five-fold by addition of TMV-RNA. Part of the synthesized protein formed a specific precipitate with an antiserum to TMV protein.

Synthetic Polynucleotides and the Code. A direct approach to the nature of the code was provided by Nirenberg and Matthaei when they reported in 1961 that the synthetic polyribonucleotide, poly U, greatly increased incorporation of C^{14}-phenylalanine into a product insoluble in trichloroacetic acid and indicated to be polyphenylalanine. Of 18 amino acids tested, only phenylalanine incorporation was markedly stimulated. Incorporation was inhibited by inhibitors of protein synthesis, *e.g.*, chloramphenicol and puromycin, and by ribonuclease but not by deoxyribonuclease. Phenylalanyl-sRNA was an intermediate in the system.

From the above, it is apparent that some portion of poly U codes for phenylalanine. If a triplet code is assumed, then the code for a single residue of phenylalanine is 3U, or UUU. To determine other code compositions, polynucleotides of mixed composition have been employed. In order to illustrate the approach used, the work of Ochoa and coworkers with poly UG may be cited. Mixed polynucleotides were prepared with *polynucleotide phosphorylase* and the nucleoside diphosphates. Since the polymer was prepared with a reaction mixture containing 5 parts UDP to 1 of GDP, the poly UG was assumed to contain the respective bases U and G in a ratio of 5:1. With this poly UG, incorporation of cysteine, valine, leucine, glycine, and tryptophan was stimulated, in addition to phenylalanine. The experimentally determined ratios proved to be Phe/CySH = 5; Phe/Val = 5; and Phe/Leu = 8. Thus the code compositions for cysteine, valine, and leucine are assigned the composition 2U1G, since the theoretically expected ratio for this composition is 5. Similarly, the experimentally found ratios were Phe/Gly = 24 and Phe/Try = 20, as compared with the theoretical value of 25 for the composition 1U2G.

In the same manner assignments have been made for all 20 amino acids. In Table 30.3 triplet compositions are listed as derived from the work in three laboratories. It is noteworthy that considerable degeneracy (page 596) has already been found; incorporation of certain amino acids is stimulated by polymers of different composition. However, there is some uncertainty of code compositions where low levels of incorporation were observed.

Code Sequences. The use of randomly polymerized ribonucleotides can indicate code compositions but cannot yield information concerning code sequences. For this problem it is essential to use polymers in which the base sequence is known. A preliminary approach to this problem has been reported by Ochoa and coworkers, who prepared polymers in which a single A is attached to a homo U

Table 30.3: SOME CODE COMPOSITIONS DERIVED FROM STUDIES WITH SYNTHETIC
POLYRIBONUCLEOTIDES

Amino acid	Probable code compositions	Amino acid	Probable code compositions
Alanine	CUG,CAG,CCG	Leucine	UAU,UUC,UGU
Arginine	GUC,GAA,GCC	Lysine	AAA,AUA,ACA,AAG
Asparagine	UAA,CUA,CAA	Methionine	UGA
Aspartic acid	GUA,GCA	Phenylalanine	UUU,UUC
Cysteine	GUU	Proline	CCC,CUC,CAC,CCG
Glutamic acid	AAG,AUG	Serine	CUU,CCU,ACG,UCG
Glutamine	AGG,ACA	Threonine	CAC,CAA,CGC,UAC
Glycine	GUG,GAG,GCG	Tryptophan	UGG
Histidine	ACC,AUC	Tyrosine	AUU
Isoleucine	UUA,AAU	Valine	UUG

SOURCE: These data have been compiled from the results of Ochoa and coworkers, Nirenberg and coworkers, and Bretscher and Grunberg-Manago. The sequence of the three code letters in each triplet is arbitrary.

polymer, *i.e.*, ApUpUp $\cdots$ UpUpU, where the A bears the unesterified 3′—OH group. This polymer produced, as expected, a large stimulation of phenylalanine incorporation, and in addition, a small stimulation of tyrosine. There was no stimulation of incorporation of isoleucine, leucine, asparagine, or lysine, amino acids whose incorporation is stimulated by UA copolymers.

In the isolated polypeptides, only phenylalanine was found at the amino-terminal end, whereas both phenylalanine and tyrosine were found at the carboxyl end. Inasmuch as peptide synthesis commences at the amino end of the chain, the polypeptide and the polynucleotide can be represented as colinear in the following manner.

$$\text{H}_2\text{NPhe—Phe—Phe} \cdots \cdots \cdots \text{TyrCOOH}$$
$$\text{UUU} \quad \text{UUU UUU} \qquad \qquad \text{UUA}$$

Unfortunately, in a previously defined convention, the sequence of this polynucleotide is written ApUpU $\cdots$ UpUpU (page 171). In order to read the coding in the same direction as peptide synthesis, it would be desirable to use the convention as given above with a direct relationship to amino acid sequence.

Code Specificity and sRNA. The present view suggests that an amino acyl–sRNA becomes attached to the ribosome, presumably by a triplet complementary to a triplet of the mRNA. For example, since the mRNA code for phenylalanine is UUU, the sRNA triplet which attaches to the mRNA is expected to be AAA. Additional residues of amino acyl–sRNA are attached with peptide bond formation along the length of the template mRNA. This presupposes, as much evidence suggests, that there is no overlapping of triplets and that there is colinearity of synthesized polypeptide, beginning at the amino-terminal residue, to the template mRNA. Furthermore, that the sRNA bears complementary coding is indicated by the experiment in which cysteinyl-sRNA was oxidized to the cysteic acid derivative but cysteic acid was, nevertheless, incorporated in place of cysteine. Additional studies with amino acyl–sRNA in conjunction with polyribonucleotides have confirmed this. C¹⁴-labeled cysteinyl-sRNA was desulfurized with Raney nickel and converted to C¹⁴-alanyl-sRNA. Poly UG stimulates the incorporation of cysteine but not of alanine (Table 30.3). When Ala-sRNA^{CySH} was tested with poly UG, there was strong incorporation, but not when Ala-sRNA^{Ala} was used. (The superscript refers to the type of sRNA.) It is evident from these results that sRNA serves as an adaptor in specifying the fit of an amino acid on a template. Once attached to sRNA, the amino acid side chain can be altered but the coding properties of the sRNA remain unchanged.

Leucine incorporation is stimulated by poly UC and by poly UG (Table 30.3). At least two sRNA acceptors for leucine from *E. coli* (page 601) have been separated by countercurrent distribution. Holley and coworkers demonstrated that incorporation of leucine attached to one sRNA is stimulated by poly UC, whereas leucine attached to the other sRNA responds to poly UG. These experiments confirm that coding specificity resides in the sRNA and in the mRNA and provide proof that there are at least two distinct leucine codes.

As already noted (page 605), only one strand of DNA appears to be active in the in vivo formation of mRNA. Information on the code is in accord with these observations. If both strands of DNA were active in forming mRNA, complementary codes of mRNA, *e.g.*, UUU for phenylalanine and AAA for lysine, would create ambiguities in the insertion of these two amino acids. Since peptide chains are uniquely determined, only one chain of DNA appears to be involved in mRNA formation. Thus it appears that the double-stranded structure of DNA is essential for its replication, but not for its role as a template in determining the sequence of mRNA, and hence for its role in protein biosynthesis.

It should be emphasized that mRNA is functional as a template only when attached to the ribosomes. The precise roles of ribosomal RNA and of ribosomal proteins in protein biosynthesis remain to be elucidated.

REFERENCES

See list following Chap. 31.

31. Genetic Aspects of Metabolism

Variation of Protein Structure. Control of Protein Synthesis. Hereditary Disorders of Metabolism

GENETIC VARIATION OF PROTEIN STRUCTURE

Mutation, whether spontaneous or induced experimentally, alters the DNA and results in a change in the amino acid sequence of the protein whose production is controlled by that DNA. The first clear proof of this was provided by the study of Hb S (sickle cell hemoglobin, page 806), when Ingram demonstrated that a valine residue is substituted for a glutamic acid residue at a unique site in the β chain (page 806). Earlier, it had been shown by Pauling and Itano that Hb A and Hb S differ not only in the solubility of the reduced forms but in electrophoretic mobility. The latter technique has been particularly valuable in detecting hemoglobin variants. Those abnormal hemoglobins for which the amino acid substitutions have been established are listed in Table 31.1. In each case, production of the

Table 31.1: SOME AMINO ACID SUBSTITUTIONS IN HUMAN HEMOGLOBIN

Type of Hb	Position	Residue in		Type of Hb	Position	Residue in	
		Hb A	Mutant			Hb A	Mutant
I	$\alpha16$	Lys	Asp	$G_{San\ José}$	$\beta7$	Glu	Gly
$G_{Honolulu}$	$\alpha30$	Glu	$GluNH_2$	E	$\beta26$	Glu	Lys
$Hb_{Shimonoseki}$	$\alpha54$	$GluNH_2$	Arg	$M_{Saskatoon}$	$\beta63$	His	Tyr
Norfolk	$\alpha57$	Gly	Asp	M_{Zurich}	$\beta63$	His	Arg
M_{Boston}	$\alpha58$	His	Tyr	$M_{Milwaukee}$	$\beta67$	Val	Glu
$G_{Philadelphia}$	$\alpha68$	$AspNH_2$	Lys	D_{Punjab}	$\beta121$	Glu	$GluNH_2$
$O_{Indonesia}$	$\alpha116$	Glu	Lys	Q_{Arabia}	$\beta121$	Glu	Lys
C	$\beta6$	Glu	Lys				
S	$\beta6$	Glu	Val				

SOURCE: Compiled from the work of many investigators. Positions refer to the residue number from the amino-terminus of the α and β chains of Hb A given in Fig. 11.1 (page 195). Many other abnormal hemoglobins, described under different names, have substitutions identical with one of those given above. A more complete listing of abnormal hemoglobins is given by W. A. Schroeder, *Ann. Rev. Biochem.,* **32,** 301, 1963.

variant protein is due to a point mutation representing the minimal alteration in the gene (cistron) and this is inherited in mendelian fashion, the cistrons for the α and β chains being distinct and probably located in different chromosomes. Presumably, the mutations responsible for the changes are alterations in a single base within the coding unit of the DNA and reflected in the complementary mRNA.

When the code compositions for various amino acids are definitely established, it should be possible to use the amino acid substitutions of hemoglobin and other proteins to test the nature of the code compositions in various species. For example, the only valine code presently known is UUG (Table 30.3). To yield the code for glutamic acid, by a single base change, as in Hb M$_{Milwaukee}$ (Table 31.1), the code for glutamic acid is expected to be AUG; a single base change cannot yield AAG, the other code known for glutamic acid. Similarly, the His to Tyr substitution can occur by a single base change only from AUC to AUU. Since the sequence of the bases for Tyr is established (page 609), the sequence for His as AUC is indicated.

It should be emphasized that the codes given in Table 30.3 were determined with the use of synthetic mRNA, utilizing the protein-synthesizing system of *Escherichia coli*. Thus far, only a part of these codes has been established for mammalian systems. It is likely that the codes will prove to be identical in many species ("universality of code"); however, it will be necessary to ascertain which codes are actually operative in a given species. For man the amino acid replacement data will aid in establishing code compositions and sequences.

Inasmuch as DNA contains predominantly only the same four bases, point mutations can be expected to occur in all genetic material and will be reflected in amino acid substitutions in proteins of the same species. Relatively few of these have been reported as yet, partly because the structure of only a few proteins is known and partly because of the difficulty of isolating a pure protein from a single individual. Hemoglobin is a favorable protein for study from both viewpoints.

Yanofsky and coworkers have produced experimentally many mutants of *E. coli* which influence the activity of the A protein of tryptophan synthetase (page 523). This protein and many of its inactive variants have been isolated in pure form, and a number of amino acid substitutions have been reported.

In a single peptide obtained from the A protein, a glycine residue was found to be substituted by Glu or Arg (Fig. 31.1), the enzyme containing either of these residues being totally inactive. A rare recombination by crossing over from the two mutant types yielded the wild-type active enzyme containing glycine. This demonstrates that the base which was altered in the code for Gly must be different in the two cases in order to yield the original code by crossing over. Other mutations from the codes for Glu or Arg have yielded additional substitutions (Fig. 31.1).

These studies have provided important information regarding the code. The cross-over recombination, noted above, provides further evidence that the smallest mutation unit, the *muton* (page 597), is a single base of a nucleotide. As in the case of hemoglobin, mutation alters only a single amino acid, indicating that the code is of the nonoverlapping type (page 597). The finding that at least six different amino acids—Gly, Glu, Arg, Val, Ala, and Ser—can occupy the same locus indicates that the coding unit must be at least a doublet and may be a larger unit.

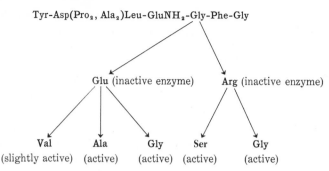

FIG. 31.1. Portion of the peptide sequence of the wild-type A protein of tryptophan synthetase of *Escherichia coli*. Mutations have been found producing the amino acid substitutions indicated with the resulting effects on enzymic activity. (*Adapted from U. Henning and C. Yanofsky, Proc. Nat. Acad. Sci.,* **48**, 1497–1504, 1962.)

It is noteworthy that the enzyme is active with the small neutral residues, Gly, Ala, or Ser, is slightly active with Val, and is inactive with the charged residues, Glu or Arg. As yet, it is unknown whether this sequence is involved in the conformation or active enzymic regions of the A protein.

Tobacco mosaic virus (TMV) RNA, which behaves as an mRNA (page 602), when treated with nitrous acid gives rise to alterations in the sequence of the TMV protein which is synthesized in the host plant by infection with the active RNA alone (page 184). The main effect of nitrous acid on RNA is expected to be deamination of cytosine to uracil and of adenine to hypoxanthine, which functions in base pairing in the same manner as guanine. No effect is expected on uracil, and deamination of guanine would produce xanthine, which either would pair as guanine does or would not pair at all. Studies of this sort, reported independently by Tsugita and Fraenkel-Conrat and by Wittmann, have furnished amino acid replacement data which are particularly valuable in several respects: (1) no amino acid substitution has been found which occurs in both directions; *i.e.,* where residue A replaces residue B, B has not been found to replace A; (2) substitutions for certain amino acids have not been found, *e.g.,* a replacement for phenylalanine. Since the code for Phe is UUU, there is no mechanism by which deamination could alter this code or certain others containing only U or G (xanthine in place of guanine appears to be ineffective).

Amino Acid Substitution and Protein Function. Specific genetic variation in the structure of a protein can furnish valuable information concerning the role of amino acid residues in the function of a specific enzyme or other protein. Human hemoglobin may be used as an example. Certain abnormal hemoglobins were first detected because of the physiological disturbances which they produce. These "hereditary hemoglobinopathies" (Chap. 42) are most striking for carriers of Hb S, Hb M, and others. On the other hand, there are amino acid substitutions which do not appear to have any significant effect on hemoglobin function, *e.g.,* Hb G$_{San José}$, Hb I, Hb G$_{Philadelphia}$ (Table 31.1).

The interpretation of these striking differences in the effects of amino acid substitutions rests on present knowledge of protein structure and function. It is known that the amino- or carboxyl-terminal ends of certain proteins may be entirely dispensable for function (page 161). It has also been shown that chemical treatment which alters certain amino acid side chains may produce no demonstrable effect on the function of certain proteins; *e.g.,* conversion of many or all lysine residues to homoarginine residues by reaction with O-methylisourea does not alter the enzymic activity of ribonuclease, lysozyme, papain, etc. Similarly, other residues of proteins can be acylated, oxidized, or treated in other ways without significant effect on function. Nevertheless, certain groups in enzymes are absolutely critical for their functions, as in the demonstrations of "active sites," elucidated with various types of inhibitors.

Evidently, then, certain residues of proteins are essential for function; others are not. As a *minimum,* we may expect that those residues which are present at "active sites," which are essential for binding substrates, cofactors, or prosthetic groups, or which determine the folding and essential conformation of the peptide chains cannot be altered by genetic or other means without profound effects on function. Examination of the conformation of the myoglobin molecule (page 158) or the chains of hemoglobin (page 194) suggests that the regions where greatest variation in amino acid sequence could occur without disturbance of function are in the sections of the chains which are in the form of an α helix. Indeed, these are the regions in which one would expect to find differences among species. It has long been known that the hemoglobins of vertebrates possess similar functional properties, yet there are substantial differences among them in amino acid composition and other properties which, nevertheless, permit oxygen transport.

Table 31.2 shows the variations found in the structures of the insulins of several mammals. Most of the variations occur in the internal loop of the A chain and at the carboxyl-terminal end of the B chain (Fig. 9.2). The carboxyl-terminal residue may be removed by carboxypeptidase A without loss of insulin activity. Since the variations in the A chain do not affect insulin activity, it may be assumed that the spacing of these residues may be important but that their exact chemical nature is not.

Table 31.2: Amino Acid Substitutions in Insulin

Source	A8*	A9*	A10*	B30*
Beef.............	Ala	Ser	Val	Ala
Pig.............	Thr	Ser	Ileu	Ala
Sheep...........	Ala	Gly	Val	Ala
Horse...........	Thr	Gly	Ileu	Ala
Sperm whale......	Thr	Ser	Ileu	Ala
Sei whale........	Ala	Ser	Thr	Ala
Man.............	Thr	Ser	Ileu	Thr
Dog.............	Thr	Ser	Ileu	Ala
Rabbit..........	Thr	Ser	Ileu	Ser

* Positions refer to the residue number from the amino-terminus of the A or B chain (Fig. 9.2; page 153). Rat insulin resembles that of rabbit but differs in having Asp instead of Glu at A4, Lys instead of AspNH$_2$ at B3, and Lys or Met at B29.

Similar comparative studies have been made on the heart muscle cytochromes c of various species (Table 31.3). As in the case of the insulins, the cytochromes all possess a similar sequence of 104 residues. It must be assumed that the species variations do not influence either the coordination of the heme iron or the conformation of the native protein, since all these are equally active and possess similar properties, *e.g.*, redox potential, absorption spectra, etc. It is noteworthy that variations have been found at 18 positions in the species listed and many more have been found in the cytochromes of the more remotely related tuna fish and yeast. Particularly noteworthy is the presence of only two histidine residues, at positions 18 and 26, in tuna cytochrome. These define the residues which probably coordinate with the heme iron. Other properties of cytochrome c are given on pages 199*ff.* and in Chap. 18.

Evolution and Protein Structure. Comparison of the proteins of various organisms reveals that, during the course of evolution, (1) those proteins which fulfill the same function at all phylogenetic levels, *e.g.*, the enzymes of glycolysis, cytochrome c, etc., synthesis of which is presumed to be directed by homologous genes, have been extensively modified; (2) some proteins have disappeared; and (3) many new proteins have appeared. Since, in the immediate sense, the structure and distribution of proteins constitute the phenotypic character of a species, these three major changes represent the operation of evolution itself.

Few data are at hand which describe a single enzyme or protein at various phylogenetic levels. It is clear, however, that the pentapeptide obtained by tryptic hydrolysis, which includes the functionally significant serine residue of phosphoglucomutase (Table 14.2), is identical in the enzyme obtained from *E. coli,* yeast, and rabbit muscle. However, this enzyme from these diverse sources has many striking differences in amino acid composition, although of approximately the same molecular weight. The enzymically significant sulfhydryl group of triose phosphate dehydrogenase has been found to occur in the same octadecapeptide obtained by proteolysis of the yeast and rabbit muscle enzymes, which are in other respects quite different. It will be apparent that the many amino acid replacements, which have occurred in these proteins as a result of mutagenic forces affecting the homologous DNA, have not impaired their enzymic function. Indeed, the function of phosphoglucomutase has been enhanced, since the turnover number of the rabbit muscle enzyme is considerably greater than that of the yeast or bacterial enzymes.

Most significant, however, is the fact that no change in amino acid composition has occurred in the region of the "active site." Presumably, any substitution at that site which alters its steric fit and substrate-binding capacity or which results in loss of a residue or group participating in the catalytic process (serine, histidine, sulfhydryl group, etc.) must destroy enzymic activity of the protein. Loss of activity might also result from replacement of a proline residue at the turn of a helix or any other substitution that alters the conformation of the protein in a manner affecting the structure at the active site. Presumably, it is just such substitutions which, at some distant time, resulted in loss of specific enzymes, thus making the vertebrates dependent on their food supply for the nutritionally essential amino acids and fatty acids, as well as for the vitamins. Such are the mutations of tryptophan synthetase of *E. coli* (page 612). Although the active site cannot be specified

Table 31.3: AMINO ACID SUBSTITUTIONS IN CYTOCHROME C

	3	11	12	15	44	46	47	50	58	60	62	66	83	88	89	92	103	104
Man.........	Val	Ileu	Met	Ser	Pro	Tyr	Ser	Ala	Ileu	Gly	Asp	Glu	Val	Lys	Glu	Ala	AspNH₂	Glu
Other species..	Ileu	Val	GluNH₂	Ala	Glu	Phe	Thr	Asp	Thr	Lys	Glu	GluNH₂	Ala	Thr	Thr(H) Gly(D,P) Ser(C)	Glu(H,P) Val(C)	Lys	Ser
	(C)	(H,D,C,P)	(H,D,C,P)	(H,D,P)	(C)	(H,C,P)	(H)	(H,D,C,P)	(H,D,C,P,M)	(H)	(H,D,C,P)	(M)	(H,D,P,C)	(D)			(D)	(C)

Note: Residues are numbered from the amino-terminus; C = chicken, H = horse, D = dog, P = pig, and M = monkey [*Macaca mulatta* (rhesus)]. The sequence of human cytochrome c is given in Fig. 11.4 (page 200). Information for the sequences of other cytochromes may be found in the following papers: horse (E. Margoliash, E. L. Smith, G. Kreil, and H. Tuppy, *Nature*, **192**, 1121, 1961); dog (M. McDowall and E. L. Smith, unpublished results); monkey (J. A. Rothfus and E. L. Smith, unpublished results); pig and chicken (E. Margoliash, S. B. Needleman, and J. W. Stewart, *Acta Chem. Scand.*, **17**, S250, 1963). Information for sequences near the heme of other species is given by S. Paléus and H. Tuppy, *Acta Chem. Scand.*, **13**, 631, 1959.

on other grounds, mutants created by irradiation synthesize enzymically inert proteins that are identical with the normal enzyme except for substitution of a single amino acid.

It is not known whether vertebrates continue to synthesize similar functionless genetic derivatives of formerly active proteins which once made possible the synthesis of tryptophan, thiamine, etc. Indeed, it is not known whether the homozygotic alkaptonuric human being who possesses no active homogentisic acid oxidase, the result of a much more recent mutation, synthesizes a homologous protein which is inactive because of one or more amino acid replacements. Not all substitutions at a given site are necessarily deleterious with respect to function, as in some mutant forms of tryptophan synthetase (Fig. 31.1). Indeed, it is clear that there is considerable tolerance for replacement, deletion, or insertion of amino acids in regions other than the active sites of enzymes. Examples of such tolerance are apparent from (1) the specific immunochemical behavior of similar proteins from different species; (2) the fact that many enzymes can tolerate acetylation of amino groups, or conversion of lysine to homoarginine residues by treatment with O-methylisourea; (3) the proteolytic removal of a substantial segment of a polypeptide chain without enzymic inactivation; and (4) the gross differences in chemical composition of phosphoglucomutase and triose phosphate dehydrogenase, cited above.

The protein for which most information is available is cytochrome c, as described previously. Although this protein is not an enzyme, and cannot be said to have an active site in the usual sense, if the protein is to be useful physiologically, it may not be altered by mutation in a manner preventing its "fit" to cytochrome oxidase, changing its potential, or interfering with its capacity for attachment to the heme moiety. Withal, in the time since yeast and man diverged from some common ancestral form, amino acid replacements have accumulated in the proteins of these species, without significant effect on their function in mitochondrial electron transport.

The increased number of proteins synthesized by higher organisms is paralleled by an increase in the amount of DNA in their genomes, and it is assumed that this reflects the occasional duplication of some or all of the genes in an individual organism. When such duplication occurs, that organism possesses for a given protein four rather than two such genes, and thereafter, each pair is free to follow an independent evolutionary path. So long as one pair continues to direct synthesis of the original functional protein, the other may undergo drastic mutational change and, indeed, ultimately become responsible for synthesis of a protein which serves a different function. If the latter offers "survival value" it will be retained and the organism will flourish and perhaps come to occupy a very different ecological niche. The result of such processes has been studied most carefully in the case of hemoglobin.

When the amino acid sequences for the α and β chains of Hb A, the γ chain of Hb F, and the δ chain of Hb A_2 were established, the number of differences among these chains could be summarized as in Table 31.4. When the α and β chains of human Hb A were compared to those of a few other mammals, such as the horse, it was evident that there were fewer differences among α chains than among β chains. Since, moreover, the α chains are common to Hb A, Hb F, and

Table 31.4: Amino Acid Variations in Chains of Human Hemoglobins

Chains compared	Number of variant amino acid residues	Time since divergence from common chain ancestor, years $\times$ 10^6
β; and δ...............	6	44
β; and γ...............	36	260
α; and β...............	78	565
α; and γ...............	83	600

Source: After E. Zuckerkandl and L. Pauling, Molecular Disease, Evolution and Genic Heterogeneity, in M. Kasha and B. Pullman, eds., "Horizons in Biochemistry," Academic Press, New York, 1962.

Hb A_2, Ingram suggested that the α chain might be the oldest of these and might be homologous with the chains of lamprey hemoglobin which is monomeric (Table 34.4, page 672) rather than tetrameric. Hence, from the observed number of differences, it was further suggested that succeeding gene duplications led from α chains to γ, β, and δ, in that sequence. Supporting evidence has come from a study of the hemoglobins of a single order, the primates. Living representatives of this order, according to the paleontological record and their comparative anatomy, appeared in the following sequence: tree shrews, lemurs, lorises, New World monkeys, Old World monkeys, man. The α chains of hemoglobins of representatives of these genera show relatively few amino acid substitutions. The β chains differ increasingly from those of man as one descends to more primitive forms; most

Table 31.5: Alterations in Structure of Cytochrome c

Species compared	Number of variant amino acid residues	Time since divergence from common chain ancestor, years $\times$ 10^6
Man; horse	12	130
Horse; pig	3	33
Horse; chicken	12	100–150
Pig; chicken	10	
Rabbit; chicken	11	
Man; chicken	14	
Horse; tuna	19	180–220
Pig; tuna	17	
Rabbit; tuna	19	
Chicken; tuna	18	
Man; tuna	21	
Man; yeast	43	465–520
Horse; yeast...........	44	
Pig; yeast	43	
Rabbit; yeast	45	
Chicken; yeast	43	
Tuna; yeast	48	

Source: From E. Margoliash, *Proc. Soc. Nat. Acad. Sci.*, **50**, 672, 1963.

striking is the fact that the substitutions occur largely at those positions in which human β chains differ from γ chains. Indeed, the hemoglobins of adult shrews and lemurs resemble human fetal hemoglobin more closely than they resemble human Hb A, including resistance to alkaline denaturation.

An interesting aspect of such studies was noted by Zuckerkandl and Pauling. The paleontological record suggests that man and the horse separated from a common ancestor about 100 to 150 million years ago. The α chains of the hemoglobins of these species differ in 18 positions; assuming that each accumulated 9 such mutations over the intervening years, it follows that such mutations occurred and remained permanent at intervals of about 12 million years. This calculation is in keeping with the number of amino acid substitutions encountered in the β chains of the primates and is also consistent with the number of differences found when the cytochromes c of various species are compared, as shown in Table 31.5.

The polypeptide hormones of the neurohypophysis (Chap. 51) provide another example of the possible evolution of structure and function. The structures of these hormones are given in Table 31.6. The vasotocin of the frog possesses weak activity both as a vasopressin and as an oxytocin, in contrast to the powerful hormones of the mammal and other higher vertebrates. The change from vasotocin to

Table 31.6: AMINO ACID SEQUENCES OF HORMONES OF THE NEUROHYPOPHYSIS

Hormone	Residue position								
	1*	2	3	4	5	6*	7	8	9
Vasotocin	CyS·Tyr·Ileu·GluNH$_2$·AspNH$_2$·CyS·Pro·Arg·GlyNH$_2$								
Vasopressin	CyS·Tyr·Phe·GluNH$_2$·AspNH$_2$·CyS·Pro·Arg·GlyNH$_2$								
Oxytocin	CyS·Tyr·Ileu·GluNH$_2$·AspNH$_2$·CyS·Pro·Leu·GlyNH$_2$								

* The half-cystine residues in positions 1 and 6 are in each case linked by a disulfide bridge.

arginine-vasopressin involves a substitution at position 3 from Ileu to Phe. Similarly, from vasotocin to oxytocin, the change in position 8 is from Arg to Leu. For the evolution from a single hormone to the presence of two or more hormones in the same species, we must assume a duplication of the genetic material, as well as point mutations, in order to have independent production of two or more hormones.

Ultimately, such data must be understood in terms of the slight physiological changes they induce and these placed in the context of the total biology of the species they serve. Meanwhile, it is gratifying to have this biochemical confirmation of the paleontological evidence for evolution. Indeed, it is not excessive to state that such studies provide a view of the fine structure of the evolutionary process.

CONTROL OF PROTEIN SYNTHESIS

In multicellular organisms, control of metabolic rates and pathways is achieved, in part, by hormonal and neural mechanisms which are particularly important in regulating and integrating various tissue and organ systems. Metabolic controls at the cellular level operate by different mechanisms (pages 490*ff.*). Here the discussion is concerned with control of enzyme (protein) synthesis.

Some enzymes are present in cells in large amounts and others in very minute quantities. Since enzyme synthesis is under genetic control, it is of interest to ascertain which genetic and other factors regulate the intracellular concentration of various enzymes. Most of the information presently available has been derived from studies with microorganisms, but less complete studies with mammalian systems indicate that similar factors may be operative.

Induced Enzyme Synthesis. It has long been known that yeast cells grown on glucose do not ferment galactose, but that if galactose is present, such cells will begin to ferment that sugar, after a brief lag period. The phenomenon was originally termed *adaptive enzyme formation* but is now usually called *induced enzyme synthesis.*

Similar induction phenomena have been observed for the formation of enzymes concerned with various aspects of metabolism in microorganisms: formation of *amylases* induced by starch, formation of *tryptophanase* in response to tryptophan, *penicillinase* formation, etc. In mammals, several enzymes have been shown to increase in activity in response to administration of their substrates. Nevertheless, not all enzymes show such changes in activity; many so-called *constitutive enzymes* remain at the same level regardless of the amount of potential inducer added to the cell culture or injected into the animal.

Many features of the induction phenomenon can be illustrated with the *β-galactosidase* of *E. coli.* Formation of the induced enzyme clearly represents a *de novo* synthesis of protein. M. Cohn demonstrated that the level of induced enzymic activity was proportional to the amount of material precipitated by antiserum specific for the galactosidase. It was also shown that induced enzyme is formed from free amino acids in the same manner as in normal protein synthesis, and that the enzyme is not derived from preexisting high molecular weight precursors. Induction begins very rapidly, β-galactosidase synthesis at 37°C. attaining its maximal rate within 3 to 4 min. after addition of inducer. The rate is constant as long as inducer is present and returns to the uninduced rate within a few minutes after removal of the inducer.

The nature of the *inducer* for β-galactosidase has been extensively studied. Some compounds, *e.g.,* methyl β-galactoside, proved to be excellent inducers and poor substrates; other compounds are good substrates and poor inducers. Nevertheless, the enzyme formed is the same regardless of the inducer; the latter does not confer any specificity upon the induced enzyme. Inasmuch as there always is a very small basal amount of enzyme present in uninduced cells, induction represents an increased production of an enzyme for which the cell already possesses the requisite genetic information.

Repression of Enzyme Formation. Enzyme formation can be repressed as well as induced. To illustrate the phenomenon, the pathway of arginine biosynthesis (pages 497*ff.*) may be considered.

$$\text{Glutamic acid} \longrightarrow \text{ornithine} \longrightarrow \text{citrulline} \longrightarrow \text{arginine}$$

$$+$$

$$CO_2 + NH_3 + ATP \longrightarrow \text{carbamyl phosphate}$$

$$+$$

$$\text{aspartic acid} \longrightarrow \text{ureidosuccinic acid}$$

When wild-type cells of *E. coli* are grown on a minimal medium, arginine is formed and the level of *ornithine transcarbamylase* is at a constant value. When arginine is supplied from the medium, the level of this enzyme falls by dilution during subsequent growth of the culture. The presence of arginine represses enzyme formation. When the cells are washed and resuspended in minimal medium, they begin to form the enzyme again. Thus, the phenomenon is the reverse of induction.

The most interesting feature of the phenomenon is the "feedback" aspect of repression. Excess of the amino acid arginine shuts off the entire pathway leading to its synthesis, and it does so at the first committed synthetic step, as already discussed (pages 490*ff.*).

The phenomenon may also be illustrated by the data of Ames and Garry for the biosynthesis of histidine in *Salmonella*. The last four consecutive steps leading to formation of histidine are catalyzed by (1) *imidazoleglycerol phosphate dehydrase*, (2) a *transaminase*, (3) *histidinol phosphate phosphatase*, and (4) *histidinol dehydrogenase* (page 526). When histidine is added in varying amount to wild-type cells or to various types of mutant cells, the relative activity of all four enzymes is decreased in parallel, indicating closely regulated control of their rates of formation.

As in the case of enzyme induction, enzyme formation by *derepression* involves *de novo* synthesis of the enzymes. The genes responsible for the formation of each of the enzymes are always present in the organism. Indeed, in many cases the genes for a given pathway of synthesis are closely linked in the chromosome. In *Salmonella*, Demerec and his colleagues have shown by recombination studies with some 450 histidineless mutants that the genes for the enzymes of histidine synthesis are close together in the chromosome. Similarly, some 77 tryptophanless mutants were utilized to show that the genes for various enzymes of tryptophan synthesis are adjacent to one another.

Mechanism of Induction and Repression. A general hypothesis to account for induction and repression has been proposed by Monod and his colleagues. Their viewpoint may be summarized as follows. (1) Both induction and repression, are primarily negative, *i.e.*, they operate by inhibiting or releasing an inhibition of protein synthesis. (2) It is suggested that there are two classes of genes, *structural genes,* which contain the information for the structures of specific enzymes, and *regulatory genes,* which are primarily concerned with rates of protein synthesis. (3) Several linked structural genes probably represent a functional unit in that they are all active or inactive simultaneously, as in the cases of the several enzymes concerned in histidine biosynthesis mentioned above. (4) It is proposed that the regulatory mechanism functions at the genetic level and therefore controls the rate of synthesis of a relatively short-lived messenger (mRNA).

The view that there are two types of genes seems to be well founded, at least in the case of microorganisms. A mutation in a structural gene influences only the activity of a single enzyme. However, point mutations have been found which lead to a failure of the regulatory mechanisms and hence to a high rate of formation of all the enzymes in a metabolic pathway. Such enzymes then become *constitutive, i.e.*, their concentration is now independent of the presence of inducers or repressors. Furthermore, although mutations in structural genes follow the one gene–one enzyme hypothesis, this is not the case for regulatory genes since the levels of several enzymes may be influenced.

Since genes carry information for synthesis of RNA, it is assumed that a regulatory gene determines the formation of an RNA or of a specific protein which is a regulator of protein synthesis.

Although regulatory genes and repressor mechanisms have been demonstrated only in microorganisms, it may be assumed that they are present in more complex organisms also. Differentiated cells of multicellular organisms possess very different levels of various enzymes; only erthyrocytes synthesize hemoglobin and muscle cells fabricate myosin despite the presumed identity of their genetic complements. Inductive and repressive phenomena may be involved in some of the differences in metabolic rates and in the relative importance of different pathways found in differentiated cells of the same organism.

HEREDITARY DISORDERS OF METABOLISM

When Garrod, in 1908, assembled the known "inborn errors" (page 266), they were few in number. Since then many additional metabolic abnormalities have been described, and the number is growing continuously.

Earlier, attention was focused on instances in which individuals or microorganisms are unable to perform specific metabolic reactions (Chap. 29). From the relationship of the gene to protein synthesis, it is evident that genetic defects represent an alteration (mutation) in DNA leading either to complete failure to produce a protein or to production of a modified protein (enzyme) whose catalytic or other function is impaired or lacking.

For many of the metabolic defects that have been studied in human beings, the anomaly has been traced to the absence of activity of a single enzyme. Table 31.7 presents a list of hereditary disorders in which the lacking or modified enzyme or protein has been identified. Individuals with these disorders are analogous to the mutants in *Neurospora* discussed earlier (Chap. 29), in which a single metabolic reaction is blocked. In man, most of these defects are apparent phenotypically only in the homozygous state. In the heterozygote, with one normal and one mutant gene, there is usually sufficient enzyme to meet physiological needs. Clearly, the older concept of *dominance* can be explained on the basis that one normal gene of each pair can stimulate sufficient protein synthesis to serve the needs of the organism. In heterozygotes with genes for the production of one normal and one abnormal hemoglobin, *e.g.*, Hb A, Hb S, Hb M, etc., there are approximately equal amounts present of each variety. Similarly, the heterozygotic parents of galactosemic infants (page 406) possess approximately 50 per cent of the normal amount of enzyme (galactose 1-phosphate uridyl transferase).

Most of the inherited enzymic abnormalities which have been described represent cases in which a complete metabolic block of some type has occurred. The consequences of such a block may be reflected in different ways: (1) there may be a complete absence of the final product of the pathway, *e.g.*, the lack of melanin in albinism (page 822); (2) there may be an accumulation of an intermediate metabolite for which there is no significant alternate pathway, *e.g.*, certain glycogen storage disorders (page 420) in which glycogen is made but cannot be utilized, or alkaptonuria in which homogentisic acid accumulates (page 548); and (3) there

Table 31.7: SOME HEREDITARY DISORDERS IN MAN IN WHICH THE SPECIFIC LACKING OR MODIFIED ENZYME OR PROTEIN HAS BEEN IDENTIFIED

Disorder	Affected enzyme or protein	Page reference
Acanthocytosis	β-Lipoproteins	639
Acatalasemia	Catalase	
Afibrinogenemia	Fibrinogen	648
Agammaglobulinemia	γ-Globulin	638
Albinism	Tyrosinase	822
Alkaptonuria	Homogentisic acid oxidase	548
Analbuminemia	Serum albumin	643
Argininosuccinic acidemia	Argininosuccinase	513
Galactosemia	Galactose 1-phosphate uridyl transferase	406
Glycogen storage diseases:		
Type I (von Gierke's)	Glucose 6-phosphatase	420
Type III	Amylo-1,6-glucosidase	420
Type IV	Amylo-(1,4 $\longrightarrow$ 1,6)-transglycosylase	420
Type V (McArdle's)	Muscle phosphorylase	420
Type VI (Hers')	Liver phosphorylase	420
Goiter (familial)	Iodotyrosine dehalogenase	834
Hartnup's disease	Tryptophan pyrrolase	553
Hemoglobinopathies	Hemoglobins	805ff.
Hemophilia A	Antihemophilic factor A	652
Hemophilia B	Antihemophilic factor B	652
Histidinemia	Histidase	550
Hyperbilirubinemia (Gilbert's disease)	Uridine diphosphate glucuronate transferase	801
Hypophosphatasia	Alkaline phosphatase	785
Maple syrup urine disease	Amino acid decarboxylase	547
Methemoglobinemia	Methemoglobin reductase	806
Orotic aciduria	Orotidine 5'-phosphate pyrophosphorylase	575
Parahemophilia	Accelerator globulin	652
Pentosuria	L-Xylulose dehydrogenase	408
Phenylketonuria	Phenylalanine hydroxylase	501
Wilson's disease	Ceruloplasmin	640
Xanthinuria	Xanthine oxidase	567

may be an accumulation of products of an alternate, and ordinarily minor, pathway of metabolism, as in phenylketonuria (page 501), leading to excretion of large amounts of compounds ordinarily produced in trace amounts.

In addition to the genetic abnormalities which have been ascribed to the lack or modification of a particular enzyme or protein, there are many hereditary disorders of metabolism in which the regulatory protein has not yet been identified; some of these are listed in Table 31.8. As biochemical knowledge increases, the protein aberration involved in these disorders will undoubtedly be identified. Furthermore, it is likely that the list will continuously increase, particularly as quantitative differences in metabolism become further defined. As in the case of the abnormal hemoglobins where the effect of the modified protein may be negligible or profound, similar findings may be expected for other altered proteins and enzymes.

Chromosomal Abnormalities. In addition to the abnormalities listed in Tables

Table 31.8: Some Hereditary Disorders in Which the Affected Protein Has Not Been Identified

Disorder	Biochemical manifestation	Page reference
Congenital steatorrhea..........	Failure to digest and/or absorb lipid	266
Cystinuria....................	Excretion of cystine, lysine, arginine, and ornithine	742
Cystinosis....................	Inability to utilize amino acids, notably cystine; aberration of amino acid transport into cells	
Fanconi's syndrome............	Increased excretion of amino acids	742
Fructosuria..................	Excretion of fructose	741
Gargoylism (Hurler's syndrome)..	Excessive excretion of chondroitin sulfate B	775
Gaucher's disease.............	Accumulation of cerebrosides and ceramides in tissues	480
Niemann-Pick disease...........	Accumulation of sphingomyelin in tissues	480
Porphyria....................	Increased excretion of uroporphyrins	742
Tay-Sachs disease.............	Accumulation of gangliosides in tissues	480

31.7 and 31.8, which are, or appear to be, due to point mutations, there are other defects which are due to the presence of an abnormal number of chromosomes. In *mongolism* one of the autosomes is present as a triploid rather than in the normal diploid condition.

Individuals are also known in whom the Y chromosome is lacking or in whom excess X chromosomes are present. Since these chromosomes carry genes concerned with sexual differentiation, such individuals present syndromes associated with abnormal sexual development and usually manifest numerous other metabolic abnormalities. The hormones associated with normal sexual development are steroids (Chap. 48), and the effect of sex chromosome polysomy or deficiency suggests that some genes concerned with steroid synthesis may be present on X and Y chromosomes.

In concluding this discussion of hereditary disorders in man, some aspects of studies of human genetics warrant comment. In the early part of this century, after Mendel's laws were rediscovered, many genetic studies were made of human traits. It soon became obvious that not all the physical, psychological, and metabolic characteristics ascribed to genetic differences are in fact inherited. The difficulties arise because of many factors. Human families are usually very small compared with those of laboratory animals, and it is impossible to obtain accurate data for more than a few generations. Populations are highly mobile, which frequently makes it difficult or impossible to study all members of a family. All too often, common social or environmental factors, which are largely uncontrolled, may simulate a genetic picture.

These cautionary remarks are necessary because in the study of human genetics many meaningless "pedigrees" have been compiled. In this connection, it may be noted that rickets, a disorder due to deficiency of vitamin D or to inadequate exposure of the skin to ultraviolet radiation (Chap. 56), was long ascribed to a genetic factor. Similarly, goiter, once so prevalent in parts of Switzerland and in the "goiter belt" of the United States, was believed to be inherited. It is now recognized that a similar environmental factor, deficiency of iodine, was one etiological factor operative in producing the enlarged thyroid gland. Nevertheless, it has been established that one form of goiter is inherited (Chap. 46). Clearly, it will be necessary, in other instances, as in the case of goiter, to disentangle the complex factors involved in metabolic abnormalities to determine the exact contribution of genetic, nutritional, and other environmental factors involved in each situation. Further, efforts must be devoted to learning how to correct the manifestations of the genetic disorder. The successes achieved in galactosemia (page 406) by withholding galactose from the diet of infants and in phenylketonuria by limiting the intake of phenylalanine (page 501) indicate approaches to these problems.

REFERENCES

Books

Allen, F. W., "Ribonucleoproteins and Ribonucleic Acids," Elsevier Publishing Company, Amsterdam, 1962.

Allen, J. M., ed., "The Molecular Control of Cellular Activity," McGraw-Hill Book Company, Inc., New York, 1962.

Anfinsen, C. B., "The Molecular Basis of Evolution," John Wiley & Sons Inc., New York, 1959.

"Cellular Regulatory Mechanisms," Cold Spring Harbor Symp. Quant. Biol., vol. **26**, Biological Laboratory, Cold Spring Harbor, N.Y., 1961.

Chargaff, E., and Davidson, J. N., eds., "The Nucleic Acids," vol. III, Academic Press, Inc., New York, 1960.

Dobzhansky, T., "Mankind Evolving: The Evolution of the Human Species," Yale University Press, New Haven, 1962.

Garrod, A. E., "Inborn Errors of Metabolism," 2d ed., Henry Frowde and Hodder & Stoughton, Ltd., London, 1923.

Harris, H., "Human Biochemical Genetics," Cambridge University Press, New York, 1959.

Ingram, V. M., "Hemoglobin and Its Abnormalities," Charles C Thomas, Publisher, Springfield, Ill., 1961.

Kornberg, A., "Enzymatic Synthesis of DNA," John Wiley & Sons, Inc., New York, 1962.

McElroy, W. D., and Glass, B., eds., "The Chemical Basis of Heredity," Johns Hopkins Press, Baltimore, 1957.

Perutz, M. F., "Proteins and Nucleic Acids," Elsevier Publishing Company, Amsterdam, 1962.

Sager, R., and Ryan, F. J., "Cell Heredity," John Wiley & Sons, Inc., New York, 1961.

Stanbury, J. B., Wyngaarden, J. B., and Frederickson, D. S., eds., "The Metabolic Basis of Inherited Disease," McGraw-Hill Book Company, Inc., Blakiston Division, New York, 1960.

Taylor, J. H., ed., "Molecular Genetics," part I, Academic Press, Inc., New York, 1963.

Wolstenholme, G. E. W., and O'Connor, C. M., eds., "Biochemistry of Human Genetics," Little, Brown and Company, Boston, 1959.

Review Articles

Berg, P., Specificity in Protein Synthesis, *Ann. Rev. Biochem.*, **30**, 293–324, 1961.

Crick, F. H. C., The Recent Excitement in the Coding Problem, in J. N. Davidson and W. E. Cohn, eds., "Progress in Nucleic Acid Research," Academic Press, Inc., New York, 1963.

Hill, R. L., The Abnormal Human Hemoglobins, *Lab. Invest.,* **10,** 1012–1030, 1961.

Jacob, F., and Monod, J., Genetic Regulatory Mechanisms in the Synthesis of Proteins, *J. Mol. Biol.,* **3,** 318–356, 1961.

Monod, J., Jacob, F., and Gros, F., Structural and Rate-determining Factors in the Biosynthesis of Adaptive Enzymes, in D. J. Bell and J. K. Grant, eds., "The Structure and Biosynthesis of Macromolecules," Biochemical Society Symposia: No. 21, Cambridge University Press, New York, 1962.

Nirenberg, M. W., The Genetic Code: II, *Sci. Am.,* **208,** 80–94, 1963.

Schroeder, W. A., The Hemoglobins, *Ann. Rev. Biochem.,* **32,** 301–320, 1963.

Spiegelman, S., Information Transfer from the Genome, *Federation Proc.,* **22,** 36–54, 1963.

32. Blood Plasma

Unicellular organisms which live in immediate contact with the external environment obtain nutrients directly from that environment and eliminate unused or unwanted materials directly from the internal to the external milieu. As living organisms evolved into more complex structures comprised of diverse anatomical forms, special means of communication were established which enabled the organism to maintain an integration among various tissues and organs, as well as to facilitate contact with the external environment. The circulatory systems represent one of the important connecting pathways among various cells, and groups of cells, which constitute the mammalian organism.

The vascular structures containing their rapidly moving red fluid, the blood, and the lymphatic vessels with their more slowly flowing whitish medium, the lymph, constitute the circulatory systems. The difference in color is due to the fact that the lymph, although having large numbers of leukocytes, or white cells, has very few erythrocytes, or red cells.

Both blood and lymph contain dissolved solutes as well as suspended insoluble components. The specific gravity of blood is 1.055 to 1.065, and its viscosity is approximately five to six times that of water. If blood is drawn from a vein and measures are taken to prevent clotting (Chap. 33), the suspended cellular elements may be separated by centrifugation. The normally clear, slightly yellow supernatant fluid is termed *blood plasma*. Should the blood be drawn and allowed to clot, there separates from the clot a clear yellowish fluid, the *blood serum*. The yellow color is due to the presence of small quantities of bilirubin, a bile pigment (Chap. 36), and of carotenoids (Chap. 6). The clot is composed largely of cellular elements, enmeshed in a network of fibrous strands of *fibrin*. Thus blood plasma represents blood minus its cellular elements, whereas blood serum lacks, in addition, fibrinogen, the precursor of fibrin. This is considered again in Chap. 33, in the discussion of blood clotting. Lymph also clots, although somewhat more slowly than blood. The composition of lymph is discussed in Chap. 36. Aspects of the biochemistry of the cellular elements of the blood are considered in Chap. 42. The present chapter is concerned with the blood plasma.

COMPOSITION OF BLOOD PLASMA

The total volume of blood in the vascular system approximates 8 per cent of the body weight. In the adult, this is equivalent to 5 to 6 liters of blood. Infants have a larger blood volume, in proportion to their body weight, than do adults; the blood volume is a function of the surface area of the body.

Dissolved in the blood plasma are solutes which comprise approximately 10 per cent of the plasma volume. Of these solutes, the plasma proteins constitute approximately 7 per cent of the plasma, inorganic salts approximately 0.9 per cent, with the remainder of the solutes consisting of diverse organic compounds other than protein. Tables 32.1 and 32.2 indicate the concentrations of the principal nonprotein organic and inorganic components, respectively, of the blood plasma of man, with the ranges of concentration for each constituent under nor-

Table 32.1: APPROXIMATE RANGES OF VALUES FOR CERTAIN OF THE PRINCIPAL NONPROTEIN ORGANIC CONSTITUENTS OF THE BLOOD PLASMA OF MAN

Constituent	Normal range, mg./100 ml.	Constituent	Normal range, mg./100 ml.
Nonprotein N:	25–40	*Carbohydrates:*	
Urea	20–30	Glucose	65–90
Urea N	10–20	Fructose	6–8
Amino acid N	4–8	Glycogen	5–6
Amino acids:	35–65	Polysaccharides (as hexose)	70–105
Alanine	3.0–3.7	Glucosamine (as poly-	
α-Aminobutyric acid	0.2–0.4	saccharide)	60–105
Arginine	1.2–1.9	Hexuronates (as glucuronic acid)	0.4–1.4
Asparagine	0.5–0.7	Pentose, total	2–4
Aspartic acid	0.01–0.07	*Organic acids:*	
Cysteine and cystine	1.1–1.3	Citric acid	1.4–3.0
Glutamic acid	0.4–1.2	α-Ketoglutaric acid	0.2–1.0
Glutamine	5–12	Malic acid	0.1–0.9
Glycine	1.3–1.7	Succinic acid	0.1–0.6
Histidine	0.8–1.5	Acetoacetic acid	0.8–2.8
Isoleucine	0.7–1.3	Lactic acid	8–17
Leucine	1.4–2.3	Pyruvic acid	0.4–2.0
Lysine	2.5–3.0	*Lipids:*	
Methionine	0.3–0.4	Total lipids	385–675
Ornithine	0.6–0.8	Neutral fat	80–240
Phenylalanine	0.7–1.0	Cholesterol, total	130–260
Proline	1.8–3.3	Cholesterol, esters	90–190
Serine	1.1–1.2	Cholesterol, free	40–70
Threonine	1.2–1.7	Phosphatides:	
Tryptophan	1.0–1.2	Total	150–250
Tyrosine	0.8–1.5	Lecithin	100–200
Valine	2.4–3.7	Cephalin	0–30
Bilirubin	0.2–1.4	Sphingomyelin	10–50
Creatine	0.2–0.9	Plasmalogens	7–8
Creatinine	1–2	Total fatty acids	150–500
Taurine	0.4–0.8	Unesterified fatty acids	8–30
Uric acid	2–6		

mal physiological conditions. Factors influencing the concentrations of blood plasma constituents, as well as their physiological functions, are considered below as well as in preceding and succeeding chapters of this book.

The nature and amount of a particular blood constituent are the resultant of a number of physiological processes: (1) the rate at which the substance is being synthesized at its site, or sites, of production; (2) the rate at which addition of the component to the blood takes place; and (3) the rate of utilization or removal of the substance from blood by various tissues. Although quantitative measurements of particular blood components may yield information of considerable value, the composition of the blood is not of itself a complete reflection of the metabolic status within tissue cells. Significant amounts of cellular products may be present in cells without appearing to a detectable degree in the circulation. This is particularly pertinent in the case of solutes which are not freely distributed between intra- and extracellular fluids.

Table 32.2: APPROXIMATE RANGES OF VALUES FOR THE PRINCIPAL INORGANIC
CONSTITUENTS OF THE BLOOD PLASMA OF MAN

Anions	Concentration meq./liter*	Cations	Concentration meq./liter*
Total	142–150	Total	142–158
Bicarbonate	24–30	Calcium	4.5–5.6
Chloride	100–110	Magnesium	1.6–2.2
Phosphate	1.6–2.7	Potassium	3.8–5.4
Sulfate	0.7–1.5	Sodium	132–150
Iodine (total)	8–15†	Iron	50–180†
Iodine (protein-bound)	6–8†	Copper	8–16†

* meq./liter, milligram equivalents per liter, or milliequivalents per liter; a meq./liter of an ion or

a substance $= \dfrac{\text{mg./liter} \times \text{valence}}{\text{atomic or formula weight}}$.

† These concentrations are in terms of micrograms per 100 ml.

THE PLASMA PROTEINS

Composition of Plasma Proteins. The total protein content of the plasma is normally in the range of 5.7 to 8.0 g. per 100 ml. Ideally, to describe all the plasma proteins, a complete list should be constructed of the constituent proteins, with the amounts and function of each indicated. Such a list is not possible because information is still inadequate concerning many of the proteins present in small amounts. Although free boundary and paper electrophoresis (see below) are convenient methods of separation and estimation of the major groups of plasma proteins, more refined procedures, e.g., density gradient centrifugation (page 179), starch gel electrophoresis (page 127), and immunoelectrophoresis (page 635), have revealed a bewildering number of plasma proteins and fractions. Some of the members of a fraction may share only one major property in common, e.g., solubility, density, molecular weight, or electrical charge at a defined pH. Some plasma proteins have been best identified or detected as a consequence of a particular biological or biocatalytic property, but have not been significantly purified. Finally, a few plasma proteins have been obtained in crystalline form and are more clearly characterizable. In the absence of a single method of delineating all plasma proteins, classification schemes have been adopted that are based largely on experimental methods. Illustrative examples will be found in the pages which follow.

One of the best methods of describing grossly the proteins of plasma and their relative amounts is on the basis of their electrophoretic distribution. The general method of free boundary electrophoresis has been described (page 126). Usually, the medium used for analysis of plasma is a buffer at pH 8.5 to 8.6 containing diethyl-barbiturate (Veronal) at an ionic strength of 0.1. Figure 32.1 shows the distribution

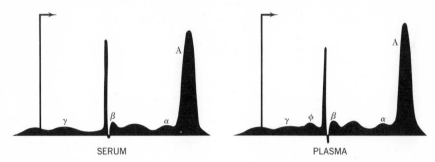

SERUM   PLASMA

Fig. 32.1. The electrophoretic patterns obtained with (*left*) normal human serum and (*right*) plasma are shown. The main components are identified as *A* for albumin, ϕ for fibrinogen, and α, β, and γ for the different globulins. Fibrinogen is lacking in serum.

of the plasma proteins obtained after migration in this medium for 250 min. at a potential gradient of about 6 volts per centimeter. The amount of each component is assessed from the area under each individual boundary. Representative average values for normal human plasma are given in Table 32.3. It should be recognized immediately that there are only six main boundaries evident in the electrophoretic

Table 32.3: Electrophoretic Distribution and Mobility of Plasma Protein Components

(Average values obtained with large pools of normal human plasma and analyzed in sodium diethyl-barbiturate (Veronal) buffer at pH 8.6. Amounts given in percentages of total protein and mobilities $\times 10^5$ in square centimeters per volt per second)

	Albumins	α_1-Globulins	α_2-Globulins	β-Globulins	Fibrinogen*	γ-Globulins
Amount....	55.2	5.3	8.7	13.4	6.5	11.0
Mobility..	5.92	4.85	3.87	2.88	2.06	1.15

* The amount of material which migrates under the "fibrinogen" boundary is much greater than the quantity of fibrinogen estimated as protein clottable by thrombin, which is about 4 per cent. The extra 2.5 per cent undoubtedly should be assigned to the γ-globulins.

Source: From S. H. Armstrong, Jr., M. J. E. Budka, and K. C. Morrison, *J. Am. Chem. Soc.*, **69**, 416, 1947.

pattern, whereas there are numerous additional proteins in plasma. Such designations as α_1-globulins, α_2-globulins, β-globulins, etc., represent groups of proteins, and each group contains additional proteins which possess similar mobilities under these experimental conditions. The pH chosen for this plasma analysis was selected in order that all the proteins should have a negative charge. This minimizes the possibility of salt formation between different proteins. At the same time, the pH is sufficiently alkaline to permit migration and separation of the *major* different groups in a reasonable length of time.

Although precise analyses are obtained with the large electrophoretic apparatus of Tiselius, a number of simpler methods are now widely used. In particular, zone electrophoresis on paper or on starch blocks is generally employed for rapid, routine analysis of plasma or serum, yielding values for several of the major protein components. The use of starch gel as a supporting medium increases markedly the resolving power of zone electrophoresis. For example, the 5 conventional zones observed in paper electrophoresis can be separated into approximately 20 zones by starch gel electrophoresis. One noteworthy new component which is thus revealed has been termed pre-albumin, because its mobility, at the usual alkaline pH values used for electrophoresis, is greater than that of albumin.

Addition to plasma of an equal volume of a saturated solution of ammonium sulfate precipitates the "globulins." Saturation of the solution with solid ammonium sulfate after removal of the precipitate now brings down the "albumin." Crude preparations of the two fractions are readily obtained in this way. A further fractionation of the globulin fraction may be made by dialysis against distilled water. The resulting precipitate contains the euglobulins (true globulins); the pseudoglobulins remain in solution. Both the eu- and pseudoglobulin fractions contain α-, β-, and γ-globulins. Precipitation with varying (increasing) concentrations of sodium sulfate can also be employed for estimations of plasma proteins.

The major protein constituents of the plasma are similar in all the vertebrates, although the relative amounts differ considerably. The electrophoretic distribution of the serum proteins of several mammalian species is given in Table 32.4. It is noteworthy that the content of γ-globulins is higher in the sera of members of other species than in man and that the amount of albumin is much lower in horse, cow, and pig sera.

Table 32.4: ELECTROPHORETIC DISTRIBUTION OF PROTEINS IN SOME MAMMALIAN SERA

(The data are given as percentages of the total protein and are averages of many individual determinations)

Animal	Albumins	α-Globulins	β-Globulins	γ-Globulins
Cow..................	41	13	8	38
Guinea pig.............	56	14.5	8	21.5
Horse.................	32	14	24	30
Pig...................	42	16	16	25
Rabbit...............	60	7	12	21
Sheep................	57	11	7	25

SOURCE: From H. Svensson, *Arkiv. Kemi. Mineral Geol.,* **22A**, No. 10, 1946.

SERUM ALBUMIN

General Properties. Albumin is the smallest and most abundant of the plasma protein constituents, with a molecular weight of 69,000, whereas most of the serum globulins have molecular weights of about 160,000 to 180,000. Its isoelectric point, pH 4.7, is also lower than that of the other major proteins; this and its high net charge explain why the electrophoretic migration of albumin is more rapid than that of the other major plasma proteins at neutral or slightly alkaline pH values (Table 32.1). The high net charge is due to the large number of titratable groups, about 180 titratable groups per mole (Table 8.1). At the pH of the blood, 7.4, albumin has a net negative charge of 18. These properties aid in explaining its extremely high solubility. At pH 7.4, 40 per cent solutions of serum albumin are readily prepared.

The albumin molecule has an asymmetry corresponding to that of an ellipsoid with a diameter of 38 Å. and a length of 150 Å. It is much more symmetrical than γ-globulin or the highly elongated fibrinogen molecules. As a result, solutions of albumin have a smaller viscosity than those of fibrinogen or of the globulins since viscosity is influenced much more by shape than by molecular size. This is an important consideration in cardiac physiology inasmuch as the work performed by the heart depends in large part on the viscosity of the blood. It has been estimated that the viscosity of blood is approximately equal to that of any of the following: twice concentrated plasma, a 25 per cent solution of albumin, a 15 per cent solution of γ-globulin, or a 2 per cent solution of fibrinogen. Human serum albumin is a mixture, as shown by its separation into at least two components after prolonged electrophoresis.

Osmotic Effect. The main function of albumin is its important role in osmotic regulation (Chaps. 35 and 36). Of the total osmotic effect of the plasma proteins, albumin is responsible for about 75 or 80 per cent. Although it constitutes slightly more than half the plasma proteins by weight, the effectiveness of albumin is far greater than that of the globulins because of its lower molecular weight. In addition, albumin gives a greater osmotic effect at the pH of the blood than would be expected from the ideal thermodynamic relationship where $\pi v = nRT$ (page 132). At pH 7.4 the 18 negative charges of albumin contribute strongly hydrophilic groups which cause a cluster of water molecules around each charge, thus producing a greater osmotic effect than would be given by a neutral molecule. Theoretically, the osmotic pressure should be linearly proportional to protein concentration, but albumin deviates strongly from this, again giving a greater effect than expected for its concentration in plasma. These two unusual properties contribute to the remarkable effectiveness of serum albumin as a factor in osmotic regulation.

Transport Function. Many substances which are sparingly soluble in water are readily dissolved in the presence of serum or plasma. Albumin solutions possess this property to a marked degree, and in each instance it has been demonstrated that the dissolved substance is actually bound to the protein. This was first observed with simple dyes but has since been found with a variety of substances of physiological interest, such as ions of fatty acids, naphthoquinone derivatives, bilirubin, sulfonamides, and other compounds. Albumin thus plays an important role in the transport of sparingly soluble metabolic products from one tissue to another. In certain diseases associated with excessive hemolysis, such as blackwater fever, the plasma contains "methemalbumin," an albumin complex with ferriprotoporphyrin (hemin).

Some of the properties of albumin and other important plasma proteins to be discussed are summarized in Table 32.5.

γ-GLOBULINS

Some Immunological Principles. When foreign proteins, *antigens,* are injected into a suitable animal, production of a specific protein called an *antibody* results.

Table 32.5: Major Protein Components of Human Plasma and Their Properties

Component	Estimated amount, g./100 ml.	Sedimentation constant, Svedberg units	Molecular weight	Isoelectric point, pH	Special properties and function
Pre-albumin	0.3	4.1	61,000	......	1.3% Carbohydrate
Albumin	2.8–4.5	4.6	69,000	4.7	Osmotic regulation; transport
Globulins, total	3.0–3.5				
α_1-Globulins	0.3–0.6				
α_1-Globulin (orosomucoid)	0.075	3.1–3.5	41,000	1.8–2.7	40% Carbohydrate
α_1-Globulin (glycoprotein)	0.030	3.5	54,000	......	14% Carbohydrate
α_1-Lipoproteins*:					
Density = 1.093	0.05–0.13	5.5	435,000	......	Lipid transport; 67% lipid
Density = 1.149	0.3–0.4	5.0	195,000	5.2	Lipid transport; 43% lipid
Haptoglobin, type 1-1	0.1	4.2	85,000	4.1	Binds hemoglobin; 23% carbohydrate; differing genetic types
α_2-Globulins	0.4–0.9				
α_2-Globulin (glycoprotein)	......	2.6	......	3.8	16% Carbohydrate
α_2-Globulin (macroglobulin)	0.2	19.6	820,000	5.4	10% Carbohydrate
Ceruloplasmin	0.03	7.1	160,000	4.4	7% Carbohydrate; copper transport
Plasminogen	......	4.3	143,000	5.6	Precursor of plasmin, a fibrinolysin (Chap. 33)
Prothrombin†	......	4.8	62,700	4.2	11% Carbohydrate; blood coagulation
β-Globulins	0.6–1.1				
β_1-Lipoproteins:					
Density = 0.98–1.002	0.13–0.20	......	$5–20 \times 10^6$	......	90% Lipid; lipid transport
Density = 1.03	0.20–0.25	......	3.2×10^6	......	79% Lipid; lipid transport
Lipoeuglobulin III, density = 1.036	......	8.2	3×10^6	5.3	75% Lipid; lipid transport
β_1-Metal-binding globulin (transferrin; siderophilin)	0.40	5.0	90,000	5.9	5.5% Carbohydrate; iron transport
Antihemophilic globulin	......	......	......	6.4	
Fibrinogen	0.30	7.6	341,000	5.8	3% Carbohydrate; blood clotting (Chap. 33)
Cold-insoluble globulins (cryoglobulins)	......	15.0	......	......	
γ-Globulins	0.7–1.5	7.0	150,000	6.3–7.3	Antibodies
γ_1-Globulins	......	7.0	......	5.8–6.6	2.5% Carbohydrate
γ_1-Macroglobulins	0.05–0.15	19.0	1×10^6	5.1–7.7	10% Carbohydrate
γ_2-Globulins	......	7.0	150,000	7.3–8.2	3% Carbohydrate

* Other data for lipoproteins are presented in Table 22.1, page 435.

† From bovine plasma.

SOURCE: The information in this table is largely taken from summaries by E. J. Cohn and associates, in *J. Am. Chem. Soc.*, **72**, 465, 1950; and from "The Plasma Proteins," F. W. Putnam, ed, vols. I and II, Academic Press, Inc., New York, 1960.

Although the stimulation of antibody production is most commonly observed with proteins, certain polysaccharides such as the capsular components of pneumococci and other microorganisms are also antigenic. The antibody may combine with the antigen to produce a visible precipitate; hence the term precipitin reaction. Antibodies which are produced to toxins are *antitoxins*. If the antigens are cells, such as erythrocytes of another species, or bacteria, and if clumping of the cells is produced by the antibodies, the latter are *agglutinins*. If the cells are lysed, the antibodies are *lysins*. Each antigen elicits formation of a different, specific antibody.

The antibodies found in blood are mainly associated with the γ-globulins, although some are found in the β-globulin fractions. Plasma plays an important role as the medium of transport for the antibodies in their mobilization for defense against invasion by microorganisms. Antibodies, like the other plasma proteins, are made in the tissues, presumably by cells of the reticuloendothelial system. Since normal individuals are exposed during their lives to many different organisms, plasma contains a large variety of antibodies. Immunity to a virus or bacterium is associated with the presence of specific antibodies to the invading pathogen.

Artificial active immunity may be produced by injecting a nonpathogenic antigen such as killed bacteria, *e.g., Hemophilus pertussis,* the causative organism of whooping cough, or a toxoid made by treating the toxins of the diphtheria or tetanus bacilli with formaldehyde. The injected individual will develop specific antibodies and possess active immunity. Temporary passive immunity is given by injection of antibodies made by immune individuals of the same species or even of another species. Antitoxins to diphtheria and tetanus toxins from horse plasma have been extensively used for treatment of these diseases for more than 50 years.

This brief statement of the principles of immunology merely indicates the tremendous medical and biological importance of this field which is so closely allied to the study of bacteriology and infectious diseases. The present objective is to present some of the more important aspects of the chemistry of the antibodies and their importance as plasma proteins.

It should be emphasized that antibodies are highly specific in character. Antibody made in rabbits to hen's egg albumin is specific for hen's egg albumin; it gives only a minimal or no precipitin reaction with albumins of other closely related species. This property has been useful in assessing the relationship of various proteins and in testing the purity of individual proteins (page 139). A pure protein elicits formation of only a single type of antibody, whereas a mixture of proteins results in formation of many antibodies. It is evident from this that the γ-globulins normally present in plasma are mixtures of many kinds of antibodies produced during the life of the individual and, in addition, may contain protein which is immunologically inert.

Physical Properties of γ-Globulins. The γ-globulin fraction was originally defined as the plasma protein component which moves most slowly during electrophoresis of plasma at alkaline pH. Plasma proteins with the electrophoretic mobility of γ-globulin have certain common physicochemical and immunological characteristics but are heterogeneous according to several criteria, *e.g.,* the wide range of electrophoretic mobility and diffuse spread on ion exchange chromatography, as well as the multiplicity of antibodies present.

When examined in the ultracentrifuge, the γ-globulins of the blood of normal individuals consist of two classes of proteins. Of the total γ-globulins, 85 to 90 per cent have a sedimentation constant of 7 S, with a corresponding molecular weight of approximately 150,000. This group is often termed 7 S$_\gamma$. The second group of proteins, comprising 10 to 15 per cent of the total γ-globulins, sediments with a value of 19 S, corresponding to a molecular weight of approximately one million, and has been termed 19 S$_\gamma$. The normal 19 S component migrates as a γ_1-globulin; hence the designation γ_1-macroglobulin. This component has also been termed β_2M, because in immunoelectrophoresis (see below) it appears to be closely related to a minor group of β_2-globulins. However, the designation γ_1M seems more appropriate (see below). Immunoelectrophoresis has also led to the identification of a third type of γ-globulin, which is mainly of molecular size similar to 7 S γ-globulin but, like the 19 S fractions, has a relatively high carbohydrate content. This 7 S γ-globulin has been designated γ_1A-globulin.

Immunoelectrophoresis. As the term indicates, immunoelectrophoresis makes possible differentiation of proteins in solution on the basis of electrophoretic and immunological properties. Electrophoretic migration is generally performed in agar gel. Immunological differentiation of the separated protein fractions is achieved by

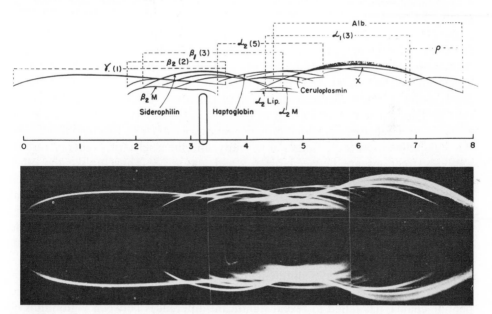

FIG. 32.2. *Lower diagram:* Immunoelectrophoresis of normal human serum developed with a horse antiserum to whole normal serum. *Upper diagram:* A drawing to scale of the immunoelectrophoretic pattern indicating the components identified immunologically. The figures in parentheses give the number of precipitin lines found in each mobility range. The Greek letter ρ designates a component that moves more rapidly than serum albumin (a pre-albumin). Another line (χ) with a mobility close to that of serum albumin is mucoprotein and corresponds to two purified fractions: a low molecular weight α_1-acid glycoprotein and orosomucoid (Table 32.5). The term siderophilin in the upper diagram is a synonym for transferrin; Alb. designates albumin and α_2Lip. designates α_2-lipoproteins. (*From F. W. Putnam, ed., "The Plasma Proteins," vol.* I, *p.* 73, *Academic Press, Inc., New York,* 1960.)

adding specific immune serum to a groove in the agar block beside the separated protein fractions. Precipitation lines or rings form within a few hours at the points of contact from diffusion of the electrophoretically separated protein fractions and of the specific immune serum in the trough. The position of these precipitation lines is determined by the electrophoretic mobility, the rate of diffusion, and the serological specificity of each of the proteins present in the solution under study. The number, shape, and intensity of the lines correspond to the incidence, nature, and extent of the precipitin reactions (Fig. 32.2).

In addition to the use of agar in rectangular dishes, an agar supporting medium in glass tubes has also been employed. After electrophoresis the agar cylinder is pushed into a tightly fitting trough previously prepared in an agar plate, and the immune serum is placed in a parallel trough to develop precipitin reactions. Similarly, another procedure combines electrophoretic separation on paper with serological testing in agar. Finally, starch gel supporting medium for electrophoresis has been combined with modified precipitin gel diffusion techniques. The technique of immunoelectrophoresis has provided additional information about the number of serum components, the characteristics and distribution of antibodies, and the nature of γ-globulin.

Chemical Properties of γ-Globulins. Many difficulties have been encountered in attempting to demonstrate differences by chemical means among the various human 7 S γ-globulins, as well as between antibody and apparently inert γ-globulin of the same electrophoretic mobility and purity. Highly purified antibodies have been prepared by precipitation with the specific antigen, followed by chemical separation of the antigen and the antibody. Such antibody preparations possess physical and chemical characteristics of the γ-globulins. Antibodies of most species have a molecular weight of 150,000 to 180,000, except for certain antibodies in the horse and related species, which may be as large as 900,000. Electrophoretically, the γ-globulins show large ranges in mobility, and the isoelectric points of various antibody fractions are between pH 6.3 and about 7.3. Thus, unlike the other plasma proteins, these molecules are almost electrically neutral at the pH of the plasma. The γ-globulins are glycoproteins and may contain from 2 to 10 per cent of carbohydrate, including galactose, mannose, fucose, glucosamine, and a sialic acid. The carbohydrate portion of γ-globulin is linked to the protein by an amide bond between a β-carboxyl groups of an aspartic acid residue and the amino group of a hexosamine residue.

Amino acid analyses of different fractions of γ-globulins show some minor differences. However, amino acid analysis, both for quantity and position in the peptide chains, has failed to reveal significant differences between γ-globulins of normal and of hyperimmunized rabbits. Present evidence suggests that antibodies differ from each other and from "normal" γ-globulin in specific conformational relationships rather than in amino acid composition, although differences due to small, narrowly localized sequences of amino acids are also possible.

One of the remarkable properties of antibodies is their susceptibility to partial digestion by the proteolytic enzymes pepsin, trypsin, papain, etc., without loss of their specific immunological properties. Antibodies can be hydrolyzed to half or even quarter molecules which are fully active, although further digestion leads to inactive products. Northrop isolated an active crystalline diphtheria antitoxin from horse plasma after digestion with trypsin. The active antitoxin had a molecular weight of 90,000 as compared with 180,000 for the undigested antitoxin.

These observations have been extended by a number of investigators, notably Porter, Edelman, Nisonoff, Pressman, and their coworkers. When human 7 S γ-globulin is reduced in the presence of $6M$ urea, approximately 15 disulfide bonds are split and the molecular weight falls from about 150,000 to 50,000. The products of reduction can be separated by chromatography but are immunologically inactive. Reduction of γ-globulin in neutral aqueous solution splits a maximum of five disulfide bonds; subsequent dialysis against acetic or propionic acids dissociates two fractions, which have been termed A and B. The A fraction comprises three-quarters of the total and has an average molecular weight of 111,000; the B fraction, comprising about 25 per cent of the total protein, has an average molecular weight of about 20,000. Immunological and immunoelectrophoretic studies indicate that the B chains reflect properties which are common to all γ-globulins, while A chains are specific for each type of γ-globulin. Thus, the antigenic cross-reactivity among the classes of γ-globulins would be accounted for by the general structural similarity of the B chains. Within each class, however, the major determinant of heterogeneity would be variations in the type of B chains in different molecules. This permits the concept of the same basic primary structure of the B chain in any individual or closely related group of individuals, accompanied by minor though characteristic modifications, e.g., in amino acid sequence and composition.

Porter and his associates have also shown that papain splits each γ-globulin molecule into three fragments separable by chromatography. Two fragments of molecular weight approximately 40,000 retained the power to combine with antigen; the third fragment, of molecular weight about 70,000 to 80,000, was antigenically active but was not itself bound by antigen, i.e., exhibited no antibody activity. The three fragments accounted for 90 per cent or more of the original molecule, and little if any biological activity was lost. In relating the properties of these fragments to the above-described chains obtained by reduction, it was possible to show that the A chain was present only in one of the fragments, while the B chain and a portion of the A chain were present in the other two fragments. These data led Porter to postulate that all 7 S γ-globulins consist of four peptide chains linked through disulfide bonds. The order of the chains is suggested as B, A, A, B, i.e., two small B chains on either side of an internal core of two larger A chains. All the carbohydrate of the three main types of γ-globulin is present in the A chains.

In view of the basically similar structure of the γ-globulins, it has been suggested that the three main γ-globulin components, i.e., the two 7 S and the 19 S (γ₁-macroglobulin) components, be designated as 7 S, γ₁A-, and γ₁M-globulins, rather than relating them to electrophoretic globulin fractions other than the γ₁-globulins.

Antibodies in the Newborn. Newborn mammals do not appear to be able to make antibodies. However, physiological mechanisms exist for creating a temporary passive immunity in the young which permits them to resist infection until the time when the mechanism of antibody synthesis has developed. In some mammals, including man, the plasma proteins of the newborn show an electrophoretic pattern similar to that of the maternal plasma. Moreover, many specific antibodies present in maternal plasma are demonstrable at birth in the blood of the young. For these species passive immunity is achieved by transfer of antibodies from the maternal blood through the placenta to the blood of the fetus.

There is a rare, congenital condition in which human beings lack the ability to form γ-globulins (*agammaglobulinemia*, page 632) and such proteins are lacking in plasma. These individuals are particularly susceptible to infectious agents. γ-Globulin may be administered at intervals as a therapeutic measure.

In the Ungulata—cow, horse, sheep, goat, etc.—γ-globulins are absent in the serum of the newborn, and, correspondingly, no antibodies can be detected in the blood. Ehrlich observed that antibodies appear in the plasma after the young of these species have suckled and received the first milk, or colostrum. Colostrum may contain as high as 20 per cent protein, five times the amount present in milk, and the predominant fraction is immune globulins. In the Ungulata, the placental barrier does not permit the passage of the large antibody molecules from the maternal to the fetal circulation, whereas the newborn can absorb these antibodies from the intestine into its blood stream. Antibodies are also present in human colostrum, but they play a secondary role since the placental transmission is more important.

Newborn ungulates also possess an unusual α-globulin with the low molecular weight of 40,000. Pedersen named this plasma component *fetuin*, since it is present in large amounts in the plasma of the fetus and the young calf or pig and its content diminishes rapidly in the older animal. Fetuin, like other α-globulins, contains carbohydrate (see below) and is a mucoprotein with a total carbohydrate content of 22 per cent.

THE LIPOPROTEINS

As indicated previously (page 434), the plasma lipids are not found free in the plasma but are associated with protein. Except for the small quantity of fatty acids present as fatty acid–albumin complexes (page 436), the remainder of the plasma lipid is present as *lipoproteins*. These migrate electrophoretically with both the α- and β-globulins (Table 32.5, page 633). Lipoprotein fractions can be separated by density gradient centrifugation and are characterized by their flotation constants (page 434).

The lipoproteins have been considered previously with regard to their lipid composition (Table 22.1, page 435) and their role in lipid metabolism (page 434). The lipoproteins present in serum range in molecular weight from 200,000 to 10,000,000 and contain from 4 to 95 per cent lipid. It should be stressed that the classes of lipoproteins described (Tables 22.1 and 32.5, pages 435 and 633) are based on empirically devised physical procedures, and that each class represents not a single molecular species but rather multiple species with similar physical properties. Indeed, there may be present in plasma on the order of a hundred or more lipoprotein classes. However, the broad chemical and structural interrelationships of lipoproteins within lipoprotein classes have permitted simplification of the characterization of lipoproteins.

In addition to the physical and chemical data given previously for the lipoproteins, certain additional properties warrant comment. The amino acid composition of each of the major classes of lipoproteins appears to be similar to one another, but different from the amino acid composition of the other serum proteins, *e.g.*, albumin, γ-globulin, and fibrinogen. However, some differences in amino acid composition and terminal residues between the low- and high-density lipoproteins have been reported.

In some pathological conditions, the β_1-lipoprotein (low-density) is often present in increased amount. This is more readily detected by density gradient ultracentrifugal studies than by electrophoresis, since the electrophoretic β-globulin fraction is a mixture of lipoprotein and many other components. Regimens designed to lower the β- and elevate the α-lipoproteins (high-density) are based on the thesis that a lowering of the former, with its accompanying cholesterol, is a desirable prophylactic and therapeutic goal (Chap. 53).

A hereditary disorder characterized by a complete absence of normal plasma β-lipoproteins or by the presence of a reduced amount of low-density lipoproteins, but with an electrophoretic mobility differing from that of the normal β-lipoproteins, has been termed *acanthocytosis*. The name is derived from the appearance of the erythrocytes, which are spherical and have numerous projecting spines and spicules (Gk. *akantha*, a thorn). More than 80 per cent of the red cells may have this appearance, which is reversible to normal in vitro by addition of certain nonionic detergents such as Tween 80. In acanthocytosis, triglycerides are virtually absent from the serum, and low cholesterol concentrations are found, ranging between 35 and 75 mg. per 100 ml. There is an accompanying malabsorption of lipid from the intestine.

THE MUCOPROTEINS

Mucoproteins of high carbohydrate content have been detected in the plasma filtrate remaining after precipitation of the other proteins by addition of trichloroacetic acid or perchloric acid. Mucoproteins are not coagulated by boiling. In Veronal buffer at pH 8.6, they migrate with the α-globulins (Table 32.5), but in acetate buffer at pH 4.0 they retain their negative charge, unlike the other plasma proteins, which possess more alkaline isoelectric points.

An acidic mucoprotein with the electrophoretic mobility at pH 8.6 of an α_1-globulin has been obtained in crystalline form from serum and from nephrotic urine. It has been termed *orosomucoid*, and is also known as α_1-acid seromucoid and acid seromucoid. The substance contains about 40 per cent carbohydrate, including galactose, mannose, fucose, N-acetylgalactosamine, and N-acetylneuraminic acid.

Haptoglobin, an α_2-globulin, is a mucoprotein which can combine with hemoglobin to form a weak peroxidase. When hemoglobin is injected or liberated by hemolysis, it combines with haptoglobin until the capacity of the latter is exceeded. In hemolytic conditions and in acute hepatitis the plasma level of haptoglobin is diminished. Haptoglobin preparations have been described with molecular weights of 85,000 and 170,000, suggesting that the protein may exist as a dimer. Starch gel electrophoretic studies by Smithies demonstrated that the type of haptoglobin occurring in a given individual falls in one of three genetic groups. Each of the haptoglobin types, in turn, shows multiple bands on starch gel electrophoresis. However, all the haptoglobins react equally well and identically with antibodies to each of the others, and all appear to have a similar amount and proportion of diverse carbohydrates.

Laurell isolated haptoglobin from single individuals of the three hereditary types, using ascitic fluid as the starting source. Haptoglobin 1-1 was homogeneous and had a sedimentation constant of 4.2 S (molecular weight, approximately 85,000); haptoglobin 2-2 was also homogeneous and had a sedimentation constant of 7.5 S, suggesting a dimer. However, the haptoglobin from type 2-1 individuals was heterogeneous in the ultracentrifuge, giving components of 5.6 and 6.4 S. It is possible that a number of polymers of a basic subunit of haptoglobin may occur.

In many metabolic disorders there is a pronounced elevation in the number of α-globulins estimated electrophoretically. This is largely because of an increase in mucoproteins. Infectious diseases, *e.g.*, pneumonia, tuberculosis, and acute rheumatic fever, and general disturbances such as cancer with metastases produce these increases, and they are frequently associated with a concurrent increase in fibrinogen and a decrease in albumin.

THE METAL-BINDING PROTEINS

A crystalline β_1-globulin capable of combining with iron, copper, and zinc has been isolated from plasma. This substance constitutes approximately 3 per cent of the total plasma protein and has a molecular weight in the region of 90,000. The protein contains about 5.5 per cent carbohydrate and is capable of binding two atoms of iron per molecule of protein. The iron complex dissociates below pH 7.0.

The main physiological function of this metal-binding protein is to transport iron. For this reason it has been termed *transferrin* and *siderophilin*. In iron deficiency and pregnancy, there is a striking increase in the plasma concentration of transferrin. In some disease states, *e.g.*, chronic infections, liver disease, and pernicious anemia, there is a reduction in the concentration of this protein.

The interaction of copper with the metal-binding protein differs from that of iron in that at pH 7, where the protein has its maximal binding capacity for iron, its capacity to bind copper is only half maximal. On addition of iron the copper is almost entirely displaced.

A blue copper-containing protein, *ceruloplasmin,* has been isolated from serum by Holmberg and Laurell. This protein contains 90 per cent, if not all, of the copper in serum. Ceruloplasmin of human plasma has been prepared in crystalline form. It is an α_2-globulin of molecular weight about 160,000, with 7 per cent carbohydrate, and contains eight atoms of copper. It can be reduced to a colorless compound with certain reducing agents, a reduction which is completely reversible in the presence of oxygen. In the rare inherited *Wilson's disease,* which is primarily a disorder of copper metabolism, there is a marked decrease in the plasma ceruloplasmin concentration and an increased level of copper in the liver and brain. The disorder is associated with neurological changes and liver damage. The function of ceruloplasmin is unknown. Ceruloplasmin copper is exchangeable with copper in the medium and the apoprotein may be reversibly separated from the copper under these circumstances. It has been suggested that ceruloplasmin functions by reversibly binding and releasing copper at various sites in the body, possibly thereby regulating the utilization of copper. The nature of the copper linkage in ceruloplasmin is obscure, but available data suggest that not all the copper atoms are bound in a similar manner.

SYNTHESIS OF PLASMA PROTEINS

Formation of fibrinogen and of the albumin of plasma appears to be limited to the liver. Damage to hepatic tissue or total liver removal (hepatectomy) causes reduction in the plasma fibrinogen and albumin. Prolonged limitation of protein intake not only diminishes the serum albumin, as a consequence of a decreased supply of amino acids to the liver, but depletes liver protein and leads to histological alteration of hepatic cells. Patients with liver cirrhosis are unable to form serum albumin and fibrinogen, even when fed amounts of protein adequate to produce a positive nitrogen balance.

Studies with the isolated perfused rat liver revealed a rate of albumin synthesis of 10 to 20 mg. per hr. It was calculated that the liver could synthesize all the plasma fibrinogen and albumin and approximately 80 per cent of the total globulins. Lipoprotein biosynthesis is largely limited to the liver. The extent of plasma protein synthesis by the liver was dependent on the presence of the essential amino acids in the perfusion fluid and, in agreement with previous discussion (page 492), was augmented when the essential amino acids were supplemented by a generous supply of the nonessential amino acids. A high level of amino acids in the perfusion fluid favored synthesis of the plasma albumin fraction; a low amino acid level resulted in preferential synthesis of plasma globulins. Under optimal experimental conditions, the rate of plasma protein synthesis by the isolated, perfused rat liver would permit a daily turnover of approximately 25 per cent of the total circulating plasma protein. This value is greater than that obtained for the half-life of plasma proteins in man (page 509), but is in good agreement with data on intact rats, which have a higher rate of metabolism than man. The rapid rate of plasma protein formation is seen in the replacement of serum albumin lost in nephritis and nephrosis. Patients may excrete 10 to 20 g. of protein daily for several months, yet in some instances no severe alteration in the concentration of serum albumin is evident.

As indicated above, some of the total plasma globulins are synthesized in extrahepatic tissues. Subjects on an inadequate protein diet maintain a normal concentration of plasma globulin, while the albumin fraction falls. Although this may be because of a propensity of the liver to produce globulin rather than albumin as the blood amino acid level falls (see above), this explanation appears inadequate in circumstances in which, despite experimental or clinical liver damage, increases in blood globulin concentration have been observed (see below). Moreover, the synthesis of antibody globulin by the widely distributed cells of the reticuloendothelial system is an additional example of extrahepatic formation of a portion of the blood globulins. Blood also has low concentrations of specialized proteins synthesized by specific tissues, *e.g.*, protein hormones and enzymes produced by various tissues. Nevertheless, the major portion of the serum proteins is of hepatic origin.

The rapid turnover of plasma proteins, and the fall in serum albumin concentration caused by restricted protein intake, indicate a continuing removal of plasma proteins from the circulation and utilization by tissues. Intravenously administered albumin is efficiently used for growth in experimental animals, and for restoration of blood volume and tissue repair in man. The liver and kidney appear to play a major role in the utilization of circulating protein, as is also the case for blood amino acids. This is probably a reflection, in part, of the more rapid turnover of proteins of these organs. Incorporation of amino acids administered as serum albumin into characteristic cellular proteins has been demonstrated. Presumably, proteins, *e.g.*, serum albumin, entering cells by a mechanism involving pinocytosis are degraded by intracellular cathepsins, with the liberated amino acids becoming available for synthesis of new protein molecules. A surprisingly large and temporary storage of intravenously administered serum albumin has been observed in the subcutaneous tissues of the rabbit.

ENZYMES OF PLASMA

Many different enzymes can be detected in plasma by measuring their catalytic effects on appropriate substrates. Under normal circumstances, the levels of activity are fairly low, and it is unlikely that most plasma enzymes play any specific metabolic role in plasma, although an exception must be made for the enzymes concerned in blood coagulation (Chap. 33). The enzymes present in plasma are presumably derived from the normal dissolution of the cells of blood and of other tissues. Nevertheless, the activity of certain enzymes in plasma is frequently a useful index of abnormal conditions in the tissues. An example is the observation that serum *amylase* is elevated in cases of acute pancreatitis.

The level in plasma of *acid phosphatase,* measured at pH 6, becomes very high in cases of prostatic cancer. Conditions which produce a regression of the cancer tissue, such as castration or administration of female sex hormones (estrogens), cause a marked decrease in the acid phosphatase levels. Thus, the estimation of plasma acid phosphatase is an important prognostic aid in the consideration of this disease. The *alkaline phosphatase* activity of blood, estimated at pH 9, is markedly increased in many bone diseases. In rapidly healing rickets and other conditions of rapid bone regeneration, high alkaline phosphatase levels are found; however, high alkaline phosphatase is also found in cases of hepatic obstruction.

In individuals with myocardial damage, the plasma level of certain enzymes, derived from cardiac tissue, is markedly increased. Estimation of glutamic-aspartic transaminase, lactic acid dehydrogenase, and other enzymes has proved to be of some value as diagnostic and prognostic aids for assessing cardiac damage. Elevation of the plasma level of these and certain other enzymes, *e.g.*, aldolase, also occurs in liver disease.

Quantitative estimation of different enzymes of plasma may be expected to play an increasing role in clinical medicine as more conditions are discovered in which specific correlations may be made between tissue destruction or growth and a specific enzyme.

ABNORMAL DISTRIBUTION OF PLASMA PROTEINS

It is important to distinguish those conditions in which disturbances of the levels of the normal proteins occur and those conditions in which abnormal proteins appear in the plasma.

The normal levels of the various plasma proteins estimated electrophoretically have been given in Table 32.3. A general effect of disease, particularly when malnutrition or marked wasting occurs, is a decrease of the serum albumin level. In *nephrosis,* there is loss of albumin in the urine, and in *cirrhosis* of the liver, there is impairment of albumin synthesis. In these same circumstances, there is usually some elevation of the globulins. These changes occur in so many conditions that they are seldom useful for diagnostic purposes, but are of value in prognosis since the changes over a period of time may indicate the severity or trend of the disorder. Thus in some cases of hepatic disease, albumin may be as low as 0.3 to 0.4 g. per 100 ml. as compared with about 4.0 g. per 100 ml. in normal plasma. In *analbuminemia,* a hereditary disorder, synthesis of plasma albumin is impaired.

In *cirrhosis* of the liver, two- to threefold increases in γ-globulins and some increases in β-globulins may accompany the marked decrease in albumin. In many infectious disorders, increases in γ-globulins also take place, although these may be small and not specific. In *kala-azar, lymphogranuloma venereum,* and *sarcoidosis,* γ-globulin increases may be so large as to provide valuable diagnostic confirmation and useful aids in evaluating treatment. In these conditions, a marked elevation of total plasma protein may occur, with γ-globulins representing more than half the total protein.

In Fig. 32.3 are shown the electrophoretic patterns found in a number of abnormal serum samples. The changes from the normal are described in the legend and indicate the usefulness of such estimations when correlated with clinical findings.

It is noteworthy that hyperglobulinemia is a frequent accompaniment of many diseases whereas hyperalbuminemia rarely, if ever, occurs except as a consequence of hemoconcentration. Also, the hyperglobulinemia is frequently associated with hypoalbuminemia. The globulin increment is customarily designated as "abnormal globulins," without regard to the question of whether they represent normal components present in excess amount or unnatural proteins formed only in disease. Certain of the abnormal globulins merit comment.

Myeloma Globulins. In multiple myeloma many small tumors of plasma cells, or "myelomas," are found in the bones. In most, if not all, cases of multiple myeloma an abnormal protein component is present, in either the plasma or the urine (see below), or both. Frequently, 50 to 70 per cent of the total plasma protein migrates electrophoretically as a homogeneous component, accounting for all the hyperglobulinemia. This component may exhibit a mobility less than that of γ-globulin, intermediate between γ- and β-globulins, the same as β-globulins, or, in rare cases, the same as α_2-globulins. Most myeloma globulins have the same sedimentation constant, 6.6 S, and a molecular weight of about 160,000, similar to that for normal γ-globulin. Occasionally, myeloma globulins have heterogeneous components sedimenting at rates intermediate between 6.6 S and 19 S (macroglobulins, see below).

All the myeloma proteins which have been examined resemble normal human γ-globulin in amino acid composition. Differences in composition and terminal residues have been obtained on analysis of various abnormal myeloma proteins from different individuals.

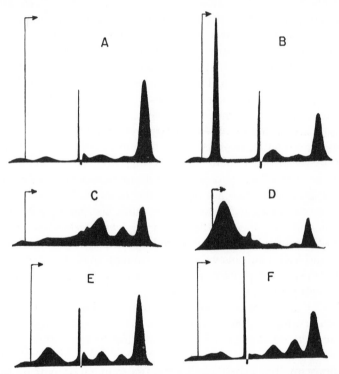

FIG. 32.3. Electrophoretic patterns of human sera. *A* is pooled serum obtained from normal individuals. *B* is from a patient with multiple myeloma; in this serum there is an abnormally large amount of γ-globulin. *C* is from an individual with nephrosis; the total protein is low, particularly albumin, and there are increased amounts of α_1- and α_2-globulins. *D* is the serum from a patient with cirrhosis of the liver; the albumin and total protein are very low, and the γ-globulin is elevated. *E* is from a patient with chronic rheumatoid arthritis; the γ-globulin and α-globulins are higher than found normally. *F* is from a patient with Hodgkin's disease; the α-globulins (including mucoproteins) are high, and the albumin and γ-globulin are abnormally low.

Bence-Jones Proteins. Bence-Jones discovered that a protein of unusual properties is excreted in the urine of many multiple myeloma patients. Heating the urine produces a cloudy precipitate at 50 to 60°C., but raising the temperature near the boiling point causes the precipitate to redissolve. The majority of the Bence-Jones proteins studied have a sedimentation constant of 3.5 S, with a molecular weight of about 45,000. The Bence-Jones proteins have many general relationships to normal human serum γ-globulin, including common antigenic properties, similar amino acid composition, and probably a common site of synthesis. This has led Putnam to suggest that Bence-Jones proteins represent incomplete or aberrant polypeptide chains of normal human γ-globulin. This has been supported by his demonstration of marked similarities in the peptide patterns obtained by enzymic digestion of Bence-Jones proteins and of normal human γ-globulins. Bence-Jones proteins can be grouped into two classes, based on differences in antigenic properties and on the presence or absence of amino-terminal aspartic acid.

Macroglobulins. The presence in normal plasma of γ-globulins of 19 S and an approximate molecular weight of one million has been considered previously (page 635). Abnormal amounts of macroglobulins have been reported for a number of clinical conditions. Occasional cases of myeloma reveal macroglobulinemia. Most striking is *Waldenström's macroglobulinemia,* characterized by a group of heterogeneous macroglobulins with a major component of about 19 S and both heavier (24 to 40 S) and lighter (14 to 16 S) components. Close immunological relationships obtain between the normal γ₁-macroglobulins and the pathological Waldenström macroglobulins. These normal and abnormal macroglobulins are immunologically related to ordinary 7 S γ-globulin.

A 19 S macroglobulin is found in the sera of a high percentage of patients with rheumatoid arthritis.

Cryoglobulins. Cryoglobulins is the name given to a group of rare serum globulins that have in common the unique property of precipitating, gelling, or even crystallizing spontaneously from solution or serum which is cooled. Though infrequent in multiple myeloma, cryoglobulins occur most often in this disease. They have also been found occasionally in rheumatoid arthritis. The cryoglobulins which have been studied have molecular weights similar to that of normal γ-globulin. Cryoglobulins have been found in normal sera in small amount after concentrating certain globulin fractions (Table 32.5).

C-Reactive Protein. The appearance in blood of a protein not present normally has been reported in the acute phase of certain infections, including rheumatic fever. Although the protein is nonspecific with respect to the inciting agent of the disease, it is detectable by a specific reaction between serum and the pneumococcal type C somatic polysaccharide in the presence of Ca^{++}. The C-reactive protein has been obtained in crystalline form. On electrophoresis the protein has the mobility of a β-globulin (free boundary electrophoresis) or a γ-globulin (starch zone electrophoresis). The isoelectric point is at pH 4.8, and the S value is 7.5. Since the titer of C-reactive protein in the serum is maximal in the active stage of infection and rapidly decreases during convalescence, the estimation of C-reactive protein is of considerable prognostic value.

From the foregoing, it is evident that studies of plasma protein distribution provide useful aids in clinical medicine. In certain conditions, such as multiple myeloma, nephrosis, cirrhosis, and lymphogranuloma venereum, the changes are so striking that plasma protein determinations are an essential aid in diagnosis. In many other conditions, the study of the plasma proteins is a useful adjunct in evaluating prognosis.

It is also evident that development of knowledge of the plasma proteins depends on their preparation in as pure a state as possible in order to assess individual properties and functions. Salt fractionation has been mentioned as a useful method of analysis; it has also been employed for preparation of a few individual proteins. Subsequent studies have been concerned with methods of obtaining as many plasma proteins as possible from a single large batch of plasma, both for characterization of individual proteins and for their production in quantities suitable for widespread clinical use. Outstanding work in this field has been performed by E. J. Cohn, J. T. Edsall, J. L. Oncley, and their associates at Harvard University. Their methods are based on the use of ethanol-water mixtures of controlled pH, ionic strength, and protein concentration at low temperatures ($+2$ to $-5°C.$) and with the addition of divalent metal ions, which form specific combinations with certain proteins.

REFERENCES

Books

Albritton, E. C., ed., "Standard Values in Blood," W. B. Saunders Company, Philadelphia, 1952.

Boyd, W. C., "Introduction to Immunochemical Specificity," Interscience Publishers, Inc., New York, 1962.

Landsteiner, K., "The Specificity of Serological Reactions," Harvard University Press, Cambridge, Mass., 1945.

Pedersen, K. O., "Ultracentrifugal Studies on Serum and Serum Fractions," Almqvist & Wiksells International Booksellers, Uppsala, 1945.

Putnam, F. W., ed., "The Plasma Proteins," vols. I and II, Academic Press, Inc., New York, 1960.

Sunderman, F. W., and Boerner, F., "Normal Values in Clinical Medicine," W. B. Saunders Company, Philadelphia, 1949.

33. Blood Clotting

The major *chemical* defense against blood loss is the formation of the blood clot. *Physiological* defense against blood loss in mammals also depends on constriction of blood vessels. In other animals, constriction of the body wall may occur, or the discarding of an injured extremity with severance of the circulation at that point may be the means of preventing blood loss. The present discussion is concerned with the chemical reactions involved in the coagulation of mammalian blood.

Blood clotting may be simply demonstrated by collection of a few milliliters of blood in a test tube. The tube is tilted at occasional intervals until clotting is observed; normal human blood will clot in 5 to 8 min. at 37°C. This poses the primary problems of coagulation: What factors are responsible for prevention of intravascular clotting, what changes are set in motion by removing blood from the vessels, and what substances are responsible for the clotting process?

The simplest scheme of coagulation was proposed in 1903 by Morawitz. The colorless protein mainly responsible for the coagulum is *fibrin*, which is formed from its soluble precursor, *fibrinogen*. The transformation is catalyzed by an enzyme called *thrombin*. Thrombin itself is not present in normal blood but is generated from its inactive zymogen, *prothrombin*. Conversion occurs only in the presence of Ca^{++} ions and another protein called *thromboplastin*. This minimal outline of the major changes may be formulated in two reactions which may be regarded as enzymic.

$$\text{Prothrombin} \xrightarrow{\text{Ca}^{++}, \text{ thromboplastin}} \text{thrombin}$$

$$\text{Fibrinogen} \xrightarrow{\text{thrombin}} \text{fibrin}$$

The participation of Ca^{++} in the coagulation mechanism is easily demonstrated since clotting can be prevented by collection of blood in the presence of decalcifying agents such as oxalate, fluoride, or citrate. Use of nontoxic citrates for this purpose made possible development of large-scale preservation of whole blood and plasma for transfusions. Various pyrophosphates, metaphosphates, and chelating agents, *e.g.*, ethylenediaminetetraacetate (EDTA), which bind Ca^{++} have also been used as anticoagulants. Preservation of whole blood has been achieved by removal of Ca^{++} ions by ion exchange resins, such as Amberlite IR 100, frequently used in the preparation of deionized water.

647

FIBRINOGEN AND FIBRIN

In human plasma, fibrinogen is present in a concentration of about 0.3 g. per 100 ml. As indicated previously (page 641), fibrinogen is produced in the liver. Normally, the regeneration of fibrinogen is rapid in animals depleted of this protein. Complete (*congenital afibrinogenemia*) and partial (*congenital hypofibrinogenemia*) absence of fibrinogen have been observed in a few infants. These rare diseases are characterized by a severe hemorrhagic tendency from birth and are usually fatal in early life.

Preparation of crude fibrinogen is simple since it is the least soluble of all plasma proteins. It is generally isolated by salting out in the cold by half saturation with sodium chloride or quarter saturation with ammonium sulfate. Precipitation from human plasma at 0 to $-3°C$. with 8 to 10 per cent ethanol gives a fibrinogen preparation which is about 65 per cent clottable protein. Repetition of the ethanol procedure gives materials which are 90 to 95 per cent coagulable with thrombin.

The fibrinogen molecule is an elongated ellipsoid, about twenty times greater in length than in cross-sectional diameter. Some additional physical properties are given in Table 32.5 (page 633). The native fibrinogen molecule is a dimer consisting of three pairs of polypeptide chains, probably linked by disulfide bridges. The presence of carbohydrate in the molecule has some significance in the clotting mechanism (see below).

The clotting of fibrinogen is normally accomplished by thrombin, but certain other enzymes, papain in particular, are also able to effect this. Trypsin does not clot fibrinogen, although it will digest fibrin clots. Certain snake venoms can cause clotting, and this is ascribed to the presence of active proteolytic enzymes. Many microorganisms, notably strains of staphylococci, can also coagulate fibrinogen.

In contrast to fibrinogen, fibrin is insoluble in salt solutions. Microscopic examination of fibrin shows a fine reticulum of fibers which exhibit birefringence under polarized light. In the conversion of fibrinogen to fibrin, at least three steps may be delineated: (1) proteolysis of fibrinogen; (2) physical aggregation of fibrin monomer to form a soft clot; and (3) an enzymic process which, in the presence of Ca^{++}, results in formation of a hard clot.

Proteolysis of Fibrin. The action of thrombin on fibrinogen (molecular weight, 330,000) results in the liberation of two peptides, termed fibrinopeptides A and B, which together have an aggregate molecular weight of approximately 9,000. Peptide A contains 18 amino acid residues, while B has 20, including tyrosine-O-sulfate. Also, approximately 18 per cent of the total sialic acid (0.6 per cent) present in fibrinogen is liberated in this conversion, as are small amounts of the other carbohydrates (mannose, galactose, and glucosamine) present in fibrinogen. It may be noted that the sialic acid residues of fibrinogen can also be removed by the action of neuraminidase (page 57), with a simultaneous increase in the ability of fibrinogen to clot. These observations indicate that the sialic acid is in some manner involved in the clotting of fibrinogen.

The protein remaining after thrombin action, *viz.*, fibrin monomer, contains four new amino-terminal glycine residues, whereas each of the liberated fibrinopeptides contains carboxyl-terminal arginine. These observations, together with studies of the action of thrombin on synthetic peptides, indicate that in the action of thrombin on fibrinogen, four arginyl-glycine linkages are split. Other enzymes, *e.g.*, trypsin and papain, can also catalyze hydrolysis of these peptide bonds, but in these instances, general and more widespread proteolysis of fibrin occurs. Thrombin also exhibits esterase activity, particularly toward arginine esters. This has led to a method for estimation of thrombin activity of plasma, with an N-substituted arginine methyl ester as substrate, by measurement of acid production.

Fibrin Monomer Aggregation; Formation of Soft Clot. The fibrin monomers resulting from the action of thrombin on fibrinogen undergo polymerization, possibly as a consequence of electrostatic attraction or of hydrogen bonding between groups unmasked by the removal of the peptides. Polymerization occurs in stages and depends on factors such as pH and ionic strength, but is independent of the presence of thrombin. Initially, end-to-end polymerization occurs with formation of primitive fibrils, followed by a side-to-side polymerization of these fibrils to form coarser fibrin strands.

The hydrolysis of fibrinogen by thrombin in the presence of a chelating agent results in the formation chiefly of a *soluble fibrin.* Clot formation, if it occurs, leads to a *soft clot,* and the fibrin present can be solubilized by buffer at pH values below 4.5 and above 9 and by $1M$ urea at pH 8.

Formation of Hard Clot. The formation of highly insoluble fibrin occurs in the presence of calcium and an enzyme which has been termed *fibrinase,* also designated as *fibrin stabilizing factor.* It appears that fibrinase modifies the fibrin monomer in a manner to permit new cross-linkages between monomers via disulfide bond formation. Since free sulfhydryl groups are absent in the soluble fibrin monomer, it has been inferred that the new disulfide bonds are created by a disulfide exchange reaction in which the intramonomer disulfide groups exchange to form intermonomer disulfides. The proteolytic activity of fibrinase somehow promotes juxtaposition of disulfide groups to permit disulfide exchange, and thus increases the degree of interaction between the fibrin monomers. Laki and his coworkers have demonstrated that fibrinase action is accompanied by liberation of sialic acid. Clots formed from fibrinogen which has been previously freed of sialic acid, by prior treatment with neuraminidase (page 57), remain soluble. The data suggest that fibrinase is an oligosaccharide-splitting enzyme, and that its effectiveness in releasing sialic acid from the soluble clot somehow allows introduction of strong bonds between the fibrin molecules; as a result, the clot becomes insoluble.

The three steps which have been described for the conversion of fibrinogen to fibrin may be summarized as follows.

(*a*) Proteolysis: **Fibrinogen** $\xrightleftharpoons{\text{thrombin}}$ **fibrin monomer** (f) **+ fibrinopeptides A and B**

(*b*) Polymerization: $$nf \rightleftharpoons f_n$$

(*c*) Clotting: $$mf_n \rightleftharpoons \textbf{fibrin}$$

In the above, f_n designates intermediate polymer, and n and m are variable numbers.

PROTHROMBIN AND THROMBIN

Thrombin is not found in normal plasma, which, however, contains the inactive precursor, prothrombin. The absence of thrombin from plasma is readily demonstrated, since intravenous injection of thrombin produces clotting promptly. It is evident that blood normally remains fluid in the vessels because of the absence of thrombin. However, the mechanism for preventing thrombin formation intravascularly has not been completely elucidated.

Prothrombin has been prepared in highly purified form by Seegers and his associates. It is a glycoprotein containing about 4 to 5 per cent carbohydrate as hexose and glucosamine. Prothrombin has the electrophoretic mobility of an α_2-globulin and an isoelectric point at pH 4.2; the molecular weight is approximately 65,000. When dissolved in 25 per cent sodium citrate solution, prothrombin slowly dissociates into three smaller particles with molecular weights of about 10,000, 15,000, and 35,000. This phenomenon is associated with the appearance of thrombin-like activity which resides only in the largest particle.

Thrombin is much less stable than prothrombin and has a similar molecular weight. "Citrate-activated thrombin" (see above) has a molecular weight of 30,000 to 35,000. Thrombin has solubility properties of a globulin; its enzymic properties and specificity were described previously (page 648). The nature of the conversion of prothrombin to thrombin is considered below.

Plasma prothrombin deficiency (*hypoprothrombinemia*) occurs frequently in obstructive jaundice and in other liver disorders. Hepatectomy in animals has also shown the importance of the liver in the synthesis of prothrombin since blood prothrombin values decline following liver removal. Normal production of prothrombin is dependent on adequate nutritional intake of vitamin K (*Koagulation-Vitamin*) (Chap. 56). The role of vitamin K in maintaining normal prothrombin levels is unknown, but it is believed to be concerned in the hepatic synthesis of prothrombin. Present evidence excludes participation of the vitamin in the coagulation mechanism itself, and it is not a part of the prothrombin molecule.

A hemorrhagic disease of cattle is caused by Dicumarol, a derivative of coumarin, the sweet-smelling substance of clover.

Dicumarol
[3,3'-Methylenebis-(4-hydroxycoumarin)]

Dicumarol fed to experimental animals or man causes a decrease of plasma prothrombin and is used clinically in cases of threatened thrombosis to reduce the clot-forming tendency. The action of Dicumarol is at the site of prothrombin formation in the liver and is partially counteracted by feeding vitamin K. The apparent similarity in structure of the fused ring systems of vitamin K and Dicumarol suggests that a competitive metabolic effect may be involved.

THROMBOPLASTIN

The term thromboplastin was used originally to describe a substance found in tissues and which, in the presence of Ca^{++}, catalyzed conversion of prothrombin to thrombin. It is now apparent that there is a group of thromboplastins, and that manifestation of the thromboplastin activity of tissue extracts requires the presence of several additional factors found in normal blood (see below). The thromboplastic activity from tissue extracts differs from that of blood. In the latter, thromboplastin activity *arises during* the clotting process, whereas this activity is evident *immediately* in certain tissue extracts, *e.g.*, of brain. This differentiation is the basis for the rapid clotting (within 12 to 15 sec.) of blood on addition of a suitable brain extract, as contrasted with the slower clotting time (5 to 10 min.) of whole blood placed in a glass tube. Lung, brain, and placenta are rich in thromboplastin activity; probably all tissues contain such material. Chargaff and his associates prepared from lung a material with thromboplastin activity which appeared to be homogeneous in the ultracentrifuge and on electrophoresis. The product had an apparent molecular weight of about 170,000,000 and contained a variety of phosphatides which accounted for 40 to 50 per cent of the material. The bulk of the remainder was protein, but carbohydrate and ribonucleic acid were also found. The intact substance is remarkably potent; 0.008 μg gives detectable conversion of prothrombin to thrombin. Removal of the lipid from thromboplastin destroys its activity. Indeed, the phosphatides which can be removed also possess some thromboplastin activity, although when they are tested in place of thromboplastin, a clotting time is found that is prolonged five- to sixfold.

As indicated above, plasma does not contain a thromboplastin, but there is evidence for the existence of a prothromboplastin which can be converted to thromboplastin through the mediation of the platelets or platelet factors, as well as of other factors present in normal blood.

FACTORS CONCERNED IN PROTHROMBIN ACTIVATION

In addition to Ca^{++} and thromboplastin, other factors have been implicated in the activation of prothrombin. Some of these appear to act on prothromboplastins, accelerating their conversion to thromboplastin, others seem to act as cothromboplastins, and still others may participate by some direct means in the conversion of prothrombin. The situation is not completely clear, partly because of the complexity of the process and partly because some of the factors have not been purified sufficiently to determine their chemical nature and relationships. Nevertheless, there is excellent evidence for the existence of at least five such factors. The evidence is derived mainly from the description of dyscrasias in which an individual factor is present in low concentration or missing entirely from the plasma of individuals whose blood does not manifest a normal clotting time. The independent discovery of these factors by several investigators has resulted in the use of different names for the same factor. Table 33.1 contains a list of these factors and the various synonyms used by different workers, together with the dyscrasia resulting from the deficiency of the substance.

Antihemophilic Factors. The hereditary defect known as *hemophilia* is inherited as a sex-linked recessive trait and thus occurs with significant frequency in males but is transmitted only through the female. The defect is manifested in a markedly prolonged clotting time. The hemophilic clotting system apparently contains normal amounts of fibrinogen, prothrombin, Ca^{++}, etc. The existence of two types of hemophilia was discovered by Pavlovsky, who observed that when the blood of one hemophiliac was added to the blood of another patient with hemophilia, the clotting time was much shorter than that of either specimen alone.

In hemophilia A, the missing factor is a labile, sparingly soluble globulin, usually precipitated with fibrinogen, which can be obtained from normal plasma. Preparations of this globulin hasten, both in vitro and, temporarily, in vivo, the clotting of blood of individuals with hemophilia A. Since thrombin formation is defective in hemophilic blood, the *antihemophilic globulin* is concerned with the conversion of prothrombin to thrombin, and is believed to be a thromboplastinogen or prothromboplastin.

Less is known concerning the factor which is deficient in individuals affected by hemophilia B, but some evidence suggests that this factor is also concerned in thromboplastin formation. The factor is, however, distinct from antihemophilic globulin and has been termed *Christmas factor,* from the name of the first patient in whom the disorder was recognized; the disease is known as *Christmas disease.*

Table 33.1: PROTHROMBIN AND THROMBOPLASTIN ACTIVATION FACTORS

Synonyms	*Dyscrasia or deficiency disease*
Antihemophilic globulin (AHG) or factor (AHF), antihemophilic factor A, thromboplastinogen A, platelet cofactor I, Factor VIII	Classical or hemophilia A
Antihemophilic factor B, plasma thromboplastin component, PTC factor, Christmas factor, platelet cofactor II, autoprothrombin II, Factor IX	Hemophilia B
Accelerator (Ac) globulin, proaccelerin, labile factor, labile component, Factor V	Congenital parahemophilia
Proconvertin, serum prothrombin conversion accelerator (SPCA), stable factor, autoprothrombin I, cothromboplastin, Factor VII	Result of treatment with Dicumarol; vitamin K deficiency

Thromboplastinogenase, platelet thromboplastic factor

Accelerator Globulin. Another factor concerned in the clotting mechanism was identified by Owren in 1944 in the study of a patient with a bleeding tendency and whose blood was deficient only in this factor. The deficiency disease is now called *congenital parahemophilia.* The responsible factor involved in the transformation of prothrombin to thrombin is *accelerator* or *Ac globulin* (labile factor). The substance is present in plasma as an inactive precursor (*proaccelerin*) which is transformed to the accelerator globulin (*accelerin*). Proaccelerin is thermolabile and disappears rapidly from stored plasma.

Proaccelerin may be deficient in the plasma of individuals with severe liver disease. The condition does not respond to vitamin K therapy but is corrected by administration of fresh, prothrombin-free plasma.

Proconvertin and Convertin. In contrast to proaccelerin, proconvertin is a relatively stable substance and persists in stored plasma. One hypothesis suggests that proconvertin interacts with thromboplastin in the presence of Ca^{++} to form convertin which is essential for prothrombin conversion. Another view, suggested by the name *serum prothrombin conversion accelerator,* is that the substance acts with thromboplastin to hasten prothrombin conversion.

Proconvertin deficiency occurs in patients treated with Dicumarol or in individuals with vitamin K deficiency (page 650). Vitamin K administration leads to an increase in plasma proconvertin levels.

Platelets. Suspensions or extracts of platelets (thrombocytes) accelerate coagulation of platelet-free blood, establishing the importance of platelets in blood coagulation, although their exact role is not clear. They contain small quantities of thromboplastin, and it has been suggested that rupture of platelets aids in initiation of coagulation by liberation of thromboplastin or, more likely, by release of an enzyme which acts as a thromboplastin activator (*thromboplastinogenase*).

Prevention of platelet dissolution may be accomplished by collection of blood with needles, tubing, and glassware which have been coated with silicones or other water-repellent polymers. Platelets remain intact on contact with these nonwettable, smooth surfaces, and coagulation is strongly retarded. In fact, if platelets are removed by high-speed centrifugation, human plasma kept in silicone containers will not coagulate for protracted periods even in the absence of calcium-binding agents. If platelet extracts or lysed platelets are added to such preparations of blood, clotting occurs rapidly.

During the dissolution of platelets, norepinephrine (Chap. 49), serotonin (page 536), and histamine (page 534) are liberated. These substances are vasoconstrictors and may aid in the physiological control of blood loss.

Prolonged bleeding time may be due to *thrombocytopenia,* a deficiency of platelets. This leads to a decreased formation of active thromboplastin with deficient production of thrombin. The condition may be caused by a variety of chemical reagents including certain drugs, by ionizing radiations, by associated blood disorders, *e.g.,* certain leukemias or anemias, or by a variety of infections.

HEPARIN

Heparin prevents the coagulation of plasma. This substance was discovered by Howell and McLean in 1916 in crude extracts of liver. Many tissues of the body contain heparin since it specifically originates in the metachromatic granules of mast cells, which are principally found along blood vessel walls. Heparin has been isolated from lung as well as liver as the crystalline barium salt. It is an acid mucopolysaccharide of molecular weight about 17,000, which, on hydrolysis, yields glucosamine, sulfuric acid, and glucuronic acid. The probable structure of heparin has been presented previously (page 56).

Sulfation of certain polysaccharides, *e.g.,* starch, can produce a product which exhibits heparin-like activity in preventing blood coagulation and also behaves as a clearing factor (page 436). This indicates that the repeating sulfate polymer structure in heparin (page 56) is the basis of these biological activities. However, the chondroitin sulfates (page 55), which also contain sulfate but have galactosamine in the repeating unit in place of glucosamine, have no anticoagulant activity. Also, a minimum molecular weight is essential for activity since lower molecular weight synthetic polymers of a monomer structure identical with that in heparin are not biologically effective.

Heparin acts in vivo as well as in vitro to prolong the clotting time of blood by interfering with the normal conversion of prothrombin to thrombin. However, heparin does not act by itself since it has no influence on purified prothrombin. A serum protein cofactor is necessary for heparin action. Heparin also inactivates thrombin in the presence of serum. Thus, the action of heparin with its protein cofactor is that of an antithrombin and antiprothrombin; this is believed to be the basis of one of the normal mechanisms for control of the fluidity of the blood.

Thrombin causes platelets to become sticky and to adhere to each other as well as to rough surfaces and to disintegrate, leading to release of thromboplastinogenase. Heparin prevents agglutination of platelets and thus aids in preventing thrombus formation.

Fragmentary evidence has been obtained that plasma contains antithrombins which are effective without addition of heparin. One such antithrombin is removed from plasma or serum by extraction with ether, and it has been claimed that the ether extract possesses the activity.

Fibrin itself can adsorb thrombin. Thus clot formation immediately sets into operation a way of preventing excessive clotting by retaining the thrombin at the site of bleeding.

A tentative summary of all the factors concerned in the coagulation mechanism still leaves us with the classical two-step reaction scheme (page 647) described by Morawitz many years ago, but with the addition of other important participants whose chemical nature and mode of action are still largely to be determined. This may be illustrated in the diagram below.

$$\text{Prothrombin} \xrightarrow{\text{blocked by inhibitors of activation}} \text{thrombin}$$

Requires: Calcium ions

Thromboplastin

Ac globulin

Platelet factors

Antihemophilic globulin

Other factors

$$\text{Fibrinogen} \xrightarrow{\text{thrombin}} \text{fibrin}$$

$$\text{Thrombin} + \text{antithrombin} \longrightarrow \text{inactive thrombin}$$

DISSOLUTION OF FIBRIN

Sterile blood clots usually dissolve after a few hours or days, and the lysis is caused by a proteolytic enzyme. It is also known that serum becomes fibrinolytic when shaken with chloroform. The present view is that this proteolytic enzyme, *plasmin* (fibrinolysin), ordinarily exists in plasma as the inactive precursor, or zymogen, *plasminogen* (profibrinolysin). Plasminogen is a protein of molecular weight approximately 143,000, is isoelectric at pH 5.6, and contains about one per cent of hexose. Activation of plasminogen by chloroform or other organic solvents is presumably due to separation of an inhibitor. Also effective are extracts of hemolytic streptococci or certain other bacteria which contain an enzyme termed *streptokinase* that catalyzes conversion of plasminogen to plasmin. Obviously, the above activators of plasminogen cannot be considered of significance in normal circumstances. However, factors present in many tissues will produce activation of plasminogen. Plasmin formation from plasminogen occurs in a variety of circumstances, *e.g.*, emotional stress, during exercise, or after injection of epinephrine. Plasminogen activator also is produced in blood vessel walls, from which it is released on vascular injury.

Plasmin, which has a molecular weight of about 100,000 and retains the carbohydrate present in plasminogen, is a true proteolytic enzyme since it acts not only on fibrin and fibrinogen but also on casein, gelatin, and other proteins. However, unlike thrombin, it does not convert fibrinogen to fibrin. Specificity studies indicate that plasmin splits arginyl-lysine linkages.

Thus information is presently available which indicates that in addition to the complex, delicately balanced mechanisms for prevention of clotting, as well as for its initiation, there is also present a system for removal of intravascular clots, or thrombi. Since antiplasmins have been shown to occur in plasma, there are physiological controls for the level of proteolytic activity in plasma. The present picture may be summarized in the following outline:

$$\text{Plasminogen} \xrightarrow[\text{and other factors (?)}]{\text{tissue enzymes}} \text{plasmin}$$
$$+$$
$$\text{inhibitors}$$
$$\downarrow$$
$$\text{inactive plasmin}$$

$$\text{Fibrin clot} \xrightarrow{\text{plasmin}} \text{soluble products}$$

REFERENCES

Books

Biggs, R., and MacFarlane, R. G., "Human Blood Coagulation and Its Disorders," 3d ed., Blackwell Scientific Publications, Oxford, 1962.

Seegers, W. H., "Prothrombin," Harvard University Press, Cambridge, Mass., 1962.

Review Articles

Dam, H., Vitamin K, *Vitamins and Hormones, 6,* 27–53, 1948.

Link, K. P., The Anticoagulant from Spoiled Sweet Clover Hay, *Harvey Lectures, 39,* 162–216, 1943–1944.

Quick, A. J., The Anticoagulants Effective in Vivo with Special Reference to Heparin and Dicoumarol, *Physiol. Revs., 24,* 297–318, 1944.

Scheraga, H. A., and Laskowski, M., Jr., The Fibrinogen-Fibrin Conversion, *Advances in Protein Chem., 12,* 1–131, 1957.

Seegers, W. H., Coagulation of the Blood, *Advances in Enzymol., 16,* 23–103, 1955.

34. Chemistry of Respiration

Primitive organisms rely on diffusion through their environmental media to provide the oxygen needed for their metabolism and to remove the carbon dioxide produced. The active metabolism of mammalian tissues remote from the atmosphere is possible because of a mechanism which provides constant delivery of oxygen and removal of carbon dioxide. The magnitude of this task may be appreciated from the fact that a man oxidizing 3000 Cal. of mixed food per day uses about 600 liters of oxygen (27 moles) and produces about 480 liters of carbon dioxide (22 moles). Through the action of hemoglobin, oxygen is abstracted from the air, carried within a few seconds to the most distant parts of the body, and delivered to the tissues at a pressure only slightly less than that at which it existed in the atmosphere. The CO_2 produced daily by the tissues becomes H_2CO_3, an acid, in an amount equivalent to 2 liters of concentrated hydrochloric acid; yet all this acid normally pours from the tissues, through the blood, and out of the lungs with a change in the pH of blood of no more than a few hundredths of a pH unit. This chapter will describe the means by which these enormous tasks are accomplished.

THE RESPIRATORY GASES

The pressure which a gas exerts, when mixed with other gases, is the partial pressure of that gas and is denoted by the symbol P. This pressure is a function of the temperature and of the number of molecules of gas in a given volume. At constant temperature and volume, equal numbers of molecules of all ideal gases exert equal pressures, and the total pressure exerted by a gas mixture is equal to the sum of all the partial pressures in the mixture. The barometric pressure of atmospheric air is thus the sum of the partial pressures of O_2, CO_2, N_2, etc.

The amount of any gas present in solution is proportional to the partial pressure of that gas in the total gas mixture with which the solution is in equilibrium; occasionally it is convenient to describe the concentration of a gas in solution by stating the partial pressure with which that solution might be in equilibrium. This is the *tension* of the gas in that solution and is expressed in the same units as the pressure in a gas phase, millimeters of mercury (mm. Hg). However, the actual amount of gas which will dissolve per unit volume of solvent at a given partial pressure varies with each gas. This is stated in the expression

$$C = kP$$

where C is milliliters gas per milliliter solvent, P is the partial pressure of the gas in the vapor phase in millimeters mercury, and k is the Bunsen absorption coefficient, a constant for a given gas in a given solvent at a specified temperature. The k values for the important respiratory gases are given in Table 34.1, which also includes the effect of temperature on the solubility of these gases. The rate of diffusion of a gas through liquid (tissue in this case) varies directly with the absorption coefficient.

Table 34.1: ABSORPTION COEFFICIENTS OF RESPIRATORY GASES

Temperature, °C.	O_2	CO_2	N_2
Water:			
0	0.049	1.71	0.024
20	0.031	0.87	0.016
40	0.023	0.53	0.012
Plasma:			
38	0.024	0.510	0.012

Note: Values are ml. of gas (measured at standard conditions) which dissolve in 1 ml. of indicated solvent when the latter is equilibrated with the specified gas at 760 mm. Hg.

Inspired air mixes with the gas mixture present in the larger passages of the respiratory tract, the trachea, bronchi, and bronchioles. Some of this mixture, tidal air, is sucked into the expanding alveolar sacs, where the gases make contact with the pulmonary capillaries. From the alveolar gas mixture, O_2 diffuses across the capillary walls and into the circulating blood while CO_2 migrates in the reverse direction. On expiration, a portion of this alveolar air is forced up into the larger passages, where it mixes with the gas mixture already present, and from the tidal air a portion leaves as expired air. By proper adjustment of this tidal flow of gas, the rates of entry of O_2 and CO_2 into the alveoli equal the rates of loss, and the composition of alveolar air remains relatively constant with respect to these gases.

Although the pressure in the alveoli fluctuates rhythmically during the respiratory cycle, the mean pressure of the alveolar gas mixture is that of the atmosphere. However, alveolar air must also be saturated with water vapor evaporated from the lung surfaces. Since, at body temperature, the partial pressure of water vapor is 47 mm. Hg and is independent of the composition of the remainder of this mixture, the aqueous tension is a significant fraction of the total alveolar gas pressure and its importance must increase at diminished total pressure, *e.g.*, at high altitudes. The composition of inspired, expired, and alveolar air is shown in Table 34.2. The composition of the alveolar gas mixture is determined by the *rate* at which alveolar air is mixed with tidal air and the latter with atmospheric air. Under normal conditions the respiratory apparatus maintains the CO_2 content of alveolar air relatively constant at 40 mm. Hg, although other components of air are not maintained with similar constancy.

Since the P_{O_2} in alveolar air is of the order of 100 mm. Hg, while that in the venous blood is about 50 mm. Hg or less, a concentration gradient exists across the capillary wall and oxygen diffuses across. As the blood rushes by, the O_2 of the alveolar gas and of arterial blood almost equilibrates and the P_{O_2} of arterial blood in man, at rest, is about 100 mm. Hg, while during vigorous exercise it may be 95 mm. Hg. This O_2 is then transported in the blood in two ways, (1) as oxygen in solution and (2) in chemical combination with the hemoglobin of erythrocytes. The limited solubility of oxygen permits transportation of only 0.3 ml. O_2 per 100 ml. of blood, and, even with a considerably increased cardiac output, this amount of oxygen does not meet metabolic requirements. However, since each gram of hemoglobin can combine with 1.34 ml. of O_2 and normal blood contains about 15 g. of hemoglobin per 100 ml., fully oxygenated blood may contain almost seventy times the amount of O_2 present in simple solution.

Thus, it will be apparent that comprehension of physiological transport of O_2 and CO_2 requires understanding of the chemistry of hemoglobin (pages 193*ff*.).

Table 34.2: COMPOSITION OF THE RESPIRATORY GASES

	Inspired air		Alveolar air		Expired air	
	mm. Hg	vols. per cent	mm. Hg	vols. per cent	mm. Hg	vols. per cent
O_2	158.2	20.95	101.2	14.0	116.2	16.1
CO_2	0.3	0.04	40.0	5.6	28.5	4.5
N_2	596.5	79.0	571.8	80.0	568.3	79.2
H_2O	5.0	. . . .	47.0	. . . .	47.0	. . . .
Total	760.0	99.99	760.0	99.6	760.0	99.8

The Combination of Hemoglobin with Oxygen. The unique feature of hemoglobin is its ability to bind oxygen reversibly. Ferroporphyrin and many of its hemochromogens can also bind oxygen, but in these instances the iron is rapidly oxidized to the ferric condition, whereas hemoglobin uniquely forms a stable oxygen complex in which the iron remains in the ferrous state. This special behavior of hemoglobin appears to be due to the fact that much of the heme of the molecule lies within a cover of hydrophobic groups of the globin, providing an environment of relatively low dielectric constant. This is suggested by the behavior of the model system previously discussed (page 197). Conjugation of the iron to the imidazole moiety of histidine is also essential to its normal properties, since hemoglobin M (page 611), in which one of the histidine residues normally linked to the heme is replaced by tyrosine, also can bind oxygen but is then rapidly oxidized to the ferric state.

Since in hemoglobin all the coordination positions of the ferrous atom are filled by virtue of coordination to the two histidine residues, it follows that reaction with oxygen involves displacement of one imidazole group. The mechanism of this reaction is obscure.

Factors Affecting the Combination of Hemoglobin with Oxygen. The hemoglobin of the lamprey eel has a molecular weight of about 17,000 and one heme group per molecule. In this regard it resembles the myoglobin of both vertebrate and invertebrate muscle. These compounds, like human hemoglobin, reversibly bind oxygen. Increasing P_{O_2} promotes the formation of their oxygenated forms. The general relationship between oxygen tension and the formation of the oxygenated compounds is shown in Fig. 34.1. The depicted curve is a rectangular hyperbola,

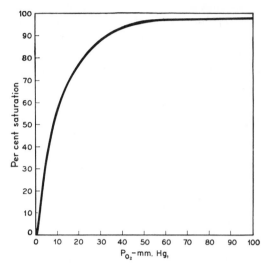

FIG. 34.1.   General form of curve showing oxygenation of myoglobin and lamprey hemoglobin as a function of oxygen tension.

the curve expected from the mass law for the dissociation of oxyhemoglobin, formulated as $HbO_2 \rightleftharpoons Hb + O_2$. In contrast, the dissociation curve for the oxyhemoglobin of normal human blood is sigmoidal (Fig. 34.2). No adequate explanation of this difference in behavior is available. The sigmoidal curve was long inter-

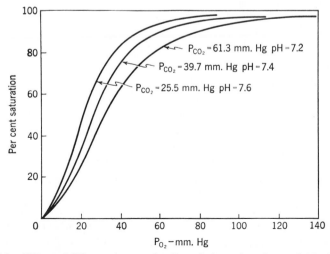

FIG. 34.2.   Effect of CO_2 tension on the dissociation of oxyhemoglobin in blood.

preted as indicating that the presence of oxygen on a heme group of hemoglobin affects the dissociation constants of the other heme groups on the same molecule, an effect which, from the shape of the curve, is thought to be greatest for the fourth dissociation. However, x-ray crystallography reveals that the four heme groups are quite remote from each other and separated by a considerable portion of the peptide chains. Hence, direct heme-heme interactions within the same hemoglobin molecule are difficult to comprehend. However, x-ray crystallography also reveals a pronounced conformational change upon oxygenation of hemoglobin, and it would appear that the successive changes in binding affinity for oxygen to the four hemes of each hemoglobin reflect these induced conformational changes. Each hemoglobin molecule may be combined with 0, 1, 2, 3, or 4 O_2 molecules; the resulting compounds may be designated as Hb_4, Hb_4O_2, Hb_4O_4, Hb_4O_6, and Hb_4O_8, respectively. The sigmoidal oxygen dissociation curve is therefore a composite of the curves shown in Fig. 34.3, but the real basis for this phenomenon

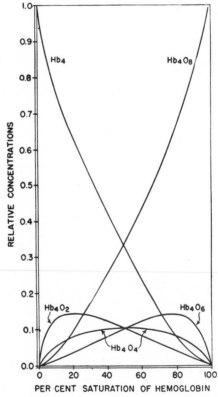

FIG. 34.3. Analysis of the oxyhemoglobin dissociation curve. (*From data of C. D. Coryell, L. Pauling, and R. W. Dodson, J. Phys. Chem.,* **43**, 825, 1939.)

remains to be established. In any case, however, the sigmoidal character of the dissociation curve of oxyhemoglobin is of great physiological significance, since, as is evident in Fig. 34.2, although the saturation of hemoglobin is affected by O_2 tension over a wide range of pressure (20 to 80 mm.), arterial hemoglobin is virtually saturated at a P_{O_2} as low as 80 mm.

As indicated previously (page 198), the oxygenation of hemoglobin results in a profound rearrangement of the electrons in the heme moiety. This effect of the strongly electrophilic O_2 extends through the iron atom to the heme-linked imidazole group; the electrons binding the imidazolium dissociable hydrogen are attracted and more closely held by the imidazole group, thereby loosening the dissociable hydrogen. The imidazolium, therefore, becomes a stronger acid, with its pK lowered from 7.9 to 6.7. Conversely, increased proton concentration, by repressing the acidic dissociation of the imidazole, attracts electrons to the dissociable hydrogen and away from the O_2, thereby weakening the bond between O_2 and the iron atom. Consequently, increased acidity causes dissociation of oxyhemoglobin, with the dissociation curve being shifted to the right. Thus, the reversible reaction between hemoglobin and O_2 may be schematically represented as

$$HHb^+ + O_2 \rightleftharpoons HbO_2 + H^+$$

although the reaction does not occur stoichiometrically.

Increased P_{CO_2} affects the oxygenation of hemoglobin just as does increased acidity, a phenomenon known as the Bohr effect after its discoverer. Presumably, this effect of CO_2 reflects the acidity of carbonic acid solutions. Since the P_{CO_2} in pulmonary and extrapulmonary capillaries differs markedly, in order to describe the process of oxygen carriage from lungs to tissues it is necessary to construct a family of curves differing in P_{CO_2}, such as those shown in Fig. 34.2. Increased P_{CO_2} displaces the curve to the right, and at a given P_{O_2}, an increase in P_{CO_2} decreases the amount of oxyhemoglobin within the red cell.

Explanation of the Bohr effect is incomplete at present. Whereas undoubtedly the influence of proton concentration on the state of the heme-linked histidine residue must be of great importance, other portions of the peptide chain and the conformation of the molecule make significant contributions also. Thus, Antonini and his collaborators have shown that removal of the terminal tyrosylhistidine from the β chain of hemoglobin by treatment with carboxypeptidase A yields a product which has three times the normal affinity for oxygen, exhibits a rectangular hyperbolic oxygen dissociation curve, and has a Bohr effect only about one-third the magnitude of normal hemoglobin A. When hemoglobin was treated with carboxypeptidase B, which removes the terminal lysyltyrosylarginine from the α chain, the resultant hemoglobin again showed a minimal Bohr effect although it retained the normal sigmoidal dissociation curve. Treatment with a combination of both carboxypeptidases abolished the sigmoidal character of the dissociation curve and the Bohr effect and yielded a product with an unusually large affinity for oxygen. Significant also is the finding that treatment of hemoglobin with N-ethyl maleimide, which reacts with one of the two sulfhydryl groups of each of the β chains (Fig. 11.2, page 196), reduces the Bohr effect to half that of the native molecule. Hence, the remaining Bohr effect has been attributed to the unaffected α chains. Noteworthy in this regard is the behavior of hemoglobin H (page 805), an abnormal hemoglobin consisting of four β chains. This hemoglobin exhibits an oxygen affinity ten times greater than that of normal hemoglobin A, shows no

Bohr effect, and its oxygen dissociation curve is not sigmoidal. From these observations, it is evident that the structure and conformation of the entire hemoglobin molecule, not merely of the heme-linked histidine residues, contribute to the affinity of hemoglobin for oxygen, the shape of the oxygen dissociation curve, and the Bohr effect.

Oxygen Transport. The transport of oxygen from lungs to tissues is described by the curves shown in Fig. 34.2. In the lung, oxygen diffuses across the capillary lining in accordance with the existing gradient, then through plasma and into the erythrocytes. The P_{O_2} in erythrocytes leaving the lungs is about 100 mm. Hg, and the P_{CO_2} in the arterial blood is of the order of 40 mm. Hg. By referring to Fig. 34.2, it may be seen that the hemoglobin of arterial blood is about 96 per cent saturated.

The P_{O_2} in the interstitial fluid surrounding extrapulmonic capillaries cannot be accurately measured but is probably about 35 mm. Hg in muscle at rest, while the P_{CO_2} must be approximately 50 mm. Hg. Consequently, O_2 diffuses from red cells through plasma to interstitial fluid and then into the tissue cells, while CO_2 moves in the opposite direction. Again, despite rapid passage of blood through the capillary, equilibration is almost complete so that venous blood returning from the tissues at rest is generally found to have a P_{CO_2} of 46 mm., while the P_{O_2} is about 40 mm. Hg. Since the diffusion coefficient of CO_2 is thirty times greater than that of O_2, the pressure gradient need not be so high for the former gas. Under these circumstances, venous hemoglobin is about 64 per cent saturated with oxygen. The difference, 32 per cent of the oxygen, has been delivered to the tissues. Assuming 15 g. of hemoglobin per 100 ml. of blood, and since each gram of hemoglobin can combine with 1.34 ml. of oxygen, then

$$0.32 \times 1.34 \times 15 = 6.4 \text{ ml. of } O_2$$

has been supplied to the tissues for each 100 ml. of blood traversing the capillaries. Further inspection of the curves in Fig. 34.2 reveals that during exercise, as P_{O_2} in the tissues falls and P_{CO_2} rises, this mechanism becomes increasingly efficient for the delivery of oxygen. Delivery of the increased amounts of O_2 required during exercise is, therefore, effected by a combination of this mechanism and by acceleration of the circulation through the working muscle.

Transport of CO_2. The total CO_2 content of a blood sample may be estimated by the addition of mineral acid and then subjecting the sample to reduced pressure. The volume of CO_2 released may be measured quantitatively. When this is done, it is found that the CO_2 content of arterial blood is about 50 ml. per 100 ml., referred to as 50 volumes per cent, while that of venous blood may be 55 to 60 volumes per cent. Thus, each 100 ml. of blood transports 5 to 10 ml. of CO_2 from tissues to lungs. Yet the difference in P_{CO_2} between arterial and venous blood at rest is only of the order of 6 mm. Hg. From the constants given in Table 34.1, it can be calculated that an increase of 6 mm. Hg in the P_{CO_2} would permit the physical solution of only an additional 0.4 volume per cent of CO_2. Further, even this increment in CO_2 content would markedly lower the pH of the venous blood, yet this is not observed. How then is the transport of CO_2 effected? To understand this mechanism, several conditions must first be described: (1) the actual state of

CO_2 in arterial and in venous blood, (2) the direct reaction between CO_2 and protein, (3) the relative behavior of hemoglobin and oxyhemoglobin as acids, and (4) the electrolyte composition of red cells and plasma.

1. Carbon dioxide in blood exists in several states. Bicarbonate, in both red cells and plasma, accounts for the major portion of all the CO_2 present. The CO_2 which diffuses across the capillary wall from the tissue space is largely in solution as CO_2 molecules since hydration to form H_2CO_3 is a slow reaction. The CO_2 generated by the various decarboxylation reactions of intermediary metabolism as molecular CO_2 diffuses from cells through interstitial fluid into the plasma largely in this form, with only a small fraction hydrated as carbonic acid. On entry into erythrocytes, hydration of CO_2 is catalyzed by a specific enzyme, *carbonic anhydrase*. This enzyme has been obtained in highly purified form; the purest preparations contain 0.3 per cent of zinc. The enzyme catalyzes both the hydration of CO_2 and the dehydration of H_2CO_3; at equilibrium the formation of H_2CO_3 is favored.

$$CO_2 + H_2O \rightleftharpoons H_2CO_3$$

At the pH of blood, most of the H_2CO_3 is present as HCO_3^-.

The history of this enzyme is of interest. In 1928, Henriques, studying the kinetics of the hydration and dehydration of CO_2, calculated that in the absence of an intervening mechanism, the rapid passage of blood through the pulmonary capillaries would permit less than 10 per cent of the blood CO_2 to escape into the lungs. The rate of liberation of CO_2 from serum *in vacuo* was of the order to be expected from the pH and the operation of diffusion, whereas escape from hemoglobin solutions was many times faster. In 1932, Roughton found that on splitting hemoglobin into hematin and globin, all the carbonic anhydrase activity was associated with the globin fraction, but in 1933 Meldrum and Roughton obtained a preparation 100 times as active as erythrocytes but containing relatively little heme or globin, thus establishing the enzyme as an independent entity.

2. Carbon dioxide reacts with undissociated aliphatic amino groups to form carbamino compounds as shown in the following equation.

$$R\!-\!NH_2 + CO_2 \rightleftharpoons R\!-\!NHCOO^- + H^+$$

A fraction of the CO_2 in plasma, about 0.5 millimole (mmole) per liter, is thus bound to the plasma proteins. The trivial difference in plasma protein carbamino content between arterial and venous blood, at rest, is of little consequence in CO_2 transport from the tissues. However, the increased acidity and P_{CO_2} of venous blood during exercise permits the existence of three times as many carbamino groups in hemoglobin as in oxyhemoglobin. The heme-linked imidazole groups do not participate in this process, and the increase in hemoglobin carbamino groups appears unrelated to oxygenation per se. Arterial blood contains about 1.0 mmole of carbamino-CO_2 per liter, whereas, at rest, 1 liter of venous blood carries 1.5 to 2.0 mmoles of CO_2 as the carbamino form.

3. Like all proteins, hemoglobin is a buffer, able to react with protons or dissociate to yield protons. At the pH within corpuscles, the imidazole groups of the histidine residues are chiefly responsible for the buffering action of hemoglobin. Figure 34.4 compares the titration of hemoglobin and oxyhemoglobin. These two

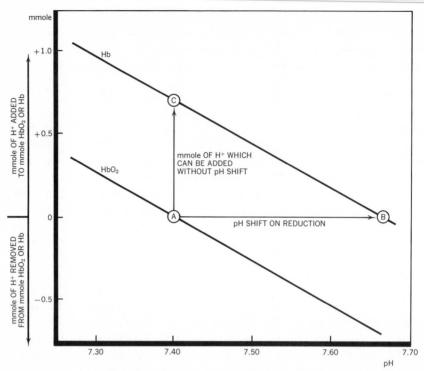

Fig. 34.4. Titration curves of hemoglobin and oxyhemoglobin; mmole denotes millimole. (*From H. W. Davenport, "The ABC of Acid-Base Chemistry," 3d ed., University of Chicago Press, Chicago, 1950.*)

curves are parallel over the physiological range of pH. If one starts with a solution of 1 mmole of either protein at pH 7.4, the addition of 2.54 mmoles of acid or alkali is required to change the pH of the solution by one pH unit. Examination of these curves reveals that oxyhemoglobin is a stronger acid than is reduced hemoglobin, as indicated previously (page 661). At pH 7.40, if 1 mmole of oxyhemoglobin were to be deoxygenated to hemoglobin, all other factors remaining constant, the pH would shift to (*B*) on the hemoglobin titration curve and would rise to about pH 7.67. The addition of 0.7 mmole of acid would be required to shift back along the curve to (*C*), where the pH would again be 7.40. Conversely, starting at (*C*), were 1 mmole of hemoglobin suddenly to be oxygenated, the blood pH would fall to about 7.13, and 0.7 mmole of alkali would be required to restore the pH to 7.4. These properties of hemoglobin and their physiological significance were first noted by Douglas and Haldane.

4. Both erythrocytes and plasma contain HCO_3^- and H_2CO_3. The following discussion assumes that all the CO_2 present is H_2CO_3. The Henderson-Hasselbalch equation (page 103) states that

$$pH = pK + \log \frac{[\text{salt}]}{[\text{acid}]}$$

and the buffer pair HCO_3^-/H_2CO_3 must adhere to this relationship. At a normal blood pH of 7.40, since the pK_a' of H_2CO_3 is 6.1, log ([salt]/[acid]) equals 1.3 and the ratio $[HCO_3^-]/[H_2CO_3]$ is 20/1. Within the physiological pH range, therefore, the main portion of the total CO_2 present in plasma and red cells exists as HCO_3^-.

A typical arterial blood sample might contain 25.5 meq. per liter of HCO_3^- in plasma and 12.7 meq. per liter of HCO_3^- within the cells. In venous blood, these values would be 26.4 meq. per liter in plasma and 13.9 meq. per liter in cells. Two factors can be cited to account for the discrepancy between the concentration of HCO_3^- within cells and plasma.

First, although red cells contain a 34 per cent protein solution, plasma is a 7.5 per cent solution of protein. Thus, if the concentrations of HCO_3^- are expressed in milliequivalents per liter of red cell and plasma *water*, instead of per liter of cells or per liter of plasma, the values are as follows: arterial blood, 27.2 meq. per liter in plasma and 19.6 meq. per liter in cells; venous blood, 28.1 meq. per liter in plasma and 21.3 meq. per liter in cells. Clearly, there remains a difference in HCO_3^- concentration between cells and plasma. This arises from the second factor, *viz.*, that within the cells, hemoglobin, which is nondiffusible, accounts for a large fraction of the total anions, while in plasma the proteins represent only a small fraction of the total anions. This results in a Gibbs-Donnan effect (page 133). Since the two solutions are in osmotic equilibrium, the total concentration of diffusible anions within cells must be smaller than the total concentration of anions in plasma. At equilibrium the ratios (r) of the concentrations of the various anions within cells (c) and plasma (p) must be constant. Thus

$$r = \frac{[HCO_3^-]_c}{[HCO_3^-]_p} = \frac{[Cl^-]_c}{[Cl^-]_p} = \text{etc.}$$

$$\frac{[HCO_3^-]_c}{[Cl^-]_c} = \frac{[HCO_3^-]_p}{[Cl^-]_p}$$

and

$$\frac{[HCO_3^-]_c}{[HCO_3^-]_c + [Cl^-]_c} = \frac{[HCO_3^-]_p}{[HCO_3^-]_p + [Cl^-]_p}$$

Since

$$[HCO_3^-]_p + [Cl^-]_p > [HCO_3^-]_c + [Cl^-]_c$$

it is apparent that the $[HCO_3^-]$ of plasma must exceed that within the cells, in agreement with the observed facts.

One further fact may be deduced from the Gibbs-Donnan equilibrium. Hydroxyl ions, as diffusible anions, must also be unequally distributed between red cells and plasma, whereas the product $[OH^-][H^+]$ must be identical in the two solutions.

$$[H^+]_c[OH^-]_c = [H^+]_p[OH^-]_p$$

Therefore

$$\frac{[OH^-]_c}{[OH^-]_p} = \frac{[H^+]_p}{[H^+]_c} = r$$

Since r is less than 1, the concentration of hydrogen ions within the red cell is greater than the concentration in plasma and, therefore, the pH of the interior of the erythrocyte is lower than that of the surrounding plasma.

The Isohydric Shift. With the above factors in mind it becomes possible to reconstruct the events in the transport of carbon dioxide from tissues to alveolar air, as first formulated by L. J. Henderson. When arterial blood arrives in the tissue capillaries, about 95 per cent of the hemoglobin is oxygenated. Because of the increased CO_2 tension and the decreased O_2 tension, the oxyhemoglobin dissociates; oxygen diffuses out into the interstitial fluid as CO_2 diffuses into the erythrocyte. A significant fraction of the CO_2 is immediately bound as carbamino hemoglobin. However, there still remains a large excess of CO_2 to be disposed of by other means. Under the influence of carbonic anhydrase this CO_2 is rapidly hydrated to carbonic acid, which then dissociates. Two opposing phenomena then come into play: (1) This carbonic acid would tend to lower the pH within the erythrocyte, but (2) the transformation of oxyhemoglobin to reduced hemoglobin involves a change of pK from 6.7 to 7.9, which tends to raise the pH within the erythrocyte. Consequently, protons formed in the dissociation of carbonic acid are accepted by the imidazole nitrogen of the reduced hemoglobin. The net result of these two events is to maintain the pH essentially unchanged, and K^+ ions within the erythrocyte, previously electrically neutralized by oxyhemoglobin, are now neutralized by the newly formed HCO_3^- ions. As a result, the major portion of the CO_2 which diffused into the erythrocyte from the tissues leaves the capillary in venous blood as red cell HCO_3^-. This set of transformations is termed the *isohydric shift* and is summarized in Fig. 34.5.

The isohydric shift entails formation of 0.7 meq. of bicarbonate for each millimole of oxygen which dissociates from oxyhemoglobin. It will be recalled that the R.Q. for the combustion of carbohydrate is 1, whereas the R.Q. for the body at rest in the fasting state is 0.82 (Chap. 16). From the values shown in Table 34.3, it appears that the quantitative operation of the isohydric shift, which is based on the difference between the acid strength of oxyhemoglobin and reduced hemoglobin, is well suited to the physiological task of removing carbon dioxide.

The Chloride Shift. Because of the isohydric shift, the ratio $[HCO_3^-]_c/[HCO_3^-]_p$ is now altered, with an excess of HCO_3^- within the cells. The ratio $[HCO_3^-]_c/[Cl^-]_c$ no longer equals the ratio $[HCO_3^-]_p/[Cl^-]_p$. The escaping tendency of HCO_3^- from the cells is increased, and HCO_3^- is replaced by Cl^- from plasma until a new equilibrium is attained. The net result of this transformation is that a significant fraction of the total CO_2 which entered the erythrocyte and was hydrated and dissociated is now found in the venous plasma as HCO_3^-. Note also that while the conversion of oxyhemoglobin to reduced hemoglobin and its subsequent buffering action do not influence the osmotic pressure due to hemoglobin within the cells, since the amount of hemoglobin is unchanged, the combined result of the isohydric and chloride shifts is to increase the total number of anions and thereby increase the effective osmotic pressure within the cells. In consequence, water is redistributed between the cells and plasma so that the relative volume occupied by the erythrocytes (the hematocrit) in venous blood is appreciably higher than that in arterial blood, rising from 45 to 48 or 49 per cent by volume. A partition of the CO_2 transported by 1 liter of blood from the tissues to the lungs of a subject at rest is shown in Table 34.3. It is apparent that about 60 per cent of the total CO_2 is transported as plasma HCO_3^-, while about 32 per cent is transported as carbamino-CO_2 and

HCO_3^- within erythrocytes. Directly and indirectly, therefore, hemoglobin makes possible the transport of more than 90 per cent of all the CO_2 carried by the blood.

When venous blood arrives in the pulmonary capillaries, this sequence is reversed. The lower P_{CO_2} in the alveoli results in a CO_2 concentration gradient favor-

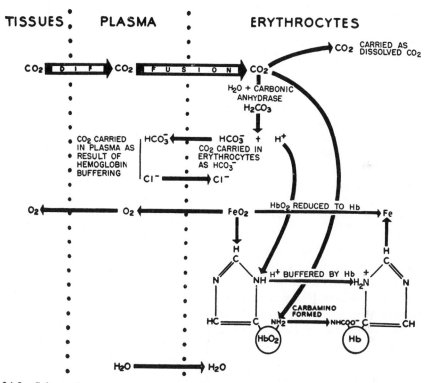

FIG. 34.5. Schematic representation of the processes occurring when carbon dioxide passes from the tissues into the erythrocytes. The imidazole ring of histidine is shown as the reactive portion of the hemoglobin molecule. (*Modified from H. W. Davenport, "The ABC of Acid-Base Chemistry," 3d ed., University of Chicago Press, Chicago, 1950.*)

Table 34.3: DISTRIBUTION OF TOTAL CO_2 IN ARTERIAL AND VENOUS BLOOD

	Arterial, mmole	Venous, mmole	Difference	
			mmole	ml.
Total CO_2 in 1 liter of blood.................	21.53	23.21	1.68	37.4
Total CO_2 in plasma of 1 liter of blood (600 ml.)	15.94	16.99	1.05	23.5
As dissolved CO_2........................	0.71	0.80	0.09	2.0
As bicarbonate ions......................	15.23	16.19	0.96	21.5
Total CO_2 in 400 ml. of erythrocytes	5.59	6.22	0.63	14.0
As dissolved CO_2........................	0.34	0.39	0.05	1.1
As bicarbonate ions......................	4.28	4.41	0.13	2.9
As carbamino-CO_2.......................	0.97	1.42	0.45	10.0

ing CO_2 flow from erythrocyte through plasma to the alveolar space. Simultaneously, oxygen flows from the alveoli into the erythrocyte, and, with diminished P_{CO_2} and increased P_{O_2}, the reduced hemoglobin is oxygenated. Plasma HCO_3^- moves into erythrocytes and combines with protons given up by dissociation of the newly formed oxyhemoglobin. Carbonic anhydrase catalyzes the dehydration of the carbonic acid so that CO_2 formed from the HCO_3^- of plasma can now diffuse out of the erythrocyte through the plasma and into the alveolar space. Carbon dioxide present as carbamino-CO_2 is also liberated because of the diminished CO_2 tension and the conversion of hemoglobin to oxyhemoglobin. The net result is the transport of oxygen from lungs to tissues in sufficient amount to meet metabolic requirements and delivery to the lungs of the carbon dioxide formed during metabolism without changing the acid-base pattern of the extracellular fluid or the erythrocytes.

Thus, the reversible reaction $HbO_2 + H^+ \rightleftharpoons HHb^+ + O_2$ is of paramount importance in the respiratory cycle, and the fact that the Fe^{++} of the heme moieties of hemoglobin is also linked to the imidazole groups of the globin histidine is of fundamental significance for the physiology of respiration. When venous blood enters the lungs, the reaction proceeds to the left since here the P_{O_2} increases, whereas the P_{CO_2}, and, consequently, the $[H^+]$ decrease and the hemoglobin is oxygenated. In capillaries outside the lungs, the increased P_{CO_2} and, therefore, increased $[H^+]$, together with the decreased P_{O_2}, favor the reaction to the right. This behavior of hemoglobin is a remarkable example of the relation of chemical structure to physiological requirements.

Fetal Hemoglobin. For maximal oxygen transport, the loading tension at which fetal blood approaches full oxygen saturation must be in the region of the unloading tension of the maternal blood in the placenta. This is indeed the case in mammals and is the consequence of the difference in structure between fetal hemoglobin (Hb F$^{\alpha_2 A \gamma_2 F}$) and adult hemoglobin (Hb A$^{\alpha_2 A \beta_2 A}$). The γ chains differ significantly from β chains in their structure (page 195), notably in the unique presence of isoleucine, which is absent in Hb A, and in the presence of a single sulfhydryl group. The oxygen dissociation curve of fetal erythrocytes, compared to adult erythrocytes, is displaced above and to the left of the curve shown in Fig. 34.2 at any given value of CO_2 or oxygen tension. Thus at 30 mm. of O_2, 37°C., and pH 6.8, maternal blood is 33 per cent saturated whereas fetal blood is 58 per cent saturated. This increased affinity of fetal erythrocytes for O_2 is not uniquely the consequence of the structure of Hb F. Indeed, the oxygen dissociation curve of pure Hb F does not differ remarkably from that of Hb A. Accordingly, the enhanced affinity for oxygen must reflect some other aspect of the structure or composition of fetal erythrocytes, as well as the structure of Hb F.

The presence of fetal hemoglobin is readily recognized by addition of alkali to a blood sample; hemoglobin of adult blood is rapidly converted to brown alkaline hematin while that of fetal blood remains bright red for a considerable period. The structural basis for this difference in behavior is not clear. After birth, fetal hemoglobin ordinarily disappears from the circulation and is entirely absent after 4 to 6 months, except in certain anemic states.

Myoglobin. The muscles of all vertebrates and invertebrates contain *myoglobin*, a hemoprotein capable of reversibly binding oxygen. The structure of whale myoglobin, which is known in detail, was discussed previously (page 158). Although its heme, like that of hemoglobin, lies in a crevice with the iron coordinated to two histidines, myoglobin exhibits no Bohr effect; the oxygen dissociation curve is constant over a wide range of pH. Since the normal protein is a monomer, the oxygen dissociation curve is a rectangular hyperbola (Fig. 34.1, page 659), displaced well above and to the left of that of hemoglobin. At a venous P_{O_2} of 40 mm. Hg, at which hemoglobin is 66 per cent saturated, myoglobin is still 94 per cent saturated. At an oxygen tension of only 10 mm. Hg, hemoglobin is 10 per cent saturated whereas myoglobin is 80 per cent saturated. Related to these considerations is the fact that cytochrome oxidase can operate at V_{max} when the medium provides oxygen at P_{O_2} of about 4 to 5 mm. Hg. Thus the affinities of these three proteins for oxygen are in the order cytochrome oxidase $>$ myoglobin $>$ hemoglobin. Consequently, myoglobin can accept oxygen from hemoglobin and store it in the muscle cell for release to cytochrome oxidase when the oxygen supply becomes limiting.

In muscle at rest, oxygen probably remains fixed to myoglobin. During contraction, when the demand for oxygen is maximal and as intracellular P_{O_2} falls, oxygen dissociates from myoglobin and is available for oxidations. In man, myoglobin is present in significant quantity only in cardiac muscle and is probably of little significance in skeletal muscle. However, in diving mammals, the myoglobin content of muscles is particularly high and probably facilitates submersion for long periods. The muscle of dolphins and seals contains 3.5 and 7.7 per cent myoglobin, respectively; these relative concentrations correlate roughly with the duration of their dives. The flight muscles of birds are also rich in myoglobin.

Carboxyhemoglobin (Carbon Monoxide Hemoglobin). Hemoglobin and the nitrogenous base derivatives of ferroprotoporphyrin bind carbon monoxide (CO). Indeed, carbon monoxide competes with oxygen in binding with hemoglobin. The affinity of human hemoglobin for carbon monoxide is more than 200 times greater than its affinity for oxygen, *i.e.*, for equal formation of HbCO and HbO₂, the required partial pressure of carbon monoxide is only about one two-hundredths that of oxygen. Claude Bernard in 1858 explained the toxicity of carbon monoxide by his discovery of its combination with hemoglobin. The brilliant cherry-red color of HbCO is very distinctive and is manifested in the skin and tissues of victims of carbon monoxide poisoning.

COMPARATIVE BIOCHEMISTRY OF RESPIRATORY PROTEINS

The need for an oxygen carrier, apparent throughout the animal kingdom, has been satisfied by various means. In the most primitive animals, which are relatively small and have low metabolic rates, the carrier is enclosed in cells suspended in the coelomic fluid. With the development of a circulation there appeared oxygen carriers dissolved in the circulating plasma, and, later still, concentrated solutions of carriers were enclosed in special circulating cells, the erythrocytes. The latter represent a great advance, as they permit the presence in the circulation of large amounts of carrier without an inordinate rise in the viscosity and colloidal osmotic pressure of the circulating medium. There are a number of oxygen carriers of markedly different properties distributed throughout the animal kingdom. Almost all vertebrates have as an oxygen carrier an intracellular hemoglobin of molecular weight 68,000 with ferroprotoporphyrin III as the prosthetic group.

A great diversity is apparent among the invertebrates. In those species in which the oxygen carrier is simply dissolved in the circulating plasma, the carrier is invariably of high molecular weight, *e.g.*, 400,000 to 6,700,000. Among these are large hemoglobin-like molecules, given the group name *erythrocruorins,* found dissolved in the blood of many polychete and oligochete annelid worms and various mollusks. Certain of the annelids, such as *Spirographis,* have green blood pigments, the *chlorocruorins,* of molecular weight 3,400,000, in which the porphyrin differs from protoporphyrin in that the 2-vinyl group has been oxidized to a formyl group.

The blood of most mollusks and crustaceans contains *hemocyanins,* blue pigments containing copper but no heme and with a molecular weight of approximately 6,760,000. The erythrocruorins and chlorocruorins, like hemoglobin, contain one heme per unit of 17,600 and bind one molecule of oxygen per iron atom, while hemocyanin binds one molecule of oxygen per two atoms of copper.

It has been assumed that the manner of binding of O_2 to the chlorocruorins is essentially similar to that in heme and involves no change in the valence state of the iron atom. However, this does not appear to be the case for those carriers in which the metal is not bound to a porphyrin. When O_2 is bound to a hemocyanin, two copper atoms are required per molecule of O_2.

Intracellular oxygen-carrying proteins are of relatively low molecular weight, varying from 17,600 to 70,400. *Hemerythrin,* molecular weight 66,000, has been found in the blood cells of sipunculoid worms. This protein contains no heme but has two times as much iron as does hemoglobin. Since it binds one molecule of oxygen per two iron atoms, it carries as much oxygen, per mole, as hemoglobin. Like hemoglobin, hemerythrin is a tetramer. Each subunit bears two atoms of iron; electron spin resonance data suggest that these may be bound in a vicinal manner similar to that of some iron flavoproteins (page 348) and thus, as in hemocyanin, a pair of metal ions may function in binding a single O_2 molecule.

It may also be noted that there are a few vertebrates, fish of the order *Chaenichthyidae,* which do not employ a respiratory pigment. These poikilothermic animals dwell in Antarctic waters, at temperatures from -2 to $+2°C.$, and their sluggish metabolism is satisfied by the oxygen carried in simple solution at this low temperature.

The peculiar suitability of these diverse oxygen carriers to their task in the organisms in which they are found is best illustrated by two considerations, (1) the operation of the Bohr effect and (2) the degree of oxygen saturation in arterial blood. Not only are there carriers which exhibit no Bohr effect, but the various oxygen carriers differ markedly in the extent to which a given change in P_{CO_2} affects the oxygen dissociation curve. This is illustrated in Fig. 34.6. Thus, in animals like the marine teleosts, which lead an active existence in ocean waters which are well oxygenated yet almost free of carbon dioxide, the Bohr effect is especially prominent. It is less pronounced in animals that live in fresh water or in air, whereas in those

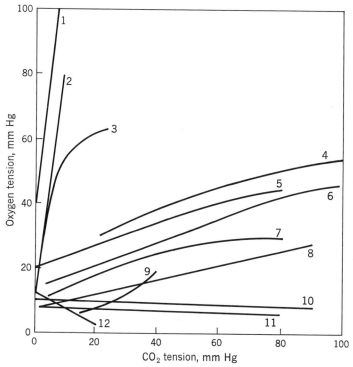

FIG. 34.6. Magnitude of the Bohr effect in the blood of various species; relationship between P_{CO_2} and the P_{O_2} necessary to maintain 50 per cent saturation of hemoglobin. A sharp slope indicates a large Bohr effect, a flat line indicates no Bohr effect, and a negative slope indicates a negative Bohr effect. 1, squid; 2, sea robin; 3, mackerel; 4, sea lion; 5, goose; 6, dog; 7, man; 8, turtle; 9, carp; 10, *Urechis*, echiuroid worm; 11, sipunculid; 12, *Busycon*, conch, a marine gastropod. (*Adapted from M. Florkin, "Biochemical Evolution," Academic Press, Inc., New York, 1949.*)

species which live in a medium poor in oxygen and rich in carbon dioxide the oxygen carrier may even exhibit an inverted Bohr effect. For each respiratory pigment it is a *sine qua non* that it should be virtually saturated with oxygen under the conditions prevailing in the arterial blood of the animal in which it is employed. While this encompasses a range of P_{O_2} from 30 to 115 mm. Hg, there is no known instance in which the oxygen-carrying protein is not at least 90 per cent saturated in its native arterial blood. The characteristics of certain of the respiratory pigments mentioned above are given in Table 34.4.

It is surprising that hemoglobin, similar to that of mammalian erythrocytes, has been found in cells of plant origin, *e.g.*, in a few strains of yeast and fungi. Of particular interest is the hemoglobin in the nodules formed by the nitrogen-fixing *Rhizobium* on the roots of Leguminosae. The pigment is a product of symbiosis since it is not formed by pure cultures of *Rhizobium* or by the plant roots in the absence of nodules. The role of hemoglobin in this biological system is not understood.

Table 34.4: CHARACTERISTICS OF RESPIRATORY PIGMENTS

Pigment	Source	Location	Atoms of metal per mole	Molecular weight	Bohr effect	Dissociation curve
Myoglobin......	Mammalian muscle	Intracellular	1 Fe	17,000	None	Hyperbolic
Hemoglobin.....	Lamprey eel	Intracellular	1 Fe	17,500	Positive	Hyperbolic
Hemoglobin.....	*Gastrophilus* larvae	Tracheal cells	2 Fe	34,000	Positive	Hyperbolic
Hemoglobin.....	Tadpole	Intracellular	4 Fe	68,000	None	Sigmoid
Hemoglobin.....	Frog	Intracellular	4 Fe	68,000	Positive	Sigmoid
Hemoglobin.....	Man	Intracellular	4 Fe	68,000	Positive	Sigmoid
Erythrocruorin...	Mollusks	Plasma	96 Fe*	1,500,000	None	Sigmoid
Erythrocruorin...	Annelids	Plasma	192 Fe*	3,000,000	None	Sigmoid
Chlorocruorin...	Polychaete worms	Plasma	192 Fe*	3,000,000	None	Sigmoid
Hemerythrin....	*Sipunculus*	Intracellular	16 Fe	66,000	None	Hyperbolic
Hemerythrin....	*Lingula*	Intracellular	......	......	Positive	Sigmoid
Hemocyanin....	Lobster	Plasma	20 Cu*	780,000	None	Sigmoid
Hemocyanin....	Snail	Plasma	200 Cu*	6,760,000	None	Sigmoid

* Approximate number.

REFERENCES

Books

Barcroft, J. S., "The Respiratory Function of the Blood. II. Haemoglobin," Cambridge University Press, London, 1928.

Davenport, H. W., "The ABC of Acid-Base Chemistry: The Elements of Physiological Blood-Gas Chemistry for Medical Students and Physicians," 4th ed., University of Chicago Press, Chicago, 1958.

Haldane, J. S., and Priestly, J. G., "Respiration," Yale University Press, New Haven, 1935.

Henderson, L. J., "Blood: A Study in General Physiology," Yale University Press, New Haven, 1928.

Prosser, C. L., and Brown, F. A., Jr., "Comparative Animal Physiology," 2d ed., W. B. Saunders Company, Philadelphia, 1961.

Roughton, F. J. W., and Kendrew, J. C., eds., "Haemoglobin," Interscience Publishers, Inc., New York, 1949.

Review Articles

Drabkin, D. L., Metabolism of the Hemin Chromoproteins, *Physiol. Revs.,* **31**, 345–431, 1951.

Millikan, G. A., Muscle Hemoglobin, *Physiol. Revs.,* **19**, 503–523, 1939.

Redfield, A. C., The Evolution of the Respiratory Function of the Blood, *Quart. Rev. Biol.,* **8**, 31–57, 1933.

Wyman, J., Heme Proteins, *Advances in Protein Chem.,* **4**, 407–531, 1948.

35. Electrolyte, Water, and Acid-Base Balance

The ability of animals to maintain constant the composition of the *extracellular fluid,* the *milieu intérieur,* first appreciated by Claude Bernard, represents one of the most significant advances of evolution, since, with it, animals became virtually independent of their environment. It is the purpose of this chapter to describe the nature and function of the intra- and extracellular fluids and the mechanisms which maintain their composition constant.

FLUID COMPARTMENTS OF THE BODY

In the human adult, an amount of fluid approximately equal to 50 per cent of the body weight is located within cells, while the extracellular fluid, *i.e., all* the fluid not present within cells, accounts for about 20 per cent of the body weight. Extracellular fluid may be further divided into several subcompartments, of which the largest are the interstitial fluid, which bathes most cells and represents 15 per cent of the body weight, blood plasma, the transport vehicle through which cells make contact with other cells and with the environment, amounting to about 5 per cent of the body weight, and relatively smaller volumes of cerebrospinal fluid, synovial fluid, aqueous and vitreous humors, lymph, etc.

The principle of the procedures for estimation of the volume of each of the various fluid compartments is essentially the same. A material, previously found to be distributed almost exclusively within the compartment to be measured, is given intravenously in known amount. After sufficient time for mixing, a sample of plasma is obtained, the concentration of administered material measured, and, from the extent of dilution, the total volume of the particular compartment calculated after correction for the quantity excreted. *Total body water,* then, may be estimated after administration of any material which is distributed throughout the body, *i.e.,* one which passes freely through capillary endothelium, cell membranes, the blood-brain barrier, etc., followed by determination of this material in any available fluid, *e.g.,* plasma or urine. The substance which most closely meets these criteria is D_2O, although total body-water measurements with this compound also include measurement of all hydrogen atoms of the variety of body substances that will exchange with deuterium. Since determination of heavy water is not always feasible, other materials, particularly antipyrine, have been employed.

Determination of *total extracellular fluid* requires a substance to which capillary walls are permeable but which fails to enter cells and, preferably, is relatively slowly excreted by the kidneys. Among the materials employed for this purpose are inulin, thiocyanate, and thiosulfate. Unfortunately, the results of these procedures are not in complete agreement; the inulin "space" appears to approximate most closely the extracellular fluid volume.

Estimation of *plasma volume* requires the intravenous administration of some material which will be retained entirely within the vascular space. For this purpose, several dyes, notably Evans' blue, have been employed, as well as serum proteins labeled with I[131].

The volume of the *interstitial fluid,* together with all the *specialized extracellular fluids,* is calculated as the difference between the volumes of total extracellular fluid and of plasma.

COMPOSITION OF BODY FLUIDS

Figure 35.1 shows the electrolyte composition of the body fluids. Although Na^+ is the chief extracellular cation, K^+ and Mg^{++} are the chief intracellular cations; Cl^- and HCO_3^- predominate outside of cells, while phosphates, sulfate, and protein constitute the bulk of the cellular anions.

The osmotic pressure within a cell must be identical with that of the surrounding fluid, since the membranes involved are freely permeable to water. The osmotic pressure considered here is that which the solution would exhibit in an osmometer with a membrane permeable solely to water, in this case about 6,000 mm. Hg. Since interstitial fluid is almost protein-free and the chief anions and cations are univalent, the height of the column in the chart indicates not only molar concentrations but also the osmolarity of this solution. In contrast, among the chief contributors to the osmotic pressure of intracellular fluid are many multivalent particles, such as Ca^{++}, Mg^{++}, protein, and phosphates. Osmotic pressure is determined, however, solely by the total number of particles in solution, regardless of their electric charge. It follows that the concentration of electrolytes within the cells, expressed in milliequivalents per liter, is appreciably greater than that outside the cells. This may be illustrated as follows.

Imagine an extracellular fluid composed exclusively of NaCl and a cellular fluid exclusively of K^+ and protein and, further, that the protein particles bear four negative charges each. If each milliliter of extracellular fluid contained 50 Na^+ ions and 50 Cl^- ions, what then must be the composition of the cellular fluid at osmotic equilibrium? Since the extracellular fluid contains 100 particles per milliliter, the cellular fluid must also contain 100 particles per milliliter. This is possible only when the latter fluid contains 80 K^+ ions and 20 protein molecules per milliliter. Expressed in milliequivalents per liter, then, the concentration of inorganic cations within the cells is eight-fifths that of the extracellular fluid. This is an exaggeration but serves to explain the observed differences depicted on the chart. Since the protein concentration of plasma is intermediate between that of cells and extracellular fluid, plasma occupies an intermediate position with respect to its electrolyte concentration.

The composition of intracellular fluid indicated in Fig. 35.1 represents a mean for cells in general. Although this may even be a valid statement for the total content of an individual cell, it seems likely that within the cell there are areas or compartments containing unusual concentrations of one or another of the cell constituents, in part because of the variable binding capacities of different protein molecules, and, in part, reflecting specific, selective transport mechanisms.

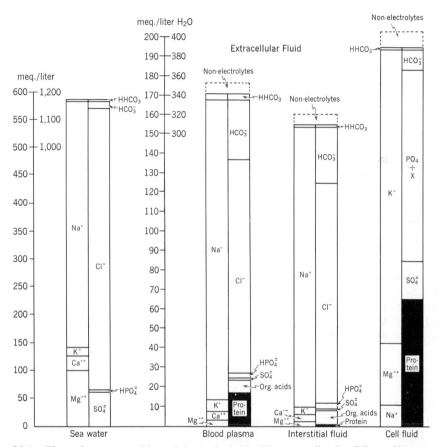

FIG. 35.1. Electrolyte composition of the body fluids. The over-all value $PO_4 + X$ (composition of cell fluid) is obtained by subtracting the equivalents found for $SO_4^= + HCO_3^- +$ protein from the total equivalents prescribed by the cations. The composition of sea water is given for comparison. (*From J. L. Gamble, "Chemical Anatomy, Physiology and Extracellular Fluid," 6th ed., Harvard University Press, Cambridge, Mass., 1954.*)

It has been suggested that the composition of extracellular fluid is not unlike that of the seas during the pre-Cambrian era, when animals with closed circulations came into existence. The sea has continued to increase in salinity, while the composition of extracellular fluid has remained fixed. The present composition of sea water is shown in Fig. 35.1 for comparison.

These differences in composition of intra- and extracellular fluid are determined by the metabolism of the cell and the properties of cell membranes. Plasma may be regarded as a special subcompartment of extracellular fluid which differs only in that it contains proteins which cannot diffuse through the endothelial lining of the capillaries. Consequently, the electrolyte composition of plasma must also differ slightly from that of interstitial fluid, as formulated by the Gibbs-Donnan equilibrium.

The electrolyte composition of intracellular fluid cannot be determined with precision but must be calculated by difference. For example, an animal is first given a known quantity of sodium thiosulfate; a few minutes later samples of plasma and muscle are obtained and analyzed for thiosulfate, Na^+, K^+, and Cl^-. The thiosulfate concentration of plasma and of interstitial fluid is assumed to be identical so that the total amount of thiosulfate in the tissue sample permits calculation of its extracellular fluid volume. Knowing the latter and the concentration of Na^+, K^+, and Cl^- in plasma, one may then calculate the extracellular Na^+, K^+, and Cl^- of the tissue sample. When these are subtracted from the total Na^+, K^+, and Cl^- concentrations found in the tissue, the differences represent the intracellular ion concentrations. Obviously, there are numerous sources of error in these procedures. The technique of isotope dilution has also been employed to determine the amount and distribution of these three ions (Na^+, K^+, Cl^-). The most striking information thus obtained is that at least one-third of the total body sodium and almost one-half the chloride are not in the extracellular fluid. By inference, except for the quantities of these ions present in bone matrix but readily "exchangeable" with ions in plasma, this signifies intracellular concentrations of the order of 20 to 40 meq. per liter.

Active Transport and the Composition of Intracellular Fluid. It is apparent from Fig. 35.1 that the electrolyte composition of intracellular fluid differs strikingly from that of the surrounding interstitial fluid. The cell membrane separating these fluids is an organized mosaic of protein, lipid, including phosphatide and ganglioside, and polysaccharide. Although this membrane exhibits selective permeability, its properties do not account adequately for the marked differences in composition of intra- and extracellular fluid. In general, small singly charged anions and cations pass through cell membranes, albeit with varying degrees of freedom. The membrane behaves as if it had pores such that hydrated ions less than 8 Å. in diameter pass freely, whereas the passage of larger ions is hindered. Thus, K^+, Rb^+, and Cs^+ ions can enter animal cells rather rapidly, whereas Na^+ and Li^+ ions enter with relative difficulty. Similarly, Cl^-, Br^-, and NO_3^- ions enter with ease, whereas HCO_3^- and CH_3COO^- ions diffuse across the membrane relatively slowly and $SO_4^=$ ions are practically excluded from cells. These relationships were established by comparing the relative rates of entry of the appropriate radioisotopes of each of these ions into animal cell preparations at 0 and 37°C.; their relative behavior is that which might be expected from the normal distribution of such ions within and outside the cell. Nevertheless, the marked disparity in composition of the fluids on either side of the cell membrane cannot be attributed solely to permeability characteristics of the membrane, which can only delay the time required for the establishment of equilibrium between the two phases with respect to each of those components which can traverse the membrane. Hence, it is necessary to postulate an "electrolyte pump" which derives its energy from the metabolic activities of the cell. The existence and operation of such a pump is indicated by many observations of the following type: human erythrocytes maintained at 0°C. lose K^+ and, in time, equilibrate with the Na^+ of the medium. If the erythrocytes are returned to 37°C., the process is reversed; Na^+ leaves the cells and K^+ reenters until the normal relationships are reestablished. However, if the cells are rewarmed in saline solution lacking glucose, redistribution of electrolytes does not occur; subsequent addition of glucose results in accumulation of K^+ within the cells, and the rate at which this occurs is a function of the rate of glycolysis. Essentially similar observations have been made with most animal tissues.

Considerable evidence indicates that the reestablishment of the normal disequilibrium in the concentrations of potassium and sodium on either side of the cell membrane results from the operation of a mechanism which, in effect, ejects Na^+ from the cell, thereby permitting accumulation of an equivalent amount of K^+, which enters the cell by diffusion. This is among the most dramatic examples of the many processes which are termed "active transport," processes whereby a solute is caused to move against an electrochemical gradient, *i.e.*, from an area of relatively low to one of higher concentration. In some instances active transport is recognized by the fact that the rate of migration of a given material, although in the direction of the electrochemical gradient, nevertheless is more rapid than can be accounted for by simple solvent drag or diffusion across the membrane.

The term "electrolyte pump" has been used to describe the operation of this process with respect to Na^+. The analogy to a mechanical pump is apt, in that energy is utilized to move material, in this case ions, against an opposing gradient. In all cases studied, the source of energy for accomplishment of this work is ATP. In erythrocytes and in fermenting yeast which actively accumulate potassium, the energy is derived from anaerobic glycolysis. Ejection of Na^+ from muscle and nerve cells, which permits maintenance of the normal high intracellular potassium concentration, secretion of HCl by the stomach, and absorption of NaCl by the renal tubular epithelium and by the intestinal mucosa, all are processes which derive the required energy from the oxidative metabolism of the respective cells. In each instance the process is inhibited by anoxia, by cyanide (which prevents reduction of oxygen by cytochrome oxidase), and by dinitrophenol (which uncouples mitochondrial oxidative phosphorylation).

Presumably involved in this process is a protein found in erythrocytes and nerves and having the apparent properties of an adenosine triphosphatase. This enzyme effects the hydrolysis of ATP only in the presence of both Na^+ and K^+ ions and is inhibited by ouabain, a cardiac glycoside which is known to inhibit active transport of sodium in cardiac muscle, in vivo. Participation of this protein in the activity of the electrolyte pump is suggested by the observation that although this protein is present in normal sheep erythrocytes, it is not present in the erythrocytes of a genetic strain of sheep which have a high $[Na^+]$ and low $[K^+]$. Of considerable interest also is the observation that the turnover of phosphatidic acid (page 73), as indicated by the rate of incorporation of P_i^{32}, in several mammalian tissues appears to be related to the rate of operation of the sodium pump in the same tissues. Thus, phosphatidic acid turnover is markedly enhanced by repeated stimulation of nerve, during the secretion of pancreatic juice, and during intestinal absorption of NaCl. However, there is no adequate hypothesis which relates the turnover of phosphatidic acid to the process of sodium transport. Also, data are not available to relate the amount of electrolyte transported to the quantity of ATP utilized during this process. If each Na^+ ion transported requires hydrolysis of one ATP molecule, then the energy expended in sodium transport may account for as much as 25 per cent of the total utilization of ATP by resting muscle.

Current hypotheses suggest the necessity for a "carrier," independent of the source of energy for operation of the pump and capable of forming a lipid-soluble complex with the cation to be transported. Such a role has been suggested for the phosphatidic acid referred to above; membrane gangliosides have also been implicated. Since the ability of various cells to concentrate amino acids diminishes during the entry of K^+ while, conversely, rapid concentration of amino acids causes loss of K^+ and accumulation of Na^+, Christensen has suggested that metal chelation by pyridoxal phosphate (page 494) may be an integral aspect of the pump. Because phosphatidyl serine has been found to have a significantly greater affinity for Na^+ than for K^+, it, too, has been suggested as a possible carrier. However, the possible role of all these substances in this regard is entirely speculative.

Active transport processes are not limited to those resulting in movement of anions or cations. Many important organic metabolites are also accumulated within cells by active concentrating mechanisms, *e.g.*, withdrawal of glucose from plasma and the accumulation of amino acids by mammalian cells. In the latter instance it does not appear that individual mechanisms are available for each of the amino acids; several independent concentrating devices, each specific for a group of amino acids, appear to be operative, although their absolute specificities are not known in detail. Since they exhibit many common features, it is generally assumed that the transcellular transport of ions, sugars, and amino acids observed in renal tubular epithelium and intestinal mucosa, as well as the secretory activities of glands such as the pancreas, stomach, and salivary glands, all represent modifications of the basic cellular transport devices.

CONTROL OF THE BEHAVIOR OF EXTRACELLULAR FLUID

Interest centers in the behavior of extracellular rather than of intracellular fluid for two principal reasons: (1) comparatively little is known about the behavior of intracellular fluid, largely because of the analytical problems involved, and (2) most disturbances of electrolyte and fluid balance originate in the extracellular fluid.

Daily Requirements for Water and Electrolytes. Under average environmental conditions, there is a daily obligatory loss of approximately 1,500 ml. of water by normal human adults. Of this, about 600 ml. is lost through the skin as insensible perspiration (page 708), 400 ml. in the expired air, and 500 ml. in the urine. Any excess of water intake over this obligatory total volume appears as an increased urine volume. To the extent to which the intake is less than this obligatory 1,500 ml., the difference must be at the expense of the total body water. Since the oxidation of glucose and lipid, in an amount sufficient to yield 2000 cal. per day, results in formation of about 300 ml. of water, there remains an obligatory water intake of the order of 1,200 ml. per day.

In contrast, there is no equivalent obligatory loss of Na^+ or Cl^- under normal conditions. Adults on a diet devoid of Na^+ and Cl^- lose these ions in the urine for only a few days, after which the urine becomes virtually Na^+- and Cl^--free, all other circumstances remaining constant. The average diet provides 100 to 200 meq. of Na^+ and Cl^- per day, all of which, except for small amounts in sweat and feces, is excreted in the urine. In the absence of dietary K^+, urinary excretion of approximately 40 to 60 meq. of K^+ per day occurs for a few days after which urine losses diminish to 10 to 20 meq. per day.

Disturbances of the normal relationships of extracellular fluid may be considered from four standpoints, (1) osmotic pressure, (2) volume, (3) composition, and (4) pH.

Control of Osmotic Pressure. No serious departure from the normal osmotic pressure of intracellular fluid can long be tolerated by the body; both hyper- and hypotonicity lead to irreversible and lethal changes in the central nervous system. Yet there is no mechanism for direct control of the osmotic pressure of cell contents, which are, at all times, in osmotic equilibrium with extracellular fluid. The osmotic pressure of the latter is regulated by one of the most complex homeostatic devices in the animal, which, like all homeostatic mechanisms, operates by a series of feedback devices. Adult kidneys can elaborate urine varying from 0 to 300 mmoles NaCl per liter, and the urinary salt concentration at any given time is determined by the influence of two hormones on the kidney. The antidiuretic action of vasopressin, released by the neurohypophysis (Chap. 51), enhances water reabsorption, and aldosterone (Chap. 49), from the adrenal cortex, stimulates Na^+ reabsorption. The circulating level of these hormones, in turn, is influenced by both the osmotic pressure and the $[Na^+]$ of the extracellular fluid. In consequence, the kidney discharges a dilute (hypotonic) urine when the salt concentration of plasma (which reflects extracellular fluid concentration) falls and a concentrated (hypertonic) urine when the salt concentration rises. In addition, water intake is regulated by the thirst mechanism, which is operative with even minute increases in the tonicity of extracellular fluid. The production of vasopressin and the sensation of thirst are both initiated by osmoreceptors in the hypothalamus (Chap. 51).

Control of the Volume of Extracellular Fluid. This is one of the least understood aspects of electrolyte and fluid metabolism. Of the four parameters here considered, *viz.*, osmotic pressure, volume, composition, and pH, volume is subject to greatest variation among a normal population. This makes determination of extracellular and plasma volumes of relatively little diagnostic use except in unusual instances when these determinations have been made in the same patient before onset of illness.

Plasma proteins are of prime importance in regulation of the osmotic balance between interstitial fluid and the plasma (see following chapter). Therefore, plasma volume is related usually to the amount of total circulating plasma protein, particularly albumin. Profound protein depletion results in diminution not only in serum albumin concentration but in plasma volume. However, removal of plasma or whole blood is followed by transfer of interstitial fluid to the vascular compartment with a temporary fall in serum protein concentration. Administration of concentrated albumin solution leads to a transitory increase in plasma volume.

The extracellular fluid volume is a function of the total sodium available. The kidney, which responds promptly to minute changes in the concentration of many electrolytes or in pH, is relatively insensitive to changes in the volume of this fluid. Administration of isotonic NaCl solution, in contrast to water, is not followed by diuresis; the salt and water are excreted over a period of several days. However, if sodium is removed from the diet, it soon disappears from the urine and is retained with sufficient water to maintain isotonicity and, therefore, the volume of extracellular fluid. Thus, the factors involved in the renal regulation of total extracellular fluid volume are not yet clearly defined.

Alterations in Electrolyte and Water Metabolism. If, for purposes of this discussion, changes in pH and composition are temporarily disregarded, there are six possible circumstances affecting the osmotic pressure and volume of the extracellular fluid. These are summarized in Table 35.1. Each of these may be produced readily in the laboratory and each has been observed clinically. However, many clinical situations exhibit features of two or more of these alterations, which will be considered in turn.

Table 35.1: ALTERATIONS IN VOLUME AND COMPOSITION OF BODY FLUIDS

Alteration in extracellular fluid	Volume		Plasma [Na$^+$]	Hematocrit, plasma proteins	Urinary excretion*	
	Intra-cellular	Extra-cellular			Na$^+$	H$_2$O
Hypotonic expansion........	↑	↑	↓	↓	↓	↑
Isotonic expansion..........	...	↑	...	↓	↑	↑
Hypertonic expansion.......	↓	↑	↑	↓	↑	↑
Hypotonic contraction.......	↑	↓	↓	↑	↓	↑
Isotonic contraction.........	...	↓	...	↑	↓	↓
Hypertonic contraction......	↓	↓	↑	↑	↑	↓

* The last two columns, showing nature of the renal response, refer to the response of the normal kidney to the stimulus of the situation summarized in the columns to the left. When the situation arises because of deranged renal function, for whatever reason, the last two columns are not applicable. ↑, increase; ↓, decrease.

SOURCE: Modified from L. G. Welt, "Clinical Disorders of Hydration and Acid-Base Equilibrium," Little, Brown & Company, Boston, 1955.

1. *Hypotonic Expansion.* The accumulation of water without an equivalent amount of salt is occasionally encountered when copious quantities of salt-free fluids, *e.g.*, glucose solution, are given to persons with inadequate renal function. The accumulated water distributes osmotically among all the fluid compartments. The cells of the central nervous system share in this process, which may lead to convulsions ("water intoxication") and even death.

2. *Isotonic Expansion.* Accumulation of water and salt in isotonic amounts expands the extracellular fluid with no alteration in intracellular volume or composition. The fluid distributes between interstitial fluid and plasma, thereby lowering the concentration of plasma proteins and the hematocrit, and may be manifest as palpable edema of the extremities or pulmonary edema, an occasionally serious complication of parenteral fluid therapy.

3. *Hypertonic Expansion.* Accumulation or retention of sodium leads to an increase in extracellular fluid volume. If, however, this sodium is not accompanied by an equivalent amount of water, the resultant extracellular fluid is hypertonic and water transfers from cells to the extracellular compartment until osmotic equilibrium is attained. Thus, the extracellular fluid expands at the expense of the cells. This is a rare phenomenon but may be illustrated by the dramatic events occurring after ingestion of sea water, as shown in Fig. 35.2. Note that sea water contains twice as much sodium as the most concentrated urine made by the kidneys of a healthy adult. If this process continues, death may occur because of damage to the central nervous system.

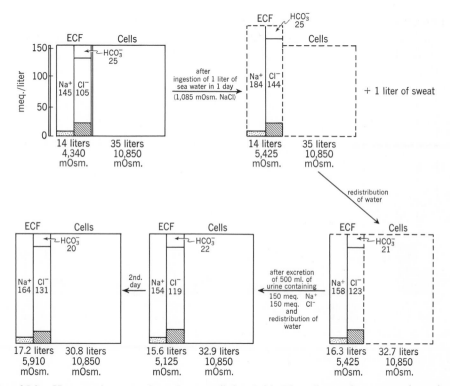

FIG. 35.2. Hypertonic expansion of extracellular fluid. The effects of sea-water ingestion. Ordinate, milliequivalents per liter. Abscissa, volume. The composition shown for extracellular fluid (ECF) is that of plasma. Only the volume and osmolar content of cellular material are presented. Broken lines denote hypothetical states, which never truly exist, as all transitions occur constantly, but which do convey the necessity for redistribution of water and the magnitude of the task confronting the kidney. The final figure (*lower left*) is based on the assumption that another liter of sea water is absorbed on the second day. Note the expansion of extracellular fluid at the expense of cellular fluid. Were no salt or water consumed, the same tendencies would be manifest except that the salt excreted in the urine would be derived from the extracellular fluid and both compartments would shrink.

4. *Hypotonic Contraction.* This results when salt is lost from the body unaccompanied by an equivalent amount of water. Several such situations are encountered in clinical practice, notably in adrenal cortical insufficiency (Chap. 49). In this

instance normal renal control of sodium excretion is lost and the urine is high in salt concentration. The water which remains is distributed among all fluid compartments so that the cells expand. However, the serious aspects are those due to diminution in plasma volume, as described below.

5. *Isotonic Contraction.* This is the most frequently encountered of the conditions under discussion. Since there is no normal obligatory sodium loss, isotonic contraction, like hypotonic contraction, can occur only by abnormal loss of sodium from the body, most commonly in one or more of the secretions of the gastrointestinal tract. These secretions are virtually isotonic with plasma (Fig. 35.3).

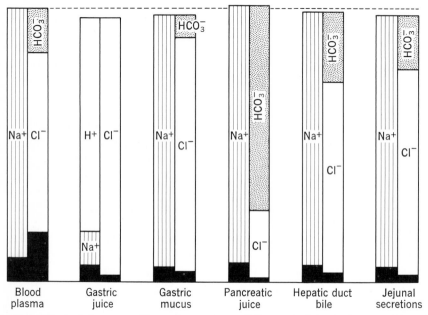

Fig. 35.3. Electrolyte composition of secretions of the gastrointestinal tract. (*From J. L. Gamble, "Chemical Anatomy, Physiology and Pathology of Extracellular Fluid," 5th ed., Harvard University Press, Cambridge, Mass.,* 1950.)

Moreover, as is evident in Table 35.2, the total daily production of these secretions is equal to 65 per cent of the volume of the entire extracellular fluids, and continued loss of these secretions would soon be serious. As these fluids are all isotonic, their loss does not occasion a change in intracellular volume, and the entire loss must be from the extracellular fluid, which contracts to an equivalent extent.

Interstitial fluid and plasma exist in a volume ratio of 3 : 1, and in isotonic contraction the fluid loss is increasingly at the expense of interstitial fluid, because of the increasing effective osmotic pressure of the plasma proteins. The clinical features of this state, frequently termed "dehydration," are due largely to the cardiovascular disturbances resulting from decreased plasma volume. Even when apparently adequate urine volumes are produced, renal insufficiency is evident by

Table 35.2: DAILY VOLUME OF DIGESTIVE SECRETIONS OF AVERAGE ADULT, IN MILLILITERS

Saliva	1,500
Gastric secretions	2,500
Bile	500
Pancreatic juice	700
Intestinal secretions	3,000
Total	8,200
Plasma	3,500
Total extracellular fluid	14,000

the rise in blood nonprotein nitrogen concentration. The kidney responds by excreting minimum volumes of urine, but without an external supply of salt and water the extracellular fluid volume cannot be restored. The oliguria is succeeded by anuria, and finally the patient may become comatose and die of circulatory collapse. Figure 35.4 depicts changes in body fluids and electrolytes as a consequence of isotonic contraction resulting from severe diarrhea.

6. *Hypertonic Contraction.* Loss of water without an accompanying isotonic loss of sodium results in shrinkage of both the cellular and extracellular compartments. This may be expected whenever the obligatory water losses are not met, as in persons to whom no water is available, elderly debilitated patients unable to feed themselves, unattended ill persons who do not respond to the normal thirst sensation, after unusual losses of sweat uncompensated by adequate water consumption, or in persons with diabetes insipidus or mellitus who lose large amounts of water in the urine uncompensated by equivalent water ingestion. Since the extracellular and intracellular compartments exist in normal ratio of 2:5, the water lost is largely at the expense of the intracellular compartment, the osmotic pressure of both compartments rising in equivalent manner. Before serious impairment of function due to contraction of the plasma is manifest, changes in the central nervous system may be the dominant feature of this syndrome, as in hypertonic expansion.

In practice pure examples of these six situations are rarely encountered. Thus, although diarrhea or vomiting may give rise to isotonic contraction, the individual may fail to ingest water in sufficient quantity to meet the obligatory water losses, thus converting the situation into hypertonic contraction. The vagaries of normal existence present minor attacks on the body fluids which, if uncompensated, might lead to one of the six situations described above. The fact that the sodium concentration and volume of extracellular fluid remain so remarkably constant is evidence of the efficiency of the homeostatic mechanisms and the effectiveness of the kidney.

Control of the pH of Body Fluids; the Buffer Systems. Little information is available concerning the pH within cells. Data obtained by staining with intravital dyes which are also pH indicators, although subject to error, indicate that intracellular pH may vary from 4.5 in the cells of the prostate to approximately 8.5 in osteoblasts. Accurate data concerning the pH of interstitial fluid are lacking. If the interstitial $[HCO_3^-]$ is less than that of plasma, as might be expected from equilibrium considerations (page 133), and if the CO_2 tension is greater, then the mean pH of interstitial fluid may be inferred to be somewhat lower than that of venous plasma.

It is convenient to regard extracellular fluid as compounded in the following manner: Consider a solution containing mixed acids (HCl, H_2SO_4, H_3PO_4, protein, etc.) to which is added a second solution containing NaOH, KOH, etc. However, the total amount of alkali, in equivalents, exceeds that of acid. After mixing, a gas mixture containing CO_2 at 40 mm. Hg is equilibrated with the solution and main-

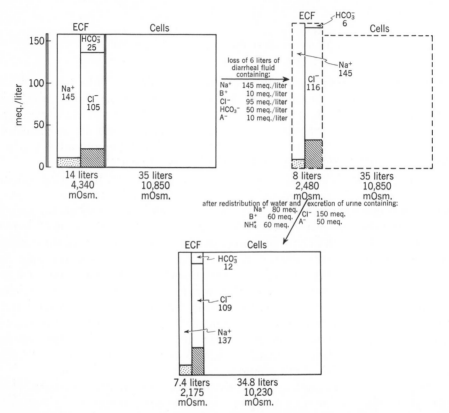

FIG. 35.4. Isotonic contraction of extracellular fluid. The effects of massive diarrhea on body fluids and electrolytes. Ordinate, milliequivalents per liter. Abscissa, volume. The composition shown for extracellular fluid (ECF) is that of plasma. The events shown occur over a 3- to 4-day period. Note the profound extracellular dehydration and relatively trivial effect on cellular volume, if water consumption is adequate. The broken lines represent a hypothetical state which never truly exists, as all transitions occur constantly. This figure does show what would happen if water redistribution and urine secretion did not occur. The final composition of extracellular fluid is conditioned by water retention and some degree of exchange of Na^+ and K^+ across cell membranes. B^+ represents the sum of cations other than Na^+ and NH_4^+; A^- represents the sum of anions other than Cl^-.

tained at the same pressure, thereby maintaining a constant $[H_2CO_3]$ in the medium. Under these circumstances an amount of HCO_3^- is generated equal to the difference between the amounts of alkali and acid in the original solutions. This concentration of HCO_3^- ion, about 25 meq. per liter in normal extracellular fluid, is a measure of the amount of alkali still available to react with additional strong acids.

The major buffer of extracellular fluid is the bicarbonate–carbonic acid system. This results from a number of factors: (1) There is considerably more bicarbonate present in extracellular fluid than any other buffer component. (2) There is a limitless supply of carbon dioxide. (3) The physiological mechanisms which operate to maintain extracellular pH function by controlling either the bicarbonate or the carbon dioxide concentration of extracellular fluid. (4) The bicarbonate–carbonic acid buffer system operates in conjunction with hemoglobin, as described in Chap. 34. As in all buffered systems, pH is dependent not on absolute concentrations of buffer constituents but rather on their *ratio,* as stated in the Henderson-Hasselbalch equation. Because the $[H_2CO_3]$ is fixed only by the alveolar CO_2 tension and is unaffected by the addition of either alkali or acid, this system is considerably more efficient in maintaining pH 7.4 than are the usual buffers employed in the laboratory. This is shown by the curves in Fig. 35.5. Curve *B* represents the behavior of a buffer whose pK_a is 7.4. Curve *A* indicates the inadequacy of a buffer constructed with a nonvolatile acid of pK 6.1 in maintaining pH 7.4. Curve *C* demonstrates the superiority of a buffer system based on an acid which is a gas of unlimited supply and whose concentration is fixed by its partial pressure in the gas phase. Since the $[H_2CO_3]$ is fixed by the gas tension, if the gas tension is equivalent to that normally present in blood, the HCO_3^-/H_2CO_3 system is more useful at pH 7.4, with a ratio of 20, than it would be at its pK, 6.1, where the HCO_3^- would be exhausted by addition of 1.25 meq. per liter of acid, and addition of this amount of alkali would result in a rise of 0.3 pH unit.

The buffer efficiency of the bicarbonate–carbonic acid system is further enhanced by the presence of erythrocytes. This is illustrated by Fig. 35.6, which depicts the results of equilibrating two solutions with CO_2 at varying tensions. These are (1) plasma which has been separated from cells and then equilibrated (separated plasma), and (2) plasma separated carefully after equilibrating whole blood at the stated CO_2 tension (true plasma). As the CO_2 tension in separated plasma is increased, CO_2 dissolves and, because of newly formed carbonic acid, the pH falls, as predicted by the Henderson-Hasselbalch equation. There is no measurable increase in bicarbonate concentration. The curve shown for "separated" plasma differs only slightly from that which would be obtained under the same experimental conditions with a solution of sodium bicarbonate in water. This difference results from the presence of other buffers in plasma, notably the proteins and phosphates, and plasma is a somewhat better buffer than is an aqueous bicarbonate solution. The behavior of "true" plasma is in marked contrast. As the P_{CO_2} is increased, an appreciable increment in plasma $[HCO_3^-]$ occurs so that the pH does not fall so rapidly as it did in the previous instances. As the P_{CO_2} is decreased below normal, the $[HCO_3^-]$ of "true" plasma also decreases, thereby preventing the expected rise in pH.

The influence of erythrocytes on the total CO_2 content of plasma at varying CO_2 tensions was described in the previous chapter (pages 662*ff.*). As CO_2 diffuses into cells, the H_2CO_3 reacts with hemoglobin, forming HCO_3^-, which then enters the plasma in exchange for chloride. This is not contingent upon deoxygenation of hemoglobin but is achieved more readily and with even less pH change when deoxygenation occurs simultaneously. Conversely, lowering the CO_2 tension results

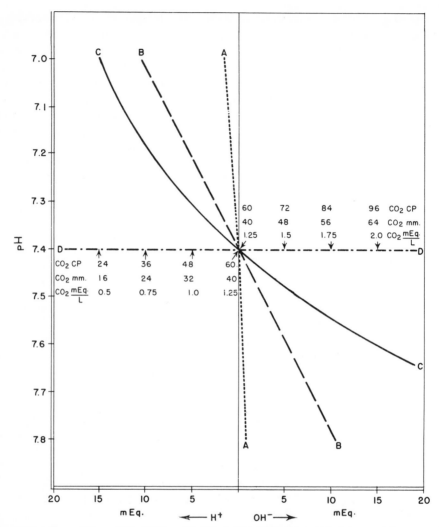

FIG. 35.5.   Comparison of the HCO_3^-/H_2CO_3 buffer with the ability of other buffers to maintain pH 7.4. Each buffer is set at pH 7.4, and then 1 liter is titrated with acid or alkali as indicated. Curve A, a buffer system of pK 6.1. At pH 7.4, $[A^-]$ is 25 meq. per liter, and [HA] is 1.25 meq. per liter. Curve B, a buffer system of pK 7.4. At pH 7.4, $[A^-]$ and [HA] are 25 meq. per liter. Curve C, a buffer system of pK 6.1, one of whose components, HA, is a gas. Titration is performed in presence of an unlimited supply of gas at a partial pressure sufficient to maintain [HA] at 1.25 meq. per liter. Curve D is made on the assumption that HA of curve C is H_2CO_3 and shows the changes, in P_{CO_2}, in gas phase, necessary to maintain a constant pH despite the addition of acid or alkali.

in a reversal of this process, with consequent diminution of plasma $[HCO_3^-]$. It is noteworthy that, although the situation does not arise under physiological conditions, only in the presence of red cells does the total CO_2 content of plasma fall to zero at a P_{CO_2} of 0 mm. Hg. This is possible because there is sufficient hemoglobin in whole blood to permit the following series of reactions to proceed to completion to the right.

$$HHb^+ + HCO_3^- \rightleftharpoons Hb^\circ + H_2CO_3 \rightleftharpoons H_2O + CO_2$$

Respiratory and Renal Regulation of the pH of Extracellular Fluid. The described combination of the properties of a buffer, one of whose components is a gas, and the automatic self-adjustments made possible by intracorpuscular hemoglobin result in the remarkably constant pH of blood plasma. In addition, the body possesses two further safeguards, the respiratory apparatus and the kidneys, which, by their control of plasma concentrations of H_2CO_3 and HCO_3^-, respectively, serve in auxiliary fashion to maintain constant the pH of extracellular fluid.

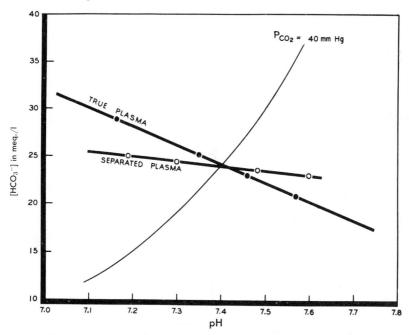

FIG. 35.6. The effect of varying CO_2 tension on the pH and $[HCO_3^-]$ of separated plasma and of true plasma (page 685). The light line is the 40-mm. CO_2 isobar, *i.e.*, at this pressure and 15 meq. per liter of HCO_3^-, pH = 7.2. Points to the left lie on isobars of increasing P_{CO_2}, those to right on isobars of lower CO_2 tension. (*After H. W. Davenport, "The ABC of Acid-Base Chemistry," 3d ed., University of Chicago Press, Chicago, 1950.*)

Unlike the $[HCO_3^-]$ or the fixed anion concentration, the $[H_2CO_3]$ is determined solely by one consideration: the partial pressure of CO_2 in the gas mixture in equilibrium with extracellular fluid, *viz.*, alveolar air. This, in turn, is dependent upon the rate at which carbon dioxide leaving pulmonary blood is diluted with atmospheric air and, hence, upon the rate and depth of respiration. These are regulated by the nervous system at two sites, the respiratory center and the carotid body, which appear to be sensitive to the pH and P_{CO_2} of the extracellular fluid.

When the pH of extracellular fluid falls below normal because of diminished $[HCO_3^-]$, respiration is stimulated, lowering alveolar P_{CO_2} and, hence, extracellular $[H_2CO_3]$. This tends to return the $[HCO_3^-]/[H_2CO_3]$ ratio to its normal value of 20:1 and, thus, to restore pH toward 7.4. The resultant fall in plasma CO_2 tension affects the controlling nerve cells in the opposite manner, and consequently compensation would never be complete if this were the sole regulatory mechanism.

With a high plasma pH, the respiratory rate falls, alveolar P_{CO_2} and, hence, plasma $[H_2CO_3]$ rise, and the pH moves toward 7.4. Again, perfect compensation is not attained since the increased plasma $[H_2CO_3]$ opposes the effect of elevated pH on the controlling centers. It is to be emphasized that the pH is dependent not on absolute concentrations but solely on the ratio $[HCO_3^-]/[H_2CO_3]$.

The buffer systems of plasma can withstand the addition of 16 meq. of acid or 29 meq. of alkali per liter and still maintain pH within the range compatible with life, viz., 7.0 to 7.8. With pulmonary compensation the normal pH range can be maintained despite addition of as much as 23 meq. of acid or 80 meq. of alkali per liter of plasma.

Whereas the respiratory mechanism compensates for disturbances of acid-base balance by regulating $[H_2CO_3]$ in extracellular fluid, the kidney augments pH control by regulating $[HCO_3^-]$. Pulmonary compensation is extremely rapid but never complete; in contrast, renal compensation requires an extended period to be effective but may result in complete restoration of normal pH. A fall in extracellular pH due to increased alveolar CO_2 or decreased $[HCO_3^-]$ is counteracted by two devices available to the kidney for elevating $[HCO_3^-]$, viz., excretion of acidic urine and of ammonium ions. Tendency toward alkaline extracellular fluid is counteracted by excretion of Na^+, HCO_3^-, and the dissociated forms of other weak acids.

By excreting acidic urine, the lower limit of which is approximately pH 4.6, weak acids which exist in dissociated form in plasma can be excreted in part in undissociated form. This occurs not only in pathological states but normally also, since the residual ash of the average diet is acidic. Primary phosphate is the principal acid of this ash.

$$\text{Dietary } H_2PO_4^- + \text{plasma } HCO_3^- \longrightarrow \text{plasma } HPO_4^= + H_2CO_3$$

The acid monovalent phosphate is transported in plasma as the divalent ion at the expense of plasma HCO_3^-. In extracellular fluid, at pH 7.4, the ratio $[HPO_4^=]/[H_2PO_4^-]$ is 4/1, but in urine at pH 5.4 this ratio is 4/100. Thus, while 80 per cent of the phosphate in plasma exists as $HPO_4^=$, virtually all the phosphate in acidic urine again exists as $H_2PO_4^-$, the form in which it originally entered plasma. Figure 35.7 summarizes these events. It is this $H_2PO_4^-$ which constitutes most of the acid conventionally measured as the "titratable acidity" of urine. As a result of the operation of this mechanism, the organism can cope with the acid constantly entering extracellular fluids without depleting the extracellular supply of sodium or appreciably lowering the plasma $[HCO_3^-]$. In acidosis this response of the kidney is initiated upon the lowering of extracellular pH, but if there has been a serious decrease in the plasma $[HCO_3^-]$ or increase in $[H_2CO_3]$, a considerable time is required before sufficient HCO_3^- can be regenerated by this process to restore pH to 7.4. A frequent and important illustration of this mechanism is that which occurs in the acidosis resulting from accumulation of ketone bodies (pages 458ff.). At pH 7.4 more than 99 per cent of acetoacetic acid exists in the dissociated form. Therefore, the following reaction must occur when this acid enters plasma,

$$CH_3-CO-CH_2-COOH + HCO_3^- \longrightarrow CH_3-CO-CH_2-COO^- + H_2CO_3$$

thereby lowering $[HCO_3^-]$ and pH. Since the pK for acetoacetic acid is 4.8, excretion of urine of pH 4.8 permits excretion of 50 per cent of the acetoacetic acid in the undissociated form. Figure 35.7 also shows these reactions.

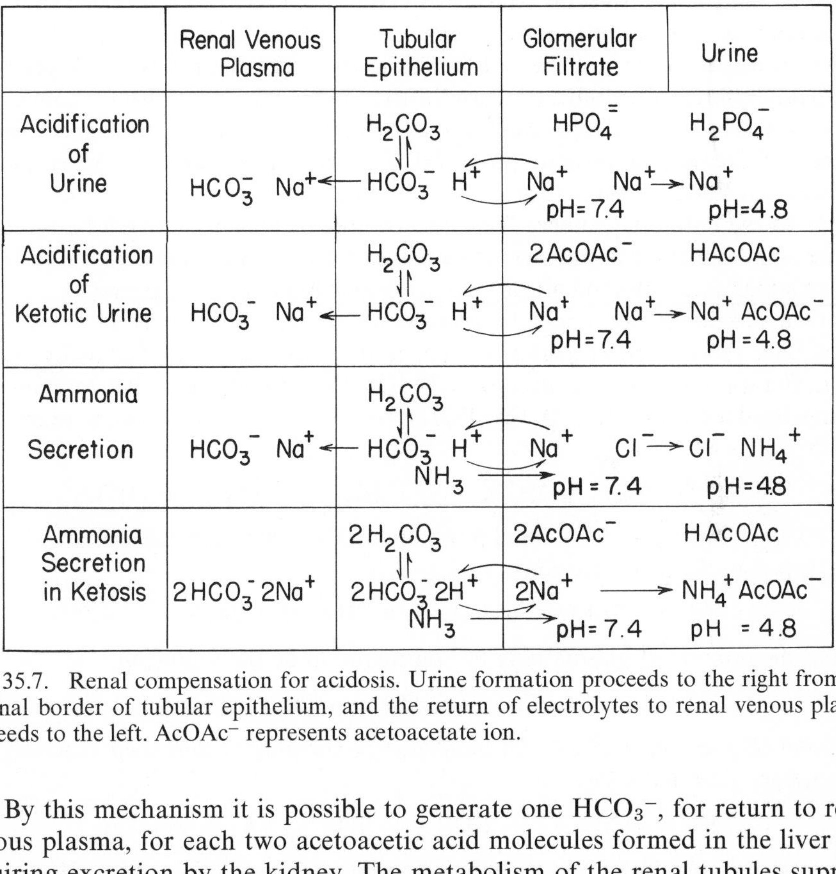

	Renal Venous Plasma	Tubular Epithelium	Glomerular Filtrate	Urine
Acidification of Urine	HCO_3^- $Na^+ \leftarrow$	H_2CO_3 ⇅ HCO_3^- H^+	$HPO_4^=$ Na^+ $Na^+ \rightarrow$ pH= 7.4	$H_2PO_4^-$ Na^+ pH=4.8
Acidification of Ketotic Urine	HCO_3^- $Na^+ \leftarrow$	H_2CO_3 ⇅ HCO_3^- H^+	$2AcOAc^-$ Na^+ $Na^+ \rightarrow$ pH=7.4	$HAcOAc$ $Na^+ AcOAc^-$ pH = 4.8
Ammonia Secretion	HCO_3^- $Na^+ \leftarrow$	H_2CO_3 ⇅ HCO_3^- H^+ NH_3	Na^+ $Cl^- \rightarrow$ pH = 7.4	Cl^- NH_4^+ pH=4.8
Ammonia Secretion in Ketosis	$2HCO_3^-$ $2Na^+$	$2H_2CO_3$ ⇅ $2HCO_3^-$ $2H^+$ NH_3	$2AcOAc^-$ $2Na^+ \longrightarrow$ pH= 7.4	$HAcOAc$ $NH_4^+ AcOAc^-$ pH = 4.8

Fig. 35.7.   Renal compensation for acidosis. Urine formation proceeds to the right from the luminal border of tubular epithelium, and the return of electrolytes to renal venous plasma proceeds to the left. $AcOAc^-$ represents acetoacetate ion.

By this mechanism it is possible to generate one HCO_3^-, for return to renal venous plasma, for each two acetoacetic acid molecules formed in the liver and requiring excretion by the kidney. The metabolism of the renal tubules supplies the energy for this process and also provides the H_2CO_3 necessary for the generation of HCO_3^- ions.

The second renal mechanism for restoring a normal extracellular pH in acidotic states is the formation and excretion of ammonium ion, a cation not present in the glomerular filtrate. Hydrolysis of glutamine is the chief source of this ammonia (page 489). This mechanism does not respond to sudden changes in extracellular pH as rapidly as does that which acidifies the urine. However, in persistent acidosis, ammonia excretion is quantitatively more significant than is acidification. Figure 35.7 schematically depicts how ammonia excretion elevates extracellular

[HCO$_3^-$]. By this means it is possible to return to the plasma, associated with HCO$_3^-$, Na$^+$ ions which otherwise would be present in association with either the dissociated fraction of weak acids or the mineral anions of urine. Only this mechanism can compensate for acidosis occasioned by the accumulation of anions of strong acids, *e.g.*, loss of alkaline digestive secretions.

The sum of ammonium ions plus titratable acid in urine is equivalent to the Na$^+$ which has been returned to the extracellular fluid in association with HCO$_3^-$, and which otherwise would have appeared in the urine had the kidney excreted urine at pH 7.4 and been unable to make ammonia. Although in the discussion above, attention has been on the bicarbonate ion, it will be recognized that these two mechanisms entail exchange of H$^+$ and NH$_4^+$ ions, respectively, for the Na$^+$ of the glomerular filtrate. The mechanism of these exchanges is considered later (see below). Since a primary function of the kidney is regulation of osmotic pressure, which, in turn, is dependent upon [Na$^+$], loss of the amount of Na$^+$ represented by the titratable acid plus NH$_4^+$ would have forced a diminution in extracellular fluid. Conservation of Na$^+$ by the renal mechanisms serves to maintain both the "alkaline reserve" and the volume of plasma. Occasionally, failure of the ammonium-forming mechanism may itself be the cause of acidosis and dehydration, as in lower nephron nephrosis and Fanconi's syndrome.

One additional mechanism is available for combating acidosis but is of significance only in prolonged acidoses. This is the substitution of Ca^{++} for Na$^+$ in urine. The source of this calcium is the Ca$_3$(PO$_4$)$_2$ of bone, which increases in solubility with decreasing pH. As Ca$_3$(PO$_4$)$_2$ from bone enters plasma, it reacts with H$_2$CO$_3$.

$$3Ca^{++} + 2PO_4^{\equiv} + 2H_2CO_3 \longrightarrow 3Ca^{++} + 2HPO_4^{=} + 2HCO_3^-$$

The HCO$_3^-$ ions formed are available to neutralize two molecules of an acid with a pK less than the pK of carbonic acid,

$$2HCO_3^- + 2HA \longrightarrow 2H_2CO_3 + 2A^-$$

so that the mixture in plasma may be considered to be the following.

$$3Ca^{++} + 2HPO_4^{=} + 2A^-$$

Addition of a second pair of acid molecules to the plasma and their reaction with bicarbonate gives the following.

$$2Na^+ + 2HCO_3^- + 2HA \longrightarrow 2Na^+ + 2A^- + 2H_2CO_3$$

The total mixture presented to the glomerulus is then 2Na$^+$, 4A$^-$, 3Ca^{++}, and 2HPO$_4^{=}$. If the usual acidification device is operative, 2Na$^+$ + 2HPO$_4^{=}$ + 2H$_2$CO$_3$ $\longrightarrow$ 2Na$^+$(plasma) + 2HCO$_3^-$(plasma) + 2H$_2$PO$_4^-$(urine). The over-all reaction, then, is

$$3Ca^{++} + 2HPO_4^{=} + 4HA \longrightarrow 3Ca^{++} + 2H_2PO_4^- + 4A^-$$

and one mole of tricalcium phosphate makes possible the excretion of four equivalents of acid. This constitutes an extremely effective mechanism for preventing depletion of the alkali reserve, although it may result ultimately in serious demineralization of the skeleton.

Renal compensation for circumstances which otherwise would result in a *rise* in extracellular pH is accomplished by lowering the [HCO_3^-] of extracellular fluid. This is possible only by excretion of Na^+ in association with anions other than those of the mineral acids. Such urine, therefore, is alkaline (pH 7.4 to 8.2) and contains unusual quantities of Na^+ associated with HCO_3^- and $HPO_4^=$. Direct excretion of Na^+ and HCO_3^- ions obviously lowers the [HCO_3^-] of extracellular fluid. Excretion of Na^+ in association with $HPO_4^=$ serves the same end. It will be recalled that urinary phosphate arises from the metabolism of organically bound phosphate of food, which entered extracellular fluid essentially as $H_2PO_4^-$ ions. As indicated previously, this acid radical reacts immediately in the extracellular fluid with HCO_3^-. In alkalosis, the phosphate, while never present in extracellular fluid in large concentration, is excreted with $2Na^+$ and, consequently, reduces the [HCO_3^-]. This removal of sodium from extracellular fluid is accompanied by sufficient water so that the extracellular fluid remains at normal osmotic pressure, and renal compensation for alkalosis is attended by isotonic contraction of the extracellular fluid, frequently increasing the severity of existing dehydration.

Cellular Buffering in Disturbances of Extracellular pH. Evidence indicates that cells also participate in regulation of extracellular pH. Muscle cells, renal tubular epithelium, and perhaps cells in general possess an ion exchange mechanism, presumed to be related to the "electrolyte pump" (page 676), which mediates an exchange across the cell membrane of Na^+ for either K^+ or H^+ or both. It is this exchange that permits the cell contents to supplement the other mechanisms which maintain extracellular pH.

In alkalosis caused by an increase in extracellular [HCO_3^-], Na^+ enters cells in exchange for both H^+ and K^+. The protons react with extracellular HCO_3^- and the resultant CO_2 is expired. The K^+ is excreted in urine with an equivalent amount of HCO_3^-. The net result is to diminish extracellular HCO_3^- by the equivalent of the amount of Na^+ which entered cells. In acidosis, Na^+ leaves cells and both H^+ and K^+ enter. For each Na^+-H^+ exchange, an HCO_3^- ion remains in plasma, since the H^+ entering cells was derived from the dissociation of H_2CO_3. The entry of K^+ into the cell has no immediate influence on extracellular [HCO_3^-], but the diminished plasma [K^+] permits more effective acidification of the urine (page 730), thus indirectly contributing to restoration of normal extracellular pH. These events are illustrated in Fig. 35.8.

Factors Altering the pH of Extracellular Fluid. Because of the acidic nature of the ash of most foods and of the organic acids which arise in metabolic processes, there is a constant addition of acid to extracellular fluid. As a consequence, the urine of man is usually acidic, as compared with extracellular fluid. The compensatory control exerted by the kidney prevents sodium loss, and normal extracellular fluid is remarkably constant in composition and volume as well as pH. Subsistence on a diet consisting largely or exclusively of fruits and vegetables results in the the opposite situation, *i.e.*, addition to the extracellular fluid of an excess of alkali which is eliminated in the urine.

Alterations in [H_2CO_3]. The respiratory system has been considered in its role as compensator, but it is, on occasion, the primary malefactor. Thus, adult hysterics or children with meningitis may markedly *hyperventilate*, lowering extracellular

[H$_2$CO$_3$] and, thereby, elevating pH; this is termed *respiratory alkalosis*. Since the arterial P_{CO_2} is lower than normal, operation of the hemoglobin buffer mechanism automatically decreases plasma [HCO$_3^-$], tending to prevent the rise in plasma pH. This cannot compensate adequately for the diminished [H$_2$CO$_3$], and hyperventilation may elevate extracellular pH to 7.65 within a few minutes. *Hypoventilation* of whatever origin (morphine poisoning, pneumonia, pulmonary edema, etc.) has the opposite effect and lowers extracellular pH. The increased P_{CO_2} results also in an increased plasma [HCO$_3^-$] because of the hemoglobin buffer mechanism, and individuals who are hypoventilating may immediately exhibit a low plasma pH, elevated [H$_2$CO$_3$], and elevated [HCO$_3^-$]; this is *respiratory acidosis*.

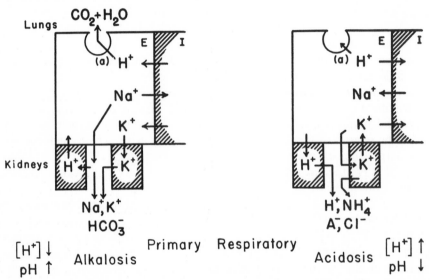

FIG. 35.8. Simplified scheme of linked transfers of cations in defense of body fluid neutrality in respiratory alkalosis and acidosis. *E* and *I* are extracellular and intracellular fluid, respectively. The primary disturbances, shown at (*a*), lead directly to respiratory alkalosis or acidosis. In alkalosis proton loss is shared by the intracellular fluid, exchanging with Na$^+$ from the extracellular phase. In acidosis exchanges take place in the opposite directions. (*After J. R. Elkinton and T. S. Danowski, "The Body Fluids," The Williams & Wilkins Company, Baltimore, 1955.*)

Compensation for either of the above circumstances of altered extracellular [H$_2$CO$_3$] is largely effected by the kidney. In the first instance, an alkaline urine is excreted, and, in the second, an acidic urine. Isotonic contraction may result from the excretion of large urine volumes but is rarely as severe as in other instances of dehydration.

The cellular exchange process also participates in these disturbances. In respiratory alkalosis, Na$^+$ exchanges for cellular K$^+$ and H$^+$ as described above, ameliorating the extracellular alkalosis but alkalinizing the cell contents and depleting cellular K$^+$, which is excreted in the urine. In respiratory acidosis, Na$^+$ is withdrawn from cells which are acidified by the entering protons and extracellular K$^+$ is diminished.

Alterations in [HCO_3^-]. More frequent and serious are those circumstances in which the alteration in pH is associated primarily with changes in [HCO_3^-]. In the simplest instances, lowering of [HCO_3^-] may be expected upon addition to the extracellular fluid of some acid stronger than carbonic acid, *e.g.*, acetoacetic acid. This is termed *metabolic acidosis* in contrast to the *respiratory acidosis* described above.

As plasma [HCO_3^-] falls in metabolic acidosis, HCO_3^- enters plasma from the red cells in exchange for Cl^-. At constant P_{CO_2} within the erythrocytes, their internal pH would be lowered and would thus repress the dissociation of the hemoglobin,

$$H_2CO_3 + Hb^\circ \rightleftharpoons HCO_3^- + HHB^+$$

thereby making more HCO_3^- available for the plasma; this would tend to restore plasma pH to normal. This is not sufficient to compensate for drastic plasma [HCO_3^-] reductions; both pulmonary and renal compensation are also required, as well as proton exchange for cellular Na^+.

Elevation in plasma [HCO_3^-] is compensated by the same mechanisms operating in reverse: the chloride shift, hypoventilation, alkaline urine, and exchange of plasma Na^+ for cellular H^+ and K^+.

The simplest means of elevating [HCO_3^-] is to administer $NaHCO_3$. This may occur in patients with peptic ulcer after overdosage with alkali or occasionally as a result of overenthusiastic use of alkali preparations for relief of gastric disorders.

Alterations Due to Fluid Loss. Those situations in which the effect on pH is based on unusual losses of fluid, particularly the various secretions of the gastro-intestinal tract, are among the most serious and frequently encountered in clinical practice. Understanding this problem requires knowledge of the composition of these fluids and the volumes which may be involved. These have been presented in Table 35.2 and Fig. 35.3. Each of these secreted fluids is elaborated from the extracellular fluid; the chief cation is sodium, except in gastric juice. However, the anionic pattern may differ considerably from that of extracellular fluid. The effect on extracellular pH is, consequently, determined by the manner in which the fluid involved differs from extracellular fluid.

Loss of a fluid which closely resembles extracellular fluid in composition is relatively infrequent but occurs occasionally when a constant suction tube is placed in the duodenum or jejunum and also occurs in simple hemorrhage and after loss of serous exudates. In these instances, there may be no great effect on pH, but serious dehydration due to isotonic contraction may result.

The ratio of [Cl^-]/[HCO_3^-] in normal extracellular fluid is about 4. If the ratio in the lost fluid *exceeds* 4, the [Cl^-] in the remaining extracellular fluid must fall while the [HCO_3^-] rises, thereby tending to elevate pH. This may be encountered during copious loss of sweat but is most frequently seen after vomiting due to pyloric or duodenal obstruction or other causes. The result is shown in Fig. 35.9. Free acid in the vomitus is not necessary in order to develop alkalosis. All that is required is the loss of a fluid in which the [Cl^-]/[HCO_3^-] ratio is greater than 4. Indeed, only very small amounts of *acidic* gastric juice are lost in prolonged vomiting; the fluid lost is largely gastric mucus, which may be contaminated with regurgitated duodenal contents. This obtains in infants who vomit and whose stomachs secrete little or no free HCl. However, loss of free acid increases the severity of the alkalosis since each mole of acid secreted results in an equivalent increase in the HCO_3^- content of extracellular fluid.

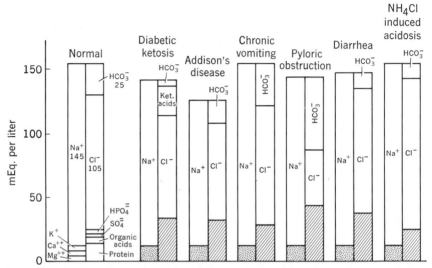

FIG. 35.9. Comparison of extracellular fluid in several pathological states. (*Modified from J. L. Gamble, "Chemical Anatomy, Physiology and Pathology of Extracellular Fluid," 5th ed., Harvard University Press, Cambridge, Mass., 1950.*)

When the $[Cl^-]/[HCO_3^-]$ of the lost fluid *is less than* 4, acidosis occurs. The chief example of this type of fluid loss is diarrhea; the fluid lost is composed of mixed secretions of the pancreas and intestine as well as bile.

Alterations Due to Ketosis. It was noted earlier that acidosis may be expected whenever an acid, HA, stronger than H_2CO_3 enters the circulation at a rate greater than that at which it can be removed. This results in accumulation of the anion, A^-, and equivalent diminution in $[HCO_3^-]$ in consequence of the reaction $HA + HCO_3^- \rightleftharpoons H_2CO_3 + A^-$. This is seen in the accumulation of ketone bodies (acetoacetic and β-hydroxybutyric acids) in diabetic patients, in persons on high-lipid diets, and during starvation. Ketosis usually complicates some other state and is not an isolated pathological phenomenon. Thus, in the diabetic person it complicates the dehydration already established by glucose diuresis, and renal compensation for the acidosis may further aggravate the dehydration. Ketosis also occurs readily in infants and young children who take no food and, therefore, is a frequent accompaniment of both vomiting and diarrhea in the young.

There is no comparable known situation of base production and accumulation, *i.e.*, there is no instance of accumulation of an unusual cation, such as ammonium, lithium, magnesium, etc., in quantities sufficient to disrupt the normal electrolyte balance.

PRACTICAL EVALUATION OF ACID-BASE BALANCE

Evaluation of the acid-base balance of a patient is ordinarily performed in a relatively simple manner. The minimal determinations required are urinary pH and plasma [HCO_3^-]. As shown in Table 35.3 these permit a decision among the four major disturbances, respiratory acidosis and alkalosis and metabolic acidosis and alkalosis, particularly if the history is known. However, at the time examination is performed the compensatory mechanisms may have restored the extracellular pH to normal, as shown by direct determination of plasma pH.

Table 35.3: EVALUATION OF ACID-BASE BALANCE

Disturbance	Urine pH	Plasma [HCO_3^-], meq./liter	Plasma [H_2CO_3], meq./liter
Normal........................	6–7	25	1.25
Respiratory acidosis............	↓	↑	↑
Respiratory alkalosis...........	↑	↓	↓
Metabolic acidosis.............	↓	↓	↓
Metabolic alkalosis.............	↑	↑	↑

A more complete picture may be obtained if arterial blood is drawn, true plasma is separated, and the pH and total [CO_2] are measured. From the nomogram in Fig. 35.10 the P_{CO_2} and [HCO_3^-] can be obtained. These values are then compared with those shown in Fig. 35.11, which is interpreted as follows: The heavy line *AB* is the normal buffer line of plasma, obtained by measuring the pH and [HCO_3^-] of true plasma from whole blood equilibrated at varying CO_2 tensions. *CD* is the P_{CO_2} 40-mm. isobar, and a family of isobars for varying CO_2 tensions could also be plotted but are omitted in this figure.

Point 1 of Fig. 35.11 lies on the normal buffer line to the left of the normal point and represents uncompensated respiratory acidosis. Point 2 lies on the 40-mm. isobar below the normal buffer line and represents uncompensated metabolic acidosis. Point 3 lies on the normal buffer line and to the right of the normal point and represents uncompensated respiratory alkalosis. Point 4 lies on the 40-mm. isobar and above the normal buffer line and represents uncompensated metabolic alkalosis. However, in clinical practice such data are very rare, and partial or complete compensation can be expected. Thus, point 5 lies above the normal buffer line but to the left of normal pH and must, therefore, represent partially compensated respiratory acidosis, while point 6 represents completely compensated respiratory acidosis. Point 7 lies below the normal buffer line and represents metabolic acidosis, but since it is to the right of the normal P_{CO_2} isobar, yet on the acid side of pH 7.4, it must represent partially compensated metabolic acidosis. Point 8 might denote completely compensated metabolic acidosis or respiratory alkalosis. Urine pH or other findings are necessary for decision. Point 9 represents partially compensated respiratory alkalosis, and point 10 partially compensated metabolic alkalosis.

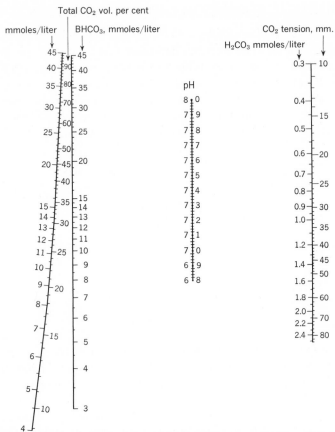

FIG. 35.10. Nomogram showing relationships between [total CO_2], [HCO_3^-], P_{CO_2}, and pH of "true" plasma. A line connecting any two of the variables will pass through the other two as formulated in the statement

$$pH = 6.10 + \log \frac{[\text{total } CO_2] - 0.0301 P_{CO_2}}{0.0301 P_{CO_2}}$$

This is derived from the Henderson-Hasselbalch equation,

$$pH = 6.10 + \log \frac{[HCO_3^-]}{[H_2CO_3]}$$

but is expressed in terms of measurements readily made in the laboratory. (*From D. D. Van Slyke and J. Sendroy, J. Biol. Chem.*, **79**, 783, 1928.)

METABOLISM OF CELLULAR ELECTROLYTES

The mean distribution of cellular electrolytes is a composite picture, obtained by analysis of a tissue, *e.g.*, muscle. Analytical data for intracellular electroytes are shown in Fig. 35.1 (page 675). No specific area within the cell is likely to have precisely this composition. Differences are to be expected in the electrolyte pattern of the cell membrane, cytoplasm, microsomes, mitochondria, nuclei, nucleoli,

Golgi apparatus, etc. However, no description of the electrolyte composition of these various cellular subdivisions is available. A significant fraction of muscle potassium is nondiffusible; presumably, this is true in all cells. At all times there is interchange between the electrolytes within and outside the cell, the rate of which may be different for each electrolyte. During the growth phase of a cell, material accumulates in relatively constant proportions. During periods of negative nitrogen balance, the cell substance is depleted, and the relative amounts of nitrogen, potassium, phosphorus, magnesium, etc., which appear in the urine in excess of the intake of these nutrients are in approximately the same proportions as those which exist within the cells.

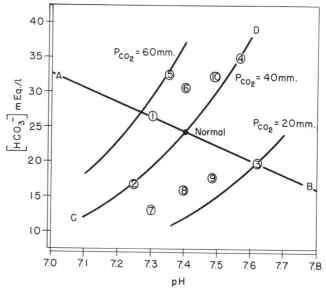

FIG. 35.11. The composition of true plasma in various disturbances of acid-base balance. Line AB, normal buffer line of plasma; CD, P_{CO_2}, 40-mm. isobar; ① entirely uncompensated respiratory acidosis; ② uncompensated metabolic acidosis; ③ uncompensated respiratory alkalosis; ④ uncompensated metabolic alkalosis; ⑤ partially compensated respiratory acidosis; ⑥ completely compensated respiratory acidosis; ⑦ partially compensated metabolic acidosis; ⑧ either completely compensated metabolic acidosis or respiratory alkalosis; ⑨ partially compensated respiratory alkalosis; ⑩ partially compensated metabolic alkalosis. (*After H. W. Davenport, "The ABC of Acid-Base Chemistry," 3d ed., University of Chicago Press, Chicago, 1950.*)

Potassium. If data obtained with dog tissues may also be applied to man, then the mean potassium concentration is about 115 meq. per liter of cell water, while the normal serum [K^+] ranges from 3.8 to 5.4 meq. per liter. The total potassium content of a 70-kg. adult is about 4,000 meq., of which only 70 meq. is in extracellular fluid.

Maintenance of normal serum [K^+] is of considerable practical importance. Characteristic electrocardiographic disturbances can be correlated with serum [K^+], and the symptoms of *hyperpotassemia* involve chiefly the heart. Electrocardiographic changes are easily detected at serum $[K^+]$ greater than 6 meq. per liter. At progressively higher concentrations, the alterations become more severe, and above 10 meq. per liter the heart may stop in diastole. These changes are referable solely to the extracellular accumulation of potassium and may even occur in the presence of a cellular deficit of this ion. It cannot be stated with equal certainty that the clinical picture of *hypopotassemia* is due to low extracellular $[K^+]$ since hypopotassemia is usually associated with cellular deficiency of potassium as well. This situation is characterized by extreme muscular weakness, lethargy, anorexia, myocardial degenerative changes, pulmonary edema, and peripheral paralysis.

Histological and functional lesions are observed in the kidneys of potassium-deficient individuals. The convoluted tubules appear engorged and the cells develop vacuoles. Concomitantly, there is a striking diminution in concentrating ability, with a conservation of K^+ and excretion of an alkaline urine containing large amounts of NH_4^+. Sodium reabsorption may be excessive, resulting in its accumulation with consequent edema.

Homeostatic control of the serum $[K^+]$ is not so well regulated as that for sodium or glucose, for example. The renal mechanism involved is well designed to prevent hyperpotassemia but is not equally effective in the prevention of hypopotassemia. Ordinarily, 60 to 120 meq. of potassium is ingested per day. In the complete absence of dietary potassium, 30 to 60 meq. per day appears in the urine for several days and then decreases to 10 to 20 meq. per day. Values below 10 meq. per day are seen only after profound K^+ depletion. Excretion may be increased still further in renal disease, diuresis, negative nitrogen balance, acidosis, alkalosis, or adrenal cortical hyperactivity. Renal excretion effectively prevents hyperpotassemia under circumstances such as increased potassium intake, tissue breakdown, or contraction of extracellular volume by dehydration.

In addition to renal excretion of potassium, other factors which may tend to decrease the serum $[K^+]$ are limited potassium intake, dilution of extracellular fluid with potassium-free fluid, loss of potassium-containing fluids, or increased glucose uptake by cells. Loss of potassium-containing fluids is particularly prominent in emesis or gastric drainage since gastric juice may at times contain as much as 40 meq. per liter of potassium, and the intestinal digestive juices normally contain 8 to 10 meq. per liter. The fluid lost in diarrhea may contain considerably higher concentrations of potassium than these values. Consequently, potassium deficiency is more frequent clinically than is hyperpotassemia. The latter obtains only in terminal states, uremia, Addison's disease, and hemoconcentration as seen in shock or following severe burns or after the injudicious administration of parenteral fluids containing potassium. Potassium deficiency, in contrast, may be expected during negative nitrogen balance, in cachexia, after the loss of digestive fluids, and as the immediate result of expansion of the extracellular fluid in the treatment of dehydration by parenteral administration of potassium-free fluids.

In several states in which there has been no primary effect on extracellular pH but a significant loss of K^+, a marked alkalosis has been observed, notably in adrenal cortical hyperactivity. The mechanism by which this alkalosis develops is not entirely certain, but it relates to the K^+-Na^+-H^+ exchange across cell membranes. Initially, K^+ leaves the cell in exchange for Na^+ and H^+, particularly the latter, thereby elevating plasma pH; the kidneys excrete a somewhat alkaline urine containing K^+, Na^+, and HCO_3^-. However, as the intracellular K^+ is depleted, serum K^+ soon falls and the kidneys excrete an acidic urine (page 730), thereby increasing the alkalosis. Therapeutic reversal of this alkalosis is possible only when the K^+ loss has been met.

A number of the enzymes of carbohydrate metabolism and electron transport have been found to be K^+-dependent. Administration of glucose or insulin results in glycogen deposition and in coincident transfer of extracellular K^+ into cells. As indicated in Chap. 38, intracellular K^+ plays a critical role in the actomyosin-ATP system of muscle. Contraction of muscle is accompanied by release into the extracellular medium of K^+, at least part of which is exchanged for Na^+. A similar phenomenon appears to be associated with the passage of the nerve impulse. Nerve fibers are rich in potassium; when nerve is stimulated, K^+ rapidly diffuses out and is replenished in the nerve cells during the rest period.

Because of the widespread distribution of potassium in foods, potassium deficiency is unlikely under normal circumstances. The minimum daily requirement for potassium by man cannot be fixed but need only be sufficient to offset expected losses. The 2 to 4 g. of potassium ordinarily available in the diet per day is more than sufficient for this purpose. Experimental potassium deficiency in rats results in slow growth, thinning of hair, renal hypertrophy, necrosis of the myocardium, and death. In dogs, perhaps the most striking finding is an early ascending paralysis of the limbs.

Aspects of the metabolism of calcium and phosphate will be considered in Chap. 41 and of other inorganic ions in Chap. 54.

REFERENCES

Books

Bland, J. H., ed., "Clinical Metabolism of Body Water and Electrolytes," W. B. Saunders Company, Philadelphia, 1963.

Elkinton, J. R., and Danowski, T. S., "The Body Fluids," The Williams & Wilkins Company, Baltimore, 1955.

Gamble, L. J., "Chemical Anatomy, Physiology and Pathology of Extracellular Fluid," 6th ed., Harvard University Press, Cambridge, Mass., 1954.

Goldberger, E., "A Primer of Water, Electrolyte and Acid-Base Syndromes," Lea & Febiger, Philadelphia, 1962.

Harris, E. J., "Transport and Accumulation in Biological Systems," Butterworth and Co. (Publishers), Ltd., London, 1956.

Maxwell, M. H., and Kleeman, C. R., "Clinical Disturbances of Fluid and Electrolyte Metabolism," McGraw-Hill Book Company, Inc., Blakiston Division, New York, 1962.

Murphy, Q. R., ed., "Metabolic Aspects of Transport across Cell Membranes," The University of Wisconsin Press, Madison, 1957.

Shanes, A. M., "Electrolytes in Biological Systems," American Physiological Society, Washington, 1955.

Welt, L. G., "Clinical Disorders of Hydration and Acid-Base Equilibrium," Little, Brown and Company, Boston, 1955.

Review Articles

Darrow, D. C., and Hellerstein, S., Interpretation of Certain Changes in Body Water and Electrolytes, *Physiol. Revs.*, **38**, 114–138, 1958.

Koefoed-Johnson, V., and Ussing, H. H., Ion Transport, in C. L. Comar and F. Bronner, eds., "Mineral Metabolism," vol. I, pp. 169–204, Academic Press, Inc., New York, 1960.

Lipsett, M. B., Schwartz, I. L., and Thorn, N. A., Hormonal Control of Sodium, Potassium, Chloride, and Water Metabolism, in C. L. Comar and F. Bronner, eds., "Mineral Metabolism," vol. I, part B, pp. 473–550, Academic Press, Inc., New York, 1961.

Robinson, J. R., Metabolism of Intracellular Water, *Physiol. Revs.* **40**, 112–149, 1960.

Steinbach, H. B., Comparative Biochemistry of the Alkali Metals, in M. Florkin and H. S. Mason, eds., "Comparative Biochemistry," vol. IV, part B, pp. 677–720, Academic Press, Inc., New York, 1962.

Ussing, H. H., The Alkali Metal Ions in Isolated Systems and Tissues, in "Handbuch der Expermentellen Pharmakologie," O. von Eichler and A. Farah, eds., pp. 1–195, Springer-Verlag, OHG, Berlin, 1960.

36. Specialized Extracellular Fluids

The mechanisms available for maintaining a constant environment for the cells of the body are described in the preceding chapter. In most organs this environment is the interstitial fluid, a portion of a complex system of extracellular fluids which intercommunicate by way of the blood plasma. In addition to the interstitial fluid and the blood plasma, there are *lymph,* formed by filtration of tissue fluids into lymphatic capillaries, and a series of extracellular fluids serving special functions and individually elaborated by the eye, joints, skin, central nervous system, gastrointestinal tract, and mammary glands. The secretion, composition, and functions of these fluids are the subject of this chapter.

THE NATURE OF CAPILLARY EXCHANGE

The classical concept of the mechanism and dynamics of the exchange of fluid between plasma and interstitial fluid across capillaries, frequently referred to as "Starling's hypothesis," is depicted in Fig. 36.1. If plasma and a protein-free ultrafiltrate prepared therefrom (a model for interstitial fluid) are separated by a membrane permeable to all solutes except the plasma proteins, the latter exert an effective osmotic pressure of about 30 mm. Hg. This is somewhat less than the hydrostatic pressure at the arteriolar end of a capillary and somewhat more than the hydrostatic pressure at the venous end. Accordingly, a net loss of fluid through the capillary wall may be expected as blood flows through the arteriolar end of the capillary, and fluid should be regained as flow continues through the venous region of the capillary. At any area along the capillary, the pressure which determines the direction of flow through the capillary wall is given by:

$$P = (\text{tension}_{\text{vascular}} + \text{osmotic pressure}_{\text{extravascular}})$$
$$- (\text{tension}_{\text{extravascular}} + \text{osmotic pressure}_{\text{vascular}})$$

If these processes are equalized, the volume of fluid entering the capillary should equal that which leaves at the venule. This flux across the capillary is relatively slow, amounting to about 2 per cent of the plasma flow through the capillaries in most tissues.

For some time it was considered that exchange of water and solutes across the capillary is accomplished in this manner. However, although this concept of a miniature circulation about each capillary provides a mechanism by which the venous return from a tissue equals the arterial input, it does not account for the very rapid rate of exchange of water and solutes between interstitial fluid and plasma. Water, electrolytes, and small organic molecules diffuse back and forth across capillaries at rates 10 to 100 times the plasma flow. The rate varies inversely with the size of the particles, suggesting a molecular "sieving" through pores in the capillary membrane. Thus, the diffusion of Na^+ is about twice as rapid as that of glucose and ten times that of inulin. At ordinary plasma flow rates, proteins do not cross the capillaries, but when plasma flow falls the diffusion of protein becomes significant. Undoubtedly, much of this diffusion occurs through "pores" in the mucoprotein gel in the intercellular spaces. However, electron microscopic evidence indicates significant passage of large molecules by pinocytotic transport through the capillary cells. Transfer of lipid-soluble materials, *e.g.*, O_2, N_2O, ethyl ether, etc., occurs so rapidly it is presumed that they pass through lipid portions of the membrane.

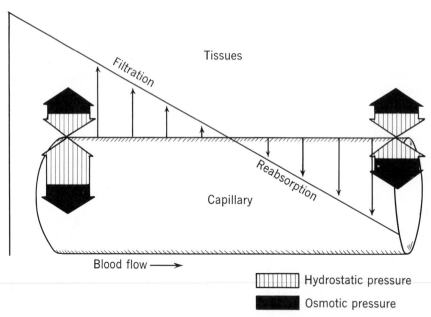

||||||| Hydrostatic pressure

■ Osmotic pressure

FIG. 36.1. The Starling hypothesis. At all points along the capillary, the hydrostatic pressure is opposed by the osmotic pressure of the plasma proteins. The relatively minor contributions of tissue tension and the osmotic pressure of the extravascular proteins are not considered. (*From W. A. Sodeman, "Pathologic Physiology," W. B. Saunders Company, Philadelphia, 1950.*)

Thus the exchange of materials across the capillary occurs at an enormous rate, perhaps 1,500 liters of water per minute in a 70-kg. man, *but by diffusion, in both directions, not by mass filtration and return.* This is not to deny the validity of the Starling hypothesis. The prime function of the hydrodynamic pressure at the arteriolar end of a capillary is to propel fluid along the capillary rather than to ram fluid through the capillary wall. However, since the capillary is porous, were this force unopposed, much more fluid would leave the capillary by filtration plus diffusion than would return by diffusion alone. This is largely compensated by the effective osmotic pressure of the plasma proteins, and the extent of movement of fluid is virtually identical in both directions.

Two clinically important problems arise from alteration of the normal balance between the fluids of the vascular and extravascular compartments. These are shock and edema.

Shock is circulatory failure resulting from loss of fluid from the vascular compartment. The fluid loss may occur by hemorrhage or through an increase in capillary permeability. In persons who have been severely burned or subjected to severe traumatic injury, or who have undergone major surgery, capillaries appear to become permeable to plasma protein, and large volumes of fluid containing albumin enter the extravascular space, thereby reducing the blood volume. The resultant diminution in blood and oxygen supply further impairs capillary permeability. Under these circumstances, the liver may release ferritin (page 804), which lowers blood pressure still further, and recovery may not occur even if fluid therapy is instituted. This is termed "irreversible shock."

Edema is the term applied to an unusual accumulation of extravascular fluid; it results from an imbalance between the transudation of fluid from the circulation and its return to the vascular system. A significant cause of edema is reduction of plasma albumin concentration which may reflect either diminished synthesis (as in malnutrition or hepatic disease) or excessive loss (as in the albuminuria of nephrosis). With hypoalbuminemia, the decreased effective osmotic pressure of the blood permits escape of fluid from the circulation. As blood volume diminishes, there is increased secretion of salt-retaining hormone of the adrenal cortex (Chap. 49) and a resulting increase of the effective osmotic pressure of the serum. This arouses thirst while also increasing secretion of the antidiuretic hormone of the neurohypophysis (Chap. 51), thus augmenting water intake and decreasing water output. The retained water and salt compose the edema fluid. "Nutritional" edema has occasionally been ascribed to hypoalbuminemia, but other significant factors must be operative as the condition has frequently been observed in children with seemingly adequate serum albumin concentrations. The *ascitic fluid,* which accumulates in the peritoneum during severe hepatic disease, is thought to result from a combination of the attendant hypoalbuminemia and portal venous hypertension.

INTERSTITIAL FLUID

Although the difference between the values for plasma volume and total extracellular fluid, determined as the I^{131}-albumin and inulin spaces, indicates that 15 per cent of the body weight is interstitial fluid, it is not possible to obtain a direct sample for analysis. Insertion of a microneedle elicits fluid only from edematous organs, and, indeed, histological examination reveals no appreciable intercellular spaces other than the capillaries and defined lymphatic channels. It is, however, noteworthy that the fluid contained within the spaces of the cellular endoplasmic reticulum is continuous with interstitial fluid and may, in sum, account for a large fraction of the total fluid volume estimated as "interstitial." The electrolyte structure of true interstitial fluid, therefore, can only be approximated from analyses of transudates low in protein content. As shown in Fig. 35.1 (page 675), the data indicate a slightly higher concentration of anions and lower concentration of cations than in plasma, in accord with expectations based on the Gibbs-Donnan formulation (page 133).

The intercellular cement which binds parenchymal cells together to form an organ appears to be a gel of highly polymerized hyaluronic acid (page 54). The latter is present in all organs but is most abundant in tissues of mesenchymal origin, *e.g.*, connective tissue, blood vessels, and lymphatic vessels. Materials in transit between blood and tissue cells must, therefore, diffuse through this gel, which is no obstacle to the passage of small inorganic ions, water, glucose, amino acids, etc., but does act as a barrier to large molecules such as proteins or discrete particles such as india ink, bacteria, viruses, etc. *Hyaluronidase* (page 773), derived from various sources, accelerates the subcutaneous spread of both particulate matter and solutions by depolymerizing the hyaluronic acid. Several virulent microorganisms have been found to secrete this enzyme and thus facilitate their spread in the host animal.

LYMPH

The terms lymph and interstitial fluid are frequently used interchangeably; however, since the precise nature of interstitial fluid is in doubt, it seems desirable to reserve the term lymph for the fluid which may be obtained from lymphatic ducts. The total daily lymphatic return in the normal human adult amounts to approximately 1 to 2 liters. The electrolyte composition of this fluid differs from that of plasma, as would be expected from equilibrium considerations. However, the protein content of lymph is variable, depending upon the source. Cervical lymph contains about 3 per cent protein; subcutaneous lymph, 0.25 per cent; and liver lymph, as much as 6 per cent. In each case the albumin to globulin ratio is considerably greater than that of plasma and is generally of the order of $3:1$ to $5:1$. There are also present in lymph sufficient fibrinogen and prothrombin to permit slow clotting.

SYNOVIAL FLUID

The precise mode of origin of synovial fluid is unknown. The electrolyte composition of the fluid is that of a transudate from plasma; in addition, the fluid contains mucopolysaccharide formed by cells of the synovium. Normally, the pH of synovial fluid is 7.3 to 7.4, and the specific gravity is approximately 1.010. The protein concentration is about 1 per cent, with an albumin to globulin ratio of approximately 4.0. No fibrinogen is present. The concentration of nonprotein nitrogenous substances is slightly below that of plasma; lipids are normally absent, and the glucose concentration is variable. Synovial fluid is highly viscous, varying from relative viscosities of 50 to 200, with an average of about 125. This high viscosity is due to the presence of about 0.85 g. per 100 ml. of hyaluronic acid.

Inflammatory joint disease, particularly rheumatoid arthritis, is usually accompanied by an increase in fluid volume of the joint as well as by an increased protein concentration in the fluid. Electrolytes and readily diffusible substances of synovial fluid exchange with plasma, while larger particles can leave the intraarticular space only via the lymphatics. Synovial fluid, then, is an extension of interstitial fluid, and not a product of secretory activity.

SECRETION

The formation of interstitial fluid from plasma may be described in physico-chemical terms based on knowledge of the diffusibility of water, the solutes of plasma, and the permeability of the capillary wall to these substances. It will be recalled that to account for the differences between the composition of intracellular and extracellular fluids, it is necessary to postulate the existence of a mechanism whereby energy, derived from metabolic processes, may be utilized to maintain the intracellular composition against an osmotic gradient. Another situation, *secretion,* may be recognized wherein cells are aligned in columnar fashion, bathed by interstitial fluid or plasma on one side and fluid of different composition on the opposite side, and in which the differences in composition of the two fluids cannot be accounted for in terms of spontaneous diffusion, osmosis, or permeability. The secretory process, operating against an osmotic, electrochemical, or hydrostatic gradient, again requires the harnessing of metabolically derived energy. It may be recognized (1) if the movement is inhibited by interruption of cellular metabolism, *e.g.*, cyanide or fluoride poisoning, (2) if, in contrast to the Donnan equilibrium, cations and anions are transported simultaneously in equivalent amounts and in the same direction, (3) if the shift takes place with nonelectrolytes, and (4) if the cells are so aligned that the transported fluid leaves by a duct and the pressure within this duct is independent of arterial pressure. The secretory activity need not involve more than one component of the secreted solution. Mammalian secretions include milk, sweat, tears, cerebrospinal fluid, aqueous humor, and the fluids of the digestive tract. Selective absorption across the intestinal mucosa, the reabsorption of water and solutes in renal tubules, and secretion into the lumen of the distal renal tubules may all be regarded from the same viewpoint. Among the more dramatic instances of secretion are the elaboration of $0.16N$ HCl by the stomach, secretion of almost pure water by sweat glands, and removal of all glucose from the urine. The fundamental mechanisms, presently unknown, may be in each case an adaptation of those by means of which all cells maintain their internal composition. The mechanisms involved in these active transfers have been the subject of much investigation but remain among the major unsolved problems in biochemistry. The term "secretion" has also been generally employed to describe the behavior of the ductless endocrine glands, the activity of the liver in adding to hepatic venous blood serum albumin, prothrombin, and glucose, and the release of mucus. In these instances, although the cells "do work" in synthesizing the material, the actual transfer, cell to plasma or lumen, operates with the osmotic gradient and no work need be done to accomplish the *transfer.*

AQUEOUS AND VITREOUS HUMOR

Aqueous Humor. The aqueous humor fills the anterior chamber of the eye, maintains the intraocular tension desirable for optical purposes, and nourishes the avascular cornea and lens. Its volume varies among animal species, depending on the size of the eyeball and the depth of the anterior chamber. In man, the volume is approximately 0.125 ml. The protein content is low in normal aqueous humor—about 0.025 g. per 100 ml. The albumin to globulin ratio is frequently of the same order as that in the plasma of the same subject. The concentrations of diffusible substances shown in Table 36.1 are not strikingly different from plasma. The concentration of ascorbic acid, however, is twenty times that in plasma. The components of aqueous humor enter at various points, and all depart through Schlemm's canal. Some of the fluid enters the anterior chamber by flow from the posterior chamber; some arises by diffusion from the blood vessels of the iris; and the remainder enters by the secretory activity of the ciliary body. Isotopic tracer experiments have indicated that the water exchange in the aqueous humor, per minute, is equivalent to approximately 20 per cent of the volume of the aqueous humor. The major portion of this turnover occurs by diffusion. However, only *water* and *nonelectrolytes* may be exchanged between the iris and the aqueous humor. In contrast, only about 1 per cent of the electrolyte content of the aqueous humor enters and leaves per minute, and this is entirely because of the secretory activity of the ciliary body. Increased secretion raises the intraocular pressure, giving rise to *glaucoma.* Administration of inhibitors of carbonic anhydrase, such as acetylamino-1,3,4-thiadiazole-5-sulfonamide, may relieve the elevated pressure, indicating a fundamental role for carbonic anhydrase in the secretory process.

When normal aqueous humor is removed, the anterior chamber rapidly refills with a fluid termed plasmoid aqueous humor. This fluid contains large quantities of protein, and if the paracenteses are repeated, the fluid which fills the anterior chamber becomes virtually identical with plasma.

Vitreous Humor. Vitreous humor fills the posterior chamber of the eye. Its fluid component is almost identical with the aqueous humor. However, this chamber also contains a gel of hyaluronic acid within a framework of collagen (page 767), Unlike the aqueous humor, this fluid cannot be removed without causing injury to the eye, as neither the gel, originally secreted by the retina, nor the collagen can be replaced. As in aqueous humor, there is an exchange of electrolytes and water of the vitreous humor with surrounding tissue by diffusion.

CEREBROSPINAL FLUID

The cerebrospinal fluid, contained within the subarachnoid space of the brain and spinal cord and the ventricles of the brain, originates in the choroid plexus and returns to the blood in the vessels of the lumbar region. Only a small fraction of the cells of the central nervous system actually make contact with this fluid; the remainder derive their nutrition from the blood vessels. The total volume of this fluid, about 125 ml. in a healthy adult, is renewed every 3 or 4 hr. If surgical drainage is instituted, several liters per day can be obtained. The composition of spinal

Table 36.1: Approximate Concentrations of the Major Electrolytes of Extracellular Fluids

Fluid	pH	Na+	K+	Ca++	Cl-	HCO3-	Protein	Other
		meq./liter of water						
Plasma	7.35–7.45	144	4.5	5.0	103	28	18 meq./liter (6.0–8.0 g./100 ml.)	Organic acids, 6 meq./liter
Edema fluid	7.4	135	3.3	3.5	105	30	<0.25 g./100 ml.	
Synovial fluid	7.3–7.4	142	4	....	117	25	1.0 g./100 ml.	
Cerebrospinal fluid	7.4	146	3.5–4.0	3.0	125	25	15–40 mg./100 ml.	
Aqueous humor	7.4	140	4.7	3.5	108	28	25 mg./100 ml.	
Tears	5.2–8.3	142	3–6	....	115	5–25	0.75 g./100 ml.	
Sweat	4.5–7.5	<85	3–6	3–5	<85	0–10	Trace	
Saliva	6.4–7.0	20–40	15–25	3–8	20–40	10–20	Variable	
Parietal gastric juice	<1.0	0	7	0	162	0	0	H+, 155 meq./liter
Gastric mucus	7.4–7.5	145	5	....	115	30	Variable	
Mixed gastric secretions	1–2	20–60	6–7	....	145	0	Variable	H+, 60–120 meq./liter
Pancreatic juice	7–8	148	7	6	80	80	Variable	
Jejunal fluid	7.2–7.8	142	7–10	....	105	30	Variable	
Ileal fluid	7.6–8.2	100–140	10–50	....	80	75	Variable	
Bladder bile	5.6–7.2	130	7–10	7–15	40–90	0–15	Variable	Bile salts, 50–100 meq./liter
Liver bile	7.4–8.0	145	5	5	75–110	25–50	Variable	Bile salts, 10–20 meq./liter

Note: Only the values given for plasma represent the mean of a large number of samples. In some instances a range is shown; in others a single value is quoted although the given figure is subject to appreciable variation. Since the values have been obtained in many laboratories, employing different analytical methods and sampling procedures, only the general pattern may be considered meaningful.

fluid suggests that it is primarily a simple transudate or ultrafiltrate from plasma. Fluid taken from the lumbar region, the cisterna magna, or the ventricles is at all times in osmotic equilibrium with plasma and contains between 15 and 40 mg. of protein per 100 ml., with an albumin to globulin ratio of 4. Plasma lipids are absent.

However, the following discrepancies in composition between cerebrospinal fluid and an ultrafiltrate of plasma indicate that formation of this fluid involves secretion, presumably by the choroid plexus. While the total cation and anion composition of the fluid is in accord with the Gibbs-Donnan equilibrium, the distribution of these ions is not. Thus, the $[Na^+]$ of cerebrospinal fluid is virtually identical with that of plasma, while the $[K^+]$ is appreciably lower. Also, while the $[Cl^-]$ of spinal fluid is greater than that of plasma, the $[HCO_3^-]$ is identical in the two fluids. Data are not available concerning the free CO_2 and H_2CO_3 content of cerebrospinal fluid, but it has been assumed to be approximately equal to that of venous blood. The calcium concentration of spinal fluid appears virtually fixed and does not respond readily to changes in plasma concentration. This is particularly striking in patients with parathyroid tumors, who show markedly elevated serum calcium levels but normal spinal fluid calcium concentrations. In general, the glucose concentration of spinal fluid is lower than that of plasma but rises and falls with changes in blood glucose levels. The concentration of nonprotein nitrogenous constituents is always appreciably lower in cerebrospinal fluid than in plasma.

SWEAT

The secretion of sweat serves, through evaporation, to cool the body. When no visible perspiration is produced, the sweat glands release virtually pure water. This *insensible* perspiration may amount to 600 to 700 ml. per day. The small amount of organic and inorganic material which accumulates on the skin under these conditions is probably associated with activity of sebaceous glands rather than with that of sweat glands. In circumstances in which visible sweat is elaborated, its volume and composition vary and are determined by rate of evaporation, previous fluid intake of the individual, external temperature and humidity, and hormonal factors. Volumes as large as 14 liters per day have been recorded. Both volume and salt content of sensible perspiration are influenced by acclimatization of the individual. Persons new to an environment which is hot and humid produce copious quantities of salt-laden perspiration; $[Na^+]$ and $[Cl^-]$ may be as high as 75 meq. per liter. Acclimated individuals, however, produce smaller volumes with a lower salt concentration. Unreplaced loss of large volumes of perspiration may result in hypertonic contraction. Miners' or stokers' cramps result from salt loss under these circumstances and can be prevented by incorporation of small amounts of salt in drinking water. In cystic fibrosis, a congenital defect involving most or all of the glandular epithelial structures of the body, sweat and tears are characteristically rich in NaCl. This analytical difference is so striking as to be diagnostic. In hot weather, victims of this disease may succumb in a state resembling acute Addisonian crisis (Chap. 49), referable entirely to Na^+ loss, and corrected by NaCl administration.

When small volumes of visible perspiration are elaborated, its concentration of nonprotein nitrogenous materials slightly exceeds that of the plasma from which it is derived. This probably reflects evaporation of water from the elaborated sweat. However, sweat glands may possess an active mechanism for the concentration of lactic acid. The lactate concentration of the sweat of athletes far exceeds that present in plasma or urine. The concentrations of potassium, magnesium, calcium, etc., are of the order expected from those found in the plasma. Specific gravities of 1.002 to 1.005 for sweat have been reported, and the pH lies between 4.5 and 7.5.

TEARS

The fluid which normally moistens the surface of the cornea is a mixed secretion of the lacrimal glands and of the accessory sebaceous glands (the glands of Zeis and the meibomian glands). Since the surface of the cornea during waking hours is exposed, there is constant evaporation of fluid on its surface, resulting in concentration of the tear fluid. Under mild stimulus with a slow rate of tear flow, the resultant fluid appears to be hypertonic, probably because of concentration due to evaporation. When rapid tear flow is induced, the resulting solution is isotonic. In most instances this fluid has a pH of 7 to 7.4, but values from 5.2 to 8.3 have been observed; alkaline tears are shed after corneal injuries.

Diffusible nitrogenous materials and electrolytes are present in tears in concentrations similar to those of plasma. The protein concentration is generally 0.6 to 0.8 g. per 100 ml., with an albumin to globulin ratio of about 2. The presence of protein in the tears, by lowering the surface tension, enables the tears to wet epithelial surfaces. The optical properties of the eye are greatly improved by this film since microscopic irregularities in the corneal epithelium are abolished, thereby producing a perfectly smooth optical surface. Further, the film protects the eye from damage by small foreign bodies such as dust or air-borne bacteria.

The most unusual component of tears is the enzyme *lysozyme,* which is also found in nasal mucus, in sputum, in tissues, in gastric secretions, and in egg white. This enzyme is a *muramidase* in that it catalyzes hydrolysis of the $\beta,1,4$-N-acetyl-glucosaminidic linkage of the repeating disaccharide unit of the muramic acid–containing mucopeptide in the polysaccharide of the cell walls of many air-borne cocci (page 58). This action of lysozyme thus protects the cornea from infection.

SECRETIONS OF THE DIGESTIVE TRACT

The major portion of ingested food must be hydrolyzed into smaller components, *e.g.*, amino acids, glucose, etc., before it can be absorbed and utilized. This process, *digestion,* is generally extracellular. Many unicellular organisms, such as the fungi, secrete hydrolytic enzymes into the surrounding medium. In higher animals, digestion is accomplished in a gastrointestinal tract, supplied with digestive secretions elaborated by special glands. In general, these glands provide three types of secretory products, *i.e.*, aqueous solutions of varying electrolyte composition and pH, enzymes, and mucus. Two main cell types may be recognized: serous cells, which elaborate the major portion of the aqueous medium as well as some of the enzymes, and the mucous cells, which secrete mucus and perhaps enzymes. Both types of cell are generally found in secretory glands.

The organic constituents of the digestive secretions, *i.e.*, enzymes and muco-proteins, are products of the metabolism of the secreting cells. This process may be observed histologically. In the resting cell, there is a clear vacuole within the cytoplasm. Within the vacuole there then appears a "granule," which gradually increases in size and virtually fills the vacuole. These vacuoles then migrate toward the apex of the cell and may almost fill the cell. Upon proper stimulation of the cell, they are mechanically extruded and washed down the duct. The precise chemical nature of these granules has not been defined. In organs whose secretions contain more than one enzyme, *e.g.*, the pancreas, it has not been possible to establish whether individual cells synthesize more than one enzyme. However, on repeated stimulation of pancreatic secretion, the relative amounts of tryptic, lipo-lytic, and amylolytic activities remain constant in the pancreatic juice. Prolonged stimulation does not exhaust the glandular ability to secrete a fluid of constant electrolyte content but may exhaust the supply of enzymes.

Saliva. Although there are numerous small glands distributed over the buccal mucosa, saliva is secreted mainly by three pairs of glands. The cells of the parotid gland are exclusively of the serous type; those of the sublingual gland, of mixed type. Parotid saliva is dilute, nonviscous, and always hypotonic; sublingual saliva is viscous because of its mucoprotein content, while that from the submaxillary gland is serous on parasympathetic stimulation and viscous when stimulated via the sympathetic nerve supply. No hormonal stimulus is known for salivary secre-tion. The flow of saliva may be stimulated by local reflexes caused by mechanical factors, including presence in the mouth of foreign materials, or by conditioned reflexes, *e.g.*, sight or smell of food. This secretion moistens and thus lubricates the food mass, thereby facilitating deglutition. Human saliva contains an *α-amylase* which catalyzes hydrolysis of polysaccharides to a mixture of oligosaccharides (page 50). Although present in saliva of many species, amylase is not secreted by the horse, dog, or cat.

The composition, pH, and volume of saliva are variable. From 1,000 to 1,500 ml. of hypotonic mixed secretions are produced daily. The $[Na^+]$ is about 20 to 40 meq. per liter; $[Cl^-]$ is subject to similar variation. Potassium is present in concen-trations four to five times that of plasma. The calcium content of saliva has been reported to be from 6 to 20 mg. per 100 ml. and, at high calcium concentrations, calculi of calcium salts may form in the ducts or, in combination with organic material, may be deposited on the teeth as "tartar." The pH of saliva is generally between 6.4 and 7.0, with $[HCO_3^-]$ of 10 to 20 meq. per liter. Mucoprotein is the chief organic constituent, together with small quantities of glucose, urea, lactic acid, phenols, vitamins, and thiocyanate. Enzymes other than amylase, including a phosphatase and carbonic anhydrase, have been reported in saliva. The large varia-tions noted in composition of saliva may be ascribed to methods of collection, the particular salivary glands which were secreting, and the varying stimuli employed to augment salivary flow.

Gastric Secretions. Secretions enter the adult human stomach from the ducts of 10 to 30 million gastric glands, most of which are in the fundus and body of the stomach. Three types of cells line the gland tubules: mucous cells at the neck of the gland, the "chief" cells of the body of the gland, and the parietal, or border, cells. Parietal cells are not found in glands of the pyloric or cardiac portions of the stomach, nor do they line the lumen of the gland. Rather they lie between and behind the chief cells and communicate with the lumen via delicate canaliculi which pass between the chief cells. The canaliculus is itself the terminal conduit of a fine network of channels within the parietal cell. The mucous cells contain mucinogen granules and secrete a thick, viscous fluid rich in mucoprotein. The chief cells elaborate and secrete *pepsinogen.* The proteins are suspended in an essentially neutral or slightly alkaline medium in which Na^+, Cl^-, and HCO_3^- are the predominant ions. The parietal cells secrete a solution of $0.16 M$ HCl and $0.007 M$ KCl, with traces of other electrolytes and little or no organic material. The concentration of hydrogen ions is thus a million times greater than that of plasma. Secretion of 1 liter of such a solution, assuming plasma to be the source of H^+, K^+, and Cl^-, requires expenditure of at least 1500 cal. if the process were 100 per cent efficient.

There can be little doubt that plasma is the source of Cl^- ion. Further, as venous blood leaving the secreting stomach contains more HCO_3^- and less Cl^- than does arterial blood, the over-all process may be represented as follows.

$$NaCl + H_2CO_3 \rightleftharpoons NaHCO_3 \text{(plasma)} + HCl \text{(secreted)}$$

Since this process occurs spontaneously to the left, cellular metabolism must provide energy for its effective reversal. However, despite intensive investigation it has not been possible to ascertain the nature of the cellular mechanism. Some of the known facts include: (1) Secretion is markedly inhibited by inhibitors of carbonic anhydrase, indicating a probable role of this enzyme in the over-all process. (2) The ratio $(H^+ \text{ secreted})/(O_2 \text{ consumed})$ exceeds 1 by a large factor. Therefore, cellular respiration does not account for total proton production. (3) Inhibitors of cellular metabolism, *e.g.*, cyanide, iodoacetate, *p*-chloromercuribenzoate, and dinitrophenol, inhibit or abolish secretion, indicating that normal metabolic pathways provide the necessary energy. (4) A potential difference of the same order of magnitude as that between cytochrome oxidase and DPNH exists across the mucosa. However, these and other data do not permit construction of an adequate model for gastric secretion, nor indeed do they exclude the possibility that gastric acid secretion is an adaptation of the $Na^+–K^+–H^+$ exchange mechanism which appears to be widely operative in biological systems.

The surface epithelial cells of the stomach, the chief cells of the necks of the fundic glands, and cells of the pyloric and cardiac glands secrete mucus of complex composition. Included are mucoproteins which contain a sialic acid (page 36) and a chondroitin sulfate (page 55). In lesser quantities are blood group substances (page 790) and a low molecular weight mucoprotein which serves as *intrinsic factor* (page 808). The mucoproteins produced by the surface epithelium are present as insoluble, stringy masses, while that from the glandular mucous cells is in solution, from which it may be readily precipitated by addition of acetone or alcohol.

Gastric juice has been studied by many investigators since the early nineteenth century. Prout recognized the existence of HCl. The foundations of modern knowledge were laid by Beaumont with the cooperation of his patient, Alexis St. Martin, who had received a gunshot wound which resulted in a gastric fistula. Later Pavlov and Heidenhain devised means of preparing isolated gastric pouches which secrete gastric juice on application of appropriate stimuli but to which food has no entry so that the secretions may be studied free of food contamination. With these preparations, and from studies of gastric juice obtained from individuals who have swallowed appropriately designed rubber tubes, it has been possible to establish some of the features of gastric secretion.

Gastric Analysis. In clinical practice it is frequently of interest to measure the amount of acid produced in the gastric secretion. The usual practice consists of withdrawal of the residuum, followed by ingestion of a simple meal or of alcohol, or subcutaneous injection of histamine, with sampling of gastric contents at 15-min. intervals. The specimens are titrated to pH 3.5 using dimethylaminoazobenzene as an indicator, and then to a phenolphthalein end point. The first titration measures free acid and the second combined acid. The results are expressed as milliliters of $0.1N$ NaOH required per 100 ml. of gastric juice. One milliliter of $0.1N$ NaOH equals one clinical unit.

Interest in these determinations arises only in instances of extreme variations. *Hypoacidity* is seldom of real consequence, but *anacidity* occurs only in pathological states, most frequently pernicious anemia and gastric carcinoma. *Hyperacidity* is considerably more frequent and is associated with chronic postprandial distress ("heartburn," "indigestion") or peptic ulcer. Peptic activity generally parallels acid secretion and is never observed in the absence of free HCl. Figure 36.2 illustrates data obtained from gastric analyses by the procedure described above.

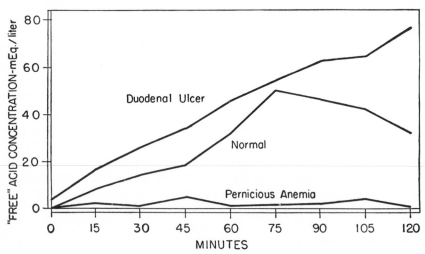

FIG. 36.2. Concentration of free acid in the gastric contents of a normal subject, a patient with pernicious anemia, and a patient with a duodenal ulcer, after administration of histamine.

Gastric and duodenal ulcers result from the digestion of mucosa by pepsin-HCl. If unchecked, digestion may continue and ultimately lead to perforation with consequent peritonitis. Alternatively, erosion into a major blood vessel, such as the pancreaticoduodenal artery, may lead to serious, even fatal, hemorrhage. The mechanism of ulcer formation has not been established. This problem may be stated in a more general fashion: Why do not the stomach and other digestive organs digest themselves? This question has intrigued such illustrious investigators as John Hunter, Claude Bernard, and Ivan Pavlov, but no definitive answer has been provided. Among the more important factors are the following: (1) The digestive enzymes are isolated within the cell in secretory vacuoles, and intracellular digestion does not occur. All the major proteases of the gastrointestinal tract are stored in the cells in which they are synthesized as inactive zymogens, *viz.*, pepsinogen, trypsinogen, chymotrypsinogen, and procarboxypeptidases; hence, active proteases never truly mix with the cell contents. (2) Once in the lumen of the alimentary tract, the enzymes cannot penetrate mucosal cells because of the selective permeability of cell membranes. (3) Mucus has both acid-binding and peptic-inhibitory properties. Since mucus is steadily renewed, and only slowly digested, the enzymes are mechanically separated from tissue itself. (4) In the stomach and duodenum, the ability of mucus to protect epithelial structures is a function of pH. At unusually high $[H^+]$, the mucus is more readily digested and the epithelium exposed to the action of pepsin. (5) Resistance of the stomach to erosion is contingent upon an active blood circulation. In emotional states, such as fear or anger, the entire gastric mucosa is occasionally blanched. Ulcer formation, known to be at least in part of psychogenic origin, sometimes occurs in individuals with gastric hyperacidity and whose gastric circulation responds in this manner to "psychic" stimuli. (6) Finally, hormonal secretions, *e.g.*, those of the adrenal cortex (Chap. 49), which provoke hypersecretory activity by the gastric mucosa and may inhibit mucopolysaccharide synthesis, contribute to ulcer formation. This is of concern in prolonged use of these hormones.

Pancreatic Secretion. The pancreas is a racemose gland similar to salivary glands in general structure. Wedge-shaped cells, containing secretory granules, line the alveoli. On repeated stimulation the secretory granules are discharged, leaving entirely clear cells. The daily volume of pancreatic secretion in the adult human being is 500 to 800 ml. per day. Pancreatic juice, in the dog, varies from pH 7 to 8, depending on the $[HCO_3^-]$ and $[CO_2]$, and is approximately isotonic, containing, in milliequivalents per liter, $Na^+ = 148$, $K^+ = 7$, $Ca^{++} = 6$, $Cl^- = 80$, $HCO_3^- = 80$, $HPO_4^= = 1$. The reactions by which the pancreas produces a fluid with a HCO_3^- concentration threefold that of plasma are unknown. Studies with $NaHC^{14}O_3$ have shown that the HCO_3^- comes from plasma and does not originate from the metabolism of the secreting cells. Since secretion of bicarbonate is virtually abolished by inhibitors of carbonic anhydrase, it is likely that this enzyme is essential to the secretory process.

The pancreatic secretion contains several enzymes of importance to the digestive process. These include *trypsinogen, chymotrypsinogen,* and *procarboxypeptidases,* precursors of *trypsin, chymotrypsin,* and *carboxypeptidases,* respectively, a *lipase* (*steapsin*) which is solely responsible for fat hydrolysis, an *α-amylase, maltase,* and *ribonuclease.* The conversion of the zymogens to active enzymes and the hydrolytic activity of each of these enzymes have been described in earlier chapters.

Secretion of pancreatic juice is under both neural and hormonal control. The presence of "secretagogues" (large polypeptides) or acid in the upper duodenum results in liberation of a hormone, *secretin,* into the circulation, resulting in augmented flow of pancreatic juice and, to a lesser extent, of bile and intestinal juices. Since secretin is effective in the atropinized animal as well as after section of the vagus, a direct action of the hormone on the secretory cells may be assumed. Secretin has been obtained in highly purified form and appears to be a basic polypeptide of molecular weight about 5,000. The pancreatic juice resulting from secretin stimulation is copious in volume, relatively deficient in enzymic activity, and of normal electrolyte composition. Vagal stimulation does not markedly enhance the volume of pancreatic secretion but results in a marked increase in enzymic activity. A second intestinal hormone, *pancreozymin,* which, unlike secretin, stimulates secretion of enzymes by the pancreas, has been partially purified from extracts of intestinal mucosa. It is not clear whether these hormones and the vagus stimulate different cells or whether the same cells respond differently to these stimuli.

Intestinal Secretions. The succus entericus, the secretion of the intestinal mucosa, has been obtained for analysis by passage of suitable tubes (Miller-Abbott) in man and from loops of intestine, isolated at various levels, in experimental animals. The secreting cells are found in glands, the crypts of Lieberkühn, which are present extensively throughout the small intestine. A second type of gland, the glands of Brünner, resembling those of the stomach in appearance, is found only in the duodenum. These glands contribute a constant supply of a slightly alkaline fluid containing mucoproteins but having no enzymic activity. Four types of cells may be distinguished in the crypts. The function of each type has not been elucidated, but it appears that the cells of Paneth, at the base of the crypt, are responsible for secretion of enzymes. The electrolyte composition of mixed intestinal juice is not constant but, except for a lower [HCO_3^-], resembles pancreatic juice.

Many enzymes have been demonstrated in extracts of intestine, but relatively few have been isolated in pure form and characterized. These enzymes include *enterokinase, aminopeptidases, dipeptidases, maltase, sucrase, lactase,* a *lipase, nucleases, nucleotidase, nucleosidase,* a *lecithinase,* and a *phosphatase.* It may be significant that relatively little enzymic activity is demonstrable in intestinal juice, particularly from isolated loops, although the mucosa of such loops gives evidence of digestive activity. Many observations of this kind suggest that digestion may, to some extent, be completed within the intestinal mucosa as smaller, dialyzable molecules, *e.g.,* disaccharides and di- and tripeptides, cross the villi.

The stimuli to secretion by the intestinal mucosa are not so well defined as those for other digestive glands. The presence of material within the intestine leads to a constant flow of juice, but there has been no clear demonstration of the role of the abundant nerve supply. Secretin administration elicits a small flow of fluid in isolated loops of intestine; a substance termed *enterocrinin* has been isolated from intestinal mucosa and may be a specific hormone controlling intestinal secretion. It does not affect pancreatic secretion but has been stated to increase both the volume and enzyme concentration of the succus entericus.

Bile. In man, bile is continually elaborated by the polygonal cells of the liver and passes along the bile canaliculi and thence through the hepatic and cystic ducts to the gallbladder. Here it is stored and concentrated and enters the intestine through the common duct when food is present. Emptying of the gallbladder occurs only under the influence of partially digested food in the intestine. In part, this seems to be under neural control, but gallbladder contraction and emptying may be observed after complete denervation of this organ and introduction of partially hydrolyzed lipid into the duodenum. Acidic extracts of duodenal mucosa contain a material called *cholecystokinin*, a hormone released by the small intestine, which stimulates contraction of the gallbladder with release of its contents into the duodenum. Cholecystokinin has not been chemically characterized, nor has the mode of its physiological behavior been elucidated.

Bile contains several compounds which are absent from all other digestive secretions, *viz.*, cholesterol, bile acids, and bile pigments. Two classes of substances may be distinguished in *hepatic* bile: (1) those which are present in concentrations differing little from those in plasma, and (2) those which may be concentrated in bile many times more than in plasma. In the first category are Na^+, K^+, Cl^-, creatinine, glucose, and cholesterol, indicating the formation of a protein-free ultrafiltrate of plasma by the polygonal cells. Representatives of the second category include bilirubin, as well as administered substances which are excreted via bile, *e.g.*, bromosulfalein (bromosulfonphthalein, BSP), *p*-aminohippurate, and penicillin. These substances are added to bile by an active secretory mechanism. Bilirubin may be concentrated as much as 1,000-fold. Since high plasma concentrations of bromosulfalein inhibit bilirubin excretion, it is thought that these two compounds compete for a single secreting mechanism. The bile acids (page 85) are made in the polygonal cells and are present in hepatic bile to the extent of 10 to 20 meq. per liter.

The capacity of the gallbladder is 50 to 60 ml. in adults. The gallbladder not only is a storage sac but also concentrates bile by absorption of water, bile salts, and electrolytes and secretes mucoproteins. The resulting solution contains only small amounts of Cl^- and HCO_3^- and may be neutral or as acidic as pH 5.6. The $[K^+]$ appears to rise slightly during the reabsorptive process, and the final $[Ca^{++}]$ may be 15 to 30 mg. per 100 ml. It is not possible to obtain accurate data for the daily production of hepatic bile in normal individuals, but biliary fistulas permit collection of 500 to 1,000 ml. per day.

The *bile acids,* synthesized in the liver, are the chief, if not the only, contribution of bile to digestion; these acids are present in bile as bile salts. In fistula bile, the concentration of bile salts may vary from 0.5 to 1.5 per cent. The role of bile salts in the emulsification, hydrolysis, and absorption of lipids has been described (page 433). The two major components, glycocholic and taurocholic acids, are present in a ratio of about 3 : 1 in human bile. Inverse ratios may be encountered in persons on very low-protein diets. Bile from carnivores contains chiefly taurocholic acid, while hog bile contains largely glycocholic acid. The daily secretion of these compounds is about 5 to 15 g. per day. Most of this is returned to the liver via the enterohepatic circulation. The daily output of bile salts falls after a few days of collection through a biliary fistula but can be reestablished by feeding cholic acid and taurine. The bile salts are formed in the liver in a manner analogous to the formation of hippuric acid (page 528), *viz.,*

$$\text{Cholic acid} + \text{ATP} + \text{CoA} \longrightarrow \text{cholyl CoA} + \text{AMP} + \text{PP}_i$$
$$\text{Cholyl CoA} + \text{glycine} \longrightarrow \text{cholylglycine} + \text{CoA}$$
$$\text{(glycocholic}$$
$$\text{acid)}$$

Taurocholic acid is synthesized similarly from cholyl CoA and taurine. Presumably, analogous derivatives are similarly formed from other bile acids, *e.g.,* deoxycholic, chenodeoxycholic, and lithocholic acids (page 85).

The normal enterohepatic circulation of bile salts may be interrupted by oral administration of ion exchange resins. By increasing the daily production of bile acids from cholesterol and by interfering with the intestinal absorption of cholesterol (see below), this procedure drains the cholesterol of the body and may significantly lower the serum cholesterol concentration. Accordingly, this approach has been of interest as a therapeutic measure in atherosclerosis (page 938).

The bile pigments are derived from degradation of porphyrins in cells of the reticuloendothelial system, notably those of the liver (Chap. 42). Fresh hepatic bile is golden yellow because of the bilirubin present. Bladder bile may be green, because of oxidation of bilirubin to biliverdin (page 796). On standing, all bile darkens progressively from gold to green to blue and then to brown as the pigments are oxidized. The total daily excretion of these pigments in man varies from 0.5 to 2.1 g. Other substances derived from heme may occasionally be encountered in bile in small quantity, including coproporphyrin and bilicyanin (Chap. 42). Bilipurpurin occurs in the bile of ruminants and appears to be derived from chlorophyll.

Cholesterol, first isolated from gallstones, is a major biliary constituent and may be present in a concentration as high as 1 per cent in bladder bile. The cholesterol is virtually all in the free form. It is not the only lipid of bile, however; fatty acids occur, as soaps, in amounts varying from 0.5 to 1.2 per cent in bladder bile, which also contains as much as 0.5 per cent of neutral fat and 0.2 per cent of phosphatides. Maintenance of this stable, supersaturated solution of cholesterol appears to be dependent on the presence of bile salts, soaps, and mucoproteins. On dialysis, bile becomes turbid, and cholesterol precipitates. Much of the cholesterol is reabsorbed in the intestine, a process which is entirely dependent on the presence and simultaneous reabsorption of bile salts.

A number of enzymes have been found in bile, of which *alkaline phosphatase* is particularly noteworthy. This enzyme enters plasma from osteoblasts and is removed by the liver. In consequence, the plasma alkaline phosphatase activity may be increased either by enhanced activity of the osteoblasts or by failure of the hepatic parenchyma to remove the enzyme, and the alkaline phosphatase activity of plasma is a useful indicator of hepatic function. Bilirubin is largely present conjugated with glucuronic acid (page 797) and with sulfate. Glucosiduronates of other cyclic alcohols are also excreted in the bile. This is a major fate of thyroxine (Chap. 46) and certain of the steroid hormones (Chaps. 48 and 49).

Gallstones are composed of normal bile components which have precipitated. Virtually all stones have an inner core of protein tinged with bile pigment. The most common stones, built of alternating layers of cholesterol and calcium-bilirubin, are about 80 per cent cholesterol. Occasionally stones are encountered which are 90 to 98 per cent cholesterol. Small calcium-bilirubin stones occur somewhat less frequently, whereas pure bilirubin or pure calcium carbonate stones are very rare in man but not uncommon in cattle. The mechanism of biliary calculus formation is not understood, but the chief contributory factors appear to be infection, biliary stasis, and perhaps the plasma concentration of cholesterol. The importance of infection is well established, and multiple cholesterol-pigment-calcium stones are generally considered of this origin. Failure of the gallbladder to acidify the alkaline hepatic bile, or premature mixing with pancreatic juice by reflux of the latter into the bile duct, would result in precipitation of calcium salts, which might then serve as centers for deposition of other relatively insoluble biliary components. Biliary stasis may be of significance in individuals ingesting diets extremely low in fat.

MILK

Prior to birth, the fetus derives all its food from the mother by means of the placenta. After birth, the newborn mammal obtains its nourishment from the milk produced by the maternal mammary glands. Preparation of the mammary glands for subsequent lactation begins early in pregnancy, and secretion of milk normally begins at the end of gestation; these processes are under hormonal control (Chap. 51).

Production of milk for the newborn is a specific mammalian adaptation, and milk is unique in being an almost complete natural food from the point of view of nutrition. Its excellent nutritive quality has led to its wide use for individuals of all ages and to production of important derived foods such as cheese, butter, etc. Milk contains proteins, lipids, carbohydrates, minerals, vitamins, etc. The most significant deficiencies are the relatively low content of iron and copper and of vitamins C and D. The special nutritive properties of milk are derived from the presence of several highly nutritive proteins unique to milk, the occurrence of the disaccharide, lactose, the high content of glycerides of the lower fatty acids, and of calcium.

Although the general composition of milk is much the same in all the Mammalia, the concentrations of certain constituents vary considerably among different species. A relation between rate of growth of the young and the protein content is readily observed by a comparison of the composition of the milk from different species. This is illustrated by some of the data of Proscher (Table 36.2) compiled some 50 years ago. It may be pointed out that the protein content of human milk

Table 36.2. GROWTH RATE AND MILK COMPOSITION OF DIFFERENT MAMMALS

Source	Time for doubling body weight of newborn, days	Protein content, per cent	Ash content, per cent
Man	180	1.6	0.2
Horse	60	2.0	0.4
Cow	47	3.5	0.7
Goat	19	4.3	0.8
Pig	18	5.9	0.8
Sheep	10	6.5	0.8
Dog	8	7.1	1.3
Rabbit	6	10.4	2.5

is very low, whereas the average protein content of rabbit and reindeer milk is more than 10 per cent, the highest recorded values. The composition of milk varies with the time after initiation of lactation. The first milk, or *colostrum,* has unique properties, which will be discussed later.

COMPOSITION OF MILK

Most of our information has been derived from studies of cow's milk, largely because of its availability and great commercial importance. However, where information is available or where important differences should be noted, data will be given for human milk also.

The average composition of human and cow's milk is given in Table 36.3. The main differences are in the higher ash and protein content of cow's milk and the greater sugar content of human milk. Modification of cow's milk for infant nutrition is accomplished by dilution with water to decrease the protein and ash content and addition of lactose or other sugars to approximate human milk. It should be noted that there are large variations in milk composition in the same species.

Table 36.3: AVERAGE COMPOSITION OF HUMAN AND BOVINE MILK

Constituent	Human, per cent	Bovine, per cent
Water	87.5	87
Total solids	12.5	13
Protein	1.0–1.5	3.0–4.0
Lipid	3.0–4.0	3.5–5.0
Sugar	7.0–7.5	4.5–5.0
Ash	0.2	0.75

The white color of milk is due partly to emulsified lipid and partly to the presence of the calcium salt of casein, the main protein of milk. The occasional yellow color is caused by the pigments, carotene and xanthophyll (page 81). Fresh milk is nearly neutral; the pH is usually 6.6 to 6.8. Unsterilized milk rapidly becomes acidic because of fermentation by microorganisms.

Ash. The distribution of inorganic constituents is very similar in human and cow's milk (Table 36.4). The most noteworthy features are the high content of calcium, phosphorus, potassium, sodium, magnesium, and chlorine. Traces of other inorganic elements are also present, but, as already noted, the copper and iron

Table 36.4: PERCENTAGE DISTRIBUTION OF ASH IN MILK

Species	Ca	Mg	P	Na	K	Cl
Human	16.7	2.2	7.3	5.3	23.5	16.5
Bovine	16.8	1.7	11.6	5.3	20.7	13.6

SOURCE: From L. E. Holt, A. M. Courtney, and H. L. Fales, *Am. J. Diseases Children,* **10,** 229, 1915.

content is low. These trace elements are apparently present in sufficient amounts for the needs of the infant, but a characteristic anemia develops in the growing child if milk is used as the sole food; this is due to insufficient copper and iron.

Milk is probably the ideal source of calcium and phosphorus in nutrition. These elements are essential for all cells and are needed in large quantities for the formation of bones and teeth. The mammary gland functions in a highly selective manner to produce differences in the concentration of inorganic constituents in blood and milk. The molar ratios of milk to blood concentration (shown in parentheses) indicate that the sodium (0.13) and chloride (0.25) contents of milk are lower than those of plasma, whereas calcium (14), potassium (7), magnesium (4), and phosphate (7) are considerably higher.

Lactose. This disaccharide of galactose and glucose occurs primarily in milk. Since free galactose is not found in mammalian tissues or in other body fluids in significant amounts, it is evident that it is formed in the mammary gland from blood glucose. Indeed, when C^{14}-labeled glucose is injected into goats, the label appears equally in the glucose and galactose moieties of lactose. The biosynthesis of lactose has been discussed earlier (page 410).

It has been reported that human infants fed cow's milk develop a mixed intestinal flora, whereas those which are breast-fed show a prevalence of *Lactobacillus bifidus* in the stool. Mild acid hydrolysis of human, but not of cow's, milk liberates compounds, previously nondialyzable, which act as growth factors for *L. bifidus*. The active compounds appear to be oligosaccharides containing N-acetylglucosamine and a sialic acid.

If unsterilized milk is allowed to stand, fermentation caused by *Streptococcus lactis* and related organisms produces lactic acid from lactose. After hydrolysis of the lactose, lactic acid production by these bacteria results from the reaction sequence of anaerobic glycolysis (page 368).

Lipids. The lipids of milk are chiefly triglycerides and are dispersed as very small globules. Since the fat has a lower density than the aqueous part of milk, it will slowly rise to the top to form cream, or milk can be centrifuged to accomplish this more rapidly. The fat of cow's milk contains all the saturated fatty acids with an even number of carbon atoms from butyric to stearic, with about 10 per cent of the total fat composed of glycerides of lower fatty acids. The principal fatty acids are oleic, 32 per cent; palmitic, 15 per cent; myristic, 20 per cent; stearic, 15 per cent; and lauric, 6 per cent. Small amounts of phosphatides and cholesterol are present. Human milk fat contains no fatty acids with a molecular weight lower than that of decanoic acid and differs from cow's milk fat in this respect. The quantities of most of the fatty acids are similar to those in bovine milk.

Vitamins. Milk contains all the known vitamins and is exceedingly rich in vitamin A and riboflavin. Vitamin C (ascorbic acid), vitamin D, thiamine, pantothenic acid, and niacin are present in lesser amounts. Pasteurization destroys most of the vitamin C. For young infants, additional vitamins C and D are usually supplied.

Proteins. The principal protein of bovine milk is casein, which represents about 80 per cent of the protein nitrogen. The ease of preparation of this phosphoprotein has long made it a favorite subject for investigation. Milk is centrifuged, and the cream skimmed off the top. The remaining fluid, *skim milk,* is acidified to pH 4.7, causing the casein to precipitate. The supernatant fluid is *whey,* which contains about 20 per cent of the total protein. It may be noted that in some types of cheese manufacture the milk is acidified by the lactic acid produced by fermentation.

Crude casein is a mixture of several related proteins of differing amino acid composition which may be distinguished electrophoretically and have been separated from one another. In order of decreasing electrophoretic mobility at alkaline pH values, these are designated as α-, β-, γ-, and κ-caseins. The γ-casein represents only about 5 per cent of the total and contains little or no phosphorus. The α- and β-caseins are rich in phosphorus. From tryptic digests of casein, a "phosphopeptone" has been isolated which is approximately a decapeptide in length; further degradation of this substance led to the isolation of phosphorylserine. As in other phosphoproteins, the phosphate is esterified to the hydroxyl group of serine. The analogous O-phosphorylthreonine has also been obtained from an acidic hydrolysate of casein. These findings are of considerable interest in connection with the structure of other important phosphoproteins. They are also significant because a considerable part of the phosphorus content of milk is due to casein. Since casein is present mostly as calcium caseinate, milk actually contains these two important inorganic constituents largely in combination with casein. For different species, the calcium and phosphate contents appear to vary with the casein content; this approximation is to be expected from the mode of binding of these substances. In addition to binding phosphate, the caseins are conjugated to a polysaccharide of uncertain structure which contains galactose, galactosamine, and N-acetylneuraminic acid, and is present in an amount approximately 5 per cent of the weight of the protein. The mode of linkage to the protein is unknown.

As indicated above, casein may be readily precipitated by addition of acid to the milk, thus bringing it to the isoelectric point of the casein. The abomasum (fourth stomach) of ruminants contains a protease, *rennin,* which causes clotting at pH 7. Rennin liberates, from κ-casein only, a glycopeptide which is nondialyzable but soluble in 12 per cent trichloroacetic acid. The remaining molecule, called *paracasein,* reacts with calcium to yield the insoluble curd. Rennin is not present in the human stomach; the enzyme has only weak proteolytic activity. However, other proteases can also catalyze the conversion of casein to paracasein, and this is the initial step in casein digestion in the infant stomach.

The whey proteins appear to be as numerous as those of serum, judged by the complex electrophoretic diagrams obtained with this fluid. The principal protein of bovine whey is β-lactoglobulin, which has been obtained in crystalline form and amounts to about 50 or 60 per cent of the whey protein. The heterogeneous fraction of whey proteins soluble in saturated magnesium sulfate or half-saturated ammonium sulfate is frequently designated the albumin fraction, or "lactalbumin." This is a misnomer since the main protein is actually β-lactoglobulin. Other important constituents of bovine whey are the immune globulins, which carry the antibodies; these account for about 10 per cent of the whey protein. They will be discussed below under Colostrum.

Many enzymes have been found in milk, and a *lactoperoxidase* has been obtained in crystalline form. Other important enzymes are *xanthine oxidase,* a *lipase,* a *protease,* etc. Since the alkaline phosphatase of milk is destroyed by heat more slowly than are bacteria, the phosphatase activity of milk samples is employed as a test for efficiency of pasteurization. It is unclear whether these enzymes are significant in the physiology of milk production.

Not only does human milk contain much less protein than bovine milk (Table 36.3), but the distribution of the proteins is different. Casein accounts for only about 40 per cent of the proteins of human milk and the whey proteins about 60 per cent. However, the composition of caseins from human milk appears to be very similar to those of bovine origin. The other proteins of human milk have not been well characterized.

The main proteins of milk, casein and β-lactoglobulin, are unique in that they are not found in other tissues and bear no obvious relationship to any of the plasma proteins; these milk proteins are synthesized by mammary tissue from amino acids furnished by the blood. Casein and β-lactoglobulin are the most important nutritive proteins of milk. They are both preeminently suited for this function, since they are complete proteins containing all the common amino acids and are very rich in the essential ones. The relatively low sulfur content of casein, 0.78 per cent, is well balanced by β-lactoglobulin, which contains 1.6 per cent sulfur and is one of the best proteins for supporting the growth of young animals.

Milk contains a small amount of albumin, which is immunologically identical with serum albumin. The immune globulins of milk are closely related to the γ-globulins of serum, although they do not appear to be identical.

COLOSTRUM

The colostral milk, or colostrum, obtained during the first few days after parturition, differs markedly from ordinary milk in physical and biological properties. Fresh milk does not coagulate on boiling, but a surface film is formed which contains casein and calcium salts. When colostrum is boiled, a large coagulum is formed. This difference in physical properties is due to the much higher protein content of colostrum and its different protein composition. Bovine milk contains about 4 per cent protein, of which 80 per cent is casein. Colostrum may contain as high as 20 per cent protein, and the predominant fraction is represented by immune globulins, which in various animals account for 40 to 55 per cent of the total protein. These globulins contain all the antibodies found in the maternal blood and are responsible for the transmission of immunity to the newborn of ungulates (page 638). The predominant change in the protein pattern which occurs in the transition from colostrum to milk is the marked decrease of the immune globulins, which occurs a few days after lactation is initiated. Correspondingly, the newborn calf can absorb these globulins from the gastrointestinal tract only during the first day or so after birth, but the passively acquired antibodies may be detected in the blood for some months. In the human and other species in which placental transmission of antibodies occurs, the colostral mechanism is a secondary means of neonatal immunization. Human colostrum has only about two or three times the protein content of milk, and the higher concentration is largely due to the immune globulins.

The lipid of bovine colostrum is usually deep yellow or orange in color, largely because of the presence of β-carotene, an important precursor of vitamin A (page 81). Colostrum contains from 50 to 100 times as much β-carotene as does ordinary milk. Larger amounts of riboflavin, niacinamide, and other vitamins are found in colostrum than in milk.

It is evident from the foregoing that colostrum serves to enhance the chances of survival of the newborn. In addition to possessing the nutritive values of milk, it also provides necessary vitamins and antibodies important to the newborn animal. It is well to reemphasize that colostrum and milk are specific adaptations distinctive for mammals.

REFERENCES

Books

Adler, F. H., "Physiology of the Eye," The C. V. Mosby Company, St. Louis, 1950.

Babkin, B. P., "Secretory Mechanism of the Digestive Glands," Paul B. Hoeber, Inc., New York, 1944.

Beaumont, W., "Experiments and Observations of the Gastric Juice: The Physiology of Digestion," F. P. Allen, Plattsburgh, N.Y., 1933.

Cantarow, A., and Trumper, M., "Clinical Biochemistry," 6th ed., W. B. Saunders Company, Philadelphia, 1962.

Conway, E. J., "The Biochemistry of Gastric Acid Secretion," Charles C Thomas, Publisher, Springfield, Ill., 1953.

Davson, H., "Physiology of the Ocular Cerebrospinal Fluid," Little, Brown and Company, Boston, 1956.

Drinker, C. K., and Yoffey, J. M., "Lymphatics, Lymph and Lymphoid Tissue," 2d ed., Harvard University Press, Cambridge, Mass., 1956.

Gray, C. H., "Bile Pigments in Health and Disease," Charles C Thomas, Publisher, Springfield, Ill., 1961.

Sobotka, H., "Physiological Chemistry of the Bile," The Williams & Wilkins Company, Baltimore, 1937.

Wolf, S., and Wolff, H. G., "Human Gastric Function: An Experimental Study of a Man and His Stomach," Oxford University Press, New York, 1943.

Review Articles

Crane, R. K., Intestinal Absorption of Sugars, *Physiol. Revs.,* **40,** 789–825, 1960.

Davson, H., The Intra-ocular Fluids, in H. Davson, ed., "The Eye," vol. 1, pp. 67–146, Academic Press, Inc., New York, 1962.

Duran-Reynals, F., The Ground Substance of the Mesenchyme and Hyaluronidase, *Ann. N.Y. Acad. Sci.,* **52,** 943–957, 1950.

Grossman, M. I., Gastrointestinal Hormones, *Physiol. Revs.,* **30,** 33–90, 1950.

Grossman, M. I., The Glands of Brunner, *Physiol. Revs.,* **38,** 675–690, 1958.

Krogh, A., The Active and Passive Exchanges of Inorganic Ions through the Surfaces of Living Cells and through Living Membranes Generally, *Proc. Roy. Soc. London, Ser. B.,* **133,** 140–199, 1946.

McMeekin, T. L., Milk Proteins, in H. Neurath and K. Bailey, eds., "The Proteins: Chemistry, Biological Activity and Methods," vol. II, part A, pp. 389–434, Academic Press, Inc., New York, 1954.

Macy, I. G., Kelley, H., and Sloan, R., The Composition of Milks, *Natl. Acad. Sci.—Natl. Res. Council Publ.* **119,** 1950.

Pappenheimer, J. R., Passage of Molecules through Capillary Walls, *Physiol. Revs.,* **33,** 387–423, 1953.

Pirie, A., The Vitreous Body, in H. Davson, ed., "The Eye," vol. 1, pp. 197–212, Academic Press, Inc., New York, 1962.

Smith, E. L., The Isolation and Properties of the Immune Proteins of Bovine Milk and Colostrum and Their Role in Immunity: A Review, *J. Dairy Sci.,* **31,** 127–138, 1948.

Steele, J. M., Body Water in Man and Its Subdivisions, *Bull. N.Y. Acad. Med.,* **27,** 679–696, 1951.

37. Renal Function and the Composition of Urine

THE KIDNEY

The preceding chapter described secretions of special composition elaborated by various cells from constituents of arterial plasma. The kidney is the major secretory organ of the body, and the fluid separated from plasma by its activity is the urine. In contrast to other secretions, however, urine exhibits a remarkable range of volume and composition, and it is by virtue of its ability to alter the nature of urine with varying metabolic and environmental circumstances that the kidney aids in regulating the volume and composition of the extracellular fluid.

Each human kidney contains about 1,000,000 functional units, or nephrons. The formation of urine is the result of three processes which occur in each nephron: (1) filtration through the glomerular capillaries; (2) reabsorption of fluid and solutes in the proximal tubule, the loop of Henle, and the distal tubule; and (3) secretion into the lumen of the distal tubule.

The volume of glomerular filtrate formed by a normal 70-kg. adult is approximately 125 ml. per min. during mild water-induced diuresis. This fluid is considered to be a protein-free ultrafiltrate of plasma. Attempts have been made to estimate the maximum size of particles which can penetrate the glomerular epithelium. Polypeptides and smaller proteins, including hemoglobin and myoglobin, appear readily in the urine when present in plasma, whereas serum albumin appears in urine only under unusual circumstances. It has been suggested that the normal glomerulus may permit passage of a significant amount of serum albumin, which is reabsorbed as it passes down the tubule. If this were of the order of 5 mg. per 100 ml. of filtrate and if none of this material were reabsorbed, a proteinuria of 9 g. per day could result. During passage through the proximal tubule, about 70 to 80 per cent of the glomerular filtrate is reabsorbed, so that about 25 to 30 ml. per min. enters the loop of Henle. This fluid is glucose-free and isosmotic and, because of the reabsorption of HCO_3^-, has a pH below that of plasma. The reabsorptive processes which occur in the proximal tubule are relatively independent of the composition and volume of the body fluids, are not known to be subject to endocrine control, and are stated to be "obligatory." Formation of urine is completed in the loop of Henle, the distal tubules, and the collecting ducts from which urine flows at the rate of 0.5 to 2.0 ml. per min. The cells of these structures possess facultative mechanisms for reabsorption of water, various electrolytes and nonelectrolytes, and for secretion into the urine of NH_4^+, H^+, and K^+ ions, among

724

others. Thus, it is here that those final adjustments in the composition and volume of urine occur which serve to regulate the constancy of the *milieu intérieur.*

Clearance. This term is used to denote the removal of a substance from the blood during its passage through the kidneys and is defined as the least volume of blood or plasma which contains all of a particular substance excreted in the urine in 1 min. Clearance is, therefore, a rate with the dimensions of milliliters of plasma per minute. Thus,

$$C = \frac{U \times V}{P}$$

where U = concentration in urine, V = urine volume, milliliters per minute, P = plasma concentration, and C = clearance, milliliters per minute.

The clearance of a substance whose concentration in plasma is identical with that in the glomerular filtrate, and which is neither reabsorbed nor secreted by the tubular epithelium, is a measure of the rate of glomerular filtration. Inulin, mannitol, thiosulfate, and creatinine meet these criteria. All yield clearance values of about 125 ml. per min. per 1.73 m.^{2} of surface area in human males, and somewhat lower values in females. It follows that any substance whose clearance is less than that of inulin, and which is not bound to plasma protein, must be reabsorbed as the glomerular filtrate flows through the tubules. Na^+, Cl^-, K^+, water, glucose, urea, amino acids, and uric acid are examples of such substances. Furthermore, any substance whose clearance exceeds that of inulin must be secreted into the urine by tubular cells. NH_4^+, H^+, and N^1-methylnicotinamide behave in this manner, as do a number of other substances, notably penicillin, *p*-aminohippurate, and phenolsulfonphthalein. At low plasma concentrations, tubular secretion of *p*-aminohippurate (PAH) is so effective that it does not appear in renal venous blood. Under these circumstances, PAH clearance is a measure of effective renal plasma flow, about 650 ml. per min. per 1.73 m.^{2}. The ratio of inulin to PAH clearance is termed the *filtration fraction* and is approximately 18 per cent in normal individuals.

Transport Maximum, T_m. Another parameter of renal excretory function is the T_m, an abbreviation for *transport maximum,* the maximum ability of the kidneys either to reabsorb or to secrete a given material. For example, since essentially no glucose is excreted when the plasma glucose concentration is 100 mg. per 100 ml., the kidneys must reabsorb 125 mg. of glucose per minute in the proximal tubules. However, at an artificially elevated plasma glucose concentration of 400 mg. per 100 ml., *i.e.*, a glomerular filtration rate of 500 mg. per min., 200 mg. per min. of glucose may be excreted. The difference, 300 mg. per min., is the maximum rate at which the kidneys can reabsorb glucose and is denoted as T_m for glucose. Similarly, by raising the concentration of PAH until it appears in the renal venous blood in appreciable quantities, the maximum amount of PAH appearing in the urine per minute represents the secretory T_m for PAH.

Renal Threshold. This term denotes the plasma concentration above which a given substance appears in the urine. Thus, in man, the renal threshold for glucose varies between 125 and 160 mg. per 100 ml. plasma. This is not so precise a concept as the reabsorptive T_m described above but is more readily determined since it does not necessitate simultaneous measurements of glomerular filtration. Any statement of the threshold value for a given compound assumes a constant glomerular filtration rate; this assumption may not be valid from interval to interval. Moreover, for no substance is there a precise threshold; after the threshold concentration has been exceeded, not all the material filtered in the glomerular filtrate is necessarily excreted quantitatively. Thus, an individual with a glucose threshold of 130 mg. per 100 ml. filters and reabsorbs 163 mg. per min. at this concentration, yet at an even higher plasma concentration may exhibit a glucose reabsorptive T_m of 300 mg. per min. Table 37.1 lists the thresholds of appearance of some major plasma solutes. Evidence for a threshold of appearance (or excretion) for a diffusible substance indicates that for its reabsorption by the tubules a device exists which can be saturated.

Table 37.1: PLASMA THRESHOLDS OF APPEARANCE AND RETENTION

Substance	Threshold of appearance	Test subject	Threshold of retention	Test subject
Glucose........	11.6 mmole/liter (208 mg./100 ml.)	Dog	6.84 mmole/liter (123 mg./100 ml.)	Rabbit
Glucose........	7.8–11.1 mmole/liter (140–200 mg./100 ml.)	Man		
Sodium........	....	......	140 meq./liter	Man, dog
Chloride.......	85 meq./liter	Rabbit	110 meq./liter	Dog
			100 meq./liter	Man
Bicarbonate....	25 meq./liter	Dog	25 meq./liter	Man, dog
Potassium......	2.8 meq./liter	Man	3 meq./liter	Man, dog
Sulfate.........	2–4 meq./liter	Dog	3 meq./liter	Dog
Calcium........	4.25 meq./liter	Man	4.8 meq./liter	Man, dog
Phosphate......	1.1–1.5 mmole/liter	Dog		

SOURCE: Adapted from A. V. Wolf, "The Urinary Function of the Kidney," Grune & Stratton, Inc., New York, 1950.

A more illuminating concept is that of the threshold of retention, the concentration at which the quantities of a given substance in plasma and urine are identical. Above this plasma concentration, urine will be more concentrated than plasma, while, below it, plasma will be more concentrated than urine. This concept describes the kidney as a regulator of the composition of the extracellular fluid more graphically than does the threshold of appearance.

RENAL EXCRETORY MECHANISMS

ELECTROLYTES

Sodium, Chloride, and Water. About 75 per cent of the Na^+, Cl^-, and water of the glomerular filtrate are reabsorbed in the proximal tubules. This occurs by an active process in which Na^+ ions are selectively removed from the tubular fluid; anions move passively in accordance with the electrical gradient established by transfer of Na^+, and water moves, passively and isosmotically, with the solute. In this manner, about 25 ml. of isosmotic filtrate arrive at the distal tubules per minute.

The subsequent facultative adjustment of the volume and osmolarity of the urine is made possible by (1) the existence of a sodium pump in the cells of the loop of Henle and in the distal portions of the tubule and collecting duct; (2) control by antidiuretic hormone (page 903) of the permeability to water of the distal tubules and collecting ducts; and (3) the architecture of the kidney. In the ascending limb of the hairpin-shaped loop of Henle an outwardly oriented sodium pump (chloride moves passively with the electrochemical gradient) operates while the same cells are relatively impermeable to water. Consequently, a gradient of about

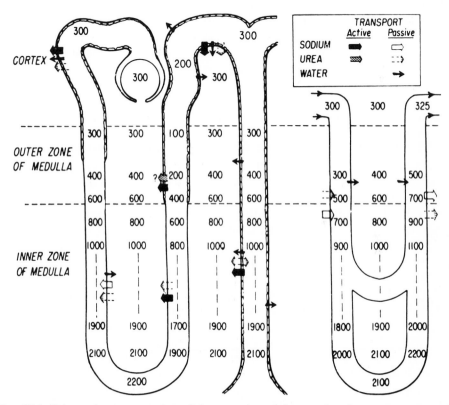

FIG. 37.1. Schematic representation of the operation of the postulated countercurrent multiplication mechanism in the formation of hypertonic urine by the kidney.

200 mOsmoles (mOsm.) per liter is established between the fluid inside the ascending limb of the loop and the surrounding interstitium. This effect is multiplied as the fluid in the thin-walled, water-permeable, descending limb achieves osmotic equilibrium with the same interstitium, thereby increasing the osmolarity of the fluid presented to the ascending limb. As the fluid travels through the distal tubule, it is diluted by water from the interstitium, with which it again attains osmotic equilibrium. Sodium may be removed throughout the distal tubule by an active process, the rate of which is determined by the adrenal cortical hormone, aldosterone (Chap.

49). This activity is maximal when Na^+ is to be conserved and can result in removal of almost all Na^+ from the presumptive urine; it is minimal at elevated plasma $[Na^+]$. As the fluid proceeds down the collecting duct, it must pass once again through an area of increasing osmolarity of the surrounding tissue. The epithelium of the collecting ducts is thought to be essentially impermeable to Na^+ whereas permeability of this tissue to H_2O is determined by the action of antidiuretic hormone (page 903). In the absence of the latter, the duct is impermeable to H_2O; the duct fluid fails to equilibrate with the surrounding medium, and a highly dilute urine is excreted. Increasing quantities of antidiuretic hormone increase permeability to H_2O until, at full activity, the duct fluid is osmotically equilibrated with the contents of the loop of Henle before entering the larger collecting passages. This hormone exerts similar effects on the water permeability of the toad bladder, which has been used to demonstrate that (1) the hormone forms a stable addition product with a thiol group on a protein of the bladder and (2) the hormone stimulates formation of cyclic adenylic acid (page 417), which, even in the absence of hormone, can also elicit a similar increase in permeability to water. The operation of this countercurrent system is shown in Fig. 37.1. Clearly, it is not possible to form a urine more concentrated than that of the contents of the bottom of the loop of Henle.

Potassium. The renal mechanisms involved in potassium excretion efficiently prevent potassium retention and ensure against hyperpotassemia. However, even on a potassium-free diet, normal adults may excrete 20 to 30 meq. per day. Although this might readily be derived from the 750 meq. filtered through the glomerulus daily, it appears likely that potassium is largely removed as fluid traverses the proximal tubules and that most urinary potassium is secreted in the distal tubules. The existence of such a secretory mechanism is suggested by the fact that K^+ clearance may exceed inulin clearance.

Whereas nothing is known of the proximal reabsorptive process, secretion of K^+ in the distal tubule is accomplished by exchange for Na^+. Only when Na^+ reabsorption is impaired, as in adrenal cortical insufficiency, does K^+ secretion fail and hyperpotassemia may result. Thus it appears that this exchange mechanism is one aspect of the aldosterone-controlled Na^+-reabsorptive process in the distal tubule (page 882). The normal operation of this mechanism enforces excretion of about 25 meq. of K^+ daily even when no potassium is ingested or at diminished plasma $[K^+]$. Exaggerated Na^+ reabsorption due to adrenal cortical hyperactivity (Cushing's disease, Chap. 49) results in augmented K^+ excretion with serious depletion of body potassium.

Acidification of Urine. In severe acidosis the $[H^+]$ of urine may be 1,000 times that of the plasma from which it is derived. This acidification begins in the proximal tubules and is completed in the distal tubules and collecting ducts. Although selective reabsorption of $HPO_4^=$ and dissociation of the dissolved CO_2 of the glomerular filtrate might account for acidification of urine in normal persons ingesting an average diet with an acidic ash, it cannot account for the maximum capacity of the kidney to produce acidic urine. The tubular ion exchange mechanism illustrated in Fig. 37.2, proposed by Pitts, is thought to represent the major mechanism for acidification of urine.

Essentially, the suggested mechanism includes metabolic CO_2 production, hydration to H_2CO_3 catalyzed by carbonic anhydrase, dissociation to $H^+ + HCO_3^-$, and exchange of the H^+ for Na^+ across the luminal border of the cell. Na^+ and HCO_3^- are assumed to diffuse to the opposite side of the cell, where the reverse process could operate, leading to appearance of Na^+ of the glomerular filtrate in

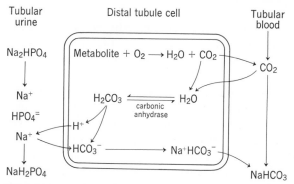

Fig. 37.2. Schematic representation of the acidification of urine by tubular cationic exchange. (*From R. F. Pitts, Am. J. Med.,* **9**, 356, 1950.)

venous blood, with HCO_3^- arising from H_2CO_3. After exchange of Na^+ and H^+ across the vascular boundary of the cell, the H^+ combines with HCO_3^-, CO_2 is produced by carbonic anhydrase catalysis, and then diffuses into the plasma. The failure of the acidification process and enhanced Na^+ excretion after administration of carbonic anhydrase inhibitors strengthen the H^+-Na^+ exchange concept and strongly suggest that cellular CO_2 is the source of the secreted protons. That this CO_2 is derived from renal oxidative metabolism rather than from the blood is indicated by the observation that the maximum rate of acidification (meq. H^+ per min.) is of the same order of magnitude as renal cellular respiration (mmoles CO_2 per min.).

Thus, both H^+ and K^+ secretion by the distal tubule are accomplished by exchange for Na^+. Moreover, these processes are not unrelated. Carbonic anhydrase inhibition results not only in alkalinization of urine and diminished Na^+ reabsorption but also in a three- to fivefold increase in urine $[K^+]$. In potassium-deficiency states, with K^+ relatively unavailable for secretion, the acidification process is hyperactive; acidic urine low in $[K^+]$ is excreted, and plasma $[HCO_3^-]$ may rise to 50 or 60 meq. per liter. Conversely, when unusual quantities of K^+ are excreted, as after potassium administration, alkaline urine is produced. In respiratory acidosis, with increased plasma and cellular P_{CO_2}, urine is acidic and low in $[K^+]$, whereas in respiratory alkalosis, urine is alkaline and high in $[K^+]$. Thus, it appears that there is a competition between K^+ and H^+ for some component of the Na^+ exchange mechanism. This process may be an aspect of the general, aldosterone-regulated Na^+ absorptive process. Acidification fails in the absence of aldosterone and is accentuated when excessive aldosterone is administered or is secreted by an adrenal tumor (Chap. 49).

Bicarbonate. Ordinarily, renal excretion of bicarbonate is very low; its concentration in urine at pH 6 or below is negligible. The major portion of the bicarbonate filtered through the glomerulus is reabsorbed, largely in the proximal tubule. Although this might occur in passive fashion similar to the behavior of Cl^- in this area, it is probable that HCO_3^- reabsorption is an active process, although both active and passive processes may obtain. In either case, the distal tubule is presented with fluid containing about 10 to 15 meq. per liter of HCO_3^-. Although there may be an HCO_3^--absorbing mechanism, HCO_3^- reabsorption occurs chiefly by Na^+-H^+ exchange, as described above for acidification of urine. In this case, cellular H_2CO_3 yields a proton which exchanges for Na^+; the HCO_3^- in the lumen accepts the proton, dehydrates, and the resultant CO_2 may diffuse into peritubular blood or rehydrate in the cell. In either instance, the HCO_3^- returned to blood derives from dissociation of intracellular H_2CO_3. All other circumstances remaining constant, this process operates so that, at plasma $[HCO_3^-]$ up to 24 to 28 meq. per liter, all filtered HCO_3^- returns to plasma; at higher $[HCO_3^-]$ virtually all the excess HCO_3^- remains in the urine, which is, accordingly, alkaline. In this manner, urine containing as much as 250 meq. per liter of HCO_3^- may be excreted.

The major factors which govern the behavior of the tubular epithelium with respect to the acidification of urine appear, with but a few exceptions, to be intracellular $[H^+]$ and $[K^+]$. At low P_{CO_2} (respiratory alkalosis), the ratio $KHCO_3/H_2CO_3$ in the cell is elevated, the supply of H^+ is low but $[K^+]$ is normal, and an alkaline, K^+-containing fluid is excreted. In respiratory acidosis with high P_{CO_2}, increased intracellular CO_2, and, therefore, increased $[H^+]$, an acidic urine may be expected. With an increase in plasma $[K^+]$, as after KCl administration, there is presumed to be an increased intracellular $[K^+]$ which competes favorably with cellular protons and urine is alkaline, whereas the reverse situation obtains after general depletion of body potassium. More difficult to rationalize in these terms are metabolic alkalosis and acidosis. In the former, the increased load of filtered HCO_3^- is presumed to be the dominant factor and urine pH is conditioned by the limit of 24 to 28 meq. of HCO_3^- per liter of glomerular filtrate which can be reabsorbed. This may, in part, be offset by increased P_{CO_2} due to respiratory compensation, but the latter is usually minimal and relatively ineffective. Finally, in metabolic acidosis, characterized by markedly diminished P_{CO_2}, and therefore lowered cellular $[H_2CO_3]$, the increased $[H^+]$ of the extracellular fluid is dominant and

Table 37.2: FACTORS CONTROLLING THE pH OF URINE

	Plasma			Cells			Urine		
	$[H_2CO_3]$	$[HCO_3^-]$	$[K^+]$	$[H_2CO_3]$	$[HCO_3^-]$	$[H^+]$	$[K^+]$	$[HCO_3^-]$	$[H^+]$
Respiratory alkalosis......	↓	...	↑	↓	...	↓	↑	↑	↓
Respiratory acidosis.......	↑	...	↓	↑	...	↑	↓	↓	↑
Potassium administration...	...	...	↑	...	...	...	↑	↑	↓
Potassium depletion.......	...	...	↓	...	...	...	↓	↓	↑
Metabolic alkalosis........	↑	↑	↓	↑	↑	↓	↑	↑	↓
Metabolic acidosis........	↓	↓	↓	↓	↓	↑	↑	↓	↑

may, by exchange for cellular K^+, titrate HCO_3^- and other cellular buffers and lower cellular pH despite the low P_{CO_2}, and thus determine the pH of urine. These interrelationships are depicted in Table 37.2.

Ammonia Excretion. Nash and Benedict demonstrated that renal tubular cells form ammonia from a precursor in arterial blood and secrete it in high concentration into tubular urine. By measurements of the renal arteriovenous differences in glutamine concentration, Archibald and Van Slyke found that in the acidotic dog some two-thirds of the urinary ammonia was derived from the amide nitrogen of the glutamine of arterial blood. In alkalosis, virtually no glutamine was removed from blood flowing through the kidney. It has been suggested that the remaining one-third of the urinary ammonia is derived from α-amino nitrogen of amino acids, and this view is supported by observations that infusion of a number of amino acids enhances urinary excretion of ammonia. Also, kidney slices, in vitro, produce ammonia and α-keto acids when incubated with amino acids. Thus, it is possible to account for all the urinary ammonia as arising from glutamine and α-amino acids present in blood traversing the kidney. Whether the relative quantities of ammonia arising from these sources are always constant is unknown.

It appears likely that NH_3, rather than NH_4^+, diffuses across the tubular lining and connecting duct epithelium and is neutralized by H^+ secreted by the ion exchange process described above. This, in turn, reduces the $[H^+]$ of the urine, permitting exchange of more H^+ for Na^+, which returns to the venous blood. Moreover, if NH_3 rather than NH_4^+ is the diffusing substance, this leads to establishment of a large concentration gradient, thereby enhancing secretion of NH_3. Conversely, if the intraluminar fluid is alkaline, formation of NH_4^+ is depressed, and NH_3 diffusion and excretion become limited to the equilibrium concentration of NH_3, which should be low. However, the $[H^+]$ of urine is not the sole factor controlling NH_3 excretion. When acidosis ensues, several days are required before maximal ammonia excretion is obtained, despite continued formation of highly acidic urine. Similarly, when ammonia excretion was compared in dogs rendered acidotic several days in advance and dogs given NH_4Cl at the start of the experiment, and then both groups were restored to normal conditions by a slow infusion of $NaHCO_3$, the animals in the first group excreted about three times as much ammonia as those in the second group at identical urinary pH levels. This effect may, in part, be due to "adaptive" increase in renal glutaminase or amino acid oxidase activity in chronic acidosis and also appears to be mediated in some manner by the adrenal cortex, since adrenalectomized animals excrete considerably less ammonia than do normal animals after administration of NH_4Cl.

Phosphate and Calcium. Phosphate clearance is, at all times, less than inulin clearance. It has not been established which segment of the tubule is responsible for phosphate absorption. However, existence of a phosphate T_m, inhibition of phosphate reabsorption by the parathyroid hormone (Chap. 47), and failure of reabsorption when serum $[K^+]$ is diminished indicate an active absorptive process. Nothing is known of the mechanisms by which phosphate excretion is enhanced in acidosis and in alkalosis.

Calcium is a threshold substance, and urine normally is virtually calcium-free.

However, calcium rapidly appears in urine when the plasma concentration is elevated to only a slight degree, indicating that the tubules normally operate rather close to their capacity, or T_m value, for calcium.

NONELECTROLYTES

Urea. Urea is the major example of a highly diffusible substance which is neither actively reabsorbed nor secreted by the tubules. Understanding of the renal mechanism for concentration of urea is as yet incomplete. Although there is suggestive evidence that urea may be actively reabsorbed by renal tubules of human beings or of herbivores during chronic ingestion of diets extremely low in protein, the behavior of urea in the nephron reflects (1) lack of any specific urea-affecting device, (2) specific mechanisms for absorption or secretion of electrolytes, and (3) osmotic equilibrium between intraluminar fluid and the renal interstitium. In the rat nephron, urea concentration increases slightly at the end of the proximal convolutions and then increases about fivefold in the loop of Henle. This urea derives from the surrounding tissue and remains in the lumen as the fluid content falls. In the distal tubule, urea again tends to remain behind as water leaves. In the collecting ducts, in the region of antidiuretic hormone-sensitive cells, with high permeability to water, concentration of urea again occurs. In general, the concentration of urea in urine, like that of $[Na^+]$, is equal to the concentration which obtains in the renal papilla.

At ordinary rates of urine flow the concentration of urea in urine is about sixty to seventy times as great as that in plasma. When urine flow is about 1 ml. per min., urea clearance is normally about 55 ml. per min. When urine excretion is 2 ml. per min. or greater, urea clearance is about 75 ml. per min., so that about 40 per cent of the urea filtered is returned to the blood, while more than 98 per cent of the water is reabsorbed. Maximum urea clearance is normally reached when the rate of urine flow is greater than 2 ml. per min.

In many renal diseases, urea clearance falls, and plasma concentration of urea rises. The fall in urea clearance merely reflects the decline in glomerular filtration. This last process is self-adjusting with respect to excretion of urea. For example, a normal individual may have a plasma urea N concentration of 10 mg. per 100 ml., a glomerular filtration of 120 ml. per min., a urea clearance of 60 ml. per min., and hence, excrete 6 mg. of urea N per minute. Thus, half the urea filtered is passively reabsorbed. In glomerulonephritis, the glomerular filtration rate may decline to as little as 60 ml. per min. Since, again, half the urea filtered is reabsorbed, then at the outset only 3 mg. of urea N is excreted per minute. In consequence, the plasma urea concentration rises. When the latter reaches 20 mg. urea N per 100 ml., at the same diminished glomerular filtration rate, 12 mg. of urea N is filtered per minute. Since half of this is reabsorbed, 6 mg. of urea N is excreted per minute, just as in the normal individual. Thus, because of the elevated plasma urea concentration, despite a striking fall in urea clearance, the nephritic person can remain in balance with respect to urea.

Creatinine. The concentration of creatinine in urine is generally thirty-five to forty times that of plasma. In man, creatinine is excreted by glomerular filtration and is partly reabsorbed by passive diffusion. However, when creatinine is injected and the plasma concentration maintained at an elevated level, creatinine clearance approaches that of inulin.

Uric Acid. The urine to plasma concentration ratio of uric acid is approximately 30. Unlike creatinine and urea, uric acid is a compound which appears in urine when the concentration in plasma exceeds values just above normal. The threshold appears to be influenced by one or more of the adrenal cortical hormones, administration of which increases urinary elimination and lowers plasma concentration of uric acid.

Glucose. Glucose is reabsorbed virtually quantitatively before the glomerular filtrate reaches the loop of Henle. When, however, the glucose threshold is exceeded, as in diabetes mellitus, glucose appears in the urine. In some individuals, glucose appears in the urine sporadically at normal, or only slightly elevated, plasma concentration of glucose. This condition is termed *renal glucosuria* and is attributed to a defective mechanism for tubular glucose reabsorption. Renal glucosuria can also be induced by administration of phlorhizin (page 46), which inhibits the tubular mechanism for glucose reabsorption. With sufficient dosage of the drug, glucose clearance may almost equal inulin clearance.

TUBULAR TRANSPORT MECHANISMS

The variable composition of urine, the absence of glucose in normal urine, and direct observation of changes in composition of glomerular filtrate within the tubules have indicated the existence of facultative mechanisms for absorption of constituents of the glomerular filtrate. Direct observation of phenol red secretion by the mesonephric kidneys of frogs, and by the tubules of the metanephric kidney in tissue culture studies in the laboratories of Marshall, Richards, and Chambers, early provided evidence of tubular secretion. Clearance techniques permit ready recognition of these processes. As the plasma concentration of a compound which is actively reabsorbed is increased, the clearance remains essentially zero until the reabsorptive capacity is exceeded. Beyond that point, clearance increases with rising plasma concentration, approaching glomerular filtration rate as a limit. Clearance of a compound that is secreted by the renal tubules exceeds that possible from glomerular filtration alone, and as its concentration in plasma increases, the clearance decreases to approach glomerular filtration as a limit.

The terms "reabsorption" and "secretion" have no meaning as applied to the cell. Both processes are "secretory" and differ only in their orientation. What, then, is the nature of the cellular transport mechanisms responsible for these processes? Many observations suggest that these processes involve enzymic systems arranged to exhibit directional orientation as well as substrate specificity. Admittedly, in no instance has the enzyme been identified, but the parallelism between the behavior of some transport mechanisms and enzymic activity is striking.

Regardless of the details of the mechanism, energy is required to transport any substance against an osmotic gradient. The immediate source of this energy is probably ATP. Tubular secretory mechanisms for secretion of phenol red and *p*-aminohippurate (PAH) fail in the presence of quinone, an inhibitor of dehydrogenases, of vinylacetic acid, which inhibits succinic acid oxidase, and of dinitrophenol, which prevents respiratory phosphorylation. Moreover, transport mechanisms appear to compete for available energy. Thus, whereas PAH is secreted and glucose and ascorbic acid are reabsorbed, reabsorption of both glucose and ascorbic acid is impaired when PAH is secreted at its T_m value.

There are numerous instances in which substances of similar structure compete for a common transport mechanism. Xylose clearance rises to that of inulin if the plasma glucose concentration is raised, although the total absorption of the two sugars exceeds that of either alone at the same concentration. The pairs leucine-isoleucine and lysine-arginine behave similarly, while PAH administration diminishes secretion of penicillin. This type of competition closely resembles that of substrates competing for a single enzyme, *e.g.*, phenylethylamine and epinephrine for liver amine oxidase. An excellent example of competitive inhibition of a transport mechanism by a substance which is not itself secreted by that mechanism is the competitive inhibition of secretion of penicillin and PAH by *p*-carboxy, N,N-diisopropylsulfonamide (Benemid). The extent of secretion is dependent, at all concentrations, on the ratio of penicillin or PAH to Benemid.

A single mechanism may serve to transport material in two directions, as in the case of the H^+-Na^+ system. In this regard it is noteworthy that Benemid, which inhibits tubular secretion of PAH and penicillin, also interferes with reabsorption of uric acid and inorganic phosphate. Additional evidence of the interdependence of secretory and reabsorptive mechanisms is the fact that if the serum $[K^+]$ is lowered, as by glucose infusion, K^+ secretion is diminished, while at the same time the renal capacity for phosphate reabsorption declines.

No normal urinary constituent is secreted as efficiently by tubules as are PAH and penicillin. Indeed, only N^1-methylnicotinamide and phenylsulfate, of the normal organic urinary constituents, are known to be secreted into the tubular urine at all, and these are excreted only in milligram quantities daily. Since PAH clearance is not affected by variations of the K^+, H^+, or NH_4^+ content of urine, or by carbonic anhydrase inhibitors, the PAH-secreting device appears to be independent of mechanisms responsible for secretion of these urinary components. Although the normal substrate for the PAH-secreting mechanism is unknown, it is possible that this substrate is absorbed rather than secreted.

The only enzymes known specifically to participate in renal transport are glutaminase, which functions in secretion of ammonia, and carbonic anhydrase, which is essential for H^+-Na^+ exchange. The high concentration of alkaline phosphatase at the luminal and vascular borders of tubular cells suggests a role for this enzyme in transport processes. Active sodium transport appears to occur along the entire length of the nephron, except in the thin, descending loop of Henle. The evidence suggests that the mechanism employed resembles closely the Na^+-K^+-H^+ exchange system of cells generally. It is noteworthy, therefore, that kidney possesses a Na^+-K^+ requiring ATPase which, like that of erythrocyte ghosts and nerve, is sensitive to the cardiac glycosides (page 47). The relationship of K^+ secretion to renal Na^+-H^+ exchange recalls the finding by Conway that acidification of the medium during yeast fermentation is also a result of a K^+-H^+ transfer, suggesting that the process of secretion of electrolytes is basically similar in all cells. It is apparent that enzymic bases for renal tubular transport have been well established although the details remain largely unknown.

RENAL HYPERTENSION

In addition to its role in maintaining the volume and composition of extracellular fluid, the kidney may also be involved in homeostatic control of arterial blood pressure. Hypertension is associated with a variety of renal disorders in man, although the role of this organ in essential hypertension is still speculative. Goldblatt produced hypertension in dogs by clamping the renal arteries to restrict renal blood flow. This procedure is also effective after renal denervation, indicating a humoral mechanism in the pathogenesis of this type of experimental hypertension. Extracts of kidney contain a protein, *renin,* which has been obtained in a relatively high state of purity. Renin is an enzyme which splits a polypeptide, *hypertensin I,* from *hypertensinogen,* a serum α_2-globulin formed by the liver. No other known proteolytic enzyme liberates hypertensin from hypertensinogen.

Hypertensin I preparations of slightly different composition have been described, depending on the sources of the renin and the substrate used. The hypertensin I obtained by incubation of hog kidney renin with horse serum globulin is a decapeptide with the amino acid sequence Asp·Arg·Val·Tyr·Ileu·His·Pro·Phe·His·Leu; this peptide exhibits no pressor activity. However, normal serum contains an enzyme which liberates the dipeptide His·Leu from the carboxyl-terminal end of the chain, yielding *hypertensin II,* the most powerful pressor agent known. All tissues, particularly intestine and kidney, exhibit peptidase activity, presumably due to leucine aminopeptidase, which rapidly destroys hypertensin II. Skeggs has shown that plasma from persons with essential hypertension contains hypertensin II in an amount sufficient to maintain an elevated blood pressure. Normal plasma is devoid of hypertensin II. The possible normal role of the renin-hypertensin system is uncertain. It may participate in homeostatic control of arterial pressure. In addition, hypertensin II acts directly on the adrenal gland to stimulate release of aldosterone (Chap. 49), resulting in Na^+ conservation.

Hypertensin has also been called *angiotonin.* A uniform nomenclature has been proposed which would designate this compound as *angiotensin.* The enzyme which cleaves this decapeptide (see above) is thus termed *angiotensinase* or *hypertensinase.* The precursor globulin, which is converted to angiotensin by renin, is termed *angiotensinogen.*

Experimental hypertension can also be produced by enveloping the kidneys with silk, cellophane, or acrylate resin, by subtotal nephrectomy, or by prolonged administration of salt and the adrenal cortical steroid, deoxycorticosterone. The relation of high salt intake or retention to hypertension is not understood, but dietary salt restriction has proved effective in management of human hypertensive disease. Restriction of protein intake alleviates the hypertension of partially nephrectomized rats, apparently because of failure of adrenocorticotropic hormone secretion (Chap. 51) secondary to protein deficiency. The role of adrenal cortical hormones is not clear, but adrenalectomy lowers blood pressure in a significant number of hypertensive human beings, renal hypertension cannot be induced in adrenalecto-mized animals, and administration of adrenocorticotropic hormone or adrenal cortical steroids produces hypertension in totally nephrectomized rats.

NATURE AND COMPOSITION OF URINE

Since the rate of formation of urine and its composition are subject to diurnal variation and to the influences of muscular activity, digestion, and even emotional phenomena, comparisons of urine specimens are generally performed by examining urines collected over a 24-hr. period.

Volume. The volume of urine voided in 24 hr. by normal adults ranges from 600 to 2,500 ml. per day. Excretion greater than this is usually indicative of disease, e.g., diabetes mellitus or insipidus, nephritis, etc. Urine volume is related to fluid intake and is increased by ingestion of large volumes of fluids, particularly beer, coffee, or tea, which contain diuretics. In the early states of kidney disease, diabetes mellitus, etc., nocturia is encountered. This is defined as the passage of more than 500 ml. of urine with a specific gravity below 1.018 during a 12-hr. period at night. Later in the course of kidney disease, however, as renal function becomes more severely impaired, nocturia ceases: urine volumes may become markedly diminished (oliguria), and, in the terminal stage of kidney disease, urine excretion may cease entirely (anuria). Oliguria is also seen as a result of dehydration, cardiac insufficiency, or fever.

Color. Urine is usually amber in color. The principal pigment is urochrome, a compound of urobilin or urobilinogen (page 798) and a peptide of unknown structure. Other pigments which may be present include uroerythrin (believed to be derived from melanin metabolism), uroporphyrins (page 792) (normally present in minute amounts), and numerous other pigments present in traces, such as riboflavin. On standing, urine usually darkens, presumably owing to formation of chromogenic material by oxidation. An unusually dark urine is due most commonly to excretion of bilirubin. Bilirubinuria is seen in icterus of the direct van den Bergh type (page 799). This includes all instances of obstructive jaundice, as well as most intrahepatic types of icterus. A darker than normal urine may also indicate the presence of porphyrins in abnormal amounts or of homogentisic acid (page 549), which is oxidized to a black polymer when urine which is slightly alkaline stands in contact with air. "Urorosein" excretion is related to ingestion of indole compounds.

Normal Sediments. Freshly voided urine is ordinarily clear. When it has been standing, a flocculent material occasionally separates; this usually consists of a small amount of nucleoprotein or mucoprotein together with some epithelial cells from the lining of the genitourinary tract. If the urine is alkaline, a mixture of calcium phosphate and ammonium-magnesium-phosphate ("triple phosphate") may also precipitate and, occasionally, oxalates and urates, which redissolve on acidification of the urine. Uric acid may precipitate from acidic urine.

Total Solute Concentration. The combined operation of the various mechanisms already described permits elaboration of urine varying in osmolarity from 50 to 1,400 mOsm. per liter, as compared with plasma at 285 mOsm. per liter. The kidneys of young children are somewhat less efficient, producing urine of from 100 to 800 mOsm. per liter. The difference between the osmolarity of a given urine and that of plasma represents the quantity of salt cleared without an equivalent loss of water, when the osmolarity of urine exceeds 285 mOsm. per liter. When the osmolarity is less than that of plasma, one may calculate the *free water clearance*. Thus, a 24-hr. specimen of urine of exactly 2 liters at 100 mOsm. per liter represents clearance of 1.43 liters of free water during this period.

In general, osmolarity, and hence specific gravity, varies inversely with urine volume, the lowest osmolarities being those of persons with uncontrolled diabetes insipidus. The high urinary concentration of glucose in diabetes mellitus may result in urine of 1,400 mOsm. per liter.

The pH of Urine. The pH of urine may vary between 4.8 and 8.0, but, because of the generally acidic nature of the ash of the diet, pH values between 5.5 and 6.5 are usually encountered. The acidic ash of the average diet is the result of oxidation of sulfur-containing amino acids to sulfuric acid, liberation of phosphoric acid from phosphoproteins and phosphatides, and intestinal absorption of anions, which, in the diet, are associated with cations that are not readily absorbable, *e.g.*, calcium or magnesium. Thus, milk yields an alkaline ash on combustion in vitro. However, in vivo much of the calcium is not absorbed in the intestine while the anions of the mineral acids of milk are absorbed; individuals restricted to a milk diet excrete urine of approximately pH 6.0. Ingestion of a diet composed largely of fruit and vegetables leads to excretion of alkaline urine. A more meaningful expression of the acidity of urine is obtained by determination of titratable acid plus ammonia; the titration is made to pH 7.4. Daily excretion by normal individuals varies from 15 to 50 meq. of titratable acid and from 30 to 75 meq. of NH_4^+; in

Table 37.3: COMPOSITION OF AVERAGE 24-HR. URINE OF A NORMAL ADULT

Component			U/P*
Sodium	2–4 g.	100–200 meq.	0.8–1.5
Potassium	1.5–2.0 g.	35–50 meq.	10–15
Magnesium	0.1–0.2 g.	8–16 meq.	
Calcium	0.1–0.3 g.	2.5–7.5 meq.	
Iron	0.2 mg.		
Ammonia	0.4–1.0 g. N	30–75 meq.	
H^+	....	4×10^{-8}–4×10^{-6} meq./liter	1–100
Uric acid	0.08–0.2 g. N	....	20
Amino acids	0.08–0.15 g. N		
Hippuric acid	0.04–0.08 g. N		
Chloride	....	100–250 meq.	0.8–2
Bicarbonate	....	0–50 meq.	0–2
Phosphate	0.7–1.6 g. P	20–50 mM.	25
Inorganic sulfate	0.6–1.8 g. S	40–120 meq.	50
Organic sulfate	0.06–0.2 g. S		
Urea	6–18 g. N	....	60
Creatinine	0.3–0.8 g. N	....	70
Peptides	0.3–0.7 g. N		

* U/P = ratio of concentration in urine to that in plasma.

severe acidosis these may rise to as much as 200 and 400 meq. per day, respectively, whereas in alkalosis, the urine may contain virtually no NH_3 and its pH may exceed 7.4.

Table 37.3 summarizes the composition of a 24-hr. sample of urine; the values given are averages for the American population living on an ordinary diet. In addition to the components listed in the table, urine contains small quantities of a large number of organic and inorganic materials.

Anions of Urine. Ordinarily, *chloride* is the chief anion of urine, and the amount excreted is roughly equal to that which has been ingested. On salt-poor diets, chloride may almost disappear from urine; thus, patients eating a rice diet for treatment of hypertension may excrete the equivalent of only 150 mg. sodium chloride per day. Even smaller amounts may be found in the urine of patients who have been vomiting. No limit to the maximum daily urinary chloride excretion may be stated, but the maximum concentration which may be attained is about 340 meq. per liter.

Virtually all the *phosphorus* in urine is present as orthophosphate. The quantity excreted varies with the dietary intake. Since the amount of phosphate absorbed in the intestine seldom exceeds 70 per cent of that ingested, balance studies include estimation of fecal phosphate. Urinary excretion of phosphate may increase in acidosis, alkalosis, and primary or secondary hyperparathyroidism. Diminished phosphate excretion may be observed as the result of renal damage, in pregnancy because of the requirement of the fetus for phosphate, or in diarrhea because of failure of intestinal absorption. Patients receiving infusions of glucose or insulin also show a temporarily diminished phosphate excretion since the plasma phosphate concentration is lowered under these circumstances.

Comparatively little *inorganic sulfate* is ingested. However, about 80 per cent of the total sulfur in urine is present as inorganic sulfate, and the amount present depends upon the previous ingestion of sulfur, largely as sulfur-containing amino acids of proteins. In addition, there is present an appreciable amount of esterified sulfate as oligosaccharides (page 55) and sulfate esters of phenolic compounds, as well as a small amount of organic sulfur.

Cations of Urine. Since *sodium* and *potassium* are the major cations of the diet, they are also the major cations of human urine. Total excretion of sodium usually varies between 2.0 and 4.0 g. per day; that of potassium is about 1.5 to 2.0 g. per day. Persons on sodium-free diets or in acidosis may excrete as little as 50 mg. of sodium per day. As explained previously, however, the excretion of potassium seldom falls below 1.0 g. per day. No limit can be placed on the maximal daily output of either of these cations, but the maximal urinary concentration of sodium is approximately 300 meq. per liter, and that of potassium is about 200 meq. per liter. These concentrations can be attained only after administration of large quantities of hypertonic solutions. The daily urinary excretion of *calcium* and *magnesium* each varies between 0.1 and 0.3 g. Since the gastrointestinal tract is the major excretory pathway of these cations at normal blood levels, the amount of calcium or magnesium excreted in urine each day is not a measure of the quantities of these elements in the diet. Above threshold levels these ions are rapidly excreted in the urine. The *ammonium ion* may vary in amount from negligible quantities in alkalosis to as much as 5 g. of NH_3-nitrogen per day in severe acidoses. The amount excreted generally varies from 0.5 to 1.0 g. (35 to 70 meq.) per day.

Organic Constituents of Normal Urine. Excretion of *urea* is a direct function of total nitrogen intake and, on average diets, may vary from 7 to 14 g. per day for a 70-kg. adult. Since excretion of other nitrogenous urinary components does not vary so much with nitrogen intake, urea nitrogen accounts for 90 per cent of the total nitrogen excretion of an individual consuming 25 g. of total dietary nitrogen, but only 60 per cent of the total urinary nitrogen of an individual eating 5 g. of total nitrogen.

On the usual American dietary, 0.7 g. of *uric acid* is excreted per day by a normal adult. Uric acid excretion rarely decreases below 0.5 to 0.6 g. even on purine-free diets but can be increased to more than 1 g. per day by ingestion of diets rich in nucleoproteins, such as glandular meats. Increased excretion of uric acid may occur in leukemia, polycythemia, hepatitis, and gout (page 567), and in response to administered aspirin, adrenal cortical steroids, or Benemid. Because of their insolubility, uric acid and its salts may precipitate in a collected urine sample or may form calculi in the lower urinary tract.

Creatinine. The amount of creatinine excreted varies, but for each individual the daily output is almost constant. This permits a simple check on the adequacy of consecutive 24-hr. urine collections. Urinary creatinine bears a direct relation to the muscle mass of the individual. This is expressed as the *creatinine coefficient,* the amount of creatinine in milligrams excreted per 24 hr. per kg. of body weight. The coefficient varies from 18 to 32 in men and from 10 to 25 in women; it is low in obese and asthenic persons and high in heavily muscled persons of average height.

Creatine excretion occurs more regularly in young children than in adults. Women may excrete more creatine and less creatinine than do men, although the creatinine excretion of women is generally as great as that of men in proportion to muscle mass. Creatine excretion rises in pregnancy and in the early post-partum period. In muscle wasting due to prolonged negative nitrogen balance, creatine excretion rises and creatinine excretion falls, with the total excretion of the two remaining roughly constant. This is seen, for example, in starvation, diabetes, hyperthyroidism, and fever. Conditions characterized primarily by muscle wasting also result in increased creatine and decreased creatinine excretion, as in various forms of muscular dystrophy. Administration of large doses of creatine leads to only small increments in urinary creatinine, the bulk of the creatine being eliminated unchanged. Administered creatinine appears quantitatively in the urine.

Hippuric acid (benzoylglycine) received its name because it was first found in equine urine. Normal excretion of hippuric acid is approximately 0.7 g. per day; ingested benzoic acid is quantitatively excreted in this form. Benzoic acid is present in natural foods, particularly fruits and berries, and is used as a preservative in various prepared foods. Since hippuric acid is formed in the liver, the rate of hippuric acid excretion after benzoic acid administration has been employed as a liver function test.

The presence of *indican* in urine is a result of bacterial action on tryptophan in the bowel, leading to formation of indole which is absorbed and oxidized in the liver to indoxyl. The latter is esterified with sulfate in the liver and excreted as the potassium salt (indican, page 555) in an amount of 5 to 25 mg. of indican per 24 hr. Increased excretion may occur in achlorhydria, because of diminished bactericidal action of the gastric juice, and in intestinal obstruction, paralytic ileus, or obstructive jaundice.

Urobilinogen appears in small quantity in normal urine. It is detected with Ehrlich's reagent (page 112), which reacts to produce a red pigment. Normal urine gives a detectable color with this reagent in dilutions of 1:20. Undiluted urine may fail to give a visible response in biliary obstruction, while large amounts of urobilinogen are encountered in hemolytic diseases.

Glucosiduronides are normal components of urine since many compounds produced in metabolism or administered are excreted to some extent in this form (page 410). Among these are chloral, menthol, phenol, morphine, aspirin, and various steroids. Certain of these substances are also excreted in part as sulfate esters.

In addition to these components of urine, small quantities of other substances are normally present. These include trace elements such as copper, zinc, cobalt, fluorine, manganese, iodine, mercury, and lead. Among the organic compounds excreted in small amounts are water-soluble vitamins, peptide hormones of the hypophysis, chorionic gonadotropin in pregnancy urine, and steroid hormones of the gonads and adrenal cortex, or their metabolic products.

ABNORMAL CONSTITUENTS OF URINE

Glycosurias. The presence of an unusual amount of reducing sugar in urine is termed *glycosuria*. This is a generic term, independent of the exact carbohydrate involved. When the specific carbohydrate has been identified, the more specific description—*glucosuria, fructosuria,* etc.—is used.

Glucosuria. Freshly voided normal urine contains between 10 and 20 mg. of glucose per 100 ml. Unusual amounts of glucose in urine may be found after anesthesia or asphyxia, and in emotional states. Approximately 25 per cent of all persons with severe hyperthyroidism have glucosuria. Renal glucosuria is occasionally observed in otherwise normal individuals as well as in association with other disorders of renal tubular function. However, the most common cause of glucosuria is diabetes mellitus. The urine of diabetic patients may vary in sugar concentration from 0.5 to 12.0 per cent glucose. The mechanism of glucosuria has been considered earlier (page 733).

Pentosuria. Alimentary pentosuria occurs after eating unusual quantities of fruit or fruit juices. The pentose excreted is that which has been ingested, *e.g.,* arabinose. Of somewhat more interest is the genetic disorder *idiopathic pentosuria* (page 408). The pentose excreted is L-xylulose (page 23), which accumulates because of lack of L-xylulose dehydrogenase. There is no accompanying clinical syndrome, and this metabolic defect is apparently innocuous. Since xylulose reduces copper more rapidly than does glucose, individuals with xylulosuria invariably show positive tests for reducing sugar, thus making possible the error of mistaking pentosuria for diabetes mellitus.

Lactosuria. Moderate excretion of lactose is a frequent finding in lactating women, but lactosuria seldom occurs during pregnancy. Glucosuria occurs during the course of about 15 per cent of all pregnancies, without accompanying hyperglycemia.

Galactosuria. Galactosuria is a consequence of galactosemia (page 406), a rare familial defect, generally detectable in very early infancy. Although no abnormality is detectable in the urine when galactose is rigorously excluded from the diet, as soon as milk, the prime dietary source of galactose, is fed, galactose may appear in the urine.

Fructosuria. Fructose rarely appears in urine. Its presence may result from a hepatic metabolic defect which may be hereditary. Fructosuria occurs less frequently than idiopathic pentosuria.

D-*Mannoheptulose,* a 7-carbon sugar, may appear in the urine of normal individuals who ingest large amounts of avocado.

Proteinuria. Normal urine contains traces of protein (including serum albumin and globulins), mucin from the lining of the genitourinary tract, and mucoproteins of other origin but does not give a positive reaction with the usual clinical tests for urinary protein. When proteinuria does occur, the major constituent is serum albumin, although globulins are invariably also present. The most common cause of proteinuria is renal disease, *e.g.,* acute glomerulonephritis, early chronic glomerulonephritis, the nephrotic syndrome (Fig. 37.3), and toxemia of pregnancy. In addition, albuminuria occurs in a variety of circumstances in which there may be

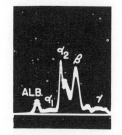
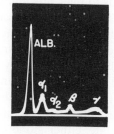

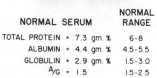

NORMAL SERUM	NORMAL RANGE
TOTAL PROTEIN = 7.3 gm. %	6-8
ALBUMIN = 4.4 gm. %	4.5-5.5
GLOBULIN = 2.9 gm. %	1.5-3.0
A/G = 1.5	1.5-2.5

NEPHROSIS SERUM (ADVANCED)

TOTAL PROTEIN = 3.4 gm. %
ALBUMIN = 0.2 gm. %
GLOBULIN = 3.2 gm. %
A/G = 0.06

NEPHROSIS URINE (ADVANCED)

TOTAL PROTEIN = 2.6 gm. %
ALBUMIN = 1.2 gm. %
GLOBULIN = 1.4 gm. %

FIG. 37.3. Electrophoretic patterns of serum and urine from a patient with advanced nephrosis; the pattern of a normal serum is given for comparison.

inadequate circulation to the kidney, *e.g.,* congestive heart failure, fever, anemia, liver disease, or various cardiac abnormalities. An occasional finding in otherwise normal individuals is postural or orthostatic proteinuria associated with long periods of standing or walking.

The urine of persons with multiple myeloma contains the unique Bence-Jones protein, which precipitates at room temperature from acidified urine and redissolves on warming (page 644).

Other Abnormal Constituents. Other substances of metabolic origin may appear in urine when their concentration in plasma is unusually elevated. Among these are the "ketone bodies," acetoacetic acid, β-hydroxybutyric acid, and acetone, which appear during ketosis (page 458); bilirubin in hepatocellular or obstructive jaundice (page 800); urobilinogen in hemolytic disease (page 808); homogentisic acid in alkaptonuria (page 549); cystine and other amino acids, notably lysine, arginine, and ornithine, in cystinuria and in other renal diseases, *e.g.*, Fanconi's syndrome.

Normal urine contains small amounts (up to 300 μg per day) of type I porphyrins (page 792). Excretion may increase ten- or twentyfold in liver disease and pernicious anemia. Congenital porphyria is a hereditary disorder characterized by an overproduction of the type I porphyrins. Uroporphyrin I and coproporphyrin I cannot be further metabolized; they are deposited in soft tissues, bones, and teeth, and as much as 100 mg. of this mixture may appear in the daily urine. The pathogenesis of acute porphyria is unknown. However, this disease is characterized by the excretion of increased amounts of uroporphyrin III and coproporphyrin III as well as large quantities of porphobilinogen (page 791) and diverse compounds formed therefrom. Coproporphyrin III excretion is also characteristic of lead poisoning (page 793).

URINARY LITHIASIS

The low solubility of several of the normal components of urine occasionally leads to their precipitation as aggregates, or "stones." Approximately one-third of all such stones are calcium phosphate, magnesium ammonium phosphate, calcium carbonate, or a mixture of these elements. The formation of such stones frequently reflects chronic alkalinity of bladder and renal pelvic urine caused by infection with bacteria which hydrolyze urea, releasing ammonia. Formation of these stones will be promoted by any situation characterized by excessive excretion of calcium, *e.g.*, hyperparathyroidism (page 848), osteoporosis due to immobilization, and unusually high calcium ingestion. About half of all kidney stones are calcium oxalate, either alone or mixed with the salts of the above group. Stones of this type are frequent among individuals ingesting vegetable diets rich in such foods as spinach and rhubarb, which contain unusual amounts of oxalate. However, calcium oxalate stones are also pathognomonic of oxaluria, a hereditary disorder of glycine metabolism (page 542) in which virtually all glycine synthesized is oxidized, via glyoxylic acid to oxalic acid. Less frequent are stones composed of insoluble organic compounds. Uric acid stones are common in gouty individuals (page 569). Xanthine stones are quite rare. Cystine deposits are almost invariably observed in cystinuric individuals, but are otherwise infrequent.

REFERENCES

Books

Braun-Menéndez, E., Fasciolo, J. C., Leloir, L. F., Muñoz, J. M., and Taquini, A. C., "Renal Hypertension," trans. by L. Dexter, Charles C Thomas, Publisher, Springfield, Ill., 1946.
Lewis, A. A. G., and Wolstenholme, G. E. W., eds., "The Kidney," Little, Brown and Company, Boston, 1954.

Lotspeich, W. D., "Metabolic Aspects of Renal Function," Charles C Thomas, Publisher, Springfield, Ill., 1959.

Pitts, R. F., "Physiology of the Kidney and Body Fluids," Year Book Medical Publishers, Inc., Chicago, 1963.

Review Articles

Beyer, K. H., Functional Characteristics of Renal Transport Mechanisms, *Pharmacol. Revs.,* **2,** 227–280, 1950.

Gilman, A., and Brazeau, P., The Role of the Kidney in the Regulation of Acid-Base Metabolism, *Am. J. Med.,* **15,** 765–770, 1953.

Goldblatt, H., Renal Origin of Hypertension, *Physiol. Revs.,* **27,** 120–165, 1947.

Kruhøffer, P., Handling of Alkali Metal Ions by the Kidney, in "Handbuch der Experimentellen Pharmakologie," O. Eichler and A. Farah, eds., pp. 233–423, Springer-Verlag, OHG, Berlin, 1960.

Page, I. H., and Bumpus, F. M., Angiotensin, *Physiol. Revs.,* **41,** 331–390, 1961.

Pitts, R. F., Acid-Base Regulation by the Kidneys, *Am. J. Med.,* **9,** 356–372, 1950.

Ulbrich, K. J., Kramer, K., and Boyland, J. W., The Countercurrent Multiplier System of the Kidney, *Progr. Cardiovascular Diseases,* **3,** 395–431, 1961.

Verney, E. B., The Antidiuretic Hormone and the Factors Which Determine Its Release, *Proc. Roy. Soc. London Ser. B,* **135,** 25–106, 1947.

Walser, M., and Mudge, G. G., Renal Excretory Mechanisms, in "Mineral Metabolism," C. L. Comar and F. Bronner, eds., vol. I, pp. 288–336, Academic Press, Inc., New York, 1960.

Wilson, C., ed., Physiology and Pathology of the Kidney, *Brit. Med. Bull.,* **13,** 1–70, 1957.

38. Muscle

The three types of muscle, striated, smooth, and cardiac, together comprise about 40 per cent of the body weight. Relatively little is known concerning possible differences in composition or metabolism among the three types of muscle. In what follows, we shall consider only those aspects of the composition and metabolism of muscle which permit it to serve as a contractile tissue.

COMPOSITION

The electrolyte composition of sarcoplasm is that shown as intracellular fluid in Fig. 35.1 (page 675). Of all mammalian tissue, muscle most closely approximates this electrolyte pattern. Other than protein, the most abundant compound is glycogen, which varies from 0.5 to 1 per cent of the weight of the fresh tissue. The metabolism of muscle glycogen is considered on pages 413*ff*. Muscle contains small quantities of free amino acids, of which glutamine, glutamic acid, aspartic acid, and alanine are present in greatest quantity. This composition resembles that of most other tissues. Anserine (page 115), carnosine (page 115), and carnitine have been isolated from skeletal muscle; their abundance in other tissues is unknown. Carnitine has been found to accelerate oxidation of fatty acids by tissue mitochondria. Acetylcarnitine is formed as follows.

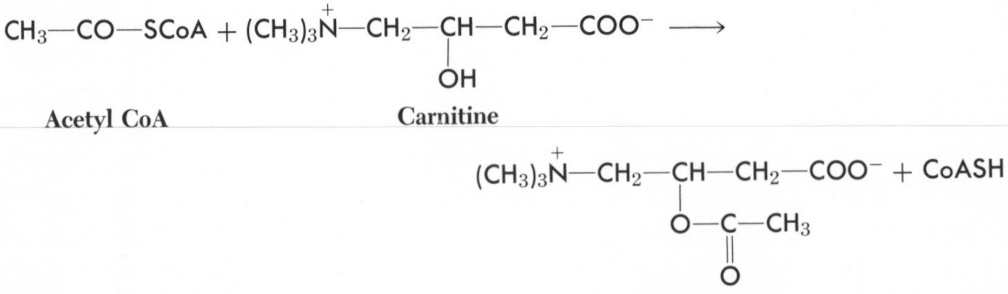

$$CH_3-CO-SCoA + (CH_3)_3\overset{+}{N}-CH_2-\underset{\underset{OH}{|}}{CH}-CH_2-COO^- \longrightarrow$$

Acetyl CoA　　　　　　　　**Carnitine**

$$(CH_3)_3\overset{+}{N}-CH_2-\underset{\underset{\underset{\overset{\|}{O}}{C-CH_3}}{|}}{CH}-CH_2-COO^- + CoASH$$

Acetylcarnitine

Acetylcarnitine is thought to react extramitochondrially with fatty acids to form acetate and the respective fatty acyl carnitine compounds. The latter then enter mitochondria and react with CoA to form acyl CoA derivatives, which are then oxidized (page 440).

The muscles contain approximately 0.5 per cent of creatine, present in resting muscle largely as phosphocreatine. The biosynthesis of creatine has been described previously (page 530). Phosphocreatine is somewhat unstable at the pH of sarcoplasm and is irreversibly transformed into creatinine, the anhydride of creatine (page 529). Creatinine serves no known metabolic function but diffuses from muscle and is excreted in the urine (page 739).

Proteins. Extraction of muscle with cold water yields a solution of proteins which consists largely of the enzymes that promote glycolysis. Extraction of the residue with 0.1M KCl dissolves about 20 per cent of the muscle proteins in an ill-defined mixture termed "globulin X." Brief extraction with alkaline 0.6M KCl of the residue remaining after the above procedure dissolves a protein fraction, of which *myosin* is the chief component. Szent-Györgyi observed that prolonged extraction with 0.6M KCl yields a myosin-containing solution of high viscosity and marked double refraction of flow, whereas brief extraction yields a solution containing almost as much protein but of much lower viscosity. In studying this phenomenon, Straub found that two different proteins are involved. These are *myosin,* the protein obtained by brief extraction with concentrated salt solution, and *actin,* prepared by various procedures which involve preliminary removal of the mixed lipids of muscle. Both proteins have been prepared in highly purified form.

Myosin has been obtained in several forms. The fundamental unit of myosin is a protein about 800 Å. long with a molecular weight of 220,000. Most solutions of myosin appear to contain an end-to-end dimer of this subunit, but some preparations behave as if three subunits are wound together in a three-stranded cable about 1,650 Å. long and 24 Å. wide. All preparations of myosin exhibit ATPase activity, which shows two pH optima at about pH 6 and 9 and is dependent on the presence of sulfhydryl groups in the protein. Incubation of myosin with trypsin or other proteinases yields, per myosin subunit, two small and one large fragment called light (L-) and heavy (H-) *meromyosins,* respectively. Only the latter retains the ATPase activity of the parent molecule.

Actin is a globular protein of 60,000 molecular weight which is soluble in dilute salt solutions. As generally prepared, one molecule of ATP is bound to each actin molecule. If the ionic strength of a solution of this globular protein (G-actin) is increased to a value comparable to that of the sarcoplasm, actin polymerizes to a high molecular weight fibrous protein (F-actin). Simultaneously, the ATP effectively hydrolyzes to ADP and inorganic phosphate, and one sulfhydryl group, per molecule of the original G-actin, becomes unreactive with the usual reagents for sulfhydryl group detection. The inorganic phosphate is released, but the ADP remains bound to the protein. If ATP is added, the latter displaces the bound ADP and depolymerization occurs. Alternately, reduction of the ionic strength of the medium results in depolymerization to yield G-actin with bound ADP. This can be reconverted to G-actin-ATP either by simple addition of ATP, which displaces the ADP, or by direct reaction with creatine phosphate in the presence of *creatine kinase* (see below). Mg^{++} is essential to the transformation of G- to F-actin.

From a dry powder of muscle which has been treated with nonpolar solvents to remove lipids, a small amount of a fibrous protein may be obtained that differs in solubility, composition, and molecular weight from myosin and has been called *tropomyosin.* Although present in relatively low concentration in mammalian muscle, tropomyosin is the dominant protein of the "catch" muscles of mollusks. Finally, if the residue from the extraction of skeletal muscle with water is subjected to a single prolonged extraction with 0.6M KCl, there is obtained *actomyosin,* a complex of myosin and actin in a ratio of about 3:1. This is the material responsible for the high viscosity of certain muscle extracts, first noted by Szent-Györgyi (see above).

Actin and myosin are the materials which compose the *myofibril,* the fundamental contractile unit of muscle, and the behavior of these two proteins in the presence of ATP is the basis for contraction.

THE CONTRACTILE PROCESS

In 1940 Engelhardt prepared threads by squirting a solution of crude myosin (which actually contained some actomyosin) into water. When these threads were suspended in a solution containing ATP, the latter hydrolyzed, with production of inorganic phosphate. This was the first observation that one of the components of the contractile system, myosin, can serve as an ATPase. If at the same time a small weight was attached to the end of the myosin thread, the latter was seen to lengthen. Thus, a relationship was discerned between the metabolism of ATP and the physical properties of actomyosin. It should be emphasized that these were synthetic threads and that the arrangement of the actomyosin molecules therein may not be similar to that within the myofibril. With more experience in the preparation of actomyosin threads, it has been observed that addition of ATP to a thread to which no weight is attached results in "contraction"; this has also been demonstrated with intact myofibrils and muscle fibers which have previously been extracted with glycerol. Such contraction occurs only in the presence of K^+ and Mg^{++}, in concentrations similar to those in muscle cell fluid, and is inhibited by Ca^{++}. Concomitant with the contraction a seemingly slower hydrolysis of ATP occurs. These events, apparently, are paralleled by changes in the viscosity of actomyosin solutions in the presence of ATP. The described observations suggest that in the presence of ATP, actomyosin dissociates into its components and re-forms when the ATP has been hydrolyzed.

The ATPase activity of myosin and actomyosin is markedly influenced in vitro by pH, ionic strength, and the concentrations of K^+, NH_4^+, Ca^{++}, and Mg^{++}. Perhaps most significant is the fact that, whereas Ca^{++} stimulates the ATPase activities of both proteins, Mg^{++} appears to inhibit myosin ATPase but stimulates actomyosin ATPase activity. At pH 7, the phosphate portions of ATP are completely dissociated and the molecule bears four negative charges. In this form, it binds divalent cations, *e.g.*, Mg_2ATP, Ca_2ATP, etc. It appears that the substrate for actomyosin ATPase must be Ca-Mg-ATP and that Mg_2-ATP cannot be hydrolyzed. Since, regardless of mechanism, the hydrolysis of ATP must serve as the source of energy for muscle contraction, the mechanism of the ATPase activity of myosin has been intensively studied. On the assumption that simple hydrolysis of ATP is wasteful, the following scheme has been proposed.

$$\text{ATP} + \text{myosin} \xrightarrow{a} \text{ADP} + \text{myosin-P} \xrightarrow{b} \text{myosin} + \text{P}_i$$

However, no phosphorylated form of myosin has been identified, and since ADP[32] does not exchange with ATP in the presence of myosin, such a reaction, if it occurs, cannot be reversible. Since some group on myosin reacts with the sulfhydryl group of p-nitrothiophenol to form a stable addition compound, but only in the presence of ATP, clearly myosin and ATP do react to yield an activated form of myosin, but the nature of this activation is unclear. The presence of myosin markedly accelerates the conversion of G- to F-actin. Whether this involves the ATPase activity of myosin and the bound ATP of G-actin is not known.

Studies of the structure of skeletal muscle by phase contrast microscopy have contributed significantly to understanding the contractile process. Muscle fibers are built of longitudinal fibrils, about 1 μ in diameter, with alternating dark and

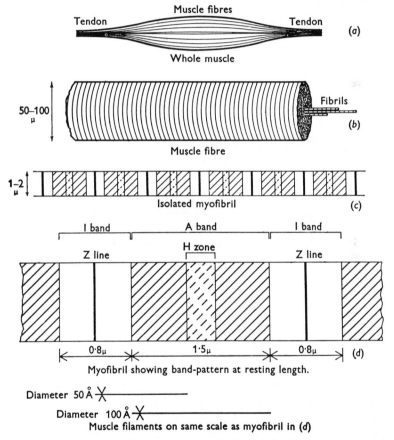

FIG. 38.1. The structure of muscle at various levels of organization; dimensions shown are for rabbit psoas muscle. (*From H. E. Huxley, Endeavour,* **15**, 177, 1956.)

light bands. The dense bands are birefringent and are called A (anisotropic) bands; the light bands are relatively nonbirefringent and are known as I (isotropic) bands. Within the I bands lies the dense Z line, which is continuous across the width of the fiber, holding the fibrils together and keeping the A and I bands of the many fibrils in "register." These features are schematically shown in Fig. 38.1. Electron microscopy of individual myofibrils reveals yet a finer structure, shown diagrammatically in Fig. 38.2. Cross sections through the denser areas of the A band show two types of filaments. The primary filaments are about 100 Å. in diameter and 200 to 300 Å. apart; around each of these are six secondary filaments about 50 Å. in diameter. These are "shared" with the surrounding six primary filaments, the fibril being built of several hundred of each type of filament. Cross sections at the

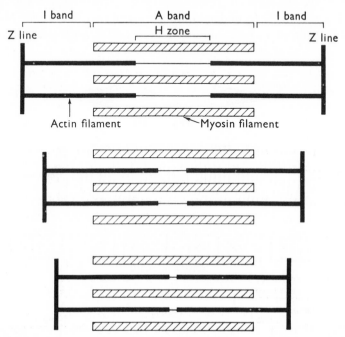

Fig. 38.2. Schematic representation of the relationships between actin and myosin filaments in extended (*above*), resting (*middle*), and partially contracted (*below*) muscle. (*Adapted from H. E. Huxley, Endeavour,* **15,** 177, 1956.)

H zone, the least dense portion of the A bands, show only primary filaments; in the I band only the smaller filaments are found. It has been suggested that the primary filaments are myosin and that the secondary filaments may be built of actin.

From such studies, Huxley has suggested the following hypothesis for the contractile mechanism. In contracted fibrils, the length and diameter of the myosin filaments are unchanged, but the I bands can virtually disappear; hence the actin filaments move together into the H zone. Since the muscle can contract or relax and remain fixed at from 65 to 120 per cent of the resting length, it is suggested that there may be many points of combination between each actin and myosin filament. Thus, in vivo, there would be no single relationship between actin and myosin and the "actomyosin" isolated by prolonged extraction of muscle is, in a sense, factitious. Contraction, therefore, would be the process in which the actin and myosin filaments slide across each other. Since the surrounding fluid, in resting muscle, contains ATP in maximal concentration, myosin ATPase activity would permit the actin and myosin fibers to separate and slide across each other to new positions. Were this the case, initiation of contraction would be accomplished by some event which initiates the ATPase activity. It must be emphasized that this hypothesis rests upon electron and phase contrast microscopic examination of muscle and that its validity remains to be established. The molecular basis for such movement of actin and myosin filaments across each other, with subsequent bonding, is not known, nor is it understood whether the G- to F-actin conversion participates in this process or represents an entirely different and independent mechanism for muscle contraction.

Conduction in Muscle. Each muscle fiber is electrically polarized; in the resting state there is a potential of 100 millivolts across its membrane and the inside is negative. Upon arrival of the nervous impulse, a wave of depolarization, the action potential, travels along the membrane, the potential reversing in sign. The rapidity with which contraction is initiated suggests that the depolarizing wave must also pass into the interior of the fiber, perhaps through the transverse membrane of Z lines. The depolarization temporarily alters the permeability of the membrane to electrolytes, and it is thought that it is the change in concentration of some critical cation which initiates the enzymic activity of the actin-myosin-ATP system. It appears most probable that a local increase in $[Ca^{++}]$ is the effective factor.

Relaxation. With cessation of nervous stimulation, contraction ceases and muscle fibrils return to the resting state. Many observations suggest the existence of a rather complex mechanism for this phenomenon, the details of which are obscure. Apparently significant are the following factors: (1) a sufficient ATP concentration which, of itself, may inhibit myosin ATPase activity if the critical concentration of divalent cations is lowered, and (2) a "relaxation factor," apparently derived from particles on the endoplasmic reticulum; this factor, in the presence of ATP, may act by promoting withdrawal of Ca^{++} from the myosin-ATPase sites. This role of "relaxation factor" is postulated solely because its activity is overcome by very low concentrations of Ca^{++} and because of the presumed role of Ca^{++} in initiating contraction (see above).

THE SOURCE OF ENERGY FOR MUSCULAR WORK

Resting muscle, like other tissues, requires a constant supply of ATP for maintenance of the constancy of its composition and for its continuing metabolism. Muscle is unusual, however, in that large amounts of energy, as ATP, must be delivered almost instantaneously for the performance of its distinctive function. The rate of ATP formation by oxidation of carbohydrate or acetoacetate is adequate to meet the requirements of resting muscle, but not of working muscle. When working maximally, frog and mammalian muscle use approximately 10^{-4} and 10^{-3} moles of ATP per gram per minute, respectively. There is, however, only about 5×10^{-6} mole of ATP present per gram of resting muscle, an amount which cannot meet the demands of mammalian skeletal muscle for more than 0.5 sec. of intense activity. Maximal activity in frog muscle increases the rate of ATP utilization almost 1,000-fold above the basal rate; yet the maximal increase in oxygen consumption is less than 200-fold. It is apparent that muscle possesses an anaerobic mechanism for rapid regeneration of ATP. In vertebrate muscles, this is the role of phosphocreatine. In the resting state, muscle has four to six times as much phosphocreatine as ATP. Muscle contains an enzyme, *creatine kinase,* which catalyzes the reversible transfer of phosphate between ADP and creatine phosphate.

$$\text{Creatine phosphate} + \text{ADP} \rightleftharpoons \text{creatine} + \text{ATP}$$

At pH 7.0, the free energy made available by hydrolysis of phosphocreatine is about 1500 cal. per mole greater than that from ATP, thus favoring formation of ATP from creatine phosphate. Phosphocreatine cannot serve as the immediate source of energy for contraction since this compound has no effect on the physical state of actomyosin, nor can it be hydrolyzed by this protein. Phosphocreatine serves, therefore, as a store of energy to be made available by way of ATP formation during contraction. Skeletal muscle contains an enzyme which catalyzes the direct transfer of phosphate from 1,3-diphosphoglycerate to creatine so that, anaerobically, the formation of creatine phosphate is facilitated by bypassing the necessity for intermediary formation of ATP. Of great interest is the observation that ADP bound to G-actin can serve as substrate for creatine kinase in the absence of any added nucleotide. Hayashi has found that G-actin, in the ADP form, reacts with creatine kinase to yield a single molecular complex, provided that creatine phosphate is present. In vivo, therefore, ADP bound to actin may be directly phosphorylated to ATP during each contraction cycle.

Among invertebrates, the metabolic role of phosphocreatine is assumed by other phosphorylated guanidine compounds, most frequently phosphoarginine. Among the annelids, this role is also served by the N-phosphate derivatives of guanidoacetic acid (*Nereis diversicola*) and taurocyamine (*Arenicola*), whereas leech muscle contains N-phosphoguanidylethylserylphosphate.

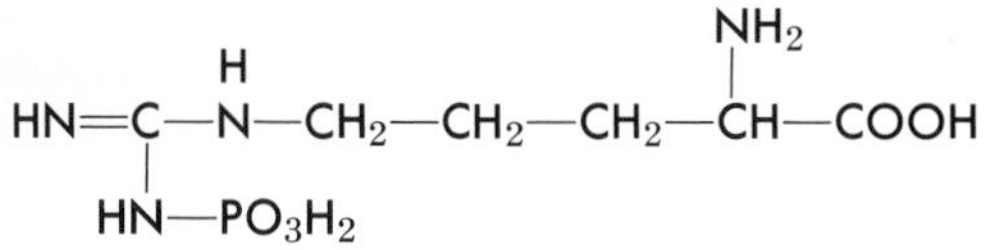

$$HN{=}\overset{H}{\underset{HN-PO_3H_2}{C}}{-}N{-}CH_2{-}CH_2{-}CH_2{-}\overset{NH_2}{\underset{}{CH}}{-}COOH$$

Phosphoarginine

$$HN{=}\overset{H}{\underset{HN-PO_3H_2}{C}}{-}N{-}CH_2{-}COOH$$

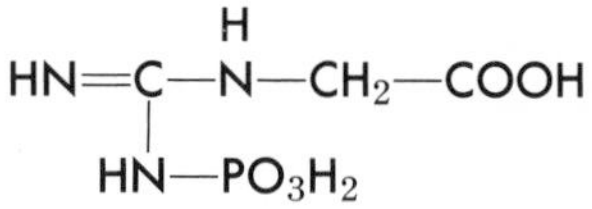

Phosphoguanidoacetic acid

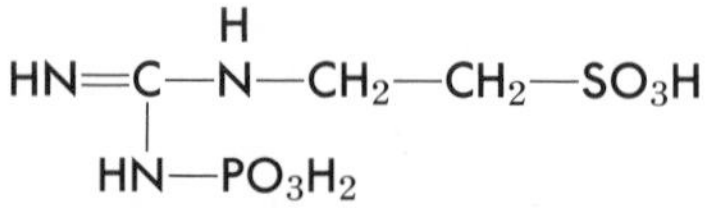

$$HN{=}\overset{H}{\underset{HN-PO_3H_2}{C}}{-}N{-}CH_2{-}CH_2{-}SO_3H$$

Phosphotaurocyamine

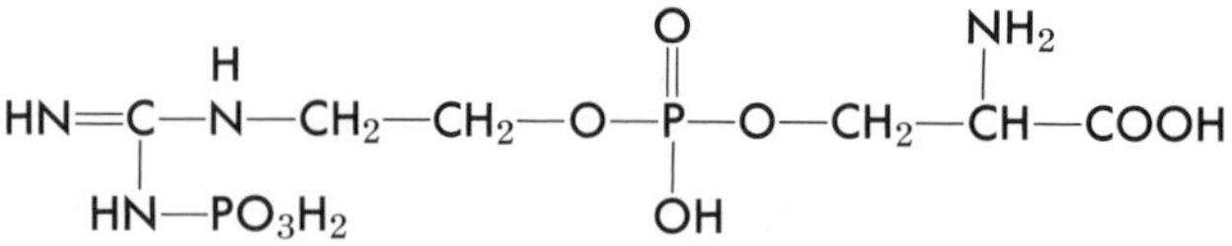

$$HN{=}\overset{H}{\underset{HN-PO_3H_2}{C}}{-}N{-}CH_2{-}CH_2{-}O{-}\overset{O}{\underset{OH}{P}}{-}O{-}CH_2{-}\overset{NH_2}{\underset{}{CH}}{-}COOH$$

Phosphoguanidylethylserylphosphate

Despite the availability of phosphocreatine in vertebrate muscle, the total supply of high-energy phosphate available per gram of muscle cannot sustain activity for more than a few seconds, *i.e.*, about 50 twitches in isolated frog muscle preparations. Thus neither stored phosphocreatine nor the respiratory metabolism of muscle is adequate to meet the energy demands of muscle for intense activity. These demands are satisfied by glycolysis of glycogen to lactic acid, which is produced by contracting muscle even in the presence of an abundant oxygen supply. The energy liberated in this process permits net synthesis of three moles of ATP per mole of glucose equivalent, as described in Chap. 20. These quantitative relationships are illustrated by the behavior of isolated muscle preparations. If the muscle is stimulated ten times per minute aerobically, contraction continues until the glycogen and the phosphocreatine supplies are exhausted, with the glycogen converted to CO_2. If, instead, the muscle is stimulated constantly, tetanus persists until the glycogen and phosphocreatine have disappeared but much of the glycogen has been converted to lactic acid. Anaerobically, contraction can continue until all the glycogen and phosphocreatine have disappeared and in their place lactic acid, creatine, and inorganic phosphate accumulate. Lundsgaard demonstrated that if the preparation is stimulated anaerobically in the presence of an inhibitor of glycolysis such as iodoacetate, contraction continues until the supply of phosphocreatine and ATP is exhausted, but glycolysis stops at the triose stage and no lactic acid is formed. Figure 38.3 presents schematically the foregoing relationships with respect to the provision of energy for muscular contraction.

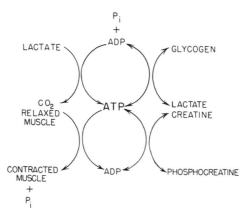

FIG. 38.3. The energy for muscular contraction. The immediate energy source is ATP, which may be regenerated from phosphocreatine and from glycolytic or aerobic phosphorylations. Resynthesis of phosphocreatine requires ATP; phosphocreatine cannot be directly employed as an energy source. In isolated muscle preparations only, resynthesis of glycogen from lactic acid requires ATP made available by complete combustion of a fraction of the lactic acid. This is indicated in the figure. However, in vivo glycogen resynthesis in muscle utilizes blood glucose, derived from glycogenolysis (see text and Fig. 38.4).

Whatever the nature of the actual mechanism by which ATP is used in contraction, it entails formation of ADP. Each molecule of the latter contains one energy-rich bond. Muscle possesses an enzyme, *adenylic acid kinase*, which catalyzes the following reaction.

$$2ADP \rightleftharpoons ATP + AMP$$

If ATP thus generated is used by the cell, the net result is the conversion of all the ATP of muscle to adenylic acid. *Adenylic acid deaminase* hydrolyzes the adenylic acid to inosinic acid, with production of a mole of ammonia. The function of this system in muscle metabolism is not known. Studies with P^{32} have shown that the rate of adenylic acid kinase activity is not appreciably affected by contraction, and it seems likely that the significance of this reaction is formation of ADP from AMP and ATP. No other reaction is known which can accomplish this end, *i.e.*, AMP cannot serve as a phosphate acceptor from either anaerobic glycolysis or oxidative reactions.

When isolated muscle, in vitro, is stimulated intermittently aerobically, it releases lactic acid during contraction and resynthesizes a large fraction of glycogen in the relaxation phase. The energy for resynthesis is obtained from the simultaneous oxidation of a sufficient fraction of the lactic acid to provide the necessary ATP, but this mechanism of oxidative recovery does not obtain in vivo. In vitro, lactic acid diffuses into the medium during contraction and reenters the muscle during relaxation. In vivo, however, lactic acid diffuses into the interstitial fluid and is carried by the circulation to the liver. Here, most of the lactic acid is utilized for glycogen synthesis at the expense of ATP derived from the oxidation of about one-sixth of the lactic acid. The liver glycogen thus formed may be stored or may provide glucose to the blood. This series of reactions is illustrated in Fig. 38.4.

The ability of muscle to sustain maximal activity anaerobically leads to the

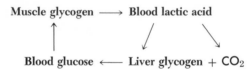

FIG. 38.4. Lactic acid, generated by working muscle in vivo, diffuses into the circulation and reaches the liver, where the lactic acid is converted to glycogen. The glycogen formed serves as a source of blood glucose, from which muscle glycogen may again be formed.

accumulation of an *oxygen debt* (page 376). This may be illustrated as follows. A sprinter running at maximal speed for about 10 sec. consumes about 1 liter of oxygen, as compared with perhaps 40 ml. in a similar period of rest. Even after he has stopped running, however, the athlete will continue to breathe at a still elevated but declining rate for some time and during this period may consume an additional 4 liters of oxygen above the basal rate. Thus, the effort of running results in a total extra consumption of 5 liters of oxygen, about four-fifths of which occurs after cessation of exercise. This oxygen is utilized for the oxidation of sufficient lactic acid to convert the remaining lactic acid to glycogen and to restore the normal phosphocreatine concentration, as described above. Ultimately, therefore, all the energy for muscular work derives from the oxidation of carbohydrate. To the extent to which energy is employed for contraction in an amount greater than that which may be supplied by oxidation during the actual period of muscular exercise, an oxygen debt is incurred which must be met during the recovery period. It is noteworthy that in this sense some of the energy for muscular work is obtained through oxidations performed in the liver. The net process is such as might have occurred had the rate of exercise been sufficiently slow to permit all the demand for ATP to be met by aerobic oxidation of glucose in the muscle between contractions.

It will be seen that the operation of the "mechanical" aspect of this system automatically accelerates operation of the energy-yielding device. The ADP released by contraction is available both to the mitochondrial oxidative phosphorylation system and to the two energy-yielding steps in glycolysis. Inorganic phosphate becomes available to the mitochondria, to triosephosphate dehydrogenase, and to glycogen phosphorylase. Since the availability of ADP and orthophosphate is rate-limiting in the resting muscle, this is an example of self-regulation or "positive feedback" in a biological system.

Whereas contracting striated muscle derives its energy largely from the anaerobic transformation of glucose or glycogen to lactic acid, resting muscle derives a large portion of its energy from the oxidation of fatty acids and acetoacetate. Indeed, determinations of the arteriovenous difference in glucose concentration across resting muscle indicate only trivial consumption of glucose. Energy for the relatively slow contraction of smooth muscle similarly is derived from oxidation of fatty acids, acetoacetate, and, to a lesser extent, glucose. Cardiac muscle, which is rich in myoglobin, the enzymes of the tricarboxylic acid cycle, and the electron transport system, utilizes largely aerobic reactions to obtain ATP for contraction. Relatively little glucose is abstracted from the blood by cardiac muscle. Instead the latter obtains ATP by oxidation of fatty acids and, to a lesser extent, of acetoacetic acid and lactic acid. During exercise, when both skeletal and cardiac muscle metabolism is accelerated, the heart abstracts from the circulation and utilizes the lactate produced in peripheral muscles.

REFERENCES

Books

Mommaerts, W. H. F. M., "Muscular Contraction," Interscience Publishers, Inc., New York, 1950.

Szent-Györgyi, A., "Chemical Physiology of Contraction in Body and Heart Muscle," Academic Press, Inc., New York, 1953.

Review Articles

Bailey, K., Structure Proteins: II. Muscle, in H. Neurath and K. Bailey, eds., "The Proteins," vol. II, part B, pp. 951–1055, Academic Press, Inc., New York, 1954.

Buchthal, F., Svensmark, O., and Rosenfalck, P., Mechanical and Chemical Events in Muscle Contraction, *Physiol. Revs.*, **36**, 503–538, 1956.

Conway, E. J., Nature and Significance of Concentration Relations of Potassium and Sodium Ions in Skeletal Muscle, *Physiol. Revs.*, **37**, 84–132, 1957.

Huxley, H. E., and Hanson, J., The Molecular Basis of Contraction in Cross-striated Muscles, in G. H. Bourne, ed., "The Structure and Function of Muscle," vol. I, pp. 183–228, Academic Press, Inc., New York, 1960.

Lilienthal, J. L., and Zierler, K. L., Diseases of Muscle, in R. H. S. Thompson and E. J. King, eds., "Biochemical Disorders in Human Disease," pp. 445–493, Academic Press, Inc., New York, 1957.

Mommaerts, W. H. F. M., Brady, A. J., and Abbott, B. C., Major Problems in Muscle Physiology, *Ann. Rev. Physiol.*, **23**, 529–576, 1961.

Needham, D. M., Biochemistry of Muscular Action, in G. H. Bourne, ed., "The Structure and Function of Muscle," vol. II, pp. 55–104, Academic Press, Inc., New York, 1960.

Perry, S. V., The Biochemistry of Muscle, *Ann. Rev. Biochem.,* **30,** 473–498, 1961.

Slater, E. C., Biochemistry of Sarcosomes, in G. H. Bourne, ed., "The Structure and Function of Muscle," vol. II, pp. 105–141, Academic Press, Inc., New York, 1960.

Szent-Györgyi, A. G., Proteins of the Myofibril, in G. H. Bourne, ed., "The Structure and Function of Muscle," vol. II, pp. 1–54, Academic Press, Inc., New York, 1960.

39. Nervous Tissue

Of the organs of the body, the brain presents one of the most complex problems of correlation of structure, composition, and function. Beginning with the work of Thudichum in the last century, it has been recognized that nervous tissue differs in several ways from other tissues. Most striking is the high content of lipid; in brain, lipids represent approximately 50 per cent of the total solids. Although studied intensively, brain composition is incompletely understood. Recent developments in quantitative methodology, notably application of various chromatographic techniques, have clarified some aspects of brain composition. However, knowledge is fragmentary of the manner in which the materials present in nervous tissue mediate its function. Some biochemical features of synaptic and neuromuscular conduction are well delineated, but still controversial is the picture of events occurring during axonal conduction. The biochemical basis of other brain functions, such as the origin of the nerve impulse, is unknown.

COMPOSITION OF NERVOUS TISSUE

With the application of milder techniques to the extraction of nervous tissue in order to preserve the tissue constituents in their naturally occurring state, it has become evident that, as in other tissues, lipids, proteins, polysaccharides, and nucleic acids are often associated with one another in a variety of linkages. Although protein-lipid complexes of nervous tissue have been isolated and characterized (see below), most information concerning the composition of the brain has been obtained by techniques designed to free each isolated material from other tissue components with which it may be associated *in situ.*

Lipids. With the exception of the neutral fats, which are not present, brain contains, in varying concentrations, representatives of all other lipid classes previously described (Chaps. 5 and 6). Some of these lipids occur only in nervous tissue; others are present only in limited amount elsewhere in the body. This is the case for the sphingomyelins, cerebrosides, and, to a lesser degree, the gangliosides. In other instances, lipids which are relatively ubiquitously distributed are present in nervous tissue in uniquely high amounts. Thus, more than half of the total phosphoinositides of brain are represented by a triphosphoinositide, and plasmalogens comprise one-third of the total phosphatides. Cholesterol, found predominantly in other tissues and the blood in ester form, is present in brain only as the unesterified sterol. This is also the case with peripheral nerve, which, however, appears to contain triglyceride. It is uncertain whether the triglyceride is in the nerve fiber proper or in the surrounding connective tissue.

The gangliosides of brain have been separated into two groups, containing one and two moles of sialic acid, respectively. In normal human brain, Svennerholm found that about 90 per cent of the monosialogangliosides consist of a compound with the molar ratio of ceramide to hexose to N-acetylgalactosamine to N-acetyl-neuraminic acid of 1:3:1:1. The hexoses are glucose and galactose. Of considerable interest is the report by the same investigator that in Tay-Sachs disease (page 480) a ganglioside which accumulates in abnormally high amounts in brain contains one less mole of hexose than described above, a mole of galactose lacking in the terminal position of the ganglioside structure.

In addition to the above lipids, brain has sulfur-containing glycolipids (page 78). A sulfate ester of phrenosin (page 78) is abundant in white matter.

Fatty acids are widely distributed in brain as components of the compounds mentioned above. Indeed, per unit weight of brain tissue, fatty acids comprise the most abundant lipid constituent. These acids are of long chain length, C_{18} to C_{26}, and include α-hydroxy acids as well as unusually high quantities of polyenoic acids. Of a polyenoic fraction of ox brain, 43 per cent was identified as C_{22} hexaenoic acids.

The lipids of myelin have received considerable attention. Cholesterol, phosphatides (largely sphingomyelins), and cerebrosides are the chief lipids of the myelin sheath in the approximate molecular ratio of 2:2:1, respectively. In addition to sphingomyelins, phosphatidyl serine, plasmalogens, and inositol phosphatides are present. The myelin lipids are characterized by a high degree of unsaturation.

Table 39.1 presents some lipid concentrations in nervous tissue. The wide ranges of values given reflect the results of different investigators and analytical methods employed. Nonetheless, the general ranges of concentrations are indicative of the composition of nervous tissue lipids. The values in the table refer, for the most part, to mammalian tissue, although in the case of peripheral nerve some figures for frog nerve are included.

Table 39.1: Concentration of Lipids in Nervous Tissue

Constituent	Gray matter	White matter	Spinal cord	Peripheral nerve
Total lipids	4.0–7.9	13.9–23.1	15.5–22.7	4.4–23.0
Total phosphatides	3.1–4.6	6.2–9.3	7.8–10.6	2.2–13.9
Cholesterol	0.6–1.4	3.6–5.4	3.9–5.9	1.1–4.8
Cerebrosides (includes all glycolipids)	0.3–1.9	4.1–7.4	3.8–6.2	1.1–4.7
Sphingomyelins	0.3–1.9	1.8–4.3	2.1–3.4	1.3–4.7

Note: All values are in grams per 100 g. fresh tissue.

Source: After R. J. Rossiter, Chemical Constituents of Brain and Nerve, in K. A. C. Elliot, I. H. Page, and J. H. Quastel, eds., "Neurochemistry," 2d ed., p. 32, Charles C Thomas, Publisher, Springfield, Ill., 1962.

Proteins. The proteins of brain account for 40 per cent of its dry weight. Although tissue proteins are usually soluble in aqueous media, the relatively high proportion of lipid in nervous tissue has made difficult the mechanics of extracting proteins with such solvents. Indeed, classes of water-insoluble, nonpolar solvent-soluble proteins are now recognized as components of nervous tissue.

Proteins Soluble in Aqueous Media. Maximal extraction of protein nitrogen from brain with aqueous media is obtained at an ionic strength of about 3.0 and pH 6 to 9. The soluble proteins include nucleoproteins, ribonucleoproteins being abundant in nerve cytoplasm. On dialysis of the extract, a small amount of lipid-free albumins remains in solution, while the bulk of the extracted proteins precipitate. The latter contain approximately 20 to 25 per cent lipid, of which one-quarter is cholesterol; these proteins may therefore be characterized as lipoproteins (page 122). Copper-containing, water-soluble proteins have been separated from brain tissue. The name *cerebrocuprein* has been given to one of these proteins which contains 0.3 per cent of copper.

Proteins Soluble in Nonpolar Solvents. Folch and his colleagues established the presence in brain of substances containing both protein and lipid but differing from the water-soluble lipoproteins (see above) in that they are insoluble in water but freely soluble in mixtures of $CHCl_3$-CH_3OH-H_2O. This class of lipid-soluble proteins has been termed *proteolipids*. The proteolipids differ from one another in the ratio of lipid to protein and in the nature of the lipids. Several have been obtained from the white matter of brain; proteolipid B, which has been obtained in crystalline form, contains 50 per cent each of protein and a lipid mixture consisting of equal parts of phosphatides and cerebrosides.

Insoluble Proteins; Residue Proteins. This is an operational description of the proteins remaining after thorough, successive extraction of brain tissue with polar and nonpolar solvents. In some laboratories, protein remaining after treatment with proteolytic enzymes, following solvent extraction, has been included in this group. Probably the most widely studied of these is *neurokeratin.* The exact nature of this protein is obscured by the variety of procedures which have been used for its preparation. Indeed, neurokeratin is probably an artifact. Histochemical techniques, together with some preparative data, suggest that neurokeratin *in situ* may represent the protein portion of some proteolipids. With the present uncertainty, further description of neurokeratin is meaningless, although amino acid analyses indicate that it differs from other keratins (page 121) with similar solubility properties.

Carbohydrates. On the basis of hexosamine determinations, fresh brain tissue contains 0.15 to 0.25 per cent mucopolysaccharide; the contribution of connective tissue to this value is not clear. Chondroitin sulfate (page 55) is the chief mucopolysaccharide present. In addition, a number of carbohydrates have been detected in the nonlipid fraction of brain extracts. These include hexosamines, hexuronic acids, and sialic acids. As noted above, other carbohydrates, *e.g.*, inositol, are present as components of lipids.

Electrolytes. The electrolyte composition of nerve is not remarkably different from that of intracellular fluids of other tissues except that there are not enough of the common anions, *e.g.*, phosphate, sulfate, bicarbonate, protein, etc., to balance the known cation content. The dicarboxylic amino acids, which are present in high concentration in brain tissue (see below), may partially compensate for the anionic deficit. Approximately 40 meq. of cations per liter are neutralized by the acidic phosphatides and sulfatides. Cations combined in this manner, however, may not be ionized, a fact which may have significance in the conduction of the nerve impulse.

METABOLISM OF BRAIN

Efforts to study the metabolism of the brain in vivo are hampered by the existence of various so-called barriers to the passage of material from blood to the brain cells. The barriers have been termed the "blood–cerebrospinal fluid barrier" and the "blood–brain barrier." The use of these terms, implying a permeability barrier between the circulating blood and the brain, is unfortunate because they are poorly defined and are used in the literature to refer to more than one concept. Thus, measurements of brain content of a substance shortly after its intravenous administration and, at a later time, in cerebrospinal fluid do not reflect the same aspect of the blood-brain barrier. Similarly, measurement of rate of staining of the brain by an intravenously administered dye does not measure the functioning of the same blood-brain barrier as that reflected by determinations of exchange rates of sodium between blood and brain, since Na^+ and K^+, unlike the dyes, play a role in transmission of the nerve impulse. For these reasons, the usual term "blood-brain barrier" probably represents a complex system in which all factors are not necessarily interconnected, rather than one real barrier.

Similar comments are pertinent with respect to attempts to designate a single histological entity as the barrier. It is likely that the barrier system consists of diverse structures utilizing several biochemical mechanisms which limit the penetration of various types of molecules, particularly those bearing a net charge, including electrolytes of extracellular fluid, and all relatively large molecules, including lipids, polysaccharides, and polypeptides. For reasons not understood, barrier permeability is occasionally altered, particularly in persons with brain tumors. This has led to methods for tumor localization. Thus iodofluoroscein does not penetrate the normal blood-brain barrier but does penetrate the blood-brain barrier in persons with brain tumors. Use of dyes containing radioactive I^{131} permits localization of tumors by means of appropriate detecting devices.

Carbohydrate Metabolism. The energy requirement of the brain *in situ* under normal physiological conditions is met almost entirely by the oxidation of glucose. Studies with labeled glucose reveal that only a portion of the glucose obtained from the blood by the brain is oxidized directly to CO_2. Approximately one-half of the glucose carbon is incorporated into tissue constituents (see below) which are utilized later as a source of energy.

The glucose removed from the blood by the brain is utilized primarily via the glycolytic pathway. Good correlation obtains between the quantity of glucose removed and the oxygen consumption plus lactic acid produced. It may be noted that, unlike liver or heart mitochondria, brain mitochondria manifest high glycolytic activity. There is also evidence for the operation of the phosphogluconate oxidative pathway in brain; its relative significance is not established. Ultimate conversion of glucose carbon to CO_2 in brain occurs via the tricarboxylic acid cycle, as in other tissues. Brain tissue also has been demonstrated to fix CO_2 in vivo into amino acids, presumably by way of oxaloacetate formation as a consequence of operation of the malic and malic acid dehydrogenase enzymes (page 380). This provides a mechanism for replenishing the supply of citric acid intermediates as a continuing source of α-ketoglutaric acid, which in turn serves as a source of glutamic acid for glutamine synthesis (see below).

The central role of the tricarboxylic acid cycle in the metabolism of nervous tissue is reflected in the neurological dysfunctions which ensue on interference with normal operation of the cycle. This is seen, for example, in thiamine deficiency, with accompanying inadequate transformation of pyruvate into acetyl CoA (page 317). The neurological signs of thiamine deficiency (Chap. 55) are classic in the history of knowledge of this vitamin.

In *hypoglycemia,* glucose consumption by brain is reduced more than is oxygen utilization, indicating oxidation of other substrates. In brain slices and homogenates, no more than 60 per cent of the oxygen consumed was due to oxidation of carbohydrates. Also, in perfusion experiments with C^{14}-labeled glucose during convulsions, when the total CO_2 production of the brain increased to twice the basal level, the $C^{14}O_2$ production was not similarly elevated. This suggested that the excess CO_2 produced by the brain during hypoglycemic convulsions was due to the oxidation of noncarbohydrate substrates, probably amino acids and lipid. Under these conditions there was a marked increase in turnover of proteins and lipids of brain (see below).

The glycogen content of brain is approximately 0.1 per cent, so that the metabolism of this organ cannot be long sustained by its carbohydrate reserves. Moreover, among all the organs studied, brain cannot produce 3′,5′-cyclic adenylic acid required for activation of phosphorylase (page 417). These facts contribute to the coma attending insulin-induced hypoglycemia. With the normal arterial blood glucose concentration of about 80 mg. per 100 ml., brain consumes 3.4 ml. of oxygen per 100 g. per min. In insulin coma, at a blood glucose level of about 8 mg. per 100 ml., oxygen consumption may be 1.9 ml. per min. It may be presumed that at this reduced level of respiration, the supply of ATP from oxidative phosphorylation is inadequate for normal brain function. The large oxygen consumption of brain, about 25 per cent of the total oxygen consumption of the body at rest, accounts for the extreme sensitivity of the brain to anoxia. Coma and irreversible damage occur even after brief hypoxia.

Amino Acid and Protein Metabolism. The free amino acid concentration in the brain is significantly higher than in most tissues and is characterized by its preponderance of glutamic acid, present in $0.01M$ concentration. This amino acid, together with aspartic acid, glutamine, glutathione, and γ-aminobutyric acid (see below), accounts for approximately 80 per cent of the nonprotein amino nitrogen content of brain. These and other nonessential amino acids are produced rapidly by brain tissue, the total rate paralleling the turnover of members of the tricarboxylic acid cycle. Indeed, the rate of conversion of carbon of labeled glucose into amino acids in the rat was several times greater in the brain than in a variety of other organs examined, including liver. Under these conditions, the specific activity of the free amino acid fraction of the brain, particularly glutamic and aspartic acids, was approximately ten times that of the other organs studied. The data suggest that the brain, with little reserve glycogen in relation to its high metabolic activity, may utilize amino acids and proteins for energy purposes. This is in agreement with the high rate of turnover of proteins in brain (see below).

Other amino acids present in brain in high concentrations include γ-aminobutyric acid, arising from decarboxylation of glutamic acid (page 534). γ-Aminobutyric acid inhibits synaptic transmission in the central nervous system. Also present in higher concentrations than elsewhere in the body and of unknown physiological significance are taurine (page 542), acetylaspartic acid, and cystathionine (page 499). The concentration of the last in brain is greatest in man, less in the anthropoid apes, still less in rodents, and extremely small in invertebrates.

The generally held concept of a high degree of impermeability of the blood-brain barrier to amino acids other than glutamine is in error, as shown by recent studies of Lajtha and his associates with isotopically labeled amino acids. Tyrosine was demonstrated to penetrate the blood-brain barrier easily. Also, although no *net* exchange of glutamic acid, lysine, or leucine was evident between brain and blood, these amino acids when added to the blood exchanged rapidly with the free amino acids in the brain. Uptake of amino acids by brain conforms to the criteria of an active transport process (page 678). These studies have also revealed anomalies in the distribution patterns of labeled amino acids in brain, suggesting compartmentalization of various free amino acids within the neurons or between neurons and glia cells.

Amino acids entering brain or arising in brain cells are rapidly incorporated into proteins. The data suggest that pathways of protein synthesis in brain are similar to those elsewhere (Chap. 30). Administered labeled amino acids appear earlier and in highest concentration in the microsomal fraction of brain tissue. Brain tissue proteins show high turnover rates, exceeded only by the albumin of plasma and the total proteins of liver. Thus, approximate half-life times of 5, 8, 10, and 14 days were found for total proteins of, respectively, the white matter, cerebral cortex, cerebellum, and spinal cord. It may be noted that brain has a high RNA content (page 762), which may suggest a correlation with its active protein synthesis (Chap. 30). On the basis of available evidence, it has been suggested that synthesis of axonal protein, which is frequently quite remote from the cell body, is the result of the combination of axonal flow and local metabolism.

Additional pathways for amino acid metabolism in brain are similar to those described previously (Chaps. 24, 26, and 27) for other tissues, including active transamination operating in conjunction with intermediates of the tricarboxylic acid cycle. Of interest, but of unknown metabolic significance, is the evidence that brain contains all the enzymes necessary for operation of the urea cycle (page 511). Brain tissue also has transamidinase (page 529) and carnosine synthetase (page 527) activities. Thus formation of both γ-guanidobutyric acid and homocarnosine (page 528) from γ-aminobutyric acid can occur in brain.

Glutamine is synthesized by brain as in other tissues (page 488). This synthesis is augmented with rising blood ammonia concentrations. This fact has been utilized in speculation concerning the cause of coma in terminal hepatic disease. Ammonia, released by either the failing liver or the intestinal tract and not removed by the liver, is thought to be used for glutamine synthesis by the brain; glutamine is markedly increased in amount in jugular blood under these circumstances. This may constitute a drain on the glutamic acid, and hence on the citric acid cycle intermediates of brain, limiting oxidative metabolism. Respiration declines and coma may ensue, presumably for much the same reason as the coma of hypoglycemia or hypoxia.

Figure 39.1 shows some of the metabolic relationships which have been described.

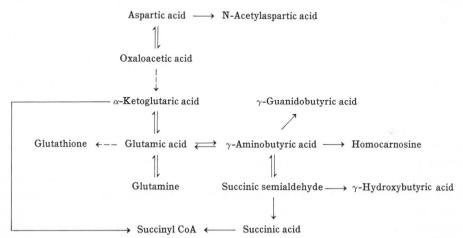

FIG. 39.1. Some general interrelationships of carbohydrate and amino acid metabolism in brain.

Another nitrogenous substance of interest in brain metabolism is serotonin, synthesized in brain and other tissues from tryptophan (page 536).

Serotonin

Serotonin, a peripheral vasoconstrictor, stimulates uterine contraction, and may play a regulatory role in the nervous system. In the brain the compound is largely present in bound form. Certain drugs which produce marked alteration in central nervous system activity are potent serotonin antagonists in vitro. Thus, administration of reserpine, a drug which diminishes the activity of the central nervous system in man, augments urinary excretion of serotonin and its major metabolic product, 5-hydroxyindoleacetic acid (page 536). Monoamine oxidase inhibitors block serotonin metabolism, leading to increased formation of N-acetyl and N-methyl derivatives of serotonin (page 537).

It should be noted that specialized areas of the brain are characterized by the presence of peptides with hormonal activity (Part Six). Certain of these peptides are produced in the hypothalamus and may be stored in the neurohypophysis; this is the case for vasopressin and oxytocin (Chap. 51). Others may be synthesized and function as mediators of release of adenohypophyseal hormones (Chap. 51).

Nucleic Acid Metabolism. Among the somatic cells of the organism, the large nerve cells are characterized by the highest content of ribonucleic acids and are probably among the most active producers of nucleoproteins, comparable in this regard to certain actively secreting cells, *e.g.*, the exocrine cells of the pancreas. The main portion of the RNA of nerve cells seems to be in the form of liponucleoproteins, correlating in content and location with the *Nissl substance.* Quantitative ultraviolet absorption techniques, developed and applied extensively by Hydén, Caspersson, and their associates, have been utilized to study the nucleic acid and protein metabolism of the brain.

The young unipolar neuroblast, two-thirds of which is nucleus, contains DNA but little RNA. As the cell proceeds through various stages of growth and development, *e.g.*, the multipolar neuroblast, the neuron, and the adult nerve cell, RNA appears and increases in quantity, with no change in the absolute amount of DNA. Concomitantly with the increase in RNA content of the cell, the concentration of protein also rises. This sequence of events is compatible with knowledge of the interrelations of DNA, RNA, and protein synthesis (Chaps. 29 and 30).

Such experiments have also revealed an active nucleic acid metabolism during nerve activity. Stimulation of the spinal ganglion cells of the rabbit for 5 min. produced an increase in cell size, in nucleolus size, and in the RNA concentration in the nucleolus. There was also a marked increase in RNA concentration in the cellular cytoplasm, as well as in the amount of protein in the cytoplasm. No alterations were observed in DNA concentration. When the cells were stimulated for an additional 10 min., they became smaller in volume and exhibited a markedly decreased content of cytoplasmic RNA and protein. From these studies it would appear that a 5-min. stimulation period represented the interval of maximal activity of the cytoplasmic protein- and RNA-forming systems under these experimental conditions, and that further stimulation led to exhaustion of synthetic capacity of the cells. Essentially identical changes were observed in motor nerves of guinea pigs made to run until exhausted in a treadmill and in the cochlear ganglion of guinea pigs subjected to intense sound for several hours.

Lipid Metabolism. *Cholesterol.* Cholesterol synthesis from labeled precursors has been demonstrated in the brain of the young animal during the period of growth, but little cholesterol is synthesized in the adult brain in vivo. However, adult brain slices in vitro do synthesize cholesterol from added acetate or mevalonate. The pathway of biosynthesis is inferred to be similar to that described previously (page 471). Apparently not all the brain cholesterol arises *in situ,* since labeled cholesterol injected intraperitoneally in the young rabbit appeared in the cholesterol of the brain, as well as in other organs. The labeled cholesterol persisted in the brain for as long as one year, in contrast to its rapid disappearance from other organs studied.

It was noted previously (page 755) that relatively little cholesterol ester is present in adult brain. However, cholesterol esters do occur in relatively high concentration at sites of active myelination.

Phosphatides. Studies with a variety of labeled precursors in vivo as well as with extracted enzymic systems in vitro indicate that rapid phosphatide turnover occurs in nervous tissue via pathways similar to those of other organs (Chap. 23).

Fatty Acids. The high total fatty acid content of brain has been noted (page 756). Isotopic studies reveal a rapid turnover of fatty acids in the brain of younger animals as compared with an appreciably slower rate in older animals. The pathways of fatty acid formation and degradation in brain are presumed to be similar to those in other tissues (Chap. 22). Evidence also supports the view that the fatty acids of brain may, under some conditions, serve as a source of energy (page 759).

Glycolipids. The unique lipids of brain reflect the presence of a group of enzymes which, also, are unique to brain. Thus, an enzymic system from rat brain has been described that forms a ceramide (page 467) from serine and palmityl CoA.

$$\underset{\text{Serine}}{\text{HO}-\text{CH}_2-\overset{\displaystyle \overset{\text{NH}_2}{|}}{\text{CH}}-\text{COOH}} + \underset{\text{Palmityl CoA}}{2\text{CH}_3(\text{CH}_2)_{14}\text{COCoA}} \longrightarrow$$

$$\text{CH}_3(\text{CH}_2)_{12}\text{CH}=\text{CH}-\underset{\displaystyle \underset{\text{OH}}{|}}{\text{CH}}-\underset{\displaystyle \underset{\overset{\displaystyle |}{\text{HN}-\overset{\overset{\textstyle O}{\|}}{\text{C}}-(\text{CH}_2)_{14}\text{CH}_3}}{|}}{\text{CH}}-\text{CH}_2\text{OH}$$

N-Palmitylsphingosine
(a ceramide)

In vivo experiments of a number of investigators indicate that brain incorporates administered glucose, galactose, glucosamine, and serine into its glycolipids. Glucose and galactose were incorporated into all the carbohydrate moieties; glucosamine appeared primarily in N-acetylneuraminic acid and galactosamine. Serine was incorporated into N-acetylneuraminic acid and sphingosine moieties, as well as into all the carbohydrates present. Uridine diphosphate hexose is the primary hexose donor in brain glycolipid synthesis, as in the synthesis of other hexose glycosides (Chap. 21). Both labeled galactose and sulfate are incorporated into the sulfatides of the brain of young rats. Apparently the sulfate is derived from 3'-phosphoadenosine 5'-phosphosulfate (page 515).

Studies with isotopically labeled precursors indicate a high rate of synthesis in brain of inositol phosphatides and gangliosides. The presence of these complex lipids in close association with proteins in proteolipids (page 757) and their high metabolic turnover have suggested that they play a role in some of the membrane structures of brain, and other tissues, and that their rapid metabolism may reflect membrane activity during function. McIlwain has suggested that gangliosides offer acidic sites in the lipid-rich membranes of cerebral tissue which function in active cation transport.

TRANSMISSION OF THE NERVOUS IMPULSE

Conduction in nerves is accomplished along the surface of the axon by an electrical current so weak that it cannot propagate itself unless there is some mechanism for its repeated amplification. A potential of about 75 millivolts exists between the inside of the axon and the surrounding medium. This polarization derives from the fact that the $[K^+]$ inside the cell is fifteen to thirty times that in extracellular fluid, whereas for [Na⁺] this relationship is reversed. During activity, a wave of negativity sweeps along the fiber and the polarity is temporarily reversed. Associated with this event, there is a marked drop in electrical impedance, Na^+ enters the fiber about 500 times more readily, and approximately 4×10^{-12} eq. per cm.² per impulse enters the cell during the ascending phase of the action potential, balanced by an equivalent outward passage of K^+ during the descending phase. There follows a refractory period when no impulse may be carried while the Na^+-K^+ relationships are restored. As a depolarized point becomes negative to the adjacent area, a local current ensues and these events are repeated, thus propagating the original impulse.

What is the nature of the alteration responsible for the transient local changes in permeability of the nerve fiber membrane? Evidence has been assembled which indicates a key role for acetylcholine in this process. Studies of Hunt, Dale, Magnus, and Loewi established that this compound is released at parasympathetic nerve endings and acts as a transmitter on the effector organ, substituting for the electric current as propagating agent. Before another impulse may be transmitted, the acetylcholine is hydrolyzed by *acetylcholine esterase.*

$$CH_3\underset{\underset{O}{\|}}{C}-O-CH_2-CH_2-\overset{+}{N}-(CH_3)_3 \longrightarrow CH_3COOH + HO-CH_2-CH_2-\overset{+}{N}(CH_3)_3$$

The evidence that acetylcholine is also involved in intracellular axonal conduction and intimately participates in the generation of electric potentials may be summarized as follows: (1) Acetylcholine and acetylcholine esterase are present in all conducting nerves. Both substrate and enzyme are localized near the surface of the axon. (2) All nerve fibers also contain *choline acetylase* which resynthesizes acetylcholine from choline and acetyl CoA. (3) Each mole of choline esterase can catalyze hydrolysis of 2×10^7 moles of substrate per minute, and the known concentration of substrate and enzyme would permit complete hydrolysis in less than 100 μsec, well within the time required by the known rate of events in nervous activity. (4) Choline esterase is concentrated in the plates of the electric organs of *Torpedo* and *Electrophorus electricus.* These are the most powerful known bioelectric generators. A direct proportionality exists between enzyme concentration and voltage. (5) Neuronal conduction is abolished by inhibitors of choline esterase in *all* types of nerves. Conduction fails when enzymic activity falls to about 20 per cent of its initial level.

These observations have permitted the formulation by Nachmansohn of a tentative concept of the events in neuronal conduction, depicted in Fig. 39.2. Initially, acetylcholine is stored, presumably bound to a lipoprotein. Depolarization of the adjacent area effects, in some manner, release of stored acetylcholine, which then makes contact with a receptor protein at the axonal surface, altering the properties of the latter so as to permit inward passage of Na^+. K^+ leaks out in exchange while the ester is hydrolyzed by acetylcholine esterase, and inward passage of Na^+ is halted. Thereafter the energy available from glucose oxidation is used to regenerate acetylcholine and to promote Na^+ and K^+ transport, thus restoring the nerve to its initial condition. Thus, during activity the two ion species move *with* the concentration gradients, whereas recovery requires active transport *against* the gradients. It may be noted that there is present in nerve an ATPase system requiring both Na^+ and K^+ which apparently plays a role in the cationic exchange described in these cells, as in others, *e.g.,* erythrocytes (page 789; cf. also pp. 677*ff.*).

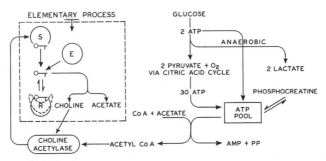

FIG. 39.2. Sequence of energy transformations associated with conduction, and integration of the acetylcholine system into the metabolic pathways of the nerve cell. The elementary process of conduction may be tentatively pictured as follows:

1. In resting condition acetylcholine ($\bigcirc\!\!\top$) is bound, presumably to a storage protein (*S*). The membrane is polarized.
2. Acetylcholine is released by current flow (possibly H^+ movements) or any other excitatory agent. The free ester combines with the receptor (*R*), presumably a protein.
3. The receptor changes its configuration (dotted line). This process increases the Na^+ permeability and permits its rapid influx. This is the trigger action by which the potential primary source of electromotive force, the ionic concentration gradient, becomes effective and by which the action current is generated.
4. The ester-receptor complex is in dynamic equilibrium with the free ester and the receptor; the free ester can be attacked by acetylcholine esterase (*E*).
5. Hydrolysis of the ester permits the receptor to return to its original shape. The permeability decreases, and the membrane is again in its original polarized condition. (*After D. Nachmansohn, Harvey Lectures,* **49**, 57, 1953–1954.)

The above picture of axonal conduction, although still incomplete and containing elements of conjecture, is in accord with most facts. It should be pointed out, however, that there is some disagreement with the hypothesis that acetylcholine metabolism is basic for the initiation of events underlying axonal conduction.

Studies of acetylcholine esterase have revealed two adjacent sites: one is anionic and binds the cationic quaternary nitrogen of acetylcholine, and the other is an "esteratic" site. The enzyme-substrate complex yields a transient acetyl enzyme which hydrolyzes to acetate and enzyme. Many substances which may bind the anionic site are reversible inhibitors; those which may also bind the esteratic site, including prostigmine and physostigmine, are remarkably effective. Others may attack the esteratic site; for example, diisopropylphosphofluoridate (page 247) forms the stable diisopropylphosphate ester of the active group at the esteratic site and thus irreversibly inhibits the enzyme. Various other alkyl phosphates react similarly; this has found application in insecticides and the so-called "nerve gases."

These considerations of the mode of action of the enzyme led to formulation of the necessary criteria for a compound which might overcome such inhibition, *viz.,* a strongly cationic group at a sufficient intramolecular distance from a nucleophilic group. Several compounds were prepared from these specifications; of these, 2-pyridine aldoxime methiodide is most effective. At low concentration it rapidly removes the diisopropylphosphate group from the esteratic site and restores enzymic activity rapidly. In vivo this compound is a successful antidote for poisoning by diisopropylphosphofluoridate.

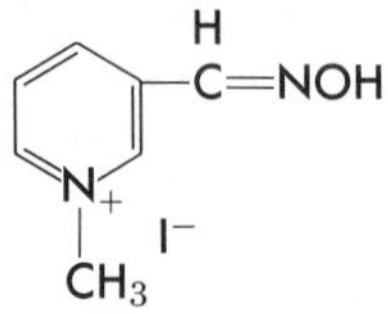

2-Pyridine aldoxime methiodide

Although acetylcholine may mediate neuronal and synaptic transmission in all nerves as well as transmit the neural stimulus to the effector organs of somatic motor fibers and parasympathetic nerves, it does not appear to be secreted by postganglionic sympathetic fibers. These secrete instead either epinephrine or norepinephrine (Chap. 49).

Some evidence suggests that γ-aminobutyrate participates in the process of transmission by inhibitory neurones. Thus both deficiency in pyridoxine and administration of isonicotinylhydrazide (Chap. 55), which decrease the level of glutamic acid decarboxylase activity in brain, result in convulsive activity which is relieved by administration of γ-aminobutyrate.

REFERENCES

Books

Caspersson, T. O., "Cell Growth and Cell Function," W. W. Norton & Company, Inc., New York, 1950.

Chagas, C., and De Carvalho, A. P., eds., "Bioelectrogenesis," Elsevier Publishing Company, Amsterdam, 1961.

Elliott, K. A. C., Page, I. H., and Quastel, J. H., "Neurochemistry," 2d ed., Charles C Thomas, Publisher, Springfield, Ill., 1962.

Himwich, H. E., "Brain Metabolism and Cerebral Disorders," The Williams & Wilkins Company, Baltimore, 1951.

McIlwain, E., "Biochemistry of the Central Nervous System," 2d ed., J. & A. Churchill, Ltd., London, 1959.

Nachmansohn, D., "Chemical and Molecular Basis of Nerve Activity," Academic Press, Inc., New York, 1959.

Richter, D., ed., "Metabolism of the Nervous System," Pergamon Press, New York, 1957.

Review Articles

Hebb, C. O., Biochemical Evidence for Neural Function of Acetylcholine, *Physiol. Revs.,* **37,** 196–220, 1957.

Hydén, H., The Neuron, in "The Cell," J. Brachet and A. E. Mirsky, eds., vol. IV, pp. 216–323, Academic Press, Inc., New York, 1960.

Hydén, H., The Neuron and Its Glia—A Biochemical and Functional Unit, *Endeavour,* **21,** 144–155, 1962.

Nachmansohn, D., Metabolism and Function of the Nerve Cell, *Harvey Lectures,* **49,** 57–99, 1953.

Waelsch, H., and Lajtha, A., Protein Metabolism in the Nervous System, *Physiol. Revs.,* **41,** 709–736, 1961.

40. Connective Tissue

Connective tissue is distributed throughout the body in cartilage, tendons, ligaments, the matrix of bone, the pelvis of the kidney, the ureters, and urethra; it underlies the skin, serves as binding for the blood vessels, and provides the inter-cellular binding substance in parenchymatous organs such as the liver and muscles. The mechanical and supportive functions of connective tissue are accomplished by extracellular, insoluble protein fibers embedded in a matrix termed the *ground substance.* The cells of connective tissue responsible for synthesis of both the insoluble fibers and the soluble matrix include not only fibroblasts, but macrophages, mast cells, and lesser numbers of other, sometimes undifferentiated, cell types.

COLLAGEN

The insoluble fiber of connective tissue is usually *collagen,* the most abundant protein in the body, comprising perhaps one-third of the total protein and, there-fore, about 6 per cent of the body weight. The amino acid composition of collagen (Table 40.1) is remarkable in that one-third of the amino acid residues are glycine; proline plus 3- and 4-hydroxyproline provide 21 per cent of the residues, and alanine, another 11 per cent.

In the native state, collagen fibers are of high tensile strength and swell in acidic or alkaline media. The fibers are resistant to trypsin and chymotrypsin but are slowly attacked by pepsin, ficin, or papain. As seen with the electron microscope, collagen fibers are built of smaller fibrils which are 200 to 2,500 Å. wide and many microns long, with characteristic cross striations at about 700 Å. (Fig. 40.1). Extremely thick fibers are characteristic of tendon, whereas the narrow fibrils found in cornea and vitreous humor (page 812) allow minimal scatter and maxi-mal passage of incident light. In the native state, most collagen is essentially insoluble. However, extraction of skin of very young animals with cold salt solution or prolonged extraction of insoluble collagen with dilute acid yields a solution of the fundamental units of collagen fibrils, termed *tropocollagen,* individual mole-cules of which are about 14 Å. wide and 2,800 Å. long, with a molecular weight of about 350,000. These are the most asymmetric molecules yet obtained from natural sources. Each of these molecules is a triple-stranded helix, with about three amino acids, in each strand, per turn. This structure is entirely dependent upon the unique amino acid composition of the three polypeptide chains. The pitch of the helix is determined by the frequent proline and hydroxyproline residues. The triple-stranded structure is possible only because of the high incidence of glycine, since in this struc-

Table 40.1: AMINO ACID COMPOSITION OF SOME COLLAGENS, ELASTIN, AND ENAMEL PROTEIN

Amino acid	Human dentin collagen	Cod-fish skin collagen	Ligamentum nuchae elastin	Pig embryo enamel protein
Glycine	329	345	322	49
Proline	116	102	121	271
Hydroxyprolines	99	53	11	0
Alanine	112	107	240	24
Serine	33	69	9	46
Aspartic acid	46	52	5	29
Glutamic acid	74	75	15	185
Threonine	17	25	8	37
Cystine/2	0	0	0	0
Valine	25	19	145	37
Methionine	5	13	0	47
Isoleucine	9	11	25	32
Leucine	24	23	48	94
Tyrosine	6	4	8	22
Phenylalanine	16	13	31	26
Hydroxylysine	10	6	0	2
Lysine	22	25	4	11
Histidine	5	7	0	72
Arginine	52	51	5	6
Tryptophan	0	0	0	12
Amide N	(38)	(33)	...	...

Note: All values are residues per thousand amino acids.

ture, every third amino acid residue, in each strand, is entirely within the interior of the molecule and only the minimal volume of glycine can fit into this structure. Accordingly, whereas there are distinct differences in the amino acid composition of collagen from diverse sources, glycine is invariably present as one-third of the total residues and the content of proline + hydroxyproline is almost as great.

Heat denaturation of collagen yields the soluble preparation called "gelatin." Examination of gelatin has helped to reveal the structure of collagen. Gelatin solutions contain four molecular species in varying amount. The smallest of these, α_1 and α_2, are separable by chromatographic means; they are of somewhat different amino acid composition but of approximately equal molecular weight and are present in the ratio 2:1. The larger molecules, β_1 and β_2, are of twice the molecular weight and are dimers of $\alpha_1 + \alpha_2$ and of two α_1 units, respectively. Thus, as shown in Fig. 40.2, the tropocollagen molecule is built of two strands of α_1 and one strand of α_2. The entire structure is joined primarily by hydrogen bonding between the strands. These are also covalently cross-linked at intervals; hence, after denaturation both types of dimers may be present. The nature of the cross-linking is uncertain but seems to be of an ester nature, involving carboxyl groups of the aspartic acid and glutamic acid residues and the carbohydrate components of the protein, as in certain glycoproteins (page 636).

Collagen fibrils are built by end-to-end and side-to-side joining of tropocollagen molecules. The end-to-end "splicing" of the cables is possible because the three

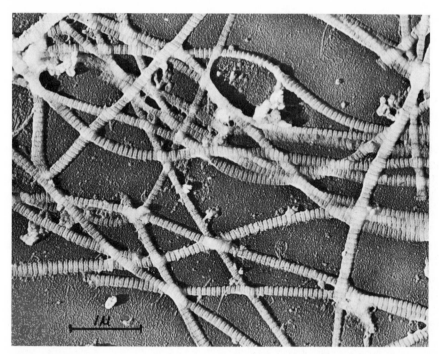

FIG. 40.1. Collagen fibrils from the corium of a 2-day-old infant. The preparation has been thoroughly washed to remove the ground substance. Note the characteristic 700-Å. repeating period and a smaller definite intraperiod structure. 18,800×. (*From J. Gross, Ann. N.Y. Acad. Sci.,* **52**, 967, 1950.)

strands are of unequal length, as shown in Fig. 40.2. Evidence exists that the end regions of each strand are rich in polar amino acids, *e.g.*, glutamic acid, tyrosine, and lysine, so that hydrogen and electrostatic bonds are responsible for the end-to-end alignment, which results in fibrils many times longer than the tropocollagen molecule. The forces which bond adjacent triple helices to each other are uncertain, but covalent bonding is unnecessary since in dilute salt solution tropocollagen recom-

$$\longleftarrow \text{--- } 86 \text{ A}° \text{ ---} \longrightarrow$$

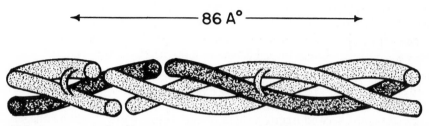

FIG. 40.2. A segment of collagen structure showing end-to-end linking of tropocollagen molecules. The tubes represent the space filled by polypeptide chains, each of which extends about 3,000 Å. The amino acid residues are 2.86 Å. apart and lie along a minor helix with a pitch of 8.6 Å. (three residues per turn). Each chain is coiled into a major helix with a pitch of 86 Å. The larger amino acid side chains extend beyond the structure shown. The U-shaped bond represents the carbohydrate cross-linking between individual strands.

bines to yield characteristic collagen fibrils when the solution is warmed to 40°C. However, cross linkage to adjacent tropocollagen units may occur with the passage of time since collagen becomes increasingly difficult to dissolve and the fibrils thicken progressively as an animal ages.

Collagen formation by fibroblasts in tissue culture establishes these cells as the source of collagen. Hydroxyprolines, primarily the 4-hydroxyproline together with a small amount of the 3-hydroxy compound, are abundant in collagen and, like hydroxylysine, are found in no other proteins. Neither administered hydroxy-proline-C^{14} nor hydroxylysine-C^{14} is incorporated into collagen, whereas administration of proline-C^{14} or lysine-C^{14} results in appearance of the respective C^{14}-labeled hydroxy acids in newly formed collagen. Thus, it appears that hydroxylation occurs after proline and lysine are each linked to the appropriate sRNA during protein synthesis (page 599), or after these amino acids are in peptide linkage.

Once formed, the collagen of most tissues appears to be metabolically inert. If turnover occurs at all, it is extremely slow; $t_{1/2}$ is measured in years. Indeed, among all mammalian tissues, collagenase activity has been observed only in the resorbing uterus. For experimental purposes, advantage has been taken of the extremely active *collagenase* of *Clostridium histolyticum,* an enzyme which, presumably, facilitates invasion of animal tissues by this organism. Clostridial collagenase exhibits specificity for rupturing the bond between glycine and proline in peptide sequences of the general structure $\cdots$Pro·X·Gly·Pro·Y$\cdots$, where the residues at positions X and Y affect the enzymic rate but do not otherwise appear significant. The amino acid composition of collagen (Table 40.1) indicates that such sequences occur frequently in collagen. Collagenase does not attack other proteins such as casein, hemoglobin, or fibrin. Nevertheless, it is clear that collagen can be degraded, *in situ.* Thus, "remolding" of the shape of growing bone entails removal of collagen from one site while it is synthesized elsewhere. Collagen also disappears from the bone of an immobilized arm or leg. During pregnancy, growth and thickening of the uterus are accompanied by significant increases in collagen, which disappears within a few days after parturition.

Ingestion of lathyrus peas has long been known to result in defective skeletal development and gross skeletal abnormalities. The active principle is aminopropionitrile, H_2N-CH_2-CH_2-CN. If given to very young animals, this compound inhibits formation of normal collagen fibers. The collagen which is formed is unusually rich in hydroxyproline; concomitantly, significant quantities of hydroxyproline-containing peptides are excreted in the urine. The mechanism by which aminopropionitrile induces the syndrome of lathyrism is not understood.

ELASTIN

Elastin is the second major protein of connective tissue. Unlike collagen, it is not converted into gelatin by boiling, and, as shown in Table 40.1, its amino acid composition differs significantly from that of collagen. Collagen is the principal protein of white connective tissue; elastin predominates in yellow tissue. Thus, the collagen content of human Achilles tendon is about twenty times the elastin content, while in the yellow ligamentum nuchae the elastin content is about five times that of collagen. As the name implies, elastin is the predominant connective tissue protein of elastic structures such as the walls of the large blood vessels. Scar formation, on the other hand, is due to deposition of collagen.

Elastin is prepared by subjecting connective tissue either to mild alkaline hydrolysis or to heat; either process dissolves collagen and the mucopolysaccharides, leaving the extremely insoluble elastin. The elastin fibers thus obtained exhibit the properties of an elastomer, *e.g.*, rubber, and are quite yellow. Both attributes are functions of the structure of elastin but are not presently understood. Elastin may be solubilized by prolonged heating in $0.25M$ oxalic acid. The resultant solution contains at least two groups of smaller proteins of molecular weight about 75,000 and 5,500, respectively, but it is not clear how these are related in the native state. The native fibers are built by cross-linking of smaller fibrous molecules; this cross-linking may well involve the unidentified yellow pigment which remains attached to peptides even after extensive proteolysis.

Native elastin fibers, even when stripped of mucopolysaccharide, are not digestible by trypsin or chymotrypsin but can slowly be hydrolyzed by pepsin at pH 2. However, pancreas secretes a zymogen, *proelastase* (page 485), which is activated by trypsin and by enterokinase to yield *elastase*. The latter is a protease of broad specificity, capable of catalyzing hydrolysis of many proteins, but unusual in its ability to effect the hydrolysis of elastin. This proceeds after a pronounced lag phase, following which amino acids and peptides appear in solution, the fibers disappear, and a mixture of yellow, cross-linked peptides remains. Elastase is inhibited by diisopropylphosphofluoridate (page 247), as are trypsin and chymotrypsin and, similarly, has been shown to have the sequence ···Gly·Asp·Ser·Gly··· at the "active site" of the enzyme (Table 14.2, page 249).

MUCOPOLYSACCHARIDES

Cells of mesenchymal origin synthesize and add to their environment a variety of heteropolysaccharides. The structure of these polymers (page 55) and the mode of their biosynthesis (page 412) have been presented. Table 40.2 summarizes the distribution of these polysaccharides among animal tissues. These data are not comprehensive. Of tissues thus far examined, vitreous humor alone has been found to contain only one of the seven polysaccharides (hyaluronic acid). Moreover, only in the case of the hyaluronic acid of vitreous and synovial fluids is the polysaccharide present free in solution, unassociated with a protein. All other mucopolysaccharides are found in combination with proteins, but neither the proteins nor the binding linkages have been characterized. Available evidence suggests that in cartilage the typical unit consists of a single protein core to which are affixed 25 to 50 chains of chondroitin sulfate A, each of molecular weight 30,000 to 50,000 and joined to the protein by a single bond.

Mucus is the secretion of mucous glands located in epithelial structures. Older literature refers to the presence in mucus of a polysaccharide, of supposedly specific structure, which was termed *mucoitin sulfate*. However, it is clear that no *specific* material is present and that mucous secretions contain a mixture of mucopolysaccharides and glycoproteins. In addition there are undoubtedly varying amounts of

Table 40.2: Distribution of Mucopolysaccharides

Tissue	Hyaluronic acid	Chondroitin	Chondroitin sulfate			Keratosulfate	Heparin
			A	B	C		
Skin................	+	...	...	+		...	...
Cartilage............	...	...	+	...	+	+	...
Tendon..............	...	...	...	+	+	...	...
Ligaments...........	...	...	...	+	...	...	...
Umbilical cord	+	...	...	...	+	...	...
Vitreous humor.......	+	...	...	...	...	...	...
Synovial fluid	+	...	...	...	...	...	...
Heart valves	+	...	...	+	...	...	...
Spinal disks..........	...	...	...	...	+	+	...
Bone................	...	...	+	...	...	+	...
Cornea..............	...	+	+	...	...	+	...
Liver................	...	...	...	...	...	...	+
Lung................	...	...	...	...	...	...	+
Arterial wall.........	...	...	...	...	...	...	+
Embryonic cartilage...	...	+	+	...	+	...	...
Mast cells...........	...	...	...	...	...	...	+

Note: + denotes positive identification of the indicated polysaccharide in the tissue shown. No + need not necessarily mean complete absence of polysaccharides other than those indicated, but does signify that these are present in very small concentration, if at all.

the chondroitin sulfates and related materials, as well as neutral polysaccharides resembling, or identical with, some of the type-specific blood group substances (page 790).

One of the most thoroughly studied of the glycoproteins is that of bovine submaxillary mucin. In contrast to the large chondroitin sulfate A chains associated with the protein of cartilage, in this instance about 800 disaccharide units, each of which is probably N-acetylneuraminyl$(2 \rightarrow 6)$N-acetylgalactosamine, are attached to a single polypeptide chain, the carbohydrate accounting for about 40 per cent of the molecular weight. The type of structure is indicated in Fig. 40.3. The bonds between the disaccharides and the protein are ester linkages between the carboxyl groups of glutamic and aspartic acid residues and the C-1 hydroxyl group of the amino sugar moiety.

Metabolism of Mucopolysaccharides. Relatively little information is available concerning the metabolism of mucopolysaccharides. The origin of the uridine diphosphate esters of the monosaccharide components, *viz.*, glucuronic acid, iduronic acid, N-acetylgalactosamine, and N-acetylglucosamine, has been described previously (Fig. 21.1, page 402). Some evidence indicates that the immediate precursors for mucopolysaccharide synthesis are in each case the appropriate derivatives of uridine diphosphate. Thus, hyaluronic acid would be formed from uridine diphosphoglucuronate (page 412) and uridine diphospho-N-acetylglucosamine, in the manner already indicated for the formation of oligosaccharides and glycogen (page 409). However, no purified enzymic system has yet been observed to catalyze this process. Increasing evidence indicates that the sulfated polysaccharides are formed by preliminary synthesis of the nonsulfated polymer followed by reaction with

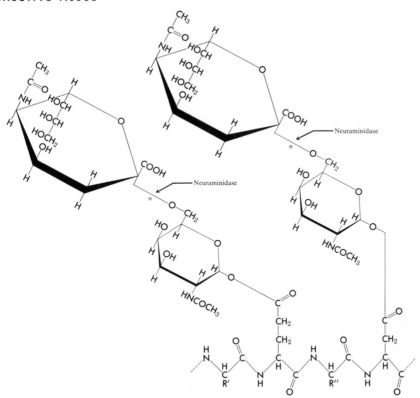

FIG. 40.3. Diagrammatic segment of bovine submaxillary gland glycoprotein, showing (1) the structure of the prosthetic group; (2) the glycosidic ester linkages joining the prosthetic groups to the β- and γ-carboxyl groups, respectively, of aspartic and glutamic acid residues; (3) the neuraminidase-susceptible α-ketosidic linkage within the prosthetic group.

phosphoadenosine phosphosulfate (page 515). Studies of the formation of chondroitin sulfate–mucoprotein indicate that rates of incorporation of amino acids, hexose units, and sulfate are similar. Thus *de novo* synthesis of the entire complex appears to characterize mucoprotein formation. In such studies, isotopically labeled precursors appear initially in the soluble mucoprotein and only subsequently in the salt-insoluble fraction, presumably indicating that the soluble material is the metabolic precursor of the insoluble component.

Hyaluronidases, which effect the hydrolysis of hyaluronic acid as well as of chondroitin and chondroitin sulfates A and C, have been found in insects, snake venom, and mammalian tissues; testis is the richest source in mammals. Hyaluronidase activity has also been observed in extracts of microorganisms, spleen, ciliary body, and autolysates of skin. With the exception of the enzyme from the leech, all hyaluronidases studied appear to catalyze hydrolysis of the glucosaminidic bond between carbon-1 of the glucosamine moiety and carbon-4 of glucuronic acid. The enzyme from the leech hydrolyzes the glucuronidic bond. Like many amylases, hyaluronidase also exhibits transglycosylase activity. Hydrolysis by mammalian hyaluronidase does not appear to proceed beyond the level of a tetrasaccharide.

Although testicular and leech hyaluronidases are normal glycosidases, bacterial hyaluronidases degrade hyaluronic acid and chondroitin by cleavage of the hexosaminidic bond with formation of a 4,5 double bond in the hexuronic acid residue. Thus, bacterial hyaluronidase cleaves the tetrasaccharide resulting from mammalian hyaluronidase action into two disaccharides, hyalobiuronic acid, the repeating unit of hyaluronic acid (page 54), plus the same disaccharide with a double bond in the 4,5 position of the glucuronic acid moiety.

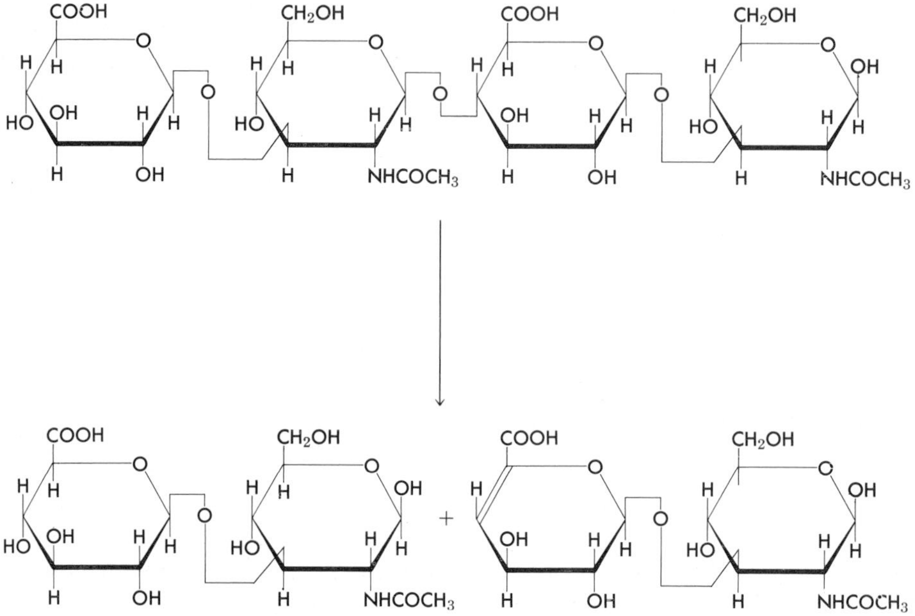

Hyalobiuronic acid   **3-O-(β-D-4,5-Glucoseenpyranosyluronic acid)-N-acetyl-D-glucosamine**

Particularly interesting is the fact that the water used for scission of the glycosidic bond derives from the uronic acid itself. When hydrolysis is carried out in O^{18}-labeled H_2O, no isotope is incorporated into the product. Bacterial enzymes that hydrolyze pectin (page 53) have been found to act in a similar manner.

β-Glucuronidases available from many sources catalyze hydrolysis of the glucuronidic bond at the nonreducing end of these oligosaccharides.

Only one mucopolysaccharide, keratosulfate (page 55), resembles collagen in being almost inert metabolically. All other mucopolysaccharides of connective tissue exhibit a continuing turnover, although at varying rates which are characteristic of individual polysaccharides in specific tissues.

Among mammalian tissues only testis is known definitely to contain an enzyme which warrants the name "hyaluronidase," although hyaluronidase *activity* has been observed in various tissue extracts, and, indeed, with mixed plasma proteins. Yet it is not clear which enzyme, if any, is responsible for the degradation of extracellular mucopolysaccharide. It appears that degradation proceeds only to the level of relatively low molecular weight polymers that leave the specific site at which they are formed, are transported to the kidney, and are excreted in the urine. No sulfatase capable of effecting hydrolysis of sulfate esters of carbohydrates is known to be present in animal tissues. Moreover, the total daily urinary excretion of sulfate esters of low molecular weight polysaccharides is compatible with estimates of the daily total synthesis of sulfated mucopolysaccharides.

Excessive mucopolysaccharide formation appears to characterize patients with *Marfan's* and *Hurler's diseases.* The tissues of patients with Hurler's disease contain unusually large amounts of chondroitin sulfate B and heparitin sulfate, which also appear in excessive amounts in the urine. Heparitin sulfate is a heteropolysaccharide of a structure resembling heparin (page 56) in that the repeating unit is a disaccharide of sulfated D-glucuronic acid and D-glucosamine moieties, probably in 1,4 linkage.

The mucopolysaccharide composition of animal tissues varies in a rather consistent manner with aging. Thus, the keratosulfate concentration of tissues which contain this material increases constantly throughout life, while the chondroitin sulfate content of cartilage and nucleus pulposus (intervertebral disks), as well as the hyaluronic acid of skin, decrease with aging. Of interest is the finding that administration of growth hormone (Chap. 51) at any age results in a pattern of mucopolysaccharide synthesis and composition which resembles that of the extremely young animal. Administration of testosterone (Chap. 48) appears, specifically, to increase markedly the rate of hyaluronic acid synthesis in such loci as heart valves, skin, the comb of the rooster, and the sex skin of the monkey. The hyaluronic acid of synovial fluid of rheumatic and arthritic joints is present in greater than normal amount but appears to be largely depolymerized. Administration of certain adrenal cortical steroids (Chap. 49) results in rapid repolymerization of existing hyaluronic acid while abruptly inhibiting further *de novo* synthesis of hyaluronic acid. The mechanism of these steroid effects remains to be established. Of interest is the report that the mucopolysaccharides of the skin of the alloxan-diabetic rat exhibited a turnover rate approximately one-third that found in normal animals; this diminished rate could be restored toward normal by administration of insulin. Since in diabetes mellitus there is a significantly greater than normal susceptibility to infection, with retarded wound healing and accelerated vascular degeneration, these characteristics may reflect, in part, the decreased ability to synthesize acid mucopolysaccharides when the insulin supply is inadequate. It will be apparent from this brief survey that much remains to be learned concerning the metabolism and biological roles of these complex polysaccharides.

REFERENCES

Books

Clark, F., and Grant, J. K., eds., "The Biochemistry of Mucopolysaccharides of Connective Tissue," Biochemical Society Symposium No. 20, Cambridge University Press, Cambridge, England, 1961.

"Connective Tissue," a symposium, Blackwell Scientific Publications, Ltd., Oxford, 1957.

Gustavson, K. H., "Chemistry and Reactivity of Collagen," Academic Press, Inc., New York, 1956.

McKusick, V. A., "Heritable Disorders of Connective Tissue," The C. V. Mosby Company, St. Louis, 1956.

Springer, G. F., ed., "Polysaccharides in Biology," Transactions of the Fourth Conference of the Josiah Macy, Jr. Foundation, New York, 1961.

Stainsby, G., ed., "Recent Advances in Gelatin and Glue Research," Pergamon Press, New York, 1958.

Wolstenholme, G. E. W., and O'Connor, M., eds., "Chemistry and Biology of Mucopolysaccharides," Little, Brown and Company, Boston, 1958.

Review Articles

Asboe-Hansen, G., Hormonal Effects on Connective Tissue, *Physiol. Revs.,* **38,** 446–462, 1958.

Dorfman, A., and Schiller, S., Effects of Hormones on the Metabolism of Acid Mucopolysaccharides of Connective Tissue, *Recent Progr. Hormone Research,* **14,** 427–456, 1958.

Dorfman, A., and Schiller, S., Mucopolysaccharides of Connective Tissue, in T. W. Goodwin and O. Lindberg, eds., "Biological Structure and Function," vol. I, pp. 327–343, Academic Press, Inc., New York, 1961.

Duran-Reynals, F., ed., The Ground Substance of the Mesenchyme and Hyaluronidase, *Ann. N.Y. Acad. Sci.,* **52,** 943–1196, 1950.

Harkness, R. D., Biological Functions of Collagen, *Biol. Revs. Cambridge Phil. Soc.,* **36,** 399–463, 1961.

Harrington, W. F., and von Hippel, P. H., The Structure of Collagen and Gelatin, *Advances in Protein Chem.,* **16,** 1–138, 1961.

Hodge, A. J., and Schmitt, F. O., The Tropocollagen Macromolecule and Its Properties of Ordered Interaction, in M. V. Edds, ed., "Macromolecular Complexes," pp. 19–52, The Ronald Press Company, New York, 1961.

Jackson, D. S., Some Biochemical Aspects of Fibrinogenesis and Wound Healing, *New Engl. J. Med.,* **259,** 814–820, 1958.

Jakowska, S., ed., "Mucous Secretions," *Ann. N.Y. Acad. Sci.,* **106,** 157–809, 1963.

Mandl, I., Collagenases and Elastases, *Advances in Enzymol.,* **23,** 163–264, 1961.

Meyer, K., Chemistry of the Mesodermal Ground Substances, *Harvey Lectures,* **51,** 88–112, 1955.

Meyer, K., and Rapport, M. M., Hyaluronidases, *Advances in Enzymol.,* **13,** 199–236, 1952.

Partridge, S. M., Elastin, *Advances in Protein Chem.,* **17,** 227–302, 1962.

Whistler, R. L., and Olson, E. J., The Biosynthesis of Hyaluronic Acid, *Advances in Carbohydrate Chem.,* **13,** 299–320, 1957.

41. Bone; Calcium and Phosphorus Metabolism

CALCIUM METABOLISM

Although more than 99 per cent of the calcium of the body is present in the skeleton, the remaining 1 per cent serves a number of important functions unrelated to bone structure. The concentration of calcium in intracellular fluid is approximately 20 mg. per 100 g. of tissue. Its presence is essential for the activity of a number of enzymic systems, including those responsible for the contractile properties of muscle and for the transmission of the nerve impulse. The concentration of calcium also appears to be critical in extracellular fluid, particularly for the response of muscle to neural stimuli and for functioning of the blood-clotting mechanism (Chap. 33).

Intestinal Absorption of Calcium. The major calcium salt ingested is calcium phosphate, since it is in this form that calcium is present in materials which serve as food. Calcium also occurs in nature as the carbonate, tartrate, and oxalate and, together with magnesium, as the highly insoluble mixed salt of phytic acid (the hexaphosphoric acid ester of inositol) (page 35), present in cereals.

From a nutritional standpoint, the intestinal absorption of calcium presents a major problem, largely because of the insolubility of most calcium salts. Within the body, moreover, the insolubility of calcium salts may lead to calcification of atheromatous blood vessels or calculus formation in the gallbladder or in the pelvis or tubules of the kidney. In increasing order of solubility, the three forms of calcium phosphate are $Ca_3(PO_4)_2$, $CaHPO_4$, and $Ca(H_2PO_4)_2$. At the pH prevailing within the stomach, the calcium phosphates readily dissolve; at the pH of the duodenum, the chief calcium salts are $CaHPO_4$ and $Ca(H_2PO_4)_2$.

Calcium passage across the duodenum occurs largely by diffusion; this process seems to be inhibited, in part, in vitamin D–deficient animals. Active transport of Ca^{++} occurs across the ileal mucosa; the system is capable of operating against a fivefold concentration gradient and requires energy, presumably ATP. This process also is diminished in vitamin D deficiency. Perhaps related is the capacity of mitochondria from many tissues to concentrate relatively large quantities of Ca^{++} from the medium provided that there is a source of ATP and an oxidizable substrate. The coupling of phosphorylation to oxidation is not essential. Subsequent release of the bound calcium is dependent upon vitamin D. This release is markedly stimulated by parathyroid hormone (Chap. 47), but only if vitamin D is also present. This relationship is in accord with several other aspects of calcium metabolism, *e.g.*, absorption of Ca^{++} from the intestine and demineralization of bone (see below), processes in which vitamin D and the parathyroid hormone exert synergistic effects.

Calcium absorption from the ileum can also be enhanced by the presence of sugars and of basic amino acids. The sugar effect is relatively nonspecific. Generally, virtually all mono- and disaccharides have been absorbed before the digested food mixture arrives at the ileum. However, lactose, uniquely, may escape digestion during this passage, and its presence markedly enhances calcium absorption. It may be noted that the only source of lactose is milk, which also provides large quantities of calcium for the growth of the young. Much of the phosphate of milk is esterified to the hydroxyl groups of the serine residues of casein (page 720). Calcium absorption may precede the complete digestion of casein so that the concentration of inorganic phosphate liberated by digestion of casein is relatively low until the calcium has been absorbed.

The presence of substantial amounts of lysine or arginine also enhances ileal calcium absorption, but under most physiological circumstances this is of little consequence. Of these factors, therefore, only vitamin D appears essential for normal absorption of calcium. A low level of *phytase,* which catalyzes the hydrolysis of phytate (see above), is present in ileal mucosa; again, this activity is diminished in vitamin D deficiency. All phytate which escapes hydrolysis renders an equivalent amount of calcium unavailable; this also occurs with fatty acids. In steatorrhea due to biliary obstruction, sprue, or regional ileitis, insoluble calcium soaps are formed which are excreted in the stool.

Regulation of Plasma Calcium Concentration. The calcium of normal human plasma varies from 9 to 11 mg. per 100 ml. (4.5 to 5.6 meq. per liter) and exists in two major forms. Ionic calcium, the form in which calcium exerts its physiological effects, is present to the extent of 5 to 6 mg. per 100 ml. The second form is calcium which is not diffusible through collodion membranes permeable to ionized calcium. This fraction consists largely of calcium bound to plasma proteins, particularly albumin. The amount of this fraction is a function of the total protein concentration; plasma low in protein exhibits a low total calcium concentration as well. The extent of calcium binding by protein increases with increasing pH. Determination of ionic calcium is possible by means of a biological assay using the frog or turtle heart, the activity of which is proportional to the ionized calcium concentration of the medium. For clinical purposes, estimation of the ionized calcium is possible from a knowledge of the total calcium and protein concentrations, using the nomogram shown in Fig. 41.1.

Maintenance of normal neuromuscular irritability is critically dependent upon the concentration of ionic calcium as one of the factors in the ratio:

$$\frac{[K^+] + [Na^+]}{[Ca^{++}] + [Mg^{++}] + [H^+]}$$

This relationship is intended only to convey the direction of the change in irritability resulting from alterations in the concentrations of these ions. A significant decrease in concentration of ionic calcium results in tetany, while an increase may so impair muscle function as to lead to respiratory or cardiac failure.

The plasma calcium concentration is homeostatically maintained. The mecha-

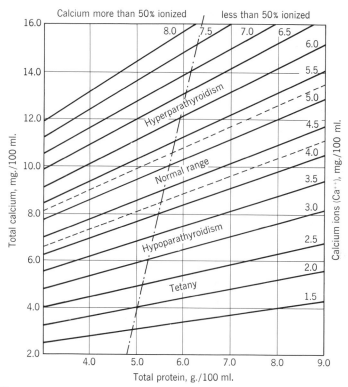

Fig. 41.1. Nomogram showing the relations between total serum calcium, protein, and ionized calcium concentrations. (*From F. C. McLean and A. B. Hastings, Am. J. Med. Sci.,* **189,** 601, 1935.)

nism includes a storage compartment, the skeleton, which may be drawn upon or into which excess may be deposited; the kidneys; excretion through the bile and intestine; and the parathyroid secretion, sensitive to the plasma concentration of Ca^{++} (Chap. 47).

Serum phosphate and Ca^{++} concentrations normally exhibit a reciprocal relationship; when the phosphate concentration is diminished, $[Ca^{++}]$ is elevated, and vice versa, as would be expected were serum the soluble phase of a saturated solution. However, in hyperparathyroidism the concentrations of both ions may be elevated, whereas in juvenile rickets both may be diminished. Thus, a simple solubility product relationship does not always obtain, and the concentrations of these ions are under cellular control.

The normal major pathway of calcium excretion is the intestinal tract. Individuals on a calcium-free diet continue to excrete calcium in the feces. This calcium is a constituent of various digestive secretions, particularly the bile. The amount of calcium excreted depends upon the plasma calcium concentration. Normally, the kidney excretes little calcium. On the other hand, chronic hypercalcemia may be accompanied by sufficient calciuria to cause formation of renal calculi. In normal individuals 99 per cent of the Ca^{++} filtered through the glomeruli is reabsorbed, even at artificially elevated plasma concentrations. However, the fraction reabsorbed decreases in several pathological conditions in which bone mineral resorption is active. Bone serves as the store of calcium in the operation of a homeostatic mechanism. Under circumstances which might otherwise lead to hypocalcemia, calcium is withdrawn from the skeleton. Conversely, hypercalcemia may be prevented by deposition of calcium in bone. The means by which this is effected will be considered below.

PHOSPHATE METABOLISM

Phosphate is ubiquitous and abundant in biological materials. In consequence, nutritional phosphate deficiency is not possible when food is ingested in amounts sufficient to meet the requirements for calories and protein. Most of the phosphate ingested is orthophosphate or organic phosphate which yields orthophosphate in the digestive tract. Although no appreciable phosphate absorption occurs in the stomach, absorption occurs throughout the small intestine. It has been suggested that phosphate transport is mediated by esterification of phosphate at the cell surface. At the present time, only the turnover of ATP is known to occur at a rate commensurate with the rate of phosphate transport, but there is no proof of its participation in this process.

The inorganic phosphate in plasma appears to be orthophosphate, with $HPO_4^=$ and $H_2PO_4^-$ present in a ratio of approximately $4:1$. All the plasma phosphate is diffusible and filtrable through the glomerulus. There also exist in plasma varying quantities of several phosphate esters. These include small quantities of hexose phosphates, triose phosphates, phosphatides, etc. The concentration of orthophosphate in normal plasma is 4 to 5 mg. of phosphorus per 100 ml. in children, and 3.5 to 4 mg. of phosphorus per 100 ml. in adults. This concentration is also regulated by a homeostatic mechanism. As in the case of calcium, the skeleton stores phosphate, which is withdrawn when the serum phosphate concentration falls or is deposited when the serum phosphate concentration rises. The chief excretory route is the kidney; the renal excretion of phosphate has been described earlier (page 731).

BONE

Composition of Bone. Although there are several different types of bone, *e.g.*, cortical bone, cancellous bone, etc., most of our information concerning the nature of bone and its formation derives from studies of the long bones. When bone is allowed to stand in a dilute acidic solution, the mineral portion dissolves, leaving a flexible, tough, and almost translucent organic residue retaining the shape of the intact bone. The mineral fraction of bone is composed largely of calcium phosphate, in addition to carbonate, fluoride, hydroxide, and citrate. Most of the magnesium, about one-quarter of the sodium, and a smaller fraction of the potassium of the body are also present in bone. Bone crystals belong to the group of hydroxyapatites, of the approximate composition $Ca_{10}(PO_4)_6(OH)_2$. The crystals are platelets, or rods, about 8 to 15 Å. thick, 20 to 40 Å. wide, and 200 to 400 Å long, with a density of 3.0. It seems likely that in bone, divalent cations other than Ca^{++}

can replace Ca^{++} in the hydroxyapatite crystal lattice, whereas anions other than phosphate and hydroxyl may be adsorbed on the vast areas of surface offered by the minute crystals, or dissolved in the hydration shell about the crystal lattice.

Inorganic material comprises only about one-fourth the volume of bone, the remainder being the organic matrix. Because of the difference in density between the organic and inorganic phases, insoluble minerals comprise half the bone weight. The organic matrix consists largely of collagen; only very small quantities of an inadequately characterized mucoprotein are present in mature dense bone. Collagen fibers in the bone matrix do not seem to differ from those present in tendon, hyaline cartilage, fibrocartilage, or other fibrous tissues. The inorganic crystal structure imparts to bone an elastic modulus similar to that of concrete.

Structure and Formation of Bone. As discussed previously (page 767), cells of mesenchymal origin (*viz.,* fibroblasts, osteoblasts) introduce into the medium about them fibrils of collagen in a milieu containing mucoprotein and mucopolysaccharides. Although this combination of collagen and mucopolysaccharide is ubiquitous in the animal body, mineralization normally occurs only in those areas destined to become bone. The mineral components must be withdrawn from the available fluid medium. It follows that this fluid phase is already supersaturated and that crystal formation is induced by "nucleation," *i.e.,* provision of a surface on which crystal lattice formation can proceed readily. Although, in chemical practice,

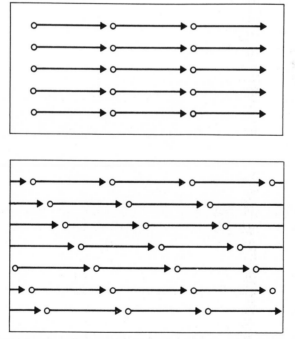

FIG. 41.2. Schematic diagram of alignment of tropocollagen molecules in collagen fibers; ▶ and ○ represent carboxyl- and amino-termini of the three strands of each tropocollagen unit. The "segment long spacing" collagen was prepared from tropocollagen in the presence of ATP and acetic acid.

"seeding" of supersaturated solutions to induce crystal formation is usually performed by addition of crystals of the same material, seeding for nucleation purposes can also be accomplished, and frequently more successfully, by addition of crystals of some other chemical species, *e.g.*, seeding of clouds with AgI to induce ice formation. It is the normal, triple-stranded collagen (Fig. 40.2, page 769) which serves as the nucleating agent for bone formation. Studies with electron microscopy and low-angle x-ray diffraction indicate that formation of the bone mineral crystal lattice is initiated within the collagen fibers. Indeed, collagen prepared from skin or tendon and solubilized and reprecipitated under conditions which lead to formation of normal fibrils (page 767), and then placed in a mineral medium identical in composition with normal blood plasma, will initiate such nucleation and be mineralized with normal hydroxyapatite crystals.

Some evidence suggests that nucleation of collagen results from binding of phosphate either to ε-amino groups of lysine and hydroxylysine or to hydroxyl groups of hydroxyproline residues. Whichever groups are responsible, the alignment of neighboring strands of the triple helix of collagen is critical. In native collagen, adjacent collagen fibrils are aligned in the fiber in a manner so that repeating groups in the tropocollagen molecules of which they are composed are not "in register" but are nevertheless aligned in a specific way (Fig. 41.2). Under certain conditions, starting with dissolved tropocollagen, one can prepare collagen fibers in which all the tropocollagen units are "in register" (Fig. 41.2), but such fibers fail to mineralize under the same conditions. During bone development, the crystals grow until they completely fill and surround the collagen and in turn serve as nucleating agents for deposition of hydroxyapatite in spaces between collagen fibers (Fig. 41.3).

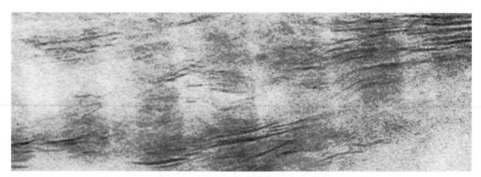

Fɪɢ. 41.3. An initial stage in bone formation. A longitudinal section through the metatarsal bone of a 12-day-old chick, magnified 200,000×, shows that nucleation and early growth of hydroxyapatite crystals is largely confined to zones occupying about 60 per cent of the axial repeat of the collagen fibrils. (*Courtesy, Dr. M. J. Glimcher and Dr. A. J. Hodge.*)

Since collagen in connective tissue other than bone does not normally calcify in the same supersaturated medium, factors other than collagen and the mineral composition of the medium must be involved. Bone formation occurs only in the vicinity of osteoblasts, with mineral deposition advancing in cartilage which consists of collagen in a mucopolysaccharide matrix. Inasmuch as the mucopolysaccharide disappears as bone is formed, it has been suggested that the mucopolysaccharides prevent mineralization of collagen, perhaps by binding Ca^{++} so that the solubility product for hydroxyapatite formation is not exceeded. This might explain the failure of collagen in skin, tendon, etc., to mineralize. Osteoblasts are unusually rich in alkaline phosphatase, which might serve to achieve a local increase in phosphate concentration, but the relationship of this enzyme to the calcification process is not clear.

It is of interest that the formation of bone as a consequence of the structure and organization of its organic matrix and with subsequent nucleation of crystallization from a supersaturated medium appears to be but one instance of a general principle. As indicated in Table 41.1, mineralized tissues appear, generally, to be formed in this manner.

Bone is not a static depot of mineral but is in a dynamic state, with simultaneous osteoblastic and osteoclastic activity maintaining the constancy of bone composition. Hevesy observed that administered P_i^{32} soon appears even in the dense portions of the shaft of the large bones. These findings have since been corroborated by studies with radioisotopes of calcium and strontium. The rapidity with

Table 41.1: EXAMPLES OF BIOLOGICALLY MINERALIZED TISSUES

Species	Tissue	Crystalline phase	Mineral form	Major organic matrix
Plants	Cell walls	$CaCO_3$	Calcite	Cellulose, pectins, lignins
Radiolaria . .	Exoskeleton	$SrSO_4$	Celestite	(?)
Diatoms	Exoskeleton	Silica	(?)	Pectins
Mollusks . . .	Exoskeleton	$CaCO_3$	Calcite, aragonite	Protein (conchiolin)
Arthropods .	Exoskeleton	$CaCO_3$	Calcite	Chitin, proteins
Vertebrates .	Endoskeleton:			
	Bone	$Ca_{10}(PO_4)_6(OH)_2$	Hydroxyapatite	Collagen
	Cartilage	$Ca_{10}(PO_4)_6(OH)_2$	Hydroxyapatite	Collagen
	Tooth:			
	Dentin	$Ca_{10}(PO_4)_6(OH)_2$	Hydroxyapatite	Collagen
	Cementum	$Ca_{10}(PO_4)_6(OH)_2$	Hydroxyapatite	Collagen
	Enamel	$Ca_{10}(PO_4)_6(OH)_2$	Hydroxyapatite	Protein

SOURCE: After M. J. Glimcher, *Rev. Mod. Phys.*, **31**, 359, 1959.

which these cations appear in bone is probably related to the vast surface of bone crystal exposed to extracellular fluid. Bone contains a high concentration of anions other than phosphate, *e.g.*, carbonate. Citrate may be present in an amount equal to about 1 per cent of the dry weight of bone mineral, and largely in association with Na^+. Bone appears to be a labile reservoir of Na^+ which may be drawn upon in acidosis and in which Na^+ accumulates in alkalosis or excessive Na^+ intake. It should be reiterated that these ions are adsorbed to the crystal surfaces, rather than being present as integral parts of the crystalline structure. Heavy metals which may enter the body are incorporated into the hydroxyapatite crystal lattice; notable examples are lead, radium, uranium, and the heavy elements derived from uranium by fission, *e.g.,* strontium.

Other Factors Influencing Bone Metabolism. Deficiency of vitamin D leads to rickets (rachitis) in the young. This vitamin promotes Ca^{++} absorption from the intestine by an unknown mechanism, and the manifestations of vitamin D deficiency derive largely from the resultant lack of Ca^{++}. In addition, however, a direct effect of vitamin D on bone is evident from the failure of calcification of rat femur, in vitro, in rachitic serum which has been fortified with calcium and phosphate.

Vitamin D toxicity has been observed both in experimental animals and in patients who have received massive doses of vitamin D, and is characterized by excessive resorption of bone, with a resultant rise in serum calcium and phosphate concentrations. This leads, in turn, to unusually large quantities of calcium and phosphate in the urine and formation of renal calculi. Indeed, renal failure has often been the presenting sign in patients suffering from vitamin D intoxication.

Vitamin A also affects bone development. In the young animal deprived of vitamin A, growth of the skeleton is impaired before that of the soft tissue. The spinal cord may thus continue to grow after growth of the spinal column has been arrested, giving rise to compression of nerve roots as they emerge from the cord; this leads to impaired function of those parts supplied by the affected nerves. Young rats given excessive but not lethal quantities of vitamin A develop multiple fractures of the long bones, and bone deformities have been observed in children receiving excessive quantities of this vitamin. These phenomena appear to reflect depolymerization and hydrolysis of the chondroitin sulfate component of cartilage.

Ascorbic acid is also essential to the development of a normal skeleton. In ascorbic acid deficiency, the mesenchymal cells fail to elaborate normal cement substance (see previous chapter), leading to impaired calcification. Skeletal growth ceases in all deficiency states, including caloric restriction. However, only in deficiencies of calcium, phosphorus, and vitamins A, D, and C are there characteristic bone lesions other than those seen in inanition.

Role of the Parathyroid Hormone. The parathyroid hormone is important in the regulation of the metabolism of calcium and phosphate. The results of parathyroid insufficiency and of overadministration of parathyroid hormone preparations are presented elsewhere (Chap. 47). The parathyroid hormone affects the metabolism of calcium and phosphate in bone, and, in the kidney, inhibits tubular reabsorption of inorganic phosphate, resulting in a lowering of the plasma concentration of phosphate. After administration of parathyroid extract, there occurs a depolymerization of the mucoprotein aggregates in the less dense areas of bone, followed by disappearance of the crystal line and matrix structures. Simultaneously, acidic mucoproteins appear in the plasma. These observations suggest that the metabolic effects of the parathyroid hormone may, in part, be mediated via the regulatory influence of the osteocytes on the structure of the ground substance. As indicated earlier, parathyroid hormone also affects Ca^{++} transport across membranes and the release of Ca^{++} from mitochondria. The parathyroid gland is sensitive to serum $[Ca^{++}]$ and secretes its active principle in response to a lowering of the concentration of circulating calcium (Chap. 47).

The local chemical factors affecting mineralization are incompletely understood. Bone cells respire and glycolyze, continually producing lactic acid. Administration of parathyroid hormone increases the rate of lactic acid production, which may result in local demineralization by lowering pH (Chap. 47). As bone crystals dissolve, citrate is released and appears in plasma. Estrogens inhibit lactic acid production, in accord with the increased bone density produced by prolonged estrogen administration (see below).

Derangements of Bone Metabolism. Deviations from normal bone metabolism are known in which either excessive or inadequate bone formation is evident. Excessive bone formation is relatively uncommon but may be produced experimentally by estrogen administration (Chap. 48). Abnormally thick and dense bones and cerebral calcification may be seen in *chronic hypoparathyroidism* and accompanying chronic tetany. Overgrowth of bones occurs in *hypertrophic osteoarthritis,* a relatively common chronic disease occurring mainly after the age of forty years.

Abnormalities of bone metabolism leading to loss of bone may arise either from failure to mineralize the bone matrix, *osteomalacia,* or because of inadequate matrix formation, *osteoporosis.* For example, osteomalacia is seen in juvenile rickets, in which bone matrix formation proceeds normally but there is inadequate calcification of the matrix. Continuing growth of uncalcified cartilage results in bone deformity. Osteoblastic activity is greater than normal, as revealed by increased plasma alkaline phosphatase activity. The deficient supply of dietary calcium leads to diminished serum [Ca^{++}] and causes release of parathyroid hormone, which through its effect on bone and on the kidney maintains a normal serum [Ca^{++}] and a diminished serum phosphate concentration. Bone deformities are not prominent in osteomalacia of adults since skeletal growth is complete, but diminished bone density and spontaneous fractures occur frequently.

Osteoporosis is most commonly observed after the menopause, presumably reflecting decreased estrogenic activity (Chap. 48). Ascorbic acid deficiency and malnutrition also result in osteoporosis because of impaired osteoblastic formation of acidic mucopolysaccharides. Hyperparathyroidism stimulates osteoclastic activity; the effect is not uniform throughout the skeleton, however, but is apparent as "punched-out" areas—*osteitis fibrosa cystica.*

Of interest are the osteomalacia and fragile bones which result from prolonged immobilization and disease. Immobilization of an extremity results in prompt negative calcium balance of that member; prolonged bed rest without exercise has the same influence on the entire skeleton. The underlying mechanism is not understood.

Hypophosphatasia is a relatively rare chronic familial disease of uncertain etiology, primarily affecting children, in whom there is deficient bone formation with histological changes resembling rickets. The disease is associated with a low level of alkaline phosphatase activity in the serum and tissues, and may occur in siblings; serum alkaline phosphatase activity is often low in one, or both, of the parents, without evidence of bone disease. One form of such "refractory rickets" has been shown to be transmitted as a sex-linked, dominant trait (Chap. 31).

Calcification in Soft Tissues. Aberrant calcification may occur in a wide variety of tissues. *Myositis ossificans* is a striking example of metastatic ossification. In skin, tendon, ligaments, and heart valves, this calcification is again associated with collagen. In the intima of large vessels, such as the aorta, it is apparently associated with elastin. Calcification of the pancreas may be related to a local increase in alkalinity due to the secretory activity of acinar tissue; calculus formation at the tooth-gum margin seems to involve participation of mucoproteins.

TEETH

The tooth is built of three layers of calcified tissue. The pulp cavity, containing blood vessels and nerves, is covered with the dentine, the major calcified tissue. Where the tooth is exposed, the dentine is covered by enamel, while the submerged roots are covered with cementum. The cementum closely resembles cortical bone in composition. Dentine is hard and dense, being almost 75 per cent mineral; the enamel is more dense and harder and is almost 98 per cent mineral. The organic matrix of dentine and cementum is much like that of bone. The protein in embryonic enamel is a fibrous protein characterized by a very high proline content and the presence of hydroxylysine (Table 40.1, page 768). This is the protein which is initially laid down and calcified. The hydroxyapatite crystals deposited within and upon the protein and in the interfibrillar spaces are much larger than are those of dentine, cementum, or bone. Analysis reveals less Mg^{++}, $CO_3^=$, Na^+, etc., in enamel than in dentine. Hevesy observed incorporation and disappearance of administered radioactive inorganic phosphate in teeth. Turnover of phosphate in dentine is about one-sixth as rapid as in long bones, but about fifteen to twenty times as rapid as in enamel. This relatively slow turnover of tooth minerals is consonant with their stability in conditions which are potentially ones of decalcification, *e.g.*, pregnancy and vitamin D deficiency.

Fluoride and Caries. Present knowledge of the relationship between fluoride and dental health stems from a noteworthy series of epidemiologic investigations commencing in 1908 with the investigation of the cause of *mottled enamel* by the Colorado Springs (Colorado) Dental Society. Teeth affected in this way are characterized by dull chalky patches distributed irregularly over the surface. The teeth are pitted and corroded and occasionally stained a yellow to dark brown color. Calcification is deficient, and cement substance may be lacking. It has been established that mottled teeth occur only in persons who have drunk water containing in excess of 1.5 mg. of fluoride per liter during the years of tooth development. An incidental important finding has been that the occurrence of caries is minimal in those communities whose drinking water provides 0.9 mg. of fluoride per liter. The fluoridation of other communal water supplies to bring the fluoride content to 1.0 mg. per liter has resulted in a significant decrease in the incidence of dental caries. Once the teeth have been fully formed, fluoride is without effect on dental caries. The mode of action of fluoride is not understood. Since the quantity of fluoride used is much too small to inhibit bacterial metabolism, it has been assumed that the fluoride in some manner increases the ability of the teeth to withstand the usual cariogenic influences.

REFERENCES

Books

Bourne, G. H., "The Biochemistry and Physiology of Bone," Academic Press, Inc., New York, 1956.

Irving, J. T., "Calcium Metabolism," John Wiley & Sons, Inc., New York, 1957.

McLean, F. C., and Urist, M. R., "Bone: An Introduction to the Physiology of Skeletal Tissue," University of Chicago Press, Chicago, 1955.

Neuman, W. F., and Neuman, M. W., "The Chemical Dynamics of Bone Mineral," University of Chicago Press, Chicago, 1958.

Sognnaes, R. F., ed., "Calcification in Biological Systems," American Association for the Advancement of Science, Washington, 1960.

Wolstenholme, G. E. W., and O'Connor, C. M., eds., "Bone Structure and Metabolism," Little, Brown and Company, Boston, 1956.

Review Articles

Bauer, G. C. H., Carlsson, A., and Lindquist, B., Metabolism and Homeostatic Function of Bone, in C. L. Comar and F. Bronner, eds., "Mineral Metabolism," vol. I, part B, pp. 609–677, Academic Press, Inc., New York, 1961.

Follis, R. H., Jr., A Survey of Bone Disease, *Am. J. Med.,* **22,** 469–484, 1957.

Glimcher, M. J., Molecular Biology of Mineralized Tissues with Particular Reference to Bone, *Rev. Mod. Phys.,* **31,** 359–393, 1959.

Nicolaysen, R., Eeg-Larsen, N., and Malm, O. J., Physiology of Calcium Metabolism, *Physiol. Revs.,* **33,** 424–444, 1953.

Urist, M. R., The Bone–Body Fluid Continuum: Calcium and Phosphorus in the Skeleton of Blood and Living Vertebrates, *Perspectives in Biol. and Med.,* **6,** 75–115, 1962.

Whipple, H. E., ed., "Comparative Biology of Calcified Tissue," *Ann. N.Y. Acad. Sci.,* **109,** 1–410, 1963.

42. The Erythrocyte and Iron Metabolism

The prime function of the erythrocyte, transport of oxygen and carbon dioxide (Chap. 34), is accomplished by the presence of a 34 per cent solution of hemoglobin. The erythrocyte contains the most concentrated protein solution in the body, thereby permitting the movement of about 16 g. of hemoglobin per 100 ml. of whole blood without the high viscosity which would attend the presence of an equivalent amount of protein in free solution. The adult mammalian erythrocyte contains no nucleus, possesses a relatively low respiratory metabolism, and is one of the few major cells of the body with a finite life span of established length. This chapter will consider the principal biochemical aspects of the erythrocyte and the metabolism of one of its important constituents, iron.

DEVELOPMENT, STRUCTURE, AND COMPOSITION OF THE ERYTHROCYTE

Development of the Erythrocyte. The red cells arise from reticular cells of the bone marrow and develop in sinusoids temporarily closed to the circulation. Rapid cell multiplication occurs at the level of the pronormoblasts, which contain large nuclei with conspicuous nucleoli. Differentiation begins with the appearance of the basophilic normoblast. This cell has lost its nucleolus, the RNA content of the cytoplasm has decreased markedly, and the total protein content of the cell is at a maximum. Heme and globin syntheses are initiated at this time. At the orthochromic erythroblast stage, the nucleus is pyknotic, the mitochondria have disappeared, only a trace of RNA remains, and the hemoglobin content has been established. Mitotic figures disappear, and the nucleus then fragments, giving rise to the reticulocyte, which still contains small amounts of RNA. Several days later the adult erythrocyte emerges containing no detectable RNA or DNA.

Structure and Composition of the Erythrocyte. The erythrocyte is a nonnucleated, biconcave disk with a diameter varying from 6 to 9 μ and a thickness of about 1 μ at the center, increasing to 2 to 2.5 μ toward the periphery. The membrane of the erythrocyte is a mosaic structure some 200 to 300 Å. thick; its chief components are an insoluble protein, *stromatin,* a mixture of lipids including lecithin and cephalin, cerebrosides, gangliosides, and unesterified cholesterol, and a group of heteropolysaccharides, one (or more) of which contains a sialic acid. The latter is of interest since attachment of specific viruses, *e.g.*, influenza, to erythrocytes occurs at "receptor" sites and, apparently, involves binding between virus and the sialic acid(s) of the cell membrane. Incubation of erythrocytes with *neuraminidase* (page 57), an enzyme which liberates neuraminic acid (page 36), alters the receptor sites, and such cells will no longer bind virus. The erythrocyte membrane also contains the specific blood group substances (see below).

As in cells generally, the chief cation of the human erythrocyte is K^+, with lesser amounts of Na^+, Ca^{++}, and Mg^{++}, while the major anions are Cl^-, HCO_3^-, hemoglobin, inorganic phosphate, and various organic phosphates, of which 2,3-diphosphoglycerate, coenzyme of phosphoglyceromutase, is particularly noteworthy. These relations are shown in Fig. 42.1.

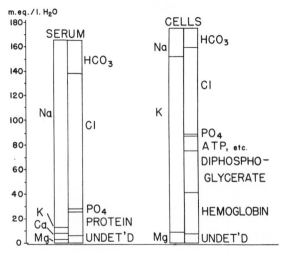

Fig. 42.1. The electrolyte structure of the oxygenated human erythrocyte. (*From G. M. Guest, Am. J. Diseases Children,* **64**, 401, 1942.)

The adult erythrocyte behaves as an osmometer, swelling and shrinking with decreases and increases in osmotic pressure of the bathing fluid. If the red cell is suspended in a sufficiently hypotonic solution, it swells, and rupture of the enclosing membrane, or *hemolysis*, occurs. Hemolysis may also be accomplished in isotonic media by various surface-active agents, *e.g.*, soaps, chloroform, and saponins (page 88). Virtually all the internal constituents of the human erythrocyte are soluble and dissolve in the medium upon hemolysis, leaving an insoluble residue, or *ghost*, which supposedly represents the original membrane.

The internal composition of the erythrocyte is maintained by energy-requiring mechanisms. The erythrocyte membrane shows an ATPase activity which is dependent upon both Na^+ and K^+ and is enhanced by the presence of low concentrations of cardiac glycosides, agents which are known to influence Na^+-K^+ transport across cardiac muscle cells. Although the glucose concentration within the red cells is generally identical with that in plasma, glucose does not appear to enter the erythrocyte by simple diffusion. Phosphate penetration of the erythrocyte is also mediated by a transport device. As in the case of nerve tissue, the behavior of the erythrocyte membrane with respect to sodium and potassium is apparently contingent on participation of acetylcholine and of choline esterase, since choline esterase inhibitors rapidly alter the cell "permeability" characteristics.

Chemistry of the Blood Group Substances. Among the most interesting constituents of the red cell membrane are the "blood group substances." These mucopolysaccharides occur not only on erythrocytes but also in secretions such as saliva, gastric juice, etc. Water-soluble products showing immunochemical blood group activity have also been obtained from tissues of various species, including the human. For example, fractionation of material from ovarian cyst fluid has yielded two substances having blood group B specificity. Both contained L-fucose, D-galactose, N-acetyl-D-glucosamine, and N-acetyl-D-galactosamine, as well as 11 amino acids. Similar constituents have been described in group A substance.

All the blood group substances isolated from a number of species show striking qualitative similarities in chemical composition, despite immunological distinctions. They are composed of carbohydrate and polypeptide, and all contain the four sugars mentioned above. Sulfur-containing and aromatic amino acids are absent. Studies of enzymic digests of immunologically active blood group substances indicate that the polypeptide portion plays no role in immunological specificity. Variations do exist among the blood group substances in the ratios of glucosamine to galactosamine which they contain, as well as in their content of fucose. They may also contain a sialic acid. The group specificity is probably associated with differences in the nature of the carbohydrate end group of the mucopolysaccharide. The most highly purified preparations of blood group substances from ovarian cyst fluids and from hog gastric mucin have molecular weights ranging from approximately 260,000 to 1,800,000.

HEMOGLOBIN SYNTHESIS

Hemoglobin is the major component of the erythrocyte. Its chemistry (pages 193*ff.*), variations in structure of its globin component (pages 611*ff.*), physiological role (pages 658*ff.*), and the biosynthesis of its porphyrin precursor, porphobilinogen (pages 532*ff.*), have been considered previously. It will be recalled that formation of porphobilinogen includes participation of glycine and succinyl CoA, via δ-aminolevulinic acid (page 532).

The pathway involved in the subsequent conversion of porphobilinogen to protophorphyrin has been intensively investigated, particularly by Granick and Mauzerall, and by Shemin, Neuberger, Rimington, Falk, and their associates. Figure 42.2 summarizes the pathway of heme biosynthesis from porphobilinogen.

Enzymic preparations utilizing porphobilinogen for porphyrin synthesis have been isolated from plant, bacterial, and animal sources. Indeed, it is apparent that a common pathway exists for the biosynthesis of heme and of chlorophyll leading

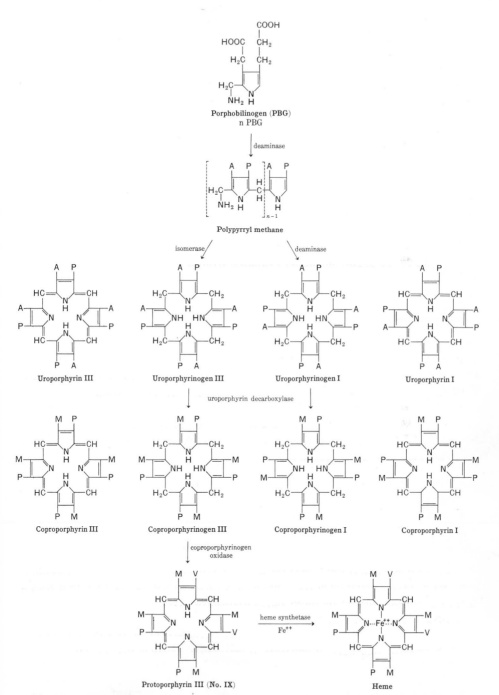

FIG. 42.2. Pathway of biosynthesis of heme and other porphyrins from porphobilinogen.
A = acetic acid; *P* = propionic acid; *M* = methyl; *V* = vinyl.

to formation of protoporphyrin IX (page 190). Insertion of iron into the latter results in heme formation. In plants, in addition to synthesis of heme, magnesium is inserted into protoporphyrin IX to form magnesium protoporphyrin, which is converted in plastids to chlorophyll.

Protoporphyrin synthesis begins with condensation of four molecules of porphobilinogen, under the influence of a *deaminase,* to a postulated intermediate, polypyrryl methane, which is converted to uroporphyrinogen I. This colorless chromogen can undergo autoxidation to form the urinary pigment, uroporphyrin I (page 742), or may be decarboxylated to yield coproporphyrinogen I, which in turn may be oxidized to coproporphyrin I. Alternatively, the polypyrryl methane, in the presence of an *isomerase,* may form uroporphyrinogen III, which can in a similar manner yield uroporphyrin III, coproporphyrinogen III, or coproporphyrin III. Coproporphyrinogen III may be oxidized and decarboxylated to yield protoporphyrin III (No. IX). The enzymes of beef liver, partially purified and studied by Sano and Granick, favor synthesis of the series III porphyrins.

Iron is incorporated at the level of protoporphyrin. No iron compounds of uroporphyrin or coproporphyrin are known to occur in nature. Extracts of nucleated, avian erythrocytes have been described which catalyze formation in vitro of either hemoglobin or myoglobin, respectively, from protoporphyrin, Fe^{++}, and either apohemoglobin or apomyoglobin. The active enzyme in such extracts has been termed *heme synthetase.* It may be noted that heme formation in vitro from a solubilized protoporphyrin and ferrous iron readily occurs in the absence of any enzyme. Iron may be made available in the form of transferrin (page 640) or ferritin (page 803) for incorporation into immature cells of the bone marrow.

Iron incorporation into hemoproteins, *e.g.,* the cytochromes, has been described in a variety of tissues. The data suggest that all aerobic cells possess independent biosynthetic capability for the manufacture of hemoproteins and that this activity is localized in mitochondria. Also, iron incorporation into protoporphyrin appears to occur after the latter has been bound to protein. Studies of London and his associates with rabbit bone marrow in vitro have demonstrated that the biosynthesis of heme and that of globin occur at approximately parallel rates. However, it was possible experimentally to influence disproportionately the rates of these two synthetic processes, indicating that they are not interdependent in that stimulation or inhibition of the one need not lead to stimulation or inhibition of the other.

The rate of protoporphyrin synthesis in the developing red cell only slightly exceeds that of hemoglobin synthesis. Erythroblasts contain no protoporphyrin; normoblasts and reticulocytes have significant quantities. The mature erythrocyte contains approximately 30 μg of protoporphyrin and approximately 1 mg. of coproporphyrin per 100 ml. of packed cells. In iron-deficiency anemia, red cells may contain as much as twenty times the normal content of protoporphyrin.

In vertebrates the heme of hemoglobin represents approximately 85 to 90 per cent of the total body heme; about 10 per cent is in muscle myoglobin and less than 1 per cent in all the other hemoproteins combined, *i.e.,* cytochromes, catalase, etc.

Abnormalities of Heme Biosynthesis; Porphyrias. Some of the clinical disorders associated with or characterized by abnormalities in heme biosynthesis result in the appearance of unusual quantities of porphyrins in the urine. These specific pathological states have been called *porphyrias.* Nonspecific excretion of porphyrins in diverse disorders, *e.g.*, alcoholism, lead poisoning, and hemolytic disease, generally characterized by increased excretion of coproporphyrin, are usually termed *porphyrinurias.*

As shown in Fig. 42.2 (page 791), type III porphyrins are most important in nature since their synthesis leads to protoporphyrin IX and thence to heme, or to chlorophyll (page 201). Type I porphyrins appear to be formed as by-products of heme synthesis and are not utilized by the body but are excreted in the urine (up to 300 μg per day) and in the stool (up to 600 μg per day). These colored porphyrins are oxidized forms of the colorless porphyrinogens.

Two types of porphyria, *erythropoietic* and *hepatic,* are believed to be hereditary disorders of metabolism. The former is a very rare disease in which there is excessive and abnormal formation of heme precursors in the developing red blood cells of the bone marrow. Skin photosensitivity is evident at an early age. Abnormal amounts of various heme precursors, notably uroporphyrin I and uroporphyrinogen I, are excreted in the urine. Several types of hepatic porphyria have been described. In general, in hepatic porphyrias, excessive and abnormal formation of heme precursors occurs in the liver. Urinary products present in higher than normal amounts include δ-aminolevulinic acid, porphobilinogen, uroporphyrin I, and uroporphyrinogen I. An unexplained interesting fact in hepatic porphyria is the excretion of most of the porphyrins as complexes of zinc. The urine darkens markedly on standing, because of the conversion of abnormal quantities of porphyrinogens and other heme precursors into porphyrins, porphobilins, and other unidentified pigments. In *acute* porphyria, porphyrins of type I as well as porphobilinogen are excreted in the urine in unusual amounts, as much as 200 mg. per day. The porphyrin excreted in lead poisoning is coproporphyrin III; greatly increased amounts of δ-aminolevulinic acid are also present.

METABOLIC ASPECTS OF THE RED CELL

Studies of the metabolism of the reticulocyte reveal the presence of functioning glycolytic and phosphogluconate oxidative pathways, the tricarboxylic acid cycle, and an intact cytochrome system and electron transfer mechanism. Moreover, the reticulocyte can synthesize globin and protoporphyrin and incorporate iron into the latter for heme formation. In addition, the reticulocyte makes diverse lipids, *viz.*, cholesterol, phosphatides, and triglycerides, and can achieve the *de novo* synthesis of purine nucleotides from small precursors (page 566) as well as from 5-aminoimidazole-4-carboxamide ribonucleotide (page 563).

In contrast to the reticulocyte, the mature erythrocyte lacks mitochondria; hence the cytochromes are absent, the tricarboxylic acid cycle is not evident, synthesis of heme and globin does not occur, and lipid synthesis is insignificant or absent. It is of interest that although the erythrocyte does not make cholesterol, rapid exchange occurs between its sterol and the cholesterol present in the plasma lipoproteins. During maturation from the reticulocyte, the erythrocyte loses the capacity for *de novo* synthesis of purine nucleotides, but can accomplish this from 5-aminoimidazole-4-carboxamide ribonucleotide. In addition, the mature erythrocyte can utilize preformed purines for nucleotide synthesis via the salvage pathway (page 566). The role of these nucleotides in maintenance of erythrocyte integrity will be considered later (page 796).

The energy of the mature erythrocyte is derived primarily from anaerobic glycolysis and glucose oxidation via the phosphogluconate oxidative pathway. Oxygen consumption of erythrocytes is low—Q_{O_2}, 0.05. Much of this oxygen is consumed by the slow oxidation of hemoglobin to methemoglobin (page 193); as much as 0.5 per cent of the total hemoglobin is converted to methemoglobin in 24 hr. However, erythrocytes appear to contain two enzymic systems which catalyze reduction of methemoglobin to hemoglobin; one utilizes DPNH, and the other, TPNH. The former coenzyme derives from glycolysis, the latter from the phosphogluconate oxidative pathway. Reduction of methemoglobin occurs only when glucose or lactate is present, and the rate of reduction in vitro is greater when methylene blue is added. Both DPNH and TPNH are oxidized by *methemoglobin reductase*. The addition of the autoxidizable dye, methylene blue, increases oxygen consumption tenfold by obviating the need for methemoglobin as the terminal oxidase in this system. Scott and Griffith have described a heme protein with a molecular weight of approximately 185,000 which catalyzes reduction of methemoglobin, utilizing DPNH as a cofactor. Activity with TPNH was only about 1.5 per cent that with DPNH. On the other hand, Huennekens and his associates have reported a ratio of 1:5.4 for DPNH/TPNH activity with a different preparation of methemoglobin reductase. Oxygen or methylene blue may act also as terminal electron acceptors. There appears to be no provision for generation of ATP incident to these oxidations. The role of methemoglobin reductase in familial methemoglobinemia will be considered later (page 806).

Glutathione, present only in erythrocytes and absent from the plasma, plays a role in maintaining the normal integrity of the erythrocyte (page 808). The tripeptide is present largely in the reduced form and is synthesized intracellularly, showing a high rate of turnover, as reflected in a half-life of only 4 days. TPNH in the presence of *glutathione reductase* maintains glutathione in the reduced state (page 360).

Life Span of the Erythrocyte. Since mature red cells are constantly destroyed and replaced by new cells, the total red cell mass is in a dynamic state. The daily turnover, calculated from the amount of bile pigment excreted during this period, represents the red cells contained in 50 ml. of whole blood, *i.e.*, 0.85 per cent of the red cell mass. It should be emphasized that the protein within the erythrocytes, in contrast to protein in other cells of the body, does not turn over during the life of the cell.

The life span of the red cell has been measured by various techniques. Thus, from human subjects given N^{15}-labeled glycine, blood samples were withdrawn at intervals, and the globin and heme were analyzed for N^{15}. The data obtained are shown in Fig. 42.3. The isotope concentration of the heme of whole blood rose

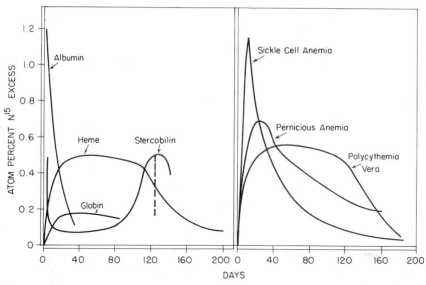

FIG. 42.3. The life span of the human erythrocyte. N[15]-labeled glycine was fed for 2 days in multiple doses; blood and stool samples were collected at intervals and the heme and globin of the red cells and the stercobilin of stool were analyzed for their N[15] content. On the left, data from a normal male. Note the life span of about 120 days, the coincidence of labeled bile-pigment formation with the death of the erythrocytes, and the early period of labeled stercobilin excretion. The behavior of serum albumin is shown to illustrate random decay. On the right, N[15] content of the heme of patients with sickle cell anemia, pernicious anemia, and polycythemia vera. (*Data adapted from D. Shemin and D. Rittenberg, J. Biol. Chem.,* **166,** 627, 1946; *I. M. London, R. West, D. Shemin, and D. Rittenberg, J. Biol. Chem.,* **179,** 463, 1949; **184,** 351, 1950.)

rapidly to a maximum, indicating formation of red cells containing a relatively high concentration of N[15] during the period of isotope administration. In the time which followed cessation of ingestion of isotopic glycine, the N[15] concentration remained relatively constant because of maintenance in the circulation of erythrocytes of high N[15] concentration. These cells were not immediately removed from circulation, but new cells, unlabeled because they had been formed in the absence of labeled precursor, were slowly replacing unlabeled cells which had previously entered the circulation before the period of isotope ingestion. When the isotope concentration of the heme of the whole blood fell relatively rapidly, there must have occurred a relatively sudden replacement of cells of high N[15] concentration by unlabeled cells. This abrupt replacement is evidence of a finite life span for individual red cells. This has been calculated from the data of Fig. 42.3 to be 126 ± 7 days.

During the period in which labeled red cells were disappearing from the circulation, N[15] appeared in the bile pigments, thus providing direct proof of the origin of bile pigments. The early spike in the curve for bile pigment suggests rapid degradation of heme compounds not incorporated in erythrocytes, and also that a fraction of the cells developed in the marrow are prematurely destroyed, with resultant production of bile pigment.

Data showing the change in N^{15} concentration of the serum albumin as a function of time are also presented in Fig. 42.3. The abrupt maximum and steady decline of isotope concentration are evidence of a random replacement of circulating albumin by newly formed albumin molecules of lower isotope concentration. Expressed in another way, this means that the renewal of serum albumin is a process which does not depend upon the age of the albumin molecule.

The life expectancy of the erythrocyte is not the same for all species, being approximately 107 days in the dog and 68 days in the cat and rabbit.

The above data establish that there is no turnover of the heme of the erythrocyte; the life span of hemoglobin, and of erythrocyte catalase as well, is the average life span of the erythrocyte itself. The turnover of heart muscle myoglobin and of cytochrome c of skeletal muscle is also very low. In contrast, the life span of liver cytochrome c of the rat has been found to be only about 8 days.

Storage of Erythrocytes. Erythrocytes may be stored, for use in transfusions, at low temperature in a medium containing glucose and citrate. With increasing time in storage, however, the viability of the cells in a recipient markedly diminishes, and after 30 to 45 days, stored blood is no longer useful for transfusion. Analysis of various cell components revealed that this "storage lesion" develops when the cellular ATP has disappeared. On warming the cells, glycolysis cannot be initiated for lack of ATP required in the hexokinase reaction, and the cells die because of lack of energy.

The useful storage time of younger cells in any blood sample may be prolonged significantly by addition of adenosine. This nucleoside is deaminated, under the influence of adenosine deaminase, to inosine, which then undergoes phosphorolysis to ribose 1-phosphate and hypoxanthine. Ribose 1-phosphate is converted to ribose 5-phosphate by phosphoribomutase, and this in turn yields triose phosphate by the nonoxidative steps of the phosphogluconate oxidative pathway (Chap. 20). The triose phosphate is metabolized to lactate, yielding ATP in the usual manner. Once some ATP has been thus generated, anaerobic glycolysis may be reinstituted. Inosine may be used in place of adenosine for this purpose.

Fate of Erythrocytes—Bile Pigment Formation. The factors contributing to destruction of the circulating erythrocyte are not clear. However, about 120 to 130 days after emerging from the marrow, red cells are phagocytized by macrophages of the reticuloendothelial system, mainly in the spleen, liver, and bone marrow. Hemoglobin appears to undergo scission of the α-methene bridge to give a biliverdin-iron protein complex known as verdohemoglobin (choleglobin) because of its green color. Iron is removed, globin is liberated, and the free biliverdin is reduced at the γ-methene bridge to yield bilirubin. Conversion of the heme of hemoglobin to bilirubin in the body is nearly quantitative and complete in 5 days. Hemoglobin released from erythrocytes is not reutilized as such. The liberated iron combines with plasma transferrin (page 640) and is transported to storage depots or to the bone marrow, where it is used in the synthesis of new hemoglobin. The globin is degraded and returned to the body pool of amino acids. These changes may be summarized as follows:

Hemoglobin $\longrightarrow$ verdohemoglobin $\longrightarrow$ biliverdin $+$ iron $+$ globin

↑	↓	↓	↓
rupture of	bilirubin	to plasma	to amino
α-methene	↓	↓	acid
bridge	to liver	to iron	pool
		stores	

In contrast to porphyrins, which contain four pyrrole rings linked by four carbon atoms in a closed-ring system, bile pigments lack one of these carbon atoms and can be pictured as an open-ring system or as a tetrapyrrole chain. The system of numbering the pyrrole rings and methene bridges in the bile pigments is derived from that used for porphyrins (Chap. 11). In the most common biological example shown below, the α-carbon has been eliminated.

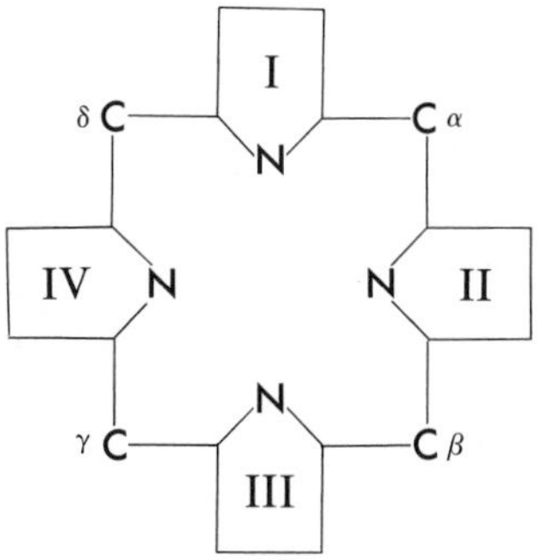

Porphyrin skeleton 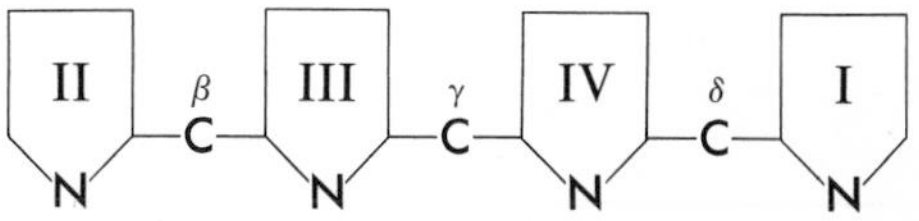   Bile pigment skeleton

Although the tetrapyrrole chain is generally used for convenience in representation, the cyclic arrangement of the pyrrole nuclei, shown at the left, is probably a more correct representation of the actual structures of the bile pigments.

Bilirubin is transported from extrahepatic reticuloendothelial cells to the liver as a protein complex, either as bilirubin-globulin or as bilirubin-albumin. On electrophoretic analysis of human serum, Bennhold observed that bilirubin migrates with albumin, while Martin has found that bilirubin combines not only with albumin but also with α-globulins. In the liver the protein is separated, and the bilirubin is converted into the corresponding diglucuronide by reaction with uridine diphosphoglucuronate (Chap. 21).

Bilirubin $+$ 2 UDP-glucuronate $\longrightarrow$ bilirubin diglucuronide $+$ 2 UDP

The compound formed between bilirubin and glucuronic acid is not a glycoside (glucosiduronide), but rather an ester between each of two propionic side chains in bilirubin and the hydroxyl group at C-1 of glucuronic acid (page 410). The soluble diglucuronide passes into the bile canaliculi and thence into the bile.

In the intestine, probably through the activity of the bacterial flora, bilirubin is further reduced to mesobilirubinogen. Formation of mesobilirubinogen involves reduction of both vinyl groups to ethyl groups, and the methene bridges are also reduced. Since resonance between the porphyrin rings is no longer possible, mesobilirubinogen is colorless.

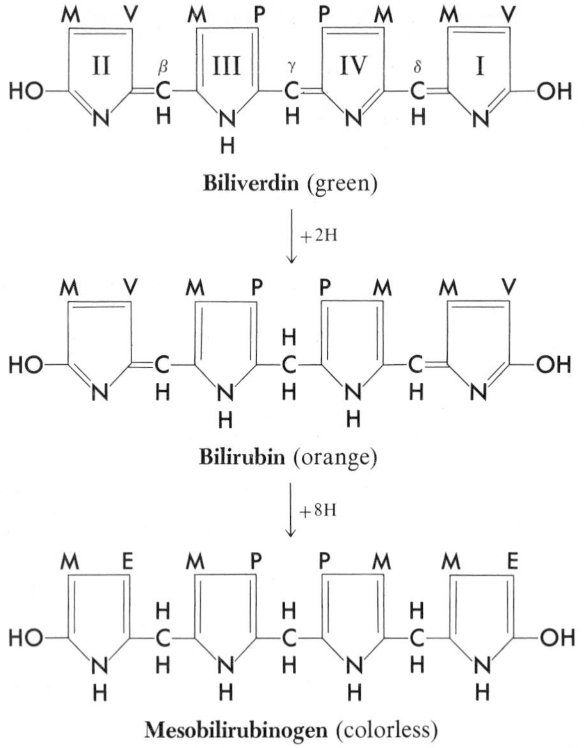

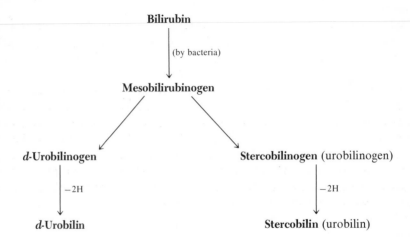

Biliverdin (green)

$\downarrow +2H$

Bilirubin (orange)

$\downarrow +8H$

Mesobilirubinogen (colorless)

It should be noted that extensive isomerism is possible in these bile pigment derivatives. However, the naturally occurring pigments appear to be largely derivatives of protoporphyrin IX, the α-methene bridge of which is preferentially ruptured.

Largely through the work of Watson and his coworkers, it is known that mesobilirubinogen undergoes further reaction. The suggested scheme may be indicated as follows.

Bilirubin

$\downarrow$ (by bacteria)

Mesobilirubinogen

d-**Urobilinogen**   **Stercobilinogen** (urobilinogen)

$\downarrow -2H$ $\downarrow -2H$

d-**Urobilin**   **Stercobilin** (urobilin)

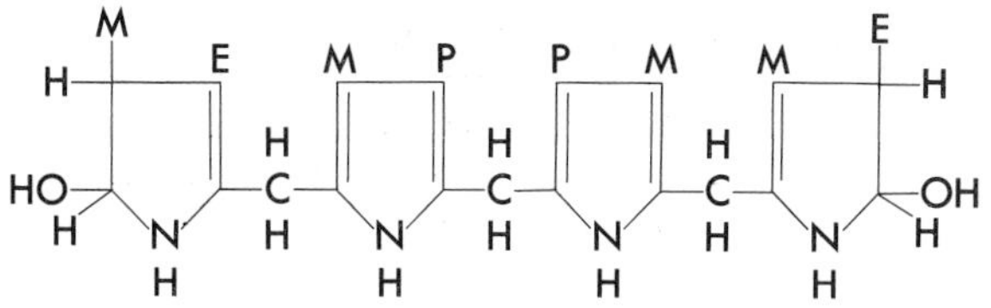

Stercobilinogen (urobilinogen)

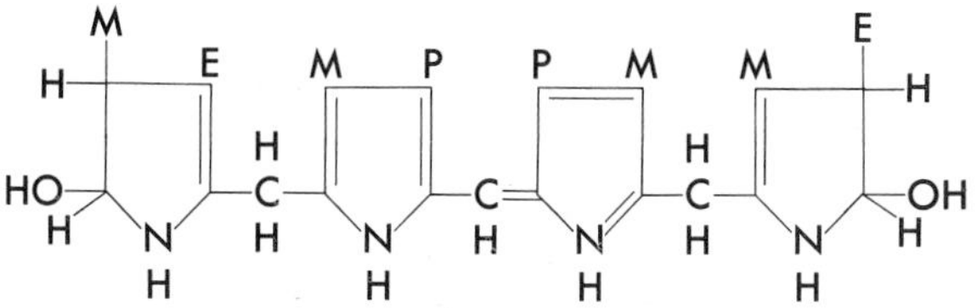

Stercobilin or urobilin (levorotatory)

d-Urobilin (dextrorotatory) has been isolated after incubation of mesobilirubinogen with bile and from urine shortly after withdrawal of antibiotic therapy; it is a dehydro derivative of *l*-urobilin in which both hydroxyl groups are oxidized to ketone groups. Stercobilin of the feces, identical with urobilin found in urine, is strongly levorotatory.

Although stercobilinogen is formed in the intestinal tract by reduction of mesobilirubinogen and is subsequently oxidized to stercobilin, some stercobilinogen is reabsorbed from the intestine, removed from the blood plasma by the liver, and reexcreted in the bile. To a small extent in the normal individual and to a greater degree in pathological conditions, some stercobilinogen is not removed by the liver and is excreted by the kidney; hence the name *urobilinogen,* which was used before its identity with stercobilinogen was recognized. When urine is exposed to light and air, urobilinogen is oxidized to urobilin. Urobilin (stercobilin) is primarily responsible for the brown color of feces. Approximately 1 to 2 mg. of bile pigment is excreted in the urine and as much as 250 mg. in the feces of a normal adult each day.

The degradation of the erythrocyte and formation of the bile pigments are summarized in Fig. 42.4.

Van den Bergh Reaction. Bilirubin can be coupled with diazonium salts, *e.g.,* diazotized sulfanilic acid, to yield azo dyes. This reaction has been developed for the estimation of bilirubin in serum and is not given by mesobilirubinogen, by other reduced compounds of this type, nor by biliverdin.

Bilirubin diglucuronide present in serum yields immediate color upon addition of diazotized sulfanilic acid to give the "direct" van den Bergh reaction. Bilirubin bound to serum proteins and unconjugated with glucuronic acid does not react with the reagent unless brought into solution by addition of alcohol; this is the "indirect" van den Bergh reaction. The diglucuronide is easily dissociable from the serum proteins to which it is loosely bound, dialyzes readily, and, in consequence, appears in the urine whenever it is present in significant amounts in plasma. Bilirubin itself is strongly bound to protein, cannot be removed by dialysis, and, hence, does not appear in urine.

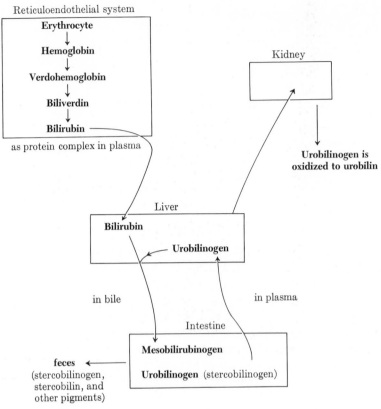

Reticuloendothelial system

Erythrocyte
↓
Hemoglobin
↓
Verdohemoglobin
↓
Biliverdin
↓
Bilirubin

as protein complex in plasma

Kidney

**Urobilinogen is
oxidized to urobilin**

Liver

Bilirubin

Urobilinogen

in bile   in plasma

Intestine

Mesobilirubinogen

feces ←
(stercobilinogen,
stercobilin, and
other pigments)

Urobilinogen (stercobilinogen)

Fɪɢ. 42.4. Metabolism of the bile pigments.

Jaundice. Jaundice is the accumulation of bile pigment in the plasma in amounts sufficient to impart a yellowish tint to the skin and conjunctiva. Three types of jaundice may be recognized. *Hemolytic jaundice* results from unusual destruction of red cells leading to bile pigment formation at a rate exceeding the capacity of the liver to remove the pigment from the circulation. The pigment which accumulates is bilirubin bound to serum proteins, so that the indirect van den Bergh reaction reveals the true concentration of bilirubin in hemolytic jaundice. Since bilirubin glucuronide excretion by the liver is maximal, excretion of stercobilinogen and urobilinogen is markedly elevated. In hepatic disease such as *infectious hepatitis* or *cirrhosis,* jaundice results from impaired capacity of the liver to conjugate bilirubin and secrete the diglucuronide into the bile. The indirect van den Bergh reaction reveals a high pigment concentration in these diseases. Stools may be light in color, and little urobilinogen is found in the urine. Occasionally, unusually large quantities of urobilinogen are observed in the urine of patients with hepatitis and little or no jaundice. This results from an impaired ability of the liver to reexcrete urobilinogen returning via the "enterohepatic circulation." The third type of jaundice arises from *obstruction of the biliary passages,* resulting in failure of bile to reach the lumen of the bowel. In the early stages of this disease, while liver function remains normal, the liver continues to secrete bilirubin, but the bile so formed is regurgitated into the circulation; thus large quantities of bilirubin diglucuronide appear in plasma, as demonstrated by the direct van den Bergh reaction. Prolonged biliary obstruction results in liver damage so that values obtained by the indirect as well as the direct assays may be high. The stools may be clay-colored, and little or no urobilinogen can be detected in the urine, although bilirubin is excreted in the urine in large amounts.

The significance of bilirubin conjugation is particularly apparent in *Gilbert's disease,* a rare congenital abnormality of the liver in which the enzyme, *uridine diphosphate glucuronate transferase,* is lacking, resulting in an intense jaundice. Apparently the capacity to conjugate bilirubin is also severely limited in the neo-natal liver, and the accumulation of bilirubin (indirect pigment) in the blood of the newborn may greatly exceed that seen in adult jaundice. This accumulation frequently has deleterious consequences for the brain, where staining of the basal ganglia may occur with permanent damage (*kernicterus*). The capacity of the liver to conjugate bilirubin increases rapidly during the first few days of life.

Bile Pigments in Nature. Pigments closely related chemically to the bile pigments have also been found in some invertebrates which do not possess hemoglobin. Most interesting are the pigments in the conjugated chromoproteins, phycoerythrin and phycocyanin, which function in the red and blue-green algae as light-absorbing substances together with the chlorophylls. Phycoerythrin and phycocyanin, which crystallize readily, are metal-free pigments that are at a stage of reduction intermediate between bilirubin and mesobilirubinogen. The side chains in the β positions of the pyrrole rings are identical with those in mesobilirubinogen, indicating the close relationship of the porphyrins, bile pigments, and related pigments in nature.

IRON METABOLISM

Dietary Requirements. The newborn infant is provided with considerably more hemoglobin than is required; both the concentration of hemoglobin in the erythro-cyte and the number of red cells per unit volume are appreciably greater than in later life. This may represent a response to the relatively low oxygen tension of uterine life, as in the case of the polycythemia of individuals living at high altitudes. For some weeks after birth, red cell destruction exceeds erythropoiesis, and jaundice may be observed. However, during this period, virtually no iron appears in the excreta. Retention of iron suffices to meet the iron requirements of the infant for some months thereafter, a fortunate circumstance since milk is virtually iron-free. Subsequent to this period, the iron requirement of the child and adult reflects the needs for growth and the rate of iron loss to the environment.

As noted previously, the daily hemoglobin turnover in the adult is equivalent to approximately 50 ml. of whole blood or 25 mg. of iron. This is far greater than the daily increment in total body hemoglobin even during the period of maximal growth. This turnover of red cells does not lead to an extra requirement for iron since the iron released within reticuloendothelial cells from phagocytized obsolescent erythrocytes is almost entirely available for reutilization. During growth, the iron requirement for formation of hemoglobin, cytochromes, catalase, and other chromoproteins is of major significance. Puberty is associated with an extraordinary increase in total body hemoglobin. The maximum iron requirement of the male thus occurs at the age of fifteen or sixteen. In the adult male, the daily iron requirement is met by replacement of relatively small losses. Although only negligible amounts of iron appear in the urine and there is no intestinal secretion of iron, there is a small daily loss through the bile.

From the menarche, the need of the female for iron is 30 to 90 per cent greater than that of the male, except for the fifteenth and sixteenth years of male life. Until the menopause, 50 per cent or more of the female's iron requirement is used in the replacement of hemoglobin lost in the menses. The average menstrual loss is about 35 ml. of blood. The replacement of this amount of blood alone requires 0.6 mg. of iron per day, in contrast to the *total* physiological iron requirement of the male adult of 0.9 mg. per day. In itself, the loss would be unimportant were it not for the fact that the average unsupplemented diet contains barely enough iron to meet the requirements. This mean catamenial requirement applies to about 60 per cent of women. In the 15 per cent with larger menstrual losses, the replacement need for iron may be almost doubled. During gestation, the requirement for iron is about 60 per cent greater than the amount lost in the menses during a similar period. An iron intake adequate to pregestational life may not be adequate to meet the demands of pregnancy. Transfer of iron to the fetus, like transfer of calcium, occurs chiefly in the last trimester of pregnancy, and it is impossible to accumulate iron stores during the earlier months of pregnancy. It is apparent therefore that the mother's food must provide unusual quantities of both iron and calcium during the last 3 months of pregnancy. This rarely obtains and may lead to a hypochromic anemia. A moderate normocytic anemia, with hemoglobin values of 11 to 12 g. per 100 ml., is "physiological" during pregnancy and due to hemodilution. Rather surprisingly, it appears that in circumstances of iron deficiency the tissue concentration of cytochromes may diminish before the blood level of hemoglobin. In summary, in adult life the iron requirement is conditioned entirely by the demand for replacement of losses, be they through the bile, placenta, uterus, or overt hemorrhage.

Although it is relatively simple to calculate the *physiological* iron requirement in terms of growth and losses, calculation of the *nutritional* iron requirement is not feasible since ingested iron is not quantitatively absorbed from the intestine. Entry of dietary iron into the body is conditioned by two factors: the chemical state of the ingested iron and the iron metabolism of the intestinal mucosa. Much of the iron ingested in natural foodstuffs is "organic iron," present in combinations such as heme, and is unavailable for absorption. Like calcium, iron forms numerous insoluble salts. The extent to which these are formed within the intestine will influence iron absorption. Thus, anemia due to iron deficiency readily results from incorporating large amounts of inorganic phosphate in the diet. The impaired iron absorption of persons with gastric achlorhydria may be related to the poor solubility of iron phosphate at the relatively alkaline pH of duodenal contents.

Many unexplained and rather striking differences in the "availability" of food iron exist. For example, iron from white flour appears to be more readily utilized than that from whole-wheat flour, while that from beef appears to be still more readily available, despite the fact that much of beef iron exists as heme compounds.

For unexplained reasons, ferrous iron is more readily absorbed from the human intestine than is the ferric form. The presence of reducing agents, such as ascorbic acid, in the diet increases the availability of iron. In view of these complications, it is impossible to calculate the desired iron intake; dietary recommendations have been based on studies of iron balance and hemoglobin formation. From these it appears that the desirable dietary level of iron should be five to ten times the actual physiological requirements. Allowances of 12 mg. of iron per day for adults and 6 to 15 mg. daily for children of various age groups are liberal.

Intestinal Absorption of Iron. Studies with radioactive Fe^{59} early demonstrated that individuals with iron-deficiency anemia absorb iron from the intestine more efficiently than do normal persons. However, when normal animals were made anemic by phlebotomy, some time elapsed before an increased efficiency of iron absorption was detected. It was postulated that normally there is a "mucosal block" to the absorption of iron, unrelated to the existence of anemia per se, and that a gastrointestinal mechanism exists which regulates passage of iron from the intestinal lumen to plasma. Granick established the relation of *ferritin* to this

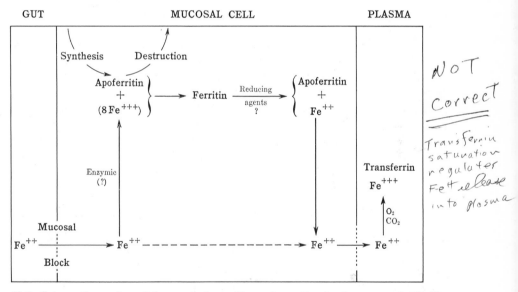

FIG. 42.5. Schematic version of the regulation of iron absorption by the mucosal cell. The amount of ferrous iron moving into the cell is regulated by the mucosal block, which is related to the level of ferrous iron in the cell and, indirectly, to the ferritin concentration. The amount of iron leaving the cell may depend upon the relative redox level of the cell, which in turn may be a function of the P_{O_2} of the blood. (*Modified from S. Granick, Physiol. Revs.*, **31**, 497, 1951.)

mucosal mechanism in the guinea pig. Ferritin is a protein containing 23 per cent of iron by weight, and isolated initially from spleen. It is composed of a protein, *apoferritin,* of molecular weight 450,000 and a ferric hydroxide-phosphate of approximate composition $[(FeOOH)_8(FeO—OPO_3H_2)]$. The isoelectric points and electrophoretic mobilities of ferritin and apoferritin are identical.

The intestinal mucosa of fasting guinea pigs contains only minute amounts of apoferritin. However, within 4 to 5 hr. after iron administration, there occurs a twenty- to fiftyfold increase in the amount of ferritin, implying rapid synthesis of apoferritin by the mucosal cells. Ferrous iron, entering the mucosal epithelial cell, is rapidly oxidized to ferric hydroxide, which combines with apoferritin. Within the mucosal cell, because of unknown circumstances which favor reduction of ferric to ferrous iron, breakdown of ferritin occurs, allowing absorption of additional iron from the intestine. It has been suggested that iron absorption is limited by the binding capacity of the apoferritin for iron. Figure 42.5 summarizes the ferritin mechanism of iron absorption.

Iron Storage. Ferritin is of importance in yet another connection. The liver of the adult male contains approximately 700 mg. of iron, present almost entirely as ferritin. After parenteral administration of Fe^{59}, much of the isotope is found in the liver as ferritin. All parenterally administered iron, in excess of the ferritin

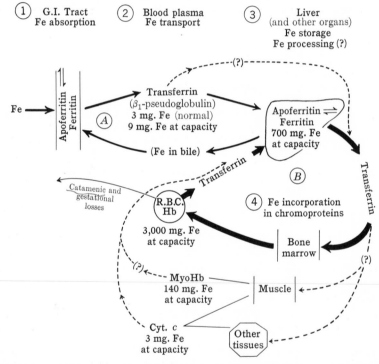

Fig. 42.6. The metabolism of iron. The cyclic movement of iron is considered in two stages, Ⓐ the absorption, transport, storage, and excretion cycle, and Ⓑ the storage, transport, and utilization cycle. Note the central role of the liver in both cycles. (*After D. L. Drabkin, Physiol. Revs., 31, 345, 1951.*)

storage mechanism, accumulates in the liver as *hemosiderin,* which is a normal constituent of most tissues and represents colloidal iron in the form of granules much larger than ferritin molecules. Hemosiderin granules contain up to 37 per cent of their dry weight as iron, are insoluble in water, and differ from ferritin in electrophoretic mobility. Hemosiderin granules are believed to be large aggregates of ferritin molecules with a higher content of iron. Since there is no excretory pathway for excess iron, continued administration of iron leads to hemosiderin accumulation in the liver in quantities sufficient to result in ultimate destruction of that organ. This has been observed in patients with aplastic or hemolytic anemia who have received multiple transfusions over several years.

In the absence of an excretory pathway for excess iron, the adjustment of iron absorption to need is essential to the organism. No other nutrient is known to be regulated in this manner.

Iron Transport. One final component of the iron metabolizing system remains to be considered. This is a protein of plasma, *transferrin* (page 640), which facilitates iron transport and is present in a concentration of approximately 0.4 g. per 100 ml. blood (Table 32.5, page 633). Transferrin binds two iron atoms per mole in the ferric form; binding occurs only in the presence of CO_2. At the normal level of plasma iron, 100 μg per 100 ml., transferrin is 30 per cent saturated. While other plasma proteins are also capable of binding iron, transferrin exhibits a much greater affinity for iron than do the other proteins. The failure of the kidney to excrete iron may result from the fact that all the plasma iron is bound to the transferrin, which is not filtrable. The homeostatic mechanisms involved in iron metabolism are summarized in Fig. 42.6.

ASPECTS OF ABNORMAL ERYTHROCYTE STRUCTURE AND FUNCTION

Aberrations in red cell structure and function represent a large area of knowledge beyond the scope of this book. However, some aspects of this topic deserve consideration because either their biochemical basis is known, or certain established biochemical alterations in erythrocytes may, in future, be shown to have significance for understanding of a particular structural or functional abnormality of the red cell.

Alterations in erythrocyte structure and function may be considered from the standpoint of the following variations from normal: (1) hemoglobin structure; (2) normal numbers of erythrocytes but with hemoglobin unavailable for transport of oxygen; (3) excessive or (4) subnormal amounts of hemoglobin accompanied by corresponding alterations in numbers of erythrocytes.

Variations in Hemoglobin Structure. In a general way, the hemoglobins exhibit three types of heterogeneity. It has already been mentioned (page 194) that the globins are species-specific and show rather extensive changes in amino acid composition. Within a species there is also heterogeneity based upon the normal ability to form β, γ, and δ chains, each of which may combine with α chains so that $\alpha_2\beta_2$, $\alpha_2\gamma_2$, and $\alpha_2\delta_2$ are normal to each individual. A few rare instances have been reported in which adult blood contains Hb H = $\beta_4{}^A$. In fetal life and early infancy the blood of such individuals contains $Hb_{Barts} = \gamma_4{}^F$. Since these components constitute only about 15 per cent of the total hemoglobin while the remainder is Hb F in fetal life and Hb A thereafter, it is apparent that these individuals possess the genetic capacity to make α chains, but do not make sufficient α chains to meet their total requirements. It is noteworthy, therefore, that in the absence of α chains, a structure is formed which is a tetramer of either β or γ chains. Although α_4 has been prepared synthetically, it has not yet been found in human blood.

The third form of hemoglobin heterogeneity occurs within individuals as a consequence of a genetic change (mutation) which has led to an amino acid replacement in either the α or β chains (Chap. 31). This was first recognized in the case of the hemoglobin of individuals with *sickle cell anemia*. This disorder is characterized by the fact that the erythrocytes of affected individuals change from their normal shape (biconcave disk) to a sickle or crescent shape when the oxyhemoglobin of the cell is reduced to hemoglobin as a result of exposure to reduced oxygen tension. Sickling occurs in the capillaries as the hemoglobin is reduced, and about 85 per cent of the hemoglobin crystallizes from solution within the erythrocyte, thereby distorting the cell. The sickled cell exhibits markedly increased fragility and tends to hemolyze in the small diameter of the capillary, leading to reduced numbers of erythrocytes; hence the term, sickle cell anemia.

Pauling and Itano demonstrated that erythrocytes which undergo sickling contain a hemoglobin distinguishable from Hb A in that the deoxygenated form migrates differently in an electrical field. The magnitude of this altered migration rate was that expected if there were two fewer negative charges per hemoglobin molecule. Ingram then showed that in sickle cell hemoglobin, Hb S, a valine residue replaces the glutamic acid residue at position 6 of the β chains (Fig. 11.1, page 195).

Many other hemoglobins with amino acid replacements have since been detected. Because of their significance to the understanding of genetic mechanisms, these amino acid replacements are summarized elsewhere (Table 31.1, page 611). It should be noted that they were detected by paper electrophoresis. Hence, replacement of a neutral, basic, or acidic residue by another of the same type would not be evident. Particularly noteworthy are Hb M, in which a glutamic acid residue replaces the valine residue at position 67, and Hb M_S in which a tyrosine residue replaces the histidine residue at position 63; both replacements occur in the β chain. These changes in the immediate environment of the heme iron result in its ready oxidation by O_2 to yield methemoglobin; hence the designation Hb M. In individuals with Hb M, no more than 30 per cent of the total hemoglobin is present as Hb M. Presumably, an individual with all his hemoglobin as Hb M could not transport O_2 in his blood at a rate sufficient to support normal physiological functions.

Alterations in Functioning of Hemoglobin. In addition to the presence of methemoglobin in individuals with Hb M, *methemoglobinemia* may result in normal persons exposed to agents which cause oxidation of the ferrous iron of hemoglobin to the ferric state. These agents include amyl nitrite, aniline, nitrobenzene, ferricyanide, etc., and methemoglobinemia has been observed clinically after administration of sulfonamides, acetanilid, phenacetin, and salicylates. A third type of methemoglobinemia, *familial methemoglobinemia* (Table 31.7, page 623), is a rare hereditary deficiency of *methemoglobin reductase* (page 794) in the erythrocytes of afflicted individuals. In these circumstances, as much as 25 to 40 per cent of the total hemoglobin may be present as methemoglobin, with accompanying evidence of cyanosis.

Carbon Monoxide Poisoning. In carbon monoxide poisoning, carbon monoxide displaces oxygen from oxyhemoglobin. The affinity of hemoglobin for carbon monoxide is more than 200 times as great as its affinity for oxygen. In the presence of CO the oxygen dissociation curve of oxyhemoglobin is "shifted to the left" (page 669), suggesting that the number of molecules of oxygen attached to hemoglobin is less than four (page 660), there being a partial replacement of O_2 by CO. These molecules of hemoglobin to which CO as well as O_2 is bound are more tenacious of O_2 than is the normal hemoglobin containing four molecules of oxygen, *i.e.*, $Hb(O_2)_4$. Consequently, the effects of carbon monoxide poisoning are more severe than would be expected on the basis of reaction of only a portion of the hemoglobin molecules with CO. Therapy in CO poisoning consists in removal of the affected individual to an atmosphere free of carbon monoxide and administration of a mixture rich in oxygen and containing 5 per cent CO_2. The oxygen "washes out" the carbon monoxide, and the CO_2 stimulates respiration.

Poisoning by cyanide or by sulfide results from formation of complexes between these anions and the ferric iron of cytochrome oxidase. Methemoglobin but not hemoglobin forms similar complexes. Since the body contains far more hemoglobin than cytochrome, therapy for cyanide-poisoned individuals consists in accelerating methemoglobin formation, *e.g.*, by amyl nitrite administration. The resulting cyanmethemoglobin is itself nontoxic and can be slowly metabolized. The sulfmethemoglobin resulting from the combination of sulfide with the ferric iron of methemoglobin cannot be further metabolized and, once formed, remains until the cell is phagocytized.

Polycythemia. Polycythemia is the term used to describe the presence of unusually large numbers of erythrocytes in the circulation. The mechanism by which low oxygen tension stimulates erythropoiesis is unknown; its effects are seen as an adaption to high altitudes and in the extremely high red cell content of children with congenital abnormalities of the pulmonary circulation ("blue babies"). This does not occur as a reaction of the erythropoietic tissue to hypoxia. Plasma from animals rendered anemic by various means induces polycythemia in normal recipient animals. This effect has been ascribed to the presence, in such plasma, of an agent called *erythropoietin,* thought to arise in the kidney. Purified preparations of erythropoietin have been obtained from sheep and rabbit plasma, and from urine. The purified preparation from sheep plasma had the properties of a mucoprotein, with approximately 30 per cent of carbohydrate, of which about 17 per cent was present as hexosamine and 15 per cent as sialic acid.

Administration of cobalt salts also results in polycythemia; the mechanism of this effect is unknown.

Anemia. Anemia due to a decrease in the number of erythrocytes has been mentioned previously in consideration of Hb S (see above). The presence of normal numbers of erythrocytes with lower than normal concentration of hemoglobin may also be the basis of anemia. This subject is beyond the scope of this textbook; brief reference will be made here, as well as in Part Seven, to some biochemical aspects of certain of the anemias.

Anemia is more accurately described by measurements of the *total circulating red cell* mass than by a statement of the hemoglobin or red cell concentration of a blood sample since the total mass is independent of fluctuations in plasma volume. Accurate estimation of the red cell mass is possible by isotope dilution analysis. A sample of blood is incubated with glucose and P^{32} as inorganic phosphate, or with radioactive Cr^{51} as inorganic chromate, which is adsorbed on the surface of the red cells. The labeled blood is then reinjected, a second sample of blood is withdrawn after a suitable time, and the red cell mass is calculated from the extent of dilution of the administered radioactivity.

Anemias of Nutritional Origin. A group of anemias of nutritional origin are those characterized by the presence of unusually large cells in the peripheral blood (mean corpuscular volume, 95 to 160 μ^3; normal, about 87 μ^3). Since their hemoglobin concentration is normal, or greater than normal, the mean corpuscular hemoglobin content is also elevated (0.03 to 0.05 mμg; normal, about 0.03 mμg). Examples of these anemias are those due to deficiency in vitamin B_{12} (cyanocobalamine) or folic acid (Chap. 55).

Pernicious (Addison's) Anemia. The pathogenesis of pernicious anemia has long been associated with impaired gastric function. The gastric juice of persons with pernicious anemia contains no "free" HCl and little or no pepsin. However, it is not the lack of pepsin or HCl which underlies the hemopoietic failure but rather a defect in production by the gastric mucosa of one or more mucoproteins (*intrinsic factor*), essential for the normal absorption of dietary vitamin B_{12} (*extrinsic factor*) from the intestinal tract. Purified preparations of intrinsic factor showed a molecular weight of approximately 53,000 and contained one mole of vitamin B_{12} per molecule of complex. About 7 per cent of reducing sugars were present, and the biological activity was rapidly destroyed by incubation with neuraminidase, indicating the presence of a sialic acid.

Lack of virtually any essential nutrient in the diet will contribute to anemia. Aspects of nutritional anemias will be considered in Part Seven of this textbook.

Anemias Due to Accelerated Erythrocyte Destruction. Hemolytic anemias may occur in malaria, blackwater fever, or other infections. Hemolysis also occurs following mismatched blood transfusion and in *erythroblastosis fetalis* (hemolytic disease of the newborn). Unusual anemia of *paroxysmal hemoglobinuria* is characterized by hemolysis and hemoglobinuria in certain individuals after exposure to cold. This phenomenon appears to be due to the presence of so-called "cold" hemolysins in the blood. The blood of persons with *familial* or *congenital hemolytic jaundice* is characterized by the presence of spherical erythrocytes of less than normal diameter (spherocytes), with a markedly increased fragility to hypotonic solutions. The reasons for this appearance of the red cell are not known. The tendency to spherocyte formation is transmitted as a mendelian dominant characteristic.

Particular interest attaches to glucose 6-phosphate dehydrogenase of erythrocytes because of a genetically transmitted disorder termed "primaquine sensitivity." In this disturbance, erythrocytes hemolyze in the presence of a wide variety of agents, including the antimalarial drug primaquine. Hemolysis seems to relate to oversensitivity to peroxides as a consequence of low concentration of reduced glutathione. In normal erythrocytes glutathione is maintained in the reduced state by glutathione reductase (page 360), which utilizes TPNH as a reductant. Primaquine-sensitive erythrocytes appear to contain an inactive form of glucose 6-phosphate dehydrogenase, which, it is claimed, can be activated by incubation with the insoluble stroma of normal erythrocytes but not by stroma from primaquine-sensitive cells. This suggests that the genetic defect may lie in the activating system, whatever its nature, rather than in the structure of the enzyme.

Thalassemia is a heritable disorder characterized by increased hemolysis based on an intracorpuscular defect. Unusually large amounts of Hb $F^{\alpha_2\gamma_2}$ and Hb $A_2^{\alpha_2\delta_2}$ have been found in some cases; these are *normal* hemoglobins appearing in *abnormal quantities.* No abnormal hemoglobin appears to be present.

In the rare disorder called *acanthocytosis* (page 639), erythrocytes are excessively susceptible to hemolysis and are short-lived; hemolytic anemia is manifest.

ASPECTS OF LEUKOCYTE COMPOSITION AND METABOLISM

The development of improved methods for separation from the blood of the two major classes of circulating leukocytes, the polymorphonuclear leukocytes and the lymphocytes, has provided adequate numbers of these cells for metabolic studies. In addition, lymphocytes are readily available either by lymphatic cannulation or by preparing cells from minced tissue which is predominately lymphocytic in cellular structure, *e.g.*, thymic tissue. Also, large numbers of polymorphonuclear leukocytes can be obtained for metabolic studies from the peritoneal cavity of suitable animals, *e.g.*, rabbits, by withdrawing peritoneal contents which have accumulated subsequent to intraperitoneal injection of an irritant such as mineral oil.

The inorganic ion content of leukocytes is unusual only in that there is present a high concentration of zinc, about twenty-five times that in erythrocytes. Unlike the erythrocytes, leukocytes possess organized systems of both respiratory and glycolytic enzymes. It is of interest that leukocytes of patients with von Gierke's disease (page 420) have a glycogen content five- or sixfold greater than normal.

The phagocytic forms of leukocytes are rich in a variety of hydrolytic enzymes, including proteinases, which are localized in the lysosomes (page 270) of these cells. In vitro studies of Karnovsky and his associates and of Hirsch and Cohn have revealed metabolic and morphological alterations which occur during particle ingestion by polymorphonuclear leukocytes. Phagocytosis is characterized by active proteolysis, although little is known of the protein metabolism of leukocytes or of the ultimate fate of the phagocytized protein. Stimulation of glycolysis is evident, and there is an increased turnover of triose phosphates, phosphatidic acid, and inositol-containing phosphatide. It is suggested that stimulated turnover of specific phosphatides at the time of transfer of particles into phagocytizing cells could involve participation of acidic phosphatides in membrane functions. In addition to the above alterations, during phagocytosis a DPNH oxidase present in the granule fraction is activated.

Particular attention has centered around the role of the lymphocytes in immune phenomena. Normal lymphocytes contain a protein identical with plasma γ-globulin, and in the immunized animal antibody can be demonstrated in lymphocytes obtained from lymphoid structures. Passive immunity can be transferred to a nonimmune recipient host by transplantation of lymphocytes from a previously immunized animal. Also, heterologous tissue transplantation is more readily effected to a host previously treated with large doses of adrenal cortical steroids or exposed to x-rays, both of which agents cause involution of lymphoid structures. Marked reduction in the numbers of circulating lymphocytes occurs shortly after administration of certain of the adrenal cortical steroids (Chap. 49). This is due in part to the involution of lymphoid tissue produced by these hormones. The role of lymphoid cells in protein synthesis and, specifically, in antibody formation has been clearly established. Of considerable interest and importance is the evidence that the thymus is the site of development of the first immunologically competent cells in the newborn.

In vitro studies with cell suspensions of lymphocytes have revealed a glycolytic pathway and a significant and continuing endogenous respiration in the absence of exogenous substrate, with an R.Q. indicative of fatty acid oxidation. Lymphocytes and separated lymphocyte nuclei in vitro are capable of incorporating labeled precursors into the total proteins and nucleic acids of these structures. Considerable attention has centered around nucleic acid metabolism of leukocytes in view of their prominent nuclei and rapid rate of cellular regeneration, both in the normal and in circumstances of exaggerated leukopoiesis. These processes exhibit a high requirement for folic acid, related to the role of this vitamin in purine biosynthesis (page 562). *Dihydrofolate reductase* has been reported to be present in high amounts in leukocytes of acute leukemic and chronic myelogenous leukemic patients, but to be in very low concentration or absent in normal cells or those from individuals with chronic lymphatic leukemia. This enzyme is specifically inhibited by folic acid antagonists, *e.g.*, being affected by these substances in concentrations of $10^{-8}M$.

REFERENCES

Books

Behrendt, H., "Chemistry of Erythrocytes," Charles C Thomas, Publisher, Springfield, Ill., 1957.

Gray, C. H., "Bile Pigments in Health and Disease," Charles C Thomas, Publisher, Springfield, Ill., 1963.

Harris, J. W., "The Red Cell: Production, Metabolism, Destruction: Normal and Abnormal," Harvard University Press, Cambridge, Mass., 1963.

Ingram, V. M., "Hemoglobin and Its Abnormalities," Charles C Thomas, Publisher, Springfield, Ill., 1961.

National Research Council, Conference on Hemoglobin, *National Academy of Sciences Publication* 557, Washington, 1958.

Wolstenholme, G. E. W., and O'Connor, M., "Haemopoiesis: Cell Production and Its Regulation," J. & A. Churchill, Ltd., London, 1960.

Review Articles

Berlin, N. I., Waldmann, T. A., and Weisman, S. M., Life Span of Red Blood Cells, *Physiol. Revs.,* **39**, 577–616, 1959.

Gordon, A., Hemopoietin, *Physiol. Revs.,* **39**, 1–40, 1959.

Granick, S., Structure and Physiological Functions of Ferritin, *Physiol. Revs.,* **31**, 489–511, 1951.

Granick, S., Porphyrin Biosynthesis, Porphyria Diseases, and Induced Enzyme Synthesis in Chemical Porphyria, *Trans. N.Y. Acad. Sci.,* **25**, 53–65, 1962.

Granick, S., and Mauzerall, D., The Metabolism of Heme and Chlorophyll, in D. M. Greenberg, ed., "Metabolic Pathways," vol. II, pp. 525–616, Academic Press, Inc., New York, 1961.

Karnovsky, M., Metabolic Basis of Phagocytic Activity, *Physiol. Revs.,* **42,** 143–168, 1962.

London, I. M., The Metabolism of the Erythrocyte, *Harvey Lectures,* **56,** 151–189, 1960–1961.

Moore, C. V., Iron Metabolism and Nutrition, *Harvey Lectures,* **55,** 67–101, 1959–1960.

Rimington, C., and Kennedy, G. Y., Porphyrins: Structure, Distribution, and Metabolism, in M. Florkin and H. S. Mason, eds., "Comparative Biochemistry," vol. IV, part B, pp. 557–615, 1962.

Shorr, E., Intermediary Metabolism and Biological Functions of Ferritin, *Harvey Lectures,* **50,** 112–153, 1954–1955.

Watson, C. J., The Problem of Porphyria: Some Facts and Questions, *New Engl. J. Med.,* **263,** 1205–1215, 1960.

White, A., Effects of Steroids on Aspects of the Metabolism and Functions of the Lymphocyte: A Hypothesis of the Cellular Mechanisms in Antibody Formation and Related Immune Phenomena, *Ann. N.Y. Acad. Sci.,* **73,** 79–104, 1958.

43. The Eye

Light entering the eye passes through the tears on the conjunctiva and then through the cornea, aqueous humor, lens, and vitreous humor before impinging on the light-perceiving apparatus of the retina. These structures will be considered in turn.

STRUCTURE, COMPOSITION, AND METABOLISM

Both the *sclera* and the *conjunctiva* are of mesenchymal origin and are built largely of collagen fibers and mucoprotein. The sclera also contains hyaluronic acid. The sclera is opaque because its collagen fibers are interwoven and cross-laminated, whereas in the transparent conjunctiva all fibers lie in parallel.

The *cornea* is a transparent structure composed of five separate layers: an outer epithelium and an inner endothelium, on the inside of each of which is a membrane enclosing the substantia propria. The corneal epithelium is easily isolated from the avascular stroma with its loosely attached single cell layer of endothelium. Descemet's membrane lies between the endothelium and the stromal connective tissue component, and consists mainly of collagen. The stroma also is collagenous, but, here, the fibrils are embedded in ground substance. The mucopolysaccharides in this matrix have been well characterized but not the proteins. Keratosulfate (page 55) is the principal corneal polysaccharide. The corneal fibrils are distinguished both by their regular arrangement and by their narrow (embryonal) cross section. Corneal vascularization occurs in numerous nutritional deficiencies.

The transparency of the cornea is dependent upon its hydration. Both the aqueous humor on the one side and the tears on the other are slightly hypertonic, but it has been assumed that this degree of hypertonicity is sufficient to draw water at all times from the cornea and maintain it in a relatively dehydrated state. An inward-directed active transport of Na^+ in the cornea has been described, in addition to ready passage of water.

Perhaps the outstanding feature of corneal metabolism is the predominance of the phosphogluconate oxidative pathway, accounting for approximately 50 per cent of the glucose utilized. The abundant lactic acid dehydrogenase in bovine corneal epithelium can function with TPNH as coenzyme. However, the three lactic acid dehydrogenase isozymes isolated from this tissue all had higher activity with DPNH than with TPNH. The high level of pyridine nucleotides and the high O_2 consumption ($Q_{O_2} = 6$) indicate that the cellular layers of the cornea are metabolically active.

812

The transparent, pale yellow *lens* is of ectodermal origin and is composed of macroscopic cells called lens fibers; within these cells lie the gel structures. The lens is surrounded by an inert membrane of unknown composition, and the interior contains 25 per cent protein and has the character of a thick gel. Three characteristic proteins have been identified: α- and β-*crystallin,* both of which are soluble, and an insoluble albuminoid related to keratin but of somewhat different amino acid composition. α-Crystallin appears to be a soluble precursor of the insoluble albuminoid. The latter is concentrated in the lens nucleus; the soluble proteins predominate in the outer layers. The lens may serve as an osmometer, being ordinarily maintained in its relatively dehydrated state by virtue of the relative hypertonicity of the fluid bathing the lens. The chief intracellular cation is potassium, and the extracellular cation is sodium. The lens has a low rate of metabolism, characterized primarily by glycolysis, with functioning also of the phosphogluconate oxidative pathway. Although all enzymes of the citric acid cycle are present, lens has little activity represented by this pathway.

Lenticular carbohydrate metabolism is markedly impaired in diabetes. There results a marked increase in glucose and fructose content of the lens, and diminished ATP formation and amino acid incorporation into lens protein.

The outer regions of the lens contain ATP and virtually no phosphocreatine, while the nucleus contains phosphocreatine and relatively little ATP. Thus, in the central region, relatively remote from oxygen and glucose which are available only by diffusion from the aqueous and vitreous humors, the lens accumulates a storage form of energy-rich phosphate which is not required in the outer layers. The usefulness of this energy is not completely clear, but one possibility is indicated below.

If kept anaerobically and aseptically, lens proteins undergo autolysis, catalyzed by two proteases which are active over a broad pH range. Some aerobic mechanism must be operative normally either to keep this proteolysis in check or to compensate by an equal rate of protein synthesis. The lens is one of the richest sources of glutathione, the cortex containing as much as 600 mg. per 100 g. of tissue. In studies with radioactive glycine, the glutathione of the lens has been found to have a half-life of about 30 hr. Continual glutathione synthesis would require an appreciable fraction of the ATP generated by glucose oxidation. It is of interest that another reducing agent, ascorbic acid, is present in lens in a concentration of approximately 30 mg. per 100 g. tissue, or almost twenty times the plasma concentration.

In addition to glutathione, several analogues of this tripeptide are found in lesser amounts in the lens. In each of these tripeptides, the cysteine residue has been replaced. In ophthalmic acid, cysteine is replaced by α-amino-*n*-butyric acid; in norophthalmic acid, by alanine; in S-sulfoglutathione, by S-sulfocysteine; and in yet another tripeptide, by S-(α,β-dicarboxyethyl)-cysteine. The significance of these additional peptides is not known. Ophthalmic acid is a potent inhibitor of glyoxalase (page 360).

The chief expression of a deranged lens metabolism is *cataract,* or opacity. The opacity results from alteration of the proteins with formation of compact fibrous aggregates, and expression of fluid from the lens. During development of senile cataract, $[Na^+]$ of the lens increases while $[K^+]$ decreases. At a later time the $[Ca^{++}]$

of the lens also increases, and [Ca^{++}] has been used as a basis for classification of the stages of cataract development. The lens then begins to swell; this corresponds temporally to the hydrolysis of α- and β-crystallins. As the amino acids which are liberated diffuse from the lens, it decreases in size. The insoluble albuminoids remain and impart increased rigidity to the lens nucleus. Similar changes have been reported for cataracts associated with diabetes in man.

Cataract also occurs in galactosemia (page 406) and can be produced in animals on a diet rich in galactose or in xylose. In experimental cataract produced by these sugars, and in alloxan-diabetic cataract, xylitol, dulcitol, sorbitol, and fructose accumulate in the lens. The opacity produced by xylose has been reported to be reversible, in contrast to that resulting from galactose feeding or diabetes, and was associated with a restoration to normal of the phosphogluconate oxidative pathway, which is depressed in the opaque lens.

It has been reported that parathyroidectomy caused decreased glucose utilization and lactate production in the lenses of young rats, and that these processes were restored to normal by addition of parathyroid hormone to lens tissue in vitro. It may be noted that clouding of the lens is often seen early in clinical hypoparathyroidism (Chap. 47). The lens also becomes opaque in various nutritional deficiencies and after poisoning with several unrelated drugs.

The interior of the eye chamber is coated with a dark (light-absorbing) substance that prevents internal reflections which would obscure the image. This material is the melanin of the pigment layer between the nerve tissue of the retina and the vascular choroid tunic. The melanin also determines the color of the iris. Brown eyes result from the presence of melanin; there is no blue pigment in blue eyes, which appear blue because of absorption of longer wavelengths as light is reflected back from the iris stroma.

The *retina* is the photosensitive portion of the eye. Here the energy of light quanta is detected and impulses are sent via the optic nerve to the cerebral cortex. The retina has the highest known rate of oxygen consumption of any tissue in the body, per unit of weight, with an active phosphogluconate oxidative pathway, a high rate of anaerobic and aerobic glycolysis, and an R.Q. of 1. Lactate is the major endogenous substrate contributing to retinal respiration. It is possible that all the major pathways of carbohydrate metabolism play roles in retinal function. Citric acid cycle activity increases markedly during maturation of the photoreceptors, localized in inner segments of the rods. Apparently, the maintenance of visual cell function is strikingly dependent on glycolysis, as evidenced by the selective toxic effect on the retina resulting from intravenous administration of iodoacetate.

The retina is essentially a network of synapses and is, therefore, rich in acetylcholine, acetylcholine esterase, and choline acetylase.

The retina, in its nine neural layers, is quite transparent. The underlying pigment epithelium and the scattered pigment in the choroid form a nearly black absorbing layer. That light which is reflected is predominantly red as a result of the rich choroidal blood supply. Many animals possess a mirror-like structure behind the retina, called the *tapetum lucidum*. In dim light, that light which is not absorbed as it passes through the retina is reflected and passed a second time through the photosensitive cells; this affords increased sensitivity of vision in dim light. The tapetum lucidum is responsible for the glowing characteristic of the eyes of cats and dogs at night, as they reflect light. The mirror quality of the tapetum lucidum of carnivores consists of an ordered arrangement of crystals of a complex of zinc and cysteine. Many fish, amphibia, and reptiles possess a tapetum lucidum in which crystalline guanine is deposited in the iris as a reflector. The guanine crystals are rather large, with one surface oriented at 45° to the visual cells.

THE PHOTOCHEMISTRY OF VISION

Light impinging on the retina is absorbed and becomes transformed into another form of energy, presumably chemical. The substances absorbing light are, by definition, pigments, and the initial phenomena of vision are concerned with retinal pigments which absorb the light. It has been assumed that at least three chemical reactions occur initially in visual stimulation: (1) a photochemical reaction in which a pigment absorbs light and is in some manner thereby altered; (2) a second chemical process, independent of light, in which the primary photoproducts of (1) somehow initiate a nerve impulse; and (3) a chemical process, also independent of light, in which the pigment is regenerated from the products of (1) or from other substances. Once the nerve impulse is initiated, the process presumably resembles other sensory mechanisms. Largely through the efforts of Hecht and associates these ideas were given kinetic formulation, and it was shown that much of the quantitative, physiological data of human and animal vision can be explained on the basis of the above assumptions. That these postulated reactions have a chemical basis has been demonstrated by investigations of the light-sensitive pigment *rhodopsin*.

The human retina normally contains two types of receptor cells, rods and cones. Animals which have vision only in bright light ("day vision"), such as the pigeon, have only cones, and animals, like the owl, which possess only "night" or "dim vision" have only rods. Thus, at the periphery of the retina in the human eye there are only rods, associated primarily with seeing at low intensities of light. Animals having only rods do not have color vision since color perception is associated with the presence of cones. Most vertebrates possess both rods and cones; only occasional species have but one of these receptors.

ROD VISION

Rhodopsin. The rods contain *rhodopsin,* or *visual purple.* This substance was discovered by Boll in 1877, who observed that the frog retina has a rose color which bleaches on exposure to light. The following year, Kühne succeeded in extracting the pigment with a solution of sodium glycocholate. Rhodopsin is a thermolabile protein which is insoluble in water but soluble in aqueous solutions of detergents like bile salts, digitonin, saponin, and sodium oleate. The molecular weight is approximately 40,000. The absorption spectrum of rhodopsin shows the typical protein absorption near 275 mμ and, more important, a broad absorption in the visible region with a maximum at 500 mμ and a small secondary peak in the ultraviolet near 350 mμ. Estimates of human rod vision in dim light show a sensitivity curve with a maximum at about 500 mμ, gradually diminishing on either side of this wavelength. The fact that the sensitivity curve for human rod vision coincides with the absorption curve for rhodopsin in the visible region (Fig. 43.1) provides strong evidence that rhodopsin is the photosensitive material of rod vision.

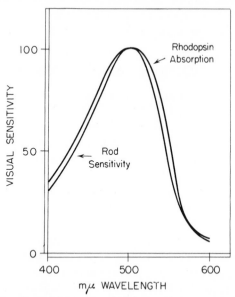

FIG. 43.1. Comparison of sensitivity of rod vision and the absorption of rhodopsin at various wavelengths. The sensitivity curve has been corrected for the effects of transmission of light through the ocular media. (*From S. Hecht, S. Shlaer, and M. H. Pirenne, J. Gen. Physiol.*, **25,** 819, 1942.)

As shown by Wald, rhodopsin is a conjugated protein which upon bleaching is split into a protein called *opsin* and a carotenoid named *retinene*. Little or no carotenoid can be extracted from dark-adapted frog retinas; immediately after bleaching isolated retinas with light, extracts of the tissue made with lipid solvents contain retinene, which absorbs maximally at about 390 mμ. If bleached retinas are allowed to stand at room temperature, the content of retinene gradually decreases and is replaced by increasing amounts of vitamin A_1. Morton and his colleagues demonstrated that retinene is vitamin A_1-aldehyde. These relationships may be illustrated as follows.

Rhodopsin $\xrightarrow{\text{light}}$ opsin + retinene (vitamin A_1-aldehyde)

$\downarrow$ dark

vitamin A_1

Vitamin A_1

The re-formation of retinene from vitamin A_1 requires an oxidation of the terminal alcohol group. The reaction is reversible and catalyzed by an alcohol dehydrogenase (*retinene reductase*) with participation of DPN.

$$
\underset{\substack{\text{Vitamin } A_1}}{C_{19}H_{27}-\overset{\displaystyle H}{\underset{\displaystyle H}{C}}-OH} + DPN^+ \underset{\text{reductase}}{\overset{\text{retinene}}{\rightleftharpoons}} \underset{\substack{\text{Vitamin } A_1\text{-aldehyde}\\\text{(retinene)}}}{C_{19}H_{27}-\overset{\displaystyle H}{C}=O} + DPNH + H^+
$$

The dehydrogenase of retina appears to be similar to the alcohol dehydrogenase of liver; crystalline alcohol dehydrogenase from horse liver will catalyze the above reaction in vitro. In the isolated system, the equilibrium is strongly in the direction of alcohol formation. Retinene reductase can also utilize TPN. Indeed, an absolute requirement for TPN was demonstrated when glucose 6-phosphate dehydrogenase was coupled to reduction of vitamin A_1-aldehyde. Balance data indicated that the phosphogluconate oxidative pathway could supply sufficient TPNH to reduce 60 per cent of the aldehyde present.

The action of light in liberating retinene from rhodopsin involves at least two colored intermediates. One is a transient product, red or orange-red in color, *lumirhodopsin*, which is stable only below about $-50°C$. If warmed to about $-20°C.$, it is converted to a second substance, also orange-red in color, called *metarhodopsin*. This substance is stable below $-15°C$. When warmed above this temperature, in the presence of water, it hydrolyzes to retinene and opsin.

Regeneration of Rhodopsin. In the retina of the intact animal, under constant stimulation, a steady state exists wherein the rate of bleaching and the rate of regeneration are equal. In the dark, regeneration of rhodopsin proceeds to a maximum. Night blindness (*nyctalopia*) in rats is produced by a diet deficient in vitamin A. The retinas of deficient rats contain less rhodopsin than do normal rat retinas, and the rate of rhodopsin regeneration is much slower than normal. These observations provided further evidence that rhodopsin is indeed the pigment concerned with rod vision.

Dietary status with respect to vitamin A can be evaluated by measuring the *visual threshold*, the minimal light intensity required to evoke a visual sensation. Dark adaptation is the change in threshold which results from a period in the dark. In man, maximal dark adaptation of the rods requires about 25 min. In experimental studies with human subjects given vitamin A-deficient diets, the visual threshold increases, *i.e.*, higher light intensities are required to evoke the sensation of light. In clinical vitamin A deficiency, the threshold after complete dark adaptation may actually be 100 or more times higher than normal; this elevation of threshold is termed *night blindness.*

It had been known since ancient times that night blindness which develops in human beings is alleviated by feeding liver or liver extracts. It was not until the period 1920 to 1925 that the curative factor was shown to be a dietary essential, vitamin A. Night blindness commonly occurs whenever famine conditions prevail, and the condition may be widespread in parts of the world where vitamin A intake is inadequate.

Solutions of rhodopsin, bleached by light, also regenerate in the dark, but the extent of regeneration is dependent upon the wavelength of the bleaching light. Light of short wavelengths (violet) permits more regeneration than does light of longer wavelengths (yellow-red). An explanation of this finding is given below.

Retinene and vitamin A_1 contain five double bonds and can therefore exist in various *cis* or *trans* configurations. Synthetic vitamin A and that in the liver of mammals and sharks is in the all-*trans* form, as is the retinene liberated by bleaching rhodopsin. However, all-*trans*-retinene cannot recondense with opsin; rhodopsin is formed by combination of opsin with the mono-*cis*-isomer, *neoretinene b* or Δ^{11}-*cis*-retinene. These structures are shown below with the hydrogen atoms omitted for simplification.

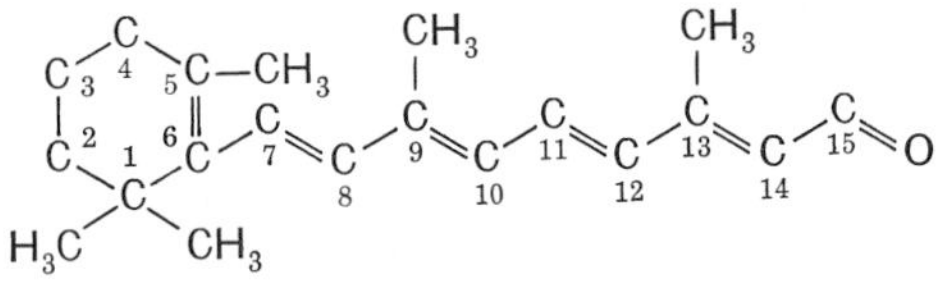

All-*trans* retinene

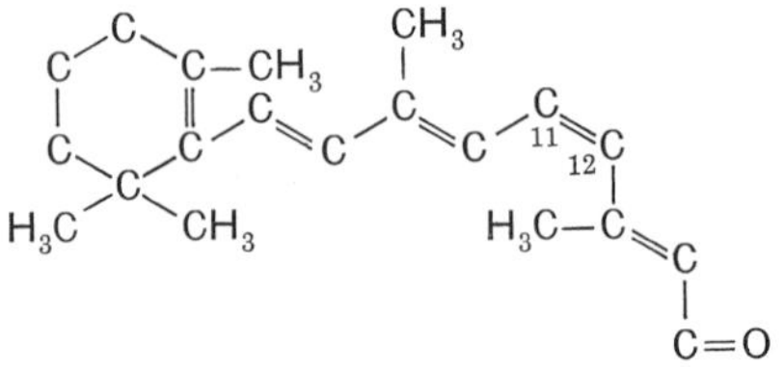

Δ^{11}-*cis*-Retinene
(neoretinene b)

Although all-*trans*-retinene and vitamin A can be isomerized to the Δ^{11}-*cis* forms by irradiation, this reaction is relatively slow and, in the eye, is catalyzed by a *retinene isomerase*. Irradiation by light of short wavelengths is most effective in the nonenzymic reaction. The major site of re-formation of the *cis* configuration may be the liver. These relationships are summarized in Fig. 43.2.

Synthesis of rhodopsin from *cis*-retinene and opsin is an exergonic process. Bleaching of rhodopsin is an endergonic process requiring light energy to initiate pigment breakdown. Present evidence suggests that one quantum is required for bleaching each chromophoric group in rhodopsin. Although each rod of the human eye contains at least 10^7 molecules of rhodopsin, Hecht has shown that a flash of light is visible when only one rhodopsin molecule in each of five to seven rods has been affected! Presumably the rest of the rod somehow amplifies this photochemical effect sufficiently to initiate a nerve impulse.

It has been noted above that bleaching of rhodopsin proceeds in distinct steps:

Rhodopsin $\longrightarrow$ lumirhodopsin $\longrightarrow$ metarhodopsin $\longrightarrow$ opsin + all-*trans*-retinene

Present interpretation of these events by Wald and coworkers is that 11-*cis*-retinene is bound as a Schiff base to an amino group of the opsin, R—HC=N—opsin. This binding is facilitated because of the over-all configuration of the *cis* form, which must fit the surface of the protein opsin. The primary photochemical event represents an isomerization of the retinene to the all-*trans* isomer, which remains attached to the opsin. The next step represents a change in opsin configuration, exposing two or three sulfhydryl groups; this is *metarhodopsin*. Finally, the Schiff base linkage hydrolyzes, with bleaching resulting.

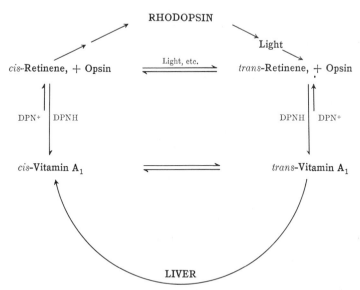

FIG. 43.2. Transformations of the carotenoids in the visual cycle.

Regeneration of rhodopsin involves the 11-*cis*-retinene and proceeds by re-formation of the Schiff base. In the light, as rhodopsin is bleached, *trans*-retinene is reduced to vitamin A_1, which migrates into the pigment epithelium. In the dark, vitamin A_1 migrates into the retina and is oxidized to retinene.

Porphyropsin. The retinas of mammals, birds, amphibia, marine fish, and invertebrates contain rhodopsins with an absorption maximum near 500 mμ, whereas retinas of all true fresh-water fish have a photosensitive pigment with a maximum absorption near 522 mμ; this pigment is *porphyropsin*. The distribution of porphyropsin and rhodopsin is of considerable biological interest. Porphyropsin is associated with fish of fresh-water origin; marine fish, like land vertebrates, possess the rhodopsin system. The retina of salmon, which develop in fresh water and migrate to the sea, contains both pigments, with porphyropsin predominant. The retina of the adult frog contains rhodopsin, whereas the bullfrog tadpole has porphyropsin. This change in visual system occurs during metamorphosis of the tadpole to the adult form.

Wald has shown that, like rhodopsin, the porphyropsin system undergoes cyclic changes on bleaching and regeneration in which vitamin A_2 and retinene$_2$ replace the analogues of the rhodopsin system. Porphyropsin is a conjugated protein containing the carotenoid, retinene$_2$, the absorption maximum of which is about 22 mμ more toward the red than that of retinene$_1$. A comparable displacement is found in the absorption maxima of vitamin A_2 and retinene$_2$ from those of their analogues in the rhodopsin system. Vitamin A_2 differs from A_1 by having one additional conjugated double bond.

Vitamin A$_2$

It should be noted that in the case of porphyropsin, as well as all other visual pigments studied (see iodopsin below), it is the 11-*cis*-retinene which is part of the photosensitive protein. Only the retinenes derived from vitamins A_1 and A_2 are known in all visual pigments; it is the opsins which differ in the various species.

CONE VISION

The pigments responsible for cone vision are of great interest inasmuch as the cones are the dominant sensory elements in the human retina and are responsible for color vision. To account for the data of color vision, it has been assumed that there are probably at least three closely related pigments in cones; this is the Young-Helmholtz trichromatic theory. The spectral sensitivity of human cone vision is greatest at 555 mμ, which indicates that the photosensitive pigment of the cone differs from the rhodopsin found in rods.

Because of the high visual threshold of cone vision, 50 to 100 times higher than that of the rods, it might be anticipated that the cone pigments are present in small amounts. Isolation of these pigments may also be complicated by the large amounts of rhodopsin present in rods. In 1937 Wald demonstrated that digitonin extracts of chicken retinas, which are composed chiefly of cones, contain not only rhodopsin but also a substance with an absorption spectrum which corresponds well with the spectrum of visual sensitivity of the fovea. This pigment, *iodopsin,* has an absorption spectrum with a maximum at 555 mμ, contains retinene, but has an opsin which differs from that in the rods. No other pigment has yet been isolated from mammalian cones. Rushton observed that after the human eye has been exposed to strong monochromatic light, the composition of the emergent light differs from the same light before the eye was exposed. It was inferred that some pigment, probably that contained in the foveal cones, had been altered or bleached. Furthermore, after bleaching with red light the composition of the emergent beam was different from its composition after bleaching with blue-green light or with white light. Rushton suggested the probable existence of two cone pigments in the normal eye; these he termed *chlorolabe* and *erythrolabe* because they absorb most actively in the green and in the red portions of the spectrum, respectively.

Wald has extended these studies and demonstrated the presence, in the cones, of three distinct pigments. The absorption maxima of two of these, at 535 and 565 mμ, suggest their probable identity with chlorolabe and erythrolabe, respectively. The properties of the latter are strikingly similar to those of iodopsin, suggesting that chlorolabe and erythrolabe are combinations of retinene with different opsins. It is not clear how combination of retinene with a third protein could also yield the third pigment with maximum absorption in the blue region, *viz.*, at about 440 mμ, yet this appears to be the case. None of these pigments has been chemically separated and identified.

Cone and rod vision may be compared with fine- and coarse-grained film, since each foveal cone communicates with the cerebral cortex via a single fiber, whereas groups of rods are connected to a single fiber. Rod vision is not only color-blind but also comparatively coarse-imaged. "In dim light, all cats are gray, and one cannot even be sure they are cats."

REFERENCES

Books

Adler, F. H., "Physiology of the Eye," The C. V. Mosby Company, St. Louis, 1950.
Dartnall, H. J. A., "The Visual Pigments," John Wiley & Sons, Inc., New York, 1957.
Davson, H., ed., "The Eye," vols. I, II, III, and IV, Academic Press, Inc., New York, 1962.
Pirie, A., and Van Heyningen, R., "Biochemistry of the Eye," Charles C Thomas, Publisher, Springfield, Ill., 1956.
Rushton, W. A. H., "Visual Pigments in Man," Charles C Thomas, Publisher, Springfield, Ill., 1962.
Smelser, G., ed., "The Structure of the Eye," Academic Press, Inc., New York, 1961.

Review Articles

Hecht, S., Rods, Cones and the Chemical Basis of Vision, *Physiol. Revs.*, **17**, 239–290, 1937.
Langham, M. E., Aqueous Humor and Control of Intra-ocular Pressure, *Physiol. Revs.*, **38**, 215–242, 1958.
Pirie, A., The Biochemistry of the Eye Related to Its Optical Properties, *Endeavour,* **17**, 171–189, 1958.
Wald, G., The Distribution and Evolution of Visual Systems, in M. Florkin and H. S. Mason, eds., "Comparative Biochemistry," vol. I, pp. 311–345, Academic Press, Inc., New York, 1960.
Wald, G., The Molecular Organization of Visual Systems, in W. D. McElroy and B. Glass, eds., "Light and Life," pp. 724–749, Johns Hopkins Press, Baltimore, 1961.

44. Skin

Keratin is the characteristic insoluble protein of the integument. Keratin obtained from different sites differs in composition. That isolated from most structures contains 3 to 4 per cent of cystine; the keratin of hair and nails, however, has approximately 15 per cent of cystine. Block has characterized as *eukeratins* those which are insoluble at any pH, are not digested by the common proteases, and contain histidine, lysine, and arginine in the ratio of 1:4:12. These are the keratins of hair, nails, horn, hoofs, etc. The *pseudokeratins* of the skin, glia, and lens are equally insoluble but are digestible by proteolytic enzymes, contain less cystine, and the ratios of the basic amino acids are not constant.

Supporting the epidermis is the *corium,* or *dermis,* consisting mainly of connective tissue collagen fibers. It is noteworthy that cells of ectodermal and mesodermal origin evolved insoluble fibers of differing amino acid composition. In contrast to collagen, keratin is rich in cystine, is devoid of hydroxyproline, and contains relatively little glycine. The corium also contains some elastic fibers, so that small quantities of elastin are present together with hyaluronic acid and chondroitin sulfate. The epidermis is the metabolically active segment of the skin; epidermal cells conduct glycolysis, the citric acid cycle, and the phosphogluconate oxidative pathway.

In the basal layer of the epidermis are melanoblasts, in which the dark pigment, melanin, is synthesized from tyrosine (Fig. 44.1). Melanin formation from tyrosine requires the action of only one enzyme, copper-containing *tyrosinase.* This catalyzes the oxidation of tyrosine to dihydroxyphenylalanine (dopa) and to dopa quinone, as shown in Fig. 44.1. Tyrosinase can also catalyze the oxidation of dopa. *Hallachrome,* so named because it was isolated from a polychaete worm, *Halla parthenolapa,* is formed nonenzymically by dismutation of two moles of dopa quinone. The oxidation of indole 5,6-quinone to melanin is probably spontaneous. Melanin (Gk. *melas,* black) has not been characterized chemically, but it is thought to be a polymer or group of polymers. The color of skin depends upon the distribution of melanoblasts, the melanin concentration, and perhaps its state of oxidation, since melanin can be reduced with ascorbic acid or hydrosulfite from a black to a tan form. Genetic absence of tyrosinase results in *albinism.*

Melanin is also normally found in the retina, the ciliary body, the choroid, the substantia nigra of brain, and the adrenal medulla. Melanoblasts occasionally give rise to highly malignant melanomas, which may or may not be pigmented. When stained with dopa, nonpigmented melanotic tumors rapidly darken and are therefore called *amelanotic melanomas.* Darkening of the human skin is initiated by

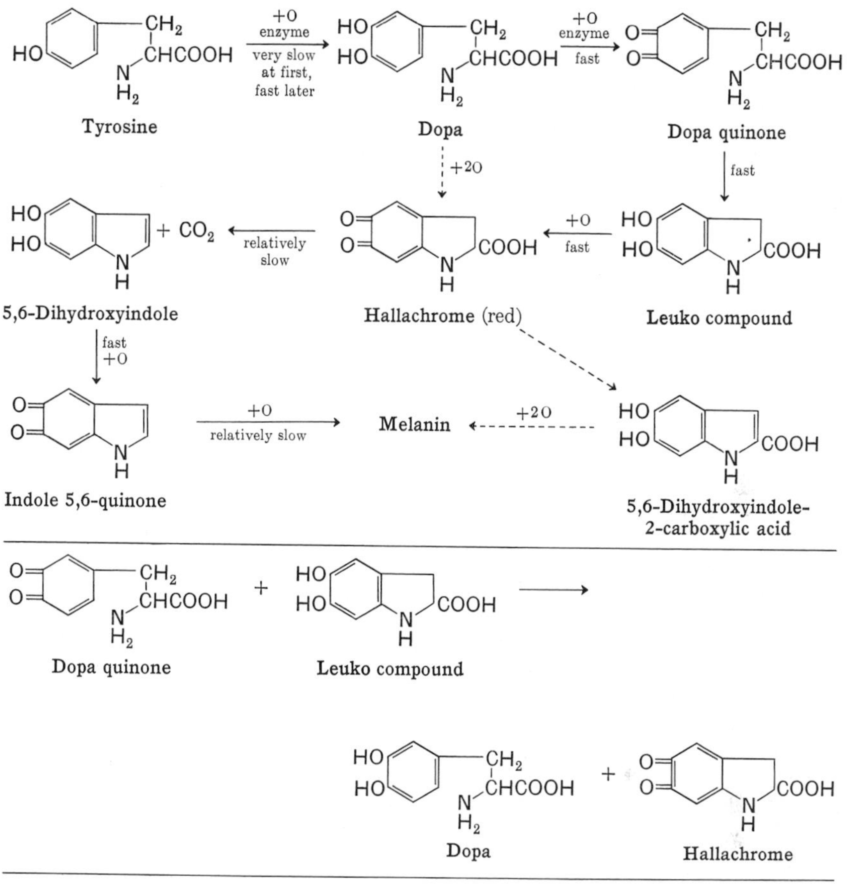

FIG. 44.1. Melanin formation from tyrosine. (*From A. B. Lerner and T. B. Fitzpatrick, Physiol. Revs.,* **30,** 91, 1950.)

ultraviolet irradiation of tyrosine, leading to formation of dopa. In albinos, either melanin-forming cells or tyrosinase, or both, may be entirely absent.

Other photochemical reactions of significance which occur in the skin are the conversion of 7-dehydrocholesterol to vitamin D, and transformations in porphyrins which result in skin photosensitization. An interesting bronzing of the skin in exposed regions is seen in Addison's disease (Chap. 49). Cutaneous sensitivity to solar radiation is an important part of the clinical picture of pellagra (Chap. 55) and porphyria (page 793). The expansion of the melanophores of cold-blooded species by melanocyte-stimulating hormone (Chap. 51) has been assumed to have no relationship to pigmentation in mammals. However, Lerner has demonstrated that administration of purified melanocyte-stimulating hormone to man results in intensification of pigmentation in previously pigmented areas of the skin, but no effect was seen on nonpigmented areas (Chap. 51).

The skin is almost impervious to water and to most electrolytes. However, if electrodes are placed upon the skin and a minute current is passed, the skin is then readily penetrated by cations. This process, known as *iontophoresis,* has had several clinical applications. Thus there appears to be in the skin an electrical or polarized barrier to the normal passage of ions. This barrier is thought to be located in the transitional layers between cornified and noncornified epithelium; this is in agreement with observations that the stratum corneum is rather acidic, whereas the mucous layer below is slightly alkaline.

The sebaceous glands lie within the skin and elaborate and secrete a complex lipid mixture. The quantity of sebaceous secretion is markedly affected by the sex hormones (Chap. 48). The secreted lipids are rich in squalene and also contain free cholesterol, waxes, triglyceride, and free fatty acids. The fatty acids include long and short, saturated and unsaturated, and both odd- and even-numbered carbon chains. The sebaceous secretions coat the skin and prevent it from being readily moistened; consequently these secretions also hinder passage of water and dissolved solutes through the skin. It may be noted, however, that there is no increase in permeability after the skin is thoroughly cleansed with lipid solvents. An illustration of the effectiveness of the waxy secretions in preventing the wetting of the epithelium is seen in the success of feathered birds in swimming because their feathers cannot be wet by water. However, if a synthetic detergent is placed in the water, ducks' feathers are rapidly wetted, and the birds will sink.

In contrast to water and electrolytes, lipid-soluble materials can penetrate the skin readily. This passage is accelerated if the materials are applied to the skin in ointment bases. When incorporated in lipid ointments, electrolytes such as potassium and lithium ions can also penetrate the skin. However, this is possible only if the ointment is applied with pressure, with resultant squeezing of air bubbles from the hair follicles; it is thought that the electrolytes then penetrate down the hair follicles, thus circumventing the electrical barrier. Among important therapeutic or toxic agents which can enter the body transcutaneously are metallic mercury (blue ointment) and benzene.

REFERENCES

Books

Carruthers, C., "Biochemistry of Skin in Health and Disease," Charles C Thomas, Publisher, Springfield, Ill., 1962.

Montagna, W., "Structure and Function of Skin," 2d ed., Academic Press, Inc., New York, 1962.

Rothman, S., "Physiology and Biochemistry of the Skin," University of Chicago Press, Chicago, 1954.

45. General Considerations of the Endocrine Glands

Examples of the manifold roles of enzymes in accelerating the rates of reactions in cells of diverse living forms have been provided *in extenso* throughout the preceding chapters of this book. A second class of substances, the *hormones,* also influence the velocity of cellular biochemical transformations and represent a group of regulators which have developed later in evolution. In contrast to the enzymes, which are essential for initiation and continuation of reactions, hormones do not *initiate* reactions but can influence the *rate* at which they proceed. However, many physiological processes may continue, although at a slower or faster rate, in the complete absence of one or more hormones. Hormones also serve as integrating influences in more complex organisms.

Higher living forms, as exemplified by mammals, operate normally in a highly integrated fashion, despite their many specialized tissues which have diverse form and function. This is possible because mechanisms have developed for the transmission of information from one organ to another. One of these mechanisms is described as *neural,* implying transmission along anatomically distinguishable tracts of the nervous system. The other is *humoral,* connoting transmission through the humors of the body, notably blood plasma.

Hormones are produced in the body by certain organs that have become specialized in hormone synthesis and which inject these products directly into their fluid environment to be carried by the circulation to other tissues, upon which the hormones exert their influence. These specialized tissues have been termed the glands of internal secretion, or *endocrine* glands. *Endocrinology* is the study of the structure and function of the endocrine glands and their secretory products, the hormones. It is the goal of the biochemist to provide explanation for the mode of synthesis of hormones, the mechanism by which they are secreted, their metabolic effects and fates, and, ultimately, their mechanism of action at cellular and enzymic levels. This last has not yet been achieved in the case of a single hormone, although the goal may be in sight for several.

Inasmuch as hormones affect the rates of most metabolic processes, endocrinology is integrated with most aspects of the studies of metabolism considered in previous chapters. Not only does each endocrine gland exert a variety of physiological influences, but these glands also affect the functioning of one another. Therefore, there exists an integrative functioning of the endocrine system of organs, reflected under normal circumstances in a high degree of hormonal balance. Derangements of this balance, either experimental or clinical, give rise to a variety of metabolic aberrations, the study of which has contributed to our understanding of health and disease.

The term hormone was first used by Bayliss and Starling in 1902 and is derived from a Greek root meaning "to excite" or "to arouse." These investigators found that intravenous injection of an acidic extract of the duodenal mucosa into dogs prepared with a pancreatic fistula produced a marked flow of pancreatic juice. This also was observed when the extract was introduced directly into a denervated loop of bowel. Thus, the physiological effect could have been mediated only by way of the blood. From this developed the concept of hormones as substances produced by specific glands, secreted directly into the blood, and transported to various organs and tissues where they exert their effects. Hormones function at low concentrations, generally less than $10^{-8}M$, are produced at a variable rate, and exert a regulatory function in response to environmental or other variations. Arbitrarily, the term hormone is limited to the products of recognized endocrine organs and does not include other agents which may fit the above description. Actually, a number of tissues synthesize, and add to the blood, substances that may induce responses in structures other than those in which they are produced. Thus, the hypothalamus secretes several polypeptides with distinct simulating action on the adenohypophysis (Chap. 51). The vasopressor peptide (page 735) liberated by renin secreted by the kidney has generalized cardiovascular effects. Indeed, the production of metabolic carbon dioxide, with its capacity to stimulate the respiratory center (page 687), could satisfy the above definition of a hormone. Nevertheless, the restriction to specific organs and their products is useful for classification of certain chemical and biological information.

Although disorders caused by endocrine dysfunctions and therefore termed *endocrinopathies* have been described since ancient times, it is only within the present century that these disorders have been related clearly to the endocrine system. For example, the effects of castration in man and animals have been known for hundreds of years, but knowledge of the hormonal role played by gonadal secretions is a contribution of contemporary science.

In the chapters to follow, each hormone will be considered from the following points of view: (1) its structure; (2) its biosynthesis; (3) its metabolic fate; and (4) its mechanism of action, including effects of insufficiency and of excess in both experimental animals and appropriate endocrinopathies of man.

Present knowledge with respect to each of the major endocrine glands is summarized in Table 45.1, which includes the names of the secretory products produced by each gland, their sites of action, and the principal phenomena affected by each hormone. The effects listed in the table are the results observed in an intact animal, generally following systemic hormone administration. Clearly, these must reflect events which occur as hormones influence processes within cells or subcellular organelles, presumably by effecting a discrete change either in the structure, organization, or metabolism of the cell or in its constituent functional components.

Table 45.1: MAJOR ENDOCRINE GLANDS IN VERTEBRATES

Endocrine gland and hormone	Principal site of action	Principal phenomena affected
Thyroid:		
Thyroxine and triiodothyronine......	General	Metabolic rate and oxygen consumption of tissues
Parathyroids:		
Parathormone....................	Skeleton, kidney, gastrointestinal tract	Metabolism of calcium and phosphorus
Testis:		
Testosterone.....................	Accessory sex organs	Maturation and normal function
	General	Development of secondary sex characteristics
Ovary:		
Estrone and estradiol..............	Accessory sex organs	Maturation and normal cyclic function
	Mammary glands	Development of duct system
	General	Development of secondary sex characteristics
Corpus luteum:		
Progesterone.....................	Uterus	Preparation for ovum implantation; maintenance of pregnancy
	Mammary glands	Development of alveolar system
Relaxin.........................	Symphysis pubis	Muscle tone
Placenta:		
Estrogens.......................	Same as ovarian hormones	Same as ovarian hormones
Progesterone.....................	Same as corpus luteum hormone	Same as corpus luteum hormone
Gonadotropin....................	Same as adenohypophyseal gonadotropins (LH and FSH)	Similar to but not identical with adenohypophyseal hormones
Relaxin.........................	Same as corpus luteum hormone	Same as corpus luteum hormone
Adrenal medulla:		
Epinephrine.....................	Heart muscle; smooth muscle; arterioles	Pulse rate and blood pressure; contraction of most smooth muscle
	Liver and muscle	Glycogenolysis
	Adipose tissue	Release of lipid
Norepinephrine..................	Arterioles	Increased peripheral resistance
	Adipose tissue	Release of lipid
Adrenal cortex:		
Adrenal cortical steroids...........	General	
Aldosterone.....................	....	Metabolism of electrolytes and water

Table 45.1: Major Endocrine Glands in Vertebrates (*Continued*)

Endocrine gland and hormone	Principal site of action	Principal phenomena affected
Adrenal cortex (Cont.): Corticosterone; 17-hydroxycorticosterone	. . . .	Metabolism of proteins, carbohydrates, and lipids; maintenance of circulatory and vascular homeostasis; inflammation; immunity and resistance to infection; hypersensitivity
Pancreas: Insulin	General	Utilization of carbohydrate
	Adipose tissue	Lipogenesis
Glucagon	Liver	Glycogenolysis
	Adipose tissue	Release of lipid
Adenohypophysis: Prolactin	Mammary gland	Proliferation; initiation of milk secretion
	Corpus luteum	Final development and functional activity
	General	Anabolic effects
Adrenocorticotropin (ACTH)	Adrenal cortex	Formation and/or secretion of adrenal cortical steroids
	Adipose tissue	Release of lipid
Thyrotropin (TSH)	Thyroid	Formation and secretion of thyroid hormone
	Adipose tissue	Release of lipid
Somatotropin (growth hormone)	General	Growth of bone and muscle; anabolic effect on calcium, phosphorus, and nitrogen metabolism; metabolism of carbohydrate and lipid; elevation of muscle and cardiac glycogen
Luteinizing or interstitial cell–stimulating hormone (LH or ICSH)	Ovary	Luteinization; secretion of progesterone (see FSH)
	Testis	Development of interstitial tissue; secretion of androgen
Follicle-stimulating hormone (FSH) . .	Ovary	Development of follicles; with LH, secretion of estrogen and ovulation
	Testis	Development of seminiferous tubules; spermatogenesis
Neurohypophysis: Oxytocin	Smooth muscle, particularly uterine	Contraction, parturition
	Mammary gland, postpartum	Ejection of milk

Table 45.1: MAJOR ENDOCRINE GLANDS IN VERTEBRATES (*Continued*)

Endocrine gland and hormone	Principal site of action	Principal phenomena affected
Neurohypophysis (*Cont.*):		
Vasopressin (antidiuretic hormone)....	Arterioles	Blood pressure
	Kidney tubules	Water reabsorption
Pars intermedia:		
Melanocyte-stimulating hormone (MSH)........................	Melanophores or chromophores	Pigment dispersal, leading to darkening of skin
Alimentary tract*:		
Secretin.........................	Pancreas	Secretion of alkali and fluid
Pancreozymin....................	Pancreas	Secretion of digestive enzymes
Cholecystokinin..................	Gallbladder	Contraction and emptying
Enterogasterone..................	Stomach	Inhibition of motility and secretion
Gastrin..........................	Stomach	Secretion of acid

* See pages 709*ff.*

SOURCE: Modified from J. A. Russell, Chap. 55, The Hormones, in J. F. Fulton, ed., "Textbook of Physiology," 16th ed., W. B. Saunders Company, Philadelphia, 1949.

REFERENCES

Books

Antoniades, H. N., ed., "Hormones in Human Plasma," Little, Brown and Company, Inc., Boston, 1960.

Cannon, W. B., "The Wisdom of the Body," 2d ed., W. W. Norton & Company, Inc., New York, 1939.

Dorfman, R. I., ed., "Methods in Hormone Research," vol. I, Chemical Determinations; vol. II, Bioassay, Academic Press, Inc., New York, 1962.

von Euler, U. S., and Heller, H., eds., "Comparative Endocrinology," vols. I and II, Academic Press, Inc., New York, 1963.

Gray, C. H., and Bacharach, A. L., eds., "Hormones in Blood," Academic Press, Inc., New York, 1961.

Pincus, G., and Thimann, K. V., eds., "The Hormones: Physiology, Chemistry and Applications," three vols., Academic Press, Inc., New York, vol. I, 1948; vol. II, 1950; vol. III, 1955.

Scharrer, E., and Scharrer, B., "Neuroendocrinology," Columbia University Press, New York, 1963.

Soffer, L. J., "Diseases of the Endocrine Glands," 2d ed., Lea & Febiger, Philadelphia, 1956.

Talbot, N. B., Sobel, E. H., McArthur, J. W., and Crawford, J. D., "Functional Endocrinology," Harvard University Press, Cambridge, Mass., 1952.

Tepperman, J., "Metabolic and Endocrine Physiology," Year Book Medical Publishers, Inc., Chicago, 1962.

Turner, C. D., "General Endocrinology," 3d ed., W. B. Saunders Company, Philadelphia, 1960.

Williams, R. H., ed., "Textbook of Endocrinology," 3d ed., W. B. Saunders Company, Philadelphia, 1962.

46. The Thyroid

CHEMICAL NATURE OF THE THYROID HORMONES

Thyroglobulin. In 1895, Baumann identified elemental iodine as a constituent of thyroid tissue. Approximately 0.5 per cent of iodine (8 mg.) is present in the thyroid and represents one-quarter of the total body iodine. The iodine of the thyroid is largely in a protein of the "colloid" named thyroglobulin, which has been isolated in partially purified form; it is a glycoprotein containing galactose, mannose, glucosamine, fucose, and a sialic acid. The iodine content varies from 0.5 to 1.0 per cent; purified preparations of thyroglobulin have a molecular weight of approximately 650,000 to 700,000.

Organic Iodine-containing Compounds. Hydrolysis of thyroglobulin yields those amino acids found commonly as constituents of proteins, and, in addition, iodinated derivatives of three amino acids, L-histidine, L-tyrosine, and L-thyronine. The 2 (or 4)-monoiodo-L-histidine present accounts for no more than 2 to 3 per cent of the total iodine of thyroglobulin, is devoid of thyroid-like activity, and is a byproduct of thyroid hormone biosynthesis. The mono- and diiodotyrosines present are also without biological activity. Only the iodothyronines have the characteristic physiological effects of thyroid preparations; they are the sole iodinated products secreted by the gland. These compounds are present chiefly as constituents of-the thyroglobulin; 1 per cent or less is present in the free state in the thyroid. Four iodinated thyronines (Table 46.1) have been identified in the thyroid; the most important physiologically are thyroxine and 3,5,3'-triiodothyronine. The L-isomers of these compounds are the natural and biologically active forms.

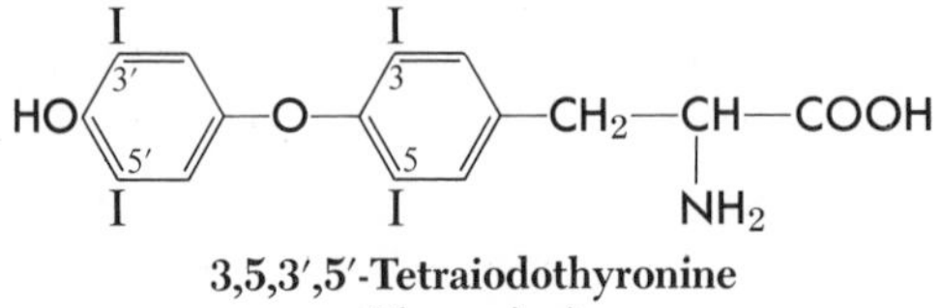

3,5,3',5'-Tetraiodothyronine
(thyroxine)

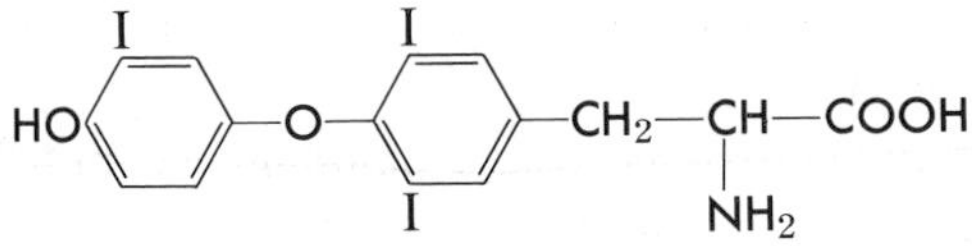

3,5,3'-Triiodothyronine

BIOSYNTHESIS AND SECRETION OF THYROID HORMONES

There is a continuous turnover of total iodine of the thyroid gland, resulting from uptake of iodide from the blood and from synthesis and secretion of thyroid hormones. This turnover has four aspects: (1) iodide entry into the gland, (2) conversion of iodide to organic iodine-containing residues of thyroglobulin, (3) proteolysis of thyroglobulin, and (4) secretion of thyroid hormones.

Iodide Accumulation by the Thyroid. The thyroid gland exhibits a remarkable capacity to collect injected or ingested iodide, which is accumulated rapidly in the colloid of the thyroid follicles. This occurs against a concentration gradient by an "active transport" mechanism (page 676). The gland normally concentrates iodide to at least twenty-five times its concentration in plasma, rapidly converting the iodide to organically bound iodine. Normally the thyroid contains approximately 10 μg exchangeable or free iodide, compared with 7,500 μg organically bound iodine.

Table 46.1: IODINE-CONTAINING ORGANIC COMPOUNDS OF THE THYROID GLAND

Compound	Date of discovery in thyroid	Per cent of total iodine in human thyroid gland	Biological activity relative to thyroxine
3,5-Diiodotyrosine.......	1911	25–42	0
Thyroxine.............	1915	35–40	100
3,5,3'-Triiodothyronine...	1952	5–8	500–1,000
3,3',5'-Triiodothyronine...	1954	<1	5
3,3'-Diiodothyronine.....	1955	<1	15–75
3-Monoiodotyrosine......	....	17–28	0

The iodide-concentrating mechanism has been referred to as an "iodide pump" or "iodide trap." Its action is dependent upon a concomitant K^+ influx and Na^+ efflux, is stimulated by adenohypophyseal thyrotropic hormone (Chap. 51), and is inhibited by certain inorganic ions, e.g., thiocyanate and perchlorate (see page 840). Other glands, e.g., the salivary and those of the gastric mucosa, also are capable of concentrating iodide. Thus, saliva, gastric juice, and milk have iodide concentrations fourteen to forty-eight times that of plasma, but the respective glands producing these fluids cannot store appreciable quantities of iodine, do not form thyroxine or triiodothyronine, and do not respond to thyrotropic hormone.

The availability of the radioactive isotopes of iodine I^{125} and I^{131} (Table 15.2, page 276) has aided in rapid expansion of knowledge of thyroid function; this will be considered below.

Formation of Organically Bound Iodine Compounds. As indicated above, iodide entering the thyroid is rapidly converted to organically bound iodine of thyroglobulin. The requisite oxidation of iodide by H_2O_2 to "active iodine," possibly iodinium ion, I^+, is catalyzed by an *iodide peroxidase*. Formation of H_2O_2 occurs by autoxidation of flavoproteins (page 345). The prosthetic group of the peroxidase is ferriprotoporphyrin IX (page 191). In congenital goitrous thyroid disorders (page 834), absence of the peroxidase results in iodide accumulation and failure to synthesize thyroid hormones. Certain "antithyroid" agents (page 841) inhibit the action of the thyroidal peroxidase.

Iodination of tyrosine, thyronines, and iodothyronines is catalyzed by *iodinase* and probably occurs with the tyrosine and thyronines in peptide linkage in thyroglobulin. There is no evidence of iodination of the free thyronines, and there is little free organically bound iodine in the thyroid (see above). The data in Fig. 46.1 illustrate the rapidity of the conversion of inorganic iodide into diiodotyrosine and thyroxine.

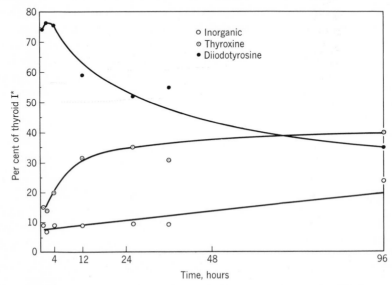

FIG. 46.1. Distribution of thyroid radioactive iodine among inorganic, diiodotyrosine, and thyroxine fractions in normal rat following administration of I[131], as iodide (I*). (*From M. E. Morton, I. Perlman, E. M. Anderson, and I. L. Chaikoff, Endocrinology, **30,** 495, 1942.*)

Biosynthesis of the hormones in the thyroid gland probably involves condensation of iodotyrosines and iodination of the phenolic ring of thyronine derivatives having position 3′ or 5′ free. These possible pathways are summarized in Fig. 46.2.

In vitro iodination of tyrosine-containing peptides and proteins, *e.g.*, casein and serum albumin, in slightly alkaline solution results in products which, when administered, exert a thyroxine-like effect on the metabolic rate. Indeed, thyroxine has been isolated from hydrolysates of these iodinated proteins. The mechanism by which iodinated thyronines arise from iodinated tyrosine residues in proteins, including thyroglobulin, is obscure. Thyronine is not known to occur as a constituent amino acid of any protein. Yet, presence of iodinated thyronines in hydrolysates of iodinated proteins suggests their ready formation, from the iodotyrosine precursors, either in the protein, at the instant of scission of peptide bonds, or in the liberated amino acid mixture.

Proteolysis of Thyroglobulin and Secretion of Thyroid Hormones. Intact thyroglobulin has no hormonal properties; these appear only after release of the iodothyronines. Thyroglobulin is the main constituent of the thyroid colloid, largely filling the lumen of the acinus, and does not enter the capillaries unless the walls are dis-

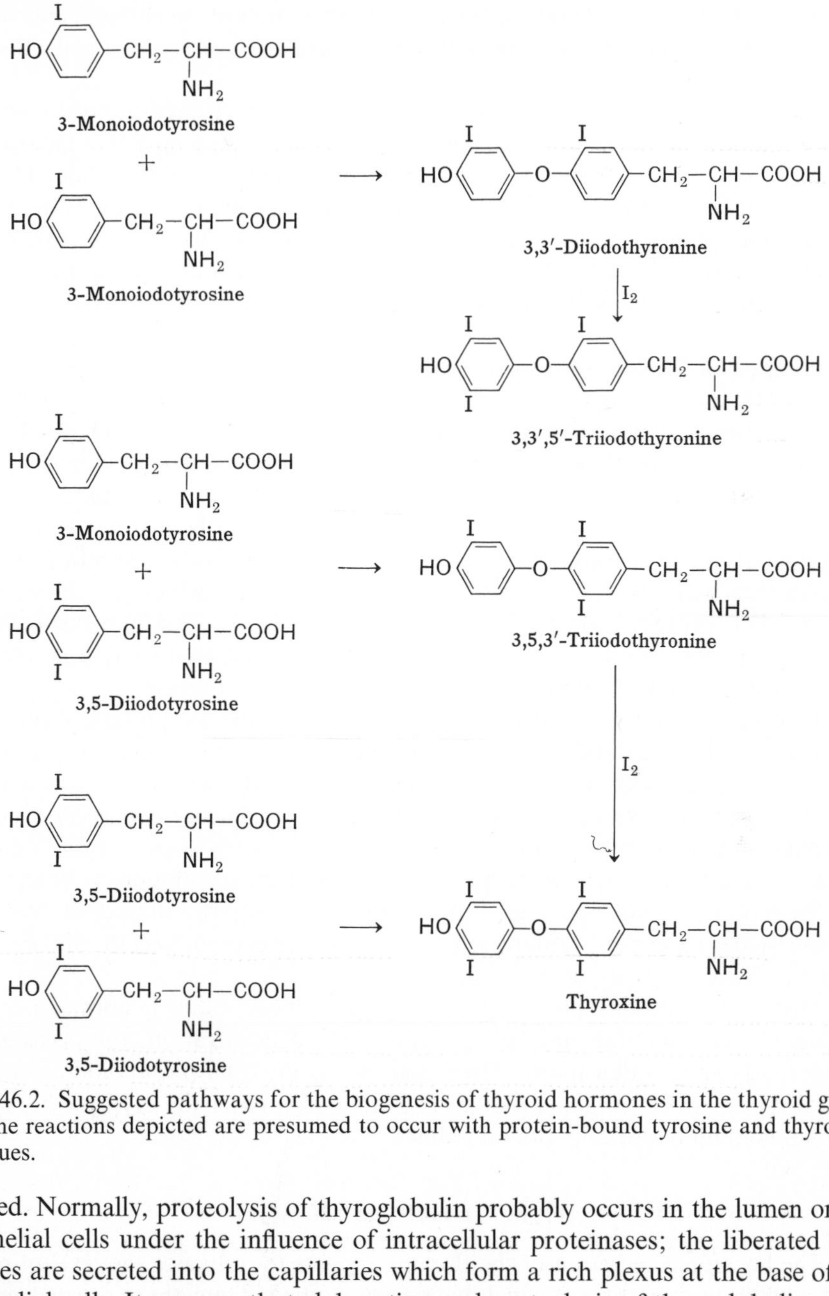

FIG. 46.2. Suggested pathways for the biogenesis of thyroid hormones in the thyroid gland. All the reactions depicted are presumed to occur with protein-bound tyrosine and thyronine residues.

rupted. Normally, proteolysis of thyroglobulin probably occurs in the lumen or the epithelial cells under the influence of intracellular proteinases; the liberated hormones are secreted into the capillaries which form a rich plexus at the base of the epithelial cells. It appears that elaboration and proteolysis of thyroglobulin occur continuously. The role of adenohypophyseal thyrotropic hormone in liberation and secretion of thyroid hormones is considered in Chap. 51.

As mentioned in the paragraph above, the process by which thyroidal hormones (thyronines) arise, during proteolysis of thyroglobulin, from iodinated tyrosine residues is obscure. Nonetheless, storage of precursors of the active thyronines, or perhaps the hormones themselves, bound in peptide linkages in thyroglobulin, provides a reserve of potentially active hormone which, however, cannot leave the cell until proteolysis of cell protein occurs.

The thyroid gland contains an active *dehalogenase* which catalyzes deiiodination of mono- and diiodotyrosines. The liberated halogen is returned to the iodide pool within the gland for reutilization, and thus conserving available iodide. The enzyme is without action on the iodinated thyronines, which are secreted. In hereditary familial goiter (page 623), lack of this enzyme results in excessive loss of the iodinated tyrosines from the thyroid. In the absence of adequate functioning of this normal iodine-conserving mechanism, thyroid deficiency symptoms (see below) may ensue.

Transport of Thyroid Hormones in the Blood. The normal plasma concentration of thyroxine, the principal thyroidal hormone of blood, is 9 μg per 100 ml. Almost all the hormone is bound loosely to a specific plasma globulin, a glycoprotein with a molecular weight of 45,000 and an electrophoretic mobility between those of α_1- and α_2-globulin; hence, the names "inter-α-globulin" and "thyroxine-binding globulin." Less than 0.1 per cent of the total plasma thyroxine is in free, or unbound, form. The hormone is readily extractable from its protein carrier with butanol, but it precipitates with plasma proteins on addition of reagents which precipitate these proteins. This protein-bound iodine, designated as PBI, is a useful measure of the level of available, circulating thyroid hormone; in the normal individual the PBI values range in concentration from 4 to 8 μg per 100 ml. of serum.

Thyroxine binding has also been described for a second protein observed in serum under specific conditions of electrophoresis. This protein has been named *pre-albumin* (page 631), because under the conditions employed it migrates at pH 8.6 with a mobility greater than that of serum albumin. The latter protein may also bind small amounts of thyroxine.

In contrast, triiodothyronine, present in blood in trace amounts, is bound very little by serum proteins and thus diffuses much more rapidly than does thyroxine into the tissues from the circulation. This is a possible explanation for the observed greater biological activity of triiodothyronine.

Thyroxine represents practically all of the total blood iodine in normal individuals. 3,3'-Diiodothyronine may be present in small concentration, and occasionally monoiodotyrosine is detectable. The remainder of the total plasma iodine, usually 10 to 20 per cent, is inorganic iodide. The latter may enter the erythrocyte, which does not contain organically bound iodine.

THYROID HYPOFUNCTION

The hormonal secretion of the thyroid appears to influence the level of metabolic activity in most tissues which have been studied. Thus, thyroid *hypofunction,* either experimental or clinical, is reflected in marked slowing of body processes. Thyroid hypofunction may result from surgical removal of the gland, its failure to develop normally, atrophy of the gland, or inadequate hormonal production. The age at which hypothyroidism ensues influences the effects seen, since adequate thyroid function is essential for normal growth and development of all structures.

If hypothyroidism is present at birth, *infantile myxedema*, or *cretinism*, results, characterized by dwarfism, with short extremities, large head, an apathetic face, and delayed development, *e.g.*, the teeth erupt late and speech is retarded. In addition, the hypothyroid individual exhibits characteristic thickening of subcutaneous tissue; initially, this was thought to be due to excess mucus formation, which led to early description of the hypothyroid state as *myxedema.*

In hypothyroidism, the basal metabolic rate and body temperature are below normal, the pulse is slow, and the cardic output and blood pressure are reduced. Other processes may also be retarded or diminished in intensity. Despite a decreased appetite, body weight may increase because of both decreased heat production, with retention of calories as depot lipid, and increased tissue hydration. Sexual activity is diminished, female sexual cycles may be interrupted, and sterility may ensue in both sexes. There is general muscular weakness.

Thyroidectomy in young animals leads most strikingly to failure of growth. Gudernatsch described the failure of metamorphosis in thyroidectomized tadpoles and the acceleration of this process in normal tadpoles placed in a medium containing thyroidal extract. This is the basis for a sensitive technique for assessing the potency of thyroidal preparations; thyroxine activity can be detected in a concentration of hormone of approximately $1 \times 10^{-6}M$.

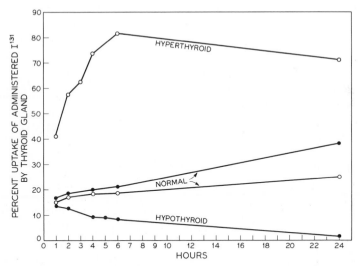

FIG. 46.3. The uptake of administered I^{131} by the thyroids of two normal individuals and by the glands of a hypo- and of a hyperthyroid subject. I^{131} given as iodide at time zero. (*Courtesy, Dr. L. J. Soffer.*)

The hypofunctioning thyroid gland has a lowered capacity to accumulate administered iodide (Fig. 46.3). The chemical basis for this fact, which is of diagnostic significance, has already been considered (page 831). Circulating thyroid hormone values in hypothyroidism are low, 1 to 2 μg of protein-bound iodine per 100 ml. of blood, as contrasted with normal values of 4 to 8 μg. An elevation of blood cholesterol level is often seen in hypothyroidism.

HYPERTHYROIDISM

Manifestations of *hyperthyroidism* result either from overmedication with potent thyroidal materials or from hyperactivity of the thyroid due to diffuse hyperplasia, focal glandular hyperplasia, or tumor (toxic adenoma). The physiological consequences are opposite to those seen in hypothyroidism in that they are characterized by an above-normal rate of activity of many functions. The clinical syndrome is generally termed *Graves' disease*. It has also been called *exophthalmic goiter* because thyroid enlargement and exophthalmos are frequently seen. The face is flushed; there is an appearance of facial anxiety accompanied by nervousness, emotional instability, and excessive reaction to stimuli. The pulse rate, pulse pressure, and blood flow are increased. Muscle tremors and weakness may be present.

Despite a generally increased appetite in the hyperthyroid individual, a persistent weight loss occurs because of increased heat production. The basal metabolic rate is strikingly elevated and may be 30 to 60 per cent above normal. Hypocholesterolemia, hyperglycemia, glucosuria, reduced glucose tolerance, and a negative nitrogen balance may obtain. The protein-bound iodine may rise to 15 to 20 μg per 100 ml. of blood, and the rate of uptake of administered iodide by the thyroid is increased (Fig. 46.3).

Experimental hyperthyroidism with its attendant metabolic alterations can be induced in animals by prolonged administration of thyroid hormone or by adding whole thyroid gland powder to the diet.

THYROID HORMONE FUNCTION

The mechanism by which thyroxine accelerates cellular reactions is not clear. Injection of the hormone into animals stimulates most enzymic systems studied, *e.g.*, glucose oxidation, incorporation of amino acids into proteins, and liver glucose 6-phosphatase, glucose 6-phosphate dehydrogenase, and TPNH–cytochrome c reductase activities. The stimulating effect of injected thyroxine in rats on the incorporation of amino acids by liver microsomes of cell-free systems prepared from the livers of these rats was localized at the step involving transfer of sRNA-bound amino acids to microsomal protein.

In contrast to the above effects, thyroxine added to mitochondria in vitro uncouples a portion of the phosphorylations occurring during oxidation of a specific substrate, *e.g.*, β-hydroxybutyrate. There is a concomitant passage of water into the mitochondria, which swell, suggesting an effect of thyroxine on the mitochondrial membrane. Uncoupling of oxidative phosphorylation could channel oxidative energy into heat rather than into the synthesis of high-energy phosphate-containing compounds. A similar uncoupling effect on mitochondrial oxidative phosphorylation has been obtained with dinitrophenol, which resembles thyroxine in calorigenic action. However, it should be emphasized that other compounds, *e.g.*, stilbestrol (page 863) and antimycin A, an antibiotic, also uncouple oxidative phosphorylation in vitro but do not exert a calorigenic effect in the intact organism. Thus, the effect of thyroxine in uncoupling oxidative phosphorylation, seen in vitro with high, nonphysiological concentrations of hormone, is of unknown significance for interpretation of the established physiological effects of thyroxine.

It may be noted that addition of thyroxine in vitro to solutions of crystalline glutamic acid dehydrogenase inhibits the activity of this enzyme. Wolff has shown that this enzymic effect is accompanied by deaggregation of the protein into subunits, as revealed in the ultracentrifuge. The significance of these observations for explanation of the mechanism of thyroxine action in vivo is not clear, inasmuch as a wide variety of substances, including steroids, metal-binding compounds, and certain surface-active agents, produce similar alterations in the physical state of glutamic acid dehydrogenase (page 864).

METABOLIC FATE OF THYROID HORMONES

The principal metabolic reactions to which thyroid hormones are subjected are (1) deamination; (2) deiodination; and (3) conjugation with glucuronic acid and sulfate. Deiodination occurs largely but not solely in extrahepatic tissues, and the other two reactions are prominent in liver, although not limited to this organ.

Hepatic Metabolism of Thyroid Hormones. The liver participates in the metabolism of thyroid hormones in two ways: (1) it destroys excess thyroid hormones in the blood, and (2) it regulates blood levels of hormone by enterohepatic circulation. As much as 40 per cent of an injected dose of thyroxine is found in the liver within 1 min. after administration. A small portion appears in the bile as iodide and as the administered hormone.

Transamination appears to be the prime mechanism for removal of the amino group of thyroid hormones in the liver with formation of the corresponding pyruvic acid analogues. The latter have a lesser degree of biological activity (see below). Transamination may also occur in kidney, which in addition contains a specific deaminase that requires oxygen, is not DPN-dependent, and catalyzes oxidative deamination of L-3,5,3'-triiodothyronine to the acetic acid analogue, triiodothyroacetic acid.

The liver also conjugates iodothyronines, with formation of glucosiduronides by linkage with the phenolic hydroxyl group of the thyronines. These conjugates are excreted in the bile. Because of the hydrolytic activity of intestinal enzymes and transmucosal transport of the liberated thyroid hormones, excretion of conjugated forms via the bile is not a significant route for their net disposal. The mechanism responsible for intestinal transport of the iodinated thyronines is similar to that for active transport of amino acid (page 486) but may in addition involve re-formation of the glucosiduronides in the intestinal mucosa.

Triiodothyronine may also be transformed in part in the liver to the O-sulfate derivative. Roche and his associates have postulated that this sulfate ester is the peripheral "storage" form of the hormone, since after its administration to rats it is less rapidly degraded than is triiodothyronine, and although the sulfate ester is found in plasma, it is not present in urine.

The metabolism of 3,3' diiodothyronine differs from that of thyroxine or triiodothyronine in that it forms little of the corresponding thyropyruvic or glucosiduronic acids. Rather, 3,3'-diiodothyronine undergoes major loss of its iodine, a significant portion of which appears in the urine as iodide.

Deiodination of the thyroidal hormones and their corresponding thyropyruvic acids in liver is catalyzed by *thyroxine dehalogenase* (see below). Only trace amounts of the deiodinated thyronines are excreted in the urine. Possible metabolic pathways for the thyronine nucleus are suggested by in vitro studies of Roche and coworkers. When thyronine was incubated with rat liver and kidney slices the products formed were tyrosine, 3′-hydroxythyronine, 3,4-dihydroxyphenylalanine, thyroacetic acid, and *p*-hydroxyphenylpyruvic acid. These findings suggest three mechanisms of thyronine metabolism: rupture of the diphenylether bridge, *o*-hydroxylation of the rings, and degradation of the alanine side chain via general pathways for amino acids.

Thus, the liver can metabolize thyroid hormones by deiodination, removal of amino groups, and disruption of the thyronine nucleus. The remainder of the thyroidal compounds, as well as certain of the metabolites, are either conjugated with glucuronic acid and channeled into an enterohepatic circulation, or, in specific instances, conjugated with sulfate and perhaps stored in this form.

Transformations in Peripheral Tissues. Deiodination appears to be the only metabolic transformation of thyroxine and triiodothyronine occurring in skeletal muscle. This tissue is thus useful as a starting material for purification of the deiodinating enzyme, thyroxine dehalogenase, although the level of the enzyme is higher in liver and kidney. Partially purified preparations, specific for thyronines, did not attack iodinated tyrosines, in contrast to the thyroid or liver *dehalogenase.*

Thyroxine dehalogenase of muscle is activated by flavins and ferrous ions and attacks thyroxine at approximately three to four times the rate with triiodothyronine. Iodide is the major product from the organically bound iodine. The enzyme is distinct from thyroid dehalogenase (page 834), which is without action on iodinated thyronines.

The physiological significance of thyroxine dehalogenase is not clear. It is not the mechanism for formation of triiodothyronine from thyroxine; the former is produced *de novo* by the thyroid. Deiodination appears to be a minor pathway for inactivating thyroid hormone, as compared with the active conjugating pathways. Suggestive evidence links the enzymic deiodination of thyroid hormones by skeletal muscle with their calorigenic action, although the exact nature of this relationship is not clear.

Excretion of Thyroidal Iodine. Only about 1 per cent of the total iodine in urine is present as iodothyronines, including the corresponding iodothyropyruvic and acetic acids; the remainder is largely inorganic iodide. Data concerning percentage and rate of elimination of iodine in urine and feces after administration of hormonal iodine are significant only in relation to the particular experimental conditions employed. The utilization of L-thyroxine in man is relatively slow, with a half-life of 7 to 12 days reported with therapeutic doses. In all cases the iodine atoms in positions 3′, or 3′,5′, of the aromatic structure are more labile than those in 3, or 3,5, since the former are excreted as iodide at a distinctly higher rate. The kidneys clear approximately 33 ml. of plasma of iodide per minute.

Relative Biological Activity of Thyronines. The relative biological activities of a number of iodothyronines are given in Table 46.2. In man, administration of the acetic acid analogues results in a thyroid-like effect which is more rapid and of shorter duration than that following triiodothyronine, which in turn acts more rapidly than thyroxine. Reference has been made previously (page 834) to the influence of the degree of protein binding, and therefore rapidity of transfer into tissues, in the expression of biological activity of thyronines. Notwithstanding this variable, the data in Table 46.2 suggest that substitution in the 3' position is significant for activity, although this must be accompanied by substitution in position 3. Further substitution of a single iodine atom also enhances activity. In all cases the 3,5,3'-triiodo derivatives are more active than the 3,5,3',5'-substituted compounds. Modifications of the alanine side chain increase potency (Table 46.2).

Table 46.2: RELATIVE BIOLOGICAL ACTIVITY OF IODOTHYRONINES AND IODOTHYRONINE ANALOGUES

Compound	Relative activity*	Compound	Relative activity†
DL-Thyroxine	100	DL-3,5,3'-Triiodothyropyruvic acid	100
DL-3,5,3'-Triiodothyronine	500–1,000	DL-3,5,3',5'-Tetraiodothyropropionic acid	9,500
DL-3,3',5'-Triiodothyronine	5	DL-3,5,3'-Triiodothyropropionic acid	27,000
DL-3,3'-Diiodothyronine	75	DL-3,5,3',5'-Tetraiodothyroacetic acid	1,100
DL-3',5'-Diiodothyronine	25	DL-3,5,3'-Triiodothyroacetic acid	1,900
DL-3,5-Diiodothyronine	0	DL-3,5,3'-Triiodothyrocarboxylic acid	155
DL-3'-Monoiodothyronine	0		
DL-3,5,3',5'-Tetraiodothyro-pyruvic acid	30		

* The relative activities are approximately the same whether based on antigoitrogenic potency in the rat or on tadpole metamorphosis.

† These data are based on assay by the tadpole metamorphosis technique only. Assay of DL-3,5,3'-triiodothyropropionic acid for antigoitrogenic activity in the rat gives a potency the same as that of DL-thyroxine, and that for DL-3,5,3',5'-tetraiodothyropropionic acid as 75 per cent that of DL-thyroxine.

SOURCE: After J. Roche and R. Michel, *Recent Progr. Hormone Research.*, **12**, 1, 1956, and R. Michel and R. Pitt-Rivers, *Biochem. Biophys. Acta,* **24,** 213, 1957.

ANTITHYROID AGENTS

The term antithyroid agent is generally employed to designate any substance inhibiting normal thyroid function. These agents include the following: (1) Those which prevent release of hormone from the thyroid by a feedback mechanism (page 490). The outstanding example is thyroxine, which affects secretion and activity of hypophyseal thyrotropic hormone; this will be considered in Chap. 51. (2) Agents which retard synthesis of hormone; this group includes thiocyanate, and certain other anions, which inhibit iodide uptake by the thyroid, iodide, and synthetic thiocarbamides and sulfonamides, which interfere with the iodination reaction (page 831). (3) Substances that inhibit utilization of thyroid hormones, viz., structural analogues. In addition, I[131] administration in high doses and deep x-ray therapy of the thyroid will also depress thyroid activity by destruction of thyroid tissue.

Iodide. The marked localization of administered iodide in the thyroid gland and its role in normal thyroid function have been discussed. It is therefore seemingly paradoxical that hyperactivity of the thyroid, as seen in toxic goiter, can be diminished by administration of large doses of iodide in the form of iodine-potassium iodide solution (Lugol's solution). This procedure has long been useful clinically in toxic, or exophthalmic, goiter and as a therapeutic measure prior to surgical removal of a portion of the thyroid gland.

Chaikoff and associates demonstrated that iodide uptake by the thyroid is completely prevented when plasma iodide rises above approximately 30 μg per 100 ml. of plasma. In vitro, iodide ion inhibits iodination of tyrosine by elemental iodine. It would appear that in simple goiter *iodine* is required for hormone synthesis, whereas in toxic goiter *iodide* may be functioning to inhibit iodine utilization, perhaps by forming a molecular complex with the latter.

Thiocyanate. In 1936 Barker observed that some hypertensive patients treated with potassium thiocyanate exhibited enlargement of the thyroid and a myxedema-like swelling of the face. Later, it was found that daily administration of small amounts of thyroid reversed within 2 weeks the changes produced by thiocyanate. The action of thiocyanate ion on the thyroid is shared by certain other anions, notably perchlorate and nitrate. The thyroid-inhibiting effect of these ions is due to inhibition of uptake of iodide by the gland (page 831). Their action differs from that of other antithyroidal agents in being readily counteracted by administration of iodide salts.

Thiocyanate is widely distributed in nature, occurring normally in blood, saliva, urine, and in many plants, such as members of the *Brassica* genus (cabbages) and Umbelliferae. Of added significance is the occurrence of substances which may be transformed into thiocyanates by the mammalian organism. These include the isothiocyanates, such as mustard oil, the organic nitriles, and the widely distributed cyanogenetic glycosides. It is possible that a large consumption of foods containing these substances would render iodine-deficient a diet otherwise adequate in iodine. This might explain the existence of endemic goiter in certain regions of the world where the iodine of the soil and water is seemingly adequate.

Thiocarbamides and Sulfonamides. There are many organic compounds which may be classed as antithyroid substances. Aside from structural analogues of thyroxine (see below), the antithyroid substances can be divided roughly into two main groups, the most active of which have in common a thiocarbamide grouping, as for example thiourea and thiouracil.

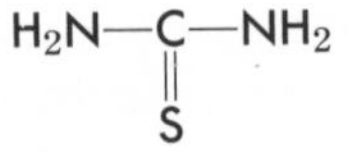

Thiourea 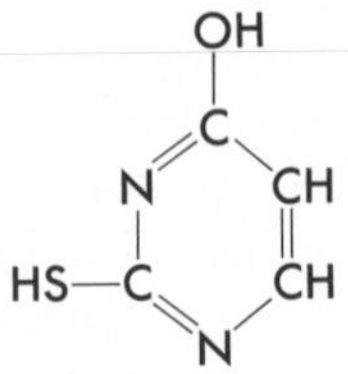   **Thiouracil**

A second group is that with an aminobenzene grouping, the best known of which are the sulfonamides; the most active of such compounds are 4,4′-diamino-diphenylmethane and 4,4′-diaminobenzil.

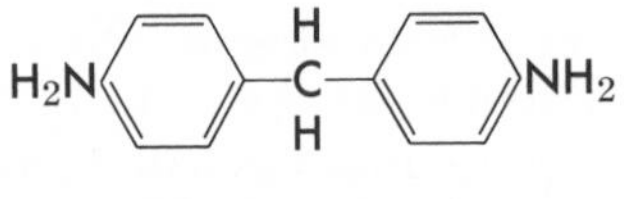

4,4′-Diaminodiphenylmethane 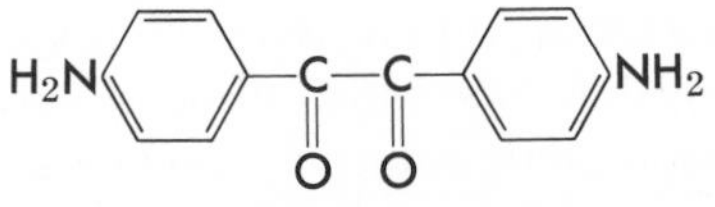   **4,4′-Diaminobenzil**

The antithyroid activity of thiocarbamides and sulfonamides was first described by Mackenzie and Mackenzie, who observed striking enlargement of the thyroid in rats ingesting a purified diet to which sulfaguanidine had been added. Concomitantly, the animals exhibited a diminished basal metabolic rate. Suppression of thyroid function as a consequence of sulfonamide therapy has been observed clinically.

It is generally agreed that the thiocarbamides and sulfonamides act to inhibit synthesis of thyroid hormone, as does the iodide ion, by forming molecular compounds with elemental iodine in the gland, thus preventing iodination and subsequent hormone formation. A few of the very active aromatic antithyroid substances act by forming stable substitution compounds with the gland iodine.

Many hundreds of synthetic compounds have been prepared in efforts to find nontoxic antithyroid drugs. Major attention has been devoted to thiouracil and its derivatives. Activity is enhanced by substitution of alkyl or aryl groups in position 6. When the alkyl group is a propyl substituent, activity is maximal and decreases with further lengthening of the alkyl side chain. Propyl thiouracil has had clinical usefulness in hyperthyroidism.

Cobalt. Kriss and his associates have described clinical and experimental evidence of depressed thyroid function, including goiters and clinical myxedema, in subjects given cobaltous chloride for treatment of anemia. Experimentally, cobaltous chloride administration suppressed I^{131} uptake. Evidence was obtained that cobalt ion acts directly on the thyroid to inhibit reactions concerned with the synthesis and secretion of thyroid hormones. These observations suggest that possibly other metals may exert undesirable influences on thyroid function.

Thyronine Analogues. A number of synthetic thyronine analogues of the thyroid hormone have antithyroid or thyroid hormone–inhibiting properties. Thus, 2',6'-diiodothyronine,

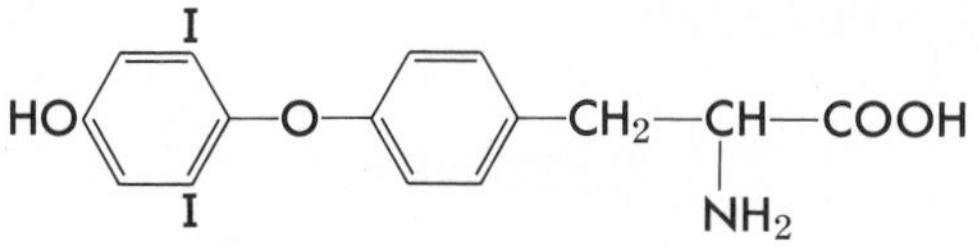

was able to antagonize thyroxine in a dose 150 times that of thyroxine and showed inhibitory action against injected thyroglobulin. Also, as in the case of compounds with thyroxine-like activity, the entire side chain is not essential for thyroxine-inhibiting action. For example, the benzyl ether of 3,5-diiodo-4-hydroxybenzoic acid,

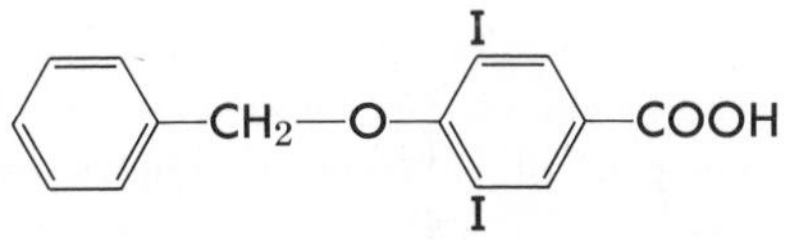

was capable of reducing the metabolic effectiveness of thyroxine. These thyroxine analogues block the effects of thyroid hormone in tissues, presumably by competing with the hormone in some essential reaction. These analogues have had little practical importance as thyroid inhibitors, chiefly because of the clinical efficacy of the antithyroid compounds described in the preceding section.

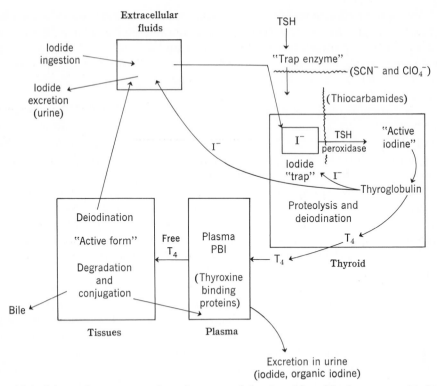

FIG. 46.4. Schematic representation of aspects of the thyroid and its hormones; T_4 designates thyroxine.

In Fig. 46.4 are depicted certain aspects of the thyroid and its hormones that have been considered in this chapter.

REFERENCES

Books

Pitt-Rivers, R., and Tata, J. R., "The Thyroid Hormones," Pergamon Press, New York, 1959.
Werner, S. C., ed., "The Thyroid," 2d ed., Harper & Row, Publishers, Incorporated, New York, 1962.
Wolstenholme, G. E. W., and Millar, E. C. P., eds., "Regulation and Mode of Action of Thyroid Hormones," Little, Brown and Company, Boston, 1957.

Review Articles

Barker, S. B., New Ideas of Thyroid Function, *The Physiologist,* **6,** 94–114, 1963.
Greer, M. A., The National Occurrence of Goitrogenic Agents, *Recent Progr. Hormone Research,* **18,** 187–219, 1962.
Hoch, F. L., Biochemical Actions of Thyroid Hormones, *Physiol. Revs.,* **42,** 605–613, 1962.
Ingbar, S. H., and Freinkel, N., Regulation of Peripheral Metabolism of the Thyroid Hormones, *Recent Progr. Hormone Research,* **16,** 353–403, 1960.
Lardy, H. A., and Maley, G. F., Metabolic Effects of Thyroid Hormones in Vitro, *Recent Progr. Hormone Research,* **10,** 129–155, 1954.

Myant, N. B., ed., Thyroid Gland, *Brit. Med. Bull.,* **16,** 89–169, 1960.

Nadler, N. J., and Leblond, C. P., The Site and Rate of Formation of Thyroid Hormone, *Brookhaven Symp. Biol.,* **7,** 40–60, 1955.

Pitt-Rivers, R., Mode of Action of Antithyroid Compounds, *Physiol. Revs.,* **30,** 194–205, 1950.

Rawson, R. W., ed., Modern Concepts of Thyroid Physiology, *Ann. N.Y. Acad. Sci.,* **86,** 311–675, 1960.

Robbins, J., and Rall, J. E., Proteins Associated with the Thyroid Hormone, *Physiol. Revs.,* **40,** 415–489, 1960.

Roche, J., and Michel, R., Natural and Artificial Iodoproteins, *Advances in Protein Chem.,* **6,** 253–297, 1951.

Roche, J., and Michel, R., Nature and Metabolism of Thyroid Hormones, *Recent Progr. Hormone Research,* **12,** 1–26, 1956.

Soderberg, U., Temporal Characteristics of Thyroid Activity, *Physiol. Revs.,* **39,** 777–810, 1959.

Symposium, Regulation of Thyroidal Function, *Federation Proc.,* **21,** 623–641, 1962.

Tata, J. R., Intracellular and Extracellular Mechanisms for the Utilization and Action of Thyroid Hormones, *Recent Progr. Hormone Research,* **18,** 187–268, 1962.

Wolff, J., Transport of Iodide and Other Anions in the Thyroid Gland, *Physiol. Revs.,* **44,** 45–90, 1964.

47. The Parathyroids

The parathyroid glands exert a striking influence on calcium and phosphate metabolism. The detailed mechanism underlying these effects is unknown, but there are suggestions that they are secondary to more direct actions of the parathyroid hormone on some aspects of carbohydrate metabolism (see below). However, this remains to be established. Products with parathyroid hormonal activity have a marked calcium-mobilizing action and promote urinary excretion of phosphate. Both these effects have been utilized in bioassay procedures necessary for isolation and characterization of the hormone, as well as to gain insight into its mechanism of action.

CHEMICAL NATURE OF THE PARATHYROID HORMONE

The existence and relative stability of the parathyroid hormone (parathormone) were established in 1925 by Collip, who showed that injection of an extract of beef parathyroid glands, prepared by the use of acid and elevated temperatures, pro-

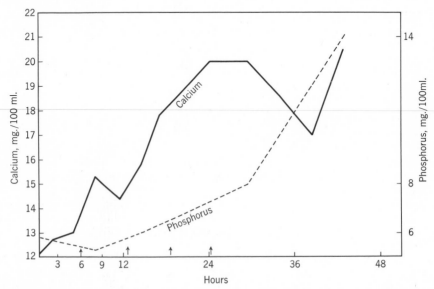

FIG. 47.1. Effect of repeated injections (indicated by arrows) of parathyroid hormone–containing extracts on the blood calcium and inorganic phosphorus concentrations of a normal dog. (*From J. B. Collip, Harvey Lectures,* **21,** 113, 1925–1926.)

844

duced a marked elevation in the serum calcium level of normal dogs (Fig. 47.1). The active principle(s) have repeatedly been shown to be polypeptide in character.

Definitive chemical characterization of active products has been achieved in recent years by Rasmussen and Craig. A group of relatively pure and biologically active polypeptides can be obtained from parathyroid tissue, depending on the methods used for extraction and purification. Table 47.1 summarizes certain of the properties of some biologically active parathyroid polypeptides. The product of largest molecular weight is obtained with initial use of a mild phenol extraction procedure, suggesting that the other polypeptides may arise as a consequence of degradative phenomena. Indeed, it is possible to prepare physiologically active products by enzymic or mild acidic hydrolysis of the largest polypeptide (molecular weight—8,500). The smallest peptide contains 33 amino acid residues and possesses, on a molecular basis, one-sixth of the activity of the parent polypeptide.

Three of the polypeptides in the table (Nos. 1, 2, and 3), shown to be pure and homogeneous by a variety of physical chemical criteria, exhibit both calcium-mobilizing and phosphaturic effects. This makes untenable earlier suggestions that the parathyroid glands may secrete two hormones, each with only one type of biological action. There also appears to be a direct correlation between the biological potency of a preparation and its size. The absence of cystine in the polypeptide chain of parathyroid hormone and the single amino-terminal alanine residue suggest a straight-chain polypeptide structure.

Table 47.1: SOME PROPERTIES OF BIOLOGICALLY ACTIVE PARATHYROID POLYPEPTIDES

Properties	Polypeptide preparation			
	No. 1*	No. 2†	No. 3‡	No. 4‡
Molecular weight...................	8,500	6,900	5,600	3,800
Relative biological activity:				
Calcium-mobilizing................	2,750	1,500	1,050	850
Phosphaturic.....................	3,000	1,400	800	§
Amino-terminal residue..............	Alanine	Alanine	§	§
Total amino acid residues.............	74	62	51	33

* Phenol-extracted.
† Acetic acid–extracted.
‡ Hydrochloric acid–extracted.
§ Data not available.
SOURCE: After H. Rasmussen and L. C. Craig, *Recent Progr. Hormone Research,* **18,** 269, 1962.

PARATHYROID HORMONE FUNCTIONS

The principal sites of regulatory influence of parathyroid hormone are the kidney, the skeleton, and the gastrointestinal tract. Although controversy has existed regarding which is the primary site of hormonal action, it seems clear that parathyroid hormone may influence directly and independently any one of the three.

Renal Actions. Hypersecretion of the parathyroids, or injection of active hormonal preparations, induces a marked phosphaturia (page 731). This is accompanied by elevation of the level of blood calcium, which is drawn from the bones, the chief reservoir of calcium ion. Conversely, hyposecretion of the parathyroids, or experimental extirpation of the glands, results in diminished phosphate excretion in the urine, with elevation of phosphate concentration in the blood, accompanied by depression of blood calcium values.

A direct influence of the parathyroids upon the mammalian renal tubule was demonstrated by infusion of purified hormone into one renal artery of the dog. This led to unilateral phosphaturia without alterations in filtration rate or renal plasma flow. Of the two mechanisms which have been suggested to account for this phosphaturia, *viz.*, (1) an increase in secretion of phosphate by the distal tubule, and

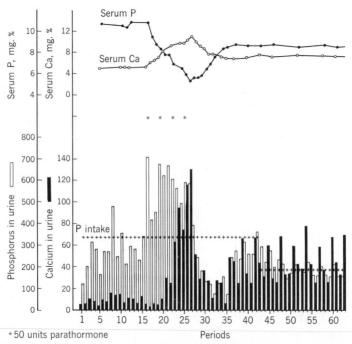

FIG. 47.2. Effects of parathyroid hormone in a patient with idiopathic hypoparathyroidism. Food intake constant in amount and composition during each 8-hr. period. Note immediate increase in excretion of phosphate (negative balance) accompanied by reversals of the high serum phosphate and low serum calcium levels. There was a much later increase in urinary calcium, as the serum calcium rose above 8 mg. per 100 ml. of plasma. The calcium and phosphorus excretion values are given as total milligrams per each 8-hr. period. (*From F. Albright and R. J. Ellsworth, J. Clin. Invest., 7, 183, 1929.*)

(2) a decrease in proximal tubular reabsorption of phosphate, considerably more experimental evidence has been accumulated in support of the first.

Renal effects noted after administration of purified parathyroid hormone to a hypoparathyroid patient include a diuresis; an increased total solute, phosphate, citrate, potassium, and magnesium excretion; and a rise in urinary pH. Some of the effects of the hormone are illustrated in Fig. 47.2.

Actions on Bone. A direct effect of parathyroid hormone on bone has been demonstrated both in vivo and in vitro. When parathyroid glands from 10-day-old mice were attached to parietal bone from the same animal and transplanted to the cerebral hemisphere of a litter mate, it was found that 10 to 14 days later, the side of the bone nearer the transplant was undergoing rapid resorption, whereas new bone deposition was occurring on the other side. In vitro, addition of parathyroid hormone to cultures of embryonic bone stimulated resorption. These data are consistent with a direct effect of parathyroid hormone on calcium transport from bone. The hormone increases osteoclastic activity with augmented connective tissue proliferation.

A stimulation of glycolytic activity in bone and kidney slices in vitro was observed when these tissues were taken from rabbits given a single injection of parathyroid hormone. The latter has also been reported to augment production of citrate and lactate by bone cells, although these changes, particularly in citrate, have not been uniformly observed. The stimulation of acid production in bone by the parathyroid hormone has formed the basis of a theory of the mechanism of bone resorption, since the lower pH could result in calcium mobilization, favoring transfer of calcium from bone to blood.

Action on Gastrointestinal Tract. Some evidence has accumulated that the parathyroid hormone augments calcium absorption from the gastrointestinal tract. This process involves calcium uptake by cells of intestinal mucosal villi, with its subsequent release to the blood. The hormone exerts its influence on the rate of release of the intracellularly bound calcium; this action is dependent on adequate nutritional status with respect to vitamin D (Chap. 56).

Other Actions of Parathyroid Hormone. Rasmussen and his associates have demonstrated that in vitro addition of purified parathyroid hormone preparations to rat liver mitochondria stimulates Ca^{++} release and phosphate entry, with an accompanying increased rate of electron transport. Stimulation of glutamate oxidation by the mitochondria, with uncoupling of oxidative phosphorylation, also resulted from addition of the hormone. The possible significance of these observations for understanding of parathyroid hormone remains to be established.

Other indicated actions of parathyroid hormone upon tissues in vitro need confirmation. Reported stimulation of glucose utilization by lens tissue in vitro upon addition of parathyroid hormone is of interest in view of the incidence of cataract in clinical hypoparathyroidism (page 814).

REGULATION OF SECRETION OF THE PARATHYROID HORMONE

The meager nerve supply of the parathyroid glands limits the likelihood that parathyroid secretion is regulated solely by the nervous system. Rather, the available data suggest that the hormone-secreting cells of the parathyroid glands are sensitive to the serum $[Ca^{++}]$. Thus, when serum $[Ca^{++}]$ falls, secretion of parathyroid hormone increases, and when the serum $[Ca^{++}]$ rises, the hormonal secretion rate declines. If serum [Ca^{++}] is lowered by injection of fluoride or oxalate, it will return to normal values only if the parathyroids are intact. In parathyroidectomized animals treated in this manner, the serum calcium level remains low. Also, Luckhardt demonstrated that when blood from a hypocalcemic animal was perfused through a parathyroid gland and then injected into another animal, the latter exhibited hypercalcemia. In contrast, if blood with a normal calcium content is perfused through the parathyroid and then administered to another animal, hypercalcemia is not observed. Thus, the blood [Ca^{++}] provides a basis for a "feedback" mechanism for regulation of parathyroid hormone secretion.

The regulatory influence of [Ca^{++}] on parathyroid activity has also been demonstrated in vitro. Addition of Ca^{++} to a medium in which parathyroid glands from 13-day-old chick embryos were cultured suppressed mitotic activity, cytoplasmic activity, and secretion of the glands. In contrast, media low in [Ca^{++}] stimulated mitotic activity, and increased secretion of parathyroid hormone by the chick glands. The responses observed were relatively specific for parathyroid tissue and for Ca^{++}.

HYPOPARATHYROIDISM

Descriptions of the effects of hypoparathyroidism resulted first from operations on the thyroid gland, with attendant inadvertent damage to, or removal of, the parathyroids. Within a few days postoperatively there result hypocalcemia, convulsions, tetany, and, in the absence of therapy, a fatal outcome. The symptoms are a reflection of the role of calcium in maintaining normal neuromuscular irritability (page 778).

HYPERPARATHYROIDISM

Symptoms resulting from an excess of parathyroid secretion may be produced in animals by prolonged administration of parathyroid extracts, and occur in man because of a tumor or hyperplasia of the parathyroids. Severe, primary clinical hyperparathyroidism leads to *osteitis fibrosa cystica,* characterized by elevation of serum [Ca^{++}], diminished phosphate concentration, and markedly increased renal excretion of calcium. The augmented calcium excretion frequently causes formation of urinary calculi, with secondary impairment of renal function. When this ensues, excretion of phosphate and calcium declines, serum phosphate level rises, and calcium returns to normal levels. However, resorption of bone mineral continues during this period, and calcium and phosphate which do not appear in the urine may be excreted in the stool. Also, with excessive loss of calcium, disseminated cystic decalcification of bone results, with markedly increased susceptibility to fractures. The alterations in bone metabolism are accompanied by an increase in serum alkaline phosphatase.

Hyperparathyroidism, and its attendant symptoms, may also be encountered in man with chronic renal insufficiency. The retention of phosphate as a consequence of renal disease depresses the serum calcium level, stimulating parathyroid hormone production (see above), and may lead to parathyroid hyperplasia.

REFERENCES

Books

Albright, F., and Reifenstein, E. C., Jr., "The Parathyroid Glands and Metabolic Bone Disease," The Williams & Wilkins Company, Baltimore, 1948.

Greep, R. O., and Talmage, R. V., eds., "The Parathyroids," Charles C Thomas, Publisher, Springfield, Ill., 1961.

Review Articles

Geschwind, I. I., Hormonal Control of Calcium, Phosphorus, Iodine, Iron, Sulfur and Magnesium Metabolism, in C. L. Comar and F. Bronner, eds., "Mineral Metabolism," vol. I, part B, pp. 387–472, Academic Press, Inc., New York, 1961.

Greep, R. O., and Kenny, A. D., Physiology and Chemistry of the Parathyroids, in G. Pincus and K. V. Thimann, eds., "The Hormones: Physiology, Chemistry and Applications," vol. III, pp. 153–174, Academic Press, Inc., New York, 1955.

Rasmussen, H., Parathyroid Hormone, Nature and Mechanism of Action, *Am. J. Med.,* **30,** 112–128, 1961.

Rasmussen, H., and Craig, L. C., The Parathyroid Polypeptides, *Recent Progr. Hormone Research,* **18,** 269–295, 1962.

48. The Gonads

Androgens (Gk. *andros,* male) and estrogens (Gk. *oistros,* a gadfly, hence: sting, frenzy) are generic terms for the hormones secreted chiefly by the testis and ovary, respectively, and responsible for the development of secondary sex characteristics. However, estrogens have been isolated from testis and androgens from ovarian tissue. The common embryological development of the testes and ovaries may account for the production of both male and female sex hormones by both sexes. These hormones are also found in other tissues of the body, *e.g.*, the adrenals and the placenta.

THE TESTES—MALE SEX HORMONES

Effects of Castration. The relation of the testes to masculinity has been known since ancient times because of the eunuchoid state resulting from castration. This operation is followed, in the immature of all species, by a failure of development of accessory sex characteristics. In the young castrated stag, the antlers do not develop. Castration in the cockerel prevents normal development of the comb, wattles, and barbels, and the sex instincts do not appear.

In the human male, castration prior to puberty retards ossification of the epiphyses of the long bones, with consequent enlargement of the stature. The lower limbs become disproportionately long; there is increased adiposity, with the distribution of lipid resembling that in the female. The larynx is not prominent, as in the mature male, and the voice remains high-pitched. Although hair may be plentiful on the head, it fails to grow on the face and body. The penis remains infantile, and sexual feelings fail to develop. Muscular strength may be significantly diminished. If castration is performed after puberty, the changes are generally those described above for the prepubertal individual, but the effect is much less intensive.

Effects of Male Sex Hormone. Administration of androgenic compounds prevents the alterations produced by castration and will to a significant degree reverse the changes in the castrate animal, restoring normal conditions. Metabolic effects of androgens on the sex organs and tissues include increased fructose production by seminal vesicles and utilization of this sugar by seminal plasma, with concomitant enhancement of the activity of both aldose reductase and ketose reductase (page 366). Administration of androgens to the rat increased the rate of amino acid incorporation into prostatic tissue proteins, and stimulated citric acid and fatty acid synthesis by this tissue. Studies of protein synthesis by broken cell preparations of prostatic tissue suggested that testosterone governs the levels of messenger RNA (page 602) attached to prostatic ribosomes.

Androgens exert a striking anabolic influence on nitrogen and calcium metabolism, increasing tissue growth in the younger animal. Testosterone has been used for enhancing growth of children prior to puberty. Androgens also augment sebaceous gland activity in the skin and are responsible in part for the severe acne vulgaris often evident at puberty.

A biological antagonism obtains between the androgens and the estrogens. Biological responses to male sex hormones are inhibited by simultaneous administration of female sex hormones, and vice versa. Thus, the stimulating effect of androgens on the growth of the capon's comb is retarded by simultaneous administration of estrogenically active substances. Use of female sex hormone in the poultry industry for caponizing young cockerels is another example of the biological antagonism between male and female sex hormones. Clinically, two examples may be cited: the resort to ovariectomy or testosterone administration for carcinoma of the breast, and the use of estrogens in treatment of carcinoma of the prostate, frequently supplemented by orchidectomy.

Chemistry of Male Sex Hormones. Brown-Séquard in 1889 probably recorded the first physiological effects of testicular extracts in experiments on himself. He noted an increased vigor and capacity for work. In 1911, Pézard produced comb growth in capons by injection of a saline extract of testicular tissue. A major advance was made in 1927 by McGee, who prepared highly potent extracts of bull testes with nonpolar solvents. A few years later, two crystalline compounds with androgenic activity, androsterone and dehydroepiandrosterone, were isolated from male human urine.

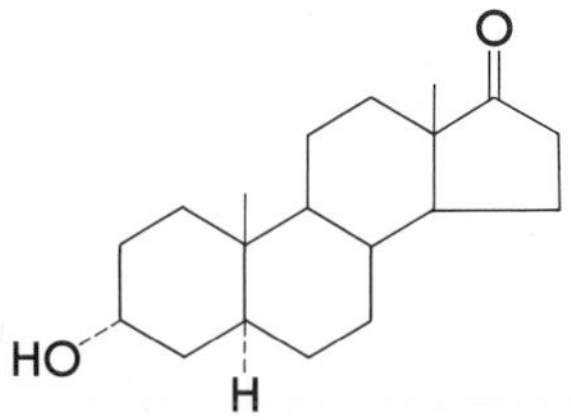

Androsterone 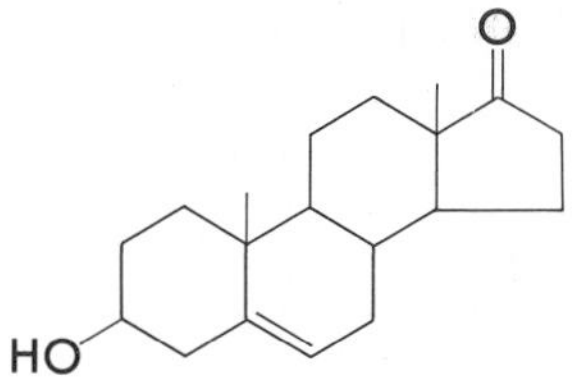   Dehydroepiandrosterone

Testosterone, which is ten times more active than androsterone, was isolated in crystalline form from bull testes by Laqueur and associates in 1935.

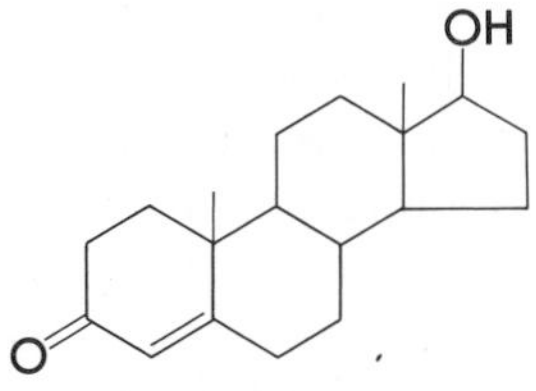

Testosterone

The source of androgens in the testes is the interstitial cells. Two additional androgens have been isolated from testes, 15α-hydroxytestosterone and 6β-hydroxytestosterone.

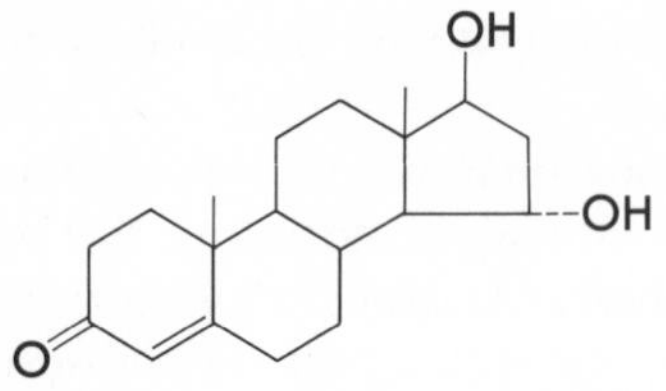

15α-Hydroxytestosterone

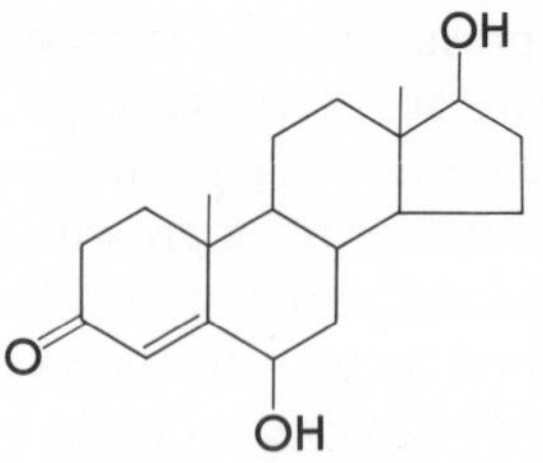

6β-Hydroxytestosterone

Compounds with androgenic activity are also synthesized in the adrenal gland (see below). These include the following:

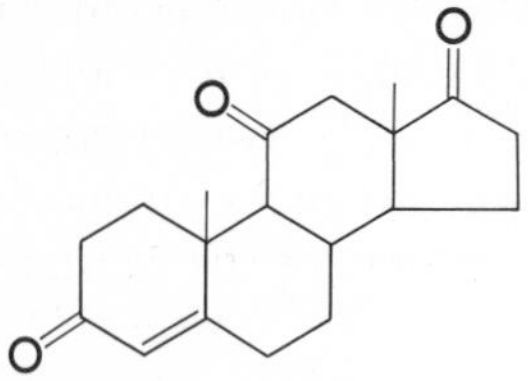

Adrenosterone

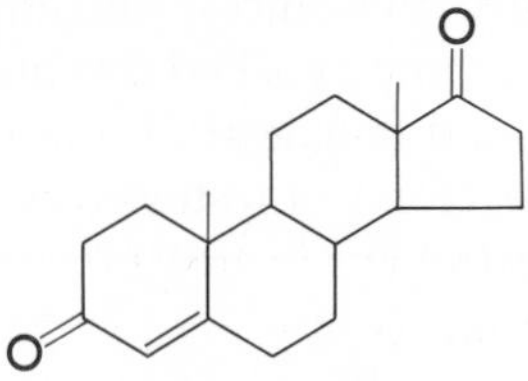

Androst-4-ene-3,17-dione

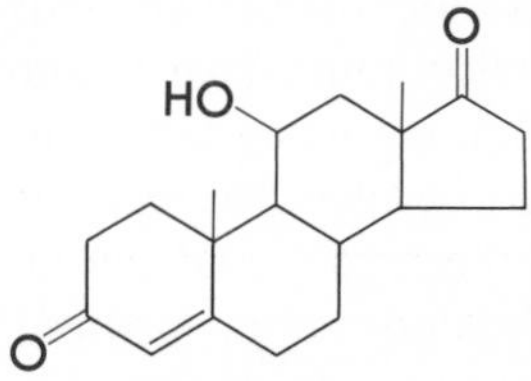

11β-Hydroxyandrost-4-ene-3,17-dione

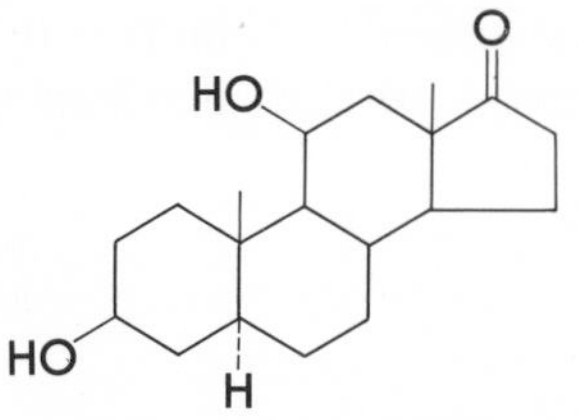

Androstane-3β,11β-diol-17-one
(11β-hydroxyepiandrosterone)

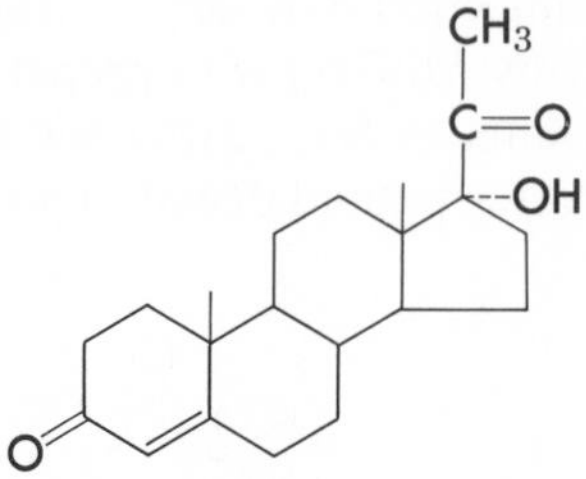

17α-Hydroxyprogesterone

In addition to the above-mentioned androgens, the 11β-hydroxy and 11-keto derivatives of androsterone and etiocholanolone (page 853) are present in urine as the glucosiduronides (page 410). Dehydroepiandrosterone is secreted by the adrenal gland primarily as the sulfate ester and appears in this form in the urine.

The 11-oxygenated C_{19} compounds are synthesized chiefly in the adrenal (see below) and may also arise from the catabolism of adrenal cortical steroids (page 888). This is an example of metabolic transformations which alter the biological activity of steroids from one type to another.

Androgen formation by the adrenal aids in understanding certain aspects of normal and abnormal adrenal function. Stimulation of the adrenal cortex by adrenocorticotropic hormone (Chap. 51) results in growth of the prostate and seminal vesicles of castrate rats, with accompanying adrenal cortical hypertrophy. This does not occur in adrenalectomized animals; therefore, the effective androgens have been derived from the adrenal cortex. The clinical features of *adrenal virilism,* due to a tumor or marked hyperplasia of the adrenal cortex (Chap. 49) and characterized by excessive masculinization of the female, furnish striking evidence for androgen production by the adrenal cortex. There is also a markedly increased excretion of urinary androgens. When abnormal growth of the adrenal cortex occurs in young children, puberty appears prematurely. Dorfman and his associates found 2.6 times as much testosterone formed in vitro from progesterone by slices of a human adrenal adenoma as compared to normal adrenal tissue under the same conditions.

Biogenesis of Androgens. The biogenesis of the steroid nucleus from acetate was discussed previously (page 471), and the conversion of cholesterol to adrenal cortical steroids is considered in the following chapter. Androgen biosynthesis from acetate and from cholesterol has also been demonstrated. Evidence for the nature of the synthetic pathways is based upon in vivo and in vitro studies, the latter using labeled precursors incubated with slices and broken cell preparations of testicular tissue derived chiefly from hog, rabbit, and man. Figure 48.1 illustrates the indicated pathways of testosterone synthesis in the testis. This sequence of reactions also occurs in the ovary, to a limited extent in the adrenal, and probably also in the placenta. A second pathway for androgen biosynthesis in the adrenal is also indicated in Fig. 48.1. In addition, androgens may be formed in peripheral tissues as a result of removal of the two-carbon side chain of circulating adrenal steroids (Chap. 49).

Metabolic Fates of Androgens. As indicated previously, androsterone and dehydroepiandrosterone were obtained from human urine prior to the isolation of testosterone from testicular tissue. Two additional C_{19} compounds, etiocholane-3α-ol-17-one (etiocholanolone) and epiandrosterone, also are present in urine.

Epiandrosterone   Etiocholane-3α-ol-17-one

Etiocholanolone and androsterone are quantitatively the *most important urinary androgen metabolites.* Etiocholanolone has a striking pyrogenic effect when administered to human subjects, and "etiocholanolone fever" of endogenous origin has been described clinically. Other pregnane metabolites share this pyrogenic effect.

Hydroxylation of the steroid nucleus at positions 11 and 18 also occurs in androgen metabolism, since the 11- and 18-hydroxy derivatives corresponding to androsterone and etiocholanolone have been isolated from the urine of a man given testosterone. Other C-11 and C-18 hydroxylated steroids will be encountered later in discussions of estrogens and adrenal cortical steroids.

The liver is a major site of metabolic transformations of androgens. In some species (*e.g.*, the rat), the bile, as well as the urine, is an important pathway for excretion of androgen metabolites; this is somewhat less significant in man. In the liver, four major types of reaction occur in androgen metabolism; the first three indicated are catalyzed by DPN- or TPN-requiring enzymic systems: (1) a reversible conver-

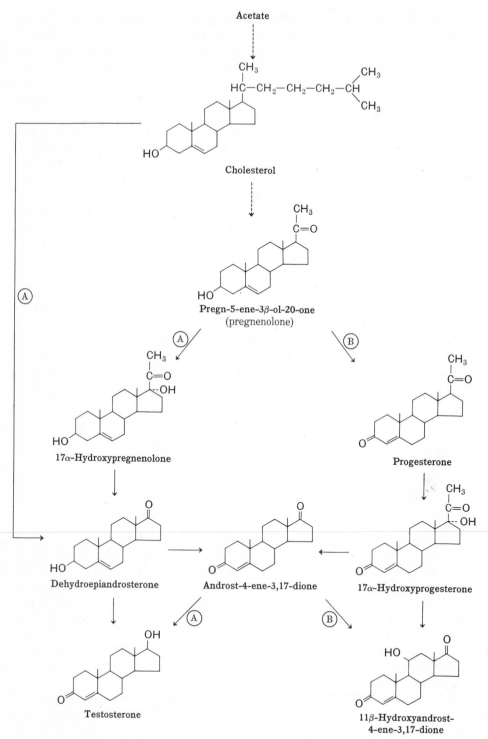

FIG. 48.1. Pathways for androgen biosynthesis; Ⓐ, in testis, ovary, adrenal gland, and placenta; Ⓑ, in adrenal gland.

sion of testosterone to androst-4-ene-3,17-dione; (2) reduction of the 4,5 double bond of ring A by a group of enzymes designated as Δ^4-*reductases;* (3) a reversible interconversion of 3-hydroxy and 3-keto derivatives, catalyzed by a group of enzymes termed *3α- and 3β-hydroxysteroid dehydrogenases;* and (4) formation of glucosiduronide conjugates of androgen metabolites. These conjugates are excreted in bile and urine. Urinary excretion of the sulfate ester of dehydroepiandrosterone was mentioned previously (page 852). Thus the androgens and their metabolites are present in urine in a conjugated, water-soluble, biologically inactive form. Treatment of urine with acid and heat, or with specific hydrolytic enzymes, *i.e.,* β-glucuronidase and sulfatase, liberates the biologically active androgens, which can then be extracted with nonpolar solvents.

Additional possible metabolic fates of androgens are suggested from observations that liver and testicular tissue can effect both dehydration of ring D, with formation of Δ^{16} derivatives, and 16α-hydroxylation. A number of 16α-hydroxy C_{19} steroids have been isolated from human urine. Experiments with C^{14}-labeled testosterone indicate that approximately 5 per cent of the administered steroid may appear as expired CO_2. The reactions involved in possible further degradation of testosterone metabolites are unknown.

Androgenic compounds other than those discussed above have been isolated from human urine in a variety of pathological conditions. These compounds are

Table 48.1: RELATIVE ANDROGENIC ACTIVITY OF SOME STEROIDS ISOLATED FROM NATURAL SOURCES

Steroid		Source	Approximate amount in μg equal to one I.U.*
Common name	Chemical name		
Testosterone..................	Androst-4-ene-17α-ol-3-one	Bull and stallion testes; spermatic vein blood	15
Androsterone..............	Androstane-3α-ol-i7-one	Human, pregnant cow, and bull urine	100
Dehydroepiandrosterone.....	Androst-5-ene-3β-ol-17-one	Human, pregnant cow, and bull urine	300
Epiandrosterone............	Androstane-3β-ol-17-one	Human and pregnant mare urine	700
Etiocholanolone............	Etiocholane-3α-ol-17-one	Human urine	Inactive at 1,200
Adrenosterone..............	Androst-4-ene-3,11,17-trione	Adrenal cortex	500
	Androst-4-ene-3,17-dione	Adrenal cortex; spermatic vein blood	100
17α-Hydroxyprogesterone....	Pregn-4-ene-17α-ol-3,20-dione	Adrenal cortex	500

* The international unit (I.U.) of androgens is established as the androgenic activity of 0.1 mg. of androsterone. The relative androgenic activities in this table are approximations on the basis of the capon's comb test and would not necessarily be similar to relative activities derived from mammalian bioassays.

SOURCE: After R. I. Dorfman, Biochemistry of Androgens, in G. Pincus and K. V. Thimann, eds., "The Hormones," vol. I, chap. 12, pp. 467–548, Academic Press, Inc., New York, 1948.

chemically related, and the term androgenic compounds is used to designate chemical relationships, *i.e.*, C_{19} steroids, not to imply that these substances are necessarily androgenically active steroids, since not all exhibit biological activity. The relative androgenic potency of certain compounds is shown in Table 48.1, which reveals that testosterone is the most potent of the biologically active androgens. This hormone is the principal androgen of the adult human male. Overproduction of androgens, *e.g.*, by adrenal cortical tumors, is relatively unimportant in the male since a degree of excess androgen does not alter overtly the physiological pattern. However, in the female, excessive androgen production by either the ovary or the adrenal cortex, more commonly the latter, may result in severe masculinization (page 886). The synthesis of androgens by patients with adrenal cancer has been noted previously (page 853).

Since each of the various urinary metabolites of testosterone has a ketone group at C-17, these substances are referred to as 17-ketosteroids, and their concentration in the urine is a useful index of endogenous production of androgenic hormones. The commonly employed methods for determination of 17-ketosteroids are based on their reaction with *m*-dinitrobenzene in alkaline solution to produce a characteristic purple color.

The daily 17-ketosteroid excretion in the normal adult female (4 to 17 mg.) is approximately two-thirds that of the male (6 to 28 mg.). Prior to puberty, 17-ketosteroid excretion is about one-third that of the adult. This difference is due to the 17-ketosteroid precursors contributed by the gonads; the remainder of the 17-ketosteroids of the urine are derived from C_{19} and C_{21} steroids of the adrenal cortex. Those 17-ketosteroids derived from the adrenal cortical hormones generally have an oxygen function (hydroxyl or keto group) at C_{11}, and are termed 11-oxy-17-ketosteroids. The relative concentrations of 11-deoxy- and 11-oxy-17-ketosteroids in urine have afforded an approximate index of the relative secretory activities of the testes and the adrenal cortex, respectively.

Plasma values reported for 17-ketosteroids in human plasma are, in μg per 100 ml., testosterone, 0.5 (men) and 0.1 (women); dehydroepiandrosterone, 90; androsterone, 60; etiocholanolone, 40; and 11β-hydroxyetiocholanolone, 15.

Reference has been made to the pyrogenic effect of etiocholanolone (page 853). It is possible that other so-called "end products" of steroid metabolism may exert biological effects. In vitro studies by Marks and his associates have revealed an interesting influence of dehydroepiandrosterone on the activity of glucose 6-phosphate dehydrogenase (page 387) of adrenal homogenates. When the concentration of enzyme was limiting, addition of dehydroepiandrosterone ($10^{-6}M$) caused a decrease in both the enzymic activity and TPNH formation. In contrast, when the concentration of TPN$^+$ was limiting, steroid addition stimulated the rate of oxidation of hexose to CO_2. The possible in vivo significance of these observations is not clear.

Androgen Analogues. Testosterone administered by mouth exhibits approximately one-sixth the potency of injected testosterone, presumably because of partial inactivation of orally administered testosterone by the liver (see above). A synthetic androgen, methyltestosterone, has the highest known androgenic potency when administered orally, and consequently has found wide clinical use.

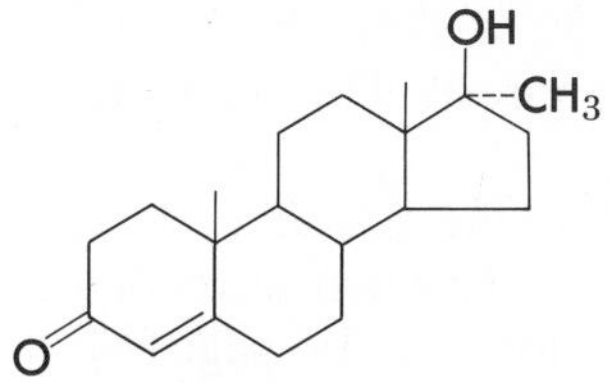

Methyltestosterone

Because of the anabolic effects of male sex hormones, as well as the therapeutic action of testosterone in carcinoma of the breast, extensive search has been made for structural analogues of androgens with the view of possible dissociation of desirable anabolic and therapeutic effects from the less desirable androgenic or masculinizing activity. Steroids without an angular methyl group in position 10 of the steroid nucleus (thus the methyl group which is C-19 is lacking) and termed *norsteroids* have proved to be of particular interest. For example, 19-nortestosterone and 17α-ethyl-19-nortestosterone,

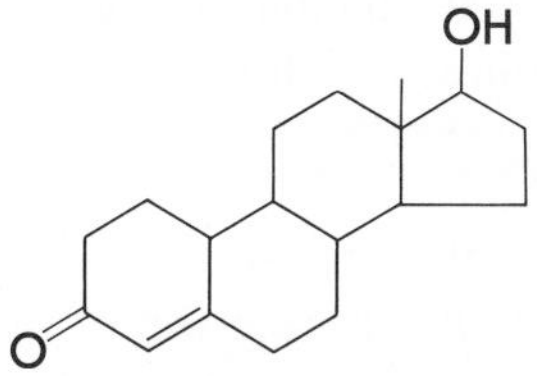

19-Nortestosterone   **17α-Ethyl-19-nortestosterone**

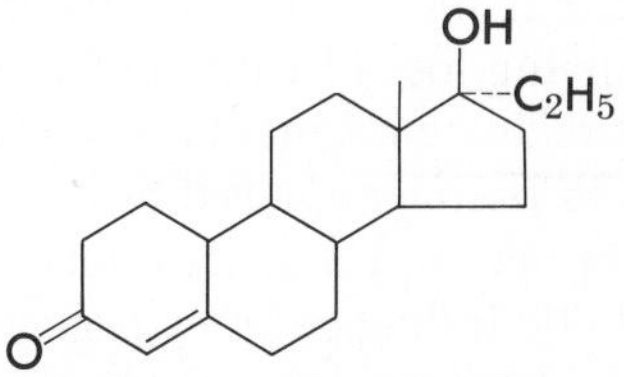

show on bioassay a relative anabolic to androgenic potency of about 20, whereas for testosterone propionate the ratio of these activities is approximately one. These two steroids also have a nitrogen-retaining activity in the human being, and favorably influence calcium balance.

THE OVARY—FEMALE SEX HORMONES

The Ovary and Sex Cycles in the Female. The ovaries are intimately concerned with two types of cyclic phenomena during which structural, functional, and chemical alterations occur: (1) the estrous, or menstrual, cycles, occurring during reproductive life; and (2) the reproductive cycle, also occurring during the span of sexually active life and repeated with each gestation. In the human being, the reproductive cycle is approximately ten times as long as the menstrual cycle.

The regulatory influence of the ovary in these cycles is the basis for the profound alterations seen following ovariectomy. If castration occurs prior to puberty, the female cycles never appear and the genital tissues remain infantile. Postpubertal castration results in cessation of the menstrual cycle, and atrophy of the uterus, vaginal mucosa, and fallopian tubes. In lower animals there is an accompanying loss of mating behavior. The secondary sex characteristics disappear at varying rates after ovariectomy. In prepubertal castrates, pubic and axillary hair is scant, the typical pelvic enlargement does not take place, and lipid deposition, distinctive of mammary growth, fails to occur. Postpubertal ovariectomy causes some involution of the mammary glands, a slow change in distribution of body hair, and gradual appearance of osteoporosis. The last is seen only after prolonged deprivation of estrogenic hormones.

Effects of Estrogens. During the ovarian cycle, estrogens induce (1) proliferation of the vaginal epithelium, (2) augmented secretion of mucus by the cervical glands, and (3) endometrial proliferation (see also page 864). Estrogen secretion is responsible for the secondary sex characteristics of the female, stimulating growth of axillary and pubic hair, maturation of the skin, alterations in body contour, and closure of the long-bone epiphyses. Estrogens stimulate proliferation of the mammary gland during pregnancy.

Estrogens exert profound metabolic effects on (1) inorganic metabolism, notably of calcium and phosphorus; (2) organic metabolism, chiefly of protein and lipid; and (3) skin and related structures. The antagonistic action of estrogens to androgenic influences has been noted previously (page 851).

Prolonged estrogen administration results in elevation of serum calcium and phosphate levels, with calcification and hyperossification of the long bones so extensive that the marrow cavity may disappear and anemia ensue. There is an accompanying loss of calcium from the pelvic bones, which become cystic. That estrogens regulate normal bone metabolism is suggested from the bone decalcification seen in postmenopausal osteoporosis.

Estrogens exert a general anabolic influence; this is marked in uterine tissue. The anabolic influence of estrogens is reflected in the stimulation of uterine and mammary gland growth produced by these hormones. Estrogen administration to rats produced in uterine tissue an acute stimulation of RNA and protein synthesis.

Estrogens exert a profound influence on lipid metabolism. In the fowl, administration of estrogen, or high levels of endogenous estrogen during egg formation, leads to a striking lipemia. In contrast, estrogen administration in man decreases the level of circulating blood lipids, particularly in individuals with hyperlipemia. This effect, together with the strikingly higher incidence of coronary disease in men as compared with women, has focused attention on a possible role of sex hormones in the etiology of atherosclerosis. However, no direct causal relationship has been established between blood lipid levels and coronary disease (see Chap. 22). Experimentally, concomitant administration of estrogens reduces the severity of the atherosclerosis induced by cholesterol feeding in chickens. This has led to a search for compounds which may similarly affect lipid metabolism but are devoid of feminizing effects produced in the male by estrogen treatment.

Estrogens are also lipotropic in mammals, *i.e.*, will prevent liver lipid accumulation when administered to animals on a diet deficient in a source of methyl groups (page 457). It is noteworthy that uterine tissue contains an estrogen-dependent lipid-synthesizing system which shows one of the earliest detectable responses of this tissue to estrogen. An early augmentation of phosphatide turnover was also seen in uterine tissue in vitro, following in vivo injection of estrogen.

The increased secretory activity of the skin sebaceous glands, induced by testosterone, is diminished by estrogen injection. The skin and associated structures are also affected by direct local application of estrogenic substances. This is seen in the growth of the mammary gland, occurring as a result of direct application of estrogens, inhibition of hair growth in rats and dogs by topical application of estrogens, and the inhibition of the chick comb growth response to androgen by simultaneous inunction with estrogen.

The carbonic anhydrase activity in the reproductive tract is influenced by estrogens. The significance of this is unknown, particularly since there are species variation in response of carbonic anhydrase activity of, for example, the uterus to estrogens. However, the marked increase in carbonic anhydrase activity of rabbit endometrium and the uterus of the immature mouse to minute quantities of injected estrogen has provided a sensitive bioassay method for estrogens.

Chemistry of Estrogens. Studies of the chemistry of secretions influencing the female sex cycles were stimulated in 1917 by Stockard and Papanicolaou, who demonstrated that the types of cells seen in smears of the vaginal epithelium of the guinea pig could be correlated with the stage of development of ovarian follicles. At the time that large follicles develop and ovulation occurs, the vaginal epithelial cells are cornified. In contrast, in castrate animals the vaginal smear contains only few leukocytes and epithelial cells. In 1923, Allen and Doisy adapted this information to a quantitative bioassay in mice and rats for estrogenic substances. The latter are administered to castrate female mice or rats, and vaginal smears of the animals examined under the microscope. The minimal dose required to produce a significant number of cornified epithelial cells is then ascertained.

In 1923, Allen and Doisy obtained a product from graafian follicles of sow ovaries and showed that it could replace the endocrine functions of the ovaries. The active substance of the extracts was termed the ovarian follicular hormone. Materials similarly active were found in corpora lutea, in blood, and in urine, the concentration being particularly high in the urine of pregnant women. From this last source, two estrogenically active compounds were isolated by Doisy and his colleagues and are known as *estrone* and *estriol*. A third crystalline estrogen, *estradiol*, was first prepared in the laboratory by reduction of the C-17 ketone group of estrone to a hydroxyl group, with formation of the α and the β isomers. *β-Estradiol*, which was isolated from follicular fluid of sows' ovaries and also from the urine of pregnant women, is *the normally secreted ovarian hormone*. The α form has also been isolated from pregnant mare urine. The structures of these four estrogens are shown below, and their relative physiological potency is indicated in Table 48.2.

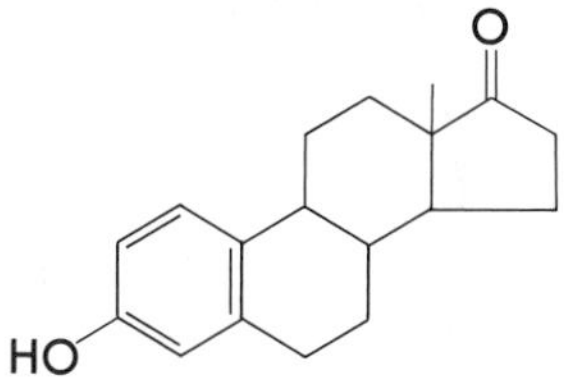

Estrone   β-Estradiol   α-Estradiol

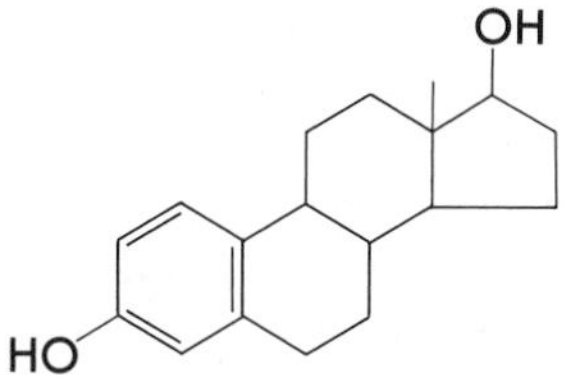

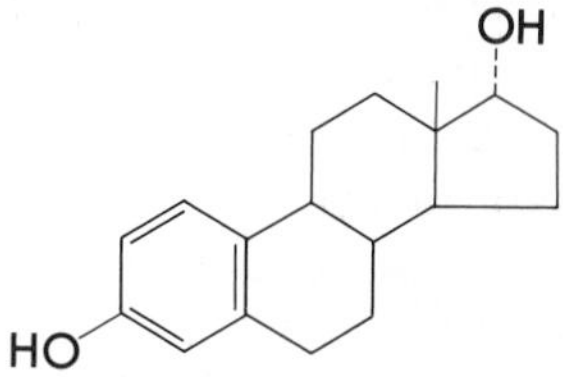

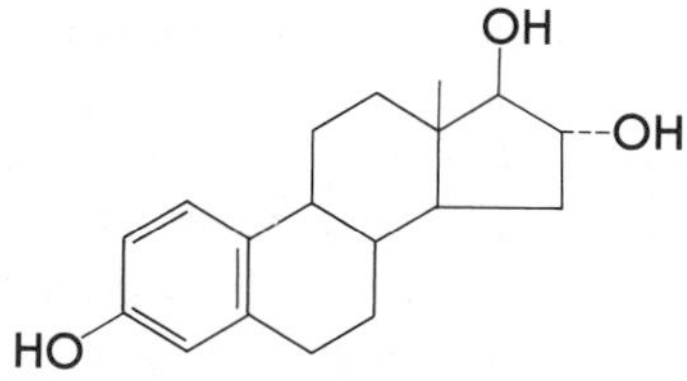

Estriol

The estrogenic steroids are C_{18} compounds, as compared with the C_{19} androgens. In the naturally occurring estrogens, there is no angular methyl group at position 10, and ring A is aromatic.

Table 48.2: COMPARATIVE PHYSIOLOGICAL POTENCY OF THE ESTROGENS

Compound	Effective dose levels for vaginal response in rats		μg per		Relative activity	
	Subcut., μg	Oral, μg	Rat unit	Mouse unit	Spayed-rat method	Immature mouse—uterine-weight method
Estrone.....	0.7	20–30	1.0	1.0	100	100
β-Estradiol..	0.3–0.4	20–30	0.08–0.125	0.05	1,000	1,000
α-Estradiol..	......	.....	3.2–12.5	1.25	10	7.5
Estriol	......	.....	....	....	20	40

SOURCE: After W. H. Pearlman, The Chemistry and Metabolism of the Estrogens, in G. Pincus and K. V. Thimann, eds., "The Hormones," vol. I, chap. 10, pp. 351–405, Academic Press, Inc., New York, 1948.

Although the ovaries and placenta are the chief sources of estrogenic hormones in the human being, the estrogenic content of horse *testis* is higher than that of any other endocrine organ. Indeed, stallion urine was early demonstrated to be rich in estrogenic substance and is the richest known source of β-estradiol. The physiological significance of these observations is not clear. Two estrogenic substances, obtained from pregnant mare urine, are apparently peculiar for this species. These are equilin and equilenin, with, respectively, approximately one-third and one-tenth the potency of estrone.

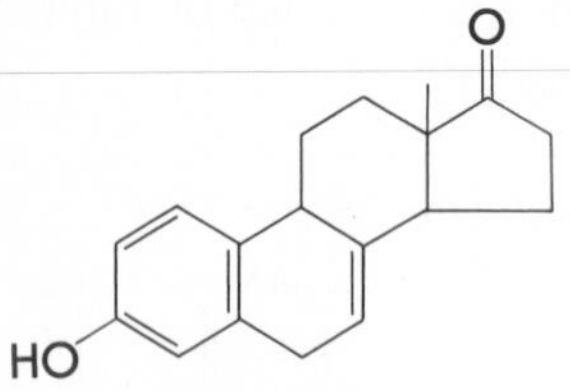

Equilin 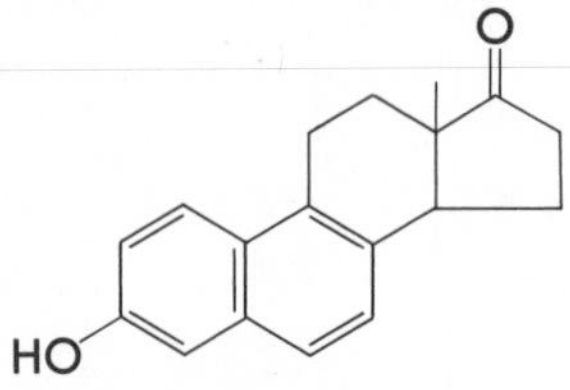   Equilenin

Biogenesis of Estrogens. The ovary is the principal site of estrogen production in the nonpregnant female. Surprisingly, the immediate precursor of the female sex hormones is the male sex hormone, testosterone. Formation of estrogens from testosterone has been observed in the presence of slices, broken cell preparations, or cell fractions of human ovarian, placental, testicular, or adrenal tissue, as well as of stallion testicular tissue. The probable pathways of estrogen biosynthesis are outlined in Fig. 48.2. The reactions leading from acetate to androst-4-ene-3,17-dione

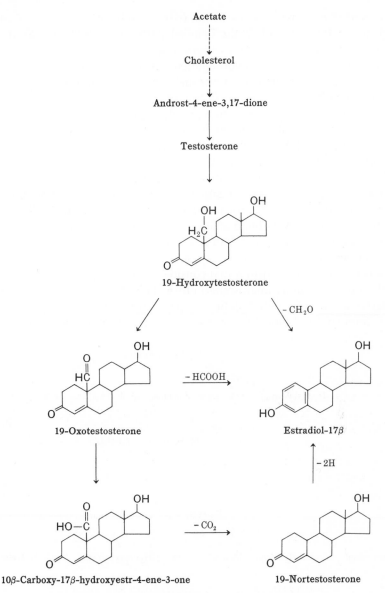

FIG. 48.2. Probable pathways of estrogen biosynthesis.

and testosterone have been indicated previously (Fig. 48.1, page 854). That testosterone conversion to estrogen can be accomplished by other peripheral tissues in the absence of the usual steroid-producing glands is indicated by the fact that testosterone-C^{14} administered to an adrenalectomized-ovariectomized woman led to urinary excretion of estrogen-C^{14}. The suggested pathways are based upon in vitro and in vivo studies with C^{14}-labeled compounds. The aromatization reaction, as studied with human placental microsomes, requires TPNH and molecular oxygen. The final products are a phenolic C_{18} steroid and formaldehyde or formic acid.

Formation of equilin and equilenin (page 860) from acetate has been demonstrated in the mare, although the detailed pathway is unknown. Studies in the pregnant mare have shown that estrone does not give rise to either equilin or equilenin, and, conversely, dihydroequilenin is not converted to either estrone or equilin. Thus, dehydrogenation of estrone or hydrogenation of equilenin does not appear to take place.

Metabolic Fate of Estrogens. Approximate values for estrone and β-estradiol in plasma, in μg per 100 ml., are in the female 0.03 for each steroid, and, in the male, 0.02 for estrone and 0.003 for estradiol. The liver is a major site of metabolic transformations of estrogens; interconversion occurs of estradiol-17β, estrone, and estriol. Estrone and estriol are major products of estrogen metabolism; their isolation from human urine was mentioned previously (page 859). Studies with C^{14}-labeled estrogens have revealed a wide variety of transformations: introduction of hydroxyl groups, reversible oxidation and reduction of hydroxyl and carbonyl groups, respectively, and methylation. Quantitatively, hydroxylation at positions 2 and 16 of the estrogens appears to be a most prominent metabolic transformation. The hydroxylation mechanism is that considered previously (page 356); the specific enzymic systems (usually microsomal) utilize TPNH and molecular oxygen. However, enzymic systems hydroxylating at position 6 have been reported to utilize DPNH. Some interrelationships of estrogen metabolism are depicted in Fig. 48.3.

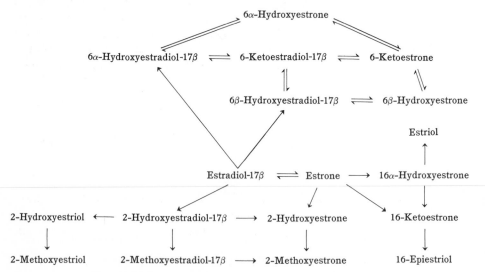

FIG. 48.3. Some interrelationships of estrogen metabolism.

Estrogens are excreted as conjugates of glucuronic and sulfuric acids, synthesized in the liver by previously described mechanisms (pages 410 and 515). The two principal conjugates are estriol glucosiduronate, with the glucosidic linkage at C-16, and estrone sulfate, with esterification at C-3. These conjugates have been isolated from pregnancy plasma and urine, and from human placenta. They are estrogenically active when given orally; this suggests that in the conjugated form estrogens are less readily degraded by the liver.

The prominent role of the liver in estrogen metabolism is reflected in a variety of experimental and clinical conditions. Nutritional factors, notably inanition, decrease the capacity of the liver to metabolize estrogens. Under these circumstances, as well as in hepatic cirrhosis, elevated blood levels of estrogens may be evident. Testicular atrophy, resulting from persistently elevated blood levels of estrogens, may be seen in patients with cirrhosis of the liver. A significant route of excretion of estrogens is the bile, and undue accumulation of these hormones may occur in conditions associated with either a decreased flow of bile or a diminished excretion of estrogen in the bile.

Synthetic Estrogens. Naturally occurring estrogens are more active when administered parenterally (Table 48.2). The most potent orally active estrogen is the synthetic compound, ethynylestradiol.

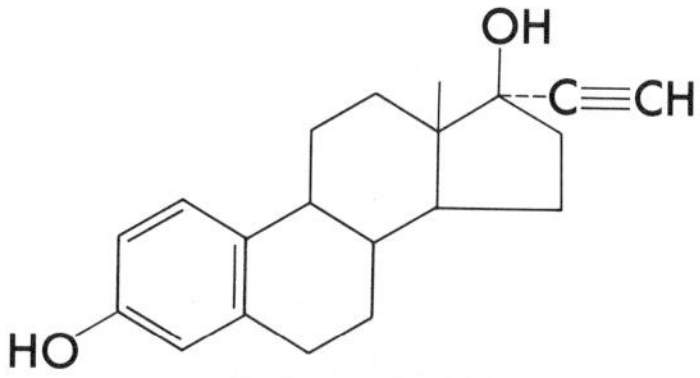

17α-Ethynylestradiol

This compound has approximately ten times the activity of estrone when each is administered by mouth. The high oral activity of ethynylestradiol is apparently due to its stability in the gastrointestinal tract and the liver. Stilbestrol, 4,4′-dihydroxy-α,β-diethylstilbene, is a synthetic product with approximately three to five times the estrogenic potency of estrone and is useful therapeutically because of its high potency when given orally.

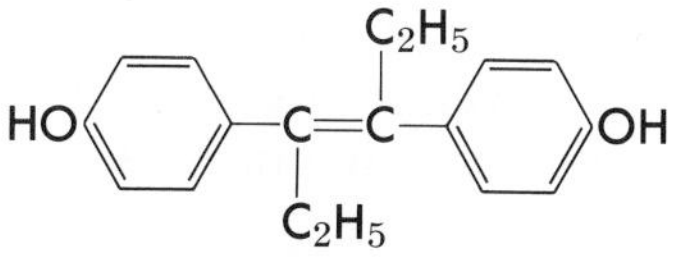

Stilbestrol

Mode of Action of Estrogens. The diverse actions of estrogens (pp. 858ff.) make it unlikely that their effects can be ascribed to a single biochemical mechanism. Effects of estrogens in vitro on several purified enzymic systems have been demonstrated.

Villee and his associates observed a marked in vitro augmentation of activity of the isocitrate dehydrogenase of endometrium and placenta on addition of estradiol. It will be recalled that isocitrate serves as a substrate for two different isocitrate dehydrogenases in animal tissues, one specific for TPN, the other for DPN (page 320). Talalay and his colleagues showed that in placenta this enzyme is TPN-linked and requires transhydrogenase (page 328) to act with DPN. These investigators have purified significantly a soluble 17β-hydroxysteroid dehydrogenase which interconverts estradiol-17 β and estrone, and reacts with DPN or TPN. These observations have led to the suggestion that estradiol functions as a coenzyme or cosubstrate in a transhydrogenation reaction catalyzed by the 17β-hydroxysteroid dehydrogenase. During the course of the hydrogen transfer between the pyridine nucleotides, estradiol undergoes cyclic oxidation and reduction with concomitant hydrogen transfer.

Frieden and coworkers, as well as Tompkins and his associates, observed that addition in vitro of $10^{-6}M$ concentration of either estradiol or stilbestrol to crystalline glutamic acid dehydrogenase produced a striking dissociation of the enzyme, with a molecular weight of 1,000,000, into units with average molecular weight of 250,000. This was accompanied by a loss of glutamic acid dehydrogenase activity and an appearance of a small degree of nonspecific L-amino acid dehydrogenase activity. The deaggregation of the enzyme, promoted by the estrogens, was prevented by AMP, ADP, DPN$^+$, and leucine. The significance of these findings for explanation of estrogen action is not clear, since thyroxine, urea, bicarbonate, and dilution produced similar effects on glutamic acid dehydrogenase.

Thus studies designed to elucidate mechanisms of hormone actions have scarcely progressed beyond the descriptive phase of documenting the effects that a hormone may produce. In general, how these effects are elicited remains to be determined.

PROGESTERONE—HORMONE OF THE CORPUS LUTEUM

Effects of Progesterone. Progesterone is secreted by the corpus luteum during the latter half of the menstrual cycle. The hormone acts upon the endometrium, previously prepared by estrogen, inducing mucus secretory activity indispensable for implantation of the ovum. If pregnancy ensues, continued secretion of progesterone is essential for completion of term. Progesterone also contributes to growth of the breasts and is thought to maintain the uterus quiescent during pregnancy. Progesterone exerts an antiovulatory effect when given during days 5 to 25 of the normal menstrual cycle; this is the basis for the use of certain synthetic progestins (page 866) as oral contraceptive agents. Progesterone in very large doses will promote retention of salt and water, its action thus resembling that of certain adrenal cortical hormones (page 882).

Chemistry of Progesterone. In 1929, Corner and Allen prepared from corpora lutea material extractable by nonpolar solvents and capable of maintaining pregnancy in ovariectomized rabbits and of stimulating development of an endometrium which could maintain an implanted fertilized ovum. These observations, which became the basis for a bioassay for following the purification of the active material, led to the isolation of progesterone, the hormone of the corpus luteum.

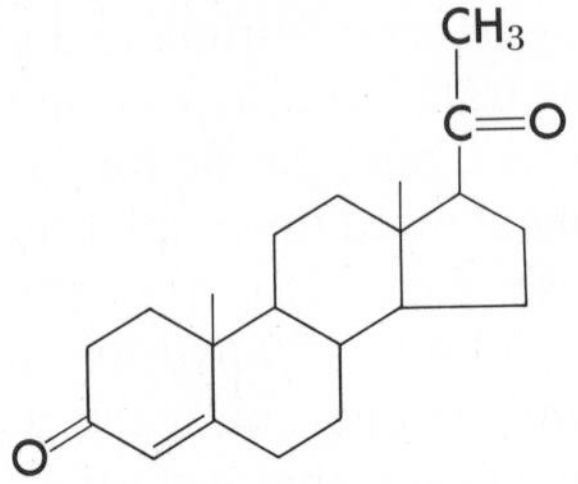

Progesterone

Biogenesis of Progesterone. Progesterone is produced not only by the corpus luteum but by the placenta and adrenals as well. Either acetate or cholesterol serves as a precursor; in the adrenals, pregnenolone is an intermediate (Fig. 48.1, page 854). Biogenesis and metabolic fate of progesterone in the adrenal glands will be referred to again in Chap. 49.

Metabolism of Progesterone. The position of progesterone in the conversion of acetate and cholesterol to C_{19} steroids has been indicated previously in Fig. 48.1. This provides explanation for the formation of 17α-hydroxyprogesterone, androst-4-ene-3,17-dione, and testosterone on incubation of progesterone with testicular, ovarian, adrenal, or placental tissues. These three products, therefore, can be considered as derived from progesterone metabolism. In addition, progesterone may give rise to estrone and estradiol, via testosterone (Fig. 48.2, page 861). Formation of these estrogens has been demonstrated experimentally in studies in which progesterone has been incubated in vitro with human ovarian tissue.

More significant quantitatively as a metabolite of progesterone is pregnane-3α, 20α-diol, a reduction product formed from progesterone chiefly in the liver, where it is coupled with glucuronic acid to form the chief urinary metabolite of progesterone, pregnanediol glucosiduronate.

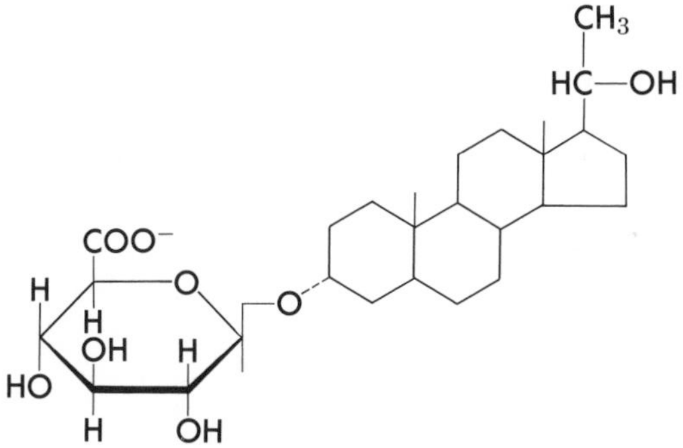

Pregnane-3α,20α-diol glucosiduronate

Reduction of the C-20 ketone group of progesterone to the 20α- and β-hydroxy isomers also occurs extrahepatically.

Although pregnanediol is not the sole metabolite of progesterone and is not derived entirely from progesterone, pregnanediol excretion in the urine is a convenient semiquantitative index of progesterone elaboration and metabolism. Pregnanediol determinations are of added significance if correlated with physiological status. In women with normal menstrual cycles the corpus luteum is the major source of progesterone; during pregnancy, progesterone arises chiefly in the placenta, especially in the later periods of gestation.

Two additional compounds with progestational activity and representing metabolites of progesterone have been isolated from human ripe follicles, corpora lutea, and placenta. These substances are pregn-4-ene-3-one-20α-ol, with approximately one-third to one-half the progestational activity of progesterone, and the corresponding 20β-ol isomer, with one-tenth to one-fifth the activity of progesterone. Of interest is the observation that some samples of human milk may contain the 20β-ol isomer of urinary pregnanediol, and that this compound specifically inhibits in vitro the enzymic formation of bilirubin diglucuronide. There appears to be an interesting correlation between the occurrence of this steroid in human milk and the appearance of hyperbilirubinemia in some breast-fed infants.

Synthetic Progestins. Progesterone is active only when given parenterally, although oral doses several hundred times the parenteral dose can elicit responses characteristic of progesterone. However, a number of synthetic steroids have been prepared which are active by mouth and with biological activity classifying them as progestins. Some of these are shown below; these compounds have a progestational activity varying from equal to that of parenterally administered progesterone, as in the case of 17α-ethynyltestosterone, to ten times as active as progesterone, e.g., 17α-ethynyl-17-hydroxy-5(10)-estren-3-one. The basis for the oral effectiveness of these compounds is not known.

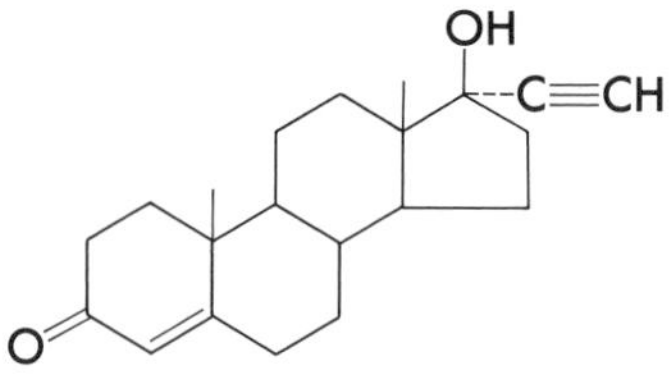

17α-Ethynyltestosterone

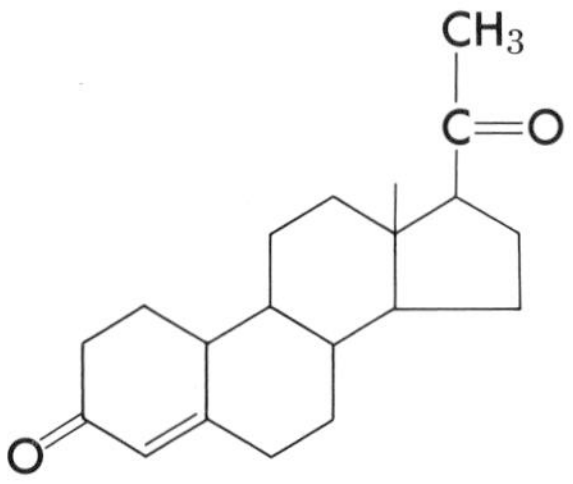

19-Norprogesterone

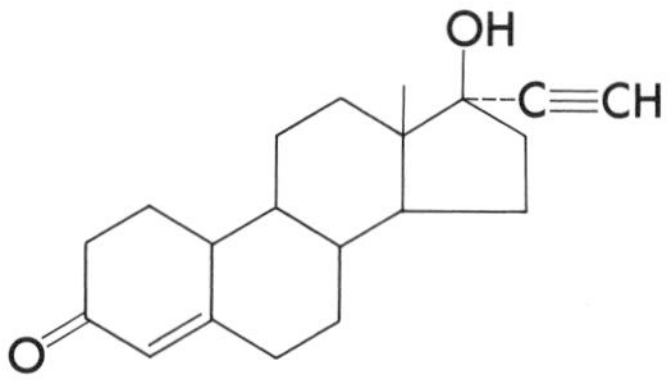

17α-Ethynyl-19-nortestosterone

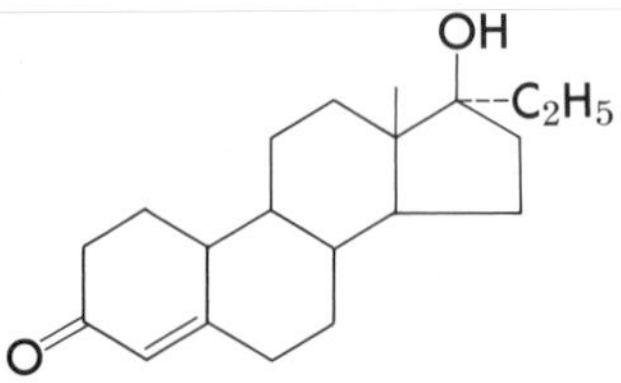

17α-Ethyl-19-nortestosterone

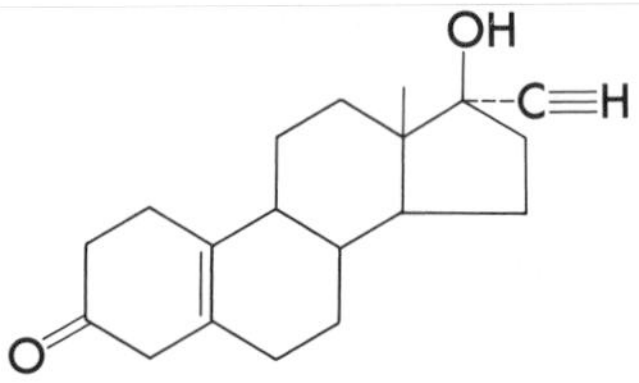

17α-Ethynyl-17-hydroxy-5(10)-estren-3-one

RELAXIN

The corpus luteum apparently produces a second hormone in addition to progesterone. There can be prepared from the corpora lutea of the sow, from the blood of pregnant females of a wide variety of species, including pregnant women, as well as from placenta, an extract which has the specific capacity to relax the symphysis pubis of the guinea pig and of the mouse. This active principle was first detected in 1926 by Hisaw in the blood of pregnant rabbits and guinea pigs, and in 1930 Fevold and his associates achieved chemical separation of the active substance from the steroid hormones in extracts of sow corpora lutea. The active principle was named *relaxin*. The material is active only when injected into an animal which is in normal or artificially induced estrus. Frieden and his coworkers have shown that the active principle is a basic polypeptide of molecular weight approximately 9,000. Further evidence for the presence of peptide linkages is the rapid disappearance of potency when relaxin is digested with proteolytic enzymes. The hormone is inactivated by reagents which reduce disulfide linkages to sulfhydryl groups.

It may be noted that progesterone and estrogens also produce relaxation of the symphysis pubis of the guinea pig. However, the steroid hormones bring about relaxation only after prolonged treatment, whereas the effect with relaxin is seen in a few hours.

REFERENCES

Books

Dorfman, R. I., and Shipley, R. A., "The Androgens: Biochemistry, Physiology, and Clinical Significance," John Wiley & Sons, Inc., New York, 1956.

Villee, C. A., and Engel, L. L., eds., "Mechanism of Steroid Hormone Action," Pergamon Press, New York, 1961.

Young, W. C., ed., "Sex and Internal Secretions," 3d ed., vols. I and II, The Williams & Wilkins Company, Baltimore, 1961.

Zuckerman, S., "The Ovary," vol. II, Academic Press, Inc., New York, 1962.

Review Articles

Dorfman, R. I., Metabolism of Androgens, in Fourth International Congress of Biochemistry, IV, "Biochemistry of Steroids," pp. 175–195, Pergamon Press, New York, 1959.

Dorfman, R. I., Steroid Hormone Biosynthesis, *Comp. Biochem. Physiol.,* **4,** 319–329, 1962.

Dorfman, R. I., Steroid Hormones in Gynecology, *Obstet. Gynecol.,* **18,** 65–116, 1963.

Drill, V. A., and Riegel, B., Structural and Hormonal Activity of Some New Steroids, *Recent Progr. Hormone Research,* **14,** 29–76, 1958.

Drill, V. A., and Saunders, F. J., Androgenic and Anabolic Action of Testosterone Derivatives, in E. T. Engle and G. Pincus, eds., "Hormones and the Aging Process," pp. 99–114, Academic Press, Inc., New York, 1956.

Eder, H., The Effects of Hormones on Human Serum Lipoproteins, *Recent Progr. Hormone Research,* **14,** 405–425, 1958.

Hall, K., Relaxin, *J. Reprod. Fertility,* **1,** 368–384, 1960.

Jensen, E. V., On the Mechanism of Estrogen Action, *Perspectives Biol. Med.,* **6,** 47–60, 1962.

Jensen, E. V., and Jacobsen, H. I., Basic Guides to the Mechanism of Estrogen Action, *Recent Progr. Hormone Research,* **18,** 387–414, 1962.

Talalay, P., Enzymatic Mechanisms in Steroid Metabolism, *Physiol. Revs.,* **37,** 362–389, 1957.

Yielding, K. L., and Tompkins, G. M., Studies on the Interaction of Steroid Hormones with Glutamic Dehydrogenase, *Recent Progr. Hormone Research,* **18,** 467–489, 1962.

49. The Adrenals

Each adrenal gland is a composite of two endocrine structures, the *medulla*, of neural origin, and the *cortex*, derived from mesodermal glandular tissue. The nature of the hormonal products and their effects are distinct for each of these two portions of the adrenal.

THE ADRENAL MEDULLA

The adrenal medulla is composed of closely packed groups of polyhedral cells containing chromaffin granules, so named because they stain a dark brown with chromates. These granules are storage sites for the medullary hormones. The gland is one of the most vascular tissues in the body and receives 6 to 7 ml. of blood per gram of tissue per minute.

Adrenal demedullation (removal of only the medullary portion of the adrenals) reveals that no obvious physiological effects ensue as a result of loss of adrenal medullary function. However, the conclusion is not unequivocal since accessory chromaffin tissue is generally associated with the ganglia and plexuses of the sympathetic chain. These chromaffin collections, *paraganglia*, are widely distributed and may preclude appearance of symptoms of adrenal medullary deficiency, if indeed these exist, following adrenal demedullation.

Hormones of the Adrenal Medulla. Crystalline epinephrine was independently isolated by Abel in 1899 and by Takamine in 1901; both were seeking the principle in adrenal extracts which, when administered to normal dogs, produced a striking elevation in blood pressure. The naturally occurring D form of epinephrine is levorotatory and has approximately fifteen times the physiological potency of the unnatural isomer. In 1946, von Euler demonstrated that some of the biological activity of adrenal medullary extracts was due in part to another compound, norepinephrine, which differs from epinephrine only in the absence of the N-methyl group. The natural D(-) form of this hormone is approximately twenty times more potent than the nonnatural isomer.

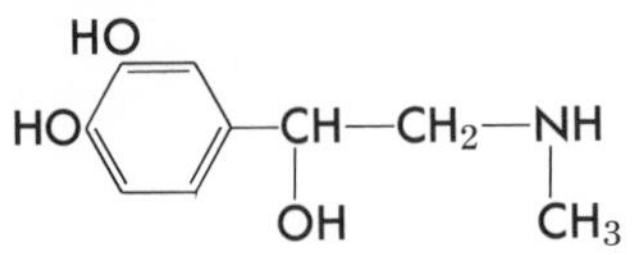

Epinephrine

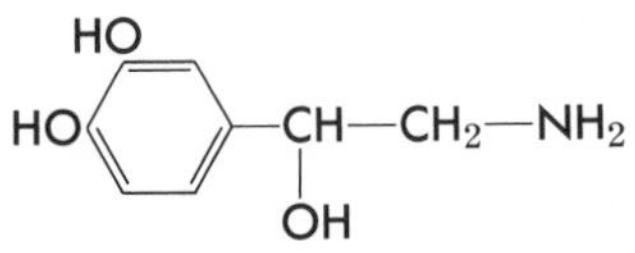

Norepinephrine

The ratios of epinephrine to norepinephrine in extracts of the adrenal medulla vary considerably with the species studied. In man, norepinephrine represents approximately one-tenth to one-third of the total. In the medulla of the cat, the two hormones are present in approximately equal amounts, whereas norepinephrine accounts for 90 to 100 per cent of the hormonal content of the whale adrenal medulla. Commercial preparations of "epinephrine" may contain 10 to 20 per cent of norepinephrine.

Norepinephrine and epinephrine are stored in separate cells of the adrenal medulla and are released by different stimuli. Insulin releases epinephrine preferentially, while stimulation of various areas of the hypothalamus yields varying proportions of the two hormones. Douglas and Rubin have demonstrated that the release of the catecholamines from the adrenal medulla under the influence of acetylcholine is dependent upon the presence of Ca^{++}, which enters chromaffin cells readily in the presence of acetylcholine.

Biogenesis of Epinephrine and Norepinephrine. The major pathway for the formation of the medullary hormones is depicted in Fig. 49.1. In rats given phenylalanine labeled with H^3 in the ring and C^{14} in the side chain, Gurin and Delluva found

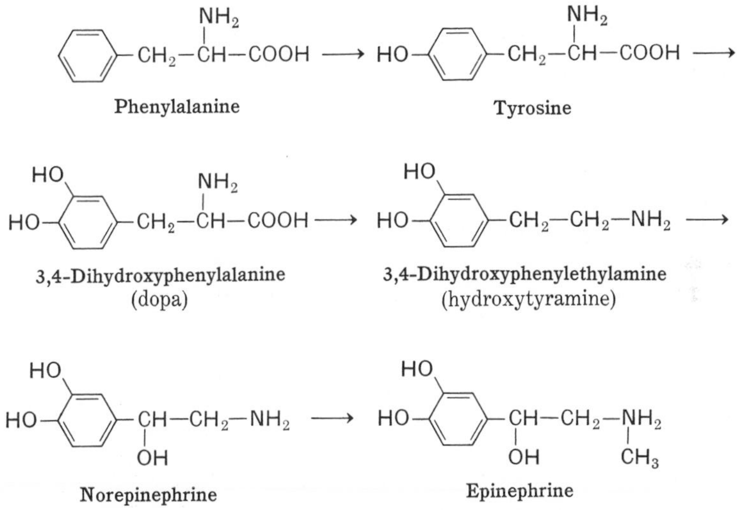

FIG. 49.1. Major pathway for biosynthesis of norepinephrine and epinephrine.

that both the aromatic nucleus and the side chain of epinephrine are derived from phenylalanine. Similarly, Udenfriend and his colleagues isolated C^{14}-labeled epinephrine from the adrenals of rats given tyrosine-C^{14}, indicating that phenylalanine is converted to tyrosine (page 500) preceding epinephrine formation. It will be recalled that this hydroxylation occurs in the liver; it has not been described in the adrenal. It is of interest that individuals having hereditary phenylketonuria (page 501), with a deficiency of liver phenylalanine hydroxylase (page 501), have low plasma epinephrine concentrations.

Oxidation of tyrosine to 3,4-dihydroxyphenylalanine (dopa) in adrenals is catalyzed by *tyrosine hydroxylase,* which resembles phenylalanine hydroxylase. An *aromatic L-amino acid decarboxylase,* requiring pyridoxal phosphate and present

in mammalian kidney, liver, and adrenal medullary tissue, catalyzes decarboxylation of 3,4-dihydroxyphenylalanine to 3,4-dihydroxyphenylethylamine (hydroxytyramine). The latter is converted to norepinephrine under the catalytic influence
of *3,4-dihydroxyphenylethylamine-β-hydroxylase*. Available data suggest that this
reaction involves direct addition of oxygen to the β-carbon atom. The enzyme also
catalyzes β-hydroxylation of other amines structurally related to hydroxytyramine.
β-Hydroxylation of hydroxytyramine appears to be the rate-limiting step in the
synthesis of the adrenal medullary hormones. Methylation of norepinephrine to

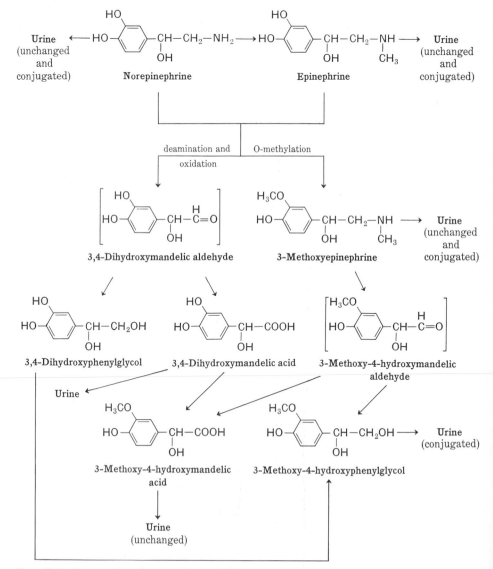

FIG. 49.2. Suggested pathways of metabolism of norepinephrine and epinephrine. As indicated in the text (page 871), conjugates are also excreted via the bile.

epinephrine is catalyzed by *phenylethanolamine-N-methyl transferase,* utilizing S-adenosylmethionine as the biological methylating agent (page 504).

Metabolism of Epinephrine and Norepinephrine. Although the adrenal medulla of man contains normally about three to ten times as much epinephrine as norepinephrine, the mean plasma concentration of epinephrine is approximately 0.06 μg per liter while the value for norepinephrine averages 0.3 μg per liter. In urine the values per 24 hr. are 10 to 15 μg for epinephrine and 30 to 50 μg for norepinephrine.

Both hormones are rapidly metabolized by three mechanisms, O-methylation, oxidative deamination (catalyzed by *monamine oxidase*), and conjugation. The liver is the major site of these transformations; O-methylation by S-adenosylmethionine is the major metabolic pathway for epinephrine. The principal metabolites of epinephrine in urine are 3-methoxy-4-hydroxymandelic acid, 3-methoxyepinephrine 3-methoxy-4-hydroxyphenylglycol, and (metanephrine). The corresponding catechols, 3,4-dihydroxymandelic acid, 3,4-dihydroxyphenylglycol, and epinephrine, are minor excretion products. Some of these metabolites are excreted both as the free compounds and as sulfates or glucosiduronides; conjugation occurs at the 4-hydroxyl group of the catechols. These conjugates are also excreted via the bile. The structures of the above metabolites, and their postulated metabolic relationships, are indicated in Fig. 49.2.

After an intravenous infusion of DL-epinephrine-2-C^{14} in human subjects, approximately 75 per cent of the radioactivity was recovered in the first 24-hr. urine. This radioactivity was distributed as follows among the various metabolites (approximate values in per cent): epinephrine and metanephrine, each 5; metanephrine conjugate, 45; 3-methoxy-4-hydroxymandelic acid, 25; and 3,4-dihydroxymandelic acid, 10.

Table 49.1: COMPARISON OF THE EFFECTS OF INTRAVENOUS INFUSION OF EPINEPHRINE AND NOREPINEPHRINE IN MAN

Index	Epinephrine*	Norepinephrine
Heart rate	+	−
Cardiac output	+ + +	0, −
Systolic blood pressure	+ + +	+ + +
Diastolic blood pressure	+, 0, −	+ +
Total peripheral resistance	−	+ +
Oxygen consumption	+ +	0, +
Blood glucose	+ + +	0, +
Blood lactate	+ + +	0, +
Blood nonesterified fatty acids	+ + +	+ + +
Central nervous system action	+	0
Eosinopenic response	+	0

* + = increase; 0 = no change; − = decrease.
SOURCE: After M. Goldenberg, *Am. J. Med.,* **10,** 627, 1951.

Effects of Epinephrine and Norepinephrine. The hormones of the adrenal medulla elicit a wide variety of effects, seen in Table 49.1, which also indicates certain differences in response produced by epinephrine and norepinephrine.

Cardiovascular and Metabolic Effects. Epinephrine administered intravenously produces a marked rise in blood pressure due to arteriolar vasoconstriction, particularly in the splanchnic bed and in the skin and mucous membranes. There is an increase in heart and pulse rate and in cardiac output. In moderate doses, epinephrine causes dilatation, rather than constriction, of the vessels of the skeletal muscles, and the coronary and visceral vessels, thus increasing blood flow in these regions.

Epinephrine produces variable effects on smooth muscle; it relaxes gastrointestinal tract musculature and causes contraction of the pyloric and ileocecal sphincters. There is a marked dilator effect on bronchial musculature.

Norepinephrine, released by stimulation of the sympathetic nervous system, mimics more closely than does epinephrine some of the effects of sympathetic stimulation. Norepinephrine exerts much weaker inhibitory influence on smooth muscle than does epinephrine, does not relax bronchiolar musculature, and augments both systolic and diastolic blood pressure owing to increased total peripheral resistance, with little effect on cardiac output (Table 49.1).

Effects on Carbohydrate Metabolism. The effects of epinephrine on carbohydrate and lipid metabolism have been considered previously (Chaps. 21 and 22, respectively). Epinephrine promotes glycogenolysis in muscle (page 419) and liver (page 419), resulting in elevation of the blood glucose level and increased lactic acid formation in muscle. These effects on carbohydrate metabolism are accompanied by an increased oxygen consumption, approximately 20 to 40 per cent in man, with an even greater increase in carbon dioxide production, raising the respiratory quotient. There is also an elevated body temperature, presumably because of an action of epinephrine on the liver. In hepatectomized animals, epinephrine exerts no effect on the falling blood sugar level or on body temperature. In contrast, norepinephrine has relatively little effect in normal animals on carbohydrate metabolism and on oxygen consumption (Table 49.1).

It will be recalled that epinephrine promotes glycogenolysis by stimulating formation of cyclic AMP from ATP; the cyclic AMP, in the presence of Mg^{++}, activates phosphorylase kinase (page 416), which in turn promotes conversion of inactive phosphorylase b to active phosphorylase a. The enzyme catalyzing formation of cyclic adenylic acid has been termed *adenyl cyclase* by Sutherland and his coworkers; it is very widely distributed in animal tissues. The activity of a particulate preparation of adenyl cyclase from dog ventricular muscle was doubled by addition in vitro of $10^{-6}M$ epinephrine. Norepinephrine had a similar action. In contrast, liver adenyl cyclase appeared to be much less sensitive to norepinephrine than to epinephrine. The latter hormone, in concentrations as low as $5 \times 10^{-7}M$, also increased the activity of adenyl cyclase preparations from cerebellum and cerebral cortex.

In a survey of various tissues, using unfractionated broken cell preparations, Sutherland and his associates found that addition of epinephrine increased formation of cyclic adenylic acid in lung, spleen, pigeon erythrocytes, and the epididymal fat pad of the rat. When added to this last tissue in vitro, epinephrine causes increased oxygen consumption and glucose utilization, with accompanying release of free fatty acids (see below). The studies of Sutherland are one of the few successful approaches to elucidation of hormone action at a molecular level

Effects on Lipid Metabolism. The catechol amines have a profound lipid-mobilizing activity, markedly increasing the blood level of nonesterified fatty acids. The basis of this appears to be the promoting effect of epinephrine and norepinephrine on the release of free fatty acids from adipose tissue, as a consequence of stimulation of lipolysis. In *pheochromocytoma* (see below), with hyperfunctioning of the adrenal medulla, blood levels of nonesterified fatty acids may be as high as several hundred times normal. Epinephrine administration to normal animals also elevates serum cholesterol and phosphatide levels.

The effects of epinephrine and norepinephrine on the release of free fatty acids from adipose tissue are counteracted significantly by a group of substances termed *prostaglandins.* The name stems from the first isolation of these compounds from seminal plasma. Subsequently, they were also obtained from lung tissue and from thymic tissue. One of the prostaglandins isolated from seminal plasma has been named prostaglandin E_1, for which Bergström and his colleagues established the following structure.

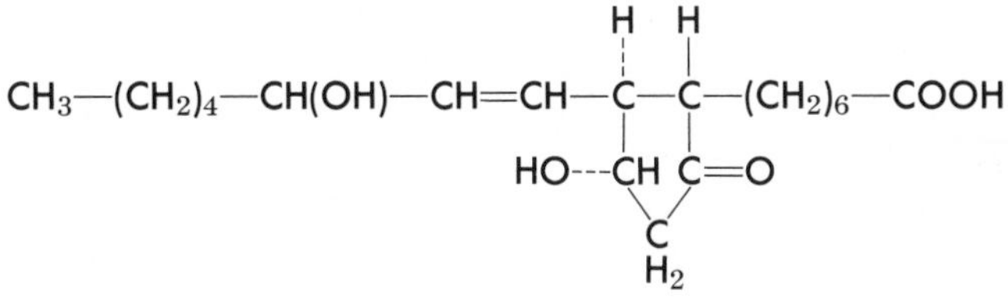

$$CH_3-(CH_2)_4-CH(OH)-CH=CH-\overset{\overset{\displaystyle H}{|}}{C}-\overset{\overset{\displaystyle H}{|}}{C}-(CH_2)_6-COOH$$

$$HO---\underset{}{CH} \quad C=O$$

$$\underset{\displaystyle H_2}{C}$$

Prostaglandin E_1

The other prostaglandins, whose presence has been detected largely by chromatographic or electrophoretic techniques, have structures apparently closely related to the above. A group of prostaglandins E, termed E_1, E_2, etc., has been described, as well as another group designated as an F series.

In addition to counteracting both the in vitro and in vivo effects of the adrenal medullary hormones on free fatty acid release from adipose tissue, prostaglandin E also significantly reduced the blood pressure elevation produced in dogs by continuous infusion of norepinephrine. It may be noted that 30 years ago, Goldblatt and von Euler reported that human seminal plasma exhibited vasodepressor and smooth muscle–stimulating activity.

Adrenal Medullary Hyperfunction. Although no experimental or clinical condition corresponding to hypofunctioning of the adrenal medulla has been described, hyperfunctioning of this structure in man is due to chromaffin tissue tumors, termed *pheochromocytomas.* These may originate in the adrenal medulla or wherever chromaffin tissue is found in the body during early life. The pathological picture may present one or several of the following features: (1) paroxysmal hypertension; (2) persistent hypertension, resembling essential or malignant hypertension; (3) a combination of hypertension, elevation of the basal metabolic rate, and glucosuria; (4) a persistent elevation of the basal metabolic rate, or hyperglycemia coexistent with intermittent hypertension.

In both the last two circumstances, insulin resistance may be encountered. Plasma levels of norepinephrine and epinephrine may rise to more than 500 times the normal (page 871), plasma nonesterified fatty acids are elevated (page 456), and there is a marked increase in urinary levels of norepinephrine, epinephrine, and 3-methoxy-4-hydroxymandelic acid. When the tumor is extramedullary, norepinephrine may represent as much as 90 per cent of the total hormone of the tissue. When the tumor is medullary, it yields increased quantities of both hormones.

THE ADRENAL CORTEX

Disease attributable to pathological changes in the adrenal glands was first described in 1855. This syndrome, known after its discoverer as Addison's disease, was ascribed by him to tuberculosis of the adrenal glands. Addison's disease is characterized by loss of appetite, gastrointestinal disturbances (vomiting and diarrhea), rapid loss of weight, weakness and prostration, a low degree of resistance to infection, anemia, and an abnormal and characteristic pigmentation which is most pronounced in regions where normal pigmentation is greatest, *i.e.*, buccal cavity, nipples, etc. The palms of the hands and the soles of the feet remain pale. The fatal consequences of Addison's disease, as of extirpation of the adrenal glands, result solely from the lack of adequate functional *cortical* tissue.

Chemistry of Adrenal Cortical Hormones. In 1927 Rogoff and Stewart first demonstrated adequate adrenal replacement therapy in the completely adrenalectomized dog by injection of aqueous extracts of adrenal tissue. Physiologically effective extracts made with nonpolar solvents were described in 1930 by Hartman and Brown and by Swingle and Pfiffner. Beginning in 1937, several groups of investigators, notably Kendall, and Pfiffner and Wintersteiner and their associates, in the United States, and Reichstein and his colleagues in Switzerland, isolated from adrenal extracts crystalline compounds with marked adrenal cortical activity (see below).

Approximately 30 crystalline steroids have been obtained from extracts of adrenal glands. With the exception of estrone (page 859), which has 18 carbon atoms, and cholesterol, containing 27 carbons, all these steroids contain either 19 or 21 carbon atoms. Some of the 19-carbon atom steroids which have androgenic activity have been considered in the previous chapter (page 852). One of the steroids isolated from adrenal tissue is progesterone, the normal hormone of the corpus luteum (page 864); this is another example of a hormone being formed by two endocrine glands.

Of the steroids isolated from the adrenal, seven are of significance for adrenal cortical activity. These compounds are the following:

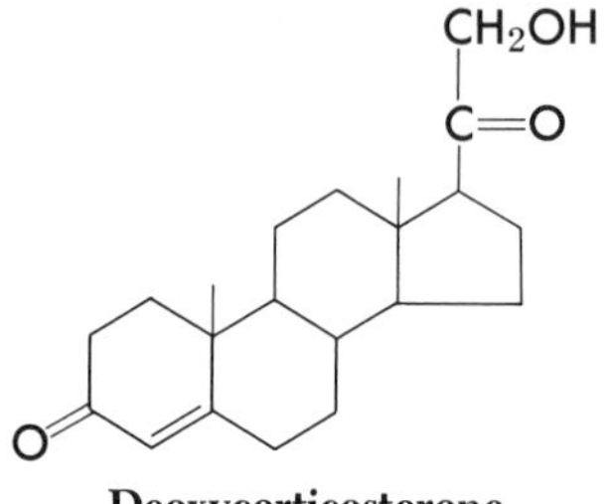

Deoxycorticosterone 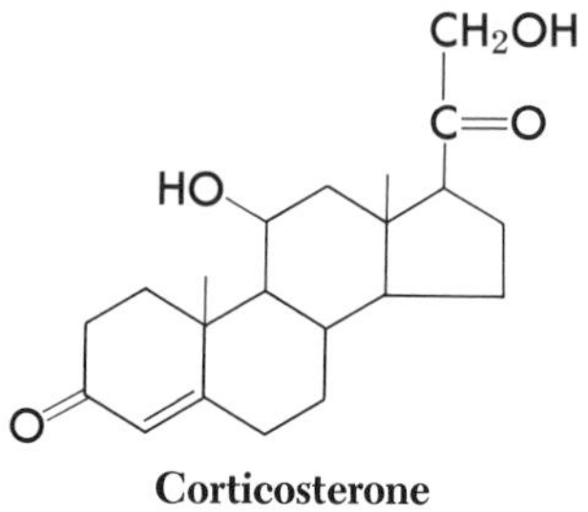   Corticosterone

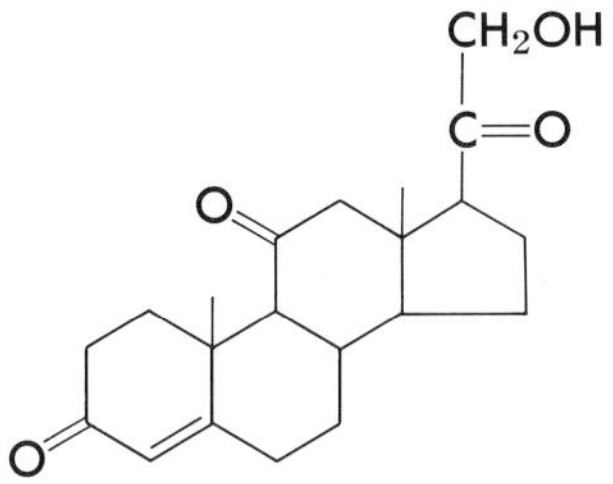

11-Dehydrocorticosterone

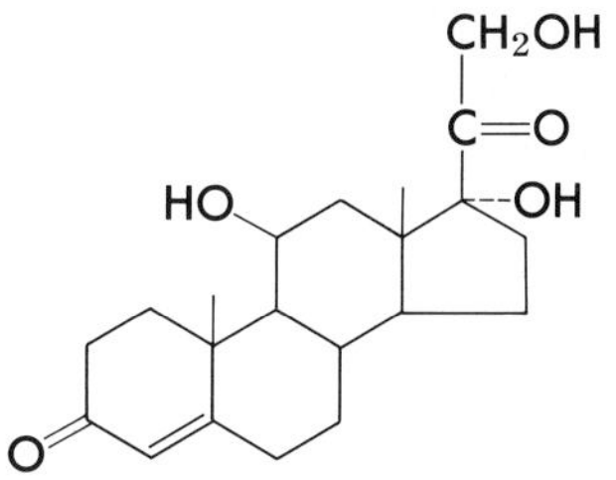

17α-Hydroxycorticosterone
(cortisol; hydrocortisone)

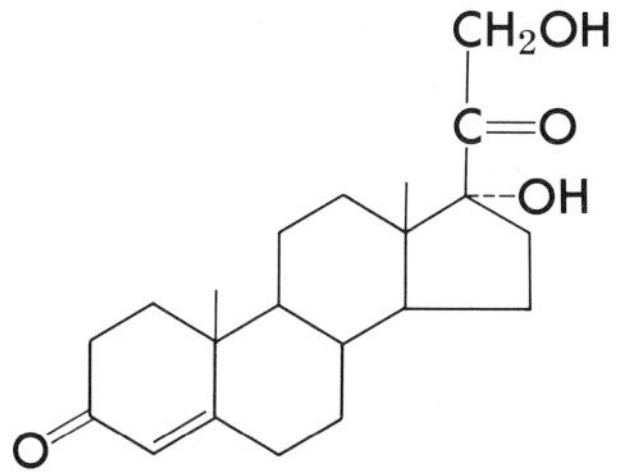

**11-Deoxy-17α-hydroxycortico-
sterone**
(11-deoxycortisol)

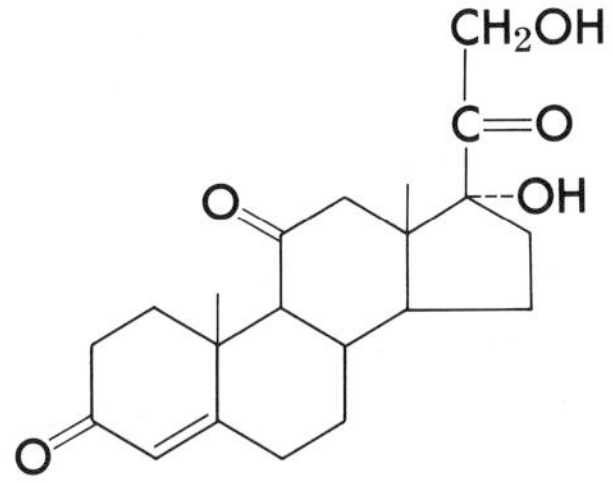

11-Dehydro-17α-hydroxycorticosterone
(cortisone)

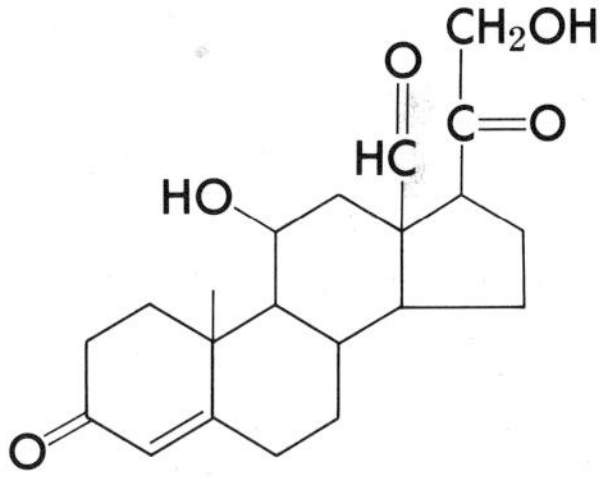

Aldosterone

It will be seen that in aldosterone the customary angular methyl group at C-13 is replaced by an aldehyde group. Solutions of aldosterone contain an equilibrium mixture of the aldehyde and the hemiacetal; equilibrium favors the latter compound.

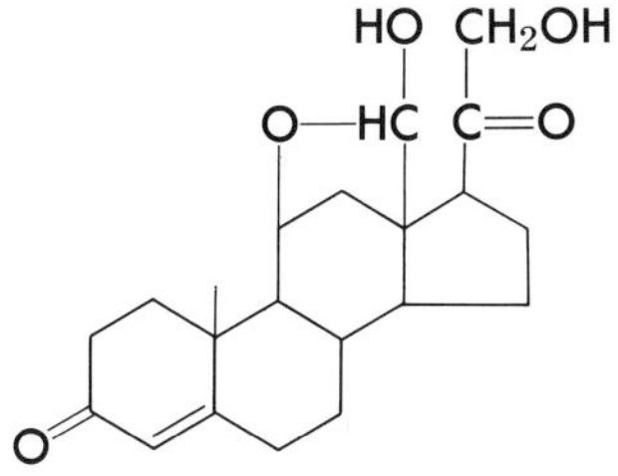

Aldosterone
(hemiacetal structure)

Placenta contains adrenal cortical activity equivalent to 1 to 2 per cent that of adrenal tissue, per gram of tissue. Hence the placenta can augment the supply of adrenal cortical hormones.

Biosynthesis of Adrenal Cortical Steroids. In the human adrenal gland, only two steroids, *viz.*, corticosterone and cortisol, appear to be normally released in relatively large amounts, the latter predominating. In addition, very small quantities of aldosterone are normally secreted. The relative quantities of these steroids secreted show some variation with species. In man, the adrenal cortex normally secretes approximately 10 to 30 mg. of cortisol, 2 to 4 mg. of corticosterone, and 300 to 400 μg of aldosterone per 24 hr. The rat adrenal apparently secretes corticosterone almost exclusively. The most prominent of the androgenic steroids secreted by the human adrenal is 11β-hydroxyandrost-4-ene-3-17-dione (page 852).

Adrenal cortical steroids may be synthesized in vivo from either acetate or from cholesterol arising from the former. The cholesterol content of the adrenal is the highest found in tissues, with the exception of nervous tissue. Adrenal cholesterol is present almost wholly in the esterified form; these esters have a high content of polyunsaturated, long-chain fatty acids, including an unusual fatty acid which represents the addition of a C_2 unit to the carboxyl-terminal end of arachidonic acid and has been termed adrenic acid (7, 10, 13, 16-docosatetraenoic acid). Stimulation of the adrenal cortex causes a marked decrease in adrenal cholesterol concentration at a time when maximal release of adrenal cortical steroids is occurring, indicating the role of cholesterol as precursor of the steroids. The adrenal cortex also contains the body's highest concentration of ascorbic acid, 400 to 500 mg. per 100 g. fresh adrenal tissue.

The biosynthetic pathways suggested between cholesterol and adrenal cortical steroids are indicated in Fig. 49.3. The steps between cholesterol and pregnenolone have been discussed previously (page 478), as has the pathway for synthesis of C_{19} steroids in the adrenal (page 854). Dehydroepiandrosterone, synthesized in the adrenal (page 852), is both stored and secreted by the gland as the 3-sulfate ester. Certain of the enzymes involved in adrenal steroid biogenesis have been obtained in soluble, partially purified form. Scission of the side chain of 20,22-dihydroxycholesterol, with formation of pregnenolone (page 478), is a TPNH-requiring reaction, catalyzed by a *desmolase*. The 3β-hydroxydehydrogenase utilizes DPN and is present in the microsomal fraction of adrenal broken cell preparations. The steroid hydroxylating enzymes, each specific for positions 11, 17, and 21 of the steroid nucleus, require TPNH and utilize molecular oxygen, as is the case for other hydroxylations of ring structures (pages 356 and 862). The 11β-hydroxylating enzyme is mitochondrial, whereas the 21-hydroxylating adrenal enzyme is microsomal. Of the steroid-producing endocrine organs, apparently the adrenal is the major site of 11-hydroxylation.

6β-Hydroxylation of C_{21} steroids has been described for adrenal tissue of several species. 6β-Hydroxycortisol is present in human urine, and large amounts of 6β-hydroxycorticosterone were produced in vitro on incubation of hyperplastic adrenal tissue and an adrenal adenoma, both removed from a patient with primary aldosteronism (page 886). 6β-Hydroxylation of other adrenal cortical compounds has been described, particularly in circumstances in which there is a deficiency in

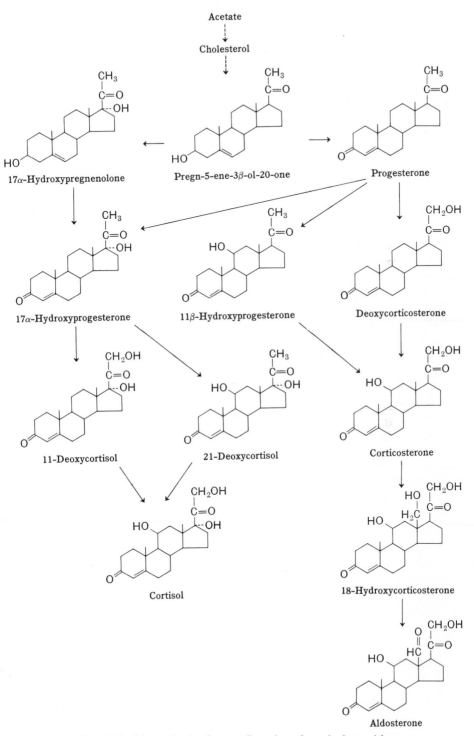

FIG. 49.3. Biosynthesis of some C_{21} adrenal cortical steroids.

11β-hydroxylase. This enzyme has been found lacking, or 11-hydroxylation is blocked, in many of the adrenal carcinomas which have been studied.

The TPNH required in the adrenals for hydroxylation reactions is provided by an active phosphogluconate oxidative pathway. Glucose phosphate is made available from stored glycogen by phosphorylase activity. As in muscle and liver (page 416), adrenal phosphorylase activity is controlled by the presence of cyclic AMP. The latter, by regulating the glucose supply, appears to be a determinant of the rate of steroid synthesis. Addition of cyclic AMP to adrenal tissue in vitro accelerates somewhat steroid formation. Stimulation of the adrenal cortex by hypophyseal adrenocorticotropic hormone (page 909) increases formation of cyclic AMP. However, it has also been established that ACTH promotes release of stored steroidal hormones, as well as enhancing their synthesis.

Regulation of Adrenal Cortical Secretion. The secretory activity of the adrenal cortex is primarily dependent upon stimulation by hypophyseal adrenocorticotropic hormone (ACTH). This will be considered later in Chap. 51, particularly with regard to the production of corticosterone and cortisol. However, secretion of aldosterone by the adrenal cortex, although influenced by ACTH, is significantly less dependent on the hypophysis and is markedly affected by other factors. These will be considered briefly here because of their importance in subsequent discussion of the effects of adrenal cortical steroids.

The $[Na^+]$ and $[K^+]$ in adrenal arterial blood are important regulators of aldosterone secretion, with decreased $[Na^+]$ being the most significant factor stimulating aldosterone release. There is, therefore, a direct, local ionic effect on the adrenal. No obligatory increase in cortisol or corticosterone secretion is evident with augmented aldosterone output. In addition to this ionic control, secretion of this steroid is augmented by constriction of the thoracic vena cava or the hepatic portal vein, suggesting an additional factor influencing aldosterone secretion. This factor appears to be angiotensin II (page 735). There may also be a rise in secretion of cortisol or corticosterone with this stimulus. The influence of angiotensin II on aldosterone secretion is independent of its pressor action.

The adrenal becomes more responsive to ACTH under circumstances of Na^+ deficiency. Hypophysectomy does not affect aldosterone secretion evoked by Na^+ depletion but does reduce output of this steroid elicited by noxious stimuli (page 885).

Adrenal venous blood contains approximately 240 μg of cortisol and 80 μg of corticosterone per 100 ml. of blood. Total adrenal steroids in *peripheral blood* in normal subjects varies from 5 to 40 μg per 100 ml. There is a pronounced diurnal variation both in the concentration in blood and in the rate of secretion in urine of these steroids; urinary concentration is maximal in early morning, slowly declines during the day, and is minimal during the night.

Transport of Adrenal Cortical Steroids. Cortisol represents approximately four-fifths of the total 17-hydroxysteroids found in blood. The hormone is present bound to a specific α_2-globulin which has been termed *transcortin* or *corticosteroid-binding protein;* this protein also specifically binds corticosterone. In contrast, aldosterone binds weakly with transcortin and chiefly to albumin, which loosely binds cortisol but only at blood levels of the latter steroid which result in saturation of binding sites of transcortin (30 to 40 μg cortisol per 100 ml. plasma). Transcortin is produced in the liver; its concentration is lowered in liver disease and in nephrosis and elevated by ACTH and by estrogen, as seen during the later stages of pregnancy.

ROLE OF THE ADRENAL CORTEX

The primary mechanism of action of the adrenal steroids is not known. There can be described, as effects of these hormones, a wide variety of biochemical and physiological responses, some of which are probably a consequence of secondary effects of a primary role, and others which may be even more indirect results of initial actions. These activities may be grouped, arbitrarily, into (1) alterations in carbohydrate, protein, and lipid metabolism, (2) effects on electrolyte and water metabolism, including an influence on circulatory homeostasis and on neuromuscular irritability, (3) hematological effects, (4) secretory action, (5) effects on inflammatory and allergic phenomena, and (6) effects on resistance to noxious stimuli.

Administration of each of the three major hormonal products of the adrenal cortex, viz., cortisol, corticosterone, and aldosterone, produces effects which have, in part, similarities. Cortisol and aldosterone may be considered at two extremes in terms of the responses they elicit, with corticosterone intermediate in its effects. Cortisol influences all the activities listed above, with, however, a very much weaker effect on electrolyte and water metabolism. In contrast, aldosterone exerts its prime action on electrolyte and water metabolism, but in the other areas listed has, at most, less than one-third of the activity of cortisol. Corticosterone spans in its effects all the activities listed, but with significantly less effectiveness in any one than is exhibited by cortisol or aldosterone in their respective areas of greatest potency.

The relative adrenal cortical activities, in animal bioassays, of certain C_{21} steroids, including the principal compounds secreted by the adrenal cortex, are shown in Table 49.2. The bioassay procedures listed in the table emphasize again

Table 49.2: APPROXIMATE RELATIVE BIOLOGICAL ACTIVITIES OF CERTAIN ADRENAL CORTICAL STEROIDS IN ADRENALECTOMIZED RATS, EXPRESSED IN TERMS OF THE ACTIVITY OF 11-DEHYDRO-17-HYDROXYCORTICOSTERONE (CORTISONE)

Steroid	Life main- tenance	Glyco- gen de- position	Sodium reten- tion*	Muscle- work test†	Growth test	Cold test	Anti- inflam- matory activity*
11-Dehydro-17-hydroxycorti- costerone (cortisone)	100	100	100	100	100	100	100
Corticostosterone	75	54	255	46	108	9	3
11-Dehydrocorticosterone	58	48	.....	32	...	33	0
17-Hydroxycorticosterone (cortisol)	100	155	150	160	219	...	1,250
Deoxycorticosterone	400	0	3,000	5	...	8	0
Aldosterone	...	30	60,000	...	...	...	0

* Adrenalectomized mice.

† Adrenalectomized-nephrectomized rats.

that the hormones of the adrenal cortex influence a wide variety of biochemical phenomena. This is further indicated in Table 49.3, which lists the diverse changes seen in adrenal cortical insufficiency.

Carbohydrate Metabolism. Certain adrenal cortical steroids, *e.g.*, cortisol, influence carbohydrate metabolism by altering the rates of three processes: (1) increasing glucose release from the liver; (2) accentuating gluconeogenesis from amino acids; and (3) decreasing the peripheral utilization of glucose. The mechanism of the first of these processes is unknown, although cortisol administration augments hepatic glucose 6-phosphatase activity. The second is a consequence of the increased availability of amino acids because of the inhibiting effect of adrenal cortical steroids on amino acid incorporation into proteins, an antianabolic effect on protein metabolism. This will be considered again below. The decreased utilization of glucose seen after cortisol administration apparently is due to an inhibitory effect of the steroid on pyruvate metabolism. A number of investigators have demonstrated that adrenal cortical steroids inhibit the oxidation of DPNH in vitro. Should this obtain in vivo, a possible result would be a reduction in the availability of DPN, essential for oxidative decarboxylation of pyruvic acid to acetyl CoA (page 317). This would also make more pyruvate available for glucose resynthesis (page 378).

As a result of the three above influences of adrenal cortical steroids on carbohydrate metabolism, there occurs, in the fasted or fed normal subject given cortisol, an elevated concentration of liver glycogen and of blood glucose. Prolonged or excessive administration of cortisol will produce a diabetic type of glucose tolerance curve (page 425) and glucosuria, and can result in permanent diabetes mellitus because of degeneration and exhaustion of pancreatic islet cells. Conversely, following adrenalectomy there is an increased sensitivity to insulin, probably related to both decreased gluconeogenesis and release of glucose from the liver. Hence, the requirement for insulin is diminished, as is the severity of any preexisting diabetes. Rapidly fatal hypoglycemia develops on fasting the hypoadrenal cortical individual, because of enhanced insulin sensitivity. In the absence of adequate adrenal cortical steroids, muscle glycogen concentration also fails to be maintained; this failure is reflected in a diminished work performance of the muscle. Work performance of adrenalectomized rats has been used for bioassay of active cortical hormones.

Only certain adrenal steroids, *e.g.*, cortisol, influence carbohydrate metabolism. Aldosterone and deoxycorticosterone are relatively without effect in this regard (Table 49.2, page 879).

Protein and Amino Acid Metabolism. Although the primary mechanism is unknown, certain adrenal cortical steroids markedly inhibit protein synthesis in muscle and other tissues. Since protein degradation in the same tissues is continuing, amino acids leave these structures, resulting in wasting of soft tissues and osteoporosis. Although there is evidence that, under these same circumstances, protein synthesis in the liver may actually be enhanced, this is insufficient to offset the exit of amino acids from other tissues, as reflected in an elevated plasma amino acid concentration. Oxidation of these amino acids with concomitant urea synthesis is indicated by an over-all negative nitrogen balance.

The stimulation of protein synthesis in liver seen following cortisol injection is a direct hormonal action on the liver since it occurs in the isolated, perfused organ

Table 49.3: BIOCHEMICAL ALTERATIONS PRODUCED BY ADRENAL CORTICAL INSUFFICIENCY

Nature of change observed	Basis for change
Alterations in blood:	
Decrease in serum sodium and increase in serum potassium; decrease in serum chloride	Disturbed kidney function reflected in failure of tubular reabsorption of Na^+ and Cl^-
Hemoconcentration......................	Loss of water through kidney, accompanying electrolyte loss
Acidosis...............................	Failure of renal Na^+-K^+-H^+ exchange mechanism
Hypoglycemia with fasting.................	Reduced level of liver glycogen in fasting; diminished gluconeogenesis and increased carbohydrate utilization
Increase in blood urea....................	Renal failure and circulatory impairment
Lymphocytosis..........................	Lack of lymphocytolytic action of 11-oxyadrenal cortical steroids, with accompanying growth of lymphoid tissue
Eosinophilia...........................	Unknown
Anemia................................	Lack of stimulation of erythropoietic tissue and of production of intrinsic factor; gastric hyposecretion
Alterations in protein metabolism:	
Diminished urinary nitrogen in fasting.......	Absence of antianabolic influence of adrenal steroids
Alterations in carbohydrate metabolism:	
Reduced levels of liver glycogen in fasting.....	Diminished gluconeogenesis
Markedly increased insulin sensitivity........	Diminished gluconeogenesis
Impairment of carbohydrate absorption from the gastrointestinal tract	Unknown; possibly related to disturbances in potassium metabolism*
Alterations in lipid metabolism:	
Impairment of lipid mobilization from depots.	Unknown
Generalized alterations:	
Intensification of inflammatory response and of hypersensitivity reactions	Increased influx of polymorphonuclear leukocytes and lymphocytes from blood into area of inflammation, accompanied by an augmented production of tissue substances contributing to reactions of inflammation and hypersensitivity, including destruction of fibroblasts.
Increased growth of lymphoid tissue.........	Lack of adrenal cortical steroid lymphocytolytic action on lymphocytes
Decreased metabolic rate..................	Unknown
Hypotension............................	Decreased extracellular volume; decreased cardiac output
Excessive pigmentation....................	Unknown; possibly due to intrinsic melanocyte-stimulating activity of ACTH (page 911)
Anorexia, weight loss; cessation of growth....	Unknown
Muscular weakness and sensitivity to stress...	Partly due to loss of potassium from cells; impaired glycogenesis.

* Passage of carbohydrate into cells is accompanied by movement of potassium in the intracellular direction. In adrenal cortical insufficiency, potassium tends to move out of cells.

when the steroid is added to the perfusion fluid. Studies of protein synthesis with fractions obtained from broken cell preparations of livers of normal rats and of rats previously injected with cortisol indicated that the hormone stimulated the amino acid–incorporating activity of ribosomal RNA (Chap. 30).

Lipid Metabolism. Adrenal cortical steroid administration to intact animals may increase peripheral lipogenesis, possibly because of an associated increase in insulin release. The latter hormone promotes lipogenesis (page 892). However, addition of cortisol in vitro to the epididymal fat pad of the rat causes release of free fatty acids and will augment the activity of epinephrine in this in vitro system. Lipid mobilization from the depots is strikingly evident in some species, notably the rabbit, following adrenal cortical steroid administration. This lipid-mobilizing effect could contribute to the marked ketogenic action of the hormone in adrenal-ectomized, depancreatized animals, as well as in human subjects with Addison's disease and concomitant diabetes. The mechanism of the lipid-mobilizing action of adrenal cortical steroids is unknown.

Electrolyte and Water Metabolism. The metabolism of electrolytes and water has been presented in Chap. 35. The adrenal cortical steroids have a regulatory influence in this metabolism, particularly in relation to the concentration of sodium and potassium in extracellular fluids. Deoxycorticosterone and aldosterone cause increased reabsorption of Na^+, Cl^-, and HCO_3^- in the distal tubules of the kidney, and by the sweat glands, salivary glands, and gastrointestinal mucosa. Thus, excessive concentrations of either of these steroids produces elevation of extracellular $[Na^+]$ and expansion of extracellular volume and $[HCO_3^-]$, with a decline in serum $[K^+]$ and $[Cl^-]$. Sodium retention is also reflected in an exchange of intracellular K^+ for extracellular Na^+, with excretion of the K^+. Mobilization of Na^+ from connective tissue occurs with transfer of this ion into extracellular compartments. The increase in extracellular volume is accompanied by increased urine volume and elevation of blood pressure. Lowering of serum $[K^+]$ by adrenal cortical steroids leads to deleterious and toxic effects on cardiac muscle, with characteristic electrocardiogram changes; elevation of extracellular $[Na^+]$ causes decreased excitability of brain tissue.

Other electrolytes, e.g., Ca^{++}, may appear in the urine in greater than normal concentrations following adrenal steroid administration. The augmented loss of Ca^{++} is due to the retardation of protein synthesis from amino acids (see above); osteoporosis results from the decreased bone formation. Ca^{++} which otherwise would be deposited in osteoid is excreted in the urine.

In contrast to the above effects of excessive quantities of adrenal cortical steroids, an inadequate supply of these compounds, i.e., hypoadrenal corticalism, results in failure of normal tubular reabsorption of Na^+, with consequent increased excretion of Na^+, Cl^-, and water, leading to diminution of plasma volume. The consequences are essentially those described in Chap. 35 for hypotonic contraction. Na^+ also moves into the tissues. Serum and tissue $[K^+]$ rise because of a diminished excretion of this cation by the kidney. Reduction in extracellular volume, hemoconcentration, and increased viscosity of the blood contribute to a decreased cardiac output and hypotension.

Metabolic acidosis develops in untreated adrenal cortical insufficiency. This acidosis has a dual origin: renal and extrarenal. In the kidney, secretion of both H^+ and NH_4^+ by the renal tubule is impaired. Under conditions of acid loading, the renal response is inadequate and acidification of the urine suboptimal. With elevation of serum $[K^+]$, there occurs a shift of bicarbonate into cells, passage of H^+ from cells into the extracellular fluid, and consequent acidosis.

The loss of extracellular sodium in adrenal cortical deficiency is reflected in undesirable effects in other tissues. For example, lowering of extracellular sodium in brain tissue is accompanied by a marked increase in excitability of this tissue, as measured by the electroshock threshold in normal and adrenalectomized rats. Alterations in the electroencephalogram have been described in Addison's disease in man. The hyperpotassemia exerts deleterious effects on cardiac muscle, reflected in changes in the electrocardiogram.

Certain of the alterations in serum electrolytes in the hypo- and hyperadrenal cortical states are illustrated in Fig. 49.4.

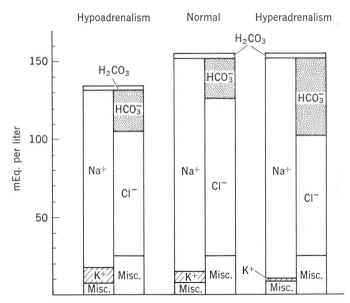

FIG. 49.4. Serum electrolytes in hypoadrenal cortical and hyperadrenal cortical states in man.

As a result of adrenal cortical insufficiency, with its consequent loss of fluid through the kidney and decrease in plasma volume, there is a decline in blood pressure with a reduced circulation through the kidneys, and renal failure. Because of the latter, the blood urea rises (Fig. 49.5), as does the blood $[Ca^{++}]$, $[P_i]$, and $[K^+]$. The excretion of extra water is also retarded, and an excessive intake of water may result in "water intoxication" (page 680).

The regulatory influence of the adrenal cortex on the capacity of the kidney to excrete water and retain salt is useful clinically as an aid in the diagnosis either of Addison's disease or of adrenal cortical hypofunctioning due to hypophyseal insufficiency. This function forms the basis for the Kepler test, which involves a

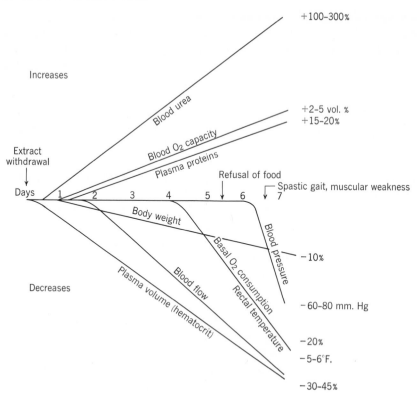

FIG. 49.5. Characteristic changes in metabolism, circulation, and concentration of certain blood constituents as seen in adrenalectomized dogs subsequent to withdrawal of adrenal cortical extract, with resultant production of adrenal cortical insufficiency. (*From R. F. Loeb, J.A.M.A.,* **104**, 2177, 1935.)

study of the urinary response to the ingestion of 20 ml. of water per kilogram of body weight. Excretion of water and of Na^+ or Cl^- is determined hourly for the following several hours. With decreased adrenal function, the urine does not become diluted; its volume is very low, but Na^+ and Cl^- continue to be excreted. The important role of sodium chloride in hypoadrenal cortical states is seen from the partial amelioration of adrenal cortical insufficiency by administration of NaCl. Recognition of the deleterious rise in serum $[K^+]$, following lowering of serum $[Na^+]$, has led to the demonstration that many of the disturbances of adrenal cortical insufficiency can be alleviated by a high sodium and low potassium intake. This regimen will rectify the mineral imbalance in adrenal cortical insufficiency and may prevent rapid deterioration and death.

Hematologic Effects. The 11-oxygenated adrenal cortical steroids other than aldosterone influence the numbers of blood lymphocytes, erythrocytes, and eosinophils, as well as the structure and function of lymphoid tissue. In the latter tissue, these adrenal steroids produce a decrease in the numbers of lymphocytes and in the size of lymphoid organs, because of a lymphocytolytic action or disintegration of lymphocytes. The basis of this phenomenon is not understood. As a consequence, fewer lymphocytes are delivered to the lymph and then to the blood, and a lymphopenia is evident. The effects of adrenal steroids on the role of lymphoid tissue in antibody formation and immune phenomena have been noted previously (page 810). Lymphoid tissue hypertrophy and lymphocytosis are seen in some species as a consequence of adrenal cortical hypofunction.

The erythropoietic action of adrenal cortical steroids indicates a stimulatory action of these hormones on bone marrow. The regulatory influence of adrenal cortical steroids on the numbers of blood erythrocytes and eosinophils is not understood. The anemia resulting from adrenal cortical hypofunctioning was noted by Addison in his original description of Addison's disease.

Secretory Action. The 11-oxygenated adrenal cortical steroids augment secretory activity of the gastrointestinal tract. Hydrochloric acid and pepsinogen secretion by the gastric mucosa, and trypsinogen secretion by the pancreas, are increased following steroid administration. These effects may be the basis of the precipitation of ulcerative lesions of the gastrointestinal tract during prolonged adrenal steroid therapy. The pernicious anemia of Addison's disease may be related functionally to gastric hyposecretion (see page 808).

Effects on Inflammatory and Allergic Phenomena. Cortisone, cortisol, and certain synthetic steroids (page 888) are anti-inflammatory substances, *i.e.*, they prevent the appearance of inflammatory responses, whether such responses are due to physical, chemical, or bacterial stimuli. The efficacy of these steroids can be demonstrated either locally, at the site of potential inflammation, or by their systemic administration. The adrenal steroids inhibit the influx of polymorphonuclear leukocytes from the blood into the local area of inflammation, and inhibit the localized destruction of fibroblasts, otherwise seen as a consequence of an inflammatory reaction.

Certain adrenal cortical steroids, *e.g.*, cortisol, are markedly effective in counteracting some manifestations of the hypersensitive state, *e.g.*, anaphylactic shock.

These activities of adrenal cortical steroids have led to the therapeutic use of these compounds in the group of clinical conditions which are diseases of mesenchymal tissue, in circumstances of hypersensitivity, and in acute inflammatory and allergic diseases of the eye and skin.

Adrenal Cortex and Resistance to Noxious Stimuli. Normally, homeostasis is maintained despite exposure to a wide variety of noxious stimuli of both endogenous and exogenous origin. In contrast, the adrenal cortical–insufficient subject does not readily cope with such challenges to homeostasis. For example, in amount considerably below those tolerated normally, hemorrhage, physical trauma, infectious agents, sensitizing antigens, or noxious chemicals may produce fatal consequences in adrenalectomized animals. As indicated previously (page 880), there is marked sensitivity to insulin, as well as to other hormones, *e.g.*, thyroxine. Such diverse types of noxious stimuli result in a markedly increased requirement for adrenal cortical hormones. This is evidenced by the increased protection against deleterious stimuli which is afforded adrenalectomized animals treated with adrenal cortical steroids prior to institution of the stimulus.

Continued maintenance of adrenalectomized animals or human beings is possible with available adrenal cortical steroids. This has led to the demonstration that partial or total adrenalectomy or hypophysectomy has an ameliorative result in some cases of malignant hypertension and in carcinoma of the breast and of the prostate.

Adrenal Cortical Hyperfunction in the Human Being. The consequences of an excessive supply of adrenal cortical steroids have been considered previously. In the human being, abnormally high secretory activity of the adrenal cortex poses special problems because of the variable chemical nature of the hormones being elaborated.

Hyperfunctioning of the adrenal cortex in the human being results from cortical cell tumors which may arise in the adrenal gland or can be extra-adrenal in location. The resulting clinical picture depends upon the nature of the predominant steroid secreted by the tumor. If *cortisol* is the major compound produced, *Cushing's syndrome* results, and the physiological alterations seen are characteristically those described previously for excessive concentrations of adrenal cortical steroids. Obesity may be marked in the supraclavicular regions, on the back of the neck (buffalo hump), and in the face (moon face). Weakness and wasting of muscle, with marked osteoporosis, are evident. The alterations in electrolyte and water metabolism are those discussed above (page 882). Either latent or overt diabetes is present in many cases, with resistance to insulin. Arteriosclerosis and hypertension are seen; there is often great lability of mood. Purple striae are evident over the abdomen, thighs, and upper arms.

If the steroid produced by the tumor is chiefly *aldosterone* (*primary aldosteronism*), there is marked Na^+ and water retention, with tendency to edema and hypertension, leading to heart failure, and extreme weakness owing to low serum $[K^+]$.

Secondary aldosteronism has been used to designate conditions in which increased aldosterone secretion is a secondary manifestation of nonadrenal disease, *e.g.*, in cardiac, renal, and hepatic disorders. A prime etiological factor relates to the influence of cardiovascular-renal stimuli in the regulation of aldosterone secretion by the adrenal cortex (page 878). Thus, in renal disease resulting in Na^+ loss in the urine, the lowered plasma $[Na^+]$ will stimulate aldosterone secretion.

In adrenal cortical hyperplasia with hypersecretion of *androgenic* steroids, the manifestations vary according to the age and sex of the patient. Adult women become masculine in appearance; hence the term *adrenal virilism.* The voice deepens, menstruation ceases, the breasts atrophy, and hair may grow on the face, chest, and limbs. In the adult male, there are overgrowth of hair, enlargement of the penis, and increased sexual desire.

When these tumors occur in young children, puberty appears prematurely. A male child of three to five years may show the sexual development of an adult, with enlargement of the penis, hair on the chest, pubis, and face, and precocious sexual desire. There may also be unusual muscular development; growth is rapid. In young girls, the breasts hypertrophy, pubic hair appears, the uterus develops prematurely, the clitoris is hypertrophied, and menstruation may occur.

Surgical removal of the tumor may be followed by symptoms of acute adrenal cortical insufficiency. However, with the availability of potent steroids, the hazards of such surgical intervention have been reduced. Administration of 11-oxyadrenal cortical steroids in some instances of juvenile adrenal virilism has become a useful

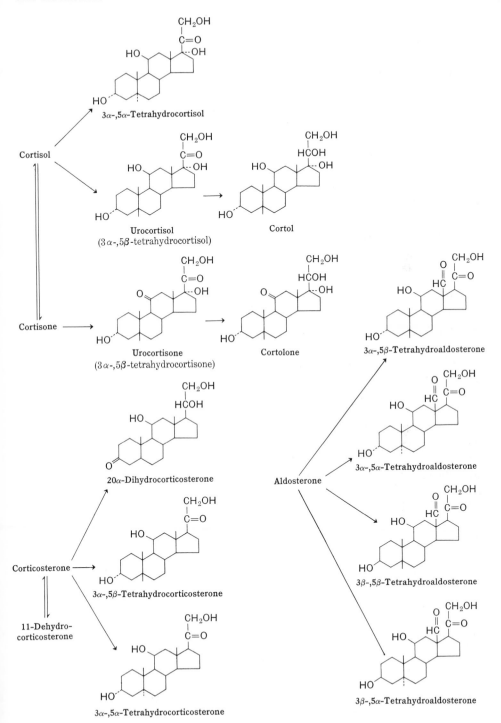

FIG. 49.6. Some metabolic products derived from adrenal cortical hormones. Structures of the latter have been presented previously (page 874). The chief metabolites, quantitatively, are indicated in the text.

therapeutic measure in place of surgery, since repeated administration of one of these steroids depresses functioning of the individual's own adrenals, with resultant atrophy of the adrenal cortex (see page 911). This also is the reason why sudden withdrawal of exogenous adrenal cortical steroid therapy may precipitate symptoms of acute adrenal cortical insufficiency.

Metabolic Fate of Adrenal Cortical Steroids. The major metabolites of adrenal cortical steroids result from reduction and conjugation reactions. Conjugates are primarily glucosiduronides at C-21, although some sulfate esters are also formed. The metabolic products are devoid of biological activity. The chief metabolites arise in the liver by a two-step reduction to the corresponding "tetrahydro" compounds. In addition, two products are present in the urine which result from further reduction at C-20. Reversible oxidation-reduction also occurs at C-11 in a variety of tissues. Some of the principal metabolites are indicated in Fig. 49.6.

After intravenous administration of C^{14}-labeled cortisol in man, 93 per cent of the hormone was eliminated within 48 hr. without scission of the steroid nucleus, 70 per cent of which appeared as urinary products and 20 per cent in the feces. Urocortisone, urocortisol, and the tetrahydroallopregnane (5α) derivative of cortisol are the major urinary metabolites of adrenal cortical steroids, approximating almost half of the total products. That portion of metabolites, both free and conjugated, excreted in the bile may be reabsorbed from the intestine in an enterohepatic circulation. As in the case of other steroid hormones (page 863), liver disease impairs metabolism of the active adrenal steroids, and in such a circumstance their level may be markedly elevated in the blood.

Approximately 5 to 10 per cent of the secreted C_{21} adrenal steroids contribute normally to the total urinary 17-ketosteroids (page 856), yielding 11-oxy-17-ketosteroids, in contrast to the 11-deoxy-17-ketosteroids formed from the C_{19} androgens.

Synthetic Adrenal Cortical Steroids. A large number of new steroids have been prepared synthetically in an effort to provide compounds with significantly greater adrenal cortical activity. In addition, it has been the goal to seek substances with single actions rather than the multiplicity of responses seen with the normally

Table 49.4: APPROXIMATE COMPARATIVE ADRENAL CORTICAL POTENCIES OF CERTAIN NATURAL AND SYNTHETIC STEROIDS, EXPRESSED IN TERMS OF THE ACTIVITY OF CORTISONE

Steroid	Sodium-retaining activity	Glycogenic activity	Anti-inflammatory activity
Cortisone	1	1	1
Cortisol	1.5	1.5	1.25
Deoxycorticosterone	30–50	0	0
Aldosterone	300–600	0	0
9α-Fluorocortisol	200–400	10–15	10–15
Δ^1-Cortisol	Minimal	3–5	4
9α-Fluoro-Δ^1-cortisol	200	30–40	10
2-Methylcortisol	100–200	5	3
2-Methyl-9α-fluorocortisol	1,000–2,000	10	10
6α-Methyl-Δ^1-cortisol	Minimal	4–6	3–5
16α-Methyl-9α-fluoro-Δ^1-cortisol	Minimal	25–30	25–35

secreted hormones. Certain of these synthetic compounds have proved to be many times more potent than cortisol, and, in certain instances, some separation of biological effects has been obtained. Some examples are shown in Table 49.4.

REFERENCES

Books

Clark, F., and Grant, J. K., eds., "The Biosynthesis and Secretion of Adrenocortical Steroids," Cambridge University Press, Cambridge, 1960.
von Eichler, O., and Farah, A., eds., "The Adrenal Cortical Hormones: Their Origin, Chemistry, Physiology and Pharmacology," part I, Lange and Springer, Berlin, 1962.
von Euler, U. S., "Noradrenaline: Chemistry, Physiology, Pharmacology, and Clinical Aspects," Charles C Thomas, Publisher, Springfield, Ill., 1956.
Krayer, O., ed., "Symposium on Catecholamines," The Williams & Wilkins Company, Baltimore, 1959. (Also published in *Pharmacol. Revs.*, **11**, 241–566, 1959.)
Soffer, L. J., Dorfman, R. I., and Gabrilove, J. L., "The Human Adrenal Gland," Lea & Febiger, Philadelphia, 1961.
Wolstenholme, G. E. W., and Cameron, M. P., eds., "The Human Adrenal Cortex," Little, Brown and Company, Boston, 1955.

Review Articles

Axelrod, J., Metabolism of Epinephrine and Other Sympathomimetic Amines, *Physiol. Revs.*, **39**, 751–776, 1959.
Beck, J. C., and McGarry, E. E., Physiological Importance of Cortisol, *Brit. Med. Bull.*, **18**, 134–140, 1962.
Berliner, D. L., and Dougherty, T. F., Hepatic and Extrahepatic Regulation of Corticosteroids, *Pharmacol. Revs.*, **13**, 329–359, 1961.
Davis, J. O., Mechanisms Regulating the Secretion and Metabolism of Aldosterone in Experimental Secondary Hyperaldosteronism, *Recent Progr. Hormone Research*, **17**, 293–352, 1961.
Davison, A. N., Physiological Role of Monamine Oxidase, *Physiol. Revs.*, **38**, 729–748, 1958.
Dorfman, A., and Schiller, S., Effects of Hormones on the Metabolism of Acid Mucopolysaccharides of Connective Tissue, *Recent Progr. Hormone Research*, **14**, 427–456, 1958.
Dorfman, R. I., Biochemistry of the Adrenocortical Hormones, in H. W. Deane, subed., "Handbuch der Experimentellen Pharmakologie Ergangungswerk, vol. XIV, part I, pp. 411–513, Springer-Verlag OHG, Berlin, 1962.
Gaddum, J. H., and Holzbauer, M., Adrenaline and Noradrenaline, *Vitamins and Hormones*, **15**, 151–203, 1957.
Grant, J. K., Studies on the Biogenesis of the Adrenal Steroids, *Brit. Med. Bull.*, **18**, 99–105, 1962.
Hagen, P., and Welch, A. D., The Adrenal Medulla and the Biosynthesis of Pressor Amines, *Recent Progr. Hormone Research*, **12**, 27–44, 1956.
Mills, I. H., Transport and Metabolism of Steroids, *Brit. Med. Bull.*, **18**, 127–133, 1962.
Sayers, G., Adrenal Cortex and Homeostasis, *Physiol. Revs.*, **30**, 241–320, 1950.
Simpson, S. A., and Tait, J. F., Recent Progress in Methods of Isolation, Chemistry, and Physiology of Aldosterone, *Recent Progr. Hormone Research*, **11**, 183–210, 1955.
Sutherland, E. W., Jr., The Biological Role of Adenosine-3',5'-Phosphate, *Harvey Lectures*, **57**, 17–34, 1961–1962.
Yates, F. E., and Urquhart, J., Control of Plasma Concentrations of Adrenocortical Hormones, *Physiol. Revs.*, **42**, 359–443, 1962.

50. The Pancreas

The pancreas produces and secretes two hormonal agents. *Insulin* is secreted by the β type of islet cells of the pancreas and exerts a profound hypoglycemic effect when administered. The other hormone, *glucagon,* is produced by the α type of pancreatic islets and exerts a hyperglycemic action. Other physiological alterations produced by each of these hormones will be considered below.

INSULIN—THE HYPOGLYCEMIC FACTOR

Four milestones are evident in the development of present knowledge of insulin: (1) the demonstration in 1889 by von Mehring and Minkowski that total removal of the pancreas in the dog or cat resulted in symptoms resembling those of human diabetes; (2) the preparation by Banting and Best in 1922 of the first extracts from pancreatic tissue effective in ameliorating the symptoms of diabetic dogs and of severely diabetic patients; (3) the demonstration by Levine and his coworkers in 1949 that a major effect of insulin is to facilitate glucose entry into cells; and (4) the establishment in 1955 by Sanger and his colleagues of the complete amino acid sequence of insulin.

Chemistry of Insulin. The first therapeutically useful preparation of insulin was obtained by Banting and Best in 1922. The hormone was isolated in crystalline form by Abel and his associates in 1926, and in 1934 Scott described the crystallization of insulin in the presence of small amounts of metallic ions, *e.g.*, zinc, cadmium, or cobalt. The zinc derivatives have been useful clinically (see below).

The chemical structure of insulin has been fully elucidated and was presented previously (page 153). Some comparative data of amino acid residue substitutions in insulins of various species have also been discussed earlier (page 614). Despite this information, there is still no understanding of the relationship between the structure of the protein and its biological action. Although removal of a single terminal amino acid residue (alanine) from bovine insulin by incubation with carboxypeptidase does not alter significantly the biological activity of insulin, digestion with other proteolytic enzymes, *e.g.*, trypsin, leads to significant lowering of the biological potency when only one or two peptide bonds have been split. It has not been possible to prepare from insulin, by partial or complete hydrolysis, a moiety with significant hypoglycemic activity. Insulin was the first hormone to be recognized as a protein and as being dependent upon its intact protein structure for its biological effects. The inactivation of insulin by proteolytic enzymes makes necessary parenteral injection to elicit the actions of the hormone.

The relatively few differences among amino acid residues of insulins from a variety of species (page 614), and the dependency of hormonal action on a relatively intact molecule, make noteworthy some recent data for the structure of insulin from cod pancreas, which has rather extensive differences in amino acid composition in comparison with other insulins. Thus, the B chain of cod insulin has one more amino acid residue, *i.e.*, 31, rather than the 30 of other insulins (page 153). However, more striking is the fact that in the A chain of cod insulin, only two amino acid residues, *viz.*, cysteine and glycine, are present in the same number as in other insulins studied. Despite this suggestion of important differences in amino acid sequences, there is no observable significant difference in potency of cod insulin in comparison with other insulins. It may therefore be assumed that the biological activity of insulin, as for other biocatalytically active proteins, is related to its conformation, and that despite probable differences in amino acid sequences between, for example, cod and ox insulins, their molecules must possess significant conformational similarities.

Available data relating the structure of insulin to its biological action suggest that (1) the free amino and aliphatic hydroxyl groups of insulin are not essential for its activity; (2) some amide, guanidine, tyrosine phenolic groups and histidine imidazole groups can be substituted without loss of activity, although extensive iodination of phenolic groups (aromatic nuclei of tyrosine) results in marked inactivation; and (3) reduction of disulfide groups or esterification of carboxyl groups leads to loss of hormonal activity.

Insulin has a molecular weight of 5,700 and is isoelectric at pH 5.4. The predominance of acidic groups in insulin results in its ready combination with bases. One such combination with basic proteins (protamines or globin) has been useful clinically because the insolubility of the protamine- or globin-insulin complex at tissue pH provides a relatively insoluble, slowly absorbed depot of insulin and results in a more prolonged action than that with ordinary insulin. This permits less frequent injections of insulin in clinical diabetes. Similar prolonged action is achieved with the crystalline zinc salt of protamine or globin insulin, also because of its relative insolubility. A neutral, crystalline protamine zinc insulin, described by Hagedorn in Denmark and termed NPH insulin (N, neutral; P, protamine; H, Hagedorn) and also known as isophane insulin, has been particularly useful. Lente (L., slowly) insulins, crystallized from an acetate buffer in the presence of Zn^{++},

Table 50.1: PROPERTIES OF VARIOUS INSULIN PREPARATIONS

Type of insulin	Time of onset of action after injection, hr.	Period of maximum action after injection, hr.	Duration of action, hr.
Regular, amorphous	1	3	6
Globin zinc insulin	2–4	8–16	16–24
Protamine zinc insulin	6–8	12–24	48–72
Isophane (NPH) insulin	2	10–20	28–30
Lente insulin	2	10–20	22–26

are also long-acting, because of the relative insolubility of the crystalline product. Lente insulin resembles NPH insulin in its duration of action but has the feature of not containing foreign protein like protamine or globin. The time of onset and duration of hypoglycemic effects of various insulin preparations are indicated in Table 50.1.

Effects of Insulin. The role of insulin in carbohydrate metabolism has been discussed previously (Chap. 21, pages 422*ff.*). The hypoglycemic effect of insulin and the hyperglycemia and glucosuria resulting from inadequate supply of insulin are a reflection of the role of insulin in the utilization of glucose by the tissues.

Evidence of Levine and his associates indicates that insulin facilitates entry of certain sugars, including glucose, into cells. The net result is a decrease in the concentration of blood glucose and an increase in formation of intracellular hexose phosphate and of products derived from the latter, including glycogen. In support of this view is the influence of insulin on the volume of distribution of D-galactose, D-xylose, and L-arabinose in the eviscerated animal. None of these sugars is utilized by the eviscerated animal, and when injected intravenously they are distributed through a volume which is considerably less than the total body water. Administration of insulin promptly increases the volume of distribution of the sugars, suggesting that insulin increases the permeability of certain cell membranes to various sugars and thereby facilitates their entry into cells. Under selected experimental conditions it has been possible to show more ready penetration of glucose itself into intracellular spaces after insulin administration.

Current evidence suggests that insulin acts by increasing penetration of cell membranes by glucose and by augmenting phosphorylation of glucose. It is possible that both events may prove to be in part different expressions of the same phenomenon. The view that insulin has an intracellular action and is not limited in its effects to transport of glucose across cells stems from observations that the rate of glucose utilization, both in intact animals and in isolated tissues, is influenced by the extracellular glucose concentration (page 423). Moreover, even in circumstances of maximal entry of glucose into cells, insulin stimulates further utilization of glucose. Sols has shown the presence in liver microsomes of a specific glucokinase, the activity of which is markedly enhanced by administration of insulin. Further, Larner and his associates demonstrated that insulin added in vitro to rat diaphragm increased by about 50 per cent the activity of glycogen synthetase (page 413), again pointing to an intracellular influence of the hormone. The basis of the effects of insulin on glucose uptake and glycogen synthesis in muscle has been discussed (pages 422*ff.*).

In addition to the effects of insulin on carbohydrate metabolism, the hormone exerts profound influences on protein and lipid metabolism as well. Certain of these actions are primary; others are secondary to glucose utilization. Insulin administration promotes protein synthesis by augmenting incorporation of amino acids into proteins. This effect is independent of glucose utilization. Insulin administration suppresses the rise in concentration of blood amino acids seen after evisceration in dogs, indicating that the hormone can exert a protein anabolic influence in extrahepatic tissues. This is also reflected in the classical demonstration by Best that fed hypophysectomized rats, which fail to grow (page 917), will exhibit approximately normal growth rates if given daily injections of insulin with adequate glucose to prevent hypoglycemic convulsions.

Evidence indicates that insulin may stimulate both the entry of certain amino acids into cells and the sequence of reactions involved in subsequent protein bio-synthesis (page 599). Korner and Robinson independently found that insulin administration to rats augmented the activity of the liver ribosomal fraction from these animals, when studied in the in vitro amino acid–incorporating system (page 598). Insulin was without effect when added to the ribosomal system in vitro. These in vitro effects of insulin are in harmony with those observed in vivo (see above).

The stimulating action of insulin on lipogenesis from carbohydrate has been obvious since the first emaciated dog or diabetic patient was treated with the hor-mone. In studies utilizing isotopically labeled glucose, Stetten calculated that in the well-nourished rat only about 3 per cent of the glucose ingested each day is con-verted to glycogen, while 30 per cent is used to make fatty acids. In the absence of insulin, the diabetic animal exhibits a much lower level of lipogenesis, as well as of glycogenesis. Aspects of lipogenesis by adipose tissue have been considered pre-viously (page 438).

Insulin added to adipose tissue in vitro increases glucose utilization, with an accompanying stimulation of synthesis by this tissue of glycerol, fatty acids, and glycogen, as well as an increased degree of pinocytosis. In contrast, fatty acid release by adipose tissue is inhibited in the presence of insulin; this may be the basis for the decrease in free fatty acids in the blood after insulin administration. Insulin added in vitro to slices of mammary gland from lactating rats increases fatty acid synthesis from added glucose and acetate, and augments the rate of incorporation of amino acids into the proteins of rat diaphragm, rat epididymal adipose tissue, and rat heart slices, as well as of adenine into the nucleic acids and of acetate into fat and phosphatides of rat diaphragm. Insulin added in vitro to the latter tissue stimulated the incorporation of C^{14} from acetate into triglyceride and phosphatide and of P_i^{32} into phosphatide and protein. These effects of insulin in vitro on the incorporation of amino acids, adenine, P^{32}, or C^{14} from acetate could be demon-strated in the absence of glucose in the medium. Insulin therefore has stimulatory effects on protein, nucleic acid, and lipid synthesis which appear to be independent of its action on glucose utilization.

In addition to the above-described effects of insulin on aspects of organic metabolism, the hormone influences inorganic metabolism, notably that of phos-phate and potassium. Insulin administration lowers the blood phosphate level and facilitates uptake of inorganic phosphate by cells, even in the absence of glucose. This phosphate appears within the cell as ATP and phosphocreatine. A similar augmentation of potassium uptake by cells is observed as a result of insulin administration.

Mechanism of Insulin Action. The statement that insulin facilitates entry of glu-cose into cells is descriptive of a process, rather than of the basic mechanism by which this transport is effected. As pointed out previously (page 825), there is no instance in which the mechanism of action of a single hormone has yet been elucidated.

Studies of the mechanism of action of insulin have been greatly stimulated by knowledge of the complete chemical structure of this protein hormone. The inactivation of insulin on reduction of its interchain disulfide linkages, and the presence of an intrachain disulfide-closed ring in the structure of insulin (page 153), have focused interest on the possible role of disulfide bonds in the binding of insulin to receptor sites in tissues. Also, the evidence that oxytocin (Chap. 51) and related disulfide peptides with oxytocic-like activity exert an insulin-like action on rat epididymal adipose tissue (page 439) is further indicative that the action of insulin may be dependent in part upon its disulfide linkages. The initiation of a series of thiol-disulfide reactions between hormone and specific membrane sites could produce alterations in the tertiary structure of membrane proteins and thereby open channels for the accelerated passage of water and specific solutes, *e.g.*, glucose, into the cell. Some data are available in support of this concept. Haft and Mirsky first reported, in 1952, that pretreatment of the isolated rat diaphragm with low concentrations of the sulfhydryl reacting agents, iodoacetate or *p*-chloromercuribenzoate, which did not alter glucose uptake did, nevertheless, inhibit the action of insulin. More recently, Cadenas and associates observed that another sulfhydryl reacting agent, N-ethylmaleimide, inhibited the action of insulin on the perfused rat heart as well as the binding of I^{131}-labeled insulin to heart tissue. Ungar and Kadis have reported also that incubation of insulin with isolated rat diaphragm decreases the total sulfhydryl groups of the tissue about 22 per cent, supporting the view that the disulfide groups of insulin combine with sulfhydryl groups of membrane proteins. Finally, Mirsky and Perisutti found that concentrations of iodoacetate and N-ethylmaleimide, which produce no significant effect on the spontaneous oxidation of glucose by rat epididymal adipose tissue in vitro, inhibit the action of insulin. However, these agents did not inhibit insulin binding by adipose tissue or diaphragm. In these last studies, therefore, the binding of insulin to the tissues studied was independent of the availability of tissue sulfhydryl groups. It is also possible that the sulfhydryl blocking agents may exert their influence on some sulfhydryl-dependent system responsible for glucose entry into the cell, and that this system may be stimulated by insulin.

Insulin Deficiency. Insulin deficiency produces the clinical picture of *diabetes mellitus.* This deficiency may be due to one or more of three factors: (1) inadequate insulin production; (2) accelerated insulin destruction; and (3) insulin antagonists and inhibitors.

Inadequate Insulin Production. This is due to degeneration of pancreatic islet tissue resulting from a primary etiologic factor in the pancreas or secondarily because of continual hypersecretion of insulin by the pancreas as a consequence of a prolonged hyperglycemia. Secretion of insulin by the pancreas is under the regulatory control of the level of blood glucose. Perfusion studies of the isolated pancreas have shown that as the level of blood glucose rises, insulin secretion is augmented; when the blood glucose concentration falls, insulin production by the pancreas declines. The blood glucose level may be maintained at hyperglycemic levels by increased gluconeogenesis due to excessive secretion of adenohypophyseal adrenocorticotropic hormone (Chap. 51) or of adrenal cortical steroids (page 880) produced by an adrenal tumor. A second hypophyseal hormone, somatotropin (growth hormone, Chap. 51), also raises the level of blood glucose, and if secretion or administration of this hormone is prolonged, a secondary destruction of pancreatic β islet cells may occur. These relationships afford an explanation for the amelioration of pancreatic diabetes observed in experimental animals and in man following surgical removal of the adrenals (Chap. 49) or of the hypophysis (Chap. 51).

Accelerated Insulin Destruction. The loss of insulin activity as a result of proteolysis has been considered previously (page 890). Mirsky and his colleagues have shown that the liver and, to a lesser extent, other tissues possess an enzymic system capable of altering and thus inactivating insulin. The enzyme, which has been extensively purified, was termed *insulinase*, although insulin may not be the specific substrate, and is active both in vitro and in vivo. This aids in explanation of the relatively short half-life of insulin, approximately 40 min. in man. The possible significance of insulinase in the etiology of diabetes mellitus is not established. With the purified enzyme, no hydrolysis of peptide bonds of insulin occurs; however, the enzyme catalyzes reductive cleavage of the disulfide bonds of insulin in the presence of reduced glutathione, which functions as the hydrogen donor. Scission of both of the interchain disulfide bonds of insulin occurs. The name *glutathione-insulin transhydrogenase* has been proposed for the enzyme. The reaction catalyzed by the enzyme can be coupled to that promoted by glutathione reductase (page 500), making possible oxidation of TPNH by insulin.

$$H^+ + TPNH + GSSG \longrightarrow TPN^+ + 2GSH$$

$$\text{Insulin} \langle \begin{smallmatrix} S \\ | \\ S \end{smallmatrix} \quad + \quad GSH \longrightarrow \text{insulin} \langle \begin{smallmatrix} S-SG \\ \\ SH \end{smallmatrix}$$

$$\text{Insulin} \langle \begin{smallmatrix} S-SG \\ \\ SH \end{smallmatrix} \quad + \quad GSH \longrightarrow \text{insulin} \langle \begin{smallmatrix} SH \\ \\ SH \end{smallmatrix} \quad + \quad GSSG$$

The reduced insulin product consists of a mixture of the separated A and B chains of the hormone (page 152). Of interest is the reported inhibition of the enzyme by glucagon, the hyperglycemic factor of pancreas (see below). This may have physiological significance for maintenance of a higher level of circulating insulin in circumstances of hyperglycemia.

Insulin Antagonists and Inhibitors. Two types of insulin antagonists which may contribute to insulin deficiency can be delineated. One type, the insulin antibodies, is produced as a result of insulin therapy. The other type, also found in blood, may be distinguished from antibodies in that it may be demonstrated without prior administration of exogenous insulin. Either group of antagonists may function to render less effective insulin available from endogenous or exogenous sources.

Berson and Yalow demonstrated that in diabetic patients previously treated with insulin, a nonprecipitating insulin antibody which binds insulin is present in the β- and γ-globulin fractions of the plasma. This affords an explanation for the slower rate of destruction of intravenously administered insulin in diabetic patients, and the lesser degree of response, as compared with the normal, to a given dose of insulin. The antigenic activity of insulin also explains the resistance to the hormone which may develop during its prolonged use. This can generally be circumvented by changing to use of an insulin preparation from another species.

The second type of insulin antagonist is associated with the β_1-lipoprotein fraction (page 638) of both normal and diabetic serum obtained from experimental animals. The active material reduces the effectiveness of either endogenous or exogenous insulin. Production of this insulin antagonist appears to be influenced by both the hypophysis and the adrenal cortex. In the human being, insulin antagonists have been reported to be associated with serum albumin and with the α_1-, α_2-, and β-globulin fractions of persons with severe diabetes. It is not clear whether the various reported fractions represent a group of differing antagonists or are due in part to discrepancies in fractionation and assay techniques. The possible role of these antagonists in maintaining blood glucose homeostasis remains to be elucidated.

The B chain of insulin has been reported to inhibit insulin activity when added to the hormone. This may be of physiological significance in view of the formation of the B chain in liver as a consequence of the action of glutathione-insulin transhydrogenase (see above).

The metabolic consequences of insulin deficiency with regard to carbohydrate (page 422) and lipid (page 461) metabolism have been referred to previously. Synthesis of protein is depressed, and accelerated protein degradation obtains in insulin deficiency. With impairment of glucose utilization, *i.e.*, in diabetes, the demand for energy results in a shift to a relatively greater degree of lipid and protein metabolism. There is increased gluconeogenesis from protein, with a greater excretion of nitrogen in the urine and a wasting of body tissues. Much of the glucose produced is also wasted, in the absence of insulin. Less pyruvate is thus available for acetyl CoA synthesis, and more of the latter is derived from lipid. The excessive mobilization of lipid from body stores leads to a lipemia and may result in a fatty liver. In addition, there is augmented production of ketone bodies, and when this production exceeds the rate of their utilization, ketosis ensues. The biochemical consequences of diabetes, and their amelioration, have been discussed earlier (pages 422 and 461*ff.*).

Certain sulfonamide derivatives, notably substituted sulfonyl ureas, *e.g.*, 1-butyl-3-*p*-tolylsulfonylurea,

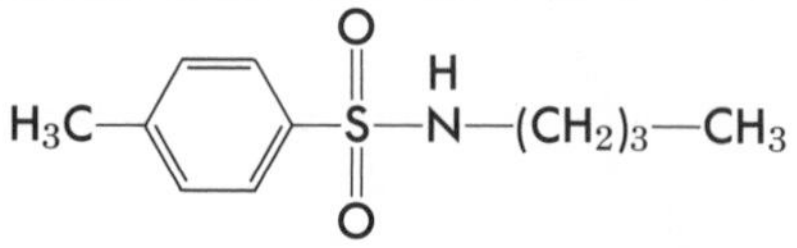

have proved useful as oral therapeutic agents in selected cases of adult diabetes. The activity of these compounds is apparently due to their ability to increase insulin release by the pancreas.

GLUCAGON—THE HYPERGLYCEMIC-GLYCOGENOLYTIC FACTOR

Although production by the pancreas of a hypoglycemic substance has been recognized since the experiments of von Mehring and Minkowski, the existence of a pancreatic hyperglycemic principle is a newer observation. It had been known that intravenous injection of insulin in a variety of species frequently resulted in an early hyperglycemia (10 to 30 min. after insulin injection) prior to appearance of the characteristic hypoglycemic effect. However, some preparations of insulin did not produce the early hyperglycemia. This suggested that certain preparations of insulin contained a hyperglycemic factor. This hyperglycemia was due to an increased rate of breakdown of glycogen in the liver, and the active hyperglycemic-glycogenolytic factor was named *glucagon.*

Other clinical and experimental studies suggested formation of a hyperglycemic principle by the pancreas. For example, total pancreatectomy in a diabetic patient decreased the insulin requirement. Also, the insulin requirement of totally depancreatized man may be less than that of many severely diabetic subjects. These findings might be expected if the pancreas produces a hormone which tends to elevate blood sugar level. Finally, dogs made diabetic by destruction of the β cells of the pancreas with alloxan (page 423) show a decreased glucosuria and insulin requirement if the pancreas is removed subsequently.

Glucagon was isolated in crystalline form from extracts of pancreas by Behrens and coworkers. The hormone is produced by the α cells of the islands of Langerhans but has also been extracted from the upper two-thirds of the gastric mucosa of the dog. The structure of glucagon is shown in Fig. 50.1. The polypeptide has a molecular weight of 3,485 and is isoelectric at pH 8.0. Its activity is lost on cleavage by proteolytic enzymes.

$$\underset{|}{NH_2} \qquad\qquad\qquad \underset{|}{NH_2} \quad \underset{|}{NH_2} \qquad \underset{|}{NH_2}$$

His·Ser·Glu·Gly·Thr·Phe·Thr·Ser·Asp·Tyr·Ser·Lys·Tyr·Leu·Asp·Ser·Arg·Arg·Ala·Glu·Asp·Phe·Val·Glu·Try·Leu·Met·Asp·Thr

FIG. 50.1. The structure of glucagon.

Glucagon augments blood glucose levels by accelerating glycogenolysis in the liver, apparently by favorably influencing the activity of phosphorylase phosphokinase (page 416), with increased formation of glucose 1-phosphate. Glucagon does not affect muscle phosphorylase. The mode of action of glucagon on liver phosphorylase activity is identical with that of epinephrine, *viz.,* stimulation of formation of 3′5′-cyclic AMP by an action on adenyl cyclase (page 416). Thus the hyperglycemic action of glucagon resembles that produced by epinephrine (page 419). However, in contrast to the latter hormone, glucagon does not cause the elevation in blood pressure characteristic of epinephrine. As a result, glucagon administration has found clinical use in circumstances of either acute or persistent hypoglycemia.

Glucagon also has profound effects on lipid metabolism, promoting ketogenesis and inhibiting the synthesis of fatty acids. The ketogenesis derives in part from the mobilization of depot lipid and hyperlipemia resulting from glucagon administration. The lipid-mobilizing action is reflected in in vitro studies demonstrating that addition of the hormone to adipose tissue increases the release of fatty acids and of glycerol, while augmenting oxygen consumption, glucose uptake, and phosphorylase activity.

Glucagon has a striking protein catabolic action. Daily administration of the hormone to rats resulted in increased urinary excretion of nitrogen, phosphorus, and creatinine, with a loss in body weight and a decreased mass of liver and muscle tissues. This action was also evident in adrenalectomized animals, suggesting a direct participation of glucagon in the regulation of protein metabolism.

Glucagon is rapidly destroyed by the liver. It is interesting that in vitro this destruction by liver slices is inhibited if insulin is present. This recalls the inhibition of insulin destruction by glucagon (page 895).

Glucagon, like insulin, will elicit formation of nonprecipitating antibodies after prolonged injection into experimental animals. This property of glucagon has been utilized for immunochemical measurement of minute amounts of the hormone.

REFERENCES

Books

Krahl, M. E., ed., "The Action of Insulin on Cells," Academic Press, Inc., New York, 1961.

Young, F. G., Broom, W. A., and Wolff, F. W., eds., "The Mechanism of Action of Insulin," Blackwell Scientific Publications, Oxford, England, 1960.

Review Articles

Ashmore, J., Cahill, G. F., Jr., and Hastings, A. B., Effect of Hormones on Alternate Pathways of Glucose Utilization in Isolated Tissues, *Recent Progr. Hormone Research,* **16,** 547–577, 1960.

Behrens, O. K., and Bromer, W. W., Glucagon, *Vitamins and Hormones,* **16,** 263–301, 1958.

de Bodo, R. C., and Altszuler, N., Insulin Hypersensitivity and Physiological Insulin Antagonists, *Physiol. Revs.,* **38,** 389–445, 1958.

Foà, P. P., Galansino, G., and Pozza, G., Glucagon: A Second Pancreatic Hormone, *Recent Progr. Hormone Research,* **13,** 473–510, 1957.

Levine, R., ed., Symposium on Diabetes, *Am. J. Med.,* **31,** 837–930, 1961.

Levine, R., and Goldstein, M. S., On the Mechanism of Action of Insulin, *Recent Progr. Hormone Research,* **11,** 343–380, 1955.

Manchester, K. L., and Young, F. G., Insulin and Protein Metabolism, *Vitamins and Hormones,* **19,** 95–135, 1961.

Miller, L. L., Some Direct Actions of Insulin, Glucagon, and Hydrocortisone on the Isolated Perfused Rat Liver, *Recent Progr. Hormone Research,* **17,** 539–568, 1961.

Mirsky, A. I., Insulinase, Insulinase-inhibitors, and Diabetes Mellitus, *Recent Progr. Hormone Research,* **13,** 429–472, 1957.

Stetten, D., Jr., and Bloom, B., The Hormones of the Islets of Langerhans, in G. Pincus and K. V. Thimann, eds., "The Hormones: Physiology, Chemistry and Applications," vol. III, pp. 175–199, Academic Press, Inc., New York, 1955.

Young, F. G., On Insulin and Its Action, *Proc. Roy. Soc.,* **B157,** 1-26, 1962.

51. The Hypophysis

The hypophysis was initially named the *pituitary* because of the erroneous concept that it is concerned with secretion of mucus or phlegm (L. *pituita,* phlegm). The term hypophysis, from the Greek meaning undergrowth, is descriptive of the location of the gland below the brain.

The hypophysis exerts a profound influence by regulating a large portion of the endocrine activity of the organism. It consists of anterior and posterior lobes, and the pars intermedia, which differ from one another embryologically, histologically, and functionally. The anterior portion, or *adenohypophysis,* is glandular and richly vascular. The posterior, or neural, portion, the *neurohypophysis,* is intimately connected with the hypothalamic areas through numerous nerve fibers and some glandular elements which comprise the hypophyseal stalk.

The adenohypophysis contains several cell types. Its blood supply is derived from branches of the internal carotid artery, the hypophyseal arteries. The latter form a rich plexus around the stalk of the hypophysis, and blood from the stalk drains into a surrounding plexus. From this plexus, blood is supplied to the adenohypophysis by what has been termed a portal circulation. This vascular supply is an important factor in the regulation of adenohypophyseal secretory activity (page 906); this lobe receives few nerve fibers.

The neurohypophyseal lobe, in contrast, has a rich nerve supply from the supraoptic nuclei and the tuber cinereum located in the hypothalamus. The blood supply of the neurohypophyseal lobe from the inferior hypophyseal arteries enters the gland posteriorly, and is distinct from that of the adenohypophysis.

There is little evidence of a direct functional relationship between the adeno- and neurohypophysis, although secretions of the latter may augment certain hormonal activities of the latter. Also, each lobe has important interactions with the hypothalamus (pages 903 and 906).

Hormones of the Hypophysis. The six known hormones produced by the hypophysis are proteins or polypeptides. Each of the isolated hormones will restore to normal, or above normal, one or more of the processes which are retarded as a consequence of removal of the hypophysis (hypophysectomy). Additional polypeptides have been isolated from adenohypophyseal tissue which either mimic the action of one of the hormones of that gland, or exhibit one of the various activities assigned to adenohypophyseal hormones. At least four hormonal products have been obtained in pure form from neurohypophyseal tissue. The hormones of the hypophysis have been listed in Table 45.1 (page 827) and will be discussed in subsequent sections of this chapter.

899

Effects of Hypophysectomy. The consequences of hypophysectomy appear to be due entirely to loss of adenohypophyseal functions and can be produced by removal of the adenohypophysis alone. Removal of only the neural lobe usually causes no striking dysfunction.

Hypophysectomy results in the following alterations: (1) cessation of growth in young animals; in the adult, loss of body tissue, with some reversion to younger characteristics, *e.g.*, appearance of juvenile hair; (2) gonadal atrophy in either sex, with loss of secondary sex characteristics in the adult, failure of development of sex characteristics in the younger individual, and sterility; (3) atrophy of the thyroid, with metabolic alterations characteristic of hypothyroidism (pages 835*ff*.); and (4) atrophy of the adrenal cortex with evidence of adrenal cortical insufficiency (pages 879*ff*.). Hypophysectomy, like adrenalectomy (page 880), results in amelioration of pancreatic diabetes; this was first demonstrated by Houssay, and the hypophysectomized, depancreatized animal has been referred to as the "Houssay animal."

In certain species, notably fish, amphibia, and reptiles, hypophysectomy also produces bleaching of the pigment cells (chromatophores) of the skin and a failure of the normal adaptive changes usually exhibited by these cells.

Uncertainty regarding the precise number of hormones secreted by the hypophysis is due to (1) evidence that this gland, as well as the hypothalamus, contains a number of polypeptides to which no known biological activity can yet be assigned, and (2) evidence that in the case of several of the hypophyseal hormones, only a portion of the molecule is essential for the hormonal functions, together with the demonstration of a similarity in portions of structures of different hormones with an accompanying overlapping of biological properties. The latter has been noted in connection with the evolution of structure and function of the neurohypophyseal hormones (page 619).

THE NEUROHYPOPHYSIS

The hormones of the mammalian neurohypophysis are *vasopressin,* which is responsible for pressor and antidiuretic effects, *oxytocin,* which causes smooth muscle contraction and milk ejection, and two polypeptides, each with melanocyte-stimulating activity, termed α- and *β-melanocyte-stimulating hormones* (α- and β-MSM). Reference has been made previously (page 619) to *vasotocin,* produced by most nonmammalian vertebrates and showing both vasopressin- and oxytocin-like activities.

CHEMISTRY

The amino acid sequences of vasotocin, vasopressin, and oxytocin have been presented in Table 31.6 (page 619). The structures of these three nonapeptide amides (the terminal glycine is present as an amide) are shown in Fig. 51.1. Vasopressin and oxytocin were first isolated, their structures were established, and their synthesis was achieved by du Vigneaud and his associates. Arginine vasotocin was prepared synthetically prior to its isolation from frog hypophyseal extracts.

Species variations in the structure of vasopressin usually occur at position 8 in the molecule, although amino acid replacements have also been found at position 3. The naming of these vasopressins is commonly based on the nature of the amino acid residue at 8. The significance of this residue in the evolution of vasopressin structures was noted previously (page 619). Thus, arginine vasopressin (Fig. 51.1) has been isolated from human, beef, sheep, and horse hypophyseal extracts. Lysine vasopressin, with lysine substituted for arginine at position 8, occurs in the pig. On

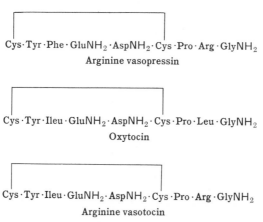

$$\text{Cys·Tyr·Phe·GluNH}_2\text{·AspNH}_2\text{·Cys·Pro·Arg·GlyNH}_2$$
Arginine vasopressin

$$\text{Cys·Tyr·Ileu·GluNH}_2\text{·AspNH}_2\text{·Cys·Pro·Leu·GlyNH}_2$$
Oxytocin

$$\text{Cys·Tyr·Ileu·GluNH}_2\text{·AspNH}_2\text{·Cys·Pro·Arg·GlyNH}_2$$
Arginine vasotocin

Fig. 51.1. Structures of arginine vasopressin, oxytocin, and vasotocin.

the other hand, oxytocin preparations from man, cow, and pig are identical. It will be noted that oxytocin differs from the vasopressins only in residues in positions 3 and 8. Arginine vasopressin and arginine vasotocin are both present in chicken hypophyseal extracts.

Although melanocyte-stimulating activity is found in the neurohypophysis, such activity is also present in adenohypophyseal extracts. Melanocyte-stimulating material is secreted by the pars intermedia, except in those species which do not possess this structure, *e.g.*, chicken, porpoise, and whale, in which this activity is found in adenohypophyseal extracts. Overlapping biological activities of various hypophyseal principles may be related to similarities in portions of the amino acid sequences of polypeptides (see below).

The structures of the melanocyte-stimulating hormones, α- and β-MSH, are shown in Fig. 51.2. Samples of α-MSH from five species studied have the same structures; α-MSH has been synthesized by Guttmann and Boissonnas. Note that the amino-terminal serine residue is N-acetylated, and the carboxyl-terminal valine is in the form of an amide. Also, α-MSH contains 13 amino acid residues, whereas β-MSH from the same species consists of 18 amino acids, with both the amino- and carboxyl-terminal groups present as aspartic acid residues. The amino acid sequence and number of amino acid residues of β-MSH differ among species (Fig. 51.2). It may be noted that the amino acid sequence in positions 7 to 13 of β-MSH from monkey, horse, beef, and pig is identical with that of positions 4 to 10 of adrenocorticotropin (ACTH, page 910). The amino acid sequence of α-MSH is identical with that of the 13 N-terminal amino acid residues of ACTH, except that its N-terminus is

Hormone	Source	Amino acid sequence
α-MSH	Monkey, horse, beef, pig, sheep	*Ac–Ser·Tyr·Ser·Met·Glu·His·Phe·Arg·Try·Gly·Lys·Pro·ValNH$_2$
β-MSH	Human	Ala·Glu·Lys·Lys·Asp·Glu·Gly·Pro·Tyr·Arg·Met·Glu·His·Phe·Arg·Try·Gly·Ser·Pro·Pro·Lys·Asp
	Monkey	Asp·Glu·Gly·Pro·Tyr·Arg·Met·Glu·His·Phe·Arg·Try·Gly·Ser·Pro·Pro·Lys·Asp
	Horse	Asp·Glu·Gly·Pro·Tyr·Lys·Met·Glu·His·Phe·Arg·Try·Gly·Ser·Pro·Arg·Lys·Asp
	Beef	Asp·Ser·Gly·Pro·Tyr·Lys·Met·Glu·His·Phe·Arg·Try·Gly·Ser·Pro·Pro·Lys·Asp
	Pig	Asp·Glu·Gly·Pro·Tyr·Lys·Met·Glu·His·Phe·Arg·Try·Gly·Ser·Pro·Pro·Lys·Asp

*Ac = Acetyl

FIG. 51.2. Amino acid sequences of α-MSH (five species) and β-MSH (five species). Adequate data are not available for α-MSH from human glands. Indeed, it is not certain that α-MSH is present in human beings. Note that although all β-MSH preparations, except human, contain only 18 amino acid residues, the peptide chains have been written to allow for the additional four residues in human β-MSH and displaced in order to show similarities in sequences. Amino acid substitutions among species, as compared with the human, are indicated by the underlined residues.

acetylated and the chain terminates with a valine carboxyamide group. These data may account for the intrinsic melanocyte-stimulating activity of ACTH (page 911).

Since the synthesis of oxytocin was achieved by du Vigneaud and his associates in 1953, more than 50 analogues of this hormone, as well as of vasopressin and MSH, have been synthesized and examined for biological activity. The data for vasopressin and oxytocin analogues suggest that the three amino acids attached to the ring structures of the hormones are essential for biological activity. In the case of oxytocin, (1) substitution of tyrosine by phenylalanine in position 2 reduces activity; (2) replacement of cysteine by thiopropionic acid at position 1 increases potency; (3) replacement of asparagine (position 5) by α-aminobutyric acid seriously reduces activity, whereas similar replacement of 4-glutamine has little effect. Vasopressin analogue studies reveal that the nature and basicity of the amino acid residue at position 8 influences the relative antidiuretic potency, with arginine vasopressin being most active and leucine vasopressin least. For α-MSH, removal of the N-acetyl group markedly diminishes activity, loss of residues 1 and 2 causes further reduction of activity, but acetylation of the N-terminal residue of this only slightly active undecapeptide results in a twenty-five–fold increase in potency. It has been suggested that presence of an N-acetyl group protects the hormone against rapid degradation by aminopeptidases. Substitution of glutamic acid for serine at position 2 of beef β-MSH produced a two and one-half–fold increase in biological potency.

The above data reveal interesting relationships of structure to biological activity and could be of value in elucidation of the mechanism of action of the neurohypophyseal hormones.

BIOLOGICAL ASPECTS

The hormones of the neurohypophysis are synthesized in the supraoptic and paraventricular nuclei. The hormones, in association with a protein of molecular weight about 30,000, migrate as granules down the nerve fibers and accumulate at the nerve endings in the neurohypophysis. Secretion of the hormones is influenced by three types of stimuli: (1) action of the central nervous system, (2) the osmotic pressure of the blood, and (3) drugs. Secretion of vasopressin has been studied more extensively than that of oxytocin, and apparently selective release of either of the hormones may occur. Thus, hemorrhage stimulates release primarily of vasopressin, while certain drugs, *e.g.*, anesthetics, cause release of both principles, with oxytocin being secreted in larger amounts.

Release of vasopressin may be stimulated by a variety of neurogenic stimuli, *e.g.*, pain, trauma, and emotional states. On the other hand, evidence of inhibition of vasopressin release may also be seen as a consequence of central nervous system activity. Thus, excessive production of epinephrine may inhibit vasopressin release. It is of interest that similar neural stimuli may also affect release of adrenocorticotropic hormone (page 910).

With respect to the role of the blood osmotic pressure, Verney demonstrated that a 2 per cent change in osmotic pressure of the blood traversing the carotid sinus will alter the rate of vasopressin secretion. This rate diminishes or increases with hypo- or hypertonicity, respectively. Verney postulated the existence of specific osmoreceptor cells in those hypothalamic nuclei responsible for production and secretion of vasopressin. "Volume receptors," or baroreceptors, have also been postulated as regulatory factors influencing vasopressin release. This concept would explain the fact that hemorrhage is one of the most powerful known stimuli of vasopressin release. It will be recalled that blood volume alteration is also a potent influence on the rate of aldosterone secretion (page 878).

Finally, the release of vasopressin is a cholinergic-mediated response and is therefore affected by acetylcholine, anesthetics, etc.

Circulatory or Pressor Action. The pressor action of vasopressin is due to peripheral vasoconstriction in the systemic arterioles and capillaries. There is a constriction of the coronary and pulmonary vessels, but a dilation of cerebral and renal vessels. The latter dilator effect is caused by the rise in systemic blood pressure.

Antidiuretic Action. The most striking and important effect of vasopressin is on the kidneys, where it accelerates the rate of water reabsorption from the early part of the distal convoluted tubules to the length of the collecting tubules. The augmented water reabsorption of a fluid that is hyposmotic with reference to serum is accompanied by excretion of a urine which contains increased concentrations of sodium, chloride, phosphate, and total nitrogen. Glomerular filtration is apparently unaffected. Although the urine volume is less, more chloride may be excreted per unit of time. In man, as little as 0.1 μg of vasopressin will produce a maximal antidiuretic effect; the half-life of the hormone is approximately 12 min.

It has been suggested that the antidiuretic hormone augments synthesis of cyclic AMP (page 417) in the renal tubules, since this anhydride exerts an antidiuretic effect in the isolated toad bladder. Also, addition of vasopressin in vitro to dog kidney preparations increased the formation of cyclic AMP, presumably by stimulating the activity of adenyl cyclase (page 416). The relation of this to the antidiuretic action of the hormone is not clear.

As indicated above, secretion of antidiuretic substance by the hypophysis is augmented in circumstances of dehydration and of increased salt intake, and is decreased when the extracellular fluid becomes hypotonic. This has been discussed in detail in Chap. 36.

The role of a principle with antidiuretic activity is seen in man in *diabetes insipidus.* This clinical condition frequently accompanies lesions of the hypophysis or hypothalamus. It is characterized by the excretion of large quantities of urine of very low specific gravity, 1.002 to 1.006, and of low chloride content. As much as 4 to 5 liters of urine (*polyuria*) may be voided per day, and volumes several times these amounts have been reported. The patient exhibits a corresponding increase in fluid intake and a marked thirst (*polydipsia*). The condition is controlled by the parenteral administration of purified vasopressin preparations.

The relation of diabetes insipidus to disturbances in the hypothalamus is based on the neural control of neurohypophyseal function. The neurohypophysis is connected to specific hypothalamic nuclei (see above); section of the hypophyseal stalk or destruction of the supraoptic nuclei produces atrophy of the neurohypophysis and diabetes insipidus.

Oxytocic Action. The term *oxytocic* (Gk., rapid birth) is descriptive of the action of this principle in causing strong contractions of the uterus. This also occurs in the isolated uterus and is the basis of a bioassay method. A concentration of the hormone as low as 0.5 mμg per ml. will cause contraction of the isolated uterus. Oxytocin finds clinical use during and after parturition.

Oxytocin also excites the musculature of the intestine, gallbladder, ureter, and urinary bladder. The hormone also causes ejection of milk; this action is distinct from that of prolactin in stimulating milk production (page 914). The release of oxytocin in response to nipple stimulation by suckling is another example of a neuroendocrine reflex.

Certain of the biological effects of vasopressin and oxytocin are indicated in Table 51.1; their comparative potencies are given in Table 51.2.

Oxytocin and vasopressin added in vitro increase glucose oxidation by slices of mammary gland taken from lactating rats. This effect is abolished by puromycin, an inhibitor of protein synthesis, suggesting that protein synthesis is coupled

Table 51.1: SUMMARY OF THE BIOLOGICAL EFFECTS OF VASOPRESSIN AND OF OXYTOCIN

Structure or function affected	Vasopressin	Oxytocin
Water diuresis	Inhibits	No effect
Blood pressure	Raises	Slightly lowers
Coronary arteries	Constricts	Slightly dilates
Intestinal contractions	Stimulates	Questionable
Uterine contractions*	Stimulates	Stimulates
Ejection of milk	Slightly stimulates	Stimulates

* Response varies with species, as well as with the stage of the normal and the reproductive cycles.

Table 51.2: POTENCY OF HIGHLY PURIFIED OXYTOCIN AND ARGININE VASOPRESSIN
IN TERMS OF UNITED STATES PHARMACOPEIA STANDARD

	Oxytocic (rat uterus, without Mg^{++})	Avian depressor (fowl)	Milk-ejecting (rabbit)	Pressor (rat)	Antidiuretic (dog)
Oxytocin.............	500	500	430	4	5
Arginine vasopressin...	12	56	68	400	400

NOTE: All figures are United States Pharmacopeia Units per mg.
SOURCE: Courtesy Dr. H. B. Van Dyke.

in the gland with the stimulating effects of the hormones on glucose oxidation. Oxytocin also exerts an insulin-like effect on the utilization of glucose by adipose tissue in vitro in that it stimulates incorporation of glucose carbon into triglycerides.

Melanocyte-stimulating Action. α- and β-MSH cause dispersal of black pigment found in the melanophore cells of certain cold-blooded animals, thus producing a generalized blackening of the skin. Evidence that this activity is of significance in man is lacking, although injection of purified MSH in man was reported to intensify pigmentation in areas previously pigmented, but not to affect nonpigmented regions.

Lerner and his associates have isolated a substance which reverses the darkening effect of MSH by stimulating aggregation, rather than dispersal, of melanin granules within melanocytes, thus causing lightening of skin color. The substance was named *melatonin* and was shown to have the following structure.

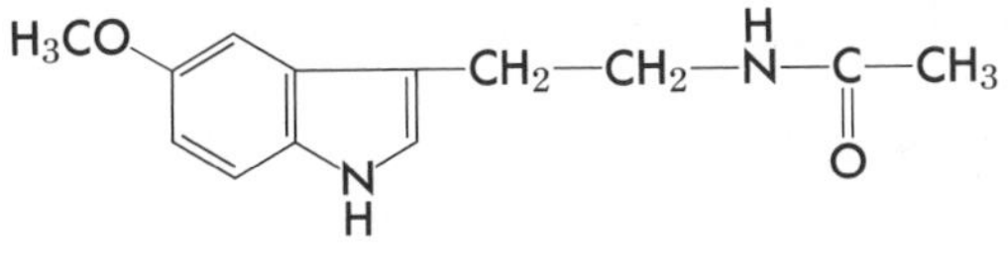

Melatonin
(N-acetyl-5-methoxytryptamine)

The compound was obtained from pineal glands, as well as from hypothalamic tissue and peripheral nerve. Melatonin biosynthesis occurs by reaction of acetyl CoA with serotonin (page 536); methylation of the N-acetylserotonin formed then occurs, utilizing S-adenosylmethionine (page 504). The enzyme catalyzing this last step was found only in the pineal gland.

Melatonin administered to mice was rapidly metabolized. The major metabolic pathway involves hydroxylation at position 6 followed by conjugation primarily with sulfate and, to a small extent, with glucuronic acid.

THE ADENOHYPOPHYSIS

The two major regulatory systems in mammals, *viz.*, the nervous system and the endocrine glands, have multiple relationships and integrations exemplified in the regulation of secretion of at least five of the adenohypophyseal hormones, *viz.*, thyrotropin, the two gonadotropins, prolactin, and adrenocorticotropin. Prolactin is discussed with the gonadotropins because of its influence on the corpus luteum.

The chain of events in the control of adenohypophyseal secretion may be depicted as (1) stimulation of neuroreceptors, (2) transmission of afferent impulses to the thalamus, hypothalamus, and cortex, (3) initiation or modification of hypothalamic activity by the thalamus and cerebral cortex, and (4) release of hypothalamic neurohumoral substances which are transmitted via the hypothalamic-hypophyseal portal circulation to excite the adenohypophysis, with resulting secretion of one or several of its hormones, depending upon the nature of the initiating stimulus.

In addition to the above neural factors, a second set of regulatory mechanisms affects adenohypophyseal secretion. The products of the target glands, over which adenohypophyseal hormones exert regulatory influence, make possible a negative feedback regulatory mechanism in that the rate of secretion of certain adenohypophyseal hormones is inversely related to the blood concentration of the hormones produced by the target gland.

These two mechanisms of influencing the secretory activity of the adenohypophysis, *viz.*, that involving the neural pathways and that concerned with blood levels of hormonal products, are the basis for the rapid responses of adenohypophyseal secretory level to a wide variety of stimuli, ranging from environmental, *e.g.*, cold, hypoxia, trauma, noxious chemicals, etc., to psychological, *e.g.*, fear, anxiety, the presence of other animals or individuals, etc. This accounts to a degree for the numerous experimental and clinical circumstances in which a similarity in physiological effects may be seen.

The envisaged mechanism for linking hypothalamic activity with the secretory level of the adenohypophysis would explain the interruption of secretion of certain adenohypophyseal hormones which follows transection of the infundibular stalk.

THE THYROTROPIC HORMONE

Hypophysectomy in mammals results in involution of the thyroid gland, with flattening of the epithelium, and development of the previously described consequences of hypothyroidism (page 834): lowered basal metabolic rate, depressed rate of iodide uptake by the thyroid, a diminished serum concentration of protein-bound iodine, and decreased cellular activity. Parenteral administration of hypophyseal extracts induces reparative effects in the thyroid of the hypophysectomized animal, with restoration of function. Assay of active thyroid-stimulating hormone (thyrotropic hormone, thyrotropin, TSH) is based on the direct effect of the hormone on the thyroid, with evaluation of alterations in the histology, weight, composition (iodine content), or metabolic activity (P^{32} uptake).

Secretion of Thyrotropic Hormone. Two mechanisms of regulation of TSH secretion exist, one neural, the other nonneural. Neurogenic and psychogenic influences have long been recognized as affecting thyroid function and contributing to *thyrotoxicosis.* The neural influence was also shown by removal of the hypophysis from its location beneath the median eminence and transplantation to other sites; marked diminution in TSH secretion resulted. Also, appropriately placed hypothalamic lesions prevented the expected rise in TSH secretion in response to lowered levels of blood thyroxine. The latter is the basis for the nonneural mechanism of regulating TSH secretion, functioning as a feedback mechanism.

The suggestion that the central nervous system influences TSH secretion via a substance released from the hypothalamus into the hypophyseal portal system led to the isolation by Schreiber and his associates, from hypothalamic tissue, of a nonapeptide which stimulated TSH release in vitro when added to rat adenohypophyseal tissue.

Chemical Properties. Highly purified preparations of thyrotropic hormone have been obtained from beef, sheep, and human hypophyses. These products are a mixture of glycoproteins with a mean molecular weight of approximately 30,000. Thyrotropin preparations have eight to nine cystine residues per mole; the disulfide groups seem to be present as intra- rather than interchain linkages. Mannose, fucose, glucosamine, and galactosamine were present, the last two probably as the N-acetyl derivatives; these sugars appeared to be present in a single oligosaccharide unit.

Effects of Thyrotropic Hormone. The thyrotropic hormone influences the rates of the following reactions: (1) removal of iodide from blood by the thyroid; (2) conversion of iodide to thyroid hormones; and (3) release of hormonal iodine from the gland.

The hypophysectomized animal has a decreased rate of iodide uptake by the thyroid and of removal of administered iodide from plasma (Fig. 51.3). Although

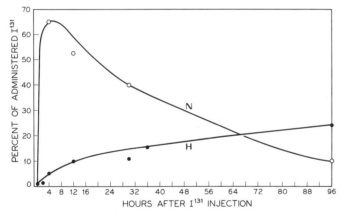

FIG. 51.3. The uptake of total radioactive iodine by the whole thyroid gland of the normal (N) and hypophysectomized (H) rat. A tracer dose of I^{131} (as iodide) was injected intraperitoneally into each rat. (*After I. L. Chaikoff and A. Taurog, Ann. N.Y. Acad. Sci.,* **50,** 377, 1949.)

in the hypophysectomized animal iodide enters the gland more slowly, following entry it is rapidly converted to diiodotyrosine. *However, the rate of conversion of diiodotyrosine to thyroxine is depressed in the absence of the hypophysis* (Fig. 51.4). Hypophysectomy in the rat leads to a 50 per cent decrease in total blood hormonal iodine (PBI, page 834) within 4 days after operation. However, although thyroid size also diminishes, the quantity of stored hormones or of total iodine in the gland does not decline. Therefore, since the thyroid becomes smaller after hypophysectomy, the concentration of iodine in the gland is elevated. Thus, the lowered hormonal iodine of the plasma is not a direct stimulus to the thyroid to release its

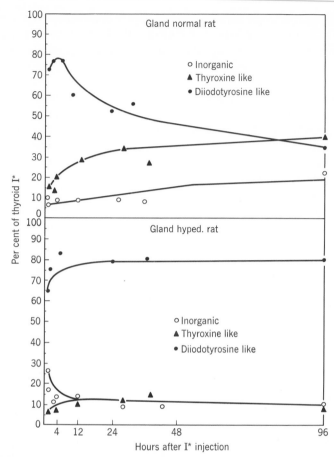

FIG. 51.4. Distribution of radioactive iodine in the thyroids of normal (*upper*) and of hypophysectomized (*lower*) rats. Each rat received intraperitoneally a tracer dose of I^{131} (I*). (*From I. L. Chaikoff and A. Taurog, Ann. N.Y. Acad. Sci.,* **50**, 377, 1949.)

hormones, and is dependent upon TSH. The proteolysis of thyroglobulin in relation to release of thyroid hormones from the gland has been considered previously (page 832).

Administration of TSH decreases the organically bound iodine of the thyroid; there is some stimulation of iodide release also. Further, thyroid glands made hyperplastic with TSH administration have a greater than normal capacity to fix iodine in all fractions, with the normal distribution between diiodotyrosine and thyroxine being shifted toward thyroxine (Fig. 51.5). There is an accompanying increase in plasma hormonal iodine. The transport and metabolic fates of thyroid hormones have been discussed (pages 834 and 837).

There is some evidence that TSH may have a direct action on orbital tissue relating to the exophthalmos of diffuse toxic goiter (page 836). However, purification of TSH is accompanied by a decrease in exophthalmos-stimulating activity, and a separate hypophyseal factor has been postulated for the latter effect.

Thyrotropin administration to rats lowered the sialic acid content of the thyroid and raised its acid phosphatase activity. Addition of the hormone to slices of thyroid stimulated amino acid entry into the tissue and augmented the phosphogluconate oxidative pathway. TSH is highly active in vitro in stimulating oxygen consumption, glucose utilization, and increased release of free fatty acids from adipose tissue.

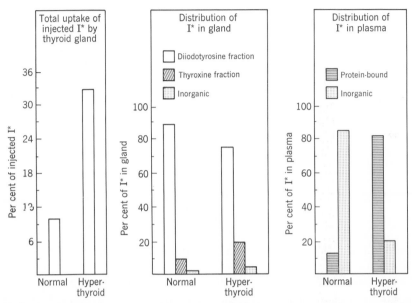

FIG. 51.5. Uptake of radioactive iodine and its distribution in the thyroid and the plasma of normal guinea pigs and of guinea pigs made hyperthyroid by injection of thyrotropic hormone. The measurements were made 16 hr. after the intraperitoneal injection of a tracer dose of I^{131} (I^*). (*From I. L. Chaikoff and A. Taurog, Ann. N.Y. Acad. Sci.*, **50**, 377, 1949.)

ADRENOCORTICOTROPIC HORMONE

The adrenocorticotropic hormone (adrenocorticotropin, ACTH, corticotropin) stimulates the secretion and growth of the adrenal cortex. The hormone will restore to normal size the atrophied adrenal cortex of the hypophysectomized animal, or, if administered postoperatively, will prevent atrophy. This effect is the basis for two methods for bioassay of adrenocorticotropin.

The high ascorbic acid and cholesterol contents of the adrenals have been mentioned previously. After administration of ACTH, these adrenal constituents decline rapidly. The ascorbic acid depletion is the basis for a widely used method for bioassay of the hormone.

Chemistry of Adrenocorticotropic Hormone. Adrenocorticotropic hormone was isolated in highly purified form by Li and his associates and by Bell and coworkers. The latter group established the structure of the hormone (Fig. 51.6). This polypeptide has been designated as α-ACTH to distinguish it from a pepsin- or acid-degraded product, β-ACTH (also termed adrenocorticotropin B).

As indicated in Fig. 51.6, the amino acid sequences of ACTH preparations from several species have been established. Hofmann and his associates have synthesized a polypeptide containing the first 23 residues of ACTH which has biological activity similar to that of the hormone isolated from hypophyses. Thus, residues 24

Ser·Tyr·Ser·Met·Glu·His·Phe·Arg·Try·Gly·Lys·Pro·Val·Gly·Lys·Lys·Arg·Arg·Pro·Val·Lys·Val·Tyr·Pro·
 1   2   3   4   5   6   7   8   9   10   11   12   13   14   15   16   17   18   19   20   21   22   23   24

I   Asp·Ala·Gly·Glu·Asp·GluNH$_2$·Ser·Ala·Glu·Ala·Phe·Pro·Leu·Glu·Phe
     25   26   27   28   29   30   31   32   33   34   35   36   37   38   39

II   Asp·Gly·Glu·Ala·Glu · Asp · Ser·Ala·Glu·Ala·Phe·Pro·Leu·Glu·Phe

III Ala·Gly·Glu·Asp·Asp · Glu · Ala·Ser·Glu·Ala·Phe·Pro·Leu·Glu·Phe

IV   Asp·Gly·Ala·Glu·Asp·GluNH$_2$·Leu·Ala·Glu·Ala·Phe·Pro·Leu·Glu·Phe

FIG. 51.6. Amino acid sequences of human (I), beef (II), sheep (III), and pig (IV) adrenocorticotropin. Note that the first 24 residues are the same in the four species, and that all variations in structures occur among residues 25 through 32.

to 33 are not essential for biological activity. It is noteworthy that the first 24 residues are identical in the ACTH of all species investigated (Fig. 51.6). Although removal of a portion of the carboxyl-terminal end of ACTH does not alter activity, removal of a few residues from the amino-terminal end of the molecule by leucine aminopeptidase destroys hormonal activity.

The smallest synthetic polypeptide having some ACTH activity is one containing the amino-terminal 16 amino acid residues of adrenocorticotropin. Elongation of the peptide chain to 19 residues resulted in a striking increase in biological activity, indicating the importance of the highly basic lysyllysylarginylarginyl sequence for high potency.

Secretion of Adrenocorticotropin. The rate of secretion of adrenocorticotropin is also influenced by the two major mechanisms previously described (page 905). The neurohumoral mechanism provides a basis for release of ACTH as a result of a wide variety of unrelated stimuli, e.g., trauma, emotional stress, drugs, chemical or bacterial toxic agents, or substances normally present in the body, e.g., insulin, thyroxine, epinephrine, and vasopressin. Initiation of the secretory mechanism, as a result of these stimuli, occurs in the posterior hypothalamus and median eminence. Nerve endings in these regions are believed to discharge humoral substances which are transmitted via the hypophyseal portal vessels to the adenohypophysis, evoking release of ACTH. There appear to be several such peptides present in the hypothalamus, as well as in the neurohypophysis; these neurohumoral agents have been termed corticotropin-releasing factors (CRF). These peptides are closely related in structure to the neurohypophyseal hormones, and one has been termed α-CRF because of its structural and biological similarity to α-MSH (page 901). The material also has some ACTH and vasopressor activity. A second substance, designated as β-CRF, has been isolated which possesses a significantly higher activity than the α-CRF and has properties very similar to those of vasopressin. Synthetic vasopressin also shows ACTH-releasing activity.

The rate of secretion of ACTH is also related inversely to the level of circulating adrenal cortical steroids. Increased rate of removal of these steroids by the tissues lowers their concentration in the blood and will evoke secretion of ACTH. On the other hand, administration of exogenous adrenal steroid will, by elevating the blood concentration of the adrenal steroids, tend to depress ACTH secretion (page 888). This mechanism would account for the adrenal cortical atrophy and hypofunction reported in animals and in patients treated for long periods with adrenal steroids. The locus of action of the adrenal steroids in suppressing ACTH secretion appears to be at the level of the hypothalamus.

Biological Properties of Adrenocorticotropin. The prime role of ACTH is stimulation of the synthesis and secretion of adrenal cortical steroids. More recently, it has been recognized that the hormone also has extra-adrenal effects which are exerted directly on specific tissues, independent of adrenal cortical mediation. These effects of ACTH are discussed below.

Adrenal-mediated Actions of ACTH. As a consequence of stimulation of production of adrenal steroids, ACTH injection mimics all the responses described for those hormones (pages 879*ff.*). Thus, ACTH administration leads to augmented gluconeogenesis, with accompanying retardation of protein synthesis in all tissues studied, except the liver. There is increased lipid mobilization to the liver, with ketonemia, and hypercholesterolemia. Promotion of salt and water reabsorption by the kidney occurs but to a lesser degree than with aldosterone; it will be recalled that secretion of this steroid is dependent only in part on the hypophyseal principle (page 878). Lymphopenia, eosinopenia, and erythropoiesis result from ACTH administration. The hormone is effective therapeutically in the variety of clinical conditions mentioned previously which respond favorably to certain adrenal cortical steroids (page 885). Addison's disease is an exception, since in this circumstance there is a limited amount of responsive, normal adrenal cortical tissue.

Certain of the in vivo effects of ACTH administration differ from those of adrenal cortical steroid injection. ACTH releases a mixture of steroids from the adrenal, whereas injection of a single adrenal cortical steroid produces effects characteristic only of the compound injected, as well as those which follow inhibition of ACTH secretion. Consequently, prolonged ACTH administration can lead to undesirable manifestations of adrenal cortical hyperfunction (page 886), including masculinization, reflecting androgen secretion by the adrenal cortex (page 852).

ACTH administration in intact animals has been reported to have an insulin-like effect (page 422) in accelerating transfer of monosaccharides and amino acids into muscle cells. Also, the defective lipogenesis from glucose in the liver of hypophysectomized rats was repaired by administration of ACTH. Both the above effects could be secondary consequences of augmented insulin release in response to ACTH injection. An additional but unexplained effect of ACTH on the liver is to prevent the striking elevation of DPN synthesis from administered nicotinamide which occurs in the liver of rats following hypophysectomy. Cortisone was also effective, indicating an adrenal-mediated action of ACTH. It is possible that some of the diverse metabolic effects of ACTH, mediated via the adrenal cortex, are based on an influence on pyridine nucleotide coenzymes.

Direct Effects of ACTH on Tissues. One of the direct actions of ACTH has been referred to previously, its intrinsic melanocyte-stimulating activity (page 902).

This may account in part for the darkening of the skin in Addison's disease (page 874), in which the blood level of ACTH is abnormally high. One of the most striking direct effects of ACTH is its in vitro stimulation of glucose utilization and fatty acid release by adipose tissue. There is an accompanying increase in phosphorylase activity. Thus, ACTH resembles epinephrine in these actions on adipose tissue. Astwood and coworkers concluded that the lipolytic effect of ACTH is due to activation of a lipase in adipose tissue. This may be an aspect of the lipid-mobilizing activity of ACTH seen in vivo (see above), since intravenous administration of ACTH to adrenalectomized rats produced a rapid increase in free fatty acids of adipose tissue and plasma. A synthetic tridecapeptide, identical in sequence with the amino-terminal portion of ACTH (page 910), also produced release of fatty acids from adipose tissue in vitro and a severalfold increase in the plasma free fatty acids of rabbits injected subcutaneously with the preparations. This so-called adipokinetic activity of these peptides and of ACTH is of interest in view of reports of a separate adipokinetic hormone in the hypophysis (page 921).

Administration of ACTH to adrenalectomized-nephrectomized rats decreased urea formation; this suggests an extra-adrenal action of the hormone on some phase of nitrogen metabolism, perhaps by facilitating amino acid transport into nonhepatic cells. ACTH administration to adrenalectomized animals or to Addisonian subjects retards the rate of disposal of both endogenous and exogenous cortisol. An inhibition of liver conjugation of injected cortisol and its metabolites has been described in adrenalectomized, ACTH-treated animals. The basis of this extra-adrenal action of ACTH is not clear. It may also be noted that injection of ACTH into the blood of an isolated heart-lung preparation augmented the heart rate significantly. In this regard, ACTH resembled norepinephrine and epinephrine.

It is apparent that ACTH has a wide variety of biological effects. Many of these are due to the influence of this hormone on the production of active steroids by the adrenal cortex. A second group of effects of ACTH are apparently not adrenal-mediated and are due to a direct influence of the hormone on a number of tissues.

Hypersecretion of Adrenocorticotropic Hormone—Pituitary Basophilism—Cushing's Disease. This clinical condition is generally attributed to hyperplasia, or tumor of the basophil cells of the adenohypophysis. The symptoms of the disease suggest that there may be overactivity of endocrine glands other than the adrenals. However, the resemblance of symptoms to those seen in primary tumors of the adrenal cortex and the adrenal hypertrophy found at autopsy suggest that Cushing's disease is characterized chiefly by an overproduction of ACTH. The main features of Cushing's disease are (1) obesity of the trunk (especially of the abdomen), face, and buttocks but not of the limbs; purplish striae, due to distention, are present over the lower abdomen; (2) cyanosis of the face, hands, and feet, pigmentation of the skin, and excessive growth of hair; women may grow a mustache or beard; (3) demineralization of the bones; (4) hypertension; (5) loss of sexual functions; (6) hyperglycemia and glucosuria; (7) acne.

Mode of Action of ACTH. Since administration of ACTH rapidly results in an increased synthesis and release of adrenal steroids, it is evident that in the absence of ACTH, the enzymic systems responsible for steroid synthesis are not functioning maximally. Available evidence indicates that a limiting factor may be the supply of TPNH required for reductions and hydroxylations (page 876). TPNH is also required in the conversion of cholesterol to pregnenolone (page 477), and an action of ACTH at this locus in steroidogenesis in the adrenal has been hypothesized. ACTH, but not epinephrine or glucagon, stimulates in the adrenal formation of cyclic AMP from ATP (page 416). The cyclic AMP activates the phosphorylase system, thereby making available a supply of glucose 6-phosphate for the phosphogluconate oxidative pathway and, hence, generating TPNH for steroid synthesis. Although ACTH may influence steroidogenesis by other means also, this presently appears to represent the major operational device.

THE GONADOTROPIC HORMONES

The hormonal influence of the hypophysis on the gonads and accessory sex organs is evident, following hypophysectomy, in the atrophy of these structures in the adult and in their failure to mature in younger individuals. This is reflected in atrophy of the human gonads, amenorrhea, and impotence, in disease caused by atrophy or degeneration of the adenohypophysis.

At least four gonadotropic hormones are known. Two are secreted by the adenohypophysis, viz., *follicle-stimulating hormone* (FSH) and *luteinizing* or *interstitial cell–stimulating hormone* (LH or ICSH). *Prolactin* also has gonadotropic activity. In addition, a gonadotropin is produced by the placenta and designated as *human chorionic gonadotropin* (CG or HCG), and a gonadotropin is present in pregnant mare's serum. The physiological bases for these designations are indicated later.

Chemistry of the Gonadotropins. The hypophyseal gonadotropins have been extensively purified; luteinizing hormone from human hypophysis has been obtained in apparently homogeneous form by Li and his associates. Prolactin and follicle-stimulating hormone have also been highly purified. Table 51.3 summarizes some of the physical and chemical properties of these hormones. Three of the gonado-

Table 51.3: SOME PROPERTIES OF GONADOTROPIC HORMONE PREPARATIONS AND PROLACTIN

Hormone	Molecular weight	Isoelectric point, pH	Total carbohydrate content, per cent
Luteinizing or interstitial cell–stimulating:			
Human	26,000	5.4	3.5
Sheep	30,000	7.3	11.0
Hog	100,000	7.5	5.0
Follicle-stimulating:			
Human	30,000	. . .	8.0–9.0
Sheep	67,000	4.5	8.0–9.0
Hog	29,000	5.1	7.0–8.0
Prolactin:			
Beef:	23,500	5.7	0
Sheep	23,500	5.7	0
Human chorionic gonadotropin	30,000	3.0	28.0
Pregnant mare's serum gonadotropin	23,000	. . .	45.0

tropins as well as prolactin are glycoproteins whose constituents include fucose, hexoses (mannose and galactose have been identified as present in hog FSH), hexosamine, and a sialic acid. Gottschalk and his colleagues have found that incubating a sheep FSH preparation with neuraminidase liberated a sialic acid, with concomitant loss of all biological activity. On the other hand, the carbohydrate moiety of chorionic gonadotropin has been reported as not essential for hormonal activity.

Secretion of Gonadotropins. Secretion of the above hypophyseal gonadotropins is also regulated by the two primary mechanisms which have been described (page 906). Thus, a wide variety of neurogenic effects on sexual activity have been described experimentally and clinically. Release of each gonadotropin from the adenohypophysis appears to be stimulated by specific agents which, in turn, are secreted in response to stimuli reaching specific loci in the hypothalamus. The circulating androgens and estrogens, which influence gonadotropin secretion, act directly on the hypothalamus. The androgen receptor lies in the posterior median eminence whereas the effect of estrogens has been localized in the arcuate hypothalamic nucleus. The hypothalamo-hypophyseal mechanism, which stimulates release of FSH and LH, simultaneously inhibits release of prolactin. Conversely, liberation of prolactin by the adenohypophysis, with consequent lactogenesis, appears to be a result of suppression of release of the other gonadotropins.

Biological Aspects of Gonadotropins. *Follicle-stimulating hormone* induces, in the female, growth of a large number of graafian follicles, resulting in an increased weight of the ovaries. In the male, FSH produces spermatogenesis in the testis by stimulating the epithelium of the seminiferous tubules, causing the appearance of large numbers of spermatocytes in various stages of development, including mature spermatozoa. The urinary excretion of FSH is significant in amount chiefly in castrates and following the menopause, and is elevated in malignancy of the reproductive organs.

Luteinizing hormone is concerned, in the female, with the final ripening of the ovarian follicles, together with the manifestations of heat, or estrus, and the rupture of the follicles with their transformation to corpora lutea. In the male, this hormone stimulates the Leydig cells, which secrete testosterone and are thus concerned with development and functioning of the secondary sex glands. It is because of its action on the interstitial cells of both the ovaries and the testes that luteinizing hormone has also been termed interstitial cell–stimulating hormone. The effect of LH on the interstitial cells of the testes may be thought of as analogous to its action on the thecal cells of the ovary.

Prolactin was first described as an adenohypophyseal principle essential for initiation of lactation in mammals at parturition. Hence its present designation as lactogenic hormone or prolactin. The hormone also promotes functional activity of the corpora lutea and, thus, progesterone secretion. Prolactin functions synergistically with estrogen to promote mammary gland proliferation, in addition to its capacity to initiate secretion of milk in the hypertrophied mammary gland. In the young pigeon, prolactin produces a proliferative hypertrophy of the normally thin crop sac. This response affords a convenient bioassay method for the hormone. Highly purified prolactin from human hypophyses also has significant growth-promoting activity (page 916). Prolactin preparations are anabolic agents.

Although *chorionic gonadotropin* is of placental and not hypophyseal origin, its biological effects resemble those of the hypophyseal hormones. Indeed, the placental principle was early described as an anterior pituitary-like (APL) factor. It appears in the urine early in pregnancy, in approximately the first week after the first missed menstrual period. This forms the basis for two commonly employed tests for pregnancy. In the Aschheim-Zondek test, urine or an alcoholic precipitate of urine is injected into immature female mice or rats. Urine from a pregnant individual, containing chorionic gonadotropin, will increase ovarian weight and cause ripening of follicles and hemorrhages into some unruptured follicles. In the Friedman test, the urine is injected intravenously into female rabbits to assess its ability to produce an ovulatory response (presence of ruptured ovarian follicles).

Markedly increased amounts of adenohypophyseal-like gonadotropin are excreted in conditions other than pregnancy and give rise to a false positive Aschheim-Zondek or Friedman test. This is seen in instances of chorionepithelioma, a malignant tumor of the placental tissue, and in hydatidiform mole, a cystic degenerative disease of chorionic tissue. High titers of urinary gonadotropin are also present in the urine of males afflicted with testicular tumors composed of malignant embryonal tissue, e.g., teratoma and epithelioma. Gonadotropin assays of urine are a useful diagnostic aid in these conditions.

It seems likely that chorionic gonadotropin supplements the hypophysis in maintaining growth of the corpus luteum during pregnancy, although this placental principle will not prevent ovarian atrophy which follows hypophysectomy in animals. Administered chorionic gonadotropin stimulates Leydig tissue and hence the male accessory organs. This has led to some success in the clinical use of this hormonal product in cryptorchidism in young males.

The role of the hypophyseal gonadotropins and certain of their interrelationships with other endocrine glands in reproduction are discussed later in this chapter.

Mode of Action of Gonadotropins. The stimulating action of gonadotropins on the synthesis of steroid hormones has been demonstrated in a variety of in vivo and in vitro studies with isotopically labeled precursors. These include FSH stimulation of in vitro conversion of acetate to estrone and estradiol by human ovaries taken from subjects following gonadotropin injection; augmented synthesis of progesterone from acetate by slices of bovine corpus luteum on addition of human chorionic gonadotropin, horse hypophyseal gonadotropin, or beef luteinizing hormone; and stimulation of testosterone formation from acetate on addition of FSH and LH to slices of rabbit testis.

Prolactin affects adipose tissue in vitro in a manner resembling that of insulin, viz., it stimulates glucose uptake and lipogenesis. The hormone from human hypophyses has marked anabolic actions (see below).

GROWTH HORMONE—SOMATOTROPIN

One of the earliest observations of hypophyseal physiology was that the adenohypophysis secretes a hormone which affects the rate of skeletal growth and gain in body weight. Hypophysectomy of younger animals results in either a greatly retarded growth rate or complete failure to grow. Growth abnormalities in man, e.g., acromegaly, gigantism, and dwarfism, associated with hypophyseal dysfunction, have provided additional evidence that the secretory activity of this gland influences skeletal growth. The generalized effects of a hormone of the adenohypophysis on growth and development led Evans to name this principle *somatotropin.*

Assay of somatotropin preparations has been based on (1) growth-promoting effect in the hypophysectomized rat, (2) growth stimulation in adult female rats which have ceased to grow, and (3) increase in width of the proximal end of the tibia of the hypophysectomized immature rat. With the availability of purified growth hormone preparations (see below), immunochemical determination of the hormone has become possible, permitting estimation of the growth hormone concentration in human sera.

Chemistry of Somatotropin. Highly purified preparations of active growth-promoting proteins have been prepared from hypophyses of many species, including the human. The hormone from bovine and human tissue has been obtained in crystalline form. Table 51.4 indicates some of the characteristics of growth hormone

Table 51.4: SOME CHARACTERISTICS OF VARIOUS GROWTH HORMONE PREPARATIONS

Source	Molecular weight	Isoelectric point, pH	Disulfide linkages	Amino-terminal residues
Beef	45,000	6.8	4	Phenylalanine Alanine
Sheep	48,000	6.8	5	Phenylalanine Alanine
Pig	41,000	6.3	3	Phenylalanine
Whale	40,000	6.2	3	Phenylalanine
Monkey	25,000	5.5	4	Phenylalanine
Human	27,000	4.9	2	Phenylalanine

SOURCE: After C. H. Li, in G. E. W. Wolstenholme and C. M. O'Connor, eds., "Human Pituitary Hormones," p. 46, J. A. Churchill Ltd., London, 1960.

preparations from various species. Of particular interest is the apparent grouping of certain of the properties, notably molecular weights, of human and monkey growth hormone as compared with hormones from other species. The beef and sheep proteins contain two polypeptide chains, whereas the hormones from other species contain one. Although all the growth hormone preparations studied show biological activity when tested in various heterologous species except the primates, only monkey and human growth hormone preparations are effective in all species studied, including man. Thus, until monkey and human hypophyseal tissue became available, there was not an effective growth hormone preparation for use in human subjects. These findings are in accord with the observation of cross reaction between monkey and human growth hormone antisera, whereas these antisera do not react with growth hormone preparations from other species. In contrast with other species, a close chemical and biological similarity obtains between *human* growth hormone and *human* prolactin. Chemical separation of the two activities, *i.e.,* growth-promoting and crop sac–stimulating (page 914), has been achieved in hypophyseal preparations from all species except the human, in which the two preparations are immunologically identical.

Data of Li and his associates suggest that only a portion of the growth hormone protein is essential for biological activity. Partial chymotryptic hydrolysis of growth hormone preparations from three species occurred without loss of biological activity. The extent of hydrolysis was 25, 20, and 10 per cent, respectively, for growth hormone from beef, monkey, and human glands.

Biological Effects of Somatotropin. The diverse effects of somatotropin are not primarily due to its influence on other endocrine glands, in contrast to the operation of other adenohypophyseal hormones. Somatotropin actions can be demonstrated in the hypophysectomized animal despite hypofunctioning of thyroid, adrenals, and gonads. However, somatotropin can act in cooperation with other hormones. For example, the anabolic effect of androgens is minimally manifest in the hypophysectomized animal, and somatotropin administration markedly enhances the nitrogen retention produced by androgens, as well as the growth of specific androgen-sensitive tissues.

In addition to its general growth-promoting and anabolic properties, somatotropin administration produces metabolic alterations which may be characterized as diabetogenic, pancreotropic, glycostatic, lipid-mobilizing and ketogenic, renal, erythropoietic, and galactopoietic.

Growth and Anabolic Effects. The designation of a single substance as the growth-promoting hormone is inaccurate in view of the influence of other hormones,

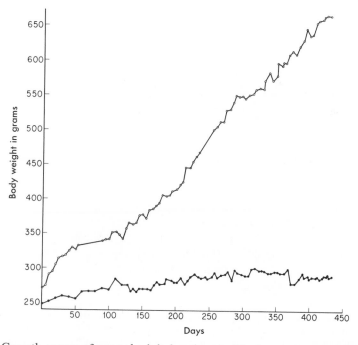

FIG. 51.7. Growth curves of normal adult female rats. The lower curve is for the control animal, which, at the body weight indicated (250 g.), had ceased to grow and received no further treatment. The upper curve is for another animal which had also ceased to grow but then received 0.40 mg. of growth hormone daily for the first 23 days, 0.60 mg. daily the next 68 days, 1.0 mg. daily the next 33 days, 1.5 mg. daily the next 115 days, 2.0 mg. daily the last 193 days; no injections on Sundays. (*C. H. Li and H. M. Evans, in G. Pincus and K. V. Thimann, "The Hormones: Physiology, Chemistry and Applications," vol. I, p.* 631, *Academic Press, Inc., New York,* 1948.)

notably those of the thyroid, adrenal cortex, and pancreas, on normal growth and development. Other factors, such as protein intake, also affect growth. Nevertheless, repeated injection of somatotropin promotes growth of both hard and soft tissue; this is reflected in a variety of effects. These include body weight gain, alterations in concentrations of nitrogen, potassium, phosphate, and sulfate in hard or soft tissues, and stimulation of mitotic activity. However, it is not known whether these manifold responses reflect a specific effect on some key metabolic process which is rate-determining, an influence on cellular permeability, or an action on a large number of diverse enzymic systems.

Depending on the amount and period of somatotropin injection, there may result both an accelerated growth rate and an extension of the growth period beyond the normal limits (Figs. 51.7 and 51.8). Administration of the hormone to animals prior to closing of the epiphyses produces accelerated growth of bones and soft tissues, with an almost symmetrical enlargement of all features. In adult animals, with closed epiphyses, somatotropin stimulates chondrogenesis and osteogenesis wherever endochondral bone exists or some remnants of cartilage remain. This produces long and characteristically misshapen bones. Animals resembling acromegalic humans (see below) can be produced by repeated administration of somatotropin (Fig. 51.8).

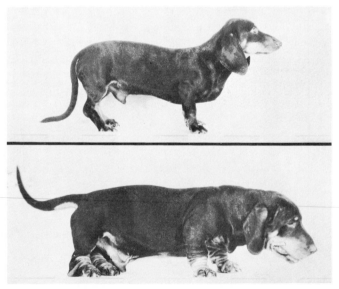

Fig. 51.8. Effect of adenohypophyseal extract on growth of the dog. Above, nontreated control; below, litter mate treated with bovine adenohypophyseal extract (daily intraperitoneal injections during 6 months). Note prominent signs of gigantism. (*From H. M. Evans, K. Meyer, and M. E. Simpson, Mem. Univ. Calif., 2, 1, 1933.*)

If the young animal is hypophysectomized, there is a cessation of chondrogenesis and osteogenesis. The epiphyses are not completely closed but remain as thin cartilaginous plates. These can be reactivated by somatotropin injection to give the appearance of young and growing bones. The primary effect of the hormone is on chondrogenesis, followed by ossification. Previous mention has been made of the use of the widening of the proximal tibial epiphyseal cartilage by somatotropin injection in young hypophysectomized rats as a method of assaying the hormone. These effects of the hormone on chondrogenesis and osteogenesis are reflected in reports that injection of somatotropin into hypophysectomized rats increased the uptake of Ca^{45} by the tibias in an amount proportional to the body weight gain induced by hormone treatment. Similarly, somatotropin administration stimulated incorporation of injected $S^{35}O_4^=$ into the costal cartilage of hypophysectomized rats as a result of augmented synthesis of chondroitin sulfate.

Somatotropin produces in all mammalian species retention of nitrogen with augmented deposition of tissue protein. There is an accompanying retention of potassium and phosphate. This is evident in hypophysectomized animals even when the food intake is restricted to that of controls not receiving hormone. Augmentation of protein synthesis under the influence of the hormone is seen in muscle, kidneys, and liver and in bone matrix.

Growth hormone administration to either intact or hypophysectomized rats lowers the concentration of serum amino acids. This is a reflection of augmented amino acid uptake by tissue cells. Addition of somatotropin to a rat diaphragm preparation in vitro promoted intracellular concentration of amino acids and their incorporation into muscle tissue proteins. Of the other hypophyseal hormones, only prolactin produced similar effects, but this hormone was much less active in this regard. The possible growth-promoting activity of prolactin has been mentioned previously (page 916). Somatotropin also stimulates RNA synthesis in the liver of the hypophysectomized rat.

Actions of Somatotropin on Carbohydrate Metabolism—Diabetogenic, Pancreatropic, and Glycostatic Effects. Hypophysectomy results in a tendency to hypoglycemia and a loss of hepatic and muscle glycogen on fasting, an increased sensitivity to insulin, and an increased rate of utilization of carbohydrate.

In the depancreatized animal, or in experimental diabetes produced by administration of either alloxan or phlorhizin, the glucosuria and ketosis are ameliorated by removal of the adenohypophysis (Houssay effect, page 900). These effects of hypophysectomy on carbohydrate metabolism can be reversed by administration of somatotropin. Indeed, purified somatotropin injections can produce hyperglycemia and glucosuria in normal dogs and cats, as well as intensify the diabetes of the hypophysectomized, diabetic dog and human being. Lack of responsiveness to administered insulin (insulin resistance) develops. The high incidence of glucosuria in acromegaly in man (see below) is known.

The above actions of somatotropin have been termed *diabetogenic effects.* It should be recalled that ACTH or adrenal cortical steroid administration may also have a diabetogenic effect (page 880), and similar observations have been made with prolactin in partially depancreatized animals. These effects of somatotropin in vivo on carbohydrate metabolism are intensified if the hormone is given together with adrenal steroids.

In contrast to the hyperglycemia caused by prolonged somatotropin administration to normal or hypophysectomized subjects (see above), a single injection of monkey growth hormone in hypophysectomized, fasted monkeys induced acute hypoglycemia, with manifest hypoglycemic convulsions. This did not occur in normal, fasting monkeys. These observations probably reflect the stimulating effect of somatotropin on insulin production by the pancreas (see below), and the diminished gluconeogenesis in the hypophysectomized animal due to insufficiency of adrenal cortical steroids (page 880).

The hyperglycemia following somatotropin administration is a result of the rapid release of glucose from the liver. This would stimulate secretion of insulin (page 894). Permanent diabetes has been produced in dogs and cats by somatotropin administration, with destruction of the β cells of the pancreas, apparently because of a period of excessive production of insulin. In this sense, somatotropin exerts a *pancreatropic effect*. It may be noted that in the rat, ACTH, and not somatotropin, will produce corresponding diabetogenic effects, including alterations in pancreatic β cells. Evidence has been adduced that somatotropin will augment secretion of glucagon by the pancreas.

The *glycostatic effect* of somatotropin is descriptive of the ability of injected hormone to prevent the fall in muscle glycogen of fasting, hypophysectomized animals. Fasting of normal animals depletes liver glycogen only. Somatotropin administration also increases the cardiac glycogen, as well as skeletal muscle glycogen, of either hypophysectomized or normal rats. Certain ACTH preparations also have been reported to exhibit a glycostatic effect.

Actions of Somatotropin on Lipid Metabolism. Somatotropin exerts a lipid-mobilizing effect. Administration of the hormone results in an acute rise in blood unesterified fatty acids and ketonemia, and may be accompanied by ketonuria. There is an increase in liver lipids consequent to accelerated lipid mobilization. These effects are particularly striking when endogenous carbohydrate stores are reduced to a minimum or exogenous carbohydrate is lacking. The rise in concentration of nonesterified fatty acids can be prevented by administration of food, glucose, or insulin. Fatty acid release from lipid depots following somatotropin administration appears to be stimulated by conditions unfavorable to fat synthesis, *e.g.*, fasting, and inhibited by conditions favoring triglyceride synthesis, *e.g.*, a supply of carbohydrate.

The mobilization of lipid produced by somatotropin injection is similar to that observed with ACTH (page 911) and adrenal steroids (page 882). The question of whether the lipid-mobilizing action of somatotropin is dependent upon simultaneous presence of adrenal cortical steroids is unsettled.

Other Effects of Somatotropin. The *renotropic* effect of somatotropin administration is reflected in increased kidney size and function, notably augmented renal clearance and tubular excretion, with retention, in adrenalectomized rats, of potassium, sodium, chloride, and nitrogen. These actions of the hormone are independent of the hypophysis or adrenal cortex.

Somatotropin has an *erythropoietic* effect, *i.e.*, an ability to stimulate reticulocytosis and increase the percentage of nucleated erythroid elements within the bone marrow, as well as to stimulate repair of the hypoplastic bone marrow of the hypophysectomized animal.

The *galactopoietic* effect of somatotropin is descriptive of the stimulation by the hormone of milk production in cows, as well as its effect on mammary gland proliferation and induction of milk secretion in hypophysectomized rats. The possible identity of somatotropin with lactogenic hormone in the human being has been indicated (page 916).

Hypersecretion of Somatotropin in Man. In man, excessive production of somatotropin after the usual age of full skeletal growth results in *acromegaly*, first described by Pierre Marie in 1895. Overproduction of the hormone in this clinical syndrome is due to an adenomatous acidophil cell-containing tumor of the adenohypophysis. The characteristic features of acromegaly are: (1) Overgrowth of the bones of the hands, feet, and face. The feet and hands are markedly increased in size; the hands appear broadened and the fingers thickened. Bowing of the spine (kyphosis) is commonly seen. The soft tissues of the nose, lips, forehead, and scalp are thickened. The scalp may appear to be folded and wrinkled and is described as a bulldog scalp. There is a general overgrowth of the body hair. (2) Enlargement of the viscera (splanchnomegaly). The tongue, lungs, heart, liver, spleen, and thymus are greatly enlarged. The thyroid, parathyroid, and adrenal glands may show hypertrophy or adenomatous growths. Hyperthyroidism may be present, as well as glucosuria and hyperglycemia, suggesting a diabetes of pancreatic origin. (3) In the early stages of the disease, increased sexual activity may be evident. Later, there occur atrophy of the gonads and suppression of the sexual functions in both sexes, with impotence in men and amenorrhea in women.

If the hypophyseal adenoma occurs prior to puberty, before ossification is complete, gigantism will result. There is a general overgrowth of the skeleton, resulting in individuals of 7 or 8 ft. or more in height. The limbs are generally disproportionately long.

Hyposecretion of Somatotropin: Pituitary Dwarfism. Dwarfism, or premature arresting of skeletal development, has been considered previously in connection with hypothyroidism (cretinism, page 835). This type of dwarfing may possibly be a manifestation of a primary hypophyseal deficiency reflecting the absence of adequate secretion of the thyrotropic hormone.

Another type of arrested growth results from a deficiency of somatotropin secretion. In contrast to the cretins, these hypophyseal dwarfs do not show deformity or, as a rule, mental inferiority and frequently do not have the unattractive appearance of a cretin. The hypophyseal dwarfs are frequently immature sexually. At adult age the dwarf may be no more than 3 or 4 ft. in height. The relative proportions of the different parts of the skeleton do not deviate markedly from normal, although the head is generally large in relation to the body.

In concluding these considerations of the individual hypophyseal hormones of established identity and biological function, mention should be made of hypophyseal preparations which are active in mobilizing free fatty acids into the serum of rabbits and are reported to be distinct from known hypophyseal hormones. This activity has been described as *adipokinetic*. As indicated previously, several of the known hypophyseal hormones stimulate release of fatty acids from adipose tissue when tested either in vivo or in vitro. In addition, preparations of polypeptide character have been obtained which appear to differ from all other purified hypophyseal hormones and produced a striking, acute rise in level of serum fatty acids of rabbits following intravenous injection. These products were only slightly effective in raising the concentration of free fatty acids of plasma of human subjects following subcutaneous administration.

Differences in response to adipokinetic preparations in various species, as compared to ACTH and other lipid-mobilizing polypeptides such as oxytocin, lend some support to the possibility that adipokinin may be a distinct adenohypophyseal hormone.

ENDOCRINE INTERRELATIONSHIPS

The biochemistry of the endocrine glands reveals a variety of integrations and interrelationships among these structures. This picture is not unlike the interrelationships which obtain among the diverse processes of intermediary metabolism, in that the influence of one upon the others is continually apparent. Certain of the interrelationships among the endocrine glands have been strikingly illustrated by the effects of the adenohypophysis on several other endocrine structures. Reference has been made to the ability of hormones to complement one another, or to act synergistically, *e.g.*, thyroxine and somatotropin in promoting growth. On the other hand, attention has also been directed to the phenomenon of hormonal antagonism, or inhibition, as seen, for example, in the mutually opposing and inhibiting actions of androgens and estrogens.

ADENOHYPOPHYSEAL-OVARIAN INTERRELATIONSHIPS

The Sexual Cycle: Menstruation. Among the most striking examples and results of endocrine interrelationships are the rhythmic sexual, or menstrual, cycles in the postpubertal female, reflecting hypophyseal-ovarian interrelationships.

The rhythmic sexual cycles, which are initiated at puberty, depend on the secretion and release of the gonadotropic hormones of the adenohypophysis. Prior to puberty, these hormones are not secreted in detectable quantities, and no significant alterations occur in either the ovaries or testes. The basis of the onset of this new activity of the hypophysis at the time of puberty is unknown. The secretion of follicle-stimulating hormone (FSH), acting synergistically with a small amount of luteinizing hormone (LH), stimulates follicle development in the ovary. As the follicle begins to ripen, growth and activity of the cells of the theca interna result in their secretion of estrogens. These estrogens induce secretion of follicular fluid by the granulosa cells and sensitize the follicle to FSH. In women, FSH stimulates maturation of a single follicle at each cycle, although occasionally two follicles may mature. The stimulated follicle continues to develop, while the other follicles that were in the process of ripening cease to grow and become, in part, atretic.

The estrogens which have been produced enter the blood stream and exert a diversified influence on the secretory activity of the adenohypophysis. FSH secretion is diminished, while secretion of LH and probably also of prolactin is augmented. LH acts upon the mature and sensitized follicle, causing its rupture, with release of the ovum (ovulation). The same hormone (LH) stimulates development of the corpus luteum in the ruptured follicle, and prolactin induces secretion by the newly formed corpus luteum. The progesterone thus produced inhibits hypophyseal secretion of LH and of prolactin; this fall in hormonal secretion coincides with menstruation. With the cessation of production of LH and prolactin, the hypophysis returns to the initial stage, *i.e.*, a new cycle begins. These events are diagrammed in Fig. 51.9.

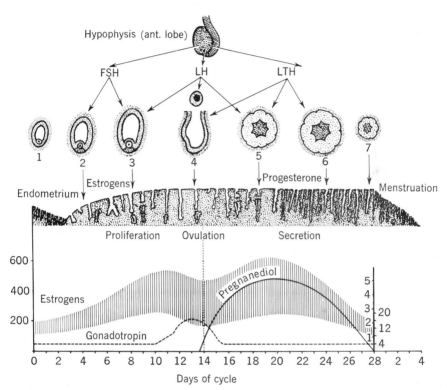

FIG. 51.9. Diagram of human female sexual cycle. The follicle-stimulating hormone (FSH) of the adenohypophysis provokes ripening of the ovarian follicle. 1, primary follicle; 2, ripening follicle; 3, ripe follicle; 4, rupture of follicle (ovulation) as a result of luteinizing-hormone (LH) action. LH stimulates corpus luteum formation (5), and prolactin (LTH) induces secretion by corpus luteum of progesterone (6). The mature corpus luteum (6) then degenerates (7) if there is no pregnancy. The endometrium proliferates under the action of estrogens in the first part of the cycle and secretes under the action of progesterone during the latter part of the cycle, which ends in menstruation. Below, urinary excretion of hormones; vertical lines, estrogens; broken line, gonadotropins; solid line, pregnanediol. On the left, the units are international units of estrogens eliminated in 24 hr.; on the right, milligrams of pregnanediol (1 to 5) and international units of gonadotropins (4 to 20) excreted in 24 hr. (*From B. A. Houssay, "Human Physiology," 2d ed., McGraw-Hill Book Company, Inc., New York, 1954.*)

Pregnancy. Secretion of progesterone by the corpus luteum prepares the endometrium of the uterus for the reception and implantation of the fertilized egg and for the maintenance of the embryo and fetus. Progesterone also decreases the tonus of the uterus and stimulates development of the mammary gland preparatory to its secretion of milk after parturition.

If the ovum is not fertilized, it is not implanted in the uterus and the corpus luteum retrogresses. With implantation of the fertilized ovum, however, the corpus luteum persists in an active stage, and the normal menstrual cycle is interrupted. There is evidence that in women the corpus luteum can be removed after the fourth or fifth month of pregnancy without inducing abortion. This is related to the fact that at this time the placenta begins to produce progesterone. Urinary excretion of pregnanediol, a normal metabolite of progesterone (page 865), rises sharply at this period in pregnancy.

Production of estrogens, progesterone, and gonadotropins is augmented following ovum implantation in the uterus. The level of gonadotropin secretion is high early in gestation and forms the basis for several laboratory tests for pregnancy (page 915).

THYROID—ADRENAL CORTICAL INTERRELATIONSHIPS

Interest in the therapeutic value of adrenal cortical hormones (pages 888*ff.*) has, with their extensive use, revealed interrelationships of the adrenal cortex with other endocrine glands. Among these is the observation that a high blood level of adrenal cortical steroids, produced either by overproduction of endogenous hormone or by administration of ACTH or of adrenal cortical steroids, may reduce thyroid secretion. This effect has been noted in patients and in experimental animals treated for long periods with cortisol or ACTH. It is assumed that the adrenal cortical steroids depress the production of thyrotropic hormone by the hypophysis. However, the effect of cortisol may be due to a direct inhibitory influence on the thyroid, and not to interference with the production of thyrotropic hormone.

An augmenting relationship apparently also obtains between the adrenal cortex and the thyroid gland. Small amounts of thyroxine stimulate the ACTH–adrenal cortical secretory mechanism. Although this may be a nonspecific effect of thyroxine, it has considerable physiological significance. Conversely, a long period of hypothyroidism may result in a secondary depression of adrenal cortical function. This has been described as a "myxedema" of the adrenal cortex, whose function can be restored to normal with appropriate thyroid therapy. Apparently, the adrenal cortex, like many of the other tissues of the body, operates at a lower than normal level in circumstances of hypothyroidism.

THYROID-OVARIAN INTERRELATIONSHIPS

The thyroid gland may influence ovarian function either indirectly via the adenohypophysis or by a direct effect on the ovary. A characteristic enlargement of the thyroid gland during the latter part of pregnancy has been known since ancient times and may be seen in medieval and Renaissance art. The thyroid hormone augments or facilitates ovum formation; this may be a reflection of the generalized influence of the thyroid on growth and differentiation of tissues. Thyroid hormone also increases the sensitivity of peripheral tissues to ovarian hormones.

The amenorrhea and infertility in human hypothyroidism have been mentioned previously (page 835). During pregnancy there is an increased requirement for thyroid hormone. Also, a number of gonadal steroids have been shown to affect the uptake of radioiodine by the rat thyroid. All the above observations suggest thyroid-ovarian interrelationships. A practical application of this interrelationship is the administration of thyroid to increase milk production in cows and egg production in hens.

OTHER INTERRELATIONSHIPS

A number of other endocrine interrelationships have been noted in the previous chapters of this part and will be briefly recalled. One of the striking interrelationships observed in endocrinology is that which exists between the level of secretion of the hormones of the adenohypophysis and the concentration in the blood of the hormones which are produced in the endocrine glands whose secretory rate is influenced by the adenohypophysis. Reference has been made to the effects of ovarian hormones on the secretion of the hypophyseal gonadotropic hormones, and to the diminution in ACTH secretion by the hypophysis which results from injection of an adrenal cortical steroid.

The effects of the adrenal cortex and of insulin on carbohydrate metabolism are of a balancing nature, in the sense that the former promotes gluconeogenesis and thus increases the glucose supply, while the latter stimulates carbohydrate utilization. The results of ACTH–adrenal cortical secretion and of somatotropin on the activity of the pancreas have been pointed out previously. It is evident that certain hormonal activities may be interrelated via their influence on specific metabolic processes, as well as because of their direct effects on the secretory activity of endocrine glands.

In several of their metabolic effects, estrogens and androgens are antagonistic in that when administered together there is no evidence of the physiological response which would have been seen had either hormone been given alone. Since the adrenal cortex also produces androgens, it participates in estrogen-androgen interrelationships.

The interrelationships among the endocrine glands described in this section reemphasize that the diverse processes of the organism are interrelated and interdependent and focus attention, with the endocrine glands as examples, on additional mechanisms in the body by which augmenting and restraining influences operate to produce the dynamic state of balance, or homeostasis, which characterizes the normal organism.

REFERENCES

Books

Berde, B., "Recent Progress in Oxytocin Research," Charles C Thomas, Publisher, Springfield, Ill., 1961.

Caldeyro-Barcia, R., and Heller, H., eds., "Oxytocin," Pergamon Press, New York, 1961.

Fields, W. S., Guillemin, R., and Carton, C. A., eds., "Hypothalamic-hypophyseal Interrelationships," Charles C Thomas, Publisher, Springfield, Ill., 1956.

Harris, G. W., "Neural Control of the Pituitary Gland," Edward Arnold (Publishers) Ltd., London, 1955.

Heller, H., ed., "The Neurohypophysis," Academic Press, Inc., New York, 1957.

Parkes, A. S., ed., "Marshall's Physiology of Reproduction," vol. 1, part 1, Longmans, Green & Co., Ltd., London, 1956.

Velardo, J. T., ed., "Endocrinology of Reproduction," Oxford University Press, New York, 1958.

Werner, S. C., ed., "Thyrotropin," Charles C Thomas, Publisher, Springfield, Ill., 1963.

Wolstenholme, G. E. W., and O'Connor, C. M., eds., "Human Pituitary Hormones," J. & A. Churchill, Ltd., London, 1960.

Young, W. C., ed., "Sex and Internal Secretions," vols. I and II, The Williams & Wilkins Company, Baltimore, 1961.

Review Articles

de Bodo, R. C., and Altszuler, N., The Metabolic Effects of Growth Hormone and Their Physiological Significance, *Vitamins and Hormones,* **15**, 205–258, 1957.

Engel, F. L., Extra-adrenal Actions of Adrenocorticotropin, *Vitamins and Hormones,* **19**, 189–227, 1961.

Finkel, M. S., Human Growth Hormone, Metabolic Effects and Experimental and Therapeutic Applications, *Am. J. Med.,* **32**, 588–598, 1962.

Greer, M., Studies on the Influence of the Central Nervous System on Anterior Pituitary Function, *Recent Progr. Hormone Research,* **13**, 67–104, 1957.

Harris, I., The Chemistry of Pituitary Polypeptide Hormones, *Brit. Med. Bull.,* **16**, 189–195, 1960.

Hofmann, K., Chemistry and Function of Polypeptide Hormones, *Ann. Rev. Biochem.,* **31**, 213–246, 1962.

Hofmann, K., and Yajima, H., Synthetic Pituitary Hormones, *Recent Progr. Hormone Research,* **18**, 41–88, 1962.

Knobil, E., and Greep, R. O., The Physiology of Growth Hormone with Particular Reference to Its Action in the Rhesus Monkey and the "Species Specificity" Problem, *Recent Progr. Hormone Research,* **15**, 1–69, 1959.

Leaf, A., and Hays, R. M., The Effects of Neurohypophyseal Hormone on Permeability and Transport in a Living Membrane, *Recent Progr. Hormone Research,* **17**, 467–492, 1961.

Lerner, A. B., and Takahashi, Y., Hormonal Control of Melanin Pigmentation, *Recent Progr. Hormone Research,* **12**, 303–320, 1956.

Li, C. H., Hormones of the Anterior Pituitary Gland. Part I. Growth and Adrenocorticotropic Hormones, *Advances in Protein Chem.,* **11**, 101–190, 1956.

Li, C. H., Hormones of the Anterior Pituitary Glands. Part II. Melanocyte-stimulating and Lactogenic Hormones, *Advances in Protein Chem.,* **12**, 290–317, 1957.

Li, C. H., Synthesis and Biological Properties of ACTH Peptides, *Recent Progr. Hormone Research,* **18**, 1–40, 1962.

Liddle, G. W., Island, D., and Meader, C. K., Normal and Abnormal Regulation of Corticotropin Secretion in Man, *Recent Progr. Hormone Research,* **18**, 125–166, 1962.

Munson, P. L., and Briggs, F. N., The Mechanism of Stimulation of ACTH Secretion, *Recent Progr. Hormone Research,* **11**, 83–117, 1955.

Raben, M. S., Human Growth Hormone, *Recent Progr. Hormone Research,* **15**, 71–114, 1959.

Riddle, O., Prolactin in Vertebrate Function and Organization, *J. Natl. Cancer Inst.,* **31**, 1039–1110, 1963.

Rudman, D., Hirsch, R. L., Kendall, F. E., Seidman, F., and Brown, S. J., An Adipokinetic Component of the Pituitary Gland: Purification, Physical, Chemical and Biologic Properties, *Recent Progr. Hormone Research,* **18**, 89–123, 1962.

Sawyer, W. H., Comparative Physiology and Pharmacology of the Neurohypophysis, *Recent Progr. Hormone Research,* **17**, 437–465, 1961.

Sawyer, W. H., Neurohypophyseal Hormones, *Pharmacol. Revs.,* **13**, 225–277, 1961.

Sonenberg, M., Chemistry and Physiology of the Thyroid-stimulating Hormone, *Vitamins and Hormones,* **16**, 205–261, 1958.

Thorn, N. A., Mammalian Antidiuretic Hormone, *Physiol. Revs.,* **38**, 169–195, 1958.

52. General Considerations of Nutrition

SCOPE OF THE SCIENCE OF NUTRITION

The science of nutrition may conveniently be considered in relation to the questions: What are the substances required by the animal for growth, maintenance, and reproduction, and in what quantities? What are the results of failure to meet these requirements, and what are the results of the ingestion of these substances in excess of the requirements? What is the physiological role of each of these nutrients? How does failure of this physiological function lead to the overt signs of deficiency? Which foods will enable the animal to meet these requirements, and in what amounts are these foods required?

Almost all the major nutrients required by man have been considered earlier in this book, particularly in those instances in which some understanding of the metabolic role of an individual nutrient is available. What follows, therefore, is a survey of the answers presently available to the questions raised above. In the main, this discussion will be confined to "essential" nutrients, *i.e.*, those necessary for normal growth, maintenance, and reproduction and which man cannot synthesize from other constituents of the diet.

The nutritional requirements of man include water, inorganic ions, and a number of organic compounds. The requirement for water has been considered in detail (Chap. 35). The inorganic substances include the major anions and cations of the extra- and intracellular fluids and skeleton and a number of elements required in lesser amounts. Carbohydrates and lipids are required as fuels and as precursors for the synthesis of diverse substances and structures. Amino acids are needed for the synthesis of proteins and of other nitrogenous compounds. Accessory food factors called vitamins are frequently employed as structural components of coenzymes. Of the organic compounds in the body, approximately 24 have been definitely established as dietary essentials. All other substances are synthesized by the organism in the presence of an adequate supply of these essential factors. In view of the complex chemical composition of living things, the list of essential nutrients shown in Table 52.1 is perhaps more remarkable for its brevity than for its length.

ASSAY ANIMALS

Recognition of the role of nutrition in the etiology of certain diseases of man led to a search for the specific nutrients which would prevent these diseases. Among the nutrients recognized in this manner have been vitamins A, D, and B_{12}, thia-

Table 52.1: NUTRIENTS REQUIRED BY MAN

Established as essential	*Probably essential*
Amino acids:	*Amino acids:*
Isoleucine	Arginine*
Leucine	Histidine*
Lysine	
Methionine	
Phenylalanine	
Threonine	
Tryptophan	
Valine	
Elements:	*Elements:*
Calcium	Fluorine
Chlorine	Molybdenum
Copper	Selenium
Iodine	Zinc
Iron	
Magnesium	
Manganese	
Phosphorus	
Potassium	
Sodium	
Vitamins:	*Vitamins:*
Ascorbic acid	Biotin
Choline†	Pantothenic acid
Folic acid	Polyunsaturated fatty acids
Niacin‡	
Pyridoxine	
Riboflavin	
Thiamine	
Vitamin B_{12}	
Vitamins A, D§, E, and K	

* Indicated to be unnecessary for maintenance of nitrogen equilibrium in adults in short-term studies but probably necessary for normal growth of children.

† Requirement met under circumstances of adequate dietary methionine.

‡ Requirement may be provided by synthesis from dietary tryptophan.

§ Requirement may be met by exposure of children to sunlight. No evidence for a requirement in adults.

mine, niacin, and ascorbic acid. These investigations required the establishment of deficiency states in experimental animals under controlled circumstances. Many animal species have been employed; the chicken and pigeon are used as assay animals for thiamine, the dog is used in niacin and vitamin D analyses, and the guinea pig for ascorbic acid assays. The animal most often employed in nutrition studies is the albino rat. The rat is omnivorous, has a gastrointestinal tract comparable with that of man, and in the main, exhibits nutritional requirements similar to those of man. However, it has rarely been possible to reproduce, in an experimental animal, a disease entity identical with that encountered in human deficiency states. Indeed, impaired growth of the young animal has frequently been the only criterion of deficiency. The fact that, when all nutrients but one are present in the diet in adequate amounts, the growth rate of an animal is proportional to the dietary supply of the limiting nutrient makes possible bioassays of natural foodstuffs and concentrates. During the period between the recognition of each new accessory food factor and its final identification, it has been the practice to adopt for comparative purposes a standard *unit* of activity, *e.g.*, the amount necessary to cause a specific quantitative response in a given animal. After the nutrient has been identified and is available in pure form, the data are then expressed in terms of the weight of the nutrient. However, when several structurally related and naturally occurring compounds are found to exert similar activity under the conditions of bioassay, it has been the practice to continue to express the activity of biological materials in units.

MICROORGANISMS AND NUTRITIONAL STUDIES

Microorganisms have been extremely useful in nutritional investigations. Inositol, pantothenic acid, and biotin were all ultimately recognized as a result of studies of the complex which, in 1901, Wildiers had termed *bios*. This was a mixture of substances present in beerwort and required for the initial growth of certain strains of yeast. Folic acid was established as an essential factor for the growth of several strains of lactobacilli several years before its importance in mammalian nutrition was discovered. Vitamin B_{12}, the antipernicious anemia factor, was identified in one laboratory because it is essential for the growth of *Lactobacillus lactis* Dorner. Many species of bacteria, molds, yeast, and fungi have been found for which one or more of the nutrients known to be essential to man are also growth factors, thus providing a basis for rapid quantitative microbiological assays for these substances.

The bacteria which inhabit the gastrointestinal tract may supply significant amounts of vitamins to the host. This fact accounts for the simpler nutritional requirements of the ruminants and of those species with large ceca, *e.g.*, the horse and rabbit. Thus these animals are provided with fermentation mechanisms which produce many essential nutritional factors. To a lesser degree, this occurs also in the intestine of man, who is thereby supplied with a major fraction of his requirement for biotin and vitamin K. The role of the intestinal flora in nutrition has been established by inclusion in the diet of antibiotics. Animals raised under sterile conditions with bacteria-free intestinal tracts have also been employed in studies of this type. The inclusion of antibiotics, particularly Aureomycin and Terramycin, in the stock rations of pigs and chicks has been found to stimulate their growth, with an increased weight per pound of ingested feed. The mechanism whereby this is accomplished is not clear but probably reflects establishment of an intestinal flora which furnishes utilizable nutrients to the host animal.

NUTRITIONAL REQUIREMENTS OF MAN

Several difficulties are encountered in studies of human nutrition. The most serious of these are the impracticality of feeding human subjects rations consisting exclusively of chemically purified materials for sufficient lengths of time and the uncertainty concerning the qualitative and quantitative activities of the intestinal flora. It has been particularly difficult to establish the quantitative requirements for many nutrients known, qualitatively, to be essential. Nitrogen balance studies have

Table 52.2: RECOMMENDED DAILY DIETARY ALLOWANCES

Age and sex	Weight, kg.(lb.)	Height, cm.(in.)	Calories	Protein, g.	Calcium, g.	Iron, mg.	Vitamin A, I.U.*	Thiamine, mg.	Riboflavin, mg.	Niacin, mg.	Ascorbic acid, mg.	Vitamin D, I.U.*
Men:												
25 yr.	70(154)	175(69)	3200	70	0.8	10	5,000	1.6	1.8	21	75	
45 yr.	70(154)	175(69)	3000	70	0.8	10	5,000	1.5	1.8	20	75	
65 yr.	70(154)	175(69)	2550	70	0.8	10	5,000	1.3	1.8	18	75	
Women:												
25 yr.	58(128)	163(64)	2300	58	0.8	12	5,000	1.2	1.5	17	70	
45 yr.	58(128)	163(64)	2200	58	0.8	12	5,000	1.1	1.5	17	70	
65 yr.	58(128)	163(64)	1800	58	0.8	12	5,000	1.0	1.5	17	70	
Pregnant (second half)	...	...	Add 300	78	1.5	15	6,000	1.3	2.0	20	100	400
Lactating (850 ml. daily)	...	...	Add 1000	98	2.0	15	8,000	1.7	2.5	19	150	400
Infants:												
2 mo.–6 mo.	6(13)	60(24)	Kg. × 120	...	0.6	5	1,500	0.4	0.5	6	30	400
7 mo.–12 mo.	9(20)	70(28)	Kg. × 100	...	0.8	7	1,500	0.5	0.8	7	30	400
Children:												
1–3	12(27)	87(34)	1300	40	1.0	7	2,000	0.7	1.0	8	35	400
4–6	18(40)	109(43)	1700	50	1.0	8	2,500	0.9	1.3	11	50	400
7–9	27(60)	129(51)	2100	60	1.0	10	3,500	1.1	1.5	14	60	400
10–12	36(79)	144(57)	2500	70	1.2	12	4,500	1.3	1.8	17	75	400
Boys:												
13–15	49(108)	163(64)	3100	85	1.4	15	5,000	1.6	2.1	21	90	400
16–19	63(139)	175(69)	3600	100	1.4	15	5,000	1.8	2.5	25	100	400
Girls:												
13–15	49(108)	160(63)	2600	80	1.3	15	5,000	1.3	2.0	17	80	400
16–19	54(120)	162(64)	2400	75	1.3	15	5,000	1.2	1.9	16	80	400

* I.U. = international unit.

SOURCE: Recommended by the Food and Nutrition Board, National Research Council, 1958. Publication 589, National Academy of Sciences, Washington, D.C.

yielded values for the amounts of the essential amino acids required for maintenance of adult human beings. However, the amino acid requirements for growth have not been established for the human species. Balance studies have also been employed to establish quantitative requirements for elements such as potassium, calcium, and iron. Perhaps the most striking result of these studies is the extreme variability found within the population. The amount of calcium required to maintain one individual in balance may be two or three times that which suffices for another. A similar situation exists with respect to iron. The quantitative requirements for the vitamins are even less securely established. The recommended dietary allowances shown in Table 52.2 represent dietary levels which, in clinical experience, are known *not* to lead to deficiency; they are not intended to represent minimal requirements but are objectives which it is presently thought desirable to seek in planning diets for normal individuals.

REFERENCES

See list following Chap. 56.

53. The Major Nutrients

Protein, Lipid, and Carbohydrate

PROTEIN

Animals do not require dietary protein, per se, but rather certain of the individual amino acids derived therefrom. The concept of nutritionally essential amino acids and the manner in which they have been identified have been presented earlier (Chap. 24). The amino acids essential experimentally for growth of the white rat are also those essential for adequate nutrition of the human infant. Rose has established the amount of each amino acid required for the maintenance of nitrogen balance in young adults (Table 53.1). Evidence from other sources suggests that the values shown may be high and that they provide an appreciable margin of safety. The fact that histidine did not appear to be necessary to maintain nitrogen balance in these studies should not be taken to mean that this amino acid is not required by the human adult, since prolonged histidine deficiency has been found to result in impaired hemoglobin production.

Table 53.1: Amino Acid Requirements of Young Adults

Amino acid	Amount, mg./kg.	Maintenance pattern*
Arginine	0	0
Histidine	0	0
Tryptophan	7	1.0
Phenylalanine	31	4.3
Lysine	23	3.2
Threonine	14	1.9
Valine	23	3.2
Methionine	31	4.3
Leucine	31	4.3
Isoleucine	20	2.8

* Molecular ratios required relative to the tryptophan requirement.
Source: From W. C. Rose, *Federation Proc.,* **8,** 546, 1949.

The values for the requirement of a single amino acid, such as those shown in Table 53.1, are not absolute but are influenced markedly by the composition of the total amino acid mixture. Clearly, the requirements for phenylalanine and methionine are significantly reduced by the provision of tyrosine and cystine, respectively.

If only minimal amounts of essential amino acids are provided, a striking growth stimulus results from the further provision of nonessential amino acids, *e.g.*, glutamic acid and arginine. However, addition of large quantities of such amino acids, particularly glycine, can result in serious growth depression. Optimal nutrition, therefore, requires a *balanced* amino acid mixture. Another example is afforded by experience with wheat gluten; this protein is relatively poor in lysine. If the protein is fed as 30 per cent of a rat diet, an additional 0.8 per cent of lysine is required to obtain good growth; if fed as 60 per cent of the diet, 1.3 per cent of lysine is required to achieve the same growth rate.

Biological Value of Protein. Much effort has been expended in the determination of the *biological value* of individual proteins. The term refers to the relative nutritional value of individual proteins as compared to a standard and includes a factor relating to the digestibility of a given protein as well as to its amino acid composition. Among the procedures employed are determinations of the growth rate of young rats with varying dietary levels of individual proteins, establishment of the minimum dietary level of a given protein which will permit nitrogen balance in adults of various species, and influence of a given amount of protein on the serum

Table 53.2: ESTIMATES OF THE PROTEIN REQUIREMENTS OF ADULT MEN FOR MAINTENANCE OF NITROGEN EQUILIBRIUM

Protein source	Required g./70 kg./day	Protein source	Required g./70 kg./day
Beefsteak	19.2	Mixed vegetable protein 2:3, and mixed meat protein 1:3*	27.1
Whole egg	19.9		
Corn germ	20.7	General mixed diet†	27.6
Haddock	21.6	Potato	29.6
Cottonseed flour	23.0	Soy-white flour‡	29.8
Yeast	24.0	All-vegetable diet§	32.4
Milk	24.4	Wheat flour	38.4
Soy flour	25.4	White flour	42.1
Beef	26.3	Whole-wheat bread	66.8

* The amount of each food in the all-vegetable diet was decreased by one-third and replaced by meats in amount necessary to supply one-third of total nitrogen.

† A cheap complete mixed American diet in which animal proteins provided 47 per cent of total nitrogen.

‡ Thirty-six per cent soy flour protein + 64 per cent white flour protein.

§ Distribution of nitrogen: 50 per cent from white flour, 12 per cent other cereals, 13 per cent potatoes, 17 per cent other mixed vegetables, 8 per cent fruits.

SOURCE: From H. H. Mitchell, in M. Sahyun, ed., "Proteins and Amino Acids in Nutrition," chap. 2, Reinhold Publishing Corporation, New York, 1948.

levels of the essential amino acids. By these procedures, proteins which lack any of the essential amino acids will have no biological value as compared with a standard protein preparation such as lactalbumin, which is known to be qualitatively complete and readily digestible. It is apparent that if the amino acid compositions of two proteins are generally similar except that A contains only half as much leucine as does B, twice as much of A is needed to meet the leucine requirement and the "biological value" of B is greater than that of A when the leucine supply of the diet is a limiting factor. In general, proteins of animal origin have greater biological value than do proteins of plant origin. Casein, lactalbumin, mixed muscle proteins, and mixed egg proteins are approximately equal in value. Table 53.2 shows the amount of protein from various sources which, as the sole source of protein in the diet, will permit maintenance of nitrogen equilibrium in adult men under normal conditions.

Vegetable proteins are not only generally nutritionally inferior to those of animal origin, but proteins are also present in relatively smaller concentration in plant materials. In general, plant proteins are lower in lysine, methionine, and tryptophan content, and are less readily digestible than are animal proteins. However, nutritional inadequacies of a given protein are likely to differ from those of other proteins, and there are many possible combinations of two or more inadequate proteins which are nutritionally satisfactory. In general, by providing protein from various sources, optimal benefit to the animal is assured. For example, Incaprina, a vegetable mixture prepared and distributed by the Institute of Nutrition of Central America and Panama, which contains 29 per cent whole corn, 29 per cent whole sorghum, 38 per cent cottonseed meal, 3 per cent Torula yeast, plus some $CaCO_3$ and vitamin A, affords a protein mixture of biological value only slightly less than that of cow's milk.

When inadequate proteins are combined in the diet, it is essential that they be present in the same meal. Animals do not store amino acids and can synthesize protein only when all the component amino acids are simultaneously present. For example, rats fail to grow when fed, each day, one of the essential amino acids 3 hr. after the others.

Effects of Protein Deficiency. No disease of man has yet been described which is attributable to a deficiency of a single amino acid. Indeed, relatively little is known of the possible consequences of deficiencies of single amino acids in man. The effects of such deficiencies in the rat, other than the invariable growth failure, are summarized in Table 53.3. When offered diets lacking in any of the essential amino acids, rats rapidly lose appetite and develop the disorders summarized in Table 53.3. However, if force-fed such diets in amounts equal to that consumed by well-nourished controls, invariably there is a sharp weight loss, shaggy coat, weakness, and the animals die in only a few days.

As the total protein content of the rat's diet is reduced, the first deficiency to limit health is usually that of methionine. Methionine deficiency results in fatty infiltration of the liver, progressing to cirrhosis. If choline is now added to the diet, fatty liver is prevented; as the dietary protein level is reduced further, an acute hepatic necrosis due to cystine deficiency appears. Addition of cystine to the ration prevents this disturbance. In order, thereafter, if casein is the protein of the diet, the amino acids which may become limiting are threonine, tryptophan, isoleucine, leucine, valine, phenylalanine, and lysine. In general, an insufficient quantity of a balanced amino acid mixture is less deleterious to the animal than an abundant supply of an unbalanced mixture.

Rats fed a low-protein, choline-supplemented diet develop pathological disturbances if the experiment is prolonged. Among the manifestations of protein deficiency are anemia, hypoalbuminemia, and edema, symptoms also commonly seen in undernourished human beings. Peptic ulcers have been observed in rats fed diets low in protein. It is interesting to note that peptic ulcers are unusually common in the population of certain areas of India in which no animal proteins are consumed and the vegetable proteins are of poor quality. A low-protein diet also leads to marked suppression of adenohypophyseal secretion in rats. This is reflected in a low basal metabolic rate, growth failure, diminished adrenal cortical activity, permanent anestrus, and suppression of lactation. Similar effects of protein malnutrition have been noted in seriously undernourished individuals in prisoner-of-war camps, and in patients in European sanatoriums after the Second World War.

Table 53.3: MANIFESTATIONS OF DEFICIENCIES OF SINGLE AMINO ACIDS IN THE RAT

Amino acid	Symptoms*	
	Young rats†	Adult rats
Arginine		Hypospermia
Cystine	Acute hepatic necrosis	
Histidine	Cataract	
Isoleucine	Anemia; hypoproteinemia	
Leucine	Hypoproteinemia	
Lysine	Anemia; sudden death	Anemia; anestrus
Methionine	Anemia; hypoproteinemia; alopecia; hemorrhagic kidneys; fatty liver and cirrhosis	Anemia; hypoproteinemia; fatty liver and cirrhosis
Threonine	Edema	
Tryptophan	Cataract; poor dentition; alopecia; gastric hyperplasia	Corneal vascularization; alopecia; testicular atrophy; fetal resorption
Valine	Locomotor dysfunction	

* All changes are reversed when the diet is supplemented with the missing component shortly following the appearance of symptoms.

† All deficiencies and any amino acid imbalance cause corneal vascularization in immature rats.

SOURCE: Modified from A. A. Albanese, *J. Clin. Nutrition,* **1**, 46, 1952.

In economically undeveloped areas such as tropical America, Central and South Africa, and India, limitation of dietary protein is an important etiologic factor in a disease in children first called *kwashiorkor* in Central Africa. This name is now frequently applied to similar syndromes in other parts of the world, and is said to mean "displaced child," since it occurs in infants displaced from the breast by younger siblings. The disease is characterized by growth retardation, anemia, hypoproteinemia frequently with edema, fatty infiltration of the liver with ensuing fibrosis, and, in young Negroes, red–light brown hair. Often there is atrophy of the acinar tissue of the pancreas, with resulting diarrhea and steatorrhea. This last alteration is thought to reflect methionine deficiency, since a similar lesion is produced by feeding a methionine antagonist, ethionine (S-ethylhomocysteine), to dogs. The lack of pancreatic digestive secretions makes unavailable even the small amount of dietary protein. Moreover, a renal lesion develops which leads to strikingly increased urinary excretion of free amino acids. If the diet contains much iron, the intestinal mucosa fails to restrict its absorption, and iron may accumulate in the liver. In general this disease appears in children who are fed almost exclusively on a gruel of a cereal such as plantain, taro, millet, cassava (manioc), or corn. In contrast to milk, which contains 5.4 g. of protein per 100 cal., these diets provide less than 2 g. of protein per 100 cal. and are deficient also in other essential dietary factors. The symptoms respond therapeutically to a high-protein diet containing considerable quantities of meat and milk products. The mortality rate in untreated children has been reported to be 30 to 90 per cent. It is probably significant that the incidence of primary carcinoma of the liver is considerably more frequent in individuals of these areas than in other population groups.

The negative nitrogen balance of severe protein restriction occurs, in large measure, at the expense of the liver, which may lose as much as 50 per cent of its total nitrogen. Mitochondria, microsomes, cytoplasmic enzymes, and RNA, but

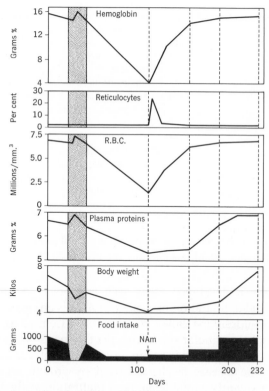

FIG. 53.1. Physiological priorities for available dietary protein. A niacin-deficient dog was carried through the blacktongue crisis with saline infusions (stippled area) (page 956) and in 4 months of niacin deficiency became severely anemic, hypoproteinemic, and emaciated. At the arrow, nicotinamide (NAm) was given and food consumption was restricted to 250 g. per day. Note the reticulocyte response and restoration almost to normal hemoglobin concentration. When the food allowance was increased somewhat, the plasma protein concentration increased with little change in weight. When ad libitum food consumption was permitted, body weight began to increase. (*From P. Handler and W. P. Featherstone, J. Biol. Chem.,* **151**, 395, 1943.)

not DNA, are all decreased under these circumstances. Of the enzymes, liver xanthine oxidase appears to be the most labile and sensitive indicator, all activity disappearing from the rat liver after 2 weeks on a protein-free regime. Indeed, so constant is this finding, that the ability to maintain xanthine oxidase activity has been employed as a test for the biological value of proteins. In general the behavior of hepatic enzymes during repletion with protein after severe deficiency falls into four categories: (1) enzymes which increase in amount and then plateau (xanthine, D-amino acid oxidases); (2) enzymes which increase in activity as dietary protein increases (arginase, transaminases); (3) enzymes which decrease in amount as dietary protein increases (phosphatase); and (4) enzymes which are unaffected (cathepsins).

The chronically niacin-deficient dog illustrates the physiological priorities which exist for available protein in the realimentation of an undernourished animal. Such dogs exhibit profound anemia and hypoproteinemia, are markedly emaciated, and voluntarily take limited quantities of the deficient diet. If niacin is given but food consumption restricted to that which the dog had previously been eating ad libitum, a marked hemopoietic response occurs with little change in body weight or serum protein concentration. If a small increase in the total food allowance is then given, the serum proteins increase in quantity although there is little or no change in body weight. Finally, if the animal is allowed to eat ad libitum, body weight is restored. These relations are shown in Fig. 53.1.

LIPID

The studies of Burr and Burr in 1929 demonstrated that the rat does not synthesize polyunsaturated fatty acids and that when these are omitted from the diet a syndrome develops characterized by a dermatitis, necrosis of the tail, sterility, and hyperemia of renal tissues with swelling of the kidneys. Subsequent studies in mice and dogs indicate that these species also have a limited ability to synthesize multiply unsaturated fatty acids. Swine ingesting diets deficient in polyunsaturated fatty acids develop a syndrome called parakeratosis in which erythema, seborrhea, and hyperkeratosis of the skin are manifest. A similar disorder appears to occur in zinc-deficient hogs (page 943).

There is no report of a deficiency syndrome in human adults resulting from lack of essential fatty acids. Although the dermatitis of the deficient rat resembles closely the lesions of follicular hyperkeratosis in man, viz., hyperplasia of surface epithelium, with well-defined layers of cutaneous fat but with the openings of the hair follicles plugged with keratin, this syndrome in man is not the result of fatty acid deficiency. However, a number of infants fed a formula diet devoid of polyunsaturated fats developed dry, leathery skin with desquamation and oozing. The dienoic and trienoic fatty acids of their sera fell to extremely low levels. This disorder improved rapidly when trilinolein was added to the diet as 5 to 7 per cent of total calories. When human adults are fed diets of similar composition for several months, the iodine number of plasma fatty acids and the concentration of polyunsaturated fatty acids decline precipitously, but no other symptoms have been observed. It seems appropriate to consider unsaturated fatty acids as essential to the human dietary, with the reservation that an absolute deficiency is unlikely in view of the wide distribution of these compounds in common foods. Although no specific function of linoleic acid is known, and although arachidonic acid, which is readily fabricated by man from linoleic acid (page 452), completely satisfies the requirement of experimental animals for polyunsaturated acids, it seems most convenient to designate these as a group of essential compounds rather than to regard linoleic acid as merely the precursor of arachidonic acid.

There is, however, increasing evidence suggesting that hyperlipemia and, hence, atherosclerosis may occur in consequence of a *relative* deficiency in polyunsaturated fatty acids. Deposition of lipid plaques on the intima of arteries (atheroma) appears to occur most readily when the serum lipids are elevated in concentration. The material deposited has a composition similar to that of the lipids of the serum at the time of deposition. The concentration of plasma lipids is determined, at least in part, by the composition of the diet. In general, variation in the amount of dietary cholesterol, as it might occur in normal diets, is without significant influence. When greater quantities are included in experimental diets, the consequences vary with the amount of cholesterol and the composition of the diet. Large quantities (2 per cent of the diet) evoke a massive lipemia; triglyceride is mobilized from the adipose tissue and deposited in the liver. Lesser quantities result in marked lipemia, including high concentrations of cholesterol itself with concomitant fall in the serum concentration of polyunsaturated fatty acids in the various lipid fractions. This is the technique used to produce experimental atherosclerosis. In contrast a diet extremely low in lipid results in prompt decline in all plasma lipid fractions, although a lipid-free, high-carbohydrate regime may elicit an increase in serum triglycerides.

When lipid is present in the diet in an amount sufficient to contribute 20 to 60 per cent of the total calories (the average American diet provides about 40 per cent of calories as lipid), the level of blood lipids appears to be influenced by the nature of the dietary lipid. When the latter is largely or exclusively saturated or monoethenoic, as when animal fats predominate in the diet, blood lipid concentrations may be as much as twice as great as when the diet is rich in polyunsaturated fatty acids. This concept was originally derived from epidemiological studies in which serum cholesterol, diet, and the incidence of atherosclerosis in the United States and Western Europe were compared with these items in economically underdeveloped areas. In the latter, vegetable oils rich in linoleic acid are the major sources of dietary lipid; the populations of these areas exhibit relatively low serum lipid concentrations, and the incidence of atherosclerotic disease in age-matched groups is stated to be decidedly lower than, for example, in the United States, England, or the Scandinavian countries. This influence of diet upon plasma lipids has been confirmed under controlled conditions in human subjects and suggests that the serum lipid concentration does not reflect the absolute level of dietary lipid but rather the *relative* contributions of saturated and unsaturated fatty acids. Safflower, corn, peanut, and cottonseed oils, in that order, appear to be most effective in maintaining a low concentration of serum lipids.

Many other factors contribute to this complex situation. As indicated previously, pyridoxine may be required for the synthesis of arachidonic acid from linoleic acid (page 452). Pyridoxine deficiency in the monkey results in hyperlipemia and formation of atheromas indistinguishable from those found in human arteries. Atherosclerosis may be produced in many species by dietary means; in the rabbit and chicken atherosclerosis is induced by inclusion of cholesterol in the ration, whereas in the rat a high-lipid diet, low in unsaturated fatty acids and rich in cholesterol, is required.

Of great potential significance is recognition of the influence of eating patterns on serum lipids. Thus, rats and chicks normally eat by nibbling throughout their waking hours. If forced to eat, equicalorically, two or three meals per day, they deposit lipid in adipose tissue, the R.Q. falls, and serum lipid levels, including that of cholesterol, increase significantly. Converse studies of multiple feedings in man have not yet been reported.

Much evidence indicates that exercise significantly decreases serum cholesterol and triglyceride levels while total unsaturated fatty acids of serum appear to increase. It is perhaps significant also that diets which increase serum lipid concentrations have been reported to result in increased blood clot strength and delayed fibrinolysis. Thus, in addition, to the complex nutritional effects, genetic tendencies, emotional variability, exercise, and even anatomical relationships must be significant in the control of serum lipid concentrations. Moreover, it is not yet established that reduction of serum lipids will delay atherosclerosis or prevent coronary artery disease in man.

Extensive efforts have been made to determine the optimal amount of lipid in the diet. Although young animals grow successfully on a diet containing only sufficient lipid to provide minimal amounts of the essential fatty acids, it appears desirable to provide approximately 30 per cent of the total calories as lipid with a large fraction of this consisting of polyunsaturated lipids. Rats, dogs, and hogs on this lipid intake achieve a greater body weight and live slightly longer than do animals fed a minimal amount of lipid. Diets yielding more than 60 per cent of calories as lipid lead eventually to obesity in all species.

CARBOHYDRATE

While dietary carbohydrate provides a source of energy and the substrates for many biological syntheses, animals and man can be maintained on diets devoid of carbohydrate. However, since dietary calories may be provided most cheaply in this form, carbohydrate supplies 50 to 60 per cent of the calories of most human dietaries.

A carbohydrate-poor ration must provide calories in the form of lipid since protein intake is limited by the feeling of satiety provided by relatively small quantities of protein. Subjects transferred from ordinary mixed rations to a lipid-rich diet rapidly develop ketosis. After some weeks the ketosis abates and may disappear entirely. Indeed, the Eskimo normally lives on such a high-lipid, low-carbohydrate ration. This problem is significant in the diabetic individual who depends on lipids for his calories, since the extent of carbohydrate utilization will depend on the amount of insulin administered. The relative tendencies of various foodstuffs to elicit or prevent ketosis are expressed as their ketogenic or antiketogenic activity. As an aid in the management of diabetes mellitus, diets are planned in terms of a balance of ketogenic and antiketogenic foods.

Sucrose has long been a major article of commerce. The free fructose liberated by hydrolysis of sucrose in the intestine has two major metabolic fates. To the extent that phosphorylation is accomplished by relatively nonspecific hexokinases, fructose 6-phosphate is formed and enters the glycolytic and other pathways (page 402). Phosphorylation by liver and muscle *fructokinases* yields fructose 1-phosphate. This cannot, directly, be phosphorylated to the diphosphate, nor is there an appropriate mutase. The only further fate of fructose 1-phosphate is cleavage by *phosphofructose aldolase* to dihydroxyacetone phosphate plus free glyceraldehyde. Phosphorylation of the latter yields 3-phosphoglyceraldehyde, permitting the pair of trioses to enter the glycolytic pathway or to undergo conversion to fructose 1,6-diphosphate by the action of aldolase.

Only extremely rare individuals cannot utilize sucrose. Those with a genetic lack of fructokinase exhibit a benign fructosuria. However, those who lack phosphofructose aldolase cannot utilize the fructose 1-phosphate formed by fructokinase. Accumulation of fructose 1-phosphate results in a bizarre syndrome of headache and acute abdominal distress.

Lactose furnishes a significant but not the major portion of the caloric value of milk. Feeding diets high in lactose or galactose to rats results in impaired growth and cataract. The growth impairment results from a limited capacity of the rat liver to convert galactose 1-phosphate to glucose 1-phosphate. Such animals have extremely high blood sugar levels, most of which is galactose; the blood glucose concentration is markedly reduced. Similar findings are encountered in infants with "idiopathic galactosemia" (page 406). The relationship between high blood galactose concentration and cataract development is obscure (page 814). The favorable influence of dietary lactose on intestinal calcium absorption has been mentioned previously (page 778). This effect is not specific for Ca^{++} but extends also to other alkaline earth metals. Diets high in lactose or galactose also evoke a demineralization of bone with resultant calciuria; the mechanism is unknown. Finally, one may note the extremely rare infants whose intestines are devoid of lactase. This condition is simply apparent as growth failure and diarrhea. Transfer to a synthetic milk containing sucrose results in prompt improvement.

REFERENCES

See list following Chap. 56.

54. Chemical Elements in Nutrition

The nutritional roles of several of the major mineral nutrients have already been considered. The elements known to be required by man, as appropriate ions, include sodium, chlorine, and potassium (Chap. 34), calcium and phosphorus (Chap. 41), iron (Chap. 42), and iodine (Chap. 46). The requirements, function, and manifestations of deficiency of these elements were described previously. In addition, man requires magnesium, manganese, and copper. The status of cobalt, zinc, fluoride, molybdenum, and selenium in human nutrition is not clearly established.

MAGNESIUM

Magnesium is indispensable in the diet, but the daily requirement is not known. The factors which influence magnesium absorption are similar to those affecting calcium (Chap. 41). The normal serum $[Mg^{++}]$ is 1.8 to 2.5 meq. per liter, of which about 80 per cent is ionized and diffusible and the remainder is bound to protein. The $[Mg^{++}]$ in erythrocytes is somewhat higher—about 3.5 meq. per liter— while tissue cells generally contain about 16 meq. per liter. Most of the Mg^{++} of the body is in the skeleton. Absorbed or administered Mg^{++} is rapidly excreted in the urine. However, the major daily excretion occurs in the feces and represents unabsorbed magnesium. Ingestion of magnesium also increases excretion of calcium in both feces and urine.

Magnesium deprivation has been studied in dogs and rats fed diets which contained less than 2 parts per million of the element. Such animals gradually developed a picture consisting of vasodilatation, cardiac arrhythmia, hyperirritability to any external stimulus, spasticity, and tonic and clonic convulsions; death invariably followed.

Spontaneous nutritional deficiency of Mg^{++} in man is extremely unlikely. However, extensive loss of this element may occur in diarrhea and become evident if such patients are rehydrated with fluids which do not contain Mg^{++}. As the serum $[Mg^{++}]$ declines to about 1.0 meq. per liter, a syndrome resembling delirium tremens may be precipitated, i.e., semicoma, tremor, carpopedal spasm, and a general tetany-like neuromuscular irritability with marked susceptibility to auditory, mechanical, and visual stimuli. Administration of Mg^{++} effects a prompt improvement.

Parenteral administration of large amounts of magnesium salts results in marked depression of both the central nervous system and peripheral neuromuscular activity. This depressive action can be antagonized by calcium; an animal anesthetized with magnesium returns to consciousness and behaves normally a few seconds after intravenous administration of sufficient calcium salt. There is no explanation for either the magnesium narcosis or the calcium antagonism. Low serum concentration of magnesium leads to tetany closely resembling that of hypocalcemia. Thus, while a low concentration of either of these ions in the blood leads to similar functional changes, an excess of calcium antagonizes rather than synergizes the effects of excessive magnesium.

MANGANESE

Manganese deficiency has been observed in the rat, chick, and pig. Male rats on diets deficient in manganese become sterile and show irreversible testicular degeneration; females on manganese-deficient diets are unable to suckle their young. In manganese-deficient pregnant sows, resorption of the fetus is common; if young are born they are undersized, weak, and ataxic. The estrus cycle of the nonpregnant animal is irregular or may cease completely. In the chick, manganese deficiency is manifested as the osteodystrophy called *perosis;* the tibial-metatarsal joint enlarges, the distal end of the tibia and the proximal end of the metatarsus are twisted, and the gastrocnemius tendon slips from its condyles. Because of the latter, this is frequently referred to as "slipped tendon disease." The chicks appear short-legged with deformed legs and spinal columns.

No precise requirement for manganese by man has been established. Manganese salts are poorly absorbed from the intestine, but after parenteral administration, manganese is concentrated in the liver and kidneys, particularly in the mitochondria, and excreted largely into the colon and bile, with only a small portion appearing in the urine. Ingestion of excessive quantities of manganese appears to interfere with absorption of iron, thus causing an anemia which is readily prevented by increasing the dietary iron.

Manganese is intimately bound to arginase of liver and activates many enzymes, *e.g.*, phosphoglucomutase, choline esterase, the oxidative β-ketodecarboxylases, certain peptidases, and muscle adenosinetriphosphatase.

COPPER

Copper deficiency has been observed in infants receiving only milk. The prime manifestation is a microcytic, normochromic anemia; this also is seen in copper-deficient rats. The anemia appears to relate to failure to absorb dietary iron and readily responds to parenteral administration of iron. Such animals also exhibit a diminution in hepatic cytochrome c and cytochrome oxidase as well as an increase in the iron-binding capacity of plasma. In continued severe copper deficiency, rats and pigs develop a rickets-like syndrome as well as neurological disturbances. Chronic copper deficiency leads to anestrus in female rats. Earlier, they may mate but gestation terminates in fetal abortion or stillbirth. In lambs, such deficiency results in "swayback," a serious demyelinating disorder of the spinal cord. Excessive tissue deposition of copper is seen in man in *Wilson's disease*, with hepatolenticular degeneration and characterized chemically by a deficiency of ceruloplasmin, the copper-binding globulin of normal plasma (page 640).

Known metabolic functions of copper relate to its presence in tyrosinase, uricase, and perhaps butyryl CoA dehydrogenase and cytochrome oxidase. Erythrocuprein, a copper-containing protein of unknown function, occurs in human erythrocytes.

COBALT

Cobalt deficiency has been observed in ruminants, particularly cattle and sheep, in many areas of the world. All the effects of deficiency appear to reflect failure of synthesis by the rumen microorganisms of vitamin B_{12}, of which cobalt is a constituent (Chap. 55). There have been no reports of the production of cobalt deficiency in nonruminating animals, all of which require dietary vitamin B_{12}. The mechanism for the polycythemia induced by parenterally administered cobalt (page 807) is not understood but appears to be unrelated to the role of cobalt as a constituent of vitamin B_{12}.

ZINC

Zinc deficiency in the rat is manifested by retarded growth, alopecia, and lesions in the skin, esophagus, and cornea. Hogs fed processed peanut meal develop a syndrome called parakeratosis (page 937), with anorexia, nausea, and vomiting. The disease is readily cured by inclusion of 0.02 per cent $ZnCO_3$ in the diet. The disease occurs only if the diet has been supplemented with calcium; a very high level of dietary calcium similarly precipitates manganese deficiency. Analyses of foodstuffs for zinc are not adequate to indicate their value as dietary sources of this element. Thus soybean, sesame, and peanut (see above) meals all contain significant quantities of zinc, yet this is unavailable when ingested. Eggs from zinc-deficient chickens produce grossly deformed, bizarre chicks. Zinc is a constituent of a number of enzymes, *e.g.*, carbonic anhydrase, alcohol and lactic acid dehydrogenases, and various peptidases. Since zinc is necessary for the activity of these enzymes, it is probably also an essential nutrient for man. However, in view of the wide distribution of zinc in foods, it is unlikely that zinc deficiency will occur in human beings eating a normal diet.

FLUORINE

The relationship of fluorine to dental caries and mottled enamel was described earlier (page 786). Since there are no other indications of a biological need for this element, classification as an essential nutrient may be largely a matter of definition. In this instance, the nutrient appears to be essential for dental health.

MOLYBDENUM

The status of molybdenum in animal nutrition is not clear. In herbivora, ingestion of minute quantities of molybdenum results in an increased copper requirement and leads therefore, in the absence of sufficient dietary copper, to anemia as well as to lesions of bone and muscle. This effect of molybdenum is observed only when the diet provides inorganic sulfate. Molybdenum deficiency results in a diminution of intestinal and hepatic xanthine oxidase activity in the rat and may be induced readily by inclusion of tungstate in the diet. This observation led to the discovery that molybdenum is a constituent of xanthine oxidase.

The relationship between molybdenum and copper recalls the relationship between magnesium and calcium (page 941) and that between zinc and copper. Excessive dietary zinc causes anemia and growth failure, which can be counteracted by administration of copper. Many similar antagonisms are known in bacteria. One of the most unusual involves potassium and rubidium. In some microorganisms, these elements have an antagonistic action; rubidium inhibits growth, but this can be overcome by increasing the concentration of potassium in the medium. Further increase in rubidium concentration produces a requirement for additional potassium to maintain growth of the colony. In other organisms no interrelationship between potassium and rubidium is apparent, while in still others rubidium actually has a synergistic effect with potassium on bacterial growth. The intrabacterial cell concentration of sodium is very low, and growth of numerous organisms is inhibited by the presence of sodium. This inhibition can be alleviated by increasing the potassium concentration in the medium.

SELENIUM

Kuhn and Schwarz observed that diets in which rigorously purified casein served as the source of protein for rats resulted, after about one month, in sudden death due to hepatic necrosis. Many natural foodstuffs were found to protect against this phenomenon. Initially it was believed that this necrosis resulted from simultaneous deficiency of cystine (page 934) and of tocopherol (page 984). However, Schwarz later demonstrated the presence of a third material (*factor 3*), which was required even when tocopherol and cystine were provided. Factor 3 has been incompletely characterized but contains selenium. Indeed, selenite added to the experimental rations affords complete protection against liver necrosis. The earlier curative effects of cystine were, at least in part, attributable to traces of selenocystine, $(-Se-CH_2-CHNH_2-COOH)_2$, among the naturally occurring amino acids. The nutritional interrelations of selenium and vitamin E are described later (page 984).

Selenium in somewhat larger doses is extremely toxic. Since this element will replace sulfur in cystine and methionine in many plants grown in seleniferous soils, selenium poisoning constitutes a public health and an agricultural problem in certain areas in the north central and southwestern United States.

OTHER METALS

Kidney has been found to contain a sulfhydryl-rich protein, termed "metallothein," to which are bound significant quantities of zinc and cadmium. The physiological role of this protein and its attached metals is unknown.

Evidence has accumulated that some factor, other than the recognized hormones, is required to facilitate transfer of glucose from plasma to cells, particularly at elevated glucose concentration as it occurs during a glucose tolerance test. This factor, which survives ashing, has been stated to be chromium ion (Cr^{+++}), but the mechanism of this effect is unclear.

In sum, deficiencies of trace elements appear to be rare in human nutrition. Exceptions are iodine deficiency in areas in which goiter is endemic and copper deficiency in infants on diets of unsupplemented milk.

REFERENCES

See list following Chap. 56.

55. The Water-soluble Vitamins

HISTORICAL BACKGROUND

In 1816 Magendie introduced the experimental procedure of feeding diets of purified materials to young animals in order to observe the effects of these diets on growth. He recognized that "animals could not remain in health when fed only the staminal principles, the saccharin, oleaginous and albuminous." Sixty-five years later, Lunin arrived at a similar conclusion. In 1905 Pekelharing made analogous observations on mice fed rations containing casein, egg albumin, rice flour, lard, and inorganic salts and noted that when this diet was supplemented with very small quantities of milk, the animals remained in good health. Pekelharing concluded that milk contains an unknown substance which "even in very small quantities is of paramount importance to nourishment." The following year, F. G. Hopkins referred to scurvy and rickets as "diseases in which for long years we have had knowledge of a dietetic factor."

The modern era in vitamin research was initiated in 1912, when Hopkins and Funk suggested the vitamin theory, *i.e.*, they postulated that specific diseases such as beriberi, scurvy, and rickets are each caused by the absence from the diet of a particular nutritional factor.

The relationship of diet to disease had been indicated considerably earlier. Hippocrates recorded the curative effect of liver on night blindness. Cod-liver oil has been employed for treatment of rickets since the eighteenth century. In his "Treatise on Scurvy," James Lind in 1757 stated that fresh fruits and vegetables are "alone effectual to protect the body from this malady," and half a century later the British navy made routine the administration of lime juice to its seamen. The correlation between the incidence of pellagra and the ingestion of maize was recognized in Italy 150 years ago by Marzari, who stated that the disease resulted from some form of dietary inadequacy. In 1887, Takaki demonstrated that beriberi was prevented by decreasing the amount of milled rice and increasing the amounts of meat, vegetables, and milk in the ration of Japanese sailors. Ten years later, by feeding polished rice to fowls, Eijkman produced a disease similar to beriberi. He noticed further that polyneuritis did not develop in birds fed unpolished rice and that an extract of rice polishings cured avian polyneuritis. These observations led Grijns a few years later to state that beriberi is the result of a deficiency in the diet of an essential nutrient. The statements of Hopkins and Funk were extensions of this concept.

The first successful preparation of an essential food factor was in the form of a concentrate of a potent antiberiberi substance from rice polishings by Funk. Since the active factor was an amine, and necessary for life, he introduced the term "vitamine." This term has been retained in its generic rather than its chemical sense and presently is employed as a name for accessory food factors which are neither amino acids nor inorganic elements. Since subsequent studies showed that these substances are not all amines, the terminal "e" has been dropped from the spelling. The earliest laboratory demonstrations of the multiplicity of such food factors were the description in 1913 by McCollum and Davis of a lipid-soluble essential food factor in butterfat and egg yolk, and the recognition two years later of a heat-labile water-soluble factor in wheat germ necessary for growth of young rats. These were designated "fat-soluble A" and "water-soluble B," respectively.

Although many essential factors have been added to the list of vitamins in succeeding years, the distinction between lipid- and water-soluble vitamins has been retained since members of each group have certain properties in common. For example, the lipid-soluble vitamins are absorbed from the intestine with the dietary lipids, so that in steatorrhea, deficiency of lipid-soluble but not water-soluble vitamins may result. Perhaps also as a consequence of their lipid solubility, significant quantities of each of the four known lipid-soluble vitamins are stored in the liver; storage of the water-soluble vitamins is not significant. Therefore, while it is possible to administer a several weeks' supply of each of the lipid-soluble vitamins in a single dose, the water-soluble vitamins must be supplied more frequently. Specific metabolic functions have been demonstrated for several of the water-soluble vitamins which are essential portions of coenzymes. In the case of the lipid-soluble vitamins, a specific biochemical role has been established only for vitamin A, in the visual process (Chap. 43).

It is difficult to formulate a completely satisfactory statement of what the term vitamin means at present. For many years vitamins were considered to be substances distinct from the major components of food, *i.e.*, carbohydrates, lipids, amino acids, minerals, and water, required in relatively minute amounts for normal nutrition, and whose absence causes specific deficiency diseases. However, in at least one instance, niacin, the vitamin may be synthesized from an amino acid precursor, tryptophan. Furthermore, there are a number of substances which are presumed to be vitamins, such as pantothenic acid and biotin, but whose significance in human nutrition has never been established and for which there do not exist corresponding deficiency diseases.

In the early years of vitamin research there was confusion as to the number and nature of the water-soluble B vitamins. At the time that only one B vitamin was known, the antiscorbutic factor was designated as vitamin C and the antirachitic factor as vitamin D. Later, the multiple nature of "vitamin B" was revealed and successively recognized factors were called vitamins B_2, B_3, B_4, etc. Most of these terms have since been discarded, either because the active factor was identified and is now known by a suitable name or because it proved to be identical with some previously recognized factor. The term "B complex" continues to be useful because in large measure these factors are found together in nature. Foodstuffs either rich or lacking in one member of the "complex" are likely to be rich or poor, respectively, in many of the others. Consequently, pure deficiencies of a single member of this group are rare in man. Moreover, the overt manifestations of deficiency of this group overlap in some degree. Thus, in the dog, individual deficiencies of niacin, riboflavin, pyridoxine, pantothenic acid, and folic acid are each characterized by a glossitis with atrophy of the lingual papillae.

THIAMINE

Thiamine was first isolated in crystalline form by Jansen in Holland and Windaus in Germany. R. R. Williams and his coworkers then developed methods of obtaining thiamine in yields of approximately 5 g. per ton of rice polishings. Many workers made significant contributions to the identification of the structure of this substance, including Windaus, Clarke and Gurin, and Williams and his coworkers, who established the structure of thiamine.

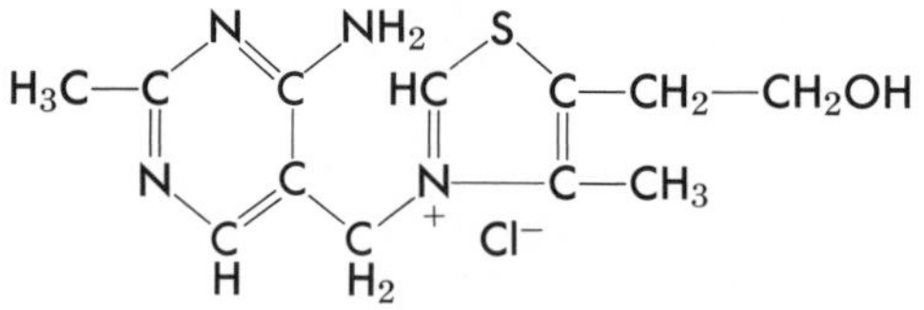

Thiamine chloride

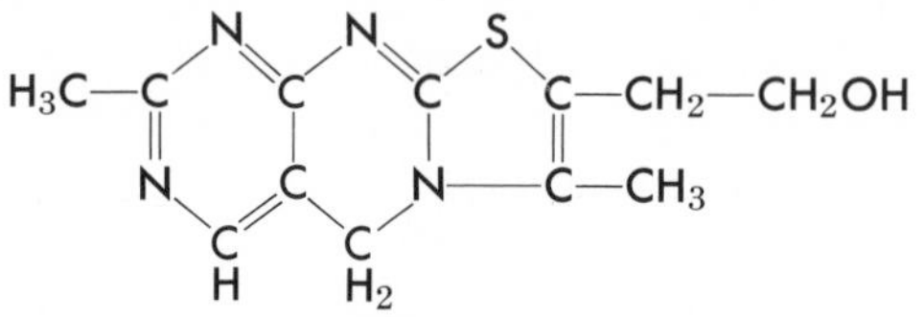

Thiochrome

Thiamine is easily converted to *thiochrome* by mild oxidants. This is a particularly useful reaction, because thiochrome exhibits a blue fluorescence, the intensity of which can be related quantitatively to thiamine concentration. Thiamine is relatively stable in acidic solutions but is rapidly inactivated by heating in neutral or alkaline solutions.

Biogenesis of Thiamine. Studies of the synthesis of thiamine by extracts of baker's yeast have revealed that the pyrimidine and thiazole moieties are formed independently. The origins of the 2-methyl-4-amino-5-hydroxymethylpyrimidine and 4-methyl-5-(β-hydroxyethyl)-thiazole shown as the starting materials in Fig. 55.1 have not been established. Thereafter, *hydroxymethylpyrimidine kinase, hydroxymethylpyrimidine phosphokinase, thiazole kinase,* and *thiamine phosphate pyrophosphorylase* catalyze the reactions indicated as *1, 2, 3,* and *4,* respectively. A phosphatase catalyzes removal of the phosphate, completing the synthesis of thiamine. Thiamine pyrophosphate, the coenzyme form of thiamine, is synthesized by direct transfer of the pyrophosphate group from ATP.

$$\text{Thiamine} + \text{ATP} \longrightarrow \text{thiamine pyrophosphate} + \text{AMP}$$

The role of thiamine pyrophosphate in the oxidative decarboxylation of α-keto acids has been discussed previously (page 317).

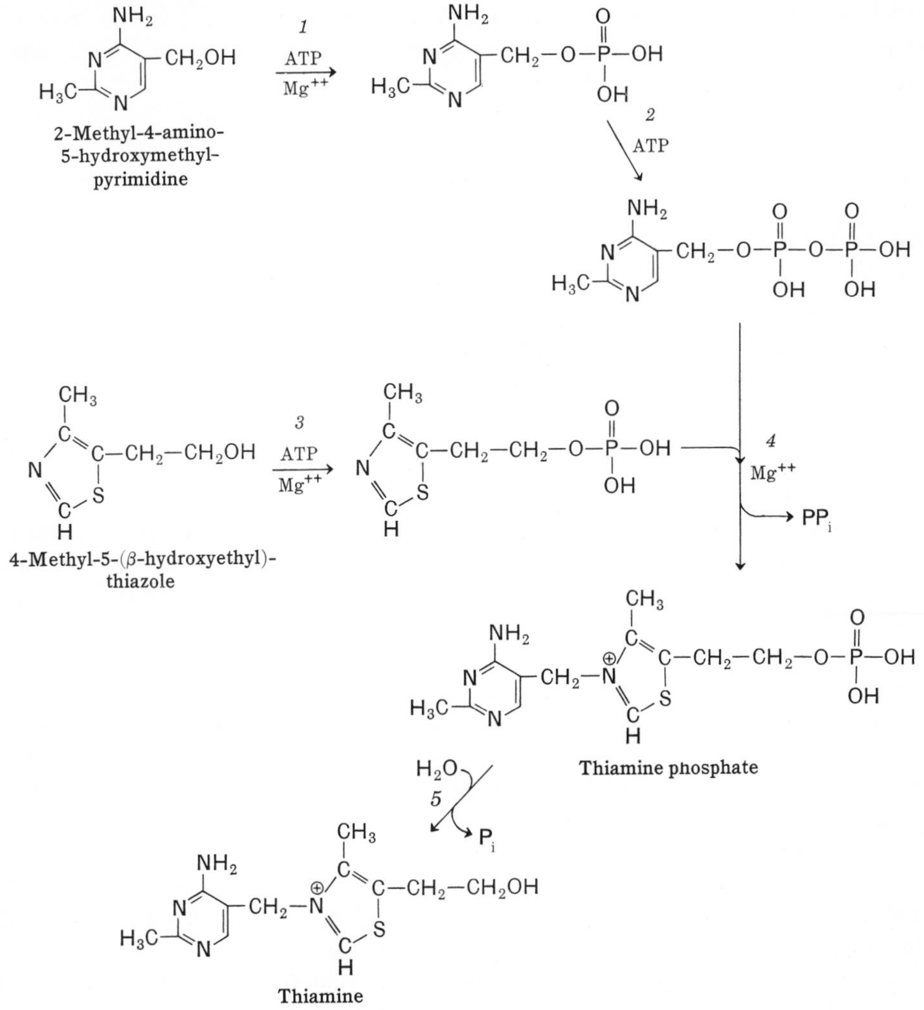

FIG. 55.1. Biosynthesis of thiamine.

Metabolic Fate of Thiamine. After administration of thiamine to animals, a portion may be recovered in the urine unchanged, and a part as *pyramin* (2-methyl-4-amino-5-hydroxymethylpyrimidine). The latter is presumed to arise from thiamine as the result of the activity of *thiaminase,* an enzyme first detected in the tissues of fish, and may reflect the activity of intestinal microorganisms rather than of any animal tissue. Normal individuals, ingesting 0.5 to 1.5 mg. of thiamine daily, excrete 50 to 250 μg of the vitamin in the urine.

The history of thiaminase is of some interest. In 1932 it was observed that domestic foxes develop a fatal disease (Chastek paralysis), characterized by polyneuritis and paralysis, after the incorporation of raw fish into the animals' rations. Thiaminase activity was demonstrated in the tissues of most fresh-water fish and mollusks and in a few salt-water species. This enzyme seems to consist of a heat-labile nondialyzable protein component and a heat-stable dialyzable material thought to be manganese. The extent of thiaminase activity may modify the quantitative requirement for thiamine.

Thiamine Deficiency. All animals other than ruminants require a dietary supply of thiamine. In man, beriberi has long been endemic in those areas in which polished rice is a dietary staple. The symptoms of incipient beriberi are anorexia, weakness, insomnia, undue fatigue after slight exertion, generalized pruritus, tachycardia, palpitation, and shortness of breath. Anesthesia and slight edema may be present over the anterior surface of the lower legs. Muscular soreness, particularly of the calf muscles, develops. There are two forms of the disease; these have been termed dry and wet beriberi. The dry form is preceded by symptoms of incipient beriberi, with subsequent rapid loss of weight and muscle wasting. Marked peripheral neuritis and muscular weakness result in the patient's becoming almost helpless. Deep reflexes are lost, sensory changes may occur, and anxiety states and mental confusion are evident. The heart becomes enlarged. In wet beriberi, there is a generalized edema which may obscure the weakness and muscular wasting. Acute cardiac symptoms may develop rapidly. Since wet beriberi can respond dramatically to thiamine administration with improved cardiac function and massive diuresis, these aspects of beriberi may be specifically ascribed to thiamine deficiency. In the Western world, frank thiamine deficiency is rarely seen except in the Wernicke syndrome of chronic alcoholics. In this syndrome cardiac and respiratory irregularities are associated with a hemorrhagic lesion of the third and fourth ventricles of the brain, similar to lesions which have been observed in thiamine-deficient pigeons and in the brains of foxes with Chastek paralysis. A characteristic sign of thiamine deficiency in birds is head retraction (opisthotonos) which rapidly responds to administration of small quantities of thiamine. This response has been employed as a basis for the quantitative assay of thiamine.

The laboratory diagnosis of thiamine deficiency is unsatisfactory. Several procedures have been suggested, none of which may be capable of diagnosing early thiamine deficiency. A most sensitive index appears to be measurement of the appearance of $C^{14}O_2$ when glucose 2-C^{14} is incubated with erythrocytes. Since these cells do not have the citric acid cycle, CO_2 from glucose arises by the phosphogluconate oxidative pathway (page 387). Formation of $C^{14}O_2$ from glucose-1-C^{14} is unaffected in thiamine deficiency but the C-2 atom can appear as CO_2 only if the complete series of reactions is operative, including the thiamine pyrophosphate-dependent transketolase reaction (page 389). The latter has been reported to be limiting before any overt signs of thiamine deficiency are apparent.

Several thiamine analogues have been prepared which are antimetabolites and which on administration rapidly induce signs of thiamine deficiency. These include *pyrithiamine,* in which the pyridine group is substituted for the thiazole ring, and *oxythiamine,* in which a hydroxyl group is substituted for the free amino group on the pyrimidine ring. The effects of each of these antimetabolites are alleviated or prevented by administration of thiamine. The mechanisms by which these compounds exert their actions are unknown. Pyrithiamine inhibits synthesis in chicken erythrocytes of thiamine pyrophosphate and lowers its concentration in the brains of pyrithiamine-treated animals. Oxythiamine appears to displace thiamine in the tissues, since its administration to rats results in an increase of thiamine excretion.

Distribution of Thiamine. As expected from the requirement for cocarboxylase by all cells, thiamine is ubiquitous in the biological world; however, its quantitative distribution varies considerably. The outer layers of the seeds of plants are especially rich in thiamine content. Whole-wheat bread, therefore, is an excellent source, whereas ordinary white bread is a poor source of the vitamin, since most of the thiamine is removed in the milling process. The practice of enriching wheat flour with thiamine restores the original thiamine content, and, because of the quantities consumed, enriched bread is an important dietary source of this vitamin. Most animal tissues are useful dietary sources of thiamine; pork products are especially rich. Although the concentration of thiamine in milk is relatively low, milk is an important dietary source of this vitamin when consumed in large volumes, as in the United States. As indicated in Table 52.2 (page 930), the recommended dietary allowance of thiamine is approximately 0.5 mg. per 1000 Cal. of diet. This recommendation assumes ingestion of a normal, varied diet. The thiamine requirement, however, varies with the composition of the diet. Both lipid and protein exert a thiamine-sparing action. The sparing action of lipid was thought to reflect a lesser metabolic demand for thiamine, but since the thiamine pyrophosphate content of the tissues of animals fed a high-lipid diet is considerably greater than that of animals on a high-carbohydrate diet, the lipid may in some manner protect thiamine from destruction.

Nutritional surveys indicate that for much of the American population, the thiamine intake is marginal; few adults consume more than 0.8 mg. per day, and many eat appreciably less. Thiamine intake can be augmented relatively cheaply by increased use of peas, beans, and enriched or whole-wheat bread, as well as by improved cooking practices. Prolonged cooking of peas and beans with soda results in destruction of as much as 60 per cent of the original thiamine content, and excessive cooking leaches the water-soluble thiamine from many foodstuffs.

RIBOFLAVIN

Three lines of investigation led to the isolation and identification of riboflavin: attempts to ascertain the nature of the fluorescent material present in milk whey, attempts to isolate a material from milk whey which is an essential dietary factor for the rat and initially designated as vitamin B_2, and isolation of the coenzyme of the "old-yellow enzyme" (page 344) from red cells.

The structure of riboflavin was established by Kuhn, and synthesis was accomplished by both Kuhn and Karrer. Warburg and Christian observed that when irradiated with ultraviolet light in alkaline solution, their yellow enzyme yielded a yellow derivative, which they named *lumiflavin*. Since, under the same conditions, lumiflavin was also obtained from the newly isolated vitamin, the structural relationship of the vitamin and the prosthetic group of the enzyme became apparent. If irradiation is conducted in an acidic medium, *lumichrome*, which exhibits an intense blue fluorescense, is produced instead of lumiflavin. These relationships are shown below.

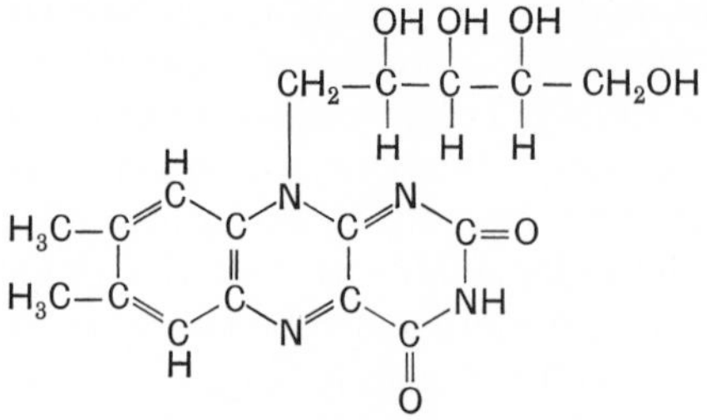

Riboflavin
(6,7-dimethyl-9-(1'-D-ribityl)-isoalloxazine)

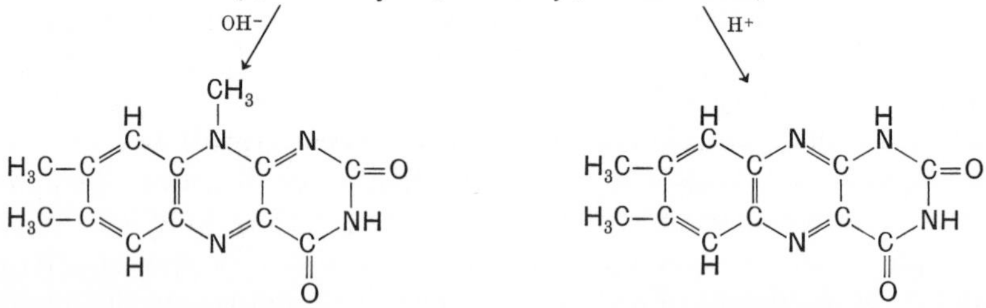

Lumiflavin

Lumichrome

Thus, the coenzyme role of riboflavin was established simultaneously with its description as an essential food factor. Cardiac muscle contains a small amount of lyxoflavin in which the D-ribitol of riboflavin has been replaced by L-lyxitol, another pentitol. Lyxoflavin is not utilized by *Lactobacillus casei* or by the riboflavin-deficient rat under conditions in which riboflavin is effective.

Biogenesis and Metabolism of Riboflavin. Riboflavin occurs ubiquitously in biological materials. Synthesis of riboflavin is effected by all green plants and by most bacteria, yeasts, molds, and fungi but, insofar as is known, not by animals. Although intensively investigated in recent years, riboflavin biosynthesis cannot yet be described in detail. Much evidence indicates that the initial stages are identical with those of purine biosynthesis. Indeed, in organisms which accumulate riboflavin, *e.g., Eremothecium ashbyii,* intact purines may be utilized for riboflavin synthesis, with all of the molecule incorporated except for C-8 of the purine ring system. An established intermediate is 6,7-dimethyl-8-ribityl lumazine, but the subsequent and immediately preceding reactions are uncertain.

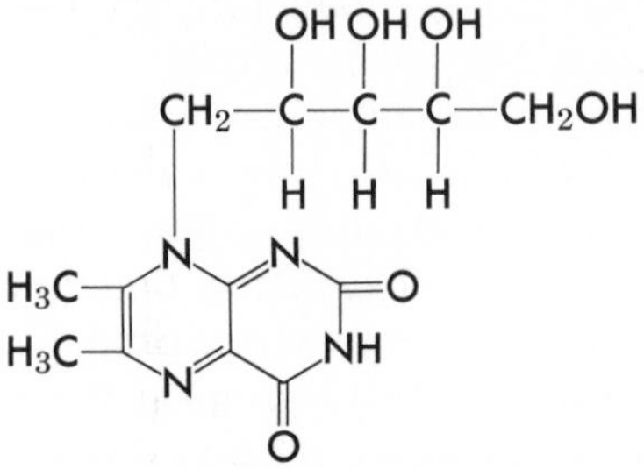

6,7-Dimethyl-8-ribityl lumazine

Observations indicate that the 4-carbon compound required to complete the synthesis is derived from one molecule of the lumazine compound and then reacts with a second. The syntheses of FMN and FAD from riboflavin have been presented previously (page 580). All biological functions of riboflavin appear to be served by these two coenzymes.

Not all bacteria can synthesize the vitamin, and it is therefore an essential growth factor for a number of bacterial species, particularly lactobacilli. The rate of acid production by these organisms, relative to the quantity of the vitamin in the medium, is the basis of quantitative assays for riboflavin. The simplest chemical assay entails measurement of the fluorescence of riboflavin solutions. In man, ingested riboflavin is largely excreted unchanged or as its phosphate ester, riboflavin 5'-phosphate (FMN, page 344).

Riboflavin Deficiency. Riboflavin does not appear to be the prime etiologic factor in a major human disease, although patients with pellagra, beriberi, and kwashiorkor are generally also deficient in riboflavin. Uncomplicated riboflavin deficiency in man is characterized by a magenta-colored tongue, fissuring at the corners of the mouth and lips (cheilosis), a seborrheic dermatitis especially at the nasal-labial folds, and corneal vascularization. Virtually each of these signs may be reproduced in other deficiency states, particularly those due to a lack of niacin and iron, and it is therefore difficult to state to what extent riboflavin deficiency occurs in man.

Riboflavin deficiency in the rat was first observed by Goldberger and Lillie while attempting to produce pellagra in this species. The main effects observed were cessation of growth, accumulation of a dried secretion on the margin of the eyelids, and, frequently, alopecia. In more recent studies of the rat, nerve degeneration, impaired reproduction, and keratitis with cataracts have been observed. Various congenital malformations in young born to riboflavin-deficient rats have also been reported. In the dog, riboflavin deficiency was originally observed by Sebrell and his associates, who noted impaired growth, followed by ataxia, weakness, bradycardia, and respiratory failure, with death ensuing within 12 hr. of onset of symptoms. Riboflavin-deficient young pigs grow poorly, have coarse hair and rough skin, slightly fatty livers, ovarian degeneration, but normal hemopoiesis.

Despite the fundamental role of the flavin enzymes in metabolism, riboflavin deficiency is not associated with any characteristic chemical changes useful for diagnosis. In general, FMN decreases more rapidly than does the FAD concentration, and both decrease more rapidly in liver and kidney than in heart and brain. In the liver the activity of the following enzymes is lost in the order shown: glycolic acid, xanthine, D-amino acid, and DPNH oxidases. Riboflavin bears some special relationship to dietary protein; on low-protein diets animals excrete increased amounts of riboflavin, resulting in decreased tissue riboflavin concentration. The concentration of riboflavin in erythrocytes is perhaps the most sensitive indicator of deficiency. Normal whole blood contains 20 μg per 100 ml.

It has not been possible to establish the human requirement for this vitamin. The recommended amount was calculated from the amount of riboflavin ingested and excreted by individuals on adequate diets. Extrapolations to man have also been made from the ratio of riboflavin to thiamine required by the rat.

There are few common foods which contain high concentrations of riboflavin; liver, yeast, and wheat germ are perhaps most noteworthy, although milk and eggs contribute a large portion of the riboflavin ingested in the usual American diet. Green leafy vegetables are also good sources of riboflavin. In most foods, riboflavin occurs as part of one of the two flavin coenzymes, and only rarely, as in retina and spleen, as the free vitamin.

Riboflavin is obtained commercially from culture media of several molds which produce the vitamin in abundance.

NICOTINIC ACID, OR NIACIN

Pellagra was recognized as early as 1735 by Don Gaspar Casal, physician to King Philip V of Spain. Although largely unknown in the United States until the twentieth century, as many as 170,000 cases were *reported* annually from 1910 to 1935 in the southeastern portion of the United States. Pellagra was established as a deficiency disease by Joseph Goldberger, who also recognized the similarity between human pellagra and canine blacktongue. This fundamental observation made possible the identification of nicotinic acid as the responsible factor by Elvehjem, Woolley, and their associates in 1937. Nicotinic acid had long been known as a product of the chemical oxidation of nicotine and was recognized as part of the molecules of TPN and DPN by Warburg and von Euler, respectively, in 1935 and 1936. Thus the metabolic role of nicotinic acid was known before its nutritional significance had been established. The term *niacin* is the official designation for this vitamin.

Biogenesis and Metabolism of Niacin. Synthesis of niacin occurs in almost all organisms, *viz.,* green plants, yeasts, molds, bacteria, fungi, and most animals, including man. The pathway for conversion of tryptophan to nicotinic acid in animals has been discussed (page 553). It should be noted, however, that this pathway is not operative in green plants and many microorganisms which must possess an unknown alternate route.

Knowledge of the metabolic fate of niacin is more detailed than that for the other vitamins. The synthesis and metabolic fate of DPN and TPN have been presented earlier (Chap. 28). Direct synthesis of nicotinamide from nicotinic acid has not been observed in plant or animal systems. Nicotinamide arises by amidation of nicotinic acid adenine dinucleotide and subsequent hydrolytic degradation of the DPN thus formed (Chap. 28). The glycosidic bond to the pyridine ring is cleaved in a reaction catalyzed by diphosphopyridine nucleotidase (DPNase), releasing nicotinamide and adenosine diphosphate ribose. The latter is hydrolyzed to AMP and ribose 5-phosphate. The nicotinamide may then be hydrolyzed by a *nicotinamidase* and the nicotinic acid reutilized for DPN synthesis.

Nicotinamide undergoes methylation in the liver, with formation of N^1-methylnicotinamide (page 531). N^1-Methylnicotinamide has no antiblacktongue activity in the dog and cannot be used as a source of methyl groups in the methionine-choline-deficient rat. It is the major urinary metabolic product of niacin. When unusually large quantities of nicotinamide are added to the diet of rats, fatty livers and growth failure ensue, probably as a result of excessive use of methyl groups for formation of N^1-methylnicotinamide. Administration of methionine prevents the fatty liver and causes resumption of growth; choline administration will prevent the fatty liver but does not restore growth.

N^1-Methylnicotinamide is oxidized by "aldehyde oxidase" (page 348) in the livers of most mammalian species, including man, with formation of the corresponding 6-pyridone (Fig. 55.2). This pyridone is excreted unchanged when administered to most mammals.

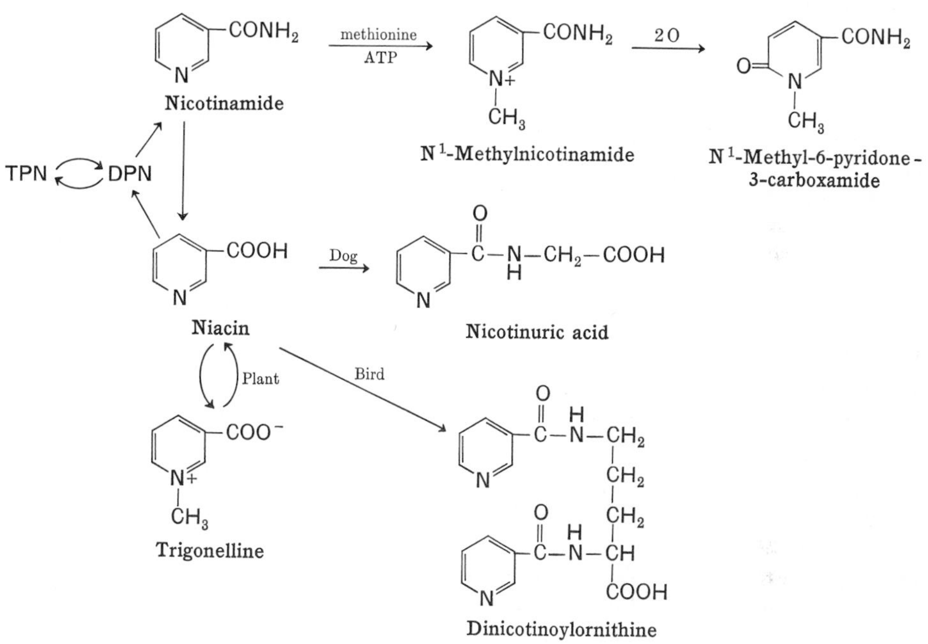

FIG. 55.2. Metabolic fates of nicotinic acid.

Administration of niacin to the dog results in excretion of nicotinuric acid (nicotinoylglycine), although this does not occur in man. Birds excrete dinicotinoylornithine when fed niacin; this is analogous to ornithuric acid excretion after benzoic acid administration (page 528).

Another derivative of nicotinic acid is trigonelline (Fig. 55.2), present in large quantities in the seeds of many plants. Trigonelline possesses no antiblacktongue activity and is quantitatively excreted on administration to dogs and man. Trigonelline is formed in plants by transfer of the methyl group from S-adenosylmethionine to nicotinic acid. During germination of seeds, trigonelline is demethylated by oxidation of its methyl group, a reaction analogous to the oxidative demethylation of sarcosine (page 531). Some of the transformations occurring in the metabolism of niacin and related compounds are summarized in Fig. 55.2.

While, in general, mammals can employ nicotinic acid as well as its esters and amides to satisfy their requirements for this vitamin, many bacteria show somewhat more specific requirements. Some species have been described which specifically require nicotinamide. Others utilize only preformed nicotinamide ribonucleoside, mononucleotide, or DPN. One such organism, *Hemophilus parainfluenzae,* which can employ the ribonucleoside, mononucleotide, or dinucleotide, has been used for the bioassay of these compounds. In species resistant to dietary niacin deficiency, *e.g.,* the mouse and many bacteria, niacin deficiency may be induced by administration of antimetabolites such as pyridine-3-sulfonic acid, 3-acetylpyridine, or 5-thiazole carboxamide.

Niacin Deficiency. It is unlikely that pellagra reflects solely a niacin deficiency; it probably represents a deficiency of many members of the B complex and of dietary protein. The disease is characterized by dermatitis of those areas which are exposed to sunlight, stomatitis, an atrophic, sore, magenta tongue, inability to digest food, and diarrhea. In severe cases the entire gastrointestinal tract may be hemorrhagic. In addition, there are frequently disturbances of the central nervous system, leading to dementia. The nervous system symptoms may, in part, be due to a concomitant thiamine deficiency. The chief manifestations of blacktongue seen in dogs fed corn-containing rations are also referable to the gastrointestinal tract and consist of stomatitis, gingivitis, thick, ropy salivation, and profuse, bloody diarrhea.

In addition, dogs with blacktongue exhibit complete loss of appetite and become markedly dehydrated. Blacktongue may be alleviated by parenteral administration of large quantities of saline solutions, and within a few weeks treated animals resume eating their corn-containing, deficient rations. Thereafter, the dogs lose weight for several months, develop profound anemia, and die, without again showing the characteristic signs of blacktongue. The ration employed in these studies contains an amount of niacin approximately equal to that which must be added as a supplement to prevent blacktongue. If adult dogs are fed instead a synthetic ration containing neither corn nor niacin, typical blacktongue may not appear, but the animals slowly develop some of the deficiency symptoms described above, and die after several months. Thus canine blacktongue and presumably human pellagra are due to more than simple dietary niacin deficiency. In this connection it is of interest that in areas where beriberi is endemic, individuals ingest rations containing considerably less niacin than do the corn-eating pellagrins, without developing symptoms of pellagra. However, the symptoms of niacin deficiency are usually apparent in persons with multiple deficiencies, as in some varieties of kwashiorkor and in Mexican children subsisting on corn gruel and who are afflicted with a summer diarrhea.

A possible explanation of these findings is supplied by observations with other species. Although rats on purified synthetic rations containing casein, sucrose, cottonseed oil, and salt mixture do not develop a niacin deficiency, this deficiency can be induced by the addition to a low-protein diet of either cornmeal, an unbalanced amino acid mixture, or glycine. The deficiency is manifested as growth failure or weight loss, both of which are alleviated by niacin. Tryptophan serves as well as niacin to support growth under these conditions; corn has long been known to be deficient in this amino acid. Thus, at least in part, the appearance of signs of niacin deficiency is related to the ingestion of an unbalanced amino acid mixture containing inadequate tryptophan. However, this explanation is not entirely satisfactory since niacin deficiency occurs in dogs on diets free of niacin but rich in casein, a tryptophan-containing protein. Addition of *free* tryptophan alleviates the niacin deficiency; therefore the fraction of tryptophan administered as the amino acid which is converted to niacin is much larger than that of dietary tryptophan present in proteins.

The only known physiological role of niacin is participation in biological oxidations as DPN and TPN. However, no serious impairment of oxidations has been demonstrated in tissues of niacin-deficient animals, and it is not possible at present to correlate the signs and symptoms of deficiency with known metabolic functions of this vitamin.

Niacin Requirements. In view of the facts presented above, it is difficult to assess the niacin requirement of man or other species. Estimates of this requirement must also consider the total composition of the diet, *i.e.*, the corn content, tryptophan content, etc. Without such knowledge, the recommended allowances shown in Table 52.2 (page 930) provide an ample margin of safety. There is no information regarding the extent of production of niacin by the intestinal flora of man.

In animal tissues, all the niacin is present as pyridine nucleotides; free niacin is not present. The vitamin is widely distributed in plant and animal sources; meat products, particularly liver, are the most important dietary sources. Although milk and eggs are almost devoid of niacin, there is no doubt of their pellagra-preventive action. This may be assumed to be related to the tryptophan content of these foods. Milling procedures used in production of white flour remove most of the niacin, which is replaced by addition of synthetic nicotinic acid. Cereal grains, including corn, contain unidentified substances which are converted to niacin by treatment with alkali, a fact of great nutritional significance in areas such as Mexico and Central America where corn is traditionally treated with lime before being baked into tortillas.

In large doses, about 1 g. given three times daily, nicotinic acid appears to lower the serum cholesterol level of hypercholesterolemic persons. Whatever the mechanism, which is unknown, this should be considered a pharmacologic property of nicotinic acid, unrelated to its normal physiological role.

VITAMIN B_6

Vitamin B_6 was defined by György as that member of the vitamin B complex responsible for the cure of a dermatitis (acrodynia, see below) developed by young rats on a vitamin-free diet supplemented with thiamine and riboflavin. Pyridoxine was isolated from liver and yeast in 1938 and synthesized in the same year. Natural sources contain two other forms of this vitamin, *pyridoxal* and *pyridoxamine.* The three substances as a group are designated vitamin B_6; no single one is considered *the* vitamin, since all three are equally effective in animal nutrition. However, for many bacteria, particularly the lactobacilli, growth is stimulated to a much greater extent by pyridoxal and its phosphate ester than by pyridoxine. Indeed, it was this observation which led to the discovery of pyridoxal and pyridoxamine by Snell.

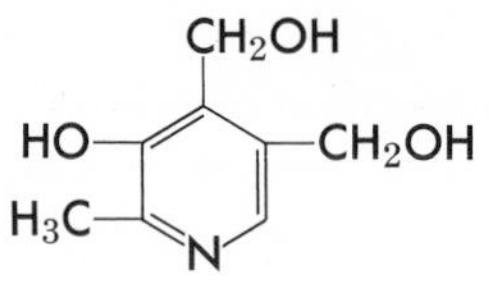

Pyridoxine

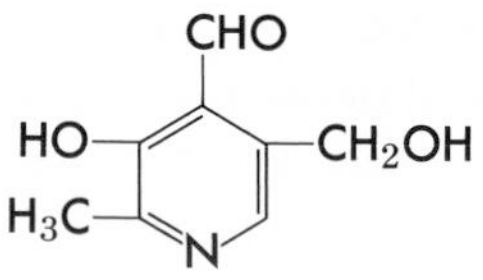

Pyridoxal

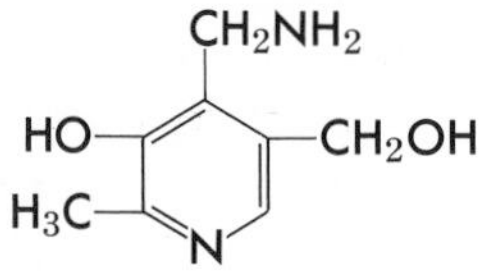

Pyridoxamine

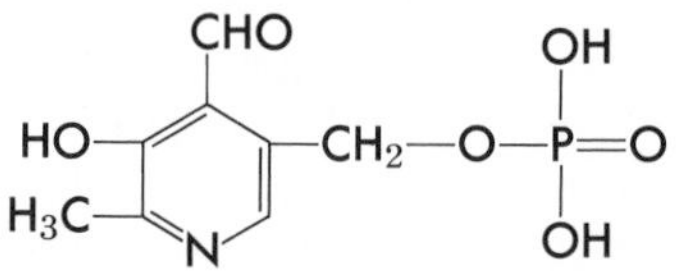

Pyridoxal phosphate

Metabolism of the B₆ Group. Pyridoxine is synthesized by green plants and many microorganisms. Nothing is known of the origin of this compound. In liver, ingested pyridoxine is phosphorylated by a specific kinase and then oxidized to pyridoxal phosphate by a specific flavoprotein. The biological role of pyridoxal phosphate in the metabolism of amino acids (page 493) and its mechanism of action (pages 494, 256) have been discussed. Approximately 90 per cent of the pyridoxine administered to man is oxidized to 4-pyridoxic acid, an oxidation product of pyridoxal, and excreted in this form.

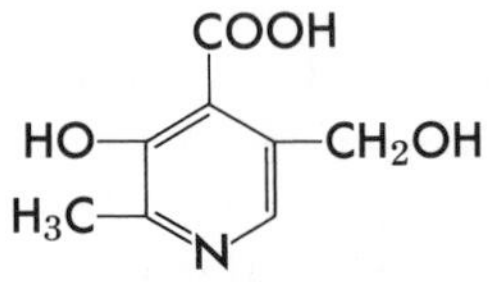

4-Pyridoxic acid

Metabolic Role of Pyridoxal. Pyridoxal phosphate plays a central role in the reactions by which a cell transforms nutrient amino acids into the mixture of amino acids and other nitrogenous compounds required for its own activities. This is most dramatically illustrated by the variation in B₆ requirements in certain bacteria. Some organisms requiring pyridoxine can grow on relatively simple media providing only a few amino acids. However, if the medium is supplemented with a mixture of amino acids, the pyridoxine requirement for maximal growth may be reduced by as much as 90 per cent. In mammals, the situation is somewhat more complex. Unlike bacteria, which absorb from their media only those amino acids which they require, animals may ingest and metabolize considerably greater quantities of amino acids than necessary for growth or nitrogen balance. Consequently, the pyridoxine requirement of animals varies directly with the protein content of the diet.

Cells from B₆-deficient animals fail to concentrate amino acids normally, and pyridoxal accelerates amino acid concentration by ascites tumor cells in vitro. These observations led Christensen to postulate a fundamental role for pyridoxal in the active transport of amino acids across cell membranes. He has also shown that pyridoxal can form uncharged chelates of alkali metals as well as more complex chelates of pyridoxal, amino acid, and metal. Since these complexes are stable in both aqueous and nonpolar media, they appear to be uniquely suitable to the task of transporting both amino acids and metal ions across cell membranes. Thus pyridoxal, or its phosphate ester, might serve as a carrier long postulated in transport mechanisms (page 677).

Pyridoxine Deficiency. In the rat, pyridoxine deficiency is characterized by growth failure and *acrodynia,* a dermatitis on the tail, ears, mouth, and paws, accompanied by edema and scaliness of these structures. Other deficiencies lead to somewhat similar lesions, and, indeed, only the edema distinguishes acrodynia from the dermatitis of rats deficient in essential fatty acids. It is entirely possible that this acrodynia, in part, reflects deficiency in polyunsaturated fatty acids because of failure of synthesis of arachidonic acid from linoleic acid (page 451), since pyridoxine-deficient rats have been found to accumulate only 10 per cent as much unsaturated fatty acids as their pair-fed controls. Pyridoxine deficiency in young pigs, dogs, and rats leads to microcytic, hypochromic anemia accompanied by an increase in plasma iron content and hemosiderosis. The nervous system is also seriously affected. Rats deficient in B_6 are extremely sensitive to noise and develop epileptiform seizures; the peripheral nerves and spinal cords are found to be demyelinated. Extensive neuropathological changes have also been found in the B_6-deficient monkey, which also develops atherosclerotic lesions.

In the human being, pyridoxine deficiency was the cause of a widespread outbreak of convulsions in infants ingesting a commercial infant-feeding formula. Similar convulsions and microcytic, hypochromic anemia appeared in infants fed a B_6-deficient ration. No specific disease syndrome occurring spontaneously in human adults is known to be due to pyridoxine deficiency. However, deficiency signs are readily induced by administration of deoxypyridoxine and by isonicotinylhydrazide (isoniazid), a drug which has proved useful in treatment of tuberculosis.

Deoxypyridoxine   Isonicotinylhydrazide

Deoxypyridoxine is phosphorylated by pyridoxal kinase, and the resulting deoxypyridoxine phosphate appears to compete with pyridoxal phosphate for the active site on specific apoenzymes. Isonicotinylhydrazide forms a hydrazone of pyridoxal and its phosphate ester, rendering these unavailable for enzymic reactions; the hydrazone is excreted in the urine.

Most of the signs and symptoms elicited by these compounds are also associated with other states, *e.g.,* nausea, vomiting, anorexia, seborrheic dermatitis, cheilosis, conjunctivitis, glossitis, polyneuritis, and a pellagra-like dermatitis; all these disappear upon administration of pyridoxine.

Particularly noteworthy is the appearance in individuals given deoxypyridoxine of oxaluria, presumably due to defective glycine metabolism (page 541), a fall in the plasma concentration of tetraenoic acids compatible with the postulated role of pyridoxal phosphate in fatty acid biosynthesis (page 452), and early excretion of xanthurenic acid. The livers from pyridoxal-deficient rats showed a more pronounced fall in kynureninase activity than in that of the transaminase which catalyzes formation of xanthurenic acid (page 553).

Pregnant women excrete as much as ten times more xanthurenic acid than do nonpregnant women after a dose of tryptophan. In this connection, pyridoxine administration has been reported to ameliorate the nausea of pregnancy.

The human requirement for vitamin B_6 is not known. Indeed, several studies have revealed that the urinary excretion of 4-pyridoxic acid may exceed the total known intake of vitamin B_6. It is not clear whether this reflects synthesis by intestinal bacteria or by the host. The B_6 group is widely distributed in nature, and those foods rich in other members of the B complex are excellent sources of these materials. Among such foodstuffs are the germs of various grains and seeds, egg yolk, yeast, and meat, particularly liver and kidney.

PANTOTHENIC ACID

This factor was originally described as a portion of the "bios" complex (page 929) necessary for yeast growth. Its ubiquitous distribution was recognized in 1933 by R. J. Williams and his colleagues, who named it pantothenic acid (Gk. *pantos,* everywhere). The significance of this substance in animal nutrition was established by Jukes, Woolley, and their associates. In 1940, pantothenic acid was isolated and its structure determined.

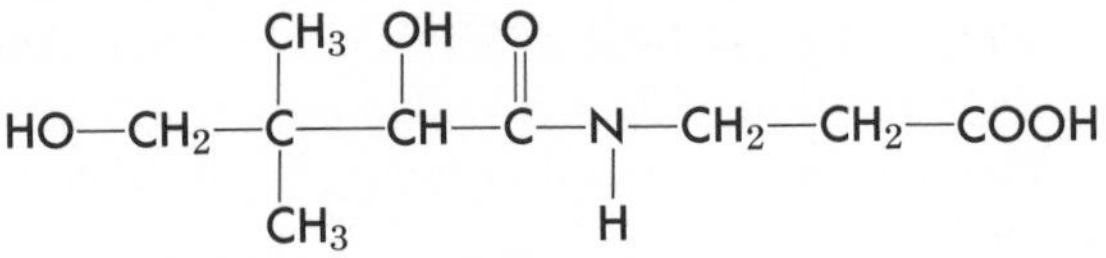

Pantothenic acid (pantoyl-β-alanine)

It will be recognized that this is an amide of α,γ-dihydroxy-β,β-dimethylbutyric acid (pantoic acid) and β-alanine.

Metabolism of Pantothenic Acid. Pantothenic acid can be synthesized by green plants and most microorganisms but not by the rat, dog, chick, pig, monkey, mouse, and fox. The biosynthetic pathway in yeast, *Escherichia coli,* and *Neurospora* is

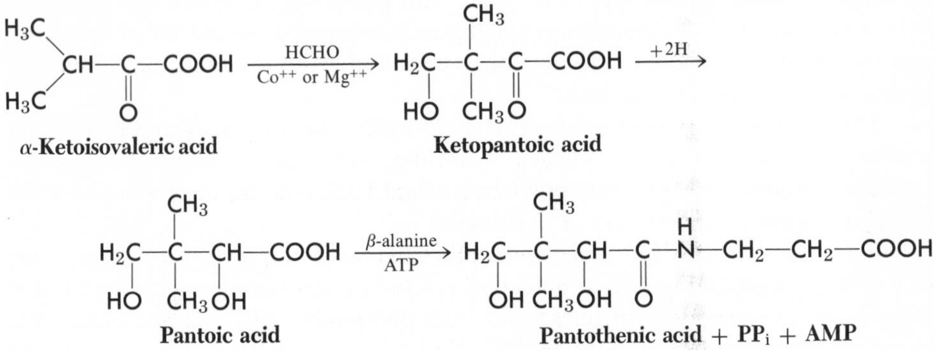

FIG. 55.3 Biosynthesis of pantothenic acid.

shown in Fig. 55.3. Synthesis begins with α-ketoisovaleric acid, which is also the immediate precursor of valine (page 520). The donor of the formaldehyde is not established. β-Alanine may be formed by decarboxylation of aspartic acid or transamination of malonic semialdehyde (page 540). Oral administration of pantoic acid together with β-alanine to pantothenic acid–deficient animals is ineffective in correcting the deficiency. On the other hand, the minimum requirement for the vitamin is satisfied by the same amount of pantothenate given orally as parenterally, indicating that the amide bond is resistant to hydrolysis in the gastrointestinal tract. The only known metabolic role of pantothenic acid is its incorporation into coenzyme A (page 316). The biosynthesis of coenzyme A has been summarized elsewhere (page 582). Nothing is known of the degradative fate of the CoA molecule. Extracts of yeast and animal tissues contain mixed disulfides of CoA and other sulfhydryl compounds, *e.g.*, glutathione or cysteine, but it is not clear whether these occur in living tissue or are artifacts of the isolation procedure.

Pantothenic Acid Deficiency. The nutritional role of this vitamin for man has not been determined, but pantothenic acid is an essential nutrient for all animal species which have been investigated. In the rat, pantothenic acid deficiency is characterized by retardation of growth, impaired reproduction, and achromotrichia, *i.e.*, graying of the hair of black rats. A striking result of pantothenic acid deficiency in the rat is hemorrhagic adrenal cortical necrosis with resultant adrenal cortical hypofunction. The survival of pantothenic acid–deficient rats may be appreciably extended by administration of sufficient quantities of salt or adrenal steroids. These observations are compatible with the reported synthesis of CoA from free pantothenic acid in the zona fasciculata of the adrenal cortex upon administration of ACTH to normal animals and a 50 per cent reduction in the ACTH-stimulated secretion of corticosterone in pantothenic acid–deficient rats. Porphyrin deposits on the whiskers and under the eyes of pantothenic acid–deficient rats come from the harderian gland and are characteristic of dehydration in this species.

Shortly before death, the liver of a pantothenic acid–deficient rat may contain as little as 50 per cent of the normal coenzyme A content and has an impaired ability to utilize pyruvate and to acetylate p-aminobenzoic acid. A number of pantothenic acid antimetabolites have been prepared, of which pantoyltaurine (thiopanic acid) and ω-methylpantothenic acid have been most frequently employed for production of deficiency states. Administration of the latter to man results in a syndrome consisting of postural hypotension, dizziness, tachycardia, fatigue, drowsiness, epigastric distress, anorexia, numbness and tingling of hands and feet, and hyperactive deep reflexes. However, this syndrome is not relieved by administration of pantothenic acid, although improvement is noted on a "good" high-protein diet, and these disturbances may reflect toxicity of ω-methylpantothenic acid rather than induced deficiency of pantothenic acid.

In general the distribution of pantothenic acid resembles that of the other B vitamins; yeast, liver, and eggs are among the richest sources. Meats and milk are important sources because of the concentration of the vitamin and of the quantities of these foods consumed. Most fruits and vegetables are relatively poor sources. Royal jelly, prepared by the bee colony for the nutrition of the queen bee, and fish ovaries before spawning are the richest known sources of this vitamin. The human requirement for this vitamin is not known.

BIOTIN

This member of the vitamin B complex was identified as a result of three separate lines of investigation. In 1936, Kögl and Tönnis isolated from 250 kg. of dried egg yolk 1.1 mg. of a crystalline growth factor which they named "biotin." A few years earlier a factor necessary for the growth and respiration of *Rhizobium* had been obtained and termed "coenzyme R." Shortly after the isolation of biotin, it was established that the two factors were identical. Many years earlier, Bateman had observed that inclusion of large amounts of raw egg white in experimental diets produced toxic symptoms in rats, and in 1926 Boas described the "egg-white injury syndrome" in rats, consisting of dermatitis, loss of hair, and muscular incoordination. She also noted that yeast, liver, and other foodstuffs contained a material which protected rats against egg-white injury. In 1940, György and du Vigneaud and their collaborators established that biotin and the anti-egg-white injury factor were identical; biotin was isolated and its structure established.

Biotin

The pathway of biotin synthesis in plants and microorganisms is presently obscure. Pimelic acid can substitute for biotin in the culture medium of several microorganisms, such as *Corynebacterium diphtheriae* and *Aspergillus niger*. These and other species incorporate pimelic acid into biotin, but the reaction sequence is unknown. In those enzymes in which it functions as a coenzyme, biotin is bound covalently in amide linkage to the ε-amino group of a lysine of the apoenzyme. Proteolysis of the enzyme liberates ε-biotinyllysine, which has been called *biocytin.*

As described previously (page 447), biotin serves as the prosthetic group of a series of enzymes, each of which catalyzes fixation of CO_2 into organic linkage. In consequence, the tissues of biotin-deficient animals exhibit reduced capacity to incorporate CO_2 into oxaloacetate, urea, and purines as well as to synthesize fatty acids.

Biotin Deficiency. Biotin deficiency cannot be produced in most animals merely by diets deficient in this nutrient, presumably because of intestinal bacterial synthesis of this compound. However, biotin deficiency has been produced in poultry, monkeys, and calves on synthetic rations. Biotin deficiency may be produced by sterilization of the intestinal tract, by the feeding of raw egg white, and by administration of biotin antimetabolites.

Shortly after the description of the effects of feeding raw egg white, Parsons postulated that raw egg white contains a material which combines with biotin and prevents its absorption from the intestine. The active agent has been identified as a protein called *avidin,* with an estimated molecular weight of 45,000. The mode of combination of avidin and biotin has not been established, nor is the normal role of avidin understood. Denaturation of avidin abolishes its biotin-binding capacity.

Many bacteria which require biotin can utilize *desthiobiotin* instead, and there is evidence that this compound is a normal intermediate in biotin synthesis in other organisms. *Oxybiotin* can substitute for biotin in the nutrition of most biotin-requiring species, including the rat and chick, and appears to be used per se, rather than being converted to biotin.

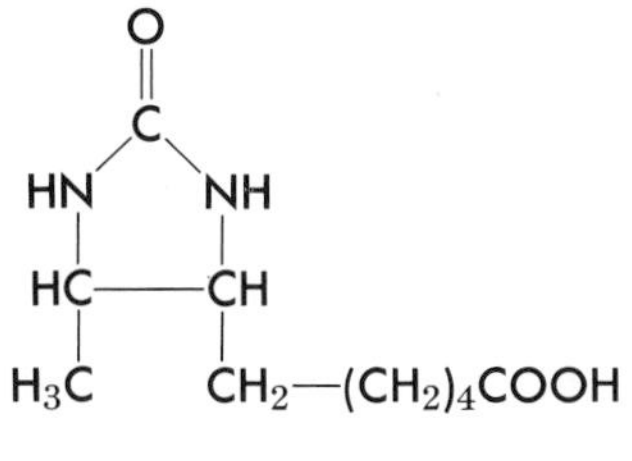

Desthiobiotin 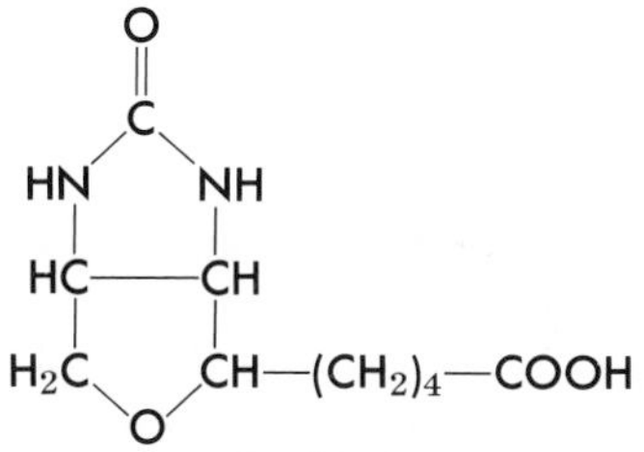   **Oxybiotin**

It is not possible to estimate the nutritional requirement for biotin. Under ordinary circumstances sufficient quantities are provided to the mammal by intestinal bacterial synthesis; the total urinary and fecal excretion of biotin by man usually exceeds the dietary intake. Biotin is widely distributed in natural products. Beef liver and yeast are among the richest sources, but most animal tissues are low in this factor. Peanuts, chocolate, and eggs contain abundant quantities. On the basis of studies of the biotin requirement of the rat, it has been suggested that the daily human requirement is approximately 10 μg. The requirement for biotin is undoubtedly smaller than for those members of the vitamin B complex discussed previously.

FOLIC ACID

Existence of this nutritional factor was first suggested by Day, who found that yeast cured a nutritional cytopenia induced in monkeys by corn-containing rations of the type which produce blacktongue in the dog. Potent concentrates were obtained from spinach leaf; this led to the name "folic acid" (L., *folium*). In 1945 folic acid was shown to have the structure presented below.

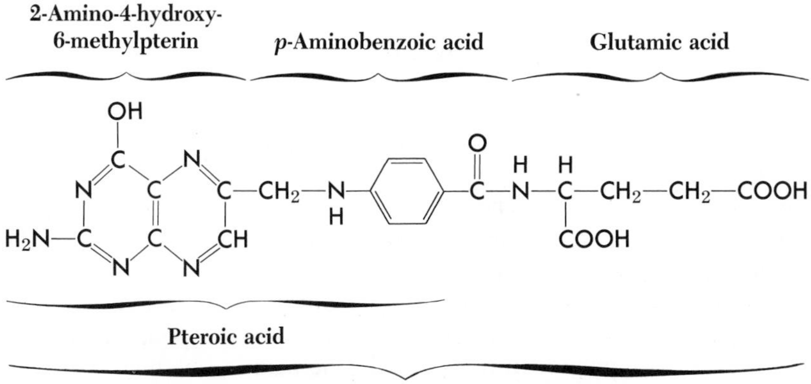

Pteroylglutamic acid (folic acid, PGA)

It will be noted that the molecule contains glutamic acid, *p*-aminobenzoic acid, and a substituted pterin. The combination of the pterin and *p*-aminobenzoic acid is termed *pteroic acid.*

The structure shown is the pteroylglutamic acid of liver. The folic acid–active material produced by bacterial fermentation contains three glutamic acid residues combined in γ-glutamyl linkage. Many animal tissues contain pteroylheptaglutamic acid, the glutamic acid residues again being in γ-glutamyl linkage. Synthetic pteroylpolyglutamic acids, in which the glutamic acid molecules are linked in α-glutamyl bonds, are active in bacterial growth assays, while pteroyl-γ-glutamic acids are effective both in bacteria and in the treatment of macrocytic anemia in man. Animal tissues contain an enzyme which hydrolyzes the naturally occurring pteroylpolyglutamic acid compounds to pteroylmonoglutamic acid and free glutamic acid.

Biogenesis of Folic Acid. Knowledge of the biological origin of folic acid stems from studies of diverse biological forms, including bacteria, *e.g.*, *Escherichia coli*, spinach leaves, moth larvae, and butterfly pupae. However, the data from all sources are consistent, and although most of the details are lacking, a general picture has emerged, as summarized in Fig. 55.4. Guanosine can be directly utilized for pteridine synthesis; in this process, C-8 of the purine ring is lost, whereas several of the carbons of the ribose moiety are retained. Shown are speculative intermediates leading to *biopterin,* which accumulates in yeast and is present in human urine but is not established as an essential intermediate in folic acid biosynthesis. Synthesis of dihydrofolic acid from 2-amino-4-hydroxy-6-hydroxymethyldihydropteridine has been observed with partially purified enzymes. The depicted pyrophosphate ester has not been found as an intermediate, but the synthetic compound is rapidly converted to dihydropteroic acid. Sulfonamides compete with *p*-aminobenzoic acid in the latter reaction.

Pterins are widely distributed in biological materials. Thus *xanthopterin* has long been known to be present in many sources and was first isolated from butterfly wings.

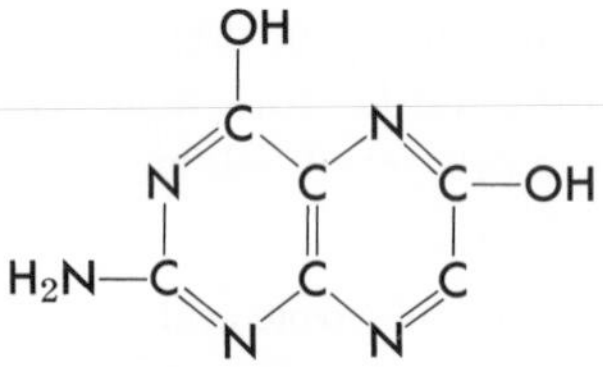

Xanthopterin

Insects contain a rich variety of pterins; at least five are present as eye pigments in *Drosophila.*

Metabolic Role of Folic Acid. The metabolic role of this vitamin has been considered earlier (page 502*ff.*). As its tetrahydro derivative, it serves as a carrier of the hydroxymethyl and formyl groups. The N-5 methyl derivative of tetrahydrofolic acid is an intermediate in the *de novo* synthesis of the methyl group of methionine (page 503). Although originally synthesized as a dihydro compound and functional as the tetrahydro compound, fully oxidized folic acid is obtained when isolated

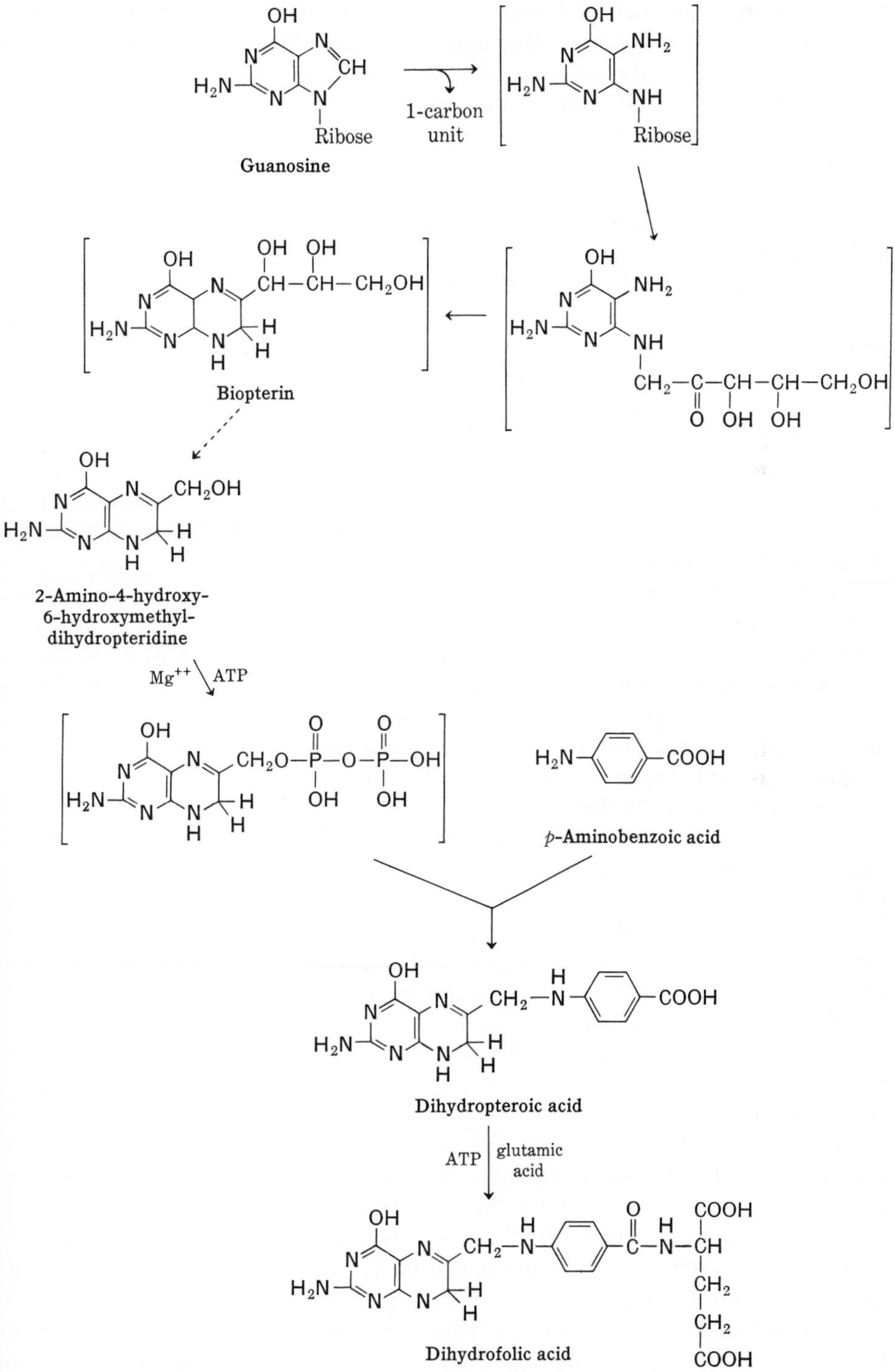

FIG. 55.4. General scheme for the biosynthesis of folic acid.

because of the spontaneous, nonenzymic oxidation of several of these derivatives. As described previously (page 501), mammalian cells have available at all times a system for reduction of oxidized folic acid, or the dihydro compound, to the tetrahydro derivative; TPNH is utilized in the reduction, which appears to require the presence of ascorbic acid.

Because of its metabolic role, folic acid deficiency is expressed primarily as failure to make the purines and thymine required for DNA synthesis. *Streptococcus faecalis*, which requires folic acid for growth, can be grown readily without this vitamin if the medium contains adenine and thymine. Cells grown in this medium possess normal amounts of deoxyribonucleic acid but no detectable folic acid, indicating that folic acid is required for purine and pyrimidine synthesis. The effects of analogues of thymine, *e.g.*, 5-bromouracil, are antagonized in bacteria both by thymine and by folic acid. The corollary is also true: growth inhibition by folic acid antimetabolites such as *aminopterin* (4-aminopteroylglutamic acid) may be alleviated in bacteria by adenine and thymine. When administered in large quantities, thymine induces a hemopoietic response, which, however, is unlike that given by folic acid in patients with pernicious anemia or sprue. Cultures of both sulfonamide- and aminopterin-inhibited bacteria accumulate in their media 5-amino-4-imidazolecarboxamide (page 563).

Folic Acid Deficiency. Folic acid deficiency is characterized by growth failure, anemia, leukopenia, or pancytopenia. Deficiency cannot always be induced in animals on folic acid–free diets. In the rat, folic acid deficiency can be more readily obtained by incorporation of sulfonamides into the diet. This effect of the sulfonamides presumably is a result of inhibition of folic acid synthesis from p-aminobenzoic acid by the intestinal bacteria. In other species, deficiency symptoms have been elicited by administration of antimetabolites.

Severe experimental anemias produced in folic acid–deficient animals led to a trial of pteroylglutamic acid in patients with macrocytic anemias of sprue, pregnancy, infancy, and pernicious anemia. Patients with sprue generally show a striking remission of all symptoms, including the steatorrhea, with a reticulocytosis and steady return to a normal blood picture. Essentially similar responses are frequently but not invariably obtained in infants and pregnant women with megaloblastic anemias. Thus, these three conditions appear to reflect true nutritional deficiency in folic acid. The megaloblastic anemia derives from a failure of DNA synthesis, since the RNA/DNA ratio of the macrocytes is about 0.85, whereas in normal cells this ratio is 0.3. Also, striking reticulocyte responses are occasionally obtained by administration of thymidine. Patients with pernicious anemia may also exhibit a marked reticulocyte response when given folic acid, but show no amelioration of the neurological disturbances characteristic of this disease, which is primarily due to lack of vitamin B_{12} (see below), rather than folic acid. The steatorrhea of sprue is a result of an atrophic jejunum, with flattened, columnar epithelium, vacuolation, and short, wide villi, reflecting the requirement for purines and thymine for DNA synthesis in the constantly dividing cells of this tissue.

A number of antimetabolites of folic acid have been synthesized and tested for therapeutic value in human leukemia, since folic acid deficiency is characterized by a leukopenia. Aminopterin (see above) and its 9-methyl derivative are effective antimetabolites of folic acid. They inhibit the growth of almost all organisms that require folic acid; the inhibition is reversible by relatively large amounts of folic acid. Aminopterin is a potent lethal agent, killing rats and mice within 1 week in a concentration of 1 part per million in the diet. The animals lose weight and develop a watery diarrhea, while the bone marrow becomes aplastic. Aminopterin may produce temporary remissions of acute leukemia in children. In the adult human being occasional remissions of tumors of lymphoid origin have been reported to follow use of this drug.

The status of folic acid in human nutrition is not certain. Although there is little doubt of the indispensability of this vitamin, the requirement for folic acid may be met, in part, as a result of its synthesis by the intestinal bacteria. Folic acid is widely distributed in the animal and plant world, and nutritional deficiency, therefore, should be infrequent. However, dietary deficiency of folic acid appears to be a factor in the etiology of sprue, as well as in the development of the macrocytic anemia of pregnancy and certain macrocytic anemias of children.

VITAMIN B_{12}

Following the demonstration by Whipple that liver promotes hemopoiesis in anemic dogs, Minot and Murphy, in 1926, showed that feeding large quantities of liver cured pernicious anemia. Later, investigators prepared from liver relatively concentrated extracts suitable for parenteral administration and therapeutically effective. Yet, despite the efforts of the next 20 years, no further progress was made in the isolation and identification of the active factor in liver. The chief obstacle in these studies was the difficult nature of the assay, *viz.*, the hemopoietic response of patients with pernicious anemia. In 1948, crystalline vitamin B_{12} was obtained independently by E. Lester Smith in England and by Rickes and his colleagues in the United States. The latter group employed a microbiological assay with *Lactobacillus lactis* Dorner, while Smith used the human bioassay procedure. Positive hematologic responses are obtained with doses as low as 3 μg of vitamin B_{12}. A coenzyme form of the vitamin was isolated first by Barker, who found it essential to the interconversion of glutamic and β-methylaspartic acids by extracts of species of *Clostridium* (see below).

The structure of the coenzyme form of vitamin B_{12}, *cobamide coenzyme*, is shown in Fig. 55.5. The central structure is the porphyrin-like *corrin* ring system, in which two of the pyrrole rings are linked directly rather than through a methene bridge as for the other rings and in porphyrins generally. Cobalt is in the position occupied by iron in the heme series. In the cobamide coenzyme shown, the cobalt is divalent; all but two bonds to the cobalt are of coordinate character. One of the coordinate bonds is to the nitrogen of a molecule of 5,6-dimethylbenzimidazole, here shown above the plane of the corrin ring, which extends in glycosidic linkage to ribose 3-phosphate. The latter, in turn, is esterified to aminoisopropanol, the nitrogen of which is in amide linkage with the carboxyl group of a propionic acid substituted in the corrin ring. Bonded to the cobalt from below the ring is a molecule of 5'-deoxyadenosine; note that the linkage is from the cobalt to the carbon atom at 5', the only instance of an organometallic compound presently known in biological systems. Lesser quantities of cobamide coenzymes are found in which the 5,6-dimethylbenzimidazole is replaced by adenine, or 5-hydroxybenzimidazole, among others. The cobamide coenzymes can be isolated only under special conditions. In the presence of anions, particularly cyanide, and of light, the cobalt is oxidized to the trivalent state and the 5'-deoxyadenosine is replaced by the attacking anion. The reaction is easily followed spectrophotometrically since the cyano-

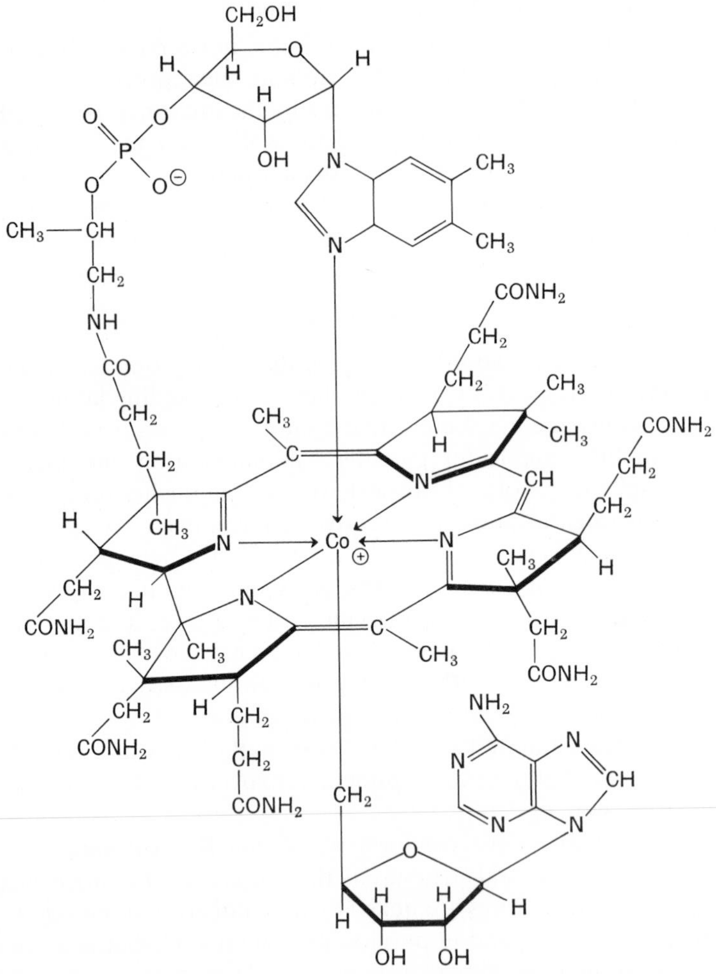

FIG. 55.5. Structure of the 5,6-dimethylbenzimidazole cobamide coenzyme.

cobalamin exhibits an absorption peak at 360 mμ which is not evident with the coenzyme forms. Some evidence suggests that, in the coenzyme forms, the cobalt is present in the trivalent state, but this is uncertain. Cyanocobalamin is the form in which vitamin B_{12} is ordinarily available, but the cyanide ion may be replaced by a variety of anions, e.g., hydroxyl (hydroxocobalamin), nitrite (nitritocobalamin), chloride (chlorocobalamin), and sulfate (sulfatocobalamin). The derivatives all have comparable biological activities.

Neither animals nor higher plants can synthesize vitamin B_{12}. Indeed, soil microorganisms appear to be the prime source of this vitamin, so that among the richest sources are activated sewage sludge (50 μg per g.), manure (0.1 μg per g.), and dried estuarine mud (3 μg per g.). Many microorganisms are unable to synthesize vitamin B_{12} and require it for growth, thus providing the basis for a microbiological assay for the vitamin.

Biosynthesis of Vitamin B_{12}. Shemin and his associates have shown that Actinomyces, which synthesize vitamin B_{12}, make the corrin portion of the vitamin molecule from δ-aminolevulinic acid in a manner analogous to the utilization of this acid for the synthesis of the porphyrin of hemoglobin (page 532). The additional methyl groups present in the vitamin are derived from methionine, while the aminoisopropanol was shown by Sprinson to arise from threonine. The origin of 5,6-dimethylbenzimidazole ribonucleoside is unknown.

Vitamin B_{12} Deficiency. Higher plants do not concentrate vitamin B_{12} from the soil and are a relatively poor source of the vitamin as compared with animal tissues. This led to the observation that cow manure and fish meal contain a nutrient required for rapid growth of chicks grown on commercial rations. This effect was attributed to an "animal protein factor," now known to be vitamin B_{12}. The requirement for the vitamin is so minute that its wide distribution in foodstuffs and retention by the animal organism would seem to preclude the possibility of nutritional deficiency in normal individuals. However, deficiency has been observed in individuals who abstain from all animal products, and have blood levels of 40 to 200 $\mu\mu$g of B_{12} per ml. as compared with normal values of 200 to 350 $\mu\mu$g per ml. Occasionally such individuals develop the hematological and neurological syndrome of pernicious anemia without the gastric disturbance usually responsible for this disease (see below).

Pernicious anemia results not from inadequate ingestion of vitamin B_{12}, but from defective gastric secretion (page 808). The "intrinsic factor" of gastric juice is required for the successful absorption of ingested vitamin B_{12} unless the vitamin is given in enormous excess. Indeed, the stool of patients with pernicious anemia is a rich source of the vitamin, and cobalamin given to these individuals may be recovered quantitatively from the stool unless given with intrinsic factor. This provides the basis for a useful diagnostic test for pernicious anemia. About 0.5 μg of cyanocobalamin labeled with Co^{60} is given orally; normal human beings excrete 5 to 30 per cent of the test dose in the stool, whereas persons with pernicious anemia excrete 75 to 95 per cent of the dose. When given with a source of intrinsic factor, normal absorption is observed. No amount of intrinsic factor can markedly increase intestinal absorption above that observed in normal persons.

Gastric juice contains a mixture of mucoproteins which bind vitamin B_{12} in varying degrees. These have been fractionated and assayed for both binding capacity and ability to serve as intrinsic factor. Although highly concentrated and effective preparations have been obtained, pure intrinsic factor has not been isolated, nor is it entirely certain that a specific single mucoprotein of the gastric juice is, uniquely, intrinsic factor. However there are structural differences among species; rats respond only to rat intrinsic factor preparations, and there is evidence that human intrinsic factor is more effective in man than that from other species. The mechanism of intrinsic factor action is not apparent, but it may be that it is not restricted to effecting the passage of vitamin B_{12} across the intestinal mucosa. The vitamin B_{12}–depleted tissues of persons with pernicious anemia in relapse clear administered vitamin B_{12} from plasma more slowly than tissues of normal individuals. Moreover, intrinsic factor preparations accelerate the uptake of vitamin B_{12} by liver slices in vitro.

Estimates of the daily requirement for cyanocobalamin are of the order of 1 μg, but there is no adequate basis for establishing this figure. The difficulty inherent in assessing this value is apparent from the fact that persons who have undergone almost total gastrectomy and no longer secrete intrinsic factor show the earliest signs of pernicious anemia only 3 to 5 years postoperatively.

Metabolic Role of Cobamide Coenzymes. Cobamide coenzymes participate in a series of seemingly diverse reactions. The reaction in *Clostridium tetanomorphum* studied by Barker, which led to discovery of these coenzymes, was the formation of β-methylaspartic acid from glutamic acid.

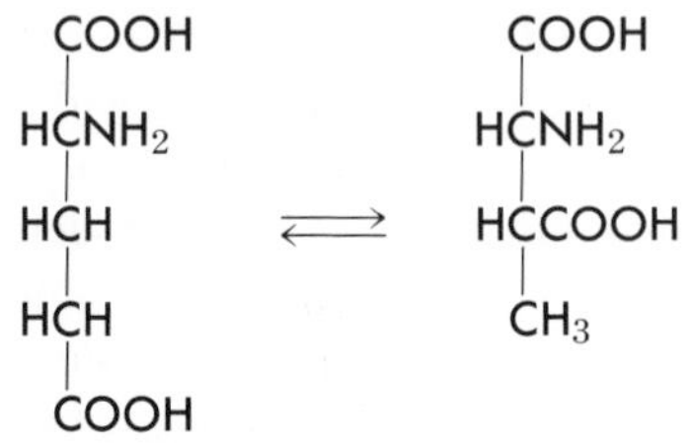

$$
\begin{array}{ccc}
\text{COOH} & & \text{COOH} \\
| & & | \\
\text{HCNH}_2 & & \text{HCNH}_2 \\
| & & | \\
\text{HCH} & \rightleftharpoons & \text{HCCOOH} \\
| & & | \\
\text{HCH} & & \text{CH}_3 \\
| & & \\
\text{COOH} & &
\end{array}
$$

Glutamic acid   **β-Methylaspartic acid**

Clearly analogous is the cobamide-catalyzed interconversion of succinyl CoA and methylmalonyl CoA (page 444). The mode of participation of the cobamide in these transformations is not known. Since C-2 of methylmalonyl CoA becomes C-3 of succinyl CoA, it is evident that it is not the free —COOH carbon that migrates but rather, as indicated previously (page 444), the entire —CO—S—CoA group. It is supposed that this involves transient substitution of the latter group for the deoxyadenosyl group of the coenzyme, but it is not clear whether the migrating group is a free radical, carbonium ion, or carbanion, and whether the cobalt must undergo alternate changes in valence during these reactions.

A second type of reaction in which cobamide coenzymes participate is the dismutation of vicinal diols, *e.g.*, propane-1,2-diol, to the corresponding aldehyde.

$$
\text{CH}_3\text{CHOHCH}_2\text{OH} \longrightarrow \text{CH}_3\text{CH}_2\text{CHO}
$$
Propane-1,2-diol   **Propionaldehyde**

Although there is no doubt of participation of cobamide coenzymes in the methylation of homocysteine to form methionine (page 504 and Fig. 26.1, page 532) and in the methylation of dUMP to form TMP (page 577), the role of the enzyme is obscure. Synthetic methyl vitamin B_{12}, in which the 5'-deoxyadenosyl group of the coenzyme is replaced by a methyl group, has been shown to be active in a liver system in which the methyl group of N^5-methyltetrahydrofolic acid is transferred to homocysteine in the presence of TPNH, ATP, and S-adenosylmethionine. Apparently, the N-5 methyl group transfer is via the methyl vitamin B_{12}; however, it is not known whether the latter is, under physiological conditions, a normal intermediate. In any case, it is the participation of vitamin B_{12} in these reactions which appears to account for the ability of rats to grow on diets lacking methionine but containing homocystine and vitamin B_{12}, as well as for the limitations placed upon TMP synthesis by a deficiency of vitamin B_{12}, with resulting macrocytic anemia.

INOSITOL

Inositol was the first component of the bios complex to be identified. It may exist in one of seven optically inactive forms and as one pair of optically active isomers. Only one of these forms, *myo*-inositol (page 35), possesses biological activity.

In 1940, Woolley described alopecia in mice on inositol-deficient diets. Deficiency of this compound has also been stated to cause the so-called "spectacled-eye" condition in rats, which is due to denudation about the eyes. The chick, turkey poult, pig, hamster, and guinea pig have also been reported to require inositol as an essential dietary nutrient. It is difficult to reconcile these observations with the fact that when glucose-C^{14} is given to the rat, inositol-C^{14} may be isolated from its tissues, indicating an unknown synthetic pathway. However, whether or not inositol is an essential nutrient for the intact animal, studies in tissue culture have revealed that it is required for growth of fibroblasts and various strains of human cancer cells in specific experimental conditions.

In special circumstances, inositol is a lipotropic agent, effectively reducing the liver lipids of rats ingesting a diet low in protein and free of lipid. However, whereas choline is effective when the low-protein diet also contains lipid, inositol is relatively ineffective in these circumstances. Although inositol-containing phosphatides are known (page 77), they have not been found in significant quantity in liver. Thus the lipotropic action of inositol is unexplained.

The rat is capable of metabolizing relatively large quantities of inositol; after its administration only minute amounts are recovered in the urine. Labeled inositol gives rise to labeled glucose in the urine of phlorhizinized rats. Inositol is also an antiketogenic substance. The initial step in its metabolism is oxidation by an oxygenase (page 356) which results in the formation of D-glucuronic acid (page 407).

Inositol is widely distributed in plant and animal cells. Large quantities are found in mammalian cardiac muscle and in the skeletal muscle of sharks. It has been suggested that in the shark, inositol may have a reserve function similar to that of glycogen in other species. In plants, mono-, di-, and triphosphate esters of inositol are found in large quantities. The hexaphosphate ester is known as phytic acid (page 778) and is found in high concentrations in grains. Dietary phytic acid is rachitogenic because the insoluble salt, calcium phytate, which may form in the gastrointestinal tract prevents normal absorption of dietary calcium (page 778). Seeds, beans, and nuts contain inositol phosphatides linked glycosidically to oligosaccharides.

CHOLINE

Choline deficiency, like that of niacin, cannot be produced in animals receiving diets adequate in protein. Nevertheless, choline may for purposes of discussion be classified as a B vitamin. At least two of the disturbances in methionine-deficient animals appear specifically to relate to the need for choline. These are fatty livers and hemorrhagic kidneys.

The synthesis of lecithin in the livers of choline-deficient animals is slower than in normal animals although the rate of addition of lecithin to the plasma by the liver is approximately the same in the two groups. It is not clear why this should result in accumulation of lipid in the liver. Perhaps equally significant is Artom's observation of impaired oxidation of long-chain fatty acids to CO_2 by liver slices from choline-deficient rats. Choline deficiency, however, is not the sole basis for fatty livers in animals on a low-protein diet, since, in the presence of limiting amounts of choline, several amino acids, notably threonine, also exert lipotropic activity.

The prolonged presence of excessive lipid in the hepatic cells of animals on low-protein rations leads to necrosis and fibrosis resembling Laennec's cirrhosis. The results of choline, methionine, and inositol therapy in human cirrhotic subjects have been disappointing.

The pathogenesis of the hemorrhagic kidneys first noted by Griffith in choline-deficient rats is still obscure. These lesions can be produced only in young rats shortly after weaning. The assumption of a relation to impaired phosphatide metabolism is based on the observation that the lesion is produced only during that period of a few days after weaning when the rate of renal phosphatide synthesis is at a maximum. Histologically the hemorrhagic kidneys somewhat resemble those of "lipoid nephrosis" but are not actually identical with any known disease entity in man. Most affected rats die in uremia. Choline administration, even at the height of the disease, appears to cure many of the animals. However, even though returned to stock rations, severe hypertension and renal arteriolosclerosis may develop some months later in animals which were previously choline-deficient, apparently because of heavy fibrosis of the renal capsule.

Chronically choline-deficient rats also develop anemia and hypoproteinemia, frequently with edema. These symptoms are not the consequence of the low-protein diet used to produce choline deficiency, since the animals respond rapidly to choline administration. In poultry, deficiency in choline, as well as many other nutrients (Mn^{++}, glycine, arginine), results in perosis. Betaine is an effective substitute for choline in all species; dimethylaminoethanol is effective in place of choline in the chick but not the rat. Presumably, the demand for choline and methionine is influenced by the amount of folic acid and vitamin B_{12} also present in the diet. Choline itself is widely distributed as a constituent of lecithin. Glandular tissues are excellent dietary sources of this compound, as are nervous tissue, egg yolk, and a few vegetable oils, *e.g.*, soybean oil.

ASCORBIC ACID

In 1907 Hölst and Frölich demonstrated that guinea pigs develop scorbutic lesions on a diet of oats and bran. Twenty years later, Zilva obtained potent concentrates of antiscorbutic material from the juice of lemons, and in 1932 King and Waugh announced the isolation of the crystalline vitamin, which had previously been termed vitamin C. From its chemical properties, they concluded that it was identical with the hexuronic acid in plants and animal tissues previously described by Szent-Györgyi.

The structure of this vitamin, renamed ascorbic acid, was established by the work of a number of laboratories, particularly that of Haworth, and is shown below.

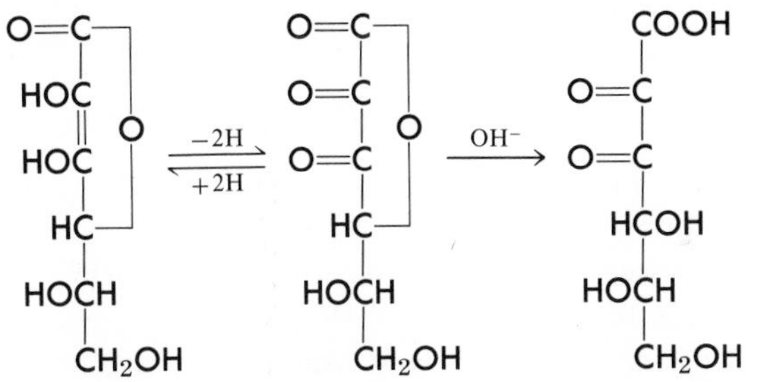

L-Ascorbic acid **L-Dehydroascorbic acid** **L-Diketogulonic acid**

The acidity of ascorbic acid is due to dissociation of the enolic hydrogen on carbon-3 ($pK_a = 4.17$). The most prominent chemical property of the vitamin is its ready oxidation to dehydroascorbic acid, which is catalyzed by small concentrations of metal ions. Dehydroascorbic acid is unstable in alkali, undergoing hydrolysis of the lactone ring, with formation of diketogulonic acid. Reduction of dehydroascorbic acid is readily accomplished by reducing agents such as H_2S, cysteine, and glutathione. The reducing power of ascorbic acid serves as the basis for most of the quantitative analytical procedures for estimation of this compound, such as titration with the dye 2,6-dichlorophenolindophenol, which, however, estimates only the ascorbic acid, not the dehydroascorbic acid present.

Biogenesis and Metabolism of Ascorbic Acid. Ascorbic acid is a dietary essential for man, other primates, and the guinea pig but can be synthesized by all other species of animals which have been investigated.

The major steps in the biosynthesis of ascorbic acid in animals appear to be the following.

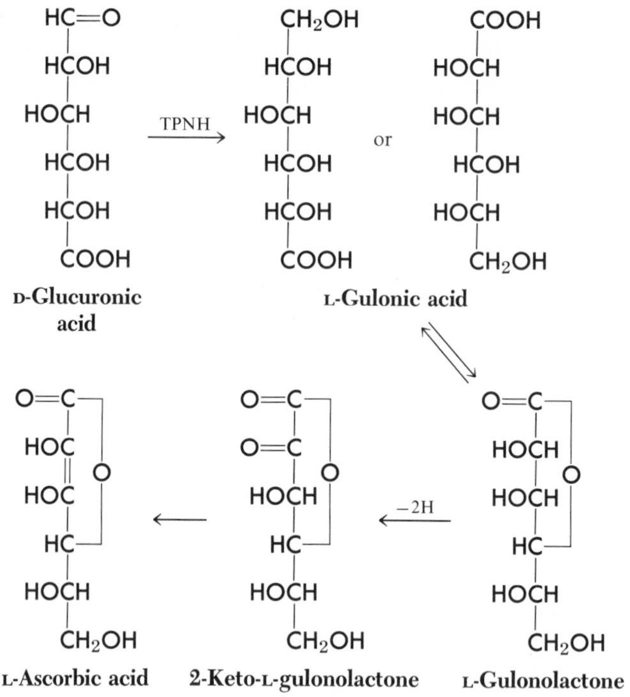

$$
\begin{array}{ccc}
\text{HC}=\text{O} & \text{CH}_2\text{OH} & \text{COOH} \\
\text{HCOH} & \text{HCOH} & \text{HOCH} \\
\text{HOCH} \quad \underset{\longrightarrow}{\text{TPNH}} \quad \text{HOCH} & \text{or} & \text{HOCH} \\
\text{HCOH} & \text{HCOH} & \text{HCOH} \\
\text{HCOH} & \text{HCOH} & \text{HOCH} \\
\text{COOH} & \text{COOH} & \text{CH}_2\text{OH}
\end{array}
$$

D-Glucuronic acid   L-Gulonic acid

L-Ascorbic acid   2-Keto-L-gulonolactone   L-Gulonolactone

Note that the two forms of L-gulonic acid merely represent the same structure rotated 180° in the plane of the paper. Primates and guinea pigs are thought to be unable to carry out the step between ketogulonolactone and ascorbic acid. Administered ascorbic acid–C^{14} is readily oxidized to $C^{14}O_2$ by the guinea pig, whereas in the human being, only diketogulonate-C^{14} and oxalate-C^{14} have been obtained. Oxidation to dehydroascorbic acid is catalyzed by a specific, copper-containing *ascorbic acid oxidase* present in plants but not in animals.

Metabolic Role of Ascorbic Acid. Since the initial studies of Szent-Györgyi, it has been assumed that the metabolic role of ascorbic acid relates to its reversible oxidation and reduction. *However, no biological oxidation system has yet been described in which ascorbic acid serves as a specific coenzyme.* A possible role for ascorbic acid in tyrosine metabolism has been considered previously (page 549). Although the vitamin activates the oxidation of *p*-hydroxyphenylpyruvic acid by rat liver homogenates, other reducing agents are equally effective and the partially purified enzyme shows no dependence upon ascorbic acid. Of interest in this regard is the observation that in the presence of oxygen, solutions of ferrous ion plus ascorbate catalyze the hydroxylation of a series of aromatic compounds. Thus, *p*-hydroxyphenylacetic acid yields homogentisic acid while tryptamine yields 5-hydroxytryptamine (serotonin). However, it seems unlikely that this system is operative physiologically.

The suggested interrelationship of ascorbic acid with folic acid has been indicated previously (page 966). Noteworthy also is the fact that ascorbic acid facilitates removal of iron from ferritin. Since the plasma iron of the anemic, scorbutic monkey is reduced to about 30 per cent of normal, this may contribute to the genesis of the anemia. At this time, therefore, except possibly for the role of ascorbic acid in hydroxyproline formation (page 496), this compound appears to serve only by poising the redox potential of cell contents. It is clear that the oxidized form, dehydroascorbic acid, may be enzymically reduced in animal tissues, with gluta-thione as the reducing agent. Indeed, in plants, this affords the basis of a respiratory system in which the electron path is the following.

$$\text{Substrate} \rightleftarrows \begin{pmatrix} TPN^+ \\ TPNH \end{pmatrix} \rightleftarrows \begin{pmatrix} 2GSH \\ GSSG \end{pmatrix} \rightleftarrows \begin{pmatrix} \text{Dehydroascorbate} \\ \text{Ascorbate} \end{pmatrix} \rightleftarrows \begin{pmatrix} H_2O \\ O_2 \end{pmatrix}$$

There is evidence that in animal tissues ascorbic acid exists both free and in a combined form. In dietary deficiency of the vitamin, the free form tends to diminish in concentration in the tissues before appreciable changes occur in the concentration of bound ascorbic acid.

Ascorbic Acid Deficiency. The manifestations of ascorbic acid deficiency are largely due to functional failure in cells of mesenchymal origin. Scurvy in adults is characterized by sore, spongy gums, loosening of the teeth, impaired capillary integrity with subcutaneous hemorrhages and edema, joint pain, anorexia, and anemia. This disease is rare in the Western world at the present time. However, scurvy in children is still seen occasionally as the result of poor feeding practices. Symptoms include tender, swollen joints, limitation of motion, petechial hemorrhages, inadequate tooth development, arrested skeletal development with characteristic bone disease, impaired wound healing, and anemia. Except for the anemia, impaired formation of collagen and chondroitin sulfate is the basis for all these changes. The collagen that is deposited is stated to be poor in hydroxyproline. In severe scurvy there is failure of formation of new ground substance and extensive depolymerization and solution of existing cement material, leading to breakdown of old, healed wounds. The anemia of scurvy may relate to impaired ability to utilize stored iron as well as to a secondary impairment in folic acid metabolism. Despite the high concentration of ascorbic acid in the adrenal cortex, there is no indication of adrenal cortical insufficiency in the scorbutic animal. In fact such animals may excrete increased amounts of adrenal cortical steroids.

Ascorbic acid deficiency in man has been studied under controlled conditions. Enlarged keratotic hair follicles were apparent after 17 to 20 weeks; these became hemorrhagic several weeks later. The buttocks and calves were first affected, but later these lesions appeared over the entire body. After 26 weeks, hemorrhages in the gums and reduced rate of wound healing were evident. The plasma concentration of ascorbic acid per 100 ml. fell from 0.55 to less than 0.05 mg. within a few weeks, while the concentration of ascorbic acid per 100 ml. in white blood cells slowly fell from 16 to less than 1 mg. In general, scorbutic signs were apparent about 1 month after the vitamin concentration in white cells had fallen to its lowest level. Ten milligrams of ascorbic acid per day prevented these changes, while administration of 20 mg. per day to subjects showing signs of scurvy resulted in complete disappearance of these signs within 3 weeks. As a result of these studies, the British Medical Research Council concluded that an ascorbic acid supply of 30 mg. daily could be considered a liberal allowance. This value is less than half of that recommended by the Food and Nutrition Board of the National Research Council

(Table 52.2, page 930). The higher recommended allowance, however, includes consideration not only of the appearance of overt scurvy but also of factors of well-being which cannot be readily evaluated. There is little doubt that the recommended intakes shown in Table 52.2 afford a generous margin of safety.

In man, the normal plasma ascorbic acid concentration is 0.7 to 1.2 mg. per 100 ml. However, these plasma values reflect dietary intake rather than potential deficiency in that levels below 0.5 mg. per 100 ml. are frequently encountered in persons who ingest 30 or 40 mg. of ascorbic acid daily, an amount which seems adequate for man. The concentration of ascorbic acid in the white blood cells may more closely reflect the concentration of ascorbic acid in tissues generally than does the amount in plasma. In "saturation tests," doses of about 500 mg. of ascorbic acid are administered; normal individuals excrete at least 50 per cent of the dose within 24 hr., while severely deficient subjects may excrete very little of the administered vitamin.

Fresh fruits and vegetables are important dietary sources of ascorbic acid. Cooking, canning, and other food-preparation procedures may result in inactivation of a portion of the ascorbic acid in foods. Therefore, tables showing the ascorbic acid content of various foodstuffs should be evaluated in terms of the manner of food preparation. In general, green leafy vegetables are excellent sources of ascorbic acid; new potatoes contain relatively large quantities. Because of the large quantities of potatoes consumed, these are an important source of the vitamin in the Western diet. The high concentrations in citrus fruits are well known. Some of the ascorbic acid may be lost in canning fruit juices but is largely preserved in frozen juices. In general, the ascorbic acid content of meats is relatively low, and cooking of meat destroys the vitamin.

REFERENCES

See list following Chap. 56.

56. The Lipid-soluble Vitamins

VITAMIN A

In 1913 McCollum and Davis, and Osborne and Mendel, noted growth failure in rats fed relatively purified rations with lard or olive oil as the source of lipid. When butterfat, cod-liver oil, or egg yolk was substituted, growth was resumed and the animals' appearance improved markedly. McCollum designated the active ingredient in these foods "fat-soluble A." Some years later, Steenbock, aware of the frequent presence of carotenoids in lipids obtained from natural sources, tested the vitamin A activity of purified β-carotene and concluded that this substance provided the same protection to rats as did the effective natural sources.

Since cod-liver oil, which is a rich source of the active factor, is only faintly colored, it appeared that some substances other than the deeply colored carotenes also possessed vitamin A activity, and because of this, relation of the carotenes to the active factor was in dispute for some time. However, in 1929, T. Moore demonstrated that when β-carotene was fed to rats depleted of vitamin A, not only did they resume growth but their livers accumulated a colorless material with vitamin A activity. This established the provitamin A status of β-carotene. The structures of vitamin A and of several natural carotenoids have been given previously (pages 80ff.). Vitamin A activity is exhibited by α-, β-, and γ-carotenes, as well as by vitamin A_1 (page 81) and vitamin A_2 (page 820). In addition, certain other carotenoids may have vitamin A activity, e.g., cryptoxanthin.

Pure vitamin A was isolated from fish-liver oil by Holmes in 1937. Vitamin A is an alcohol and forms esters with fatty acids; most of the vitamin A in the livers of both mammals and fish is present in esterified form. The vitamin A activity of plant materials is due entirely to carotenoids. Vitamin A is readily oxidized, with rapid destruction of its biological activity. Aeration of heated cod-liver oil results in complete loss of vitamin A activity. Oxidation of the vitamin by atmospheric oxygen may be inhibited by "antioxidants" such as hydroquinone or vitamin E (page 983).

In anhydrous media, vitamin A reacts with antimony trichloride to form a vivid blue compound with an absorption maximum at 620 mμ, while the β-carotene derivative is green with an absorption maximum at 590 mμ. This reaction is the basis of the most widely employed chemical method for determination of these substances.

The carotenes possess no vitamin A activity and are useful nutritionally only insofar as they are converted to vitamin A. β-Carotene is a symmetrical molecule so that two moles of vitamin A are obtained for each mole of β-carotene administered.

Since, however, in α- and γ-carotenes, as well as in *cryptoxanthin,* one of the two rings differs in structure from that of vitamin A, these carotenoids yield only one mole of vitamin A and, therefore, on a weight basis are only half as effective as vitamin A and β-carotene. *Lycopene* and *xanthophyll,* in which neither of the two ionone rings is identical with that of vitamin A, are devoid of vitamin A activity.

The biological specificity of the β-ionone ring in vitamin A is not absolute. As noted previously (page 820), the carotenoid present in the retinas and livers of fresh-water fish differs from that in salt-water fish and in most mammals. The form present in fresh-water fish, vitamin A_2, differs from A_1 (page 818) in that the ring contains an additional double bond. However, this material is as active as vitamin A_1 in promoting the growth of vitamin A–deficient animals. Generally, A_1 is found in the all-*trans* configuration, but some marine crustacea contain the *neo b* form (11-*cis*).

Although pure vitamin A and carotene are available as standards, it remains the convention to state the vitamin A content of foodstuffs in international units rather than as the weight of vitamin A. β-Carotene, which was available before vitamin A_1, was adopted as the international standard; one international unit (I.U.) of vitamin A is equivalent to the activity of 0.6 μg of crystalline β-carotene.

Biogenesis and Metabolism of Vitamin A. Carotenoids are present in virtually all green plants. The repeating unit in the side chain is the isoprene group, which also appears frequently in other natural products (page 80). The distribution of carbon atoms in vitamin A conforms to that expected from polymerization of four isoprene units. However, little is known of its biogenesis other than that this can occur from acetate and involves intermediates, notably mevalonic acid, which also occur in cholesterol synthesis, and that the α-carbon of glycine, via δ-aminolevulinic acid, can be incorporated into the final carotenoid.

The mode of cleavage of β-carotene to vitamin A has not been established. For many years, the liver was considered to be the sole organ in which this scission was accomplished, since the liver content of vitamin A increases after administration of carotene. Also, administration of carotene to persons with severe liver disease results in a rise in plasma concentration of carotene but not of vitamin A as in normal individuals. However, Deuel and his associates have concluded that the intestine rather than the liver is the major site of the conversion of β-carotene to vitamin A; other tissues may also be active in this regard. *Parenteral* administration of β-carotene to vitamin A–depleted rats resulted in deposition of carotene rather than of vitamin A in the liver, and manifestations of vitamin A deficiency were not alleviated. Nevertheless, persons with liver disease may have an impaired capacity to convert carotene to vitamin A; the explanation for this is not clear if the intestine is the major locus of this reaction.

When ingested, vitamin A is readily stored in the liver, esterified to long-chain fatty acids. Since excess vitamin A cannot be excreted by any route, all vitamin A which is absorbed must be stored. The active form of vitamin A, except for the role of retinene in vision (page 815), is not known. Vitamin A acid, in which the terminal carbon of the side chain has been oxidized to a carboxyl group, readily replaces vitamin A for all functions other than vision and maintenance of reproduction (see below). The latter failures indicate that the acid cannot be reduced to the aldehyde or alcohol. However, vitamin A acid cannot be recovered from the tissues of animals to which it has been administered. Hence, it may be some further metabolic product which is the physiologically active substance. The acid form cannot be stored, and the signs of vitamin A deficiency appear shortly after its administration has ceased. The ultimate metabolic fate of vitamin A is not known. These relationships can be summarized as follows:

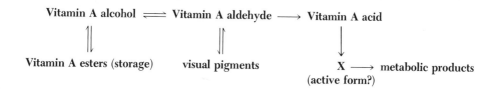

Vitamin A deficiency has a profound effect on virtually every organ. However, there has been no clue to the function of vitamin A in any metabolic reaction except for its highly specialized role in the visual process (page 815). A possible role of vitamin A in chondroitin sulfate synthesis is referred to below.

Vitamin A Deficiency. The sequelae of vitamin A deficiency show little species variation. Young animals invariably fail to grow; epithelial cells in all structures undergo keratinizing metaplasia. The best-known changes are in the eyes, giving rise to xerophthalmia. Increased susceptibility to infection of the respiratory tract is frequent. The cells of the kidney medulla may cornify and renal calculi form. The ducts of glands of all types may become blocked and the glands atrophy. Atrophy of the germinal epithelium causes sterility in the male. The vaginal smear in the female shows cornification of cells. Nevertheless, normal ovulation and implantation occur, but normal young are seldom born to the vitamin A–deficient animal because of defective placentas. Rat fetuses removed by cesarean section from vitamin A–deficient females show various abnormalities. Mammary tissue of vitamin A–deficient animals exhibits an increased sensitivity to estrogens.

The earliest sign of vitamin A deficiency in man and experimental animals seems to be night blindness. The relationship between vitamin A and vision has been presented previously (page 817). It should be emphasized that there is no relation between the defect in night blindness and that in xerophthalmia.

Wald was able to observe the ultimate consequences of vitamin A deficiency in the rat retina by supplying vitamin A acid to protect the animal in other respects. After 5 months, the visual threshold (the luminance of a 0.02-sec. flash which evokes a perceptible electroretinogram) was increased to 2,500 times normal. In 10 months, the rats were blind. The visual cells decreased in number, and the outer segments of the rods disintegrated and then disappeared. At this time the damage could no longer be reversed by vitamin A administration.

Cessation of skeletal growth is an early manifestation of vitamin A deficiency, although histologically the bones resemble those observed in animals in which growth has ceased because of inanition. Failure of skeletal growth appears to reflect a defective synthesis of chondroitin sulfate which has been reported to be due to inability to make phosphoadenosine phosphosulfate (page 515). The early failure in the growth of endochondral bone results in lesions in the central nervous system, because of continued growth of nervous tissues after arrest of development of the bony casing. Increased cerebrospinal pressure occurs before other changes are manifest.

Hyperkeratotic papules around the hair follicles have been considered a characteristic finding in vitamin A–deficient human beings, leading in extreme cases to a "toad skin." Similar skin lesions do not appear in animals fed a diet adequate in all respects except for vitamin A. However, if the young rat is placed on a diet deficient in both vitamin A and in most of the B complex, analogous changes in the skin do occur as the innermost layers of the dermis atrophy. The skin lesions of man with vitamin A deficiency may occur only in the presence of a concomitant deficiency of the vitamins of the B complex.

Evidence of vitamin A deficiency is more difficult to produce in adult than in young animals because of two factors. First, the changes characteristic of vitamin A deficiency, particularly in the skeleton and nervous system, can be observed only in growing animals; this is also true, to some extent, with respect to epithelial changes. Second, the store of vitamin A present in the liver of normal, well-fed animals may be sufficient to meet the demands of an adult for some years. The newborn, however, does not possess a hepatic store of vitamin A. Xerophthalmia thus affects large numbers of children but relatively few adults.

Attempts have been made to produce vitamin A deficiency in volunteer human adults. In general, only impaired dark adaptation has resulted in subjects on a vitamin A–poor diet for more than 2 years. Indeed, various reports have shown conflicting results with respect to the ease with which impaired dark adaptation may be produced. In a recent study, only one subject in a group of 71 showed persistent diminution in dark adaptation during a 2-year period. In other subjects, dark adaptation impairment was variable; occasionally adaptation fell to low levels but then returned to normal, even though there had been no increase in the vitamin A allowance.

Vitamin A Toxicity. When the young rat is overdosed with vitamin A, the bones become extremely fragile, leading to numerous spontaneous fractures. The findings in children who have received overdosages of as much as 500,000 units of vitamin A per day over a considerable period are not so dramatic but are manifest as tender swellings over the long bones, with limitation of motion, and definite hyperostoses. Human adults receiving 500,000 units per day show calcification of pericapsular, ligamentous, and subperiosteal structures similar to that seen in rats. At still higher dosage levels, severe headache, nosebleed, anorexia, nausea, weakness, and a dermatitis become evident within a few days. Related phenomena were noted by Fell in studies of the effects of excess vitamin A on rudimentary limb buds in tissue culture. Bone formation ceased, and existing cartilage was destroyed. This has been traced to the release and activation of the lysosomes (page 270) of the cartilage cells. The hydrolytic enzymes of these particles readily account for the destruction of cartilage and of bone matrix. Presumably similar phenomena explain the grossly malformed offspring produced by administration of massive doses of vitamin A to the pregnant rat. It will be recognized that these manifestations of vitamin A excess, like those of iron (page 804) and of vitamin D (page 983), are the penalty to the animal for his inability to excrete surplus quantities of these materials.

Vitamin A in Human Nutrition. Fruits and vegetables supply approximately 65 per cent of the vitamin A of the American diet. About half this vitamin intake is derived from leafy green and yellow vegetables; lettuce, spinach, chard, escarole, carrots, and sweet potatoes are particularly good sources of a mixture of carotenoids. It is not possible to state to what extent these carotenoids are absorbed by man and converted to vitamin A. Bile salts are not directly necessary for the absorption of vitamin A or carotenes; however, steatorrhea results in fecal excretion of a large fraction of the dietary vitamin A and carotenoids. Measures which improve gastrointestinal absorption of lipids, such as prior emulsification of the lipid mixture, also improve absorption of vitamin A.

Oxidation of vitamin A and the carotenes may result in significant destruction of these compounds present in the usual diet; this can be prevented by an adequate concentration of vitamin E (see below). Fish-liver oils are the most potent natural sources of vitamin A; depending upon the species of fish and the time of year of catch, fish livers contain 2,000 to 100,000 vitamin A I.U. per gram. In contrast, human livers appear to contain 500 to 1,000 I.U. per gram. The vitamin A content of cod-liver oil is the lowest of all fish-liver oils used as commercial sources of this vitamin; those of the shark and halibut are among the highest.

Experiments designed to establish the minimum adequate dietary level of vitamin A for adult men have been inconclusive because of the large hepatic stores of the vitamin in adults. The recommended allowances shown in Table 52.2 (page 930) are liberal, and deficiency is unlikely if the vitamin A intake remains at these levels.

VITAMIN D

In 1918, Mellanby produced experimental rickets in puppies and showed clearly the preventive and therapeutic effectiveness of cod-liver oil. A few years later, McCollum found that cod-liver oil was also effective in preventing rickets induced in the rat by a low-calcium diet and that no activity was lost when the oil was aerated at 100°C., a procedure known to inactivate vitamin A. This was the first demonstration of the existence of a substance now designated as vitamin D.

Recognition of the chemical nature of vitamin D resulted from a long series of investigations. Knowing that rickets was prevalent in areas in which children were exposed to a minimum of sunlight, Huldschinsky demonstrated in 1919 that ultraviolet light exerted a curative action on rickets. Hess and Steenbock, in seeking an explanation of the effect of ultraviolet light, independently discovered that irradiation conferred antirachitic properties on otherwise rachitogenic diets. The activatable material was identified as *7-dehydrocholesterol* by Windaus. Meanwhile, it was observed that irradiation of yeast ergosterol yielded an extraordinarily potent antirachitic agent. However, whereas irradiated 7-dehydrocholesterol was as active in curing rickets in the chick as in the rat, irradiated ergosterol was much less effective in the chick than in the rat. This indicated that the active materials produced by irradiation of the two sterols were different. Irradiation of ergosterol yields a series of isomeric sterols, one of which, *calciferol,* is markedly antirachitic and is designated vitamin D_2. Further irradiation inactivates calciferol. Irradiated 7-dehydrocholesterol is designated vitamin D_3. The material for which the term vitamin D_1 was originally reserved proved to be a mixture of calciferol and other sterols, and this designation is no longer employed. The structures of these natural precursors and their biologically active photoderivatives have been given previously (page 84). There may be other sterols, active as vitamin D, distributed in nature. Thus, some fish oils contain a ketonic sterol which, in its enolic form, is about twice as active as calciferol.

Of the series of compounds obtained from irradiation of ergosterol, only calciferol (vitamin D_2) possesses antirachitic activity. However, one of the series, *tachysterol,* may be catalytically reduced to dihydrotachysterol, which is antirachitic. Irradiation of 7-dehydrocholesterol in the skin accounts for the antirachitic efficacy of sunlight and ultraviolet irradiation. Commercial vitamin D is obtained by irradiation of ergosterol. By convention, one international unit of vitamin D is the activity of 0.01 ml. of average medicinal cod-liver oil and is approximately equivalent to 0.05 μg of calciferol.

The presence of vitamin D in fish-liver oils has not been adequately explained. If it be assumed that vitamin D can arise only through solar irradiation of sterols, then fish liver contains vitamin D only because fish have preformed vitamin D in their diet. The ultimate source of the vitamin in fish-liver oils would therefore appear to be the plant and animal plankton near the sea surface. However, assay of such materials has consistently given negative results, and the problem remains unsolved.

Since milk, the chief source of calcium in the diet, is widely consumed by children, it is logical that this foodstuff should be chosen for fortification with vitamin D. Fortification may be accomplished by irradiation with ultraviolet light, a universal practice in the preparation of evaporated milk, or by addition of vitamin D concentrates. In the former procedure, activated 7-dehydrocholesterol is produced; in the latter, calciferol is added. Another means of augmenting the vitamin D content of milk is to feed irradiated yeast to cows; a portion of the calciferol fed appears in the milk. Since fish-liver oils are not normally included in the diet and no other foodstuffs contain quantities of vitamin D, the growing child ordinarily relies upon irradiation by sunlight to provide his vitamin D. Prior to the era of routine administration of fish-liver oils or concentrates to infants, rickets was common among children of the northern latitudes, where winter is long and the sun may be obscured for several consecutive months.

Vitamin D in Metabolism. All the manifestations of vitamin D deficiency are due to defective bone formation, but it is not possible to explain adequately the role of vitamin D in its prevention or cure. As indicated earlier (page 777), vitamin D mediates absorption of calcium from the intestine, either by enhancing active transport or by facilitating diffusion. This, however, is not an adequate explanation for the effectiveness of the vitamin in the treatment and prevention of rickets. Rachitic cartilage fails to calcify when incubated in serum from rachitic animals even if calcium and phosphate are added, yet calcification occurs readily in serum from normal animals with identical concentrations of calcium and phosphate. Further, healing of rickets is initiated much more rapidly than can be accounted for on the basis of the additional calcium absorbed in the first several days after vitamin D therapy is initiated. At present, it can be stated only that in the presence of dietary vitamin D, calcification of the matrix of bone occurs, while in vitamin D deficiency this does not take place.

Rickets is a disease of growing bone. The last stage of bone growth, deposition of inorganic bone minerals in the newly formed matrix, fails to occur, but matrix formation continues. The provisional zone of calcification is no longer clearly demarcated but is irregular and deformed. Bowlegs, knock knees, rachitic rosary (a beaded appearance of the ribs), and "pigeon breast" are skeletal deformities seen in rachitic children.

Although severe rickets is seldom seen in the United States, mild early rickets may be prevalent. Histological evidence of rickets was found in almost 50 per cent of 700 children dying of all causes in the Johns Hopkins Hospital during the period 1940 to 1942. Since the newborn infant has virtually no reserve stores of vitamin D, vitamin D supplementation or adequate exposure to sunlight must be provided.

The ability of mammals to store vitamin D is relatively limited. However, it is possible to administer single doses which provide a several weeks' or months' supply of vitamin D. The fate of administered vitamin D in the mammal is not clear. Some is excreted in the bile, but the sum of urinary and fecal excretion is usually considerably less than the amount ingested. When calciferol-C^{14} is given, about 15 per cent is found in the liver, much smaller amounts appear in other tissues, and the major portion of the administered material is degraded to unidentified products.

Toxicity of Vitamin D. Excessive quantities of calciferol given either to children or to adults produce demineralization of bone, and multiple fractures may occur after only minimal trauma. Serum concentrations of both calcium and phosphate are markedly elevated, resulting in metastatic calcification of many soft tissues and formation of renal calculi. The latter may block the renal tubules sufficiently to cause a secondary hydronephrosis; frequently it is the renal disease which leads to the need for medical assistance. The basis of these effects of vitamin D overdosage is not known.

VITAMIN E

In 1920 Mattill and Conklin observed that rats fed cow's milk were incapable of bearing young. During the next few years, other laboratories noted this relationship between diet and fertility, and it was soon found that oils, particularly that from wheat germ, were rich in some factor which restores fertility in both male and female rats. The active factor was designated vitamin E.

Although ordinarily stable at high temperature and to acids, the active material is rapidly inactivated in the presence of rancid fat. On the other hand, the material inhibits both the development of rancidity and oxidative destruction of vitamin A in natural fats. Once rancidity is initiated, however, the products of the oxidation of the unsaturated fatty acids destroy vitamin E. Indeed, the independent discovery of vitamin E in Evans' laboratory was due in part to the accidental use of slightly rancid lard in a ration which otherwise would not have induced E deficiency.

Vitamin E was isolated from wheat-germ oil in 1936 by Evans, Emerson, and Emerson and given the name *tocopherol* (Gk. *tokos*, childbirth; *phero*, to bear; *ol*, an alcohol). α-Tocopherol is an oil which was isolated as a crystalline ester of allophanic acid. The structure of α-tocopherol was established by the efforts of several laboratories, notably those of Todd, Evans, Karrer, and Fernholz. Seven tocopherols, derivatives of the parent substance *tocol*, 2-methyl, 2-[trimethyl-tridecyl], 6-hydroxychromane, have been found in nature; of these, α-tocopherol has the widest distribution and greatest biological activity.

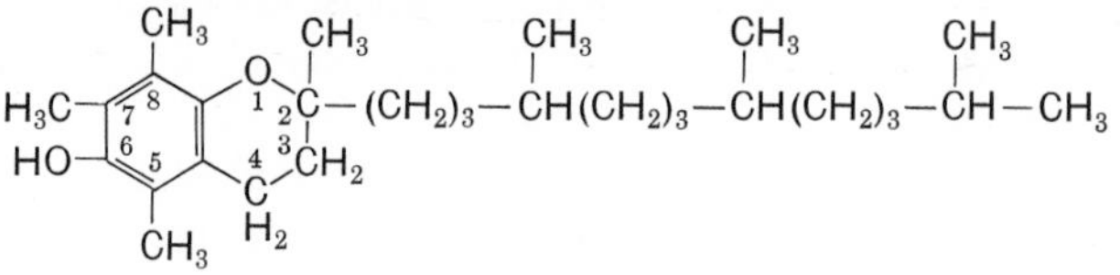

$$\text{H}_3\text{C} \overset{7}{\underset{6}{\fbox{}}} \overset{8}{\underset{5}{}} \quad \overset{1}{\underset{4}{}} \overset{2}{\underset{3}{}} \text{C}-(\text{CH}_2)_3-\text{CH}(\text{CH}_2)_3-\text{CH}(\text{CH}_2)_3-\text{CH}-\text{CH}_3$$

α-**Tocopherol**

The structures of six tocopherols are summarized below.

Tocopherol	Substituents
Alpha	5,7,8-Trimethyltocol
Beta	5,8-Dimethyltocol
Gamma	7,8-Dimethyltocol
Delta	8-Methyltocol
Eta	7-Methyltocol
Zeta	5,7-Dimethyltocol

Vitamin E Deficiency. The manifestations of vitamin E deficiency in laboratory animals vary considerably, and, at first observation, the diverse disturbances appear to have no common basis. The classical manifestation in the rat is infertility, but the reasons for this infertility differ in males and females. In the female rat, there is no loss in ability to produce seemingly healthy ova, nor is there a defect in the placenta or uterus. However, some time after the first week of embryonic life, fetal death occurs, and the fetuses are resorbed. This can be prevented if vitamin E is administered at any time up to the fifth or sixth day of embryonic life. In the male, the earliest observable effect of vitamin E deficiency is immotility of spermatazoa; later, there is degeneration of the germinal epithelium. However, there is no alteration in the secondary sex organs or diminution in sexual vigor, although the latter may disappear with continued vitamin E deficiency.

Other striking changes in the vitamin E–deficient rat include degeneration of the renal tubular epithelium, depigmentation of the incisors, and the appearance in lipid depots of a brown pigment of unknown nature. This pigmentation occurs only if an unsaturated lipid like cod-liver oil is included in the diet. Rats fed diets deficient in vitamin E and protein develop acute hepatic necrosis, which may be prevented by cystine, methionine, tocopherol, or factor 3 (see page 944). This hepatic necrosis also occurs only if the diet contains appreciable quantities of unsaturated lipid. Another manifestation of vitamin E deficiency is in vitro hemolysis of red cells in the presence of peroxide or alloxan derivatives such as dialuric acid. Vitamin E deficiency in rats ultimately produces muscular dystrophy with progressive paralysis of the hind legs, decreased muscle creatine concentration, creatinuria, and a slight decline in creatinine excretion. Signs of vitamin A deficiency may also develop because of the destructive oxidation of vitamin A in the ration in the absence of the antioxidant properties of vitamin E.

Herbivorous animals such as the rabbit and guinea pig are more sensitive to vitamin E deficiency than is the rat even when their diets contain relatively little unsaturated lipid. In these species, muscular dystrophy develops very rapidly, and the animals may succumb after a few weeks. Similar observations have been made in calves, lambs ("white muscle disease"), and ducklings. Young chicks placed on a vitamin E–deficient feed exhibit extensive capillary damage and encephalomalacia. Eggs from vitamin E–deficient hens have a low hatchability. The embryos develop hemorrhages on the third or fourth day of incubation and are dead by the fifth day. Deficiency in the monkey results in a hemolytic anemia.

A single case of what was reported to be authentic tocopherol deficiency in an adult human being has been described. A woman with chronic xanthomatous biliary cirrhosis and impaired intestinal lipid absorption also evidenced low serum tocopherol concentration, muscular weakness, creatinuria, and red cells which were unusually fragile in the presence of dialuric acid. These signs of vitamin E deficiency disappeared after administration of α-tocopherol. Sensitivity of erythrocytes to peroxide and dialuric acid, which diminishes with tocopherol administration, has also been observed in premature infants and infants with steatorrhea.

Metabolism of Tocopherol. The property of tocopherol which appears to be related to most manifestations of deficiency is its ability to inhibit the autoxidation of unsaturated fatty acids. Dam and his associates demonstrated that methylene blue, thiodiphenylamine, and N,N,-diphenyl, p-phenylenediamine (DPPD), substances which participate in reversible oxidation-reduction reactions but which do not resemble tocopherol in structure, prevent many of the manifestations of vitamin E deficiency. In the chick, methylene blue prevented capillary damage and encephalomalacia; in the rat, it prevented appearance of sensitivity to the in vitro dialuric acid–hemolysis test, depigmentation of the incisors, accumulation of brown pigment in the lipid stores, and hepatic necrosis in animals on low-protein diets. DPPD has been shown to substitute for vitamin E through three generations of rats. Like tocopherol, methylene blue also increased hepatic storage of vitamin A in animals on diets containing marginal amounts of this vitamin. Many different substances whose structures bear some resemblance to that of tocopherol (coumarins, chromanes, phenols, quinones, etc.) show some vitamin E activity. It is not known whether the relative biological activity of these compounds correlates with their potency as antioxidants.

The tissues of vitamin E–deficient animals, particularly cardiac and skeletal muscle, consume oxygen more rapidly than do normal tissues. α-Tocopherol does not readily undergo reversible oxidation. Chemical oxidation yields α-tocopherylquinone and α-tocopheryloxide; the former may be reduced to α-tocopherol, but it is not known whether similar events occur in biological electron transport systems. The increased oxygen consumption of vitamin E–deficient muscle appears to relate to peroxidation of unsaturated fatty acids. In other tissues, *e.g.*, liver, this leads to disturbance of the structure of mitochondria and reduced respiration. According to one report, peroxidation of unsaturated fatty acids in the endoplasmic reticulum of muscle results in release of lysosomal hydrolases, thereby causing the muscular dystrophy. In sum, vitamin E is not utilized for biosynthesis of a coenzyme. All manifestations of vitamin E deficiency appear to be secondary to the uninhibited peroxidation of polyunsaturated fatty acids.

The interrelationship of vitamin E and selenium, or factor 3 (page 944), remains obscure. Vitamin E seems specific with respect to prevention of reproductive impairment and of muscular dystrophy in rabbits, but selenium abolishes the requirement for vitamin E with respect to muscular dystrophy in lambs and to hepatic necrosis in all species. An ample dietary supply of selenium abolishes all requirement for vitamin E in the chick. The mechanism of action of selenium or its physiological derivatives is not known.

Both the chromane ring and the side chain of α-tocopherol are oxidized by man; the product, shown below, is excreted in the bile conjugated with two moles of glucuronic acid via the two hydroxyl groups.

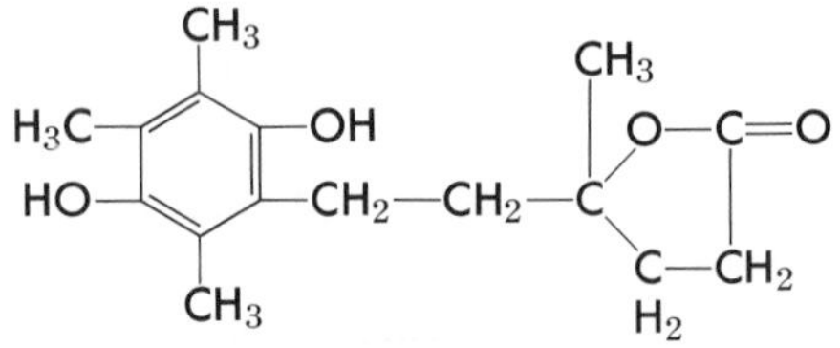

Vitamin E Requirements. The reported signs of tocopherol deficiency in a single person with defective fat absorption (page 985) are the only evidence that vitamin E is required by the human being. In view of the universal requirement by other animal species it appears that tocopherols are essential in the human diet and that their widespread distribution suffices to prevent manifestations of deficiency under most circumstances. The quantitative requirement by man for vitamin E is unknown; the richest natural sources are plant oils, *e.g.*, wheat germ, rice, cottonseed, as well as the lipids of green leaves. Fish-liver oils, abundant in vitamins A and D, are devoid of tocopherol.

VITAMIN K

Henrik Dam observed that chicks fed synthetic rations develop a hemorrhagic condition characterized by a prolonged blood-clotting time. The preventive substance in various foodstuffs was designated vitamin K (*Koagulations* vitamin) by Dam. Dam, Karrer, and their associates isolated the vitamin from alfalfa concentrates and established its structure in 1939. The same year, Doisy and his colleagues obtained substances with vitamin K activity from alfalfa and fish meal and noted differences in their physical properties and absorption spectra. The material in alfalfa was then designated vitamin K_1 and that from fish meal K_2.

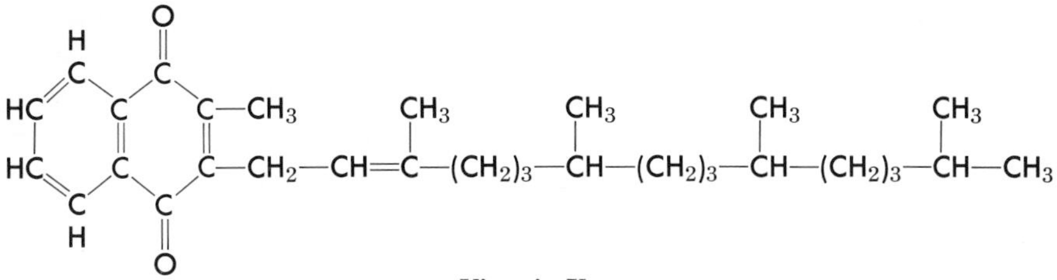

Vitamin K₁
(2-methyl-3-phytyl-1,4-naphthoquinone)

A number of vitamin K_2 analogues are known which differ only in the length of the side chain; that from fish meal has 30 carbon atoms.

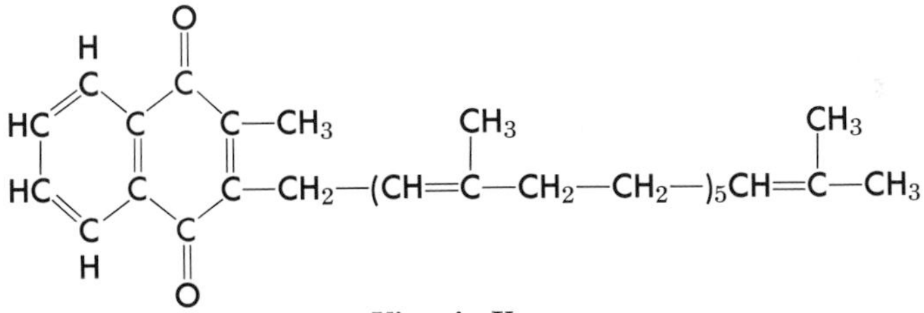

Vitamin K₂₍₃₀₎
(2-methyl-3-difarnesyl-1,4-naphthoquinone)

The symbol (30) connotes the number of carbon atoms in the side chain.

Synthesis of vitamin K_1 was accomplished almost simultaneously by three independent groups in 1939. The same year, Ansbacher and Fernholz discovered that 2-methyl-1,4-naphthoquinone (menadione) possesses marked vitamin K activity.

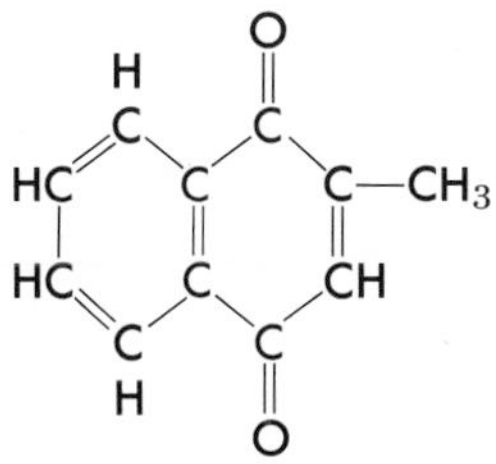

Menadione
(2-methyl-1,4,-naphthoquinone)

Many related compounds have also been tested and found to have vitamin K activity. Of these, 2-methyl-1,4-naphthoquinone is as effective as vitamin K_1 on a molar basis. The reduced form of menadione, 2-methyl-1,4-naphthohydroquinone, is almost as active as the parent compound in chick assays. The nitrogen analogue, 4-imino-2-methyl-1-naphthoquinone, is three to four times as potent as vitamin K_1 and is the most effective compound yet studied.

Vitamin K Deficiency. Vitamin K deficiency resulting from dietary lack of the vitamin does not occur in the usual laboratory rodents, not because they do not require this material, but because it is supplied constantly as a result of synthesis by intestinal bacteria. If growth of the intestinal flora is inhibited by sulfonamide feeding, if germ-free animals are employed, or if care is taken to prevent coprophagy, such animals rapidly develop signs of vitamin K deficiency. In man, steatorrhea due to biliary obstruction, sprue, pancreatic failure, or other causes, with attendant diminished intestinal absorption of lipids, results in vitamin K deficiency.

The role of the vitamin in blood clotting has been discussed previously (Chap. 33). Deficiency in vitamin K is marked by diminished plasma prothrombin concentration. However, the prolonged blood-clotting time results primarily from failure of hepatic synthesis of proconvertin (page 653). Relatively minor injuries which ordinarily are innocuous may, in vitamin K–deficient animals, result in bleeding sufficient to cause shock and death. Since deficiency may exist as an indirect consequence of biliary obstruction, vitamin K is generally administered parenterally before surgery for repair of this condition.

Newborn infants may also show signs of vitamin K deficiency. This is manifested as "hemorrhagic disease of the newborn," which persists only until the establishment of a bacterial flora in the infant's intestine. Administration of vitamin K to pregnant mothers before parturition has decreased the incidence of this disease. No manifestations of vitamin K deficiency other than impaired blood clotting have been observed. No statement can be made about the human requirement for vitamin K. Indeed, it would appear that no dietary supply of this vitamin is necessary as long as intestinal absorption of lipids is adequate. The total amount required, whether provided by the diet or by the intestinal flora, is not known at present.

Metabolic Role of Vitamin K. The functional basis for the effect of vitamin K on hepatic synthesis of prothrombin and proconvertin (Chap. 33) is unknown. However, the wide distribution of this vitamin in plant, animal, and bacterial cells may indicate a fundamental metabolic significance entirely unrelated to its special role in the blood-clotting mechanism. Martius has observed "uncoupling" of oxidative phosphorylation in mitochondria from vitamin K–deficient chicks and after Dicumarol administration. Dicumarol uncouples the electron transport chain both from DPNH to cytochrome c and from ferrocytochrome c to oxygen. Liver contains a flavoprotein which catalyzes reduction of menadione by DPNH. However, it is uncertain whether there is any vitamin K in mitochondria, and the suggestion that this vitamin is required for normal oxidative phosphorylation, which has stimulated much research, has not gained acceptance.

The physiologically active form of this vitamin appears to be vitamin $K_{2(20)}$. This is the form of the vitamin found in liver after administration of menadione-C^{14}. The work of Martius indicates that the side chain of vitamin K_1 is removed and that a 20-carbon vitamin K_2 side chain is affixed to the ring. Presumably the enzyme catalyzing this reaction is the same as that which, in liver, also promotes addition of the side chain to the ring structure of ubiquinone (page 314). The ultimate fate of vitamin K is unknown, but some menadione is excreted as a mixture of the monosulfate and diglucosiduronide of the reduced form, 2-methyl-1,4-naphthohydroquinone.

VITAMINS—SOME CONCLUDING REMARKS

It is unlikely that any new dietary requirements will be revealed by the classical techniques by which the essential food factors were discovered. There remains, however, the possibility that man and other animals require additional, as yet unknown compounds which are either provided by intestinal bacteria or, perhaps, transferred from mother to fetus in sufficient quantity to maintain adequate growth and health for one generation or more. These possibilities are illustrated by the histories of vitamin K, biotin, folic acid, and cobalamine. It should be emphasized that, as yet, no animals have been grown or maintained on a diet of exclusively synthetic ingredients. The minuscule requirements noted for cobalamine and biotin are a reminder that as long as natural products are fed, the possible existence of undiscovered factors must be recognized.

Review of the present knowledge of the metabolic role of the various food factors, and of the pathogenesis of the corresponding deficiency syndromes caused by lack of these factors, reveals that in virtually no instance can the deficiency syndrome be adequately explained in metabolic terms. Thus, the "three Ds" of pellagra (diarrhea, dermatitis, dementia) cannot be explained in terms of the function of the pyridine nucleotides. The mesenchymal failure of scurvy cannot yet be related to the chemical properties of ascorbic acid; the polyneuritis of beriberi cannot be explained in terms of diminished pyruvic acid dehydrogenase (page 317) activity. The dermal manifestations of many deficiencies presumably reflect failure of certain of the metabolic activities in which the essential nutrients are involved, but the basis for the relationships is unknown. Indeed, the participation of vitamin A in the visual process is the only instance of a clear relationship between the known function of a vitamin and a manifestation of the deficiency state.

Further, there is no reason to be certain that, for each of the essential food factors, all the possible manifestations of deficiency have been described. Deficiency of an essential factor may result in a profound disturbance of the function of a single organ or cell type, and the animal may die before it becomes possible to observe the effects of the deficiency in other organ systems. Nevertheless, the factor in question may be equally essential to the function of all cells. Thus, the vitamin E–deficient rabbit dies rapidly with symptoms only of muscular dystrophy and pathology of skeletal and cardiac muscle. Yet chronic vitamin E deficiency in the rat leads to disturbances in many other organs. Niacin deficiency in the dog on corn-containing rations results in blacktongue; yet this disease can be alleviated by administration of saline solution, and then a new disease syndrome develops. In each case the animal dies of failure of that essential process first effected by the dietary deficiency. To uncover other reactions influenced by the particular dietary factor, it may be necessary first to devise procedures which permit prolongation of life by circumventing in some manner the primary effects of the deficiency.

MALNUTRITION

Despite significant advances in understanding of nutrition and the fact that, from the standpoint of available information, no one need be malnourished, malnutrition is increasingly prevalent among the world's population. Nor is it entirely true that the roots of malnutrition are solely economic; in many cases ignorance is an equally important factor. Beriberi, kwashiorkor, pellagra, sprue, and xerophthalmia still exist on a large scale; severe rickets and scurvy may be somewhat less frequent.

Surveys of nutritional habits of peoples in economically underdeveloped areas frequently indicate an appallingly low intake of essential nutrients. This does not, however, always result in the appearance of deficiency diseases. The explanation for this is to be found in one of the basic concepts of nutrition, the *balanced diet*. In both man and experimental animals it is well established that a balanced dietary mixture, even if restricted in *total quantity*, is preferable to a regime that is adequate in most respects but badly deficient in only *one* nutrient. Inadequate quantity may lead to delayed growth, anemia, or hypoproteinemia, but the imbalanced diet results in pellagra, beriberi, scurvy, etc. The rat fed a diet completely lacking in B vitamins survives for a surprising length of time, while a deficiency of thiamine alone may be fatal in a few weeks. It should be noted that genetic differences among individuals may drastically alter the quantitative or even qualitative composition of the balanced dietary mixture desirable for optimal health. Thus, galactosemic children must eschew lactose, phenylketonuric individuals must ingest a minimum of phenylalanine, diabetics must carefully balance dietary carbohydrate and lipid. It seems likely that this list will be extended in the future.

Improved methods of laboratory diagnosis permit the detection of early deficiencies of many of the essential nutrients. Application of these techniques, particularly in large-scale nutritional surveys of populations, has helped to improve the nutritional status of the Western world while revealing the enormous magnitude of the problem of undernourishment of peoples living in the equatorial belt. Indeed, in the United States it almost becomes necessary to redefine malnutrition. This term has classically implied undernutrition of one or more elements of the diet. If, instead, it is taken to imply a deviation from *balanced nutrition*, then a large segment of the American population is malnourished in that obesity is a most serious nutritional problem. It is estimated that at least 15 per cent of the population is overweight in comparison with accepted standards and that at least 5,000,000 people in the United States are pathologically overweight, *i.e.*, their weights exceed by more than 20 per cent the accepted standards for their heights and skeletal structures. If indeed hypercholesterolemia is significant in the pathogenesis of atherosclerosis, improper nutrition contributes to the leading single cause of death in the United States and Europe.

Relatively few investigations of the conditions for *optimal* nutrition have been reported; even the criteria for optimal nutrition have not been established. The criterion generally employed in experimental nutrition has been the weight response of young rats. However, it is not established that the ingestion of a diet which permits maximum weight gains through childhood and adolescence contributes to long and healthy adult life. Indeed, available experimental evidence suggests that diets which provide the minimal intake of essential nutrients compatible with health also promote longevity. Should this prove generally to be the case, many of the recommendations that have been given in Table 52.2 (page 930) may require revision.

REFERENCES

Books

Albanese, A., ed., "Protein and Amino Acid Nutrition," Academic Press, Inc., New York, 1959.

Brock, J. F., "Recent Advances in Human Nutrition," Little, Brown and Company, Boston, 1961.

Burton, B. T., ed., "Heinz Handbook of Nutrition," McGraw-Hill Book Company, Inc., New York, 1959.

Ciba Foundation Study Group, "Mechanism of Action of Water-soluble Vitamins," Little, Brown and Company, Boston, 1962.

Cooper, L. F., Barber, E. M., and Mitchell, H. S., "Nutrition in Health and Disease," J. B. Lippincott Company, Philadelphia, 1960.

Crampton, E. W., and Lloyd, L. E., "Fundamentals of Nutrition," W. H. Freeman and Company, San Francisco, 1960.

Davidson, S., Meiklejohn, A. P., and Passmore, R., "Human Nutrition and Dietetics," E. & S. Livingstone Ltd., Edinburgh, 1959.

"Endemic Goiter," World Health Organization, Publ. 44, Geneva, 1960.

Follis, R. H., Jr., "Deficiency Disease," Charles C Thomas, Publisher, Springfield, Ill., 1958.

Gillman, J., and Gillman, T., "Perspectives in Human Malnutrition," Grune & Stratton, Inc., New York, 1951.

Goldsmith, G., "Nutritional Diagnosis," Charles C Thomas, Publisher, Springfield, Ill., 1959.

Goodwin, T. W., "The Biosynthesis of Vitamins and Related Compounds," Academic Press, Inc., New York, 1963.

Griswold, R. M., "The Experimental Study of Foods," Houghton Mifflin Company, Boston, 1962.

Jukes, T. H., "B-Vitamins for Blood Formation," Charles C Thomas, Publisher, Springfield, Ill., 1952.

Keys, A., Brozek, J., Henschel A., Mickelsen, O., and Taylor, H. L., "The Biology of Human Starvation," vols. I and II, University of Minnesota Press, Minneapolis, 1950.

McCance, R. A., and Widdowson, E. M., "The Composition of Foods," Her Majesty's Stationery Office, London, 1960.

Monier-Williams, G. W., "Trace Elements in Food," John Wiley & Sons, Inc., New York, 1949.

Moore, T., "Vitamin A," Elsevier Publishing Company, Amsterdam, 1957.

"Nutrition Surveys; Their Techniques and Value," *Natl. Research Council (U.S.) Bull.* 117, Washington, 1949.

"Present Knowledge of Nutrition," The Nutrition Foundation, Inc., New York, 1956.

"Progress in Meeting Protein Needs of Infants and Children," *Natl. Acad. Sci.-Nat. Research Council,* Publ. 843, Washington, 1961.

Sebrell, W. H., ed., "Control of Malnutrition in Man," American Public Health Association, New York, 1960.

Sebrell, W. H., Jr., and Harris, R. S., "The Vitamins," vols. I, II, and III, Academic Press, Inc., New York, 1954.

Sinclair, H. M., ed., "Essential Fatty Acids," Academic Press, Inc., New York, 1958.

Watt, B. K., and Merrill, A. L., "Composition of Foods, Raw, Processed and Prepared," *U.S. Dept. Agr. Handbook* 8, Washington, 1950.

Wohl, M. G., and Goodhart, R. S., eds., "Modern Nutrition in Health and Disease," Lea & Febiger, Philadelphia, 1960.

Woolley, D. W., "Antimetabolites," John Wiley & Sons, Inc., New York, 1951.

Review Articles

Allison, J. B., Interpretation of Nitrogen Balance Data, *Federation Proc.,* **10,** 676–683, 1951.

Best, C. H., and Lucas, C. C., Choline—Chemistry and Significance as a Dietary Factor, *Vitamins and Hormones,* **1,** 1–59, 1943.

Block, R. J., and Mitchell, H. H., Correlation of the Amino Acid Composition of Proteins with Their Nutritional Value, *Nutr. Abstr. & Revs.,* **16,** 249–278, 1946.

Booher, L. E., Hartzler, E. R., and Hewston, E. M., A Compilation of the Vitamin Values of Foods in Relation to Processing and Other Variants, *U.S. Dept. Agr. Circ.* 638, 1942.

Braude, R., Kon, S. K., and Porter, J. W. G., Antibiotics in Nutrition, *Nutr. Abstr. & Revs.,* **23,** 473–495, 1953.

Bronte-Stewart, B., The Effect of Dietary Fats on the Blood Lipids and Their Relation to Ischaemic Heart Disease, *Brit. Med. Bull.,* **14,** 243–252, 1958.

Burr, G. O., and Barnes, R. H., Non-caloric Functions of Dietary Fats, *Physiol. Revs.,* **23,** 256–278, 1943.

Chatfield, C., and Adams, G., Proximate Composition of American Food Materials, *U.S. Dept. Agr. Circ.* 549, 1940.

Chick, H., The Causation of Pellagra, *Nutr. Abstr. & Revs.,* **20,** 523–547, 1951.

Chow, B. F., ed., Symposium on Mechanisms of Intestinal Absorption, *Am. J. Clin. Nutr.,* **12,** 161–227, 1963.

Cotzias, G. C., Manganese in Health and Disease, *Physiol. Revs.,* **38,** 503–532, 1958.

Cruickshank, E. K., Dietary Neuropathies, *Vitamins and Hormones,* **10,** 2–46, 1952.

Daniel, L. J., Inhibitors of Vitamins of the B-complex, *Nutr. Abstr. & Revs.,* **31,** 1–13, 1961.

Elvehjem, C. A., Nutritional Significance of the Intestinal Flora, *Federation Proc.,* **7,** 409–418, 1948.

Flodin, N. W., ed., Protein Nutrition, *Ann. N.Y. Acad. Sci.,* **69,** 855–1066, 1958.

Garry, R. C., and Wood, H. O., Dietary Requirements in Human Pregnancy and Lactation, *Nutr. Abstr. & Revs.,* **15,** 591–621, 1946.

Glass, G. B. J., Gastric Intrinsic Factor and its Function in the Metabolism of Vitamin B_{12}, *Physiol. Revs.,* **43,** 529–849, 1963.

Handler, P., The Present Status of Nicotinic Acid, *Intern. Rev. Vitamin Research,* **19,** 393–451, 1948.

Holman, W. I. M., Distribution of Vitamins within the Tissues of Common Foodstuffs, *Nutr. Abstr. & Revs.,* **26,** 277–304, 1956.

Holmes, J. O., The Requirement for Calcium during Growth, *Nutr. Abstr. & Revs.,* **14,** 597–619, 1945.

Horwitt, M. K., Investigations of Human Requirements for B-complex Vitamins, *Natl. Research Council Bull.* 116, 1948.

Hutner, S. H., Nathan, H. A., and Baker, H., Metabolism of Folic Acid, *Vitamins and Hormones,* **17,** 2–53, 1959.

Isler, O., and Wiss, O., Chemistry and Biochemistry of the K Vitamins, *Vitamins and Hormones,* **17,** 54–91, 1959.

James, A. T., and Lovelock, J. E., Essential Fatty Acids and Human Disease, *Brit. Med. Bull.,* **14,** 262–266, 1958.

Jansen, B. C. P., The Physiology of Thiamine, *Vitamins and Hormones,* **7,** 84–110, 1949.

Keys, A., The Caloric Requirement of Adult Man, *Nutr. Abstr. & Revs.,* **19,** 1–21, 1949.

Knight, B. C. J. G., Growth Factors in Microbiology—Some Wider Aspects of Nutritional Studies with Microorganisms, *Vitamins and Hormones,* **3,** 108–228, 1945.

Krehl, W. A., Nutritional Factors and Skin Diseases, *Vitamins and Hormones,* **20,** 121–140, 1960.

Kruse, H. D., ed., Inadequate Diets and Nutritional Deficiences in the United States, *Natl. Research Council Bull.* 109, 1943.

Leitch, I., and Hepburn, A., Pyridoxine, Metabolism and Requirement, *Nutr. Abstr. & Revs.,* **31**, 389–401, 1961.

Mayer, J., Physiological Basis of Obesity and Leanness, *Nutr. Abstr. & Revs.,* **25**, 597–611, 871–883, 1955.

Meiklejohn, A. P., Physiology and Biochemistry of Ascorbic Acid, *Vitamins and Hormones,* **11**, 62–96, 1953.

Meites, J., and Nelson, M. M., Effects of Hormonal Imbalances on Nutritional Requirements, *Vitamins and Hormones,* **20**, 205–236, 1960.

Morton, R. A., Ubiquinones, Ubichromenols and Related Substances, *Vitamins and Hormones,* **21**, 1–42, 1961.

Nicolaysen, R., and Eeg-Larsen, N., Biochemistry and Physiology of Vitamin D, *Vitamins and Hormones,* **11**, 29–61, 1953.

Nieman, C., and Klein Obbink, H. J., Biochemistry and Pathology of Hypervitaminosis A, *Vitamins and Hormones,* **12**, 69–101, 1954.

Pett, L. B., Vitamin Requirements of Human Beings, *Vitamins and Hormones,* **13**, 214–238, 1955.

Platt, B. S., ed., Recent Research on Vitamins, *Brit. Med. Bull.,* **12**, 1–90, 1956.

"Recommended Dietary Allowances," Publ. 589, National Academy of Sciences, Washington, 1958.

Richter, C. P., Total Self-regulatory Functions in Animals and Human Beings, *Harvey Lectures,* **38**, 63–103, 1941–1942.

Rose, W. C., Amino Acid Requirements of Man, *Federation Proc.,* **8**, 546–552, 1949.

Smith, E. L., Vitamin B_{12}, *Nutr. Abstr. & Revs.,* **20**, 795–816, 1951.

Snell, E. E., Chemical Structure in Relation to Biological Activities of Vitamin B_6, *Vitamins and Hormones,* **16**, 77–125, 1958.

Sobel, A. E., The Absorption and Transportation of Fat-soluble Vitamins, *Vitamins and Hormones,* **10**, 47–68, 1952.

Sydenstricker, V. P., The History of Pellagra, Its Recognition as a Disorder of Nutrition and Its Conquest, *Am. J. Clin. Nutr.,* **6**, 409–414, 1958.

Terroine, T., Physiology and Biochemistry of Biotin, *Vitamins and Hormones,* **20**, 1–42, 1960.

Vasington, F. D., Reichard, S. M., and Nason A., Biochemistry of Vitamin E, *Vitamins and Hormones,* **20**, 43–88, 1960.

Yudkin, W. H., Thiaminase, the Chastek-paralysis Factor, *Physiol. Revs.,* **29**, 389–402, 1949.

INDEX

Entries in boldface type are pages on which formula or structure of a substance is given. The term, properties, connotes physical and chemical properties and behavior. The term, composition, is used to include all constituents except enzymes. Isomeric forms of compounds, e.g., of carbohydrates and of amino acids, are entered under the most general, single term, except where particular significance is indicated. Thus, glucose may include D-, L-, and α-D, etc., forms; carotene(s) includes α-, β-, and γ- forms. Acid references include the ion as well as the acid, e.g., acetoacetic acid includes acetoacetate; aspartic acid includes aspartate.